Kirk-Othmer

ENCYCLOPEDIA
OF CHEMICAL
TECHNOLOGY

Second Edition

VOLUME 16

Polyamides

to

Quinones

*Interscience Publishers
a division of John Wiley & Sons, Inc.
New York · London · Sydney · Toronto*

Kirk-Othmer

ENCYCLOPEDIA

OF CHEMICAL

TECHNOLOGY

Second completely revised edition

VOLUME 16

Polyamides
to
Quinones

CONTENTS

EDITORIAL STAFF FOR VOLUME 16

Associate Editor: EVA PAROLLA DUKES

Christopher Coleman   Phyllis Hirsch   Gloria Joyce

Paul van Reyen   Carolyn C. Wronker

CONTRIBUTORS TO VOLUME 16

R. A. Abramovitch, *University of Alabama*, Pyridine and pyridine derivatives

Leland K. Beach, *Enjay Chemical Laboratory*, Propylene

M. B. Berenbaum, *Thiokol Chemical Corporation*, Polymers containing sulfur (Polysulfides)

Harris J. Bixler, *Amicon Corporation*, Polyelectrolyte complexes

M. Blum, *Atomergic Chemetals Company*, Potassium

Michael H. Bruno, *International Paper Company*, Printing processes

R. A. Budenholzer, *American Power Conference, Illinois Institute of Technology*, Power generation

Richard W. Burg, *Merck & Co., Inc.*, Pyridoxine, pyridoxal, and pyridoxamine

A. J. Cofrancesco, *GAF Corporation*, Polymethine dyes (Cyanine, hemicyanine, and styryl dyes)

Charles F. Cusick, *Honeywell Inc.*, Pressure measurement

William H. Davis, *Texas National Bank of Commerce*, Propylene

H. Dressler, *Koppers Company, Inc.*, (Polyhydroxy)benzenes

James D. Dutcher, *The Squibb Institute for Medical Research*, Polyene antibiotics

Herbert Ellern, *Pyrotechnics Consultant, formerly UMC Industries, Inc.*, Pyrotechnics

G. Farrow, *Fiber Industries, Inc.*, Polyester fibers

Lance Funderburk, *Toms River Chemical Corp.*, Quinoline dyes

I. Goodman, *Imperial Chemical Industries, Ltd.; and University of Manchester, Institute of Science and Technology*, Polyesters

Maxwell Gordon, *Smith, Kline & French Laboratories*, Psychopharmacological agents

Elbert E. Harris, *Merck & Co., Inc.*, Pyridoxine, pyridoxal, and pyridoxamine

Stanton A. Harris, *Merck & Co., Inc.*, Pyridoxine, pyridoxal, and pyridoxamine

Henry H. Hausner, *Consulting Engineer*, Powder metallurgy

James F. Hendricks, *Worthington Corporation*, Pumps and compressors (Compressors)

Lee C. Hensley, *GAF Corporation*, Polymethine dyes

E. S. Hill, *Fiber Industries, Inc.*, Polyester fibers

J. L. Hollowell, *E. I. du Pont de Nemours & Co., Inc.,* Poromeric materials

Lee H. Horsley, *The Dow Chemical Company,* Propylene oxide

Eugene V. Hort, *GAF Corporation,* Pyrrole and pyrrole derivatives

Hugo Illy, *Toms River Chemical Corp.,* Quinoline dyes

Joseph J. Jacobs, *Jacobs Engineering Co.,* Potassium compounds

R. N. Johnson, *Union Carbide Corporation,* Polymers containing sulfur (Polysulfone resins)

James J. Julian, *Worthington Corporation,* Pumps and compressors (Compressors)

Robert Kobberger, *Worthington Corporation,* Pumps and compressors (Pumps)

Marshall Kulka, *Uniroyal (1966) Ltd.,* Quinoline and isoquinoline

Robert W. Lenz, *University of Massachusetts,* Polymerization mechanisms and processes

John H. Madaus, *MSA Research Corporation,* Potassium

Herman Mark, *Polytechnic Institute of Brooklyn,* Polymers

Alan S. Michaels, *Amicon Corporation,* Polyelectrolyte complexes

C. E. Morrell, *Enjay Chemical Intermediates Laboratory,* Propane

Arnold R. Poster, *Metals Sintering Corp.,* Powder metallurgy

Richard A. Reck, *Armour Industrial Chemical Co.,* Quaternary ammonium compounds

R. J. Richardson, *Allied Chemical Corporation,* Polyamides (Fibers)

H. Schnell, *Farbenfabriken Bayer AG,* Polycarbonates

Elmer C. Schule, *Allied Chemical Corporation,* Polyamides (Plastics)

Richard F. Smith, *GAF Corporation,* Pyrrole and pyrrole derivatives

O. E. Snider, *Allied Chemical Corporation,* Polyamides (Fibers)

Samuel Strelzoff, *Chemical Construction Corporation,* Pressure vessels

W. Sweeny, *E. I. du Pont de Nemours & Co., Inc.,* Polyamides (General)

J. R. Thirtle, *Eastman Kodak Company,* Quinones

G. H. Tomlinson, II, *Domtar Limited,* Pulp

Michael V. Tracey, *CSIRO (Commonwealth Scientific and Industrial Research Organization), Division of Food Preservation, Australia,* Proteins

Glenn E. Ullyot, *Smith, Kline & French Laboratories,* Psychopharmacological agents

B. C. Walton, *Chemical Construction Corporation,* Pressure vessels

E. J. Wickson, *Enjay Chemical Laboratory,* Propyl alcohols (Iso)

Paul F. Wiley, *The Upjohn Company,* Pyrazoles, pyrazolines, pyrazolones

S. Wilkinson, *The Wellcome Research Laboratories, Beckenham, Kent, England,* Polypeptide antibiotics

Joseph J. Wocasek, *Celanese Chemical Co.,* Propionaldehyde; Propionic acid; Propyl alcohols (Normal)

ABBREVIATIONS AND SYMBOLS

A	ampere(s)	AOCS	American Oil Chemists' Society
A	anion (eg, HA)		
Å	Angstrom unit(s)	APHA	American Public Health Association
AATCC	American Association of Textile Chemists and Colorists	API	American Petroleum Institute
abs	absolute	app	apparatus
ac	alternating current	approx	approximate(ly)
ac-	alicyclic (eg, ac-derivatives of tetrahydronaphthalene)	aq	aqueous
		Ar	aryl
		as-	asymmetric(al) (eg, as-trichlorobenzene)
accel(d)	accelerate(d)		
acceln	acceleration	ASA	American Standards Association. Later called USASI
ACS	American Chemical Society		
addn	addition		
AEC	Atomic Energy Commission	ASHRAE	American Society of Heating, Refrigerating and Air-Conditioning Engineers
AGA	American Gas Association		
Ah	ampere-hour(s)		
AIChE	American Institute of Chemical Engineers		
		ASM	American Society for Metals
AIME	American Institute of Mining and Metallurgical Engineers	ASME	American Society of Mechanical Engineers
AIP	American Institute of Physics	ASTM	American Society for Testing and Materials
AISI	American Iron and Steel Institute	atm	atmosphere(s), atmospheric
alc	alcohol(ic)	at. no.	atomic number
alk	alkaline (not alkali)	at. wt	atomic weight
Alk	alkyl	av	average
AMA	American Medical Association	b	barn(s)
		b (as in b_{11})	boiling (at 11 mm Hg)
A-min	ampere-minute(s)		
amt	amount (noun)	bbl	barrel(s)
anhyd	anhydrous	bcc	body-centered cubic
AOAC	Association of Official Analytical (formerly Agricultural) Chemists	Bé	Baumé
		Bhn	Brinell hardness number
		bp	boiling point

BP	*British Pharmacopoeia* (General Medical Council in London)	cpd, compd	compound (noun)
Btu	British thermal unit(s)	cps	cycles per second
bu	bushel(s)	crit	critical
C	Celsius (centigrade); coulomb(s)	cryst	crystalline
		crystd	crystallized
C-	denoting attachment to carbon (eg, *C*-acetyl-indoline)	crystn	crystallization
		cSt	centistokes
		cu	cubic
ca	circa, approximately	d	density (conveniently, specific gravity)
CA	Chemical Abstracts		
cal	calorie(s)	*d*	differential operator
calcd	calculated	*d-*	*dextro-*, dextrorotatory
cfm, ft³/min	cubic foot (feet) per minute	D	Debye unit(s)
		D-	denoting configurational relationship (as to *dextro*-glyceraldehyde)
cg	centigram(s)	db	dry-bulb
cgs	centimeter-gram-second	dB	decibel(s)
Ci	curie(s)	dc	direct current
CI	Colour Index (number); the CI numbers given in *ECT*, 2nd ed., are from the new *Colour Index* (1956) and Suppl. (1963), *Soc. Dyers Colourists*, Bradford, England, and *AATCC*, U.S.A.	dec, decomp	decompose(s)
		decompd	decomposed
		decompn	decomposition
		den	denier(s)
		den/fil	denier(s) per filament
		deriv	derivative
		detd	determined
		detn	determination
CIE	Commission Internationale de l'Eclairage (see also ICI)	diam	diameter
		dielec	dielectric (adj.)
		dil	dilute
cif	cost, insurance, freight	DIN	Deutsche Industrienormen
cl	carload lots	distd	distilled
cm	centimeter(s)	distn	distillation
coeff	coefficient	dl	deciliter(s)
compd, cpd	compound (noun)	*dl-*, DL	racemic
		dm	decimeter(s)
compn	composition	dp	dewpoint
concd	concentrated	dyn	dyne(s)
concn	concentration	*e*	electron; base of natural logarithms
cond	conductivity		
const	constant	ed.	edited, edition, editor
cont	continued	elec	electric(al)
cor	corrected	emf	electromotive force
cp	chemically pure	emu	electromagnetic unit(s)
cP	centipoise(s)	en	entropy unit(s)

eng	engineering	hp	horsepower(s)
equil	equilibrium(s)	hr, h	hour(s)
equiv	equivalent	hyd	hydrated, hydrous
esp	especially	hyg	hygroscopic
ESR	electron spin resonance	Hz	hertz(es)
est(d)	estimate(d)	i, insol	insoluble
estn	estimation	^{i} (eg, Pr^i)	iso (eg, isopropyl)
esu	electrostatic unit(s)	i-	inactive (eg, i-methionine)
eV	electron volt(s)	IACS	International Annealed Copper Standard
expt(l)	experiment(al)	ibp	initial boiling point
ext(d)	extract(ed)	ICC	Interstate Commerce Commission
extn	extraction	ICI	International Commission on Illumination (see also CIE); Imperial Chemical Industries, Ltd.
F	Fahrenheit; farad(s)		
F	faraday constant		
FAO	Food and Agriculture Organization of the United Nations	ICT	International Critical Tables
fcc	face-centered cubic	ID	inner diameter
Fed, fedl	federal (eg, Fed Spec)	in.	inch(es)
fl oz	fluid ounce(s)	insol, i	insoluble
fob	free on board	IPT	Institute of Petroleum Technologists
fp	freezing point		
frz	freezing	ISO	International Organization for Standardization
ft	foot (feet)		
ft-lb	foot-pound(s)	IU	International Unit(s)
ft³/min, cfm	cubic foot (feet) per minute	IUPAC	International Union of Pure and Applied Chemistry
g	gram(s)		
g	gravitational acceleration		
G	gauss(es)	J	joule(s)
G	Gibbs free energy	K	Kelvin
gal	gallon(s)	K	dissociation constant
gal/min, gpm	gallon(s) per minute	kbar	kilobar(s)
		kc	kilocycle(s)
g/den	gram(s) per denier	kcal	kilogram-calorie(s)
gem-	geminal (attached to the same atom)	keV	kilo electron volt(s)
g-mol	gram-molecular (as in g-mol wt)	kg	kilogram(s)
		kG	kilogauss(es)
g-mole	gram-mole(s)	kgf	kilogram force(s)
G-Oe	gauss-oersted(s)	kJ	kilojoule(s)
gpm, gal/min	gallon(s) per minute	kp	kilopond(s) (equals kilogram force(s))
gr	grain(s)	kV	kilovolt(s)
h, hr	hour(s)	kVA	kilovolt-ampere(s)
hl	hectoliter(s)	kW	kilowatt(s)
hmw	high-molecular-weight (adj.)	kWh	kilowatt-hour(s)

l	liter(s)	mm	millimeter(s)
l-	*levo-*, levorotatory	mM	millimole(s)
L-	denoting configurational relationship (as to *levo*-glyceraldehyde)	m*M*	millimolar
		mo(s)	month(s)
		mol	molecule, molecular
lb	pound(s)	mol wt	molecular weight
LC$_{50}$	concentration lethal to 50% of the animals tested	mp	melting point
		mph	miles per hour
		MR	molar refraction
lcl	less than carload lots	mV	millivolt(s)
LD$_{50}$	dose lethal to 50% of the animals tested	mμ	millimicron(s) (10^{-9} m)
		^{n} (eg, Bu^{n}),	
liq	liquid	*n-*	normal (eg, normal butyl)
lm	lumen	*n* (as, n_{D}^{20})	index of refraction (for 20°C and sodium light)
lmw	low-molecular-weight (adj.)		
ln	logarithm (natural)	*n-*, ^{n}	normal (eg, *n*-butyl, Bu^{n})
log	logarithm (common)	*N*	normal (as applied to concentration)
m	meter(s)		
m	molal	*N-*	denoting attachment to nitrogen (eg, *N*-methylaniline)
m-	meta (eg, *m*-xylene)		
M	metal		
M	molar (as applied to concentration; not molal)	NASA	National Aeronautics and Space Administration
mA	milliampere(s)	ND	*New Drugs* (NND changed to ND in 1965)
mAh	milliampere-hour(s)		
manuf	manufacture	NF	*National Formulary* (American Pharmaceutical Association)
manufd, mfd	manufactured		
manufg, mfg	manufacturing	nm	nuclear magneton; nanometer(s) (10^{-9} m)
max	maximum	NMR	nuclear magnetic resonance
Mc	megacycle(s)	NND	*New and Nonofficial Drugs* (AMA) (1958–1965). Later called ND
MCA	Manufacturing Chemists' Association		
mcal	millicalorie(s)	NNR	*New and Nonofficial Remedies* (1907–1958). Later called NND
mech	mechanical		
meq	milliequivalent(s)		
MeV	million electron volt(s)	no.	number
mfd, manufd	manufactured	NOIBN	not otherwise indexed by name (ICC specification for shipping containers)
mfg, manufg	manufacturing	*o-*	ortho (eg, *o*-xylene)
mg	milligram(s)	*O-*	denoting attachment to oxygen (eg, *O*-acetylhydroxylamine)
min	minimum; minute(s)		
misc	miscellaneous		
mixt	mixture	Ω	ohm(s)
ml	milliliter(s)	Ω-cm	ohm-centimeter(s)
MLD	minimum lethal dose	OD	outer diameter

Oe	oersted(s)	RI	Ring Index (number); from *The Ring Index*, Reinhold Publishing Corp., N.Y., 1940
owf	on weight of fiber		
oz	ounce(s)		
p-	para (eg, *p*-xylene)		
P	poise(s)	rms	root mean square
pdr	powder	rpm	revolutions per minute
PhI	*Pharmacopoeia Internationalis*, 2 vols. and Suppl., World Health Organization, Geneva, 1951, 1955, and 1959	rps	revolutions per second
		RRI	Revised Ring Index (number); from *The Ring Index*, 2nd ed., American Chemical Society, Washington, D.C., 1960
phr	parts per hundred of rubber or resin	RT	room temperature
pos	positive (adj.)	s, sol	soluble
powd	powdered	ˢ (eg, Buˢ), *sec-*	secondary (eg, *sec*-butyl)
ppm	parts per million		
ppt(d)	precipitate(d)	*s-, sym-*	symmetrical (eg, *s*-dichloroethylene)
pptn	precipitation		
Pr. (no.)	Foreign prototype (number); dyestuff designation used in *AATCC Year Books* for dyes not listed in the old *Colour Index* (1924 ed.; 1928 Suppl.); obsolete since new *Colour Index* was published (1956 ed.; 1963 Suppl.)	*S-*	denoting attachment to sulfur (eg, *S*-methylcysteine)
		SAE	Society of Automotive Engineers
		satd	saturated
		satn	saturation
		scf, SCF	standard cubic foot (feet) (760 mm Hg, 63°F)
		scfm	standard cubic feet per minute
prepd	prepared	Sch	Schultz number (designation for dyes from *Farbstofftabellen*, 4 vols., Akademie Verlag, Leipzig, 1931–1939)
prepn	preparation		
psi	pound(s) per square inch		
psia	pound(s) per square inch absolute		
psig	pound(s) per square inch gage	sec	second(s)
pt	point	*sec-,* ˢ	secondary (eg, *sec*-butyl; Buˢ)
pts	parts		
qual	qualitative	SFs	Saybolt Furol second(s)
quant	quantitative	sl s, sl sol	slightly soluble
qv	which see (quod vide)	sol, s	soluble
R	Rankine; roentgen; univalent hydrocarbon radical (or hydrogen)	soln	solution
		soly	solubility
		sp	specific
rad	radian	sp, spp	species (sing. and pl.)
Rep	roentgen(s) equivalent physical	Spec	specification
		sp gr	specific gravity
resp	respectively	SPI	Society of the Plastics Industry
rh	relative humidity		

sq	square	USP	(*The*) *United States Pharmacopeia* (Mack Publishing Co., Easton, Pa.)
St	stokes		
STP	standard temperature and pressure (760 mm Hg, 0°C)		
		uv	ultraviolet
subl	sublime(s), subliming	V	volt(s)
SUs	Saybolt Universal second(s)	*v-, vic-*	vicinal (attached to adjacent atoms)
sym, s-	symmetrical (eg, *sym*-dichloroethylene)	var	variety
		vic-, v-	vicinal (attached to adjacent atoms)
^t (eg, Bu^t), *t-, tert-*	tertiary (eg, tertiary butyl)	vol	volume(s) (not volatile)
t-, tert-, ^t	tertiary (eg, *t*-butyl)	v s, v sol	very soluble
TAPPI	Technical Association of the Pulp and Paper Industry	vs	versus
		v/v	volume per volume
		W	watt(s)
tech	technical	Wh	watt-hour(s)
temp	temperature	wt	weight
tert-, t-, ^t	tertiary (eg, *tert*-butyl)	w/v	weight per volume
theoret	theoretical	w/w	weight per weight
Twad	Twaddell	xu (ca 10⁻¹¹ cm)	x unit(s)
USASI	United States of America Standards Institute (ASA changed to USASI in 1966)	yd	yard(s)
		yr	year(s)

Quantities

Some standard abbreviations (prefixes) for very small and very large quantities are as follows:

deci (10^{-1})	d		deka (10^{1})	dk
centi (10^{-2})	c		hecto (10^{2})	h
milli (10^{-3})	m		kilo (10^{3})	k
micro (10^{-6})	μ		mega (10^{6})	M
nano (10^{-9})	n		giga (10^{9})	G (or B)
pico (10^{-12})	p		tera (10^{12})	T
femto (10^{-15})	f			
atto (10^{-18})	a			

P continued

POLYAMIDES

POLYAMIDES, GENERAL

Polyamides are condensation products which contain recurring amide groups as integral parts of the main polymer chains. Linear polyamides are formed as the products of condensation of bifunctional monomers. If the monomers are amino acids (eg, ϵ-aminocaproic acid), the polymers are called AB types (A, representing amine groups, and B, carboxyl groups). If the polymers are formed from condensation of diamines and dibasic acids, they are called AABB types. Polyamides are frequently referred to as *nylons* (a generic term). Although they are generally considered to be condensation polymers, polyamides may also be formed by addition polymerization. This method of preparation is especially important for some AB polymers where the monomers are cyclic lactams, such as ϵ-caprolactam or pyrrolidone.

Typical structural formulas of linear polyamides may be represented as H_2N-$RNH(COR'CONHRNH)_nCOR'COOH$ or, in the case of self-condensation of an amino acid, $H_2NRCO(NHRCO)_nNHRCOOH$, where R and R' represent chains between functional groups in the reactants and n represents the degree of polymerization or number of recurring groups in the polymer chain.

Numerous combinations of diacids, diamines, and amino acids have been interacted, and copolymers containing various proportions of two or more diacids, diamines, and amino acids have been prepared. The chains between functional groups in the reactants may comprise linear or branched aliphatic hydrocarbons, or alicyclic or aromatic rings; they may contain hetero atoms such as oxygen, sulfur, and nitrogen (for example, piperazine or even hydrazine). Secondary diamines lead to the formation of N-substituted polyamides. Polyfunctional reactants, in which the sum of the functional groups in the polyfunctional amine and acid is greater than four, lead to the formation of crosslinked or network polymers. Thus it is apparent that it is theoretically possible to synthesize a tremendous number and variety of polyamides. Of these, only a few combinations, primarily linear polyamides, have been chosen for commercial exploitation because of low cost, availability of intermediates, and generally satisfactory physical and chemical properties.

Nomenclature. A common form of shorthand which serves to identify aliphatic polyamides involves the use of numbers which signify the number of carbon atoms in the respective monomers. For AABB polymers, two numbers are used. The first gives the number of carbon atoms separating the nitrogen atoms of the diamine, and the second gives the number of straight-chain carbon atoms in the dibasic acid.

Table 1. Typical Polymer Intermediates and Their Codes

Intermediate	Structure	Code
diamine		
hydrazine	H_2NNH_2	0
ethylene	$H_2N(CH_2)_2NH_2$	2
hexamethylene	$H_2N(CH_2)_6NH_2$	6
piperazine	HN⟨ ⟩NH	Pip
diacid		
carbonic	$HOCO_2H$	1
oxalic	HO_2CCO_2H	2
adipic	$HO_2C(CH_2)_4CO_2H$	6
terephthalic	HO_2C⟨◯⟩CO_2H	T

For example, a 6,6 (pronounced "six-six") polyamide is derived from a six-carbon (hexamethylene) diamine and a six-carbon (adipic) acid. In the same way, 2,6, 2,8, 8,2, etc polyamides are derived from the corresponding straight-chain diamines and diacids in which two, six, or eight carbons are present. In this system, the diamine component is always named first, followed by the diacid component; for example, polymer-2,8 from ethylenediamine and suberic acid, and polymer-8,2 from octamethylenediamine and oxalic acid. The self-condensation polymer derived from ε-aminocaproic acid (6-aminohexanoic acid) or its lactam is known as polymer-6, because it is made from a six-carbon amino acid. Ring-containing intermediates are usually coded with single letters or short combinations thereof representing the ring structure. For example, terephthalic acid and isophthalic acid are commonly coded T and I, respectively. Thus, 6,T represents the polyamide from hexamethylenediamine and terephthalic acid. In an alternative coding system, diamine and diacid codes are separated by a hyphen. Thus, poly(hexamethyleneadipamide) becomes 6-6. Further illustrations of codes for several polymer intermediates are shown in Table 1.

In representing copolymers, the major component is named first, followed by the minor components in order of decreasing percentages. The percentages by weight are then written in parentheses. For example, if hexamethylenediamine, adipic acid, and sebacic acid (ten-carbon) are copolymerized, the product is named 6,6–6,10 (95:5) in the case where the 6,6 and 6,10 components are present in the copolymer in the proportion 95:5.

Those polyamides which have sufficiently high molecular weight, or degree of polymerization, to be fiber-forming are known as superpolyamides.

History. Systematic research on high-molecular-weight synthetic polyamides with unit lengths greater than eight is derived primarily from the theoretical studies of Carothers and co-workers (1). Analysis of the results of the fundamental polycondensation program indicated strongly that polyamides would possess a combination of properties suitable for commercial fibers. Initial work was started with 9-aminononanoic acid (ω-aminopelargonic acid). Its high-molecular-weight polyamide had a melting point of 195°C; and, after spinning and cold drawing, it yielded fibers similar to silk in strength and elasticity. Numerous polyamides were then synthesized from various combinations of amino acids, dibasic acids, and diamines. (Carothers' first patents in 1937 broadly cover polyesters and polyamides.)

The superpolyamide from hexamethylenediamine and adipic acid was selected for further development because it appeared to have the best balance of properties and prospective manufacturing cost. Commercial development of poly(hexamethylene-adipamide) required concurrent development of economical manufacturing processes for hexamethylenediamine and adipic acid (qv). The latter was originally produced from phenol and the hexamethylenediamine from adipic acid, via hydrogenation of adiponitrile. In April 1937, samples of the polyamide fiber were made into experimental stockings. The polymerization and spinning processes were developed to a pilot-plant scale in 1938 and the term "nylon" was adopted as a generic term for these synthetic polyamides. A full-scale plant went into operation at Seaford, Delaware, late in 1939 and nylon hosiery was put on general sale in May 1940.

During World War II, all nylon-yarn production was allocated for military use in parachutes, airplane tire cords, glider tow ropes, and various items of military apparel. At the end of the war, nylon production was expanded considerably, and the use of nylon, in multifilament yarn, fine monofilament yarn, high-tenacity cord, and staple yarn, was extended to many areas of textile and industrial applications. In addition, nylon became important as film, plastic, and resin.

U.S. manufacturers of nylon presently include E. I. du Pont de Nemours & Co., Inc., Monsanto Co., Celanese Corp. of America, Allied Chemical Corp., Beaunit Corp., American Enka Corp., Phillips Petroleum Co., Rohm and Haas Co., and The Firestone Tire & Rubber Co.

Table 2. The Growth of the Production of Textile Raw Materials and the Contribution of Fully Synthetic Fibers

Year	Production, million tons	Production, %
1950	9.4	1
1955	13.3	2
1960	14.9	5
1965	18.2	11

Table 3. Approximate World Production of Fully Synthetic Fibers in 1966 (3)

Fiber	Production, %	Fiber	Production, %
nylon-6	21	polyacrylic	18
nylon-6,6	28	other types	9
polyester	24		

Economic Aspects. Nylons are used chiefly in the production of synthetic fibers. The total market for all synthetic fibers has been growing vigorously since the appearance of nylon-6,6 in the U.S. in 1938, and of nylon-6 in Germany in 1941–1942. These two types still comprise >50% of the market of fully synthetic fibers. Growth of the wholly synthetic fiber market is shown in Tables 2 and 3 (2).

Advantages of nylons relative to other natural and synthetic fibers are relatively low specific gravity, high strength, and good durability. The four largest uses of nylon fibers are in tires, carpets, stockings, and upholstery. Approximately 1 billion lb of nylon fiber was produced in the U.S. in 1966 (4). World production of nylon was 2.656 billion lb in 1966 (4).

Nylon-6 and 6,6 are used not only for textile purposes, but also as molding resins for the plastics industry. In the U.S., 8% of polyamides (approx $\frac{1}{3}$ of the world production) went into plastics (5).

Although current commercial polyamides fulfill a considerable number of end-use requirements, certain deficiencies in selected applications (eg, flat-spotting in tires, insufficient dimensional stability in industrial plastics (gearings), electrostatic charge in carpets, etc) have directed research efforts toward product improvement and discovery of even better polyamide types.

Synthetic Methods

Polyamides have been prepared by many routes though only the more important will be described here. See also the following sections on individual polyamides, and reference 5a.

Direct Amidation. Direct amidation is the reaction of amine groups with carboxyls accompanied by elimination of water. This route has been studied most extensively. The groups may be together in a single molecule, eg, amino acid,

$$H_2NRCO_2H \rightarrow H(NHRCO)_nOH + H_2O$$

or they may be provided from different molecules (eg, the reaction of diamines with dicarboxylic acids). In this case, balance of the reactive ends is usually obtained by prior isolation and purification of the polymeric salt.

$$H_2NRNH_2 + HO_2CR'CO_2H \rightarrow (H_3N^+RN^+H_3{}^- O_2CR'CO_2{}^-) \rightarrow$$
$$H(HNRNHCOR'CO)_nOH + 2 H_2O$$

The above routes may be modified by using derivatives of the acid moiety.

$$H_2NRNH_2 + R'O_2CR''CO_2R' \rightarrow H(HNRNHCOR''CO)_nOR' + 2 R'OH$$

Phenyl or higher alkyl esters are preferred because partial N-methylation sometimes occurs when methyl esters are used.

$$H_2NRNH_2 + MeO_2CR'CO_2Me \rightarrow H(MeNRNHCOR'CO)_nOMe + MeOH + H_2O$$
$$H_2NRNH_2 + H_2NOCR'CONH_2 \rightarrow H(HNRNHCOR'CO)_nNH_2 + 2 NH_3$$

Acyl derivatives of the diamines may also be reacted with dicarboxylic acids to yield polyamides by acidolysis. This route is particularly important as a basis for the

$$RCONHR'NHCOR + HO_2CR''CO_2H \rightarrow RCO(HNRNHCOR''CO)_nOH + 2\,RCO_2H$$

preparation of block polyamides resulting from interchange between two polyamides.

Polyamides by Reaction of Acid Chlorides. Low-temperature polycondensation of diamines and diacid chlorides is an important route for preparing high-melting polyamides, such as aromatic polyamides, which would decompose or crosslink if prepared by high-temperature melt routes (6).

Condensation of diamines and diacid chlorides may be effected by the following methods:

1. Interfacial polymerization in which the diacid chloride in a water-immiscible solvent is added to an aqueous solution of the diamine, inorganic base, and surface-active agent. Polymerization takes place in the organic layer at the interface.

$$H_2NRNH_2 + ClCOR'COCl \xrightarrow{NaOH} H(HNRNHCOR'CO)_nCl + 2\,NaCl$$

2. Solution polymerization in which only one phase is present and an organic base is the acid acceptor.

$$H_2NRNH_2 + ClCOR'COCl \xrightarrow{R''_3N} H(NHRNHCOR'CO)_nCl + 2\,R''_3N.HCl$$

3. With weak aromatic bases, sometimes acid acceptors are not necessary to ensure complete polymerization. Heating of the amino acid hydrochloride acid chloride (or diamine dihydrochloride and diacid chloride) in an inert solvent is sufficient to remove the hydrogen chloride formed and allow polyamidation to continue (7).

$$Cl^-H_3N^+RCOCl \xrightarrow{\Delta} \text{---}(HNRCO)_nCl + HCl$$

Ring-Opening Polymerization. This is an effective and important commercial route for preparing high-molecular-weight polymer. Ring opening may be effected without elimination of another molecule (as in the polymerization of caprolactam) by the following methods:

1. High-temperature polymerization in which water, amino acid, or amine carboxylate (eg, 6,6 salt) are used as initiators.

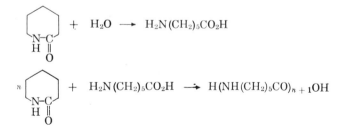

2. Low-temperature anionic polymerization in which ring opening is effected by strong base, usually with addition of an acylating cocatalyst (eg, acetic anhydride).

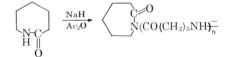

3. Ring-opening polymerization of carboanhydrides, with elimination of carbon dioxide, has been used as a route to prepare high-molecular-weight poly(α-amino acids) (8).

$$\begin{array}{c} \underset{R}{\overset{\overset{\displaystyle H}{\underset{|}{N}}}{\diagup}}\underset{\underset{\displaystyle O}{\overset{\|}{C-O}}}{C=O} \overset{\Delta}{\longrightarrow} \quad -(HNRCO)_n \quad + \quad CO_2 \end{array}$$

Miscellaneous Routes. Polyamides have also been prepared by other routes.

1. Addition of amines to activated double bonds (9).

$$H_2C=CRCONH_2 \rightarrow -(CH_2CHRCONH)_n$$

2. Polymerization of isocyanates (10).

$$RN=C=O \rightarrow -(NRCO)_n$$

3. Reaction of formaldehyde with dinitriles (11).

$$NCRCN + HCHO \rightarrow -(HNOCRCONHCH_2)_n$$

The major polymerization routes will be discussed in detail in the following section.

Chemical Properties

Hydrolysis. Most nylon fibers and plastics are unaffected by room temperature or boiling water, though at higher temperatures, and especially in the melt, hydrolysis and degradation occur. Nylons are usually stable to aqueous alkali. For example, 10% sodium hydroxide solution at 85°C has no effect on nylon-6,6 over a period of 16 hr. However, aqueous acid degrades nylon fibers rapidly. The kinetics of hydrolysis of polycaprolactam with aqueous sulfuric acid have been studied (12). Acid hydrolysis of polyamide-6,10 is slower than that of 6,6, which in turn is less than that of nylon-6 (13). Effects of hydrolysis on polyamides have been reviewed (14).

Acidolysis and Aminolysis. Polyamides undergo rapid acidolysis and degradation on heating with monobasic acids at elevated temperature, especially in the melt (15). Exchange reactions leading to block and random copolymers also proceed between different polyamide macromolecules, probably by this mechanism (16).

Heating of nylon-6,6 with hexamethylenediamine results in rapid reduction of molecular weight (15), presumably by aminolysis. Kinetics of this reaction have not been studied.

Solubility. Aliphatic polyamides, such as polyhexamethyleneadipamide, are usually soluble in phenols, formic acid, chloral hydrate, mineral acids, and similar substances at room temperature. At higher temperatures, alcohol-halogenated hydrocarbon mixtures, unsaturated alcohols, nitro alcohols, and calcium chloride–methanol mixtures are often solvents. Some copolymers (such as 6,6–6,10 (40:60)) are soluble in methanol–chloroform though the respective homopolymers are not. Nylon-6,6 is also soluble in methanol under pressure.

Aliphatic–aromatic polyamides are slightly less soluble than the all-aliphatic polyamides and are soluble in trifluoroacetic and sulfuric acids.

Aromatic polyamides are distinctly different from aliphatic polyamides in solubility in usually being soluble in basic solvents such as dimethylacetamide and N-methylpyrrolidone (sometimes with added salts such as LiCl or $CaCl_2$) (18,19). The aromatic polyamides are usually not soluble in formic acid.

Substitution of the Amide Hydrogen. Heating of polyamides in an autoclave with ethylene oxide results in hydroxyethylated polyamides characterized by high elasticity and vapor permeability. The products have been reported to be block copolymers (17).

$$\text{—CONH— } + \text{ H}_2\text{C—CH}_2 \rightarrow \text{—CON(CH}_2\text{CH}_2\text{O)}_n\text{H}$$
$$\diagdown_\text{O}\diagup$$

Ethylene carbonate also reacts with polyamides to form block copolymers by reaction with the amino and carboxyl end groups and with the amide NH group. Nylons 6,6 and 6 yield water-soluble products (20).

Elastic N-methoxymethylated polyamide nylons have also been prepared by treating nylon-6,6 with formaldehyde and methanol in the presence of an acidic catalyst (21). The melting temperatures of these polymers decrease rapidly with the extent of N-substitution until finally a viscous liquid is obtained with complete substitution.

Formaldehyde reacts with polyamides in the solid state or in formic acid solution to yield N-methylol derivatives. These polymers are thermosetting and become insoluble on heating (22).

$$\text{—CONH— } + \text{ HCHO} \rightarrow \text{—CON(CH}_2\text{O)}_n\text{H} \rightarrow \text{—CON(CH}_2\text{O)}_n\text{CH}_2\text{NCO—}$$

Grafting with Unsaturated Acids. Exposure of polyamides to high-intensity radiation (eg, α rays, x rays, etc) leads to the formation of free radicals on the polymer chains, which can be used as sites for polymerization with vinyl monomers.

$$\text{—H}_2\text{CCONHCH}_2\text{— } \rightarrow \text{ —H}_2\text{CCONH\.CH— } \xrightarrow{\text{H}_2\text{C=CHR}'} \text{—H}_2\text{CCONHCH(CH}_2\text{CH}_2\text{)}_n\text{R}$$

The predominant free radical in irradiated nylon is believed to be one with the unpaired electron on the carbon adjacent to the amide nitrogen (—ĊHNHCO—) (23). Graft copolymers have been prepared from nylons 6,6 and 6 with acrylonitrile (24) or styrene (25). The various techniques to prepare graft copolymers using ionizing radiation have been reviewed (26).

One of the intriguing possibilities opened up by radiation-induced grafting is the preparation of polymers combining the hydrophobic properties of polyamides and hydrophilic properties of selected vinyl polymers. Modification occurs mainly in the amorphous areas so that tensile properties such as tenacity and stiffness, which are functions of crystalline areas, are retained in the graft. On the other hand, properties which depend on amorphous areas, such as moisture regain and dyeability, are vastly changed. Hydrophilic grafts have been prepared from nylon-6,6 with acrylic or maleic acids (27). These two acids lead to grafts covering a wide range of properties. Acrylic acid polymerizes readily, and as a result, forms grafts composed of long polymeric chains. Maleic acid, on the other hand, does not homopolymerize and gives short grafts.

Grafting is carried out by soaking nylon-6,6 fibers in the monomers and irradiating with 2 MeV electrons from a Van de Graaff generator. Small doses (1 Mrad) are sufficient to graft 10% acrylic acid, as compared to large doses (20–40 Mrad) for equivalent amounts of maleic acid.

Weight gains of maleic acid on grafting reflect a high transfer from a grafted monomer unit to the nylon. The G yield for radical production in nylon has been reported (27) to be about 6. (See Radiation technology.) Since grafting occurs only in the amorphous areas (about 50% of the nylon), the G yield is actually 3. On this basis, 20 Mrad would give $3 \times 20 = 60$ radical sites/10^6 g of nylon.

Characterization of the nylon–acrylic acid grafts is complex because of the homopolymerization tendency of the acrylic acid. The chemical composition, proportions, and molecular weights of the various components of the grafted product have been determined and are shown below (Table 4).

nylon + acrylic acid monomer →

ungrafted nylon + ungrafted polyacrylic acid + nylon–acrylic acid

Table 4. Composition of Nylon–Acrylic Acid Grafted Product (17.5% Weight Gain)

| | | Molecular weight | |
Product	Weight, %	Number average	Weight average
initial nylon substrate		17,400	
polyacrylic acid homopolymer	1		
nylon, ungrafted	52	13,500	
nylon–polyacrylic acid graft	45	37,000	
nylon portion	33	24,500	
polyacrylic acid portion	15	12,500	60,000

The acid forms of the nylon grafts of acrylic and maleic acids have the same melting points and fiber melting characteristics as the unmodified nylon and the x-ray crystallinity patterns are about equivalent.

The acrylic acid and maleic acid grafts on nylon fibers are readily interconverted to the corresponding sodium or calcium salts by treatment with sodium carbonate or calcium acetate. The sodium salts of the grafts are highly hydrophilic as measured by moisture regain, polymer conductivity, and antistatic properties. Conversion of the grafts to the sodium or calcium form increases the fiber melt temperature considerably. The fiber melt temperature is increased from 240 to over 400°C for the calcium form of the acrylic acid graft. The sodium salts, however, are not as high melting as the calcium salts, which are essentially ionically crosslinked. The crystalline portions of the nylon in the graft melt at the usual melting point of nylon (260°C), but the inorgano–organic framework of the amorphous area remains infusible.

Crystallinity

Symmetrical, hydrogen-bonded, linear polyamides are invariably highly crystalline and owe their excellent mechanical behavior to this property. Yield point, tensile strength, elastic and shear moduli, hardness and abrasion resistance increase with increasing crystallinity, whereas moisture absorption and impact strength drop slightly. Some of these effects are indicated in Figures 1, 2, and 3 (28).

Nylons are crystalline in the sense that they give well-defined x-ray patterns. The maximum crystallinity that can be obtained varies with the nature of the polymer repeat unit, and high crystallinity (40–50%) is obtained with polymers such as nylons

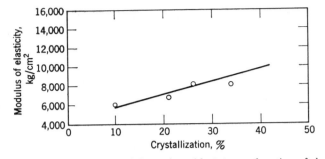

Fig. 1. Modulus of elasticity of dry polyamide-6,6 as a function of degree of crystallinity.

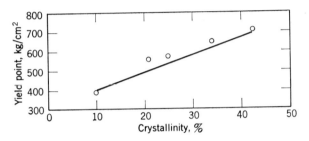

Fig. 2. Yield point of dry polyamide-6,6 as a function of crystallinity.

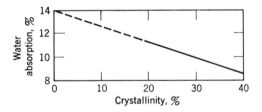

Fig. 3. Water absorption of polyamide-6,6 as a function of crystallinity at 100% rh and room temperature.

6,6, 6,10, and 6, whose regular structures permit good chain alignment and a high degree of hydrogen bonding in the plane of the chains.

An interesting feature of the crystallization of nylon-6,6 is the formation of spherulites which apparently are spherical arrangements of crystalline polymer or fibrils. Under polarized light, spherulites may appear as Maltese crosses. They are formed upon slow cooling of the melt and are found in molded polyamide plastics and fibers. Spherulites are not limited to nylon, but exist in other polymers such as polyethylene terephthalate and polyethylene.

Recently, considerable evidence has been presented (29) to show that some of the molecules in oriented nylon-6,6 fibers changed from an elongated to a folded conformation without change in crystal orientation when samples were heated to 160–255°C under zero tension. The transformation was supported by a combination of measurements of structural and physical properties, such as wide- and small-angle x-ray diffraction, broad- and narrow-line nuclear magnetic resonance, sonic modulus, density, shrinkage, and tensile properties. For example, a fortyfold increase of the intensity of the discrete small-angle x-ray diffraction, an increase of the length of the long period, and a change from a smeared four-point to a sharp two-point diagram, resulted from the heat treatment. The wide-angle x-ray measurements showed little change in crystallite orientation on heating to 250°C even though appreciable shrinkage occurred. The amount of shrinkage appeared to be controlled by the number of folds which were introduced. Tensile strength was reduced by chain folding, possibly because there are fewer extended chains to bear the applied load.

High crystallinity is not confined to aliphatic polymers, but also occurs in ring-containing polymers. Polyterephthalamides from even-numbered straight-chain diamines C_2–C_{12} show the high three-dimensional crystallinity characteristic of nylon-6,6, whereas those from the odd-chain diamines exhibit longitudinal order only (30). Chain stiffness, symmetry, and capacity to bond are especially important in the aliphatic–aromatic series to give good chain packing and high crystallinity.

Hydrogen bonding also is not necessary for good crystallinity if chain stiffness and symmetry are sufficiently high. The polyterephthalamides of piperazine and alkyl-substituted piperazines are highly crystalline.

Crystallinity has also been observed in wholly aromatic polyamides. Para orientation favors high crystallinity because of the high degree of chain stiffness and symmetry; however, highly crystalline polymers have been reported for all meta polymers (eg, poly(m-phenyleneisophthalamide)) and for copolymers composed of ordered sequences of meta and para rings (31). Apparently short-chain dissymmetry does not greatly reduce the degree to which these stiff chains pack.

Although many ring-containing polymers with high glass transition temperatures (T_g) have been reported as being amorphous or noncrystalline, this should not be taken to mean that the polymers are not crystallizable, even to a high degree of perfection. Lack of crystallinity, as shown by the x-ray method, is sometimes a consequence of the polymer sample history (eg, rapid quenching, preparation method) and crystallinity is often induced by near-solvent treatment or by thermal treatments.

Degradation

Thermal Degradation. Thermal degradation of polyamides has been the subject of many investigations (32). The rate and type of degradation depend on temperature, polymer structure, and whether the heating is carried out in the presence or absence of oxygen (32).

In the degradation of nylons 6,6 and 6 at 305°C, the volatile products are carbon dioxide, water, ammonia, hexamethyleneimine, n-hexylamine, n-heptylamine, and methylamine. About half the nitrogen is eliminatd as ammonia. With polycaprolactam and its copolymers, caprolactam is eliminated, and decrease in molecular weight is proportional to the caprolactam evolved provided it is removed continuously.

Degradation of many polyamides in the absence of air is most probably related to homolytic cleavage of the C—N bond with formation of a double bond and nitrile group. The following simplified scheme has been proposed (32) for the primary degradation process.

$$R'CONH_2 + H_2C{=}CHR{-} \longrightarrow R'CN + H_2O + H_2C{=}CHR{-}$$

Other degradation schemes have been proposed (32) but become quite complex because they try to account for all degradation products, many of which result from secondary degradation reactions (eg, hydrolysis from the H₂O by-product). In addition, many of these reaction schemes apply to the degradation of nylon-6,6 only, under specific conditions.

From the mechanism proposed above it is obvious that steric hindrance or absence of hydrogens at the position β to the amine should result in more thermally stable polyamides. The literature substantiates this (33); for example, α,α-dimethyl nylon-3 (**1**) is more thermally stable than β,β-dimethyl nylon-3 (**2**).

(**1**)   (**2**)

Nylon-6,6 is much less thermally stable than nylons 6,10 or 6, and starts to gel (crosslink) after about 14 hr heating under steam at 300°C. This is highly undesirable especially when the polymer is used for fiber preparation, because the gel particles cause quality defects in the spun and drawn yarns. Although the average holdup time in continuously operating equipment is much shorter than that required for gelation, there are dead pockets, especially along the equipment walls, where the polymer velocity approaches zero and the retention time is long. The gelation of 6,6 is uniquely related to the adipic acid moiety because polymers from higher acids (6,10 and 6,12) do not gel on heating for extended periods. Although it has been suggested that the amine ends are involved, this would not distinguish between 6,6, 6,10, and 6,12 unless products of decomposition of the acid group are also involved (32).

The mechanism for gelation of nylon-6,6 has not been defined yet but probably involves the well-known cyclization of the 6,6 acid end groups (32).

These reactions explain the decrease of COOH and the increase of NH₂; however, the cyclopentanone group must then undergo additional reaction and rearrangement for crosslinking to occur.

It has been suggested (32) that the branching and gelation result from condensation of dihexamethylenetriamine, which is formed by reaction of the amine ends.

$$2 \text{ —CONH(CH}_2)_6\text{NH}_2 \rightarrow \text{ —(CONH(CH}_2)_6)_2\text{NH} + \text{NH}_3$$

However, this mechanism has been disputed (32) and no satisfactory mechanism has been proposed yet.

Gelation of nylon-6 has been reported (32) but appears to be different from that of 6,6, and may result from oxidative crosslinking resulting from the presence of traces of oxygen or peroxides.

Heating of polyamides in the presence of oxygen results in chain scission and crosslinking. Poly(hexamethyleneadipamide) becomes brittle after 2 hr at 250°C but only after 2 yr at 70°C (32). The degradation appears to result from a free-radical chain reaction, probably initiated at the carbon alpha to the nitrogen (34), and is diffusion controlled. Plots of the reciprocal of the tenacity at break $(1/T_B)$ vs time are linear and an apparent activation energy of thermal oxidative degradation of 27 kcal/mole has been obtained for nylon-6,6 (35). The peroxide-catalyzed chain degradative mechanism is supported by the fact that small amounts of antioxidants drastically reduce thermal degradation in polyamide fibers. Copper salts are mostly used, but organic antioxidants such as N,N'-di-β-naphthyl-p-phenylenediamine have also been used (36).

Thermal degradation studies have been made on aromatic polyamides (37) mainly by thermogravimetric analysis and by analysis of the decomposition products. Relative thermal stability is greatly dependent on polymer structure and on the ring orientation of the amide unit. This is illustrated in the structures below.

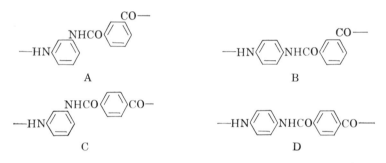

order of thermal stability of aromatic polyamides (A<B<C<D)   (38)

Thermal degradation of aromatic polyamides in the absence of oxygen probably involves direct cleavage of the amine (C—N) bond. Degradation in the presence of oxygen is more complex because the polymers crosslink rapidly, possibly by free-radical coupling of the aromatic rings.

Degradation by Light. Exposure to sunlight causes a deterioration in the properties of many artificial and natural textile materials due to loss of strength and elasticity of the individual fibers. There is an accompanying reduction in the molecular weight and slight changes in chemical constitution. The changes which occur can be reproduced using artificial light.

Although considerable work has been published on the photodegradation of nylons (39), few attempts have been made to study chemical changes occurring in the polymers. Both chain breaking and crosslinking have been shown to occur, the latter chiefly at shorter wavelengths. In the absence of oxygen, the formation of hydrogen, carbon monoxide, and hydrocarbons has been observed with both nylons 6,6 and 6. Evidence for the role played by water is conflicting (39–41).

For photodegradation to occur, the presence of oxygen is necessary at longer wavelengths, whereas at shorter wavelengths it is not, conforming to the concepts of a photosensitized oxidation and a photolysis (39–41), respectively.

Photolysis. In the process of photolysis occurring at wavelengths below 3000 Å, both direct scission of the polyamide chains and crosslinking should result. The probable scissions of, for example, the nylon-6,6 chains are as follows:

$$COCH_3 + H_2C{=}CHCH_2CO{-}$$
$$\mathop{NH(CH_2)_6NH{-}}\limits$$
$$CO(CH_2)_4CO{-}$$
$$NH(CH_2)_6NH{-} \quad \cdot CO(CH_2)_4CO{-} + \cdot HN(CH_2)_6NH{-}$$
$$\cdot CO(CH_2)_4CO{-} \rightarrow CO + \cdot(CH_2)_4CO{-}$$
$$\cdot(CH_2)_4CO{-} + XH \rightarrow H_3C(CH_2)_3CO{-} + X\cdot$$

Compounds of the type $RCONHC(R'')_2R'$ (where R'' is alkyl) were found to be resistant to photooxidation. The mechanism is summarized below.

Initiation

$$RCONHCH_2R' \xrightarrow{h\nu} RCO\cdot + \cdot HNCH_2R'$$
$$RCO\cdot + RCONHCH_2R' \rightarrow RCHO + RCONH\dot{C}HR'$$
$$R'CH_2NH\cdot + RCONHCH_2R' \rightarrow R'CH_2NH_2 + RCONH\dot{C}HR'$$

Propagation

$$\overset{OO\cdot}{\underset{|}{RCONH\dot{C}HR'}} $$
$$RCONH\dot{C}HR' + O_2 \rightarrow RCONH\dot{C}HR'$$

$$\overset{OO\cdot}{\underset{|}{RCONH\dot{C}HR'}} + RCONHCH_2R' \rightarrow \overset{OOH}{\underset{|}{RCONH\dot{C}HR'}} + RCONH\dot{C}HR'$$

$$\overset{OOH}{\underset{|}{RCONH\dot{C}HR'}} \rightarrow \overset{O\cdot}{\underset{|}{RCONH\dot{C}HR'}} + \cdot OH$$

$$\cdot OH + RCONHCH_2R' \rightarrow RCONH\dot{C}HR' + H_2O$$

$$\overset{O\cdot}{\underset{|}{RCONH\dot{C}HR'}} + RCONHCH_2R' \rightarrow \overset{OH}{\underset{|}{RCONH\dot{C}HR'}} + RCONH\dot{C}HR$$

Subsequent reactions

$$\overset{OH}{\underset{|}{RCONH\dot{C}HR'}} \rightarrow RCONH_2 + R'CHO$$

$$R'CHO + O_2 \rightarrow R'COOH$$

Stabilization of nylons toward photooxidation can be accomplished by use of ultraviolet screeners (eg, Geigy AC-865), which have a high screening factor up to at least 400 mμ, or by inorganic antioxidants (eg, Cu^{2+} or Mn^{2+} salts). Polyamide structures with hindrance or alkyl substitution at the carbon α to the amide nitrogen (eg, $-H_2CCONHC(CH_3)_2-$) are most stable to light. In comparing the two isomeric forms of dimethyl nylon-3, (**2**) is found to be more stable to light and less stable to heat than (**1**) (33).

Effect of Delusterant. Titanium dioxide as delusterant in nylon polymer increases the photodegradation above 3000 Å, and then, only in the presence of oxygen, and hence is connected with the photooxidation rather than the photolysis reactions. Titanium dioxide does not appear to change the nature of the oxidation processes but acts as a photosensitizer. Certain additives, particularly manganous salts, reduce this photo-catalytic action and are normally added to delustered commercial nylon yarns (41).

Aromatic polyamides become highly colored on exposure to light and rapidly lose tensile properties. The mechanism of degradation has not been reported (42).

Degradation by High-Intensity Radiation. Considerable research indicates that though nylon is primarily crosslinked by ionizing radiation (43), scission must also play an important role since the degree of crosslinking saturates at a rather low value (44). Differences in radiation effects have been attributed to the absence or presence of oxygen (45). The effects of pressure are quite notable, apparently because this affects the rate of diffusion of the oxygen and subsequent reaction with the radicals formed by irradiation. The importance of postirradiation diffusion of oxygen into irradiated polymers has been discussed in some detail (46). It has been recognized that the solubility of oxygen in a polymer is usually not sufficiently great to account for much degradation and that most of the damage is done by oxygen diffusing into the polymer after the free radicals have been formed by irradiation.

Structure–Property Relationships

A great amount of data dealing with physical properties of condensation polymers and covering a wide variety of structures has been accumulated since the early work by Carothers. Attempts have been made to systematize the data and correlate polymer structure with properties such as melting point, amorphous transition temperature, crystallinity, solubility, water absorption, and modulus (47,48). This is discussed below. It is always assumed that polymers of sufficiently high molecular weight are compared, so that differences in molecular weight give negligible differences in properties of the polymer types under discussion.

Linear polyethylene has been considered to be the parent polymer of all other classes of polymers (47). Insertion of various polar groups or ring structures in the hydrocarbon chain considerably changes the softening point from that of polyethylene (approx 132°C). In general, introduction of urea, amide, and urethan groups yields polymers which melt higher than polyethylene, whereas the aliphatic polyesters melt considerably lower (Table 5).

In another interpretation (49) of the effects of polymer groups on melt temperatures, any series of homologous homopolymers is considered to be composed of copolymers of polyethylene and of the simplest modifying element. The melt temperatures

Table 5. Influence of Polar Linkage on Polymer Softening Point

Polymer structure	Polymer type	Softening point, °C	
		$n = n' = 6$	$n' = 10$ $n = 6$
—COCH$_2$(CH$_2$)$_n$CH$_2$CONH(CH$_2$)$_{n'}$NH—	polyamide	215	194
—COO(CH$_2$)$_n$OCONH(CH$_2$)$_{n'}$NH—	polyurethan	145	154
—COCH$_2$(CH$_2$)$_n$CH$_2$COO(CH$_2$)$_{n'}$O—	polyester	67	73
—COCH$_2$(CH$_2$)$_n$CH$_2$COS(CH$_2$)$_{n'}$S—	polythioester		100
—CSCH$_2$(CH$_2$)$_n$CH$_2$CSNH(CH$_2$)$_{n'}$NH—	polythiolamide		85
—CONH(CH$_2$)$_n$NHCONH(CH$_2$)$_{n'}$NH—	polyurea	>300	
—CH$_2$CH$_2$(CH$_2$)$_n$CH$_2$CH$_2$(CH$_2$)$_{n'}$CH$_2$—	polyethylene	132	132

of the copolymers go through a minimum (eutectic) at some point in the composition which depends on the nature of the modifying group. The minimum melt temperature thus is always below that of linear polyethylene (mp approx 132°C).

Influence of Polar Linkages on Polymer Melt Temperatures. The intermolecular forces which hold condensation polymer chains together result primarily from the polar linkages in the chains. The types of polar linkages and their spacings directly affect the temperature at which the polymer melts (50). The melt temperature (T_m), in °K, can be defined as

$$T_m = \Delta H_u / \Delta S_u$$

where ΔH_u and ΔS_u are the heat and entropy of fusion (per mole of repeating unit), respectively, for a 100% crystalline polymer. The enthalpy is a measure of the attractive forces between the chains. The entropy of fusion may be considered as consisting of two contributions, where ΔS_{exp} represents the change in entropy associated

$$\Delta S_u = \Delta S_{exp} + (\Delta S_c)_v$$

with the increase in volume (expansion), and $(\Delta S_c)_v$ represents the change in entropy due to the increase in the number of conformations a macromolecule can assume on passing from the solid to the liquid state. As the polymer chain becomes less flexible, ΔS obviously decreases.

Entropy and heat of fusion for various polyamides have been calculated by Kirshenbaum (50) and compared with experimental data obtained by various methods. Similar calculations have been made for aliphatic and aromatic polyesters, and gave values for ΔS_u and ΔH_u which agreed well with the observed values.

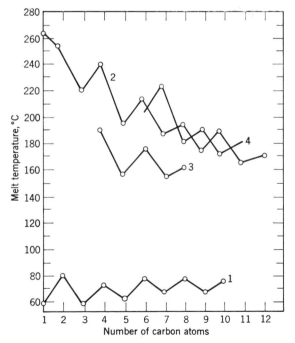

Fig. 4. Effect of polar linkage concentration on melt temperature. LEGEND: 1, acid for polyesters from decamethylene glycol; 2, diamine for polyamides from sebacic acid; 3, diamine for polyurethans from tetramethylene glycol; and 4, ω-amino acid polymers.

Table 6. Comparison of Polyesters and Polyamides

Polymer	ΔH_u/chain unit,[a] kcal	ΔS_u/chain unit,[a] eu
polyester-2,10	590	1.5
10,6	605	1.7
10,10	610	1.7
nylon-10,10	780	1.6
6,10	720	1.6
6,6	800	1.5
2,10	780	1.5

[a] Calculated.

The aromatic polyesters have high melting points, primarily because of their low entropies of fusion. The aliphatic polyesters, in contrast, have extremely low melting points primarily due to their low heat of fusion, as shown by the comparison with polyamides in Table 6. The data in this table are the heat and entropy of fusion per chain atom (ie, C, N, etc) for several polyesters and polyamides. It should be noted that the heats of fusion for polyamides are higher than those for similar polyesters.

As shown previously in Table 5, the type of polar linkage present in a polymer markedly affects melt temperature. In polyamides and polyureas, the CO—NH bond

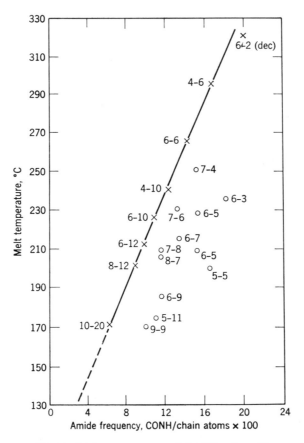

Fig. 5. Melt temperatures of AABB polyamides.

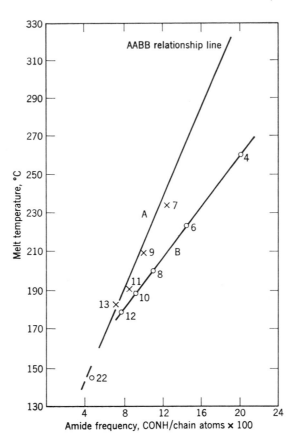

Fig. 6. Melt temperatures of AB polyamides. LEGEND: A, odd-number
carbon atoms; and B, even-number carbon atoms.

has some double-bond character. It has been estimated that the barrier for rotation about the C—N bond in amides may be 15 kcal or higher (51). Thus, the restricted rotation (lower ΔS) and higher intermolecular forces, primarily hydrogen bonding (ΔH), explain why polyamides and polyureas melt higher than the corresponding polyesters and polyurethans.

Effects of Polar Linkage Concentration. In addition to the nature of the polar linkage, the factor which most affects the polymer melt temperature is the distance between the polar groupings. In the various polymer types, the polymers which have even numbers of CH_2 groups between the polar linkages form a higher-melting series than do polymers which contain odd numbers of CH_2 groups (52). This results in a series of melting-point curves which have a zigzag form (Fig. 4), and possibly results from higher entropy of melting of the odd-number (CH_2) series.

Polyamides melt at increasingly higher temperatures as the concentration of amide linkages increases. When polyamide melt temperatures are plotted against amide group concentration, a smooth curve develops in the AABB series for the polymers with even numbers of carbon atoms, but wide scatter is shown for those with odd numbers of carbon atoms. The former are invariably highly crystalline and melt sharply, whereas the latter are often amorphous and recorded values are often softening points rather than crystalline melt temperatures. In the AB series, both the even-

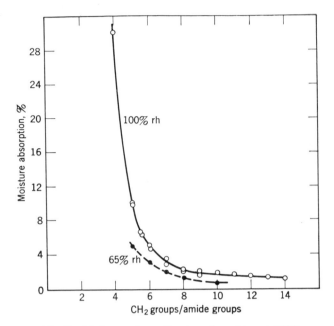

Fig. 7. Moisture absorption in polyamides at 20°C.

and odd-carbon-unit polymers yield smooth curves and, interestingly, the polymers with odd numbers of carbon atoms melt higher than those with even numbers of carbon atoms. Figures 5 and 6 were constructed, using most probable values, from a large number of data from several sources (53). A few of the values are indicated for easy reference.

Increased amide frequency also results in increased moisture absorption in polyamides. Figure 7 shows moisture absorption as a function of CH_2 groups per amide linkage (nylon-6,6 has five CH_2 groups per —CONH—).

Similar effects are observed in the AB polyamide series.

Polymer	Moisture absorption, % by wt	
	65% rh	100% rh
nylon-6	4.3	9.5
nylon-7	2.8	5.0
nylon-12	1.3	2.7

Effects of Lateral Substituents. The high melting point and crystallinity of a polyamide such as 6,6 are a result of the strong polar forces between amide linkages. The introduction of hydrocarbon side chains on the carbon skeleton of the polymer chain causes lateral disorder by forcing the chains apart and interferes with the intermolecular cohesion of the existing polar groups. When 6,6 is substituted on the α-carbon atom of the dibasic acid with hydrocarbon groups of varying size, the melt temperature decreases as the size of the hydrocarbon group increases, and the water absorption increases at the same time. Thus, the effect of a methyl group is less than that of ethyl and larger groups (Table 7). The effect of two methyl groups, one on each α-carbon atom, is equivalent to that of one larger alkyl group. On the other

Table 7. Effects of α Lateral Substituents on Polyamide-6,6

(—HN(CH$_2$)$_6$NHCOC(R)H(CH$_2$)$_3$CO—) Melt Temperatures

Code	T_m, °C	Water absorption, %
6,6	265	8.0
6,αMe6	166	9.2
6,αEt6	95	12.8
6,αn-Bu6	105	12.0
6,αBz6	115	34.0
6,α,α'diMe6	115	
6,α,α,α',α'tetraMe6	115	

hand, four methyl groups, in the α positions, do not appear to lower the melting point further, possibly because the chain is stiffened and ΔS_u decreases.

It would seem to be logical that the farther removed the lateral substituent is from the polar group, the less will be its effect on the physical properties (Table 7). Thus for methyl and ethyl groups, the melting point is lowered less when the substituent is on the β-carbon atom. In polycaprolactams, the lateral substituents also lower the melt temperatures; however, the incremental decrease is not as great as in 6,6 and the effects of α-methyl are actually less than those of β- or δ-methyls (Table 8).

Table 8. Melting Temperatures of Some Substituted Polycaprolactams (54)

Substituent	Approx melt temp, °C	Substituent	Approx melt temp, °C
none	220	δ-methyl	134
α-methyl	190	ϵ-methyl	185
β-methyl	145	γ-ethyl	80–85
γ-methyl	164		

The more pronounced effect of α-methyl groups in lowering the T_m in nylon-6,6 compared to nylon-6 (approx 100° vs 30°) may result from introduction of additional disorder in the former because the amide groups adjacent to the α substituent are not arranged in regular sequence. Nylon-6 leads to the repeated structure

$$—(CH_2CH_2CH_2CH_2CHCONH)—$$
$$\underset{R}{|}$$

By contrast, nylon-6,6 can give rise to three kinds of units, of which two are symmetrical, and one nonsymmetrical, as shown below.

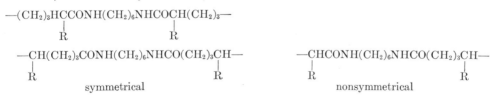

Thus an effect similar to copolymerization results.

Lateral substituents on the nitrogen atom of the amide linkage are doubly effective and not only decrease the polar forces by removing hydrogen bonding, but also introduce lateral disorder. Although the effect of one methyl group appears to be

Table 9. Effect of *N*-Substituents on Polymer Softening Point and Modulus

N-Isobutyl polyamide-6,10

N-Isobutyl substitution, %	Softening point, °C	Modulus, g/den
0	225	25.0 (hardest)
25	180	2.8
40	170	2.0
50	155	0.6
60	145	0.3
75	105	0.03 (softest)

N-Methyl Polyamide-6,6

Acid	Diamine	Softening point, °C	Crystalline
6	6	265	yes
	N-methyl 6	115	yes
	N,N'-dimethyl 6	−75	no

somewhat similar to that of an α-methyl group in nylon-6,6, the effects of larger groups (eg, isobutyl) and *N,N'*-substitution by methyl is much more pronounced (Table 9). In fact, appreciable substitution of amide hydrogens in nylon-6,6 by isobutyl groups results in a rubbery polymer. The effects are probably due both to removal of the hydrogen bonding and to gross lateral disorder which lessens the van der Waals forces as well as the polar forces.

Elastic *N*-substituted polyamides have been studied in detail (55) and the effects of *N*-isobutyl substitution on softening point and modulus are shown in Table 9. Melting point and modulus lowered markedly with increasing *N*-substitution. The *N*-substituted polyamides are also much more soluble in common organic solvents than the corresponding unsubstituted polyamides.

Effects of Introducing Rings into Polyamide Chains. When an aliphatic section of a polyamide chain is replaced by a ring segment, the flexibility of the chain is decreased and the melt temperature is increased because of the decrease in the entropy (ΔS) factor. Introduction of aromatic rings in general also decreases flexibility, solubility, and moisture absorption.

The effect on melt temperature is most pronounced when the replacement unit is a para-oriented aromatic acid group, as for example when adipic acid segments are replaced by those of terephthalic acid, and in these cases the melt temperatures of the corresponding polymers are raised approx 100–170°C (Table 10). When the ring substituent is not conjugated with the amide carbonyl, the melt temperature is raised

Table 10. Comparison of Melt Temperatures of Aliphatic Terephthalamides and Adipamides (56)

Polyamide	T_m, °C	ΔT_m, °C	Polyamide	T_m, °C	ΔT_m, °C
4,6	295	160	6,6	265	106
4,T	455		6,T	371	
5,6	230	169	7,6	220	121
5,T	399		7,T	341	

Table 11. Comparison of Melt Temperatures of Polyamides of *p*-Xylene-α,α'-diamine (XD) with Aliphatic Analogs (57)

Polyamide	T_m, °C	ΔT_m, °C	Polyamide	T_m, °C	ΔT_m, °C
6,6	265		6,10	225	
XD,6	333	68	XD,10	281	56
6,8	240		6,12	212	
XD,8	300	60	XD,12	270	58

about 50–70°C. This is amply illustrated in Table 11 in which polymers from *p*-xylene-α-α'-diamine (xylylenediamine) are compared with their all-aliphatic counterparts. This indicates that direct connection of the amide carbonyl to an aromatic ring provides the greater stiffening effect.

Complete replacement of the aliphatic segments with aromatic rings yields wholly aromatic polyamides (eg, *p*-phenyleneterephthalamide) which decompose (at >400°C) prior to melting so that comparisons of the effects of structure on melt temperature are difficult.

Symmetry is also important in affecting melt temperature in ring-containing polymers. For example, introduction of a meta ring in place of a para ring reduces the polymer melt temperatures considerably. This is shown in Table 12. Polyamides

Table 12. Effect of Position Isomerism on Polymer Melt Temperatures (48)

Code	T_m, °C	ΔT_m, °C	Code	T_m, °C	ΔT_m, °C
*p*2B2,6[a]	310		10,T	350	
*m*2B2,6[b]	210–250	~80	10,I	210	140
7,6	237	0	10,5	185	25
6,T	360		10,*p*PDA[c]	245	
6,I	210–260	130	10,*m*PDA[c]	175	70
6,5	290	20	10,7	170	0

[a] *p*2B2 is bis(*p*-aminoethyl)benzene.

[b] *m*2B2 is bis(*m*-aminoethyl)benzene.

[c] *p*PDA and *m*PDA are *p*- and *m*-phenylethylenediacetic acid.

Table 13. Comparison of Effects of Cyclohexane and Aromatic Rings on Polymer Melt Temperatures (57)

Dicarboxylic acid	*trans*-1,4-Cyclohexanebis(methylamine)		*p*-Xylene-α,α'-diamine	
	$[\eta]$	T_m, °C	$[\eta]$	T_m, °C
glutaric	0.29	280–290		
adipic	0.85	345[a]	1.02	333[a]
pimelic	1.45	290–293	1.00	280–284
suberic	1.34	308–311	0.93	300–305
azelaic	1.04	270–275	0.68	259–263
sebacic	1.68	295–300	0.82	279–281
dodecanedioic	1.38	275–278	0.89	268–272
isophthalic	0.58	305–310	insol	270–290

[a] Obtained by the extrapolation of the mp of a copolyamide series with 1,6-hexanediamine.

from para isomers are higher melting in every case and, in fact, the meta isomers do not increase the melting point appreciably over the aliphatic analogs.

Compared with the all-aliphatic analogs, *trans*-1,4-cyclohexane rings are just as effective as aromatic rings in raising polymer melt temperatures. Examples of this are shown in Table 13.

It is apparent from comparison of the two polyamide series that the polyamides from *trans*-1,4-cyclohexanebis(methylamine) melt at a somewhat higher temperature than the corresponding polyamides from *p*-xylene-α,α'-diamine. It must be concluded that the *trans*-1,4-cyclohexylene ring is at least equivalent to the *p*-phenylene ring in its effect on polymer melt temperature. Similar effects have been noted with polyesters prepared from *trans*-1,4-cyclohexanedimethanol and *p*-xylene-α,α'-diol. These conclusions are further substantiated by the fact that 10,T and 10,HT both melt at 350°C (58).

In the cases discussed, the polyamides have been prepared from the trans isomer. Mixed cis–trans isomers give lower-melting polymers.

Piperazine Polyamides. N,N'-Disubstituted diamines ordinarily yield polymers that are very low melting, and rubbery because they lack hydrogen bonding and thus, ΔH_u is low. On the other hand, polyamides from piperazine (qv) ($HN(CH_2CH_2)_2NH$) are relatively high melting because the stiff ring contributes to decreased ΔS_u on melting. For example, although the polyamide Pip,10 melts at 180°C, which is lower than the analogous aliphatic polymer 2,10 (T_m, 260°C), this is considerably higher than N,N'-dimethylethylene sebacamide (T_m, <100°C) which is the nearest N,N'-disubstituted analog. Similar effects are noted with other piperazine polymers. When the polymer contains no flexible linkage (eg, aliphatic unit) in the main chain the resultant polymers (eg, Pip,T) melt at over 400°C (59).

Copolymerization. The melt temperature of a polymer is depressed when the regularity with which the monomer groups are spaced along the backbone chain is reduced. This occurs in random copolymerization. The effect is illustrated in Figure 8 in which the melt temperatures of a range of copolymers of nylon-6,10 and nylon-6,6 are plotted against copolymer composition. The lowest melting point (190°C) is

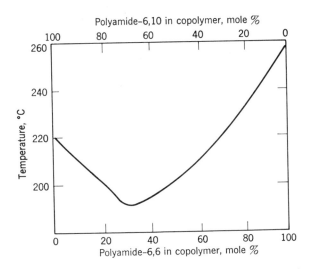

Fig. 8. Reduction in melt temperature of polyamide-6,6 by copolymerization with 6,10.

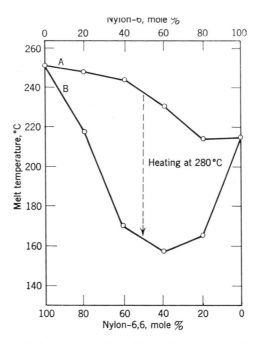

Nylon-6, mole %

Fig. 9. Effects on melt temperature in melt copolymerization of nylons 6,6 and 6.
LEGEND: A, polymer blend; and B, equilibrated random polymer (60).

reached in the neighborhood of a 70:30 composition. The lower melt temperature results because hydrogen bonding, and thus ΔH, is reduced. Similar effects result when poly(hexamethyleneadipamide) and polycaprolactam are blended and equilibrated in the melt to form a copolymer. This is illustrated in Figure 9.

Longitudinal disorder and reduced crystallinity also result from copolymerization; however, in certain instances, crystallinity is not reduced because the copolymerized segment is similar in size to that which is replaced. For example, terephthalic acid yields polyamides isomorphous with those of adipic acid because the segment lengths are similar (61).

Thus, copolymers of 6,6 and 6,T are crystalline and do not have an eutectic in the melt temperature/composition curve (Fig. 10). In contrast, when 6,10 is copolymerized with 6,T, the eutectic effect is marked (62).

Aromatic Polyamides (aromatic in both the diamine and the dibasic acid). Very little information is available in the literature (other than patent literature) describing the properties of aromatic polyamides. Many of the polymers decompose (at approx 400°C) prior to melting so that the effects of structure on melt temperature are difficult to obtain. Selected polymers are compared in Table 14. These show that para polymers are highest melting and that replacement of ortho by meta and meta by para raises the melt temperature about 50°C.

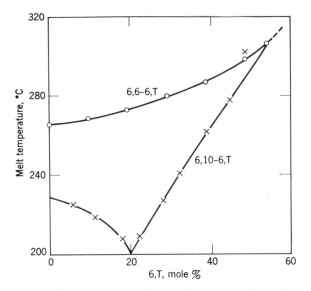

Fig. 10. Melt temperatures of 6,6–6,T and 6,10–6,T copolymers.

Symmetrical aromatic polyamides are highly crystalline (18), even when totally meta oriented. Aromatic polyamides are much more thermally stable than aliphatic polyamides and at least one (Nomex, E. I. du Pont de Nemours & Co., Inc., see p. 42) is in commercial production for high-temperature uses.

Table 14. Effects of Structure on Melt Temperature in Aromatic Polyamides (63)

Acid	Diamine	T_m, °C	ΔT_m, °C
terephthalic	o-phenylene	295	
isophthalic	o-phenylene	240	50
phthalic	o-phenylene	185	55
terephthalic	2,4-diaminotoluene	365	
isophthalic	2,4-diaminotoluene	330	35
terephthalic	bis(4-aminophenyl)methane	>360	
isophthalic	bis(4-aminophenyl)methane	350	>10

One gross distinction between aliphatic and aromatic polyamides is in their solubility characteristics. The former are soluble in acidic solvents (eg, formic and trifluoroacetic acids), whereas the latter are soluble in basic solvents (eg, dimethylformamide) (19).

Individual Polyamides or Polymer Classes

POLY(HEXAMETHYLENEADIPAMIDE), NYLON-6,6

Poly(hexamethyleneadipamide), first prepared by Carothers in 1936, is the most important polyamide commercially and is now used extensively in fibers and plastics. Current world production is about 3 billion lb/yr.

Raw Materials. The raw materials for nylon-6,6 are adipic acid and hexamethylenediamine. Adipic acid (qv) can be manufactured from various starting materials.

1. Phenol by reduction and then oxidation (64).

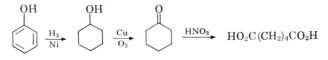

2. Cyclohexane by oxidation (64).

$$\text{cyclohexane} \xrightarrow{\text{HNO}_3} \text{HO}_2\text{C(CH}_2)_4\text{CO}_2\text{H}$$

3. Butadiene by chlorination, cyanation, hydrolysis, and reduction (64).

$$\text{H}_2\text{C=CHCH=CH}_2 \xrightarrow{\text{Cl}_2} \text{ClCH}_2\text{CH=CHCH}_2\text{Cl} \xrightarrow{\text{NaCN}} \text{NCCH}_2\text{CH=CHCH}_2\text{CN} \rightarrow$$

$$\text{HO}_2\text{CCH}_2\text{CH=CHCH}_2\text{CO}_2\text{H} \xrightarrow[\text{Ni}]{\text{H}_2} \text{HO}_2\text{C(CH}_2)_4\text{CO}_2\text{H}$$

4. Tetrahydrofuran by carbonylation (64).

$$\text{THF} \xrightarrow{\text{CO}} \text{lactone} \xrightarrow{\text{CO}} \text{HO}_2\text{C(CH}_2)_4\text{CO}_2\text{H}$$

The chief criteria of purity are melting point, color, neutralization equivalent, steam-volatile acids, and ash content. Steam-volatile acid content, usually monobasic aliphatic acids, must be low because these acids act as chain terminators in polymer preparation. Ash and iron content must also be low because inorganic impurities lead to colored polymer.

Hexamethylenediamine (65–67) can be manufactured from the following:

1. Adipic acid via the ammonium salts, dehydration, and reduction (64).

$$\text{HO}_2\text{C(CH}_2)_4\text{CO}_2\text{H} \xrightarrow{\text{NH}_4\text{OH}} \text{H}_4\text{NOOC(CH}_2)_4\text{COONH}_4 \xrightarrow{-4\,\text{H}_2\text{O}} \text{NC(CH}_2)_4\text{CN} \xrightarrow[\text{NH}_3]{\text{H}_2} \text{H}_2\text{N(CH}_2)_6\text{NH}_2$$

2. Butadiene by chlorination, cyanation, and reduction (64).

$$\text{H}_2\text{C=CHCH=CH}_2 \xrightarrow{\text{Cl}_2} \text{ClCH}_2\text{CH=CHCH}_2\text{Cl} \xrightarrow{\text{NaCN}} \text{NCCH}_2\text{CH=CHCH}_2\text{CN} \xrightarrow[\text{Ni}]{\text{H}_2} \text{H}_2\text{N(CH}_2)_6\text{NH}_2$$

3. Tetrahydrofuran by hydrolysis, cyanation, and reduction (64).

$$\text{THF} \xrightarrow{\text{HCl}} \text{Cl(CH}_2)_4\text{Cl} \xrightarrow{\text{NaCN}} \text{NC(CH}_2)_4\text{CN} \xrightarrow{\text{H}_2} \text{H}_2\text{N(CH}_2)_6\text{NH}_2$$

Melting point, color, neutralization equivalent, and steam-volatile bases are indications of purity and suitability for polymer manufacture. Steam-volatile base content must be low because these impurities may act as chain terminators or disturb the acid–diamine balance in 6,6 salt. Hexamethylenediamine is a skin and tissue irritant and care (especially around the eyes and mucous membrane) must be taken in its use.

Polymerization. Technology for the production of poly(hexamethyleneadipamide) has been reviewed in detail (64). The first step in the preparation of nylon-6,6 is formation, isolation, and purification of the hexamethylenediamine salt of adipic acid. This ensures balances of the reactants required for the preparation of high-molecular-weight polymer.

Commercially, hexamethylenediammonium adipate (6,6 salt) is made by mixing stoichiometric proportions of hexamethylenediamine and adipic acid in water (in which it is 47% soluble at 18°C). The salt solution is then decolorized with activated carbon and adjusted to the proper pH (7.6) and concentration prior to the polymerization process. A 9.5% aq soln of the salt has a pH of 7.6.

When the crystalline salt is desired, methanol is used because the salt is only 0.4% soluble at 25°C. The salt of 6,6 forms white, diamond-shaped monoclinic crystals melting at 190–191°C (other sources say 195°C, but this is affected by rate of heating and partial polymerization) with partial polymer formation. The salt is fairly stable when dry or in solution at room temperature, but above 200°C polymerization occurs.

Conversion of the nylon salt to polymer involves heating it to a temperature at which the condensation of the —NH₂ and —CO₂H groups occurs, releasing water and forming —CONH— linkages. The operation must prevent loss of the amine component of the salt when the steam is released during heating so that proper reactant balance is maintained and sufficiently high molecular weights are attained. Commercial polymerization of nylon-6,6 is controlled by temperature and equilibrium water concentration in the melt as described in the following equations:

$$\text{—NH}_2 + \text{—CO}_2\text{H} \rightleftharpoons \text{—CONH—} + \text{H}_2\text{O}$$

$$K' = [\text{—CONH—}][\text{H}_2\text{O}]/[\text{—NH}_2][\text{—CO}_2\text{H}]$$

For all practical purposes —CO₂NH— is a constant, hence, where P is steam pressure,

$$K' = P/[\text{—NH}_2][\text{—CO}_2\text{H}]$$

At one atmosphere of steam and a temperature of 275°C, [—CO₂H][—NH₂] equals approx 3600.

In practice it has been found convenient to control the average chain length by addition of small amounts of monofunctional reactants (eg, 0.2–1.5 mole % acetic acid) which react with the —NH₂ groups and prevent further growth at these ends. Hence, the number average molecular weight is given by $M_n = 2 \times 10^6/([\text{—CO}_2\text{H}] + [\text{—NH}_2] + [\text{stabilizer}])$. The equilibrium number average molecular weight of nylon-6,6 containing 0.75 mole % acetic acid stabilizer at 275°C under 1 atm of steam is approx 14,000.

The starting material for 6,6 polymer is a 10% aq salt soln, which is first concentrated to approx 60% by evaporation at atmospheric pressure, and then charged to an autoclave, together with about 0.6–1.2 mole % of acetic acid stabilizer (depending upon whether the final polymer is to have a high or low viscosity). After purging air from the autoclave, heat is applied with all outlet lines closed. The pressure in the autoclave rises slowly until it reaches 250 psig, at which point steam is slowly bled off so as to maintain this pressure, while the temperature continues to rise as the concentration of the batch increases. During the heating-up and pressure-holding periods sufficient condensation of the salt occurs to "fix" the originally volatile diamine by partial polymerization. Furthermore, by operating at 250 psig pressure, the boiling point of the batch is raised sufficiently to prevent precipitation of a solid polymer phase, which would otherwise occur as soon as the salt started to polymerize. At a temperature of about 275°C, the pressure on the batch is allowed to fall slowly, until atmospheric pressure is reached. Experience has enabled this rate to be regulated so

Table 15. Physical Constants of Poly(hexamethyleneadipamide) (68)

Property	Value
brittleness temperature, dry, °C	−85
coefficient of friction	
nylon–nylon, static	0.42
kinetic	0.35
nylon–steel, static	0.37
kinetic	0.34
coefficient of thermal expansion, 1/°F	$4.5\text{–}5.7 \times 10^{-5}$
crystal structure change, triclinic below,	
pseudohexagonal above, °C	165–175
density, g/cm³	
drawn fiber	1.14–1.16
amorphous	1.07–1.09
crystalline	1.22–1.24
dielectric constant, ϵ	
1000 cycles, 22°C, 18% rh	4.0
wet	20.0
60 cycles, dry, 33°C	3.8
90°C	7.0
dielectric strength, 50% rh, 21°C, V/mil	
9-mil unrolled film	1,300
2-mil rolled film	3,000
entropy of fusion, cal/(°C)(mole)/repeat unit	20.6
flammability, °C	532
glass transition temperature, dry, °C	50
hardness, Rockwell, 23°C	
dry	M79
	R118
50% rh	M59
	R108
heat capacity, cal/(g)(°C)	
−4.5–28.5°C	0.343
20–250°C	0.55
25°C	0.35
100°C	0.48
180°C	0.56
heat distortion temperature, °C	
66 psi	182–204
264 psi	66
heat of crystallization, cal/g	12.8
heat of fusion, kcal/mole	11
heat of wetting, cal/g	7.3
impact strength	
Izod, ft-lb/in., 25°C	2.0–2.7
4°C	0.4–1.4
tensile, psi	76
melting point, °C, in air	250
nitrogen	265
molecular weight,	
repeat unit	226.32
nonfiber forming	6,000 or less
fibers, brittle and weak	6,000–10,000
optimum range	12,000–20,000
difficult to melt-spin	20,000 or more

(continued)

Table 15 (*continued*)

power factor, %	
1000 cycles, 22°C, 18% rh	5.0
wet	11.0
60 cycles, dry, 33°C	1.8
90°C	13.0
refractive index	
index of parallel refraction	1.580–1.582
index of perpendicular refraction	1.519–1.520
undrawn or molded	1.53
principal values for single crystals	
α, calcd	1.475
β, calcd	1.565
γ, observed	1.580
resistivity, ohm-cm, film, 18% rh	4×10^4
wet	5×10^9
shear stress, psi	9,600
shrinkage	
boiling water, %	
unrelaxed multifilament	8.5–10.0
unrelaxed monofilament	10.3–11.8
mold shrinkage, in./in.	
thickness, $\frac{1}{32}$ in.	0.010
$\frac{1}{16}$ in.	0.012
$\frac{1}{8}$ in.	0.015
$\frac{1}{4}$ in.	0.022
thermal conductivity,	
Btu/(hr)(ft²)(°F/in.)	1.7
toughness, g-cm/den-cm	0.78–0.97

as to prevent freezing the batch. Finally, the batch is held at atmospheric pressure and about 270°C (mp of 6,6 polymer is 265°C) for about half an hour, to permit escape of water vapor. (In certain cases it is necessary to carry the polymerization further toward completion. This is accomplished by holding the batch under partial vacuum at the end of polymerization, and is called "vacuum finishing.") At the end of the holding period, the batch is extruded in the form of a ribbon onto a water-cooled casting wheel, additional cooling being obtained by spraying water on the ribbon. The ribbon is then dried and cut into chips or flake in a rotary cutter.

Possible variations in polymer properties within a batch or from batch to batch are minimized by thoroughly blending several batches in flake form. The flake is then kept out of contact with atmospheric air to avoid moisture pick-up until it is ready to be used. The polymer is then characterized by relative viscosity (η_{rel}), moisture content, and end-group ($-NH_2$ and $-CO_2H$) analysis.

Delustering and Pigmentation. Yarn from unmodified polymer has too high a luster to be suitable for most apparel purposes. A dull appearance is obtained by adding titanium dioxide as a delusterant during the polymerization cycle.

Physical Properties. Bulk nylon-6,6 polymer normally is a tough, white, translucent crystalline material which melts at 265°C. An amorphous, clearer form is obtained if the melt is quenched rapidly below room temperature, but this is unstable and will crystallize on standing at room temperature or if annealed.

Physical properties of nylon-6,6 are shown in Table 15. See also under Polyamide fibers, Polyamide plastics, below.

POLYCAPROLACTAM NYLON-6

Poly(ϵ-caproamide) was first obtained by Gabriel and Maas (69) in 1889 by heating ϵ-aminocaproic acid; cyclic lactam was also obtained. The polyamide did not become of practical importance until 1938 when Schlack discovered that ϵ-caprolactam was converted to polymer by heating with water (70).

At present, poly(ϵ-caprolactam) is second only to nylon-6,6 in world production. World capacity for caprolactam (1968) exceeds 2.5 billion lb. U.S. capacity is 600 million lb; Allied Chemical Corp. (300 million lb), Dow-Badische Chemical Co. (175 million lb), Union Carbide Corp. (50 million lb), and E. I. du Pont de Nemours & Co., Inc. (50 million lb) being the chief producers (71). Essentially all caprolactam produced in the U.S. is used for making nylon-6, which has about 25% of the total U.S. nylon market; nylon-6,6 has the remainder. Nylon-6 is used largely for fiber production and the annual capacity in the U.S. is about 340 million lb. Major uses are carpeting, tire cord, and textiles. Polycaprolactam is characterized by deeper dyeing properties than nylon-6,6. Nylon-6 is also used as a molding and extrusion resin and current annual capacity in the U.S. is about 40 million lb.

Monomer Synthesis. Prior to 1961, caprolactam was prepared from phenol via cyclohexanone oxime. Recently other commercial processes (71,72) have been developed from cyclohexane via (a) air oxidation to cyclohexanone, (b) nitration to nitrocyclohexane, and (c) photooximation to cyclohexanone oxime. The last route is particularly low in cost and has been developed in Japan. The major synthetic routes to caprolactam are summarized below.

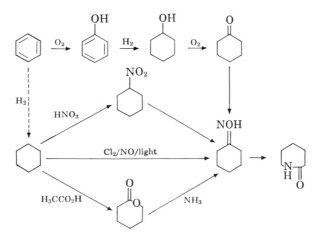

The cyclohexanone oxime is converted to caprolactam by the Beckmann rearrangement. This is done by heating the oxime with weak oleum under anhydrous conditions. The reaction is usually conducted as a continuous process and the concentration of the

oxime is kept low because the reaction is quite exothermic and may become violent if not adequately controlled. The temperature is kept at 100–120°C and the contact time is 15–30 min. The reaction mixture is then cooled, diluted with water, and

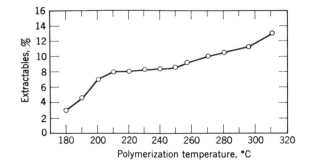

Fig. 11. Equilibrium monomer and oligomer content in polycaprolactam at various polymerization temperatures (64).

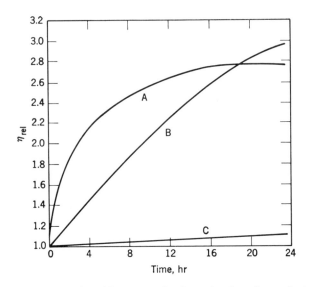

Fig. 12. Effect of aminocaproic acid on rate of polymerization of caprolactam at 260°C. LEGEND: A, B, and C have 5, 2, and 0.5% aminocaproic acid added, respectively (64).

neutralized with ammonia at <40°C. The crude caprolactam is separated by extraction with benzene and purified by distilling under vacuum (bp 120–125°C at 10 mm). Preparation and purification of caprolactam have been described (73).

Polymerization. Polycaprolactam technology has been described in detail (64). Batchwise polymerization of caprolactam is effected by heating at 260°C in an autoclave under pressure using water, 6,6 salt, or ω-aminocaproic acid initiators; acetic acid is usually added as an end-group stabilizer to limit chain length. At equilibrium, conversions of about 90% are realized. The polymer is then extruded, quenched with water, and cut into chips. Monomer (8.5%) and oligomers (1.5%) are extracted from the crude polymer with water at 95–100°C, and the polymer is dried before further processing.

Industrially, caprolactam is polymerized continuously. A concentrated aqueous solution containing the initiator is fed to a tubular reactor (single vertical tube or a number of tubes in series) and heated gradually during passage (20 hr) through the tube to 250–260°C. A slurry of titanium dioxide is often added as delusterant while

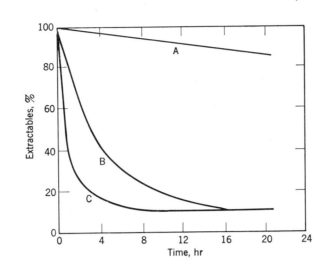

Fig. 13. Effect of aminocaproic acid on monomer and oligomer content in polycaprolactam at 260°C. LEGEND: A, B, and C have 0.5, 2, and 5% aminocaproic acid added, respectively (64).

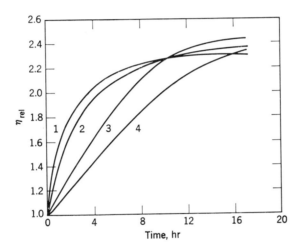

Fig. 14. Effect of 6,6 salt on rate of polymerization of caprolactam at 260°C. LEGEND: 1, H_2O + 5% 6,6 salt; 2, H_2O + 2% 6,6 salt; 3, H_2O + 0.5% 6,6 salt; and 4, H_2O (64).

the polymer is still at low molecular weight. The polymer issuing from the tube is either quenched and cut into chips or fed directly to a screw extruder and converted to yarn. Monomer and oligomers are removed prior to fabrication by aqueous or vacuum (5–10 mm pressure) extraction. The equilibrium content of monomer and oligomers in caprolactam at various polymerization temperatures is shown in Figure 11.

The mechanism of aqueous polymerization of caprolactam has been discussed in detail (74). Though water effects polymerization, the true initiating species is the aminocaproic acid formed by hydrolysis. The effect of aminocaproic acid on polymer yield and on extractants is shown in Figures 12 and 13. The hexamethylenediamine salt of adipic acid (6,6 salt) is also an effective initiator and its effect on the polymerization is compared with that of water alone in Figures 14 and 15.

Table 16. Physical Properties of Nylon-6 (77)

Property	Value
specific gravity of unoriented polymer, g/cm³	1.13
refractive index, n_D, unoriented	1.530
water absorption at saturation, %	9.5
65% rh	4.3
softening temperature, °C	210
melt temperature, °C	223
second-order transition, dry, °C	~50
brittleness point, °C	−25 to −30
Vicat softening point, °C	160–180
heat of fusion, kcal/mole	5.5
entropy of fusion, eu	11.3
spe ific heat, cal/(g)(°C)	0.4–0.5
Moldings	
tensile strength, psi	7,000–12,000
elongation, %	25–320
tensile modulus, 10⁵ psi	1.5–4.5
compressive strength, psi	6,700–13,000
impact strength, ft-lb/in. of notch	
(½ × ½ in. notched bar, Izod test)	1.0–5.5
Rockwell hardness	R103–R119
flexural modulus, dry	395,000–410,000
compressive modulus	245,000–248,000
thermal conductivity,	
cal/(sec)(cm²)(°C/cm) × 10⁻⁴	5.85
specific heat, 25°C, cal/(°C)(g)	0.38
thermal expansion, 10⁻⁵ per °C	8.3
deflection temperature, °F	
at 264 psi fiber stress	150–175
at 66 psi fiber stress	300–365
volume resistivity, 50% rh, 23°C, ohm-cm	10¹²–10¹⁵
dielectric strength, step-by-step	
⅛ in. thickness, V/mil	300–440
dielectric constant, 60 cycles	3.9–5.5
10³ cycles	4.0–4.9
10⁶ cycles	3.5–4.7
dissipation (power) factor, 60 cycles	0.040–0.06
10³ cycles	0.011–0.06
10⁶ cycles	0.03–0.04

Properties. Nylon-6 is similar to nylon-6,6 in physical and chemical properties and in response to mechanical stresses. However, its crystalline melt temperature (223°C) and softening temperature (210°C) are considerably lower. Typical properties for nylon-6 are shown in Table 16.

The relationship of limiting viscosity number (intrinsic viscosity) $[\eta]$ and molecular weight for nylons 6 and 6,6 (in cresol) derived from the Mark-Houwink equation, $[\eta] = KM^a$ (M = viscosity average molecular weight, and K and a are constants), has given the following values (75):

Polyamide	*K*	*a*	*Molecular weight range*
6	3.2×10^{-3}	0.62	500–5,000
6,6	3.5×10^{-4}	0.79	150–50,000

Data relating intrinsic viscosity and M for nylon-6 (76) and several polyamides are shown in Figure 16.

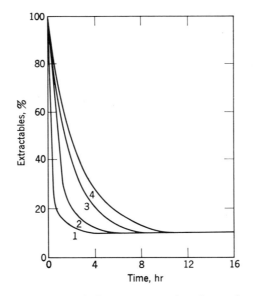

Fig. 15. Effect of 6,6 salt on monomer and oligomer content in polycaprolactam at 260°C. LEGEND: 1, H_2O + 5% 6,6 salt; 2, H_2O + 2% 6,6 salt; 3, H_2O + 0.5% 6,6 salt; and 4, H_2O (64).

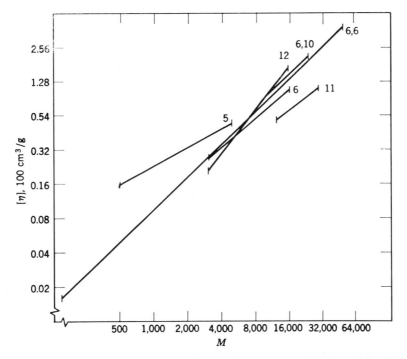

Fig. 16. Relation between $[\eta]$ in m-cresol and viscosity average molecular weight (M) for some polyamides.

OTHER AB POLYAMIDES

In recent years AB polyamides other than polycaprolactam have resulted from improved lactam syntheses and new polymerization technology; none, however, has yet assumed the commercial importance of nylon-6.   Melt temperatures of several of these polymers are shown in Table 17.

Table 17.   Melt Temperatures of Homologous AB Polyamides ($-(CH_2)_nCONH-$)

Polyamides made from	n	T_m, °C
propiolactam	2	>320
3,3-dimethylpropiolactam	2	250
4,4-dimethylpropiolactam	2	296
pyrrolidone	3	260
caprolactam	5	223
enantholactam	6	233
capryllactam	7	200
ω-aminopelargonic acid	8	209
azacycloundecan-2-one	9	188
ω-aminoundecanoic acid	10	190
laurolactam	11	179

Poly(propiolactams), Nylon-3.   β-Propiolactam is not readily prepared in high yield and its polymerization has not been investigated thoroughly.   No commercial utility has yet been found for poly(β-propiolactam).   Substituted β-propiolactams have been examined extensively (33) and possible commercialization of poly(4,4-dimethylpropiolactam), which is reported to have physical properties similar to those of silk, has been suggested.

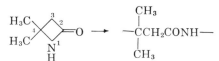

Fibers of poly(4,4-dimethylpropiolactam) are remarkably stable to oxidative heat yellowing because two methyl groups adjacent to the nitrogen shield the site of normal oxidative attack (33).   In contrast, the isomeric poly(3,3-dimethylpropiolactam) discolors on heating as do nylons 6,6 and 6 (33).

Substituted propiolactams are prepared in a low-cost process by condensing a variety of olefins with chlorosulfonyl isocyanate as shown in the following equations:

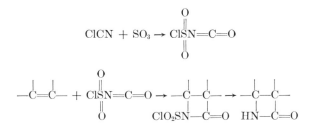

The β-lactam N-sulfonylchlorides are hydrolyzed under weakly acid conditions to give the free β-lactams. This synthesis works well with styrene and with olefins of the following types: $RR'C{=}CH_2$, $RR'C{=}CHR^2$, and $RR'{=}CR^2R^3$. The nitrogen always add to the electron-rich (most-substituted) carbon atom.

Poly(pyrrolidone), Nylon-4. For a long time, it was considered impossible to polymerize the C_4 lactam, pyrrolidone (see Pyrrole). However, in 1951, Ney (78) found that an insoluble polymeric powder (2% yield) separated when a solution of pyrrolidone stood for 203 weeks in the presence of alkali. Organic acyl compounds (acid chlorides, anhydrides, esters, and lactams) considerably accelerated the alkali-initiated polymerization of pyrrolidone. The mechanism of the anionic polymerization of pyrrolidone—without considering side and termination reactions—is the same as for nylon-6.

Pyrrolidone has been polymerized in yields of 80–85% to high molecular weights at <60°C and at economically acceptable rates using the combination of anionic initiator and acylating agent. When polymerized as a dispersion in nonsolvents (eg, hydrocarbons), fine suspensions are obtained which are suitable for dry spinning because they can be dissolved readily. The monomer and basic catalyst residues, however, must be removed from the polymer by aqueous extraction prior to dissolving since they accelerate decomposition at elevated temperatures. Poly(pyrrolidone) has not been melt spun commercially because it decomposes rapidly with reversion to monomer at 265°C.

Decomposition of poly(pyrrolidone) under nitrogen at elevated temperatures (eg, 240°C) follows first-order kinetics with respect to the weight of extractable monomer (79). About 25% of the weight is lost after 2 hr but the inherent viscosity of the extracted polymer is practically unchanged. This has been explained by preferential decomposition and unzippering of the lower-molecular-weight chains. Fibers have been obtained from poly(pyrrolidone) by dry spinning from formic acid. Typical dry and wet tensile properties are compared with those of related polyamides in Table 18.

Table 18. Tensile Properties of Poly(pyrrolidone) and Related Polylactam Fibers

Fiber	Dry tenacity, g/den	Elonga-tion, %	Denier	Wet tenacity, g/den	Elonga-tion, %	Denier	Tenacity retained when wet, %	Modulus retained when wet, %
poly(pyr-rolidone)	4.1	31	3.0	3.1	32	3.0	70–80	45–65
poly(capro-lactam)	8.3	30	6.0	7.1	29	6.0	85–90	55–70
nylon-6,6	7.8	20	6.0	6.7	17	5.9	85–90	55–70
poly(capryl-lactam)	7.5	24	5.6	7.1	22	5.6	93–97	90–95
poly(lauro-lactam)	7.2	24	5.1	7.3	24	5.1	100	90–95

Poly(pyrrolidone) has a much higher moisture absorption than its higher homologues (Table 19) and is similar to cotton in its absorbance over the whole rh range.

Poly(ω-enanthamide), Nylon-7. Although polymerization of enantholactam has been described (80), nylon-7 (known commercially in the U.S.S.R. as Enant) is more conveniently prepared by melt polycondensation of 7-aminoheptanoic acid. Aminoheptanoic acid has been prepared chiefly by two routes.

Table 19. Water Absorption of AB Polyamides

Polyamide made from	Number of CH₂ groups	Water absorption of polymers	
		65% rh	99% rh
pyrrolidone	3	9.1	28
caprolactam	5	4.3	9.5
enantholactam	6	2.8	5.0
capryllactam	7	1.7	3.9
ω-aminopelargonic acid	8	1.5	3.3
azaundecan-2-one	9	1.4	1.9
ω-aminoundecanoic acid	10	1.3	2.8
azacyclotridecan-2-one	11	1.3	2.7

1. Telomerization of ethylene in the presence of carbon tetrachloride (81), and amination and hydrolysis of the telomer. However, this route has the disadvantage

$$H_2C{=}CH_2 + CCl_4 \rightarrow Cl(CH_2CH_2)_6CCl_3 \xrightarrow{NH_3/H_2O} H_2N(CH_2)_6CO_2H$$

$$H_2N(CH_2)_6CO_2H \rightarrow -(HN(CH_2)_6CO)-$$

that the telomerization is not highly selective and relatively low yields of the desired intermediate are obtained.

Table 20. Properties of Polyenanthamide (70)

Property	Value
melting point, °C	223
specific gravity, g/cm³	1.13
heat resistance, Vicat, °C	200
moisture absorption, boiling during 1 hr, %	1.65
specific impact viscosity, kg-cm/cm²	125–150
ultimate strength in static bending, kg/cm²	750
ultimate tensile strength, kg/cm²	580–600
elongation, %	100–200
Brinell hardness, kg/cm²	14–15
ultimate shear strength, kg/cm²	600
surface resistivity, ohm	7×10^{13}
after 7 days in water	1.3×10^{12}
volume resistivity, ohm-cm	2×10^{14}
after 7 days in water	8×10^{13}
tangent of the dielectric loss angle	0.02
after 7 days in water	0.04
dielectric constant	4.4
after 7 days in water	5.5
breakdown voltage, kV/mm	19.0
after 7 days in water	20.0

2. Conversion of phenol to caprolactone, followed by ring opening with hydrogen chloride, cyanation, and reduction.

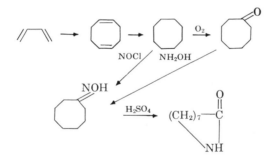

In either case, monomer costs are considerably greater than those of caprolactam so it is unlikely that Enant will be produced commercially on a large scale. Poly-enanthamide is prepared by heating aminoheptanoic acid (or ester) in the presence of water at 260°C. Typical polymer properties which are similar to those of nylon-6 are shown in Table 20.

Polymerization of enantholactam at 230°C in the presence of 4% water has been described (82). Specific viscosities of about 1.2 were obtained in 5 hr at 280°C or in 13 hr at 200°C.

Poly(capryllactam), Nylon-8. Capryllactam (79) is prepared industrially by dimerization of butadiene to cyclooctadiene, reduction to cyclooctane, oximation to cyclooctanone oxime, and then Beckmann rearrangement to the lactam. The oxime is prepared from the cyclooctane either by oxidation to cyclooctanone followed by reaction with hydroxylamine or directly by reaction with nitrosyl chloride. Both routes are shown below.

Polymerization of capryllactam (79) takes place readily in the melt using small amounts of amino acid initiator because ring strain is high. The heat of reaction is high and cooling is needed to prevent the monomer from vaporizing. Comparison of the heats of polymerization (ΔH, liquid–liquid) of capryllactam and those of close homologs is shown in Table 21.

Table 21. Enthalpies of Polymerization of Several Lactams

Monomer	ΔH, kcal/mole	Monomer	ΔH, kcal/mole
caprolactam	−3.2	capryllactam	−9.6[a]
enantholactam	−5.2	laurolactam	−1.4[a]

[a] Estimated from the temperature rise during rapid adiabatic alkaline polymerization.

Poly(capryllactam) is quite thermally stable and the melt contains only small amounts of monomer and oligomer even at long holding times. Melt spun fibers, therefore, do not have to be extracted to remove monomer. The low melt temperature (200°C) and high raw-material costs relative to nylon-6 have limited the usefulness of this polymer. Fiber properties have already been described with those of poly-(pyrrolidone) in Table 18.

Poly(ω-pelargonamide), Nylon-9. Poly(ω-pelargonamide) is prepared by melt condensation of ω-aminopelargonic acid. This intermediate is prepared by the telomerization reaction of ethylene (below), already discussed for ω-aminoenanthic acid (see p. 36).

$$H_2C=CH_2 + CCl_4 \rightarrow Cl(CH_2CH_2)_4CCl_3 \rightarrow H_2N(CH_2)_8CO_2H \rightarrow -(HN(CH_2)_8CO)-$$

Aminopelargonic acid polymerizes rapidly above 230°C. High-molecular-weight polymer (T_m, 210°) is obtained in 2–4 hr at 260°C. Though fiber properties have been reported (80), nylon-9 has not been evaluated extensively because of relatively high intermediate cost.

Poly(aminodecanoic acid), Nylon-10. Detailed evaluation of this polymer has not been described because of difficulties in preparing the monomer. Polymer melt temperature is reported to be 188°C (79).

Poly(ω-undecaneamide), Nylon-11. Poly(ω-undecaneamide) was first prepared by Carothers in 1935. Industrial manufacture is primarily carried out in France where the polymer is known as Rilsan. The monomer is prepared from castor oil via undecylenic acid, according to the scheme below (83):

$$H_3C(CH_2)_5CH(OH)CH_2CH=CH(CH_2)_7CO_2H \xrightarrow[\text{tion}]{\text{oxida-}} H_3CCH=CH(CH_2)_7CO_2H + H_3C(CH_2)_5CHO$$

$$H_3CCH=CH(CH_2)_7CO_2H \xrightarrow{\text{HBr}} BrCH_2(CH_2)_9CO_2H \rightarrow H_2N(CH_2)_{10}CO_2H$$

High-molecular-weight nylon-11 is prepared in about 3 hr by melt condensation of the ω-aminoundecanoic acid under nitrogen at 215°C. Typical properties of poly(ω-

Table 22. Properties of Poly-ω-undecaneamide (84)

Property	Value
specific gravity of nonoriented polymer, g/cm³	1.10
water absorption at saturation, %	1.6
softening temperature, °C	175
melting temperature, °C	185
brittleness point, °C	−70
ultimate tensile strength, kg/cm²	600–800
elasticity modulus, kg/cm²	1000–2000
elongation, %	90–120
surface hardness, Brinell (25-kg load), kg/cm²	465
compression strength, kg/cm²	11
volume resistivity, ohm-cm	10^{14}
dielectric constant at 10^6 cycles/sec	3.2
tangent of the dielectric loss angle at 10^6 cycles/sec	0.02–0.03

undecaneamide) are shown in Table 22. This polyamide is quite hydrophobic and has excellent electrical insulating properties. Major uses include pressure moldings and fibers. Sales of Rilsan in 1965 have been estimated at 5 million lb and capacity was approx 12 million lb.

POLYAMIDES FROM LONG–CHAIN FATTY ACIDS

Another class of polyamide resins is based on condensation of diamines or tri-amines (ethylenediamine or diethylenetriamine) with relatively high-molecular-weight dibasic acids or esters, such as dimer acid obtained from thermal polymerization of linoleic acid. (See Vol. 8, p. 848.)

The polyamides vary from tacky to high-melting (175°C) resins and are used as heat-sealing adhesives and as moisture-barrier coatings for paper, wood, cellophane, etc. The polymer coatings are applied from solution, dispersion, or powder.

PARTLY AROMATIC POLYAMIDES

The properties of aliphatic–aromatic polyamides have been discussed in detail under Structure–property relationships (see p. 14). A typical example of an aliphatic–aromatic polyamide which has been evaluated as a more thermally stable polymer with better property retention at moderately high temperatures is 6,T. However, none of the aliphatic–aromatic polyamides has yet assumed commercial importance, possibly because the lower-melting ones offer insufficient advantages over present all-aliphatic polymers (eg, 6,6) and because the higher-melting ones (such as 6,T) are difficult to prepare and fabricate, and do not offer the long-term thermal stability of the all-aromatic polyamides.

Poly(hexamethylene terephthalamide), 6,T. The only aliphatic–aromatic polyamide that appears to have been examined extensively is 6,T. The incentives to evaluate 6,T have been (a) cheap intermediates, (b) good tensile properties, and (c) dimensional stability up to 200°C. However, these attractive features are counterbalanced by (a) solution fabrication being required by the high melt temperature

Table 23. Property Comparison of 6,T; 6,6; and 2,GT

Property	Nylon-6,T	Polyester-2,GT	Nylon-6,6
melting point, °C	370	265	265
density, g/cm³	1.21	1.38	1.14
glass transition temperature, °C	180	115	60
moisture regain, %	4.5	0.6	4.5
tensile properties			
tenacity, g/den	4.5	4.8	4.9
elongation, %	35	54	57
modulus	45	40	40
strength retained after 5 hr, %			
at 150°C	100	100	85
at 185°C	100	95	40
at 220°C	60		0

(370°C), (b) being soluble only in strongly acid solvents such as sulfuric or trifluoro-acetic acids, and (c) requiring relatively expensive polymerization methods (eg, interfacial polymerization or solid-phase polymerization). Fiber and polymer properties reported (85) for 6,T, which has been wet spun from sulfuric acid, are compared with those of nylon-6,6 and poly(ethylene terephthalate) in Table 23.

Fiber Blends of Aliphatic Polyamides and Aliphatic–Aromatic Polyamide. A deficiency of nylons 6 and 6,6 when used in tires is flat-spotting. It has been shown (86) that when selected aliphatic–aromatic polyamides are melt blended with nylons 6 or 6,6 the modulus is raised and creep is reduced. Several of the aliphatic–aromatic polymers used and the effects of reducing set (at 10% rh) are reported in Table 24. The set value is a measure of the permanent increase in length (growth) of the fiber after exposure to elevated temperatures (approx 77°C) in a laboratory test which simulates tire running temperatures; fibers with set values <1.0 are considered to be nonflat-spotting. The set value obviously decreases as the aromatic content of the blend polymer increases.

Table 24. Set Values of Selected Block Copolyamides (86)

Aromatic polymer	Wt, %	Nylon-6,6, wt %	Nylon-6, wt %	Set,[a] %	Tenacity, g/den
		100		1.7	8.5
			100	2.1	
$-HN-C_6H_4-NHCO(CH_2)_4CO-$	30	70		0.56	8.7
$-HN-C_6H_4-NHCO(CH_2)_4CO-$	20	80		1.04	7.6
$-HN-C_6H_4-NHCO(CH_2)_4CO-$	20[b]	80[b]		2.3	3.1
$-OC-C_6H_4-CONH(CH_2)_6NH-$	30	70		0.86	5.4
$-OC-C_6H_4-CONH(CH_2)_3NH-$	20	80		0.64	4.7
$-HN-C_6H_4-NHCO(CH_2)_4CO-$	30		70	0.79	
$-OC-C_6H_4-CONH(CH_2)_6NH-$	35	65	65	1.07	

[a] Determined at a relative humidity of less than 10%.

[b] Random copolymer obtained by copolymerizing rather than melt blending.

The polymer blend is usually prepared by melting both components together with shearing and, at the required temperatures, amide interchange takes place resulting in *block copolymer* formation. Too high a degree of randomization results in loss of the desired stiffening effects of the aromatic component. The degree of randomization depends on time, temperature, intimacy of blending, molecular weight of both components, ratio of the blend components, and end groups (because of end-group catalysis).

WHOLLY AROMATIC POLYAMIDES

There has been a growing need for high-temperature-resistant fibers and fiber-based materials for industrial and military uses such as high-temperature filtration, protective clothing, conveyor belting, electrical insulation, and reinforcement. Such polymers must maintain a favorable balance of chemical and physical properties over a wide range of temperatures to have broad utility. One polymer which appears to meet many of these high-temperature requirements is Nomex which is a wholly aromatic polyamide (87). The chemical structure of Nomex has not been disclosed.

All-aromatic polymers reported in early polyamide patents were prepared by melt polymerization and were probably highly degraded or crosslinked because most aromatic polyamides decompose before melting. Properties alleged for the aromatic polyamides (such as softening below their melting points, noncrystalline, colored) do not agree with properties as now reported. Recent progress in synthesis and fabrication of all-aromatic polyamides results from (a) low-temperature polymerization methods from acid chlorides and (b) the discovery of solvents which do not cause side reactions during polymer preparation or degradation in spinning. The literature on low-temperature polycondensation up to 1965 has been reviewed and the preparation of several aromatic polymers has been described (6). Interfacial polymerization in general is not satisfactory for preparing high-molecular-weight aromatic polyamides ($\eta_{\text{inherent}} \geq 0.8$). In general, the best method of preparing high-molecular-weight wholly aromatic polyamides is low-temperature solution polycondensation (6,19).

AABB Polyamides from Intermediates Containing Preformed Amide Linkages. Ordered aromatic copolyamides have also been prepared by low-temperature polycondensation from diamines or diacid chlorides which contain preformed amide link-

Table 25. Polyamide Intermediates to Heterocyclic Polymers

Polyamide intermediate	Derived polymer

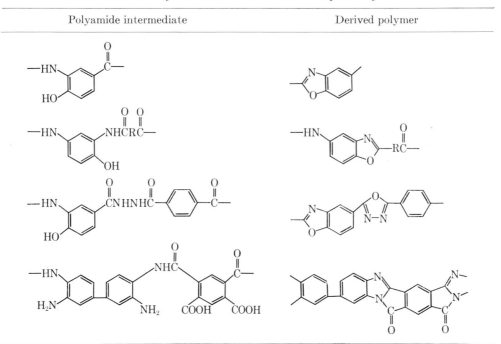

ages. Under the conditions of polymerization, no reorganization of the structural units occurs (88).

AABB Polyamides Containing Heterocyclic Units. Aromatic polyamides containing heterocyclic units have been prepared by low-temperature solution polycondensation, to determine if such polymers had better thermal stability than the comparable homocyclic polyamides (89); however, no significant improvement has been reported.

Aromatic Polyamides as Intermediates for Thermally Stable Heterocyclic Polymers. Aromatic polyamides with substituents which can be further reacted to form heterocyclic rings, have been used as soluble precursors to intractable, thermally stable polymers. For example, polyamides with *o*-carboxyl groups have been used to form polyimides (see below); polyamides with *o*-hydroxyls have been used to form polybenzoxazoles; and polyhydrazides have yielded polyoxadiazoles. A selection of these polyamides and their products is shown in Table 25. The importance of the soluble polyamides is that they can easily be fabricated into fibers and films prior to conversion to the desired intractable polymer (19,90).

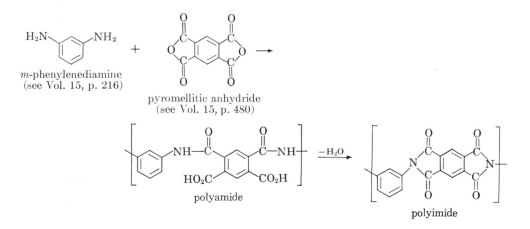

m-phenylenediamine
(see Vol. 15, p. 216)

pyromellitic anhydride
(see Vol. 15, p. 480)

polyamide

polyimide

General Properties. Aromatic polyamides, in general, are colorless, high melting ($T_m > 300°C$), and crystalline. Many aromatic polyamides discolor on exposure to light; however, the discoloration apparently acts as an effective ultraviolet shield that tends to reduce the rate of strength loss (42).

Selected aromatic polyamides have been used as high-temperature fibers and films which are superior to natural and many other synthetic polymers in retention of properties on long-term exposure. The major advantages of wholly aromatic polyamides over aliphatic polyamides are (a) superior long-term thermal stability at elevated temperatures (200–300°C), (b) excellent retention of physical and electrical properties at elevated temperatures, (c) high resistance to property loss on exposure to chemicals and solvents, (d) low flammability, (e) high stiffness (modulus), (f) high dielectric strength, and (g) resistance to ionizing radiation. One aromatic polyamide, Nomex, is now in commercial production. Fiber and paper properties and its uses in electrical insulation and protective clothing have been described in detail (42). The superiority of Nomex fiber to nylon-6,6 and to poly(ethyleneterephthalate), Dacron (E. I. du Pont de Nemours & Co., Inc.), at elevated temperatures is illustrated in Figure 17.

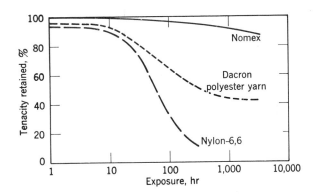

Fig. 17. Tenacity retentions of yarns exposed to air at 175°C (42).

In addition to their good retention of properties at elevated temperatures, aromatic polyamides burn only with difficulty and even then form a thick char which is an effective thermal insulator, so that they are very useful for protective clothing. Aliphatic nylons and polyesters, in contrast, melt on burning, and serious burns may result if the melt is not removed from contact with the skin.

Wholly aromatic polyamides have excellent electrical properties (eg, high volume resistivities and dielectric strengths) which are largely retained at elevated temperatures. Such properties make aromatic polyamides useful as insulators in motors and transformers. For example, the dielectric strength and useful operating temperature of Nomex paper is about twice that of high-quality rag paper, which is used widely in electrical motor insulation (Table 26).

Table 26. Electrical Properties of 10-mil Nomex Paper Compared With Rag Insulation Paper (42)

Property	Nomex paper	High-quality rag paper
volume resistivity, ohm-cm		
at 50% rh	2.3×10^{15}	4.1×10^{10}
at 95% rh	6.3×10^8	3.8×10^6
dielectric strength,		
V/mil	560	350
dielectric constant at		
50% rh, 50 cps	3.3	3.5
dissipation factor at		
50% rh, 60 cps	0.01	0.03
operating temperature, max, °C	>200	105

Resistance of crystalline aromatic polyamides to hydrolysis, or degradation by solvents in general, is very good. Nomex is reported to have good resistance to many chemicals, to hydrocarbons, and to many other organic solvents. Resistance of Nomex to acid hydrolysis is greater than that of nylon-6,6, but less than that of poly(ethylene terephthalate). On the other hand, resistance to aqueous alkali is slightly lower than that of nylon-6,6, but considerably better than that of poly(ethylene terephthalate).

Aromatic polyamide fibers, like their aliphatic counterparts, are degraded by ultraviolet radiation. However, the resistance of wholly aromatic amides to ionizing radiation is greatly superior to that of nylon-6,6. For example, Nomex fiber retains 76% of its original strength after 600 megareps in a Van de Graaff generator, whereas the strength of nylon-6,6 fiber is reduced to zero after the same exposure. The greater resistance of Nomex fibers to degradation compared with nylon-6,6 fiber is just as marked with gamma radiation and x rays (Table 27).

Table 27. Resistance of Nylon Fibers to Ionizing Radiation Degradation (42)

Type of radiation	Tenacity retained, %	
	Nomex	Nylon-6,6
beta radiation (Van de Graaff),		
200 megareps	81	29
600 megareps	76	0
gamma radiation (Brookhaven pile),		
200 megareps	70	32
2000 megareps	45	0
x rays (50 kV),		
50	85	22
100	73	0

Bibliography

"Polyamides" in *ECT* 1st ed., Vol. 10, pp. 916–937, by Ferdinand Schulze, E I. du Pont de Nemours & Co., Inc., and Harold Wittcoff, General Mills, Inc.

1. H. Mark and G. S. Whitby, eds., *Collected Papers of Wallace Hume Carothers on High Polymeric Substances*, Vol. I of *High Polymers*, Interscience Publishers, Inc., New York, 1940.
2. *Textile Organon* **37**, 97 (1966).
3. D. W. Van Krevelen, *Chem. Weekblad* **62**, 45 (1966); *Mod. Textiles Mag.* **46**, 25 (June 1965).
4. *Textile Organon* **38**, 98 (1967).
5. *Hydrocarbon Process. Petrol. Refiner* **42**, 157 (1963).
5a. "Polyamides," in N. M. Bikales, ed., *Encyclopedia of Polymer Science and Technology*, Vol. 10, Interscience Publishers, a division of John Wiley & Sons, Inc., New York (in press).
6. P. W. Morgan, *Condensation Polymers: by Interfacial and Solution Methods*, John Wiley & Sons, Inc., New York, 1965.
7. U.S. Pat. 3,296,201 (May 3, 1967), C. W. Stephens (to E. I. du Pont de Nemours & Co., Inc.).
8. D. Coleman and A. C. Farthing, *J. Chem. Soc.* **1950**, 3213–3222.
9. U.S. Pat. 2,672,480 (March 16, 1954), A. S. Matlack (to Hercules Powder Co.).
10. V. E. Shashoua et al., *J. Am. Chem. Soc.* **82**, 866 (1960).
11. A. Cannepin et al., *J. Polymer Sci.* **8**, 35 (1952); E. E. Magat et al., *J. Am. Chem. Soc.* **73**, 1031 (1951).
12. A. Marthes, *Makromol. Chem.* **5**, 165 (1950).
13. J. Haslam and S. D. Swift, *Analyst* **79**, 82 (1954).
14. E. M. Fettes, ed., *Chemical Reactions of Polymers*, Vol. XIX of *High Polymers*, Interscience Publishers, a division of John Wiley & Sons, Inc., New York, 1964, p. 561.
15. V. V. Korshak et al., *Acta Phys. USSR* **21**, 723 (1946).
16. C. W. Ayers, *J. Appl. Chem.* **4**, 444 (1954).
17. S. R. Rafikou et al., *Vysokomolekul. Soedin.* **1**, 378 (1959).
18. U.S. Pat. 3,287,324 (Nov. 22, 1966), W. Sweeney; U.S. Pat. 3,133,138 (May 12, 1964), E. L. Alexander; Belg. Pat. 569,760 (to du Pont).
19. W. B. Black and J. Preston, *Fiber Forming Aromatic Polyamides*, Interscience Publishers, a division of John Wiley & Sons, Inc., New York (in press); U.S. Pat. 3,063,966 (Nov. 13, 1962), Kwolek et al.; U.S. Pat. 3,068,188 (Dec. 11, 1962), L. F. Beste and C. W. Stephens (to du Pont).
20. S. Sönnerskog, *Acta Chem. Scand.* **10** (3), 467 (1956).
21. J. R. Lewis and R. J. W. Reynolds, *Chem. Ind.* (*London*) **1951**, 958.

22. E. E. Magat et al., *J. Am. Chem. Soc.* **73**, 1031 (1951); R. E. Wright and M. Harris, *Kunststoffe* **38**, 145 (1948).

23. E. J. Burrell, *J. Am. Chem. Soc.* **83**, 574 (1961).

24. J. C. Bevington and D. E. Eaves, *Nature* **178**, 1112 (1959).

25. V. V. Korshak et al., *Vysokomolekul. Soedin.* **1**, 1604 (1959).

26. A. Chapiro, *J. Polymer Sci.* **29**, 321 (1958); **34**, 439 (1959); Okamura, *Chemistry (Kyoto)* **11** (2), 44 (1956).

27. E. E. Magat et al., *J. Polymer Sci.* **4C**, 615 (1963).

28. H. W. Starkweather et al., *J. Polymer Sci.* **21**, 189 (1956).

29. P. F. Dismore and W. O. Statton, *J. Polymer Sci.* **13C**, 133 (1966).

30. W. O. Statton, *Ann. N.Y. Acad. Sci.* **83**, 27 (1959).

31. J. Preston, *J. Polymer Sci.* **1A** (4), 529 (1966); U.S. Pat. 3,094,511 (June 18, 1963), H. W. Hill et al. (to du Pont).

32. "High Temperature Resistance and Thermal Degradation of Polymers," *Soc. Chem. Ind. (London) Monograph* **13** (1961).

33. R. Graf et al., *Angew. Chem. Intern. Ed. Engl.* **1**, 481 (1962).

34. W. H. Sharkey and W. E. Mochel, *J. Am. Chem. Soc.* **81**, 300 (1959).

35. J. Zimmerman, private communication.

36. L. G. Tokareva et al., *Vysokomolekul. Soedin.* **2**, 1728 (1960).

37. W. W. Wright et al., *J. Polymer Sci.* **2B**, 369 (1964).

38. Y. P. Krasnov et al., *Vysokomolekul. Soedin.* **8** (3), 380 (1966).

39. G. N. Harding and B. J. McNulty, *Symposium on High Temperature Resistance and Thermal Degradation of Polymers, London, Sept. 1960.*

40. C. V. Stephenson et al., *J. Polymer Sci.* **55**, 451 (1961).

41. R. F. Moore, *Polymer* **4**, 493 (1963).

42. *Nomex Technical Information Bulletins, N-201,* E. I. du Pont de Nemours & Co., Inc., p. 195.

43. E. J. Lawton et al., *Nature* **172**, 76 (1953); A. Charlesby, *Nature* **171**, 167 (1953); O. Sisman and C. D. Bopp, *Oak Ridge National Laboratory Rept. ORNL-928* U.S. Govt. Printing Office, Washington, D.C., 1951; reference 14, pp. 751, 1080.

44. C. W. Deeley et al., *J. Appl. Phys.* **28**, 1124 (1957).

45. K. Little, *U.S. At. Energy Comm. Rept. GP/R-1402;* M. Schwemmer, *Textil-Rundschau* **11**, 1 (1956).

46. A. Charlesby and S. H. Pinner, *Proc. Roy. Soc. (London) Ser. A* **249**, 367 (1959).

47. O. B. Edgar and R. Hill, *J. Polymer Sci.* **8**, 1 (1952).

48. E. L. Wittbecker, *Symposium of Minnesota Am. Chem. Soc. Sect., June 1953;* H. Batzer, *Makromol. Chem.* **10**, 13 (1953); C. W. Bunn, *J. Polymer Sci.* **16**, 323; **17**, 159 (1955).

49. E. F. Izard, *J. Polymer Sci.* **8**, 503; **9**, 35 (1952).

50. I. Kirshenbaum, *J. Polymer Sci.* **3A**, 1869 (1965).

51. M. Dole and B. Wunderlich, *Makromol. Chem.* **34**, 29 (1959).

52. C. S. Fuller et al., *J. Am. Chem. Soc.* **59**, 344 (1937); **61**, 2575 (1939).

53. D. D. Coffman et al., *J. Polymer Sci.* **2**, 306 (1947); J. B. Quig, *Textile Res. J.* **23**, 280 (1953); W. Scheele, *Kolloid Z.* **98**, 222 (1942); R. Hill and E. E. Walker, *J. Polymer Sci.* **3**, 614 (1948); G. Champetier et al., *Bull. Soc. Chim. France* **1948**, 683; **1956**, 855; A. Parisot, *Bull. Inst. Text. France* **54**, 7 (1955).

54. W. Ziegenbein et al., *Chem. Ber.* **88**, 1906 (1955).

55. J. R. Lewis and R. J. W. Reynolds, *Chem. Ind. (London)* **1951**, 958; E. L. Wittbecker et al., *Ind. Eng. Chem.* **40**, 875 (1948).

56. V. E. Shashoua and W. M. Eareckson, *J. Polymer Sci.* **40**, 343 (1959).

57. A. Bell et al., *J. Polymer Sci.* **3A**, 19 (1965).

58. C. E. Schildknecht, ed., *Polymer Processes,* Vol. X of *High Polymers,* Interscience Publishers, Inc., New York, 1956.

59. M. Katz, *J. Polymer Sci.* **40**, 337 (1959).

60. S. J. Allen, *J. Textile Inst.* **44**, 286 (1953).

61. O. B. Edgar and R. Hill, *J. Polymer Sci.* **8**, 8 (1952).

62. M. H. Kaufman et al., *J. Polymer Sci.* **13**, 3 (1954).

63. A. H. Frazer, *High Temperature Resistant Polymers,* Vol. XVII of *Polymer Reviews,* Interscience Publishers, a division of John Wiley & Sons, Inc., New York, 1968; W. A. Lee et al., AD 482067, Royal Air Force Establishment, Great Britain, 1966.

64. H. Klare, *Synthetische Fasern und Polyamide*, Akademie-Verlag, GmbH, Berlin, 1963; H. Hopff, *Die Polyamide*, Springer-Verlag, Berlin-Wilmersdorf (West), 1954.
65. L. F. Hatch, *Hydrocarbon Process. Petrol. Refiner* **42** (4), 160–161 (1963).
66. R. J. W. Reynolds, "Polyamides, Polyesters and Polyurethans," in R. Hill, ed., *Fibers from Synthetic Polymers*, Elsevier Publishing Co., Amsterdam, 1953, pp. 123–124.
67. D. E. Floyd, *Polyamide Resins*, Reinhold Publishing Corp., New York, 1958, p. 32.
68. J. Brandrup and E. H. Immergut, *Polymer Handbook*, Interscience Publishers, a division of John Wiley & Sons, Inc., New York, 1966, p. 79.
69. S. Gabriel and T. A. Maas, *Chem. Ber.* **32**, 1266 (1899).
70. U.S. Pat. 2,241,321 (May 6, 1941), P. Schlack (to I. G. Farbenindustrie A.G.).
71. *Chem. Eng. News* **45**, 84 (Aug. 28, 1967); **45**, 21 (July 3, 1967).
72. Reference 65, pp. 161–162.
73. I. Vilea et al., *Rev. Chim. (Bucharest)* **14** (10), 122 (1963); P. W. Sherwood, *Melliand Textilber.* **43** (11), 182 (1962).
74. O. Wichterle et al., *Fortschr. Hochpolymer.-Forsch.* **2**, 578 (1961).
75. Reference 68, p. 37.
76. R. Vergoz, *Ann. Chim. (Paris)* **8**, 140 (1953); J. L. A. Jansen, *Proefschrift, Tech. Hoch*, Delft, Holland, 1967.
77. V. V. Korshak and T. M. Frunze, *Synthetic Hetero-chain Polyamides*, Davey, Daniel & Co., Inc., New York, 1964; J. Frados, ed., *Modern Plastics Encyclopedia*, McGraw-Hill Book Co., Inc., New York, 1965.
78. U.S. Pat. 2,739,959 (March 27, 1956), W. O. Ney and M. Crowther (to Arnold Hoffman & Co.).
79. K. Dachs and E. Schwartz, *Angew. Chem. Intern. Ed. Engl.* **1**, 430 (1962).
80. A. N. Nesmeyanov et al., *Chem. Tech. (USSR)* **9**, 139 (1957).
81. A. Strepinkheev et al., *Vopr. Ispolz. Pentozansoderzh. Syr'ya, Tr. Vses. Soveshch., Riga* **1955**, 281–287 (1958); *Chem. Abstr.* **53**, 14933 (1959).
82. R. Cubbon, *Polymer* **4**, 545 (1964).
83. H. Tatu, *Rev. Textile* **50**, 32 (1952); Fr. Pat. 958,178 (March 3, 1950), H. Tatu (to Société Organico).
84. R. Dumon, *Ind. Textile (France)* **67**, 106 (1950); *Ind. Plastiques Mod. (Paris)* **2**, 19 (1950).
85. B. S. Sprague and R. W. Singleton, *Textile Res. J.* **35** (11), 999 (1965).
86. Brit. Pat. 918,637 (Feb. 13, 1963), J. Zimmerman (to du Pont).
87. L. K. McCune, *Textile Res. J.* **32** (9), 762 (1962).
88. J. Preston and F. Dobinson, *J. Polymer Sci.* **1A** (4), 2093 (1966).
89. J. Preston and W. B. Black, *J. Polymer Sci.* **4B**, 267 (1966).
90. C. S. Sroog et al., *J. Polymer Sci.* **3A**, 1373 (1965).

W. Sweeny

E. I. du Pont de Nemours & Co., Inc.

POLYAMIDE FIBERS

History, Growth, and Economic Importance. Nylon was the first major fiber made from wholly synthetic polymer. It was probably first observed by Gabriel and Maas in 1899 (1). In 1929 Carothers initiated research which ultimately resulted in the transformation of a laboratory curiosity to a commercially practical fiber (2–4). This fundamental research resulted in the application for U.S. patents 2,071,250 and 2,071,253, applied for in June 1931 and January 1935. These included working examples of polyamides made from aliphatic amino acids and lactams which included nylons 6, 7, 8, 9, 11, and 17. This research work was followed by diamine–diacid polyamide in U.S. patents 2,130,523 and 2,130,948 filed in January 1935 and April 1937. These latter patents contained working examples of diamine–diacid aliphatics for aromatic, alicyclic, and heterocyclic components in combination with each other or with other aliphatic monomers as one of the polyamide components.

Research work undertaken by Schlack in 1929 and 1930, related to amino acid synthesis, was successful in January 1938 in obtaining spinnable polycaproamide and in June 1938 German patent 748, 253 was applied for (5).

In the U.S., E. I. du Pont de Nemours & Co., Inc. (du Pont) began experimental production of nylon in 1938 at Seaford, Delaware, and was in commercial production by December 1939. The first nylon stockings were introduced to the public in May 1940, and were an immediate and outstanding commercial success. The Seaford plant was followed by a plant at Martinsville, Virginia, in 1941; a third plant at Chattanooga, Tennessee, in 1947; and a fourth plant in Richmond, Virginia, in 1954.

In Germany, I. G. Fabenindustrie, A.G. started production of coarse nylon monofilaments under the trade name Perluran in the autumn of 1939 (6). Large-scale production of nylon-6 was started in 1941 at Landsberg (now renamed Gorzow Wielkopolski) and, by July 1944, the forecast monthly production rate was equivalent to an annual production rate of 8.7 million lb of nylon-6 and 1 million lb of nylon-6,6. After World War II, production of nylon-6 was started by Vereinigte Glanzstoff-Fabriken, A.G., at Obernburg; and nylon-6,6, by Deutsche Rhodiaceta, A.G., at Freiburg, in 1949 (7).

In Italy, nylon-6,6 was made by Italian Rhodiacetà at Pallanza using a spinning machine imported from the U.S. by du Pont in 1939 (8). In England, Courtaulds and Imperial Chemical Industries, Ltd. (ICI) formed British Nylon Spinners and began the production of nylon-6,6 at a plant in Covington in January 1941. This was succeeded by a second plant built at the same location in December 1942 (9). Other early producers of polyamide fibers were Canadian Industries Ltd. (du Pont and ICI), in Kingston, Ontario, 1942; Argentina Ducilo (du Pont), in Buenos Aires, 1948; Société Rhodiaceta, in Lyon-Vaise, France (nylon-6,6); Algemene Kunstzijde Unie, in Arnhem, Netherlands, 1949 (nylon-6); and Toyo Rayon, in Nagoya, Japan, 1949 (nylon-6,6).

The second nylon-6,6 producer in the U.S. was Chemstrand Corp., now Monsanto Textiles Division, which began production of nylon-6,6 in July 1952, at Pensacola, Florida.

Commercial production of nylon-6 in the U.S. began with large-scale availability of caprolactam, first produced in quantity in February 1955 by Allied Chemical Corp. During the same year, American Enka Corp., Industrial Rayon Corp., and Allied Chemical started production of nylon-6 in the U.S. The Firestone Tire & Rubber Co. was commercially producing nylon-6 monofilaments at this time.

The outstanding and fundamental research of Carothers (9a) which initiated the commercialization of nylon was extensively built upon by others who accomplished the complex and technically difficult task of conceiving, designing, and building the machinery for the first major industrial polymerization, spinning, and drawing of synthetics. Significant contributors at a research scale were P. J. Flory, J. W. Hill, G. J. Berchet, R. A. Jacobson, and G. W. Rigby. In the important transition of nylon-6,6 from a laboratory curiosity to a practical industrial fiber, important contributors were H. Worthington (engineering), W. W. Heckert, D. D. Coffman, and D. R. Hull. The work of these researchers and the host of others following them has developed into a major growth industry, ie, the synthetic-fibers industry.

In 1950, fourteen plants in ten countries produced 123 million lb of polyamide fibers (10). By 1966 this had expanded to 207 plants in forty-five countries, which had

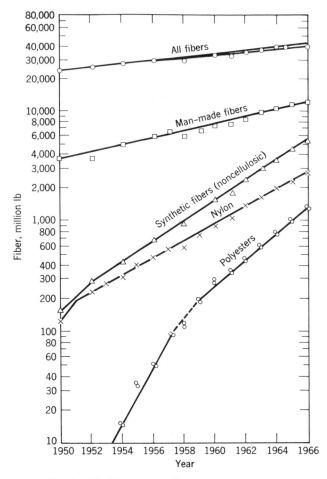

Fig. 1. World synthetic fiber production (11).

a production of 2.66 billion lb (11). As can be seen from Figure 1, world production of polyamides has increased exponentially with time from 1951 through 1966. The projected growth of polyamide fibers in the period 1966–1970 is expected to be equal to the entire growth of polyamides for the previous twenty-six years. This enormous growth is attributed to the utility and value of polyamides in the world's economy and continued dynamic research and development.

It is a tribute to the vision of the earlier developers of polyamide fibers, such as Carothers and Schlack, that nylon-6 and nylon-6,6, twenty-six years later, represented more than 98% of the total polyamides being converted to fibers, and that competition between these major polyamides has tended to spur each other's growth.

It is interesting to note that Hopff (12) reported that I. G. Farbenindustrie, A.G. had, in 1945, evaluated more than 3000 polyamide constituents without finding any important improvement over nylon-6,6 and nylon-6.

Figure 2 illustrates the competition between polyamides (13,14). The greater growth of nylon-6 over nylon-6,6 may be ascribed to three major factors: (a) greater availability of raw materials for nylon-6 at lower costs; (b) greater availability of necessary technological information; and (c) the more complex technology required to

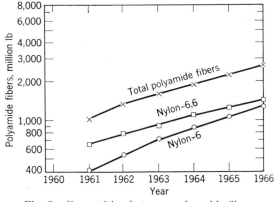

Fig. 2. Competition between polyamide fibers.

produce nylon-6,6 of equivalent quality to nylon-6 during spinning and drawing operations.

Manufacture

Outline of Operations. The major proportion of polyamide fibers are melt spun. The polymer is melted and extruded through spinnerets, forming filaments which are then solidified by cooling in a current of air.

The next step is drawing the fibers. They are heated and stretched to 400–600% of their original length. This brings about oriented crystallization, and greatly improves the tensile strength, typically from about 500 to 3000–4000 kg/cm², ie, 7000 to 400,000–570,000 psi. (The textile technologist reports tensile strength as tenacity. This is measured in grams per denier. The denier of a fiber (or of a yarn made from it) is the weight in grams of 9000 meters (see also p. 66).)

ADDITIVES

A variety of substances are normally added to the reaction mixture before or during polymerization in order to change the properties and nature of the polymer.

Delustering. This is done in order to reduce transparency, increase whiteness, and prevent undesirable gloss in finished fabrics (15–20). It is usually accomplished by dispersing finely divided titanium dioxide particles within the fiber (21,22). Semi-dull nylon yarns contain about 0.3% TiO_2; full-dull yarns about 2.0% TiO_2.

The incorporation of TiO_2 into molten monomer or polymer (23) is one of the most critical operations. If it is not done properly, one or more of the following problems may result:

1. Premature clogging of sand filter packs, leading to frequent replacement of packs and spinnerets.

2. Nubs and drips during spinning.

3. Poor drawing performance; poor yield, increased breaks and wraps, and variable denier.

4. Excessive yarn abrasiveness; rapid wear of processing machinery.

5. Poor dyeability; fabric streakiness.

6. Poor light stability; rapid loss of tensile properties upon exposure to sunlight or other ultraviolet radiation.

The anatase crystalline modification of titanium dioxide is generally used even though it catalyzes light degradation of nylon more than the rutile type (24). Moreover, it is not as effective a delusterant as rutile. However, rutile TiO₂ is generally rejected because it is not quite as white (25), and it is much more abrasive than anatase. Abrasiveness is particularly undesirable because of its costly effects on the machinery used in fiber production and textile processing.

Titanium dioxide powder with an average particle size of 0.1–0.5 μ is generally used as delusterant (25,26).

Nylon-6 and nylon-6,6 delusterant technologies differ; aqueous hexamethylene-diamine–adipic acid salt is a polar substrate in which it is difficult to disperse TiO₂ without agglomeration, while caprolactam is a substantially less polar liquid in which TiO₂ can be dispersed with ease to form a stable suspension. This characteristic enables caprolactam suspensions containing up to 30% TiO₂ to be polymerized to make low-molecular-weight master batches (27).

Spin Dyeing. Spin dyeing (mass or "dope" dyeing) is the process of coloring yarn by incorporating dyes or pigments into the polymeric mass prior to spinning (28,29). Although the pigments may be added during polymerization, they can also be added immediately prior to spinning in order to confine the colored material to as small a zone of the process as possible (30,31). The primary advantage of spin dyeing is that a stable, colorfast yarn requiring no subsequent dyeing can be produced. On the other hand, the variety of shades is limited, since each shade requires separate facilities and/or extensive flushing (with high waste) between runs.

The delusterant titanium dioxide is no more than a white pigment. After TiO₂, carbon black is the next most frequently used pigment. It can greatly enhance the resistance toward light degradation.

Inorganic pigments are often used for spin coloration (32). Organic pigments are usually more intensely colored than the inorganic, but few are available which will not degrade during spinning. The somewhat lower spinning temperature of nylon-6 (255–270°C vs 280–290°C for nylon-6,6) makes the selection of stable pigments for the former somewhat easier. Table 1 shows some typical pigments used for spin-dyeing nylon-6.

Table 1. Pigments Used for Spin-Dyeing Nylon-6 (31,43)

Pigment	Color	Pigment	Color
titanium dioxide	white	Phthalocyanine Green	green
carbon black	black	Phthalocyanine Blue	blue
cadmium sulfide	yellow	Quindo Magenta	pink
cadmium selenide	yellow	cadmium sulfoselenide	red

Russian workers have incorporated amine-containing organic dyes during polymerization to produce colored, terminated nylon-6 yarns (33–38). In one example (28) they used 0.2–1.0% of an aminoanthraquinone; the substance acted as a molecular-weight regulator, reacting with the carboxyl group, and was said to impart good color while still retaining physical properties of the uncolored products.

A method for adding color to nylon yarns which differs from that for spin dyeing has been disclosed (39). The coloring agent (pigment or dye) is dispersed in the yarn lubricant and applied at the finish roll to freshly spun yarn.

A number of optical brighteners (see Brighteners, optical) are available for incorporation in molten polymer (30,31). The portion of radiation absorbed in the ultraviolet portion of the spectrum is reemitted as visible (usually blue) light. Derivatives of diaminostilbene (40), dibenzothiophene, coumarin, benzoxazole (41), and benzimidazole (42) have been claimed for this application.

SPINNING AND DRAWING

Figure 3 illustrates a *conventional spinning* apparatus where pellets of polymer are melted in a large extruder which in turn feeds a manifold spinning line. Alternatively, the spinning manifold can be fed directly from a continuous polymerization process bypassing the large extruder.

The molten polymer feed lines are made as short as possible, and the polymer is distributed via lines to a series of manifolds where the yarn is quenched. The yarn

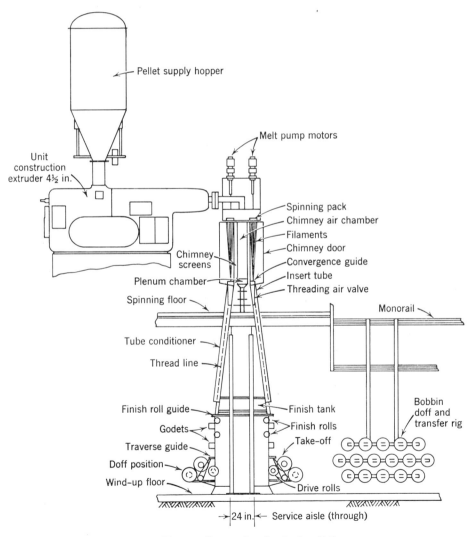

Fig. 3. Conventional spinning (44).

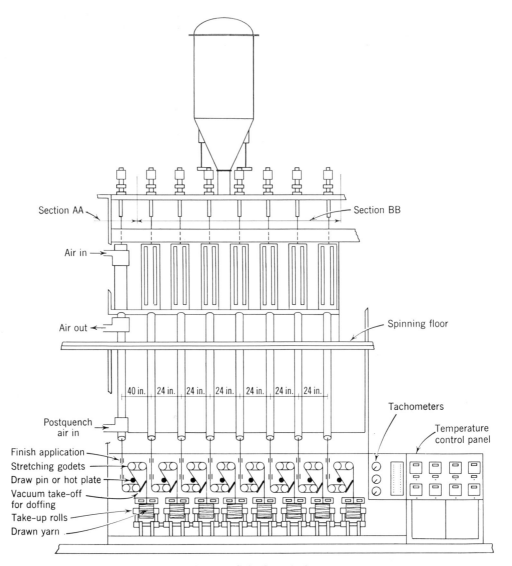

Section AA

Section BB

Air in

Air out

Spinning floor

40 in. | 24 in. | 24 in. | 24 in. | 24 in. | 24 in. | 24 in.

Tachometers

Temperature
control panel

Postquench
air in

Finish application
Stretching godets
Draw pin or hot plate
Vacuum take-off
for doffing
Take-up rolls
Drawn yarn

Fig. 4. Spin draw (45).

passes to the tube conditioners and over finish rolls, over take-up godets, and finally to winders where a spare winder is used to switch over rapidly to a new roll during the doffing operation to avoid loss of yarn. The yarns then pass on monorail conveyors to the drawing areas (44).

A great improvement on spinning and drawing separately is *spin drawing*, where both operations are performed on one piece of equipment (45). The spin-draw equipment shown in Figure 4 is similar to that shown in Figure 3, being generally a double-sided unit. The major difference is the addition of stretch godets and relaxation equipment for spin-draw processes (46–48).

Metering pumps which have a central input channel and will discharge two to four streams of polymer through two to four separate spinnerets can be employed. In section BB (Fig. 4), crossflow quenching is illustrated. In section AA, a combination

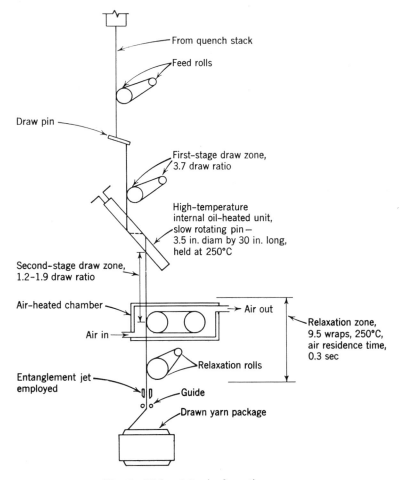

Fig. 5. Nylon-6,6 spin-draw tire yarn.

of concurrent and countercurrent quenching systems is employed. In a typical spin-draw process, at least two individual packages are taken up simultaneously on the indicated take-up rolls (49,50).

A major factor which has perhaps delayed the commercialization of spin-draw technology has been the feeling that the problem involves adapting existing equipment for the spin-draw process, since it is generally believed that the use of "tried and proven" equipment would be the shortest route to the solution of the multiplicity of problems which must be resolved.

An alternative approach is to change the spinning and drawing equipment entirely, to permit processing substantially more strands per unit spinning manifold, per unit filtration system, per unit per quench stack, and per unit drawing system.

Today, only a few companies are spinning more than one end of heavy industrial or carpet yarn per quench stack. The synthetic fiber industry, in its fiber manufacturing phase, has not always taken advantage of its enormous increase in volume output to reduce capital cost. In expanding other segments of the chemical industry, the increased capital required varies as the 0.6 exponent of the increment of capacity increases. In general, in the synthetic fiber industry, each new unit of added fiber capacity requires essentially the same amount of additional capital.

Other problems in spin drawing which have been resolved are (a) use of a very light weight traverse to avoid the high g forces encountered at high-speed winding, and (b) transfer of heat to the fibers by circulation of heated air in cages to avoid the cost and maintenance problems related to use of heated rolls.   Figure 5 illustrates a typical drawing operation in sequence with a continuous spinning operation to form high-strength tire yarn (51).   Conditions of operation are listed.

Considerations in Spinning.   In a large polyamide plant, producing 80–120 million lb/yr of industrial-type fibers, a large number of "ends" (or strands) of yarn will be spun simultaneously.   It is desirable, even mandatory, that each end of yarn be of uniform quality, along any segment of its length, in order to meet the specifications set up by the yarn manufacturer and required by industry.   At this rate of production the length of 840-den yarn produced per hour is equal to about 1.2–1.8 times the distance around the earth.   It can be appreciated that the problem of maintaining a multiplicity of strands of yarn of precisely equivalent quality over this distance is intensely challenging.   Further adding to the complexity of spinning industrial yarns, is the fact that there may be 140 filaments per yarn end.   Thus, the combined length of the individual filaments produced every hour is between 4.2 and 6 million miles, a distance equal to 9–13 round trips to the moon.   It is a general rule of thumb that any defect greater than 20% of the diameter of the filament may result in a filamentary break.   For industrial yarns, usually made up of 6-den filaments, the maximum defect can be 5.4 μ.   For a textile yarn with filaments of 2–3 den, the maximum defect should be no greater than 3–4 μ.   In producing textile-grade polyamide fibers, the total length of filament involved may be twenty times greater than that discussed for high-strength yarn.   Here, a single end of yarn with different orientation, or different heat treatment or change in moisture can result in an optically apparent streak in woven fabrics.   From the foregoing, it can be appreciated that any portion of the polymer in the yarn must be as rheologically uniform as possible.   Each defect in quality interjected by the polymer and the spinning operation will necessarily end up in the drawing operation.   Thus, it is generally considered that about 80% of the problems related to obtaining a uniformly drawn, high-strength fiber are solved by absolute control over the processing operations up to a distance of approx 6 in. below the spinneret face. While other operations are fundamental to the final product uniformity, it is probable that this phase of the operation is the most critical.

In the spinning of polyamides the following factors must be considered (46–48):

1.   Uniform residence time in the molten state for each portion until it reaches the individual spinneret holes, with plug flow throughout the whole system.   Design must avoid dead spaces as well as provide for equal residence time for the polyamide to arrive at each spinneret.

2.   Positive liquid metering system with the shortest practical time for the polyamide to arrive at each spinneret.

3.   Uniform filtration of polymer through sand packs or porous stainless steel to reduce defects in the yarn by removal of gels and traces of impurities and to avoid clogging of spinneret orifices.

4.   Extrusion of molten polymer through the spinneret orifice with specific attention to the rheology of the polymer as to design of the orifice length-to-diameter ratio and its angle of entry and exit.

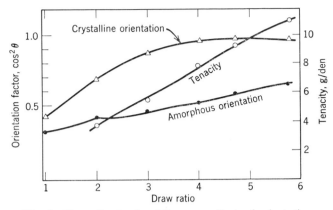

Fig. 6. Strength of nylon-6,6 yarns—effects of orientation.

5. Critical and precise quenching of the molten polymer over the first 6 in. of its length under conditions which avoid mechanical disturbance of the molten filament, then final quenching of the fibers to avoid relatively uncontrolled orientation which might otherwise occur in the quench stack.

6. Posttreatment of the fibers as they exit from the main quench stack may be used for specific polyamides.

7. Uniform application of finish materials at a precise moisture level for reduced friction, reduced electrical resistance, and to provide for filament bundle coherency.

8. Separation of the yarn ends at the exit from the quench stack.

9. Sequential drawing of the yarn using a means to establish the draw point such as a draw pin. Heat may be employed to assist in shrinking and annealing or drawing.

10. Take-up of the yarn or winding of the yarn at uniform winding tensions with sufficient yarn overlap to yield a shippable or transportable package.

Of the ten listed spinning steps, step 3 (filtration), step 4 (extrusion), step 5 (quenching), and step 7 (application of finish materials) are probably the most dominant in their effect on quality, strength, and uniformity of the fiber obtained (52).

Considerations in Drawing. Hayes et al. (53) have described some factors during the drawing of nylon-6 which influence the attainment of high-strength properties (54). These factors are the following:

1. Use of high-number-average-molecular-weight nylon-6.

2. Attainment of very small crystallites of imperfect uniformity.

3. Minimization of the differences in properties between the crystalline and amorphous phases, eg, increasing the degree of orientation of the amorphous phase (54,55).

Figure 6 shows the effect of increasing draw ratio on tenacity and other properties of nylon-6.

FIBER MODIFICATIONS

Modified Cross Sections. Conventionally, spinneret orifices are circular and produce a fiber that is round in cross section. Improved machining methods (56,57), advances in fiber production technology, and the study of the effect of profiled fibers on fabric characteristics (eg, luster, sparkle, opacity, air permeability, resistance to showing soil, and heat insulation (58–60)), have given greater importance to the production of noncircular (modified cross-section) filaments.

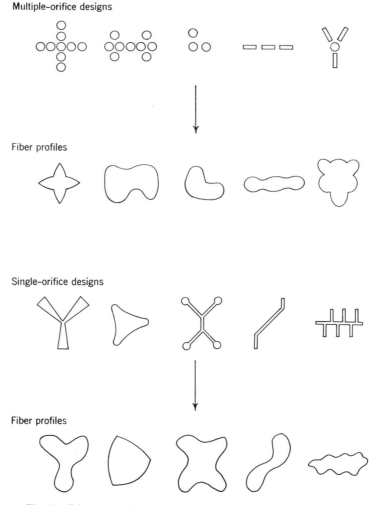

Fig. 7. Schematic orifice designs and resultant solid profiled fibers.

The spinning equipment and process for production of noncircular-cross-section yarn are very similar to those used in the manufacture of round-cross-section yarn, except for the shape of the spinneret orifice. Some of the process conditions which have been found to aid in producing well-defined cross sections include higher melt viscosity, lower polymer temperature, and rapid quench just below the spinneret (61,62). There is little difference in the technology used to make modified cross-section fibers from nylon-6 and 6,6 polymers.

In all nylon spinneret manufacture, the final orifice is produced after counterboring all but thin sections of the spinneret blank (63). Noncircular spinneret orifice shapes have been made by engraving and punching, but with difficulty in maintaining hole dimension tolerances. More advanced methods are now used, and are referred to as "electron-beam milling" and "electrodischarge machining." Both of these methods are capable of producing a wide variety of noncircular orifices with extreme accuracy. Electrodischarge machining is described as the controlled erosion of electrical conductors by rapidly recurring electrospark discharges (64). During electron-beam milling, the beam is absorbed by a very thin surface layer of the material and its energy is converted into heat, causing the material below the shaped electrodes to melt and vaporize (65).

Two basic spinneret designs are used to produce modified yarn shapes. The first method depends upon the coalescence or fusing of melt streams below the spinneret, forming a noncircular single filament (66,67). The second method consists of the extrusion of the melt through profiled capillaries, which form the basic fiber shape.

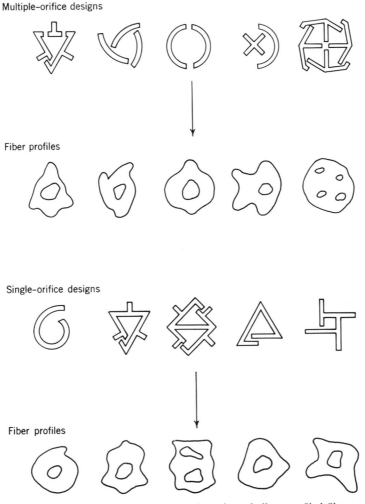

Fig. 8. Schematic orifice designs and resultant hollow profiled fibers.

Various specific orifice shapes have been developed (68,69), and fiber cross sections have been defined with mathematical relationships by Holland (70), McKinney (71,72), and Stanley (72). The simultaneous spinning of a combination of 50% round and 50% profiled filaments has been shown (73) to decrease the fiber-bundle density, giving warmth and moisture permeability to the textile fabric. Synthetic yarns have also been produced in which the cross-sectional shape varies, although the cross-section area remains constant along the filament, producing an apparent variable denier and random receptivity to dyeing, and which imparts a novel handle, luster, and porosity to textile filaments (74).

Figure 7 shows some of the spinneret hole arrangements and shapes which will produce solid profiled fibers.

Hollow filaments are produced by the proper arrangement and design of orifices so as to coalesce the melt streams below the spinneret (58,75) or through the design of spinning equipment which forms the hollow cross section within the capillary. These may include the injection of a gas into the filament in the melt stage (76–78). Figure 8 shows some of the single- and multiple-orifice shapes used to produce hollow filaments.

FIBER FINISHES

The three main functions of a fiber finish are surface lubricity, plasticizing action, and static protection. At any point where a yarn or fiber contacts another surface (draw pins, guides, or other fibers within the bundle), a lubricant is essential in order to maintain the fiber in useful form. From the time the filaments are formed until they are made into the final product, a finish must be present to prevent damage to the fiber and to accomplish the various steps in their processing. The principal causes of filament breakage during the drawing process are buildup of excessive tension and generation of a static charge on the yarn. These may be caused by interfilament friction and by the friction generated, for example, as the yarn passes over the draw pin and draw heater. These steps also generate heat, and temperatures are approached which make the operation impossible without adequate lubrication protection (79).

The term "lubricant" as applied to a finish may be misleading, since "to lubricate" generally means to reduce friction to a minimum. In textile processing this is not always desirable; sometimes it is necessary to raise or otherwise adjust friction to meet specific conditions.

Finishes applied to the fiber during spinning, which enable the fiber to be drawn in order to obtain the necessary properties, are known as "spin finishes." Overfinishes are sometimes applied by the producer for special purposes; for example, the service life of nylon-6 used in cordages was increased by a finish which had an oxidized polyethylene wax base (80). The term "yarn lubricant" (or coning oil) includes all lubricants added subsequent to application of spin finish. Yarn lubricants are the concern of textile mills and processors, and cover operations such as picking, coning, slashing, weaving, and knitting.

Composition—Lubricants and Antistats. Compounds which contribute lubricity to a fiber include a large group of chemicals. Mineral oils have long been used as lubricants, and still retain a prominent position. The fatty acids furnish the largest group; compounds with functional groups C_6 to C_{18} are known to provide excellent lubricity. These may be straight-chain esters, such as methyl, ethyl, or butyl esters of fatty acids. Polyglycols or their esters of fatty acids and fatty glycerides, refined or synthesized, are widely used; the triglycerides are most stable to higher temperatures (81). More complex chemicals are finding increased use where still greater stability is desired. These include the esters of dibasic acids, and pentaerythritol, neopentylene glycol, and polyglycerols; also aryl, alkyl, and alkyl aryl phosphates; and silicones, silicate esters, fluoroesters, and polyphenyl ethers (82). Lubricants and their modifications, used to obtain specific properties, are almost endless. In the development of synthetic lubricants, modifications have been made by ester interchange, ethoxylation or acetylation; properties such as degree of lubricity, scroop, cohesiveness, and plasticity are affected.

Antistatic agents (qv) are generally more complex than lubricants. On nonconductive surfaces, such as most textiles, charges remain isolated; effective discharge cannot be accomplished through grounding techniques. Both positive and negative charges can be acquired by various fibers. These factors are discussed in reviews of electrostatic formation and antistatic agents by Henshall (83) and Shashoua (84).

As described by Fine (85), water is an important factor which must be considered in the selection of an antistat. Since water (containing inorganic substances) has a relatively high dielectric constant, its presence may reduce the intensity of the contact potential and result in a reduced charge. In addition, water is a good conductor of electricity and can cause a nonconductive surface to exhibit some characteristic conductive properties. Therefore, hygroscopic chemicals are potentially good antistatic agents.

Organic compounds, such as those in the class of surface-active chemicals, are generally incorporated in finish formulations for their static protection. Their action is attributed to their ability to become molecularly oriented on the fiber surface and thus exhibit some dielectric shielding and conductivity.

Antistatic agents can be classified into four groups: nonionics, cationics, anionics, and ampholytes (85–87). Nonionics include the polyoxyethylene derivatives of fatty acids, alcohols, amines, and amides, as well as derivatives of hydroxy amino compounds (alkanolamines, qv). Quaternary ammonium compounds (qv), such as the alkylmorpholinium type, are examples of cationics. Anionics are represented by soaps, esters of sulfuric and phosphoric acid, and by alkane and alkylaromatic sulfonic acid derivatives. The last class, ampholytes, dissociate into either positively or negatively charged ions. Compounds of the betaine type are included in this category. (See also Surfactants.)

Antistatic properties of nylon can be substantially improved by incorporation of so-called "permanent" antistatic agents into the polymerization melt prior to spinning. Such additives are reported to be relatively resistant to bleaching and dyeing. One process uses at least 2–3% of a polyalkylene ether for this purpose (88). Another method, using a copolymer of sodium ethylenesulfonate and acrylamide, also claims good durability of antistatic properties (89).

Spin finish greatly influences the processing of fibers into yarns and fabrics; its correct performance is often an important competitive advantage to the fiber producer. If, for example, due to excessive friction during manufacture, the component fibers and yarns of a fabric do not have sufficient mobility to adjust because of improper lubrication, strains are introduced into the fabric. These may produce uneven dyeing, decreased strength, or unpleasing esthetic qualities (90).

In evaluating and selecting a fiber finish, the fiber manufacturer must consider processability, economics, and physical properties of the fiber, as well as the versatility of its end use by his many customers.

Application. After the finish has been prepared in proper concentration, usually in an aqueous emulsion, it is pumped to a holding or storage tank from which it is circulated through the finish system feeding the trough or trays on the spinning machines. Finish concentration and level of pickup are balanced to give the final weight of lubricant, antistat, water, or other finish additive required for subsequent operations. Some of the various methods of application employed in the fiber industry are passing the bundle of fibers through the circulating finish (employed mostly in nonaqueous systems), passing the yarn bundle across a constantly revolving roll, or spraying directly the constantly moving fiber bundle. Klare (91) discusses European finish technology and describes some typical finish formulations.

CONTINUOUS–FILAMENT BULK AND STRETCH YARNS

In general, textured yarns are filament yarns which have been given greater volume or made more extensible by distortion of the filaments through mechanical means. This distortion may be produced by buckling the filaments under end-load compression, bending them over an edge of small radius, or twisting the strands as a whole. Hathorne (92) has discussed texturing processes in detail. Those used more widely are summarized in this section. Bulked nylon-6 yarns which are commercially

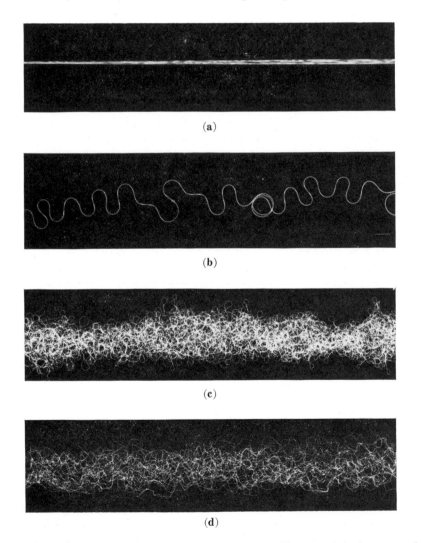

(a)

(b)

(c)

(d)

Fig. 9. Textured fine-denier yarns for apparel. LEGEND: (**a**) Untextured feeder yarn; (**b**) knife-edge textured; (**c**) false-twist textured; and (**d**) stuffer-box textured. Magnified 10×.

produced generally fall into one of two areas: fine denier (15–200 den) for woven and knitted stretch and textured fabrics in apparel applications (Fig. 9) (92), and heavy denier (1000–3600 den) for carpet. Yarns are textured to obtain increased cover, greater recovery from deformation, more pleasing hand, and greater warmth.

Requirements of texture uniformity for continuous-filament textured yarns are much more exacting than those for staple. They do not have the advantages of thorough blending, with the leveling out of nonuniformities that the latter has through its processing to spun yarn. Hutton and Morris have surveyed the literature and patents relating to textured continuous-filament yarns (including heat-setting and testing) (93).

Fine-Denier Texturing Processes. *Stuffer-tube crimping* of fine denier yarns (15–200 den) is described in a series of U.S. patents (94,95). Generally, commercial fine-denier crimping has been limited to one or a few ends. However, in the "Spunize" system, by employing a ball warper in conjunction with multiple end winding, 400 or more ends of fine denier may be simultaneously crimped and wound (95a). Drawn yarn accelerated by feed rolls impacts against yarn in a stuffer tube where it bends, folds, and forms crimps due to heat softening from preheating or heat controllers in the stuffer tube. Crimped yarn is pulled from the stuffer tube at a constant rate. The amount of texture and texture permanence are controlled by yarn residence time and temperature in the stuffer tube. Increased residence time may be accomplished with increased weight or back pressure on the stuffer tube, resulting in increased crimp. The converse effect results from decreased weight. Yarns from the process are frequently plied to reduce nonuniformity of individual ends.

In the somewhat similar Anilon process used in Czechoslovakia, the major part of the back pressure is supplied by an inclined wedge, which deflects the material through an angle of 45° (96). Gray, Bhattacharya (97), and others (98) discuss the theory of stuffer crimping.

Edge crimping to produce a bulked yarn can be accomplished by drawing a heat-plasticized yarn over a blunt knife edge. In one process, yarn is produced under U.S. patents (99–101) issued to Deering Milliken Research Corp. and sold under the trademark Agilon. In this process, two or more ends of drawn yarn are delivered to each bulking position. The yarns are fed to a rotating heated cylinder which stretches and heats them; the plasticized yarn bundle is then drawn over an edge, which can be heated. The acute angle through which the yarn travels causes the surface of each filament nearest the crimping edge to be compressed and the outside to be stretched. The filaments can have 10–20% or more of their surfaces flattened or, in some cases, practically no visible deformation at all (101). The yarn still appears untextured at this point, but the distortions and strains which have been developed are retained by passing the yarn over a cooling roll. The yarn can then be wound directly onto a package, or sent over another heated roll where the latent crimping energy can be stabilized and later released at different levels as minute coils or crimps (Fig. 9) by varying tension and temperature. In other cases the texture is not developed until the fabric is dyed and finished.

False-twist texturing, to a large extent, has replaced the tedious twist-set-detwist of the Helanca (102) process. Special manufacturing techniques are used to produce a nylon-6 feeder yarn with excellent false-twisting properties. In the false-twisting operation, the drawn yarn, heated by a radiant or contact heater to a temperature close to its melting point, is twisted to as high as 70–100 turns per inch (tpi), cooled, and untwisted to its original twist level (103). Machines with spindle speeds of up to 360,000 rpm have made this process much more economical and more competitive with other texturing processes than in the past. Equipment in which a friction twist is superimposed on false twist yielding equivalent rpm as high as 3 million is in commercial operation (103a).

The product is primarily a stretch rather than a bulk yarn. However, a modified false-twist process, in which stretch is reduced by subsequent heating and tension under controlled conditions, is used to produce a nylon-6 bulked yarn by false twist.

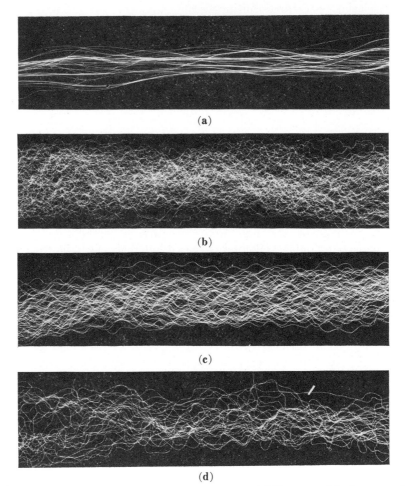

(a)

(b)

(c)

(d)

Fig. 10.   Textured heavy-denier yarns for carpet. LEGEND: (a) Untextured feeder yarn; (b) stuffer-box textured; (c) gear textured; and (d) fluid-jet textured. Magnified 10×.

This is done either by following the heat-twist-untwist step with a second heat-twist-untwist step at a lower temperature, or by a steam or hot-water treatment of the yarn on perforated tubes in a pressure dyeing machine (104).

Air-jet texturing, or Taslan (du Pont) texturing, in which continuous-filament nylon-6 yarn or other synthetics are fed to an air jet, is, in a sense, a process for controlled tangling. The yarn is introduced into a venturi tube in the air jet, where turbulence from a stream of compressed air causes loops and texture to be developed.

Many variations of this process (105–107) have been used to obtain different bulk and novelty effects. The product is characterized by having substantial bulk and practically no stretch.

Bicomponent fibers, in which each filament is composed of two or more different polymers with different responses to environmental conditions, can also be used to obtain textured yarns (see below).

Heavy-Denier Texturing Processes. Heavy-denier textured yarn is used primarily for tufting into carpets (Fig. 10) although other applications are growing. The more important manufacturing processes are described in the following section.

Several patents (108–110) have been issued which describe a *gear-crimping* process for producing textured yarn. They disclose a texturing process adaptable to a draw twister or to a spin-draw texture operation. In the process, heat-plasticized drawn yarn is delivered to a pair of meshed gears. The crimp frequency obtained is a function of the pitch of the gear teeth. Crimp permanency of the yarn depends on its temperature during crimping and the setting temperature immediately thereafter.

In *fluid-jet texturing*, the yarn, along with hot air or superheated steam, is fed at high speed into a small chamber (111–114). The yarn is first heat-plasticized by the steam, for example, and then textured by controlled turbulent flow of the same fluid. In some designs, the yarn is textured by impingement on a baffle plate or the walls of a specially shaped chamber. Fluid-jet texturing differs from Taslan texturing in that texture in each filament of the former has a random, three-dimensional, curvilinear configuration, and the whole bundle is essentially free of loops.

Stuffer-box crimping of heavy-denier yarns (800–5000 den) is basically similar to that described for the Spunize process for fine-denier yarns (95a). Heavy-denier crimping differs from conventional fine-denier processes in that generally multiple ends are fed simultaneously into the stuffer box (115–119). The operation is similar to that used in crimping tow for staple except for the separation of individual ends of textured yarns and the packaging as a parallel wound package or cones. A major portion of the crimped nylon produced in the U.S. is processed by stuffer-box, gear or fluid-jet crimping.

The basic *false-twist* process employed in producing bulked fine-denier yarn is also used in texturing heavy-denier nylon-6 yarns for carpet applications. The application of false-twist texturing to heavy-denier yarns has not been as widespread as some other processes because of economic limitations due to the low rates attainable with the maximum spindle speeds available.

Heat Setting. A heat-setting operation is usually carried out in the production of a bulked or stretch yarn. Heat setting is required to obtain a texture which is stable to dyeing and washing treatments, and which will recover from stresses applied during wearing or use of the finished goods. In nylon-6 bulking processes, yarn temperatures of 100–190°C are usually obtained before the yarn is deformed by mechanical action; then, while in the deformed state, the yarn is cooled significantly before the deforming force is removed to set the crimp. The exact temperature used depends on whether steam or dry heat is used, the amount of mechanical deforming energy, and the degree of heat set required. It has been reported that the optimum temperature for heat setting of nylon-6 fiber with wet steam is about 130°C and with dry heat is about 190°C (151). In bulking, crystallinity and orientation may be altered at points of deformation. The permanence of the deformation will be controlled by the degree of heat setting used.

Entanglement. Yarn entanglement is not a texturing process, although certain process principles and equipment bear a resemblance. A cohesive yarn bundle, usually essential for efficient textile mill processing of continuous-filament yarn, can be obtained by entangling nylon fiber. In an entanglement process, yarn is passed at high speed through a chamber into which compressed air has been injected (120). Thus, the yarn is exposed to an air stream of controlled turbulence which causes random oscillation of individual filaments. The result is a cohesive continuous-filament yarn in which filaments are randomly intertwined and comingled. For some applications entanglement can replace twisting of yarn.

STAPLE FIBER

Although it may seem paradoxical, continuous-filament yarns of nylon, polyester, acrylic, and rayon are crimped and cut into staple fibers corresponding to the natural fibers they replace, or with which they may be blended. The staple is converted into spun yarns by one of the textile spinning systems (121,122). Esthetic results and economics justify this extensive processing.

An essential feature of almost all synthetic staple fibers is crimp. Defined as waviness in a fiber, crimp determines the capacity of the fibers to cohere under light pressure, as in card webs. It is the principal feature controlling the bulking power of a textile material, and thus the specific volume of yarns and fabrics. Crimp is usually uniplanar, but may vary in form.

Semiplant production of nylon-6 staple was initiated by I. G. Farbenindustrie, A.G. in 1939 (123). Allied Chemical produced the first nylon-6 staple in the U.S. in 1955. The consumption of polyamide in staple remained relatively static at approx 20 million lb/yr, with its principal use as a blend in apparel yarns. Then, with the enormous growth of nylon filament yarns from 1950 to 1960, in carpets, there occurred a simultaneous growth of nylon staple in carpets which was 30 million lb in 1962, 50 million lb in 1964, and 60 million lb in 1966. Nylon staple in all other applications remained at a level 20–30 million lb/yr during this same period. Substantial quantities of nylon staple are manufactured in Europe and this technology is described by Klare (124).

Crimping. Stuffer-box crimping is generally accepted as the most productive method for crimping nylon for staple. Multiple ends of tow are forced continuously into a constricted stuffer box by a precisely adjusted set of feed rolls. The box is sealed by means of an adjustable hinged and weighted gate. The strands filling the chamber are folded in uniform waves by compression. When the pressure in the stuffer box exceeds the pressure of the hinged gate, the gate rises permitting discharge of the crimped tow. The operation is repetitive and proceeds continuously (94).

Nylon-6 staple also may be crimped by treatment with dilute mineral acids. The preferred procedure is to immerse the fibers in 26% sulfuric acid solution at a carefully controlled temperature. The fiber surface is etched slightly, thus decreasing the gloss. An alkaline wash follows to remove the absorbed acid prior to drying (123).

In another crimping process, cutting of hot-stretched tow permits some relaxation and crimping of the fibers; this is accentuated by dropping the cut sections into hot water. This treatment also removes monomer and oligomers. The crimp frequency developed is fairly low, thus reducing the utility of the staple produced by this relatively inexpensive method (123).

Tow Cutting. Cutting of nylon-6 tow is carried out with equipment similar to that used for making cellulose staple. The tow is usually moistened slightly prior to cutting to reduce the static charge which otherwise may cause fiber to stick to the cutters (121). Moistening the tow also increases the life of the knives. Since the toughness of polyamide fibers causes rapid wear of the cutting knives, special hardened steel has to be used.

Properties

The uses of a fiber depend upon its properties. The dynamic growth of nylon in the textile industry is due mainly to a combination of unique and inherent properties which, even today, are unavailable in any other fiber. The sustained efforts of the fiber manufacturers to modify fiber properties and improve product quality have opened up one market after another to nylon. Research inspiration and competitive pressures from other manufacturers usually have generated further improvements; these have enabled applications in other markets and resulted in increased value to the consumer.

New products are judged commercially by a complex medley of standards; these can be classified into two groups: acceptance and value criteria. The textile buyer will make his choice among several similar products on the basis of their value factors, but only after acceptance standards have been met. In apparel, the acceptance criteria depend on specific end uses that are often related to styling, comfort, and merchandising potential. Value factors are usually dyeing uniformity and economics. Acceptance criteria in carpeting are resilience and performance; controlling value factors are tufting economics and cover. The two segments of the tire-cord market have different acceptance criteria but the same value factors. Thus, in replacement tires the acceptance criteria are performance and safety; original equipment also requires nonflatspotting characteristics. Specific gravity and strength are the value factors in both (125).

While nylon-6 and 6,6 are quite similar in many properties and are competitive in most end uses, it is clear that each fiber has individual areas of usefulness where one polyamide may be preferred to the other.

It should be noted here, however, that in comparisons of examples of products as similar as nylon-6 and 6,6, it is often difficult, if not impossible, to determine whether a certain property characteristic is inherent with the fiber. One is sometimes unable to say whether a specific behavior is due primarily to basic chemical and physical structure, or whether it is a consequence of the skill of the manufacturer who made the particular sample under test. Thermal stability in tire yarn, for instance, is certainly related to the heat stabilizer used by the producer; adhesion and flex fatigue are affected by the fiber finish as well as by chemical structure. Specific processing techniques of fiber manufacturing play a very important role in affecting fiber properties.

Comparisons of properties of the different yarns discussed below are generally based on tests of typical commercial products in the field. Caution must be used, however, in concluding that the results are always representative of other examples of each nylon type.

A definite demarcation line has been established to distinguish between the medium- and heavy-denier industrial yarns and the light-denier of fine-denier apparel yarns. Usually yarn deniers above 140 are considered medium and heavy, those below 140 are rated as light, while 140-den yarns are included in both categories (126). This demarcation is observed generally by all producers.

PHYSICAL PROPERTIES

(This section and certain parts of other sections of this contribution are derived from an article written by Allied Chemical Corp. staff and edited by H. H. Weinstock, to appear in E. L. Wittbecker and N. G. Gaylord, eds., *Polyamides: Technology and Applications*, to be published by Interscience Publishers, a division of John Wiley & Sons, Inc., New York.)

Tensile Properties.   The major tensile properties of representative nylon-6 and 6,6 yarns are shown in Table 2.   The properties which are listed in the table and discussed elsewhere are defined below.

Table 2.   Physical Properties of Nylon-6 and 6,6 Continuous-Filament Yarns[a]

Property	Normal-tenacity	High-tenacity
tenacity, g/den, conditioned	5.0–6.8	8.5–9.3
wet	4.1–5.8	7.2–8.0
loop	4.5–5.6	6.5–6.7
knot	4.0–4.7	5.9–6.5
tensile strength, psi	$84\text{--}92 \times 10^3$	$124\text{--}134 \times 10^3$
elongation at break, %, conditioned	23–43	12–17
wet	28–41	17–21
tensile modulus, conditioned,[b] g/den	25–35	33–47
average toughness,[b] g-cm/den-cm	0.8–1.6	0.7–0.8
moisture regain, 70°C, 65% rh	4.5	3.3
95% rh	7.1–7.8	7.8

[a] Conditioned at 65% rh and 70°F.   Tests run on IP4 unless otherwise indicated (127,144).
[b] Tests run on Instron (128).

Linear density—denier is the weight in grams of 9000 meters of yarn.   Tex is the weight in grams of 1000 meters of yarn.

Tenacity is the tensile stress at break.   It is expressed as force per unit linear density of unstrained specimen; for example, g/den or g/tex.

Knot tenacity is the tensile stress required to rupture a single strand of yarn having an overhand knot tied in the portion of sample between the testing clamps. It is expressed as force per unit linear density (g/den), and is used as an approximate measure of brittleness of the yarn.

Loop tenacity is the tensile stress required to rupture yarn when one strand of yarn is looped through another and then broken.   It is expressed as force per unit linear density (g/den).   Loop tenacity is an indication of brittleness, but is not considered as sensitive as the knot test.   Reported values are one-half actual test values.

Breaking strength is the maximum load required to rupture a fiber.   It is expressed as grams or pounds.

Tensile strength is the maximum stress or load/unit area.   It may be expressed as pounds per square inch (psi) and calculated as

$$\text{tensile strength (psi)} = \text{tenacity (g/den)} \times \text{specific gravity} \times 12861$$

Elongation at break is the increase in sample length during a tensile test.   It is expressed as a percentage of original length.

Tensile modulus (Young's modulus, also called initial modulus or elastic modulus) is the load required to stretch a specimen of unit cross-sectional area by a unit amount.

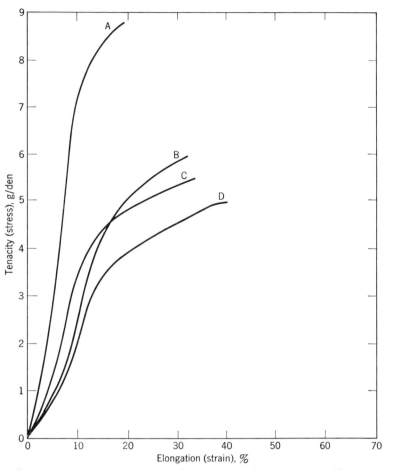

Fig. 11. Stress-strain curves of representative nylon-6 and 6,6 continuous-filament yarns. Yarns conditioned and tested at 65% rh, 70°F (130). LEGEND: A, 840-den, 136-filament tire yarn; B, 200-den, 16-filament automotive upholstery yarn; C, 70-den, 12-filament apparel yarn; and D, 1050-den, 70-filament yarn for texturing.

It is expressed as the ratio of change in strain in the initial straight-line portion of the stress-strain curve extrapolated to 100% sample elongation.

Values for the tensile modulus of a polyamide fiber decrease at slower rates of extension because primary and secondary creep have time to contribute more to the observed stress-strain curve. Modulus in semicrystalline fibers is dependent on degree of crystallinity and orientation, and thus manufacturing and processing conditions affect the modulus of nylon-6 yarns. For instance, high-tenacity yarns drawn to relatively low elongation will have a higher modulus than yarn with higher elongation. The temperature and humidity of the testing atmosphere also affect the modulus.

Stretch modulus is the ratio of change in stress to change in strain in the initial straight-line portion of the stress-strain curve for a 1% sample elongation, eg,

$$\text{stretch modulus} \times 100 = \text{tensile modulus}$$

Work to break is the actual work required to rupture the material. It is proportional to the total area under the stress-strain curve.

Breaking toughness is the actual work per unit linear density required to rupture the material. It is usually calculated by dividing work to break by denier or tex.

Average toughness (toughness index) is an estimate of the breaking toughness assuming a straight-line stress-strain curve (as approached by cotton). It is expressed as work per unit linear density of fiber which would cause rupture (129). This is not the measured area under the load-elongation curve (130).

average toughness = (g/den at break) (% elongation at break)/(2 × 100)

Yield point (elastic limit) is the point on the stress-strain curve where the load and elongation cease being directly proportional. It is the point at which the stress-strain curve deviates from the tangent drawn to the initial straight-line portion of the curve, as in tensile modulus determinations.

Creep is the change in shape of a material while subject to a stress; it is time dependent. *Primary creep* is the recoverable component of creep. *Secondary creep* is the nonrecoverable component of creep.

Elasticity is the ability of a material to recover its size and shape after deformation.

Stress-Strain Relationships. Plots of the stress-strain behavior of representative nylon-6 and 6,6 yarns are shown in Figure 11. Under normal conditions, the stress-strain (load-elongation) curves of a well-orientated nylon yarn or fiber show an initial straight-line portion in which the stress is proportional to the strain. This is followed by a yielding of the fiber structure, indicated by an S-shaped curve; first, concave to the stress axis, then a curvature concave to the strain axis—up to the break point. In the initial portion of the curve (after removal of slack, crimp, or twist effects) stress is proportional to the strain; it is referred to as the Hookean region. Its extrapolation provides data for calculating the tensile or Young's modulus.

When a nylon fiber is extended, the intermolecular forces which have kept the fiber from retracting now oppose its extension. This short-range elasticity produces the initial straight-line portion of the curve. In this region, the fiber can return to its normal length upon removal of the stress. As portions of the chain molecule are extended further, the network of chain molecules becomes more oriented. The chains are straightened and come in closer contact with each other so that more intermolecular bonding (hydrogen bonds and van der Waals forces) becomes effective. Thus the fiber passes through a yield region beyond which the molecular segments are unable to return to their original configuration upon release of the stress. The mechanism mainly responsible for this (the force which resists strain beyond the yield point) is the tendency of the chain molecules in the amorphous region to assume a random configuration, ie, the tendency toward maximum entropy. The crystalline regions also hinder the movement of the chain segments. The sum of all these forces and the resistance to chain movement equals the total stress required to break the sample. It is unlikely that any molecular bonds are broken when filaments are ruptured.

Smith (129), in 1944, was among the first to use engineering terms in interpreting stress-strain curves. Booth (131), Kaswell (132), Meredith (133), and Morton and Hearle (134) describe later interpretations of these curves. Each portion of the curve could represent an important fiber parameter, and may one day be fully correlated with end-use performance of processability of the fiber or yarn.

Stress-strain curves from tests of adjacent portions of a strand are generally quite similar until just before rupture occurs. After plotting thousands of stress-strain curves of 6-den filaments, Busch (135) concluded that the confidence range along

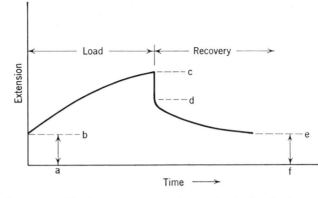

Fig. 12. Creep under constant load and recovery under zero load, showing instantaneous extension, a–b; creep, b–c; instantaneous recovery, c–d; delayed recovery, d–e; and permanent set, e–f.

the stress-strain curve was no greater than that of the breaking point. He found the coefficient of variation of the breaking strength of nylon-6 filaments (presumably Perlon, Vereinigte Glanzstoff-Fabriken A.G.) to be 2–3%, and of its breaking elongation to be 3.5%.

Creep and Recovery. Time is a most important factor in any consideration of the facets of elastic recovery. When a load is applied to a fiber, it undergoes an instantaneous extension, and will continue to extend (creep) as time goes on. On removal of the load there is an instantaneous recovery of part of the extension followed by contraction (delayed recovery) over a period of time. When recovery is incomplete, the residual is called "permanent set" (136). This behavior is shown in Figure 12. Creep is the extension with time under an applied load and recovery is the reverse process. Wegener (137) has measured creep and recovery with respect to time on nylon-6 yarns under different initial loads for different total elongations. Initially, recovery is rapid, most occurring within a few minutes after release of the load.

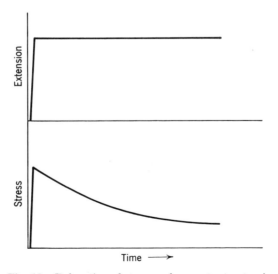

Fig. 13. Relaxation of stress under constant extension.

The conditions of extension and recovery (load, rate of extension and recovery, time of extension, etc) affect quantitative comparisons of nylon with other fibers. Contrasted with other fibers, however, the nylon yarns have an outstanding degree of elasticity, recovering well from high loads and extensions. Meredith (138) measured elastic recovery and Beste and Hoffman (139) measured work recovery of a number of different fibers and found that nylon had the best recovery properties of any tested.

Relaxation is an effect complementary to creep. In one case, stress maintained at given extension is reduced with time (136). This is illustrated in Figure 13. An instantaneous stress is set up when a nylon-6 fiber is stretched, for example, but this gradually decreases as time passes. In another sense, the reduction of stress when a fiber shrinks is also called relaxation.

Elastic recovery is the ability of a material to regain its original form after being stretched. It enables fabrication of products which will maintain their original shape or will conform to specific contours of the body. The outstanding elastic recovery of the nylons is responsible, for example, for the cling or fit in women's hosiery, and for their extensive market acceptance. Morton and Hearle (140) discuss at length the elastic recovery, creep, and relaxation of nylon and other fibers.

Staple Properties and Applications. The use of nylon staple rather than nylon continuous filament stems from a need to satisfy the demand of the consuming public for a "soft and warm" staple hand. An even more important desire is to combine some of the more advantageous properties of nylon with those of other staple fibers, natural as well as regenerated cellulosics.

Best performance in many types of fabrics usually requires fiber-to-fiber blends. Since intimate blending can only be achieved in fiber form, the combining of the blend components takes place early in the textile spinning process, either before or immediately after carding. The properties of nylon staple must therefore be compatible not only with each of the other blend components, but the fiber itself must also be adaptable to processing on the respective spinning systems. The outstanding contributions of nylon staple to carpet, apparel, and upholstery fabrics are its abrasion resistance and its low moisture absorption. The former property increases the wear life of the textile structure, the latter contributes to faster drying.

The strength of nylon continuous filament, which makes it so outstanding in industrial applications such as tire cord and webbing, is a handicap in the staple used in the apparel field. Here high fiber tenacity in conjunction with high abrasion resistance could result in unsightly pill formations and fabric structure distortions. Furthermore, high tenacity and the corresponding low elongation do not always match natural fiber properties in the respective blends. It is not surprising, therefore, that nylon staple fiber tenacities and extensions normally fall in the upper staple fiber range of 3–5 g/den and 50–100% extension. Elongation and moduli are even more important than strength considerations, since unmatched strain properties of blend components can easily overload one component to the detriment of the blend as a whole. The nylon fiber blend component, when used in the proper blend ratio, is thus able to match and enhance the strength of wool, cotton, and rayon fibers.

Most other fiber properties of nylon staple differ little from those of the continuous filament. There is little difference in the property characteristics between nylon-6 and 6,6; distinctions due to degree of crimp, finish, heat set, and other properties of products furnished by producers of one type are often greater than those between the two types of nylons.

The multiplicity of nylon blends, processing systems, and end uses requires a rather large variety of types of staple. These are classified according to the properties listed below.

fiber denier	1.5–20
staple length	cotton system (1.5 in.); woolen system (2–3 in.); worsted system (up to 4.5 in.); and special applications (up to 6 in.)
fiber cross section	round and modified
luster	bright and semidull
crimp	crimped and noncrimped
heat set	heat set and nonheat set

ELECTRICAL PROPERTIES

Electrical conductance of nylon is very low, as might be expected from its low moisture regain. Conductivity increases as moisture content rises; its value for nylon-6 yarn increases by several orders of magnitude as relative humidity increases from 0 to 100%. The absolute values, of course, depend upon the specific spin finish or after-finish applied to the fiber.

The insulating properties of nylon are manifested in the readiness with which it accumulates static electrical charges. Positive or negative charges may be generated rather easily on the surface of nylon by rubbing or contact with other appropriate substances, followed by separation. These charges are not readily dissipated.

The combination of ease of formation and difficulty in losing electrostatic charges are unfavorable characteristics of nylon and other synthetic fibers with low moisture regain. Increasing the relative humidity, application of conductive finishes, or incorporation of certain substances in the polymer melt prior to spinning help to dissipate static charges.

Some of the more important electrical constants for nylon-6 are given below. Values for nylon-6,6 are about equal except for the dielectric constant, which is lower than that for nylon-6.

surface resistance (141)	2×10^{12} ohm	dielectric strength (141)	90 kV/cm
specific resistance (141)	2.6×10^{14} ohm-cm	dielectric constant (142)	3.4

TEMPERATURE AND MOISTURE EFFECTS

The thermal behavior of nylon-6 fiber and the interrelated effects of water moisture have a pronounced influence on the physical properties of the yarn and its products. They are of basic importance in fiber manufacture, in processes of converting the yarn into fabric, and in end use. Sometimes temperature is the most important factor, sometimes it is moisture; more often the interrelated action of the one upon the other is found to be predominant. These effects and their interdependence are discussed in this section.

Thermal Properties. Thermal properties of fibers have not been extensively investigated, because much of the practical thermal behavior of textiles is so influenced by other factors. For example, temperature and heat changes are substantially affected by absorbed moisture, and thermal expansion of a nylon filament is much less than is its swelling due to moisture.

Table 3. Polyamide Temperature Index[a]

	Temperature, °C	
Property	Nylon-6	Nylon-6,6
melting point	215; 220[b]	250
zero strength[c]	232[d]	240[d]
maximum setting temperature	190	225
softening point	170	235
starts to become plastic	160	220
critical temperature, in air	163[e,]	158[e,f]
	93[g]	130[g]
in steam	137	140
maximum ironing temperature	150	180
optimum setting (steam)	128	130
maximum wash temperature, set		
by saturated steam	60	71
set by dry state	30	60

[a] Data from ref. 143,
unless otherwise noted.
[b] Data from ref. 144.

[c] Heat-stabilized tire yarn,
3.5-lb load.
[d] Data from ref. 145.

[e] Data from ref. 146.
[f] Heat-stabilized tire yarn.
[g] Unstabilized yarn.

Nylon-6 is lower in melting point and in some other thermal properties than nylon-6,6 (see Table 3).

The change in the moisture regain with relative humidity for nylon-6 and other fibers is shown in Figure 14. It is important to note that the values for moisture regain are not absolute for a particular fiber, but will vary with factors such as degree of orientation and extractable content. Nylon-6 and 6,6 have different moisture regains depending on whether equilibrium is established from a wet or dry state, as do some other fibers. The absorption and desorption of nylon-6, compared with wool, is shown in Figure 15.

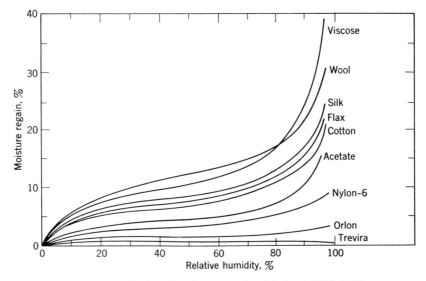

Fig. 14. Variation of moisture regain with rh at 20°C (147).

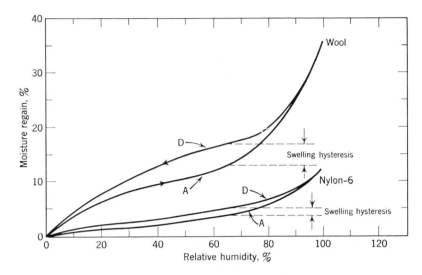

Fig. 15. Absorption (A)–desorption (D) of nylon-6 and wool (147).

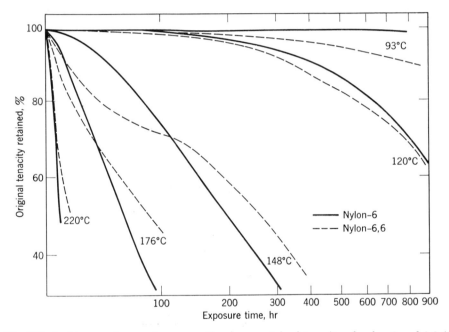

Fig. 16. Effect of temperature and exposure time upon retained tenacity of nylon-6 and 6,6 (148).

Heat Stability. The heat resistance of the nylons is of outstanding commercial importance in tire yarns and other industrial applications. Because of this, fiber manufacturers have made, and are continuing to make, constant improvements in the thermal stability of their products.

In any discussion of thermal (and light-resistant) properties of commercial products, particularly when comparisons are involved, it must be kept in mind that the results are to a large extent related to the specific stabilizing substances used and to certain aspects of the processes by which the yarns are made. These vary from pro-

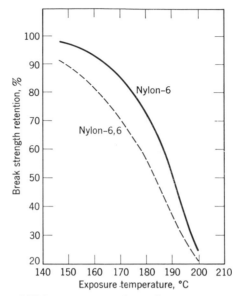

Fig. 17. Effect of 77-hr exposure to elevated temperatures upon retained strength of nylon-6 and 6,6 (149).

ducer to producer, and are changed from time to time by each producer. The information discussed here is believed representative of products typical of those in the field at the time the test was made.

Moncrieff (148) compared the thermal stability of nylon-6 and 6,6, with results shown in Figure 16. Figure 17 indicates that nylon-6 retains more than 90% of its strength after being heated 77 hr at 160°C.

DYEABILITY

The major factors which affect the dyeability of nylon are the characteristics of the particular fiber type used, the conditions of the dyebath, and the dye type and dye used.

Effect of Fiber Characteristics. Chemical structure, crystallinity, molecular orientation, and fabric preparation all play major roles in the rate and extent of dyeability of nylon. Nylon-6 and 6,6 differ in the arrangement of the carbonyl and amido groups between the hydrocarbon chains of the polymer. In nylon-6,6 their order is alternately reversed so that there is no difference in the order of occurrence from either end of the chain, ie, the order might be designated AB BA . . . . Nylon-6 has a uniform order of these functional groups, AB AB . . ., and the chain has a right and left end. When the molecules of the noncrystalline portions of the extruded fiber are aligned (oriented) by drawing, the nylon-6 molecules have a random, end-to-end occurrence, and have a different spatial relation to each other than in nylon-6,6 (150). Nylon-6 allows greater "openness" between the molecules. The rate of diffusion of dyes into this open structure is more rapid. The opportunity for dye fixation on the greater number of available hydrogen bonds is increased. Thus, nylon-6 is generally more dyeable than nylon-6,6 (151).

The nylon-6 chain normally terminates with an amine group at one end, which is a most active dye site. The ratio of such groups will vary with the molecular weight, which can also be controlled by the introduction of other chain-terminating additives for specific end uses. Nylon-6 is reported to have a higher ratio of amino end groups than 6,6, contributing to its dyeability.

It should be noted that, as with other synthetic and natural fibers, nylon consists of a mixture of crystalline and noncrystalline regions. The molecules in crystalline arrangement are so closely packed and so much less responsive to chemical influences, that they are probably not dyeable. The portion of the fiber comprised of such material, determined by polymerization and spinning conditions, is a significant factor in dyeability (152).

The physical boundary between crystalline and amorphous regions in the fiber is probably not sharply defined, but is rather a gradual transition. When the fiber is drawn to impart controlled tensile and elongation properties, a more regular spatial arrangement between molecules is established, as when a heap of match sticks is arranged in parallel. The extent to which this orientation is completed also affects dyeability (152).

When the amido and carbonyl groups of adjacent molecules chance to be in close proximity, the hydrogen atom of the amido group has a strong electrostatic affinity for the oxygen atom of the carbonyl group. The formation of this hydrogen bond releases energy and makes the polymer less responsive and more impervious to dyeing. During drawing, many of these bonds are broken, others are formed, and some are strained. During subsequent fiber handling the strains tend to return to a more relaxed state. Uncontrolled relaxation may introduce variations in these characteristics and thus, in dyeability. Nonuniform application of heat, as form guides overheated by friction during conversion to fabric, may introduce barré streaks evident after dyeing. Heat setting introduces energy under controlled conditions; this breaks the strained bonds and reforms them at more appropriate locations. Variations in heat-setting conditions from side-to-side or end-to-end of a piece may cause unevenness in dyeing (153).

The mechanism of nylon dyeing has been widely examined. Various studies have related dyeability to rate of diffusion (solubility of dye in the polymer), hydrogen bonding of dye to polymer, formation of ionic bonds between dye and polymer, the strength (affinity) of these bonds, and the aggregation of dye molecules into particles trapped in interstices between the molecules. Considerable uncertainty still prevails because each dye responds a little differently to one or more of these mechanisms, which in turn are influenced by variations in fiber and fabric preparation.

Effect of Dyebath Characteristics. Many methods have been proposed to ensure uniform dyeing results. In general, uniformity is most easily achieved when dyeing conditions are selected so that dye, diffusing into and out of the fiber, establishes an equilibrium with appreciable dyestuff remaining in the bath. Under this condition, nonuniform fabrics eventually achieve a more level shade. Disperse dyes are unexcelled for this purpose.

The nitrogen atoms in nylon absorb hydrogen ions with increasing avidity as the pH of the dyebath is lowered from about 9 (154). The terminal amino groups are most active and will fix the neutral dyeing acid colors at relatively high pH, either by reaction with the free dye acid or by addition of a hydrogen ion to form a cationic group which absorbs the dye anion. The acid dyes fixed at high pH are generally only slightly ionized (weakly acidic). At a pH below about 6.5 the fiber becomes strongly cationic and absorbs dye anions much more rapidly. Under such conditions the dye is rapidly

Table 4. Application and Performance Properties of Various Dye Classes on Nylon-6 (151)

Dye group	Ease of application	Uniformity of appearance	Leveling potential	Insensitivity to merge variations	Brightness	Light-fastness	Wet-fastness
disperse	excellent	excellent	excellent	very good to excellent	good to very good	fair to good	fair to good
acid	good to excellent	good to excellent	fair to very good	fair to very good	very good to excellent	good to very good	good to very good
metal-complex-disperse	good	fair	fair	good	fair	very good to excellent	very good to excellent
1:1 metal-complex	fair to good	fair to good	poor to fair	poor to fair	fair	very good	very good
1:2 metal-complex	very good	good	fair	fair	good	excellent	excellent
chrome	fair to good	good	poor to fair	poor to fair	poor to fair	excellent	excellent
direct	good	poor to good	fair	fair	fair to very good	good	fair to very good
naphthol	poor	good	good	good	good	fair to very good	excellent

exhausted on the most readily accessible dye site and fiber variations become very apparent as barré streaks. Because these dyes are more firmly bonded, they have very little tendency to level by migration. A direct relationship can be demonstrated between the low ionizability of a dye and its level-dyeing capacity. The relationship between oligomers (low-molecular-weight constituents), their effect on fiber dyeability, and analysis has been described in references 155–157.

Many attempts have been made to develop dyebath additives which will temporarily combine and inactivate either the cationic group in the fiber or the anionic groups of the dyestuff for slower, more level dyeing. Generally, they provide only a partially satisfactory expedient. It is worth noting that cationic dyebath additives sometimes adversely affect the lightfastness of dyes.

Many dyes will not build up to deep shades except from a dyebath at low pH (about 2). The available amino groups are not sufficient to fix more dye. At a pH below about 3.5 the amido groups absorb hydrogen ion and become effective dye sites for the acid-dyeing acid colors. These dyes are polybasic and require a greater number of dye sites to fix them. Experience has shown that when the neutral-dyeing colors (usually monobasic) are used in mixture with polybasic colors the latter may be blocked or even displaced, because the monobasics require fewer strong dye sites for effective fixation.

Choice of Dye. Nylon-6 has a marked affinity for virtually every class of dyestuff. Those classes with the widest applications are the disperse, acid, premetalized, chrome, selected directs, and certain naphthol combinations (Table 4).

The choice of dye classes to be used for nylon-6 will usually fall on disperse dyes for easy application. Since they are fixed only by easily broken hydrogen bonding, they level well but also have poor washfastness. Brightness of shade and lightfastness are usually minimal. The acid dyes contribute brighter shades and some improvement in washfastness, but require greater care in application. The neutral dyeing, weakly acidic types can be used even in solid shades on well-prepared (uniform) fabric. The acid-dyeing colors and the neutral-dyeing premetalized (strongly acidic) colors provide the ultimate in performance. They are generally usable only where tone-on-tone effects or other devices obscure nonuniformity.

Basic dyes and vat colors are generally not used with polyamides. The basic dyes are used primarily with anionic-modified polyamides with other polyamides in a muticolor fabric for a single dyebath dyeing system. Basic dyes are handicapped by their poor lightfastness. The vats suffer from difficulty of application, high cost, low migration power, and again, poor lightfastness.

To the dyer, differences between the polymer types are less significant than fiber and fabric uniformity. However, the combination of uniformity with nylon-6 polymer can substantially improve his results.

Modified Fibers and Fiber Treatments

BICOMPONENT FIBERS

These are produced by melting, separately, two different components, and extruding them through a common spinneret as shown in Figure 18. The resulting fibers may have configurations as shown in Figure 19. The sheath-core arrangement recalls the structure of wool (qv) with its cortex and cuticle.

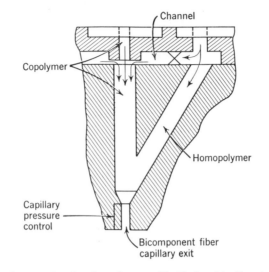

Fig. 18. Bicomponent spinneret for sheath-and-core. If side-by-side fiber is desired, interconnecting channel X is not employed.

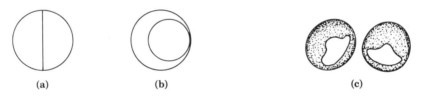

Fig. 19. Some polyamide bicomponent structural forms. LEGEND: (**a**) Side-by-side; (**b**) sheath-core; and (**c**) cantrece kidney-shaped sheath-and-core.

Conventional drawing or spin-draw procedures are used, but after the drawing stage the yarn passes through an essentially tensionless heating zone where the structure of the fiber leads to a helical crimp. It is then wound on the final sales package at very low tension.

Components used in some commercial bicomponent fibers, and their percentages, are shown in Table 5. Some properties of fabrics made from bicomponent fibers are compared with other polyamide fibers in Table 6.

Fabrics made from bicomponent yarn have unique properties of shape configuration, which is a consequence of their helical crimp. They are used in hose and tricot fabrics. Beginning as a pilot-plant operation in 1963, they grew to sales of 5 million lb in 1967, in the form of 15-den yarns which had a sales value 3–5 times greater than that of conventional nylon of equivalent denier.

Table 5. Components Used in Some Commercial Bicomponent Fibers

Component A copolymer	Copolymer composition, %	Component B homopolymer	Type
6,6–6,10 (113)	50:50	6,6	sheath-and-core
6,6-6,I (166a)	80:20	6,6	side-by-side
6,6–6 (166b)	80:20	6,6	side-by-side
6–6,T (166c)	40:60	6	sheath-and-core

Table 6. Comparative Properties of Some Polyamide Types, in a Fabric of 3.8 oz/yd^2

	Bicomponent fiber	Conventional nylon	Stuffer-box crimped Y cross-section nylon	Spun staple nylon
bulk, cm^3/g	2.4	1.8		
compressibility thickness, ratio of thickness at 3 g/cm^3 to thickness at 230 g/cm^3	1.3	1.1	1.15	1.45
air permeability, ft^3/(min)(ft^2)^a	35	20		
covering power at equal tension, % surface uncovered in hosiery	4.0	9.0		

^{a} ASTM D737-46.

RANDOM COPOLYMERS (MULTIPOLYMERS)

There has been an enormous body of literature and patents published related to copolymers (ref. 158 cites more than 360 publications on random copolymers). The largest suggested use is in the bicomponent-fiber field.

The principal limitations of random copolymers are their high shrinkage, low softening point, reduced wet-strength properties, tackiness, low ironing temperatures, and rate at which creep failure occurs.

Future commercial utility of this type of fiber may be in the field of nonwovens, heat molding of fabrics, and bonding of fabrics. There are two commercial fibers, Eftrelin, 90% nylon-6,6 and 10% nylon-6, which has good creasing or pleating properties and a soft hand; and Wetrelin, 43% nylon-6 and 57% nylon-6,T, whose properties are good compression elasticity, good creasing or pleating, better alkali resistance than nylon-6 or 6,6, and a wool-like hand. Most other polyamide copolymer systems introduced to date have not presented sufficiently improved engineering properties to justify the additional cost of production (159).

GRAFTING BY IRRADIATION

Like random copolymers, graft polymers in the polyamide field have been studied extensively, but little or no commercialization of this technology has been attained despite indications of important improvements in physical properties over the present nylons. The major limitation is an economic method for grafting either oriented or nonoriented fibers at sufficiently high speed and/or at a sufficiently large unit mass, eg, a sufficient number of fiber ends, for economical productivity.

Richardson (160) has demonstrated the relationship between the irradiation dose and the percentage of styrene grafted, and their effect on nylon strength as well as the resistance of grafted nylon tent fabric to water penetration.

Some of the numerous polyamide graft polymers which have been studied are given in refs. 160–166. Basic improvements in fiber properties which are obtained using a simple graft agent such as sodium polyacrylate are (a) better wet crease recovery properties; (b) higher stick temperature or amorphous melt point; and (c) higher moisture absorption. Other improvements are reduction in static propensity and improved dyeability. By use of special graft materials, the antisoiling properties, weathering properties, and rubber adhesion properties of polyamides can be improved.

Graft technology that is nearest to commercialization is that where a drawn sheet of yarns or greige fabric is treated with a vinyl monomer, irradiated, and finally heat-treated to dry the fabric and to complete the reaction.

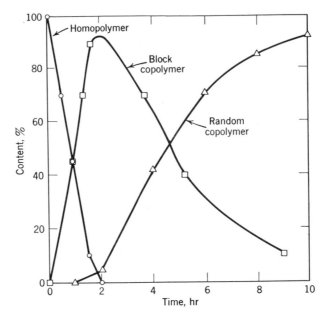

Fig 20. Typical composition change with time for conversion of two homopolymers, first to a block copolymer, then to a random copolymer.

Costs of irradiation may vary between 2 and 30¢/lb, dependent upon the irradiation dose employed, but it is believed these costs may be reduced by one-half to one-third. By combining a grafting operation with a continuous "nonwoven" operation, these costs may be significantly reduced.

BLOCK COPOLYMERS (167)

There are four common methods of producing block copolymers: (a) combination in the melt of two or more homopolyamides; (b) use of a diamine or diacid monomer which already contains an amide linkage and then reacting it with another diamine or diacid; (c) reaction of a complex molecule such as bisoxazolones with a diamine to produce a wide range of multiple amide sequences along the chain; and (d) reaction of a diisocyanate and a diamine.

Irrespective of the route selected to form block polyamides, the percentages of homopolymer, block copolymer, and random copolymer are a function of time and temperature of the mixture of these polyamides in the molten state, as shown in Figure 20. In actual practice, however, time is much more critical than is indicated in Figure 20. It has been found in the production of a polyamide-block-copolymer tire yarn that in a matter of 3–4 min there is a rather large difference in the flatspot set point and flatspot in mils. There is also considerable amide interchange at the end of 13 min (168). It is this rapid rate of amide interchange which poses a major problem in producing tire cord of equivalent flatspot values and uniformity in an industrial operation (168).

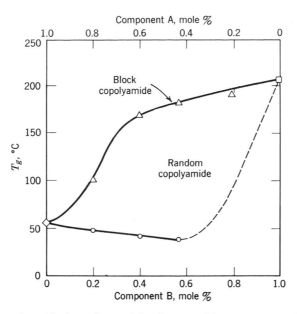

Fig. 21. Block copolyamide dependence of the glass transition temperature (T_g) on the composition of block and random copolyamides vs mole composition of nylon-6 (component A) and 2,5-dimethylpiperazine 4,4′-biphenylene-3,3′-dimethyldicarboxamide (component B).

Figure 21 illustrates a fundamental difference between block copolyamides and random copolyamides with respect to glass transition temperature as a function of composition. As can be observed, the two curves are essentially mirror images of each other, with the block copolymer having significantly improved properties and the random copolymer a degradation in properties (158).

HEAT AND LIGHT STABILIZATION

Stabilization Against Light Degradation. The successful solution of problems related to stabilization of polyamide fibers against light and other degrading conditions has been one of the major reasons for their continued dynamic growth. In the presence of light, rutile TiO_2, which is normally used as a delusterant, results in autocatalytic formation of peroxide which rapidly degenerates polyamides in the absence of stabilizers. This has been overcome by use of stabilizers such as manganese salts, along with additives such as hypophosphorous acids, phosphites, phosphates, and the like (169).

The major degrading portion of the sun's radiation is that due to ultraviolet because of its high energy, about 96 kcal/mole (170). This is double that of the carbon–nitrogen bond energy of 48 kcal/mole.

Stabilization Against Degradation by Heat and Light. Studies of the pyrolysis of nylon-6 indicate that water, carbon dioxide, and ammonia are the three major gaseous products given off (171,172). In the protection of nondelustered fibers from degradation by heat and light, the preferred stabilizers are copper salts (173). Copper salts are normally added prior to polymerization and are typically present in filamentary yarn at a concentration of 45–60 ppm Cu. Figure 22 shows the very marked effect that copper salts have upon nylon-6 and 6,6 stabilization. The effect on nylon-6 is really striking, because nylon-6 shows essentially the same heat resistance as nylon-6,6 despite a melting point which is 35°C lower (174).

Several organic or inorganic materials have been found to act as synergistic co-stabilizers with copper salts. Some of these are alkali metal iodides (175); stannous salts (176); 2-amino-3,5-diiodobenzoic acid (177); hydroxybenzothiazole; hydroxybenzimidazoles (178); and 2-mercaptobenzomethylthiazole (169).

Stabilization Against High-Temperature Strength Loss at High Loads. One of the significant factors which has made it possible to produce a nylon-6 tire yarn is the ability to increase the breaking temperature under high loads. Indeed, it has

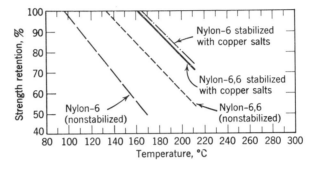

Fig. 22. Effect of 24-hr exposure to air at various temperatures on strength retention for polyamide fibers stabilized with copper salts vs unstabilized nylon-6 and 6,6.

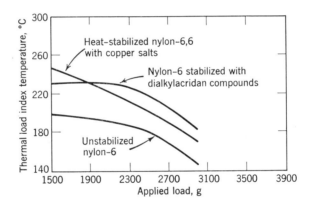

Fig. 23. The temperature at which nylons break under different applied loads. The test yarns were 840 den.

been possible to obtain greater stability than that for nylon-6,6 conventionally stabilized with copper (179). In Figure 23 it can be noted that stabilized nylon-6, under a 2.5-kg load, breaks at 209°C whereas nylon-6,6 breaks at 203°C, and unstabilized nylon-6 breaks at approx 190°C (179). 9,9-Dialkyldihydroacridine compounds (see structure below) are employed in polyamide stabilization at high temperature and high loads (180). These stabilizers are added in the amount of 0.4–1.0% by wt of monomer before or during polymerization. Certain Schiff bases, such as 3,4-methylene dioxybenzal-p-aminodiphenylamine and n-4-oxy-3-methoxybenzal-p-aminodiphenylamine (181), are said to have good thermal load index properties.

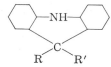

Stabilization to Heat Disorientation in the Presence of Liquids (High-Pressure Steam Vulcanization, etc). The disorientation of polyamides as vulcanization temperatures of tires are raised higher and higher, in order to gain greater productivity, has become an increasingly significant problem. This disorientation is most pronounced during the time in which tire yarns are exposed to moisture at low load during the vulcanization process, or when the pressure is released after vulcanization. This problem can be partially alleviated by maintaining some degree of tension on the tire cord at the end of the pressure release.

It can also be partially avoided by minimizing the moisture content of tire yarns prior to vulcanization, and by incorporation of various desiccants.

Stabilization Against Hot-Wet Degradation. Undrawn nylon filaments of either nylon-6,6 or nylon-6 are susceptible to degradation in wet or humid conditions at temperatures between 50 and 90°C (182). Since nylons possess a very high, largely irreversible, extensibility with the absorption of large quantities of energy, this property can be converted to a practical device in emergency arrestor gear in aircraft carriers. However, the undrawn nylon is generally prone to humid degradation. It has been found that by exposure of these arrestor ropes to 8-hydroxyquinoline, effective protection against degradation for a period of 500 days is obtainable.

A similar oxidation phenomena occurs with nylon carpet yarns, leading to extensive fading of certain disperse dyes when exposed to hot humid climates.

Bibliography

"Polyamides" in *ECT* 1st ed., Vol. 10, pp. 916–937, by Ferdinand Schulze, E. I. du Pont de Nemours & Co., Inc., and Harold Wittcoff, General Mills, Inc.

1. Gabriel and Maas, *Ber.* **32,** 1266 (1899).
2. D. G. Bannerman, *Synthetic Fibers in Papermaking,* Interscience Publishers, a division of John Wiley & Sons, Inc., New York, 1964, pp. 57, 58.
3. J. G. Cook, *Handbook of Textile Fibers,* 3rd ed., Menon Publishing, Watford, Herts, England, 1964, pp. 265–271.
4. P. A. Koch, *Fibres Plastics* **22,** 196 ((July 1961).
5. P. A. Schlack, *Chemiefasern* **17,** 961–966 (Dec. 1967).
6. H. Klare, *Technologie und Chemie der synthetischen Fasern aus Polyamiden,* Verlag Technik, Berlin, 1954, p. 13.
7. H. Hopff, *Synthetic Fiber Development in Germany,* Part II, H. M. Stationery Office, London, 1945, p. 719.
8. *Ibid.,* pp. 458, 459.
9. J. G. Cook, *Handbook of Textile Fibers,* 1st ed., Menon Publishing, Watford, Herts, England, 1959, p. 234.
9a. H. Mark and G. S. Whitby, eds., *Collected Papers of Wallace Hume Carothers on High Polymeric Substances,* Vol. I of *High Polymers,* Interscience Publishers, Inc., New York, 1940.
10. *Textile Organon* **24** (6), (June 1953).
11. *Textile Organon* **38** (6), (June 1967).
12. H. Hopff, *Synthetic Fiber Development in Germany,* Part II, H. M. Stationery Office, London, 1945, p. 101.
13. *Informations—Chimie* 86 (Nov. 1966).

14. O. E. Snider, "Polyamide Fibers," in N. Bikales, ed., *Encyclopedia of Polymer Science and Technology*, Vol. 10 (in press).
15. U.S. Pat. 1,692,372 (Nov. 11, 1929), H. A. Gardner.
16. U.S. Pat. 1,875,894 (Sept. 6, 1933), J. A. Singmaster.
17. U.S. Pat. 1,980,428 (Nov. 13, 1935), R. H. Parkinson (to Celanese Chemical Co.).
18. U.S. Pat. 2,205,722 (June 25, 1940), G. D. Graves (to E. I. du Pont de Nemours & Co., Inc.).
19. U.S. Pat. 2,278,878 (April 7, 1942), G. P. Hoff (to du Pont).
20. U.S. Pat. 3,002,947 (Oct. 3, 1961), D. E. Maple (to du Pont).
21. U.S. Pat. 2,671,770 (March 9, 1954), J. C. Lyons (to Société Rhodiaceta).
22. Brit. Pat. 504,714 (April 28, 1939) (to du Pont).
23. U.S. Pat. 2,689,839 (Sept. 21, 1954), W. W. Heckert (to du Pont).
24. A. Sippel, *Melliand Textilber.* **38,** 898 (1957).
25. R. J. Fahl, *Chem. Can.* **3,** 23 (1962).
26. U.S. Pat. 2,819,173 (June 7, 1958), K. Dithmar (to Degussa).
27. U.S. Pat. 2,846,332 (Aug. 8, 1958), G. A. Nesty (to Allied Chemical).
28. Fr. Pat. 938,012.
29. Ger. Pat. 1,111,771 (March 15, 1962), H. J. Twitchett and A. S. Weld (to Imperial Chemical Industries, Ltd.).
30. P. Schaeffer, *Chem. Tech.* **12,** 742 (1960).
31. U.S. Pat. 3,160,600 (Dec. 8, 1964), J. R. Holsten and J. S. Tapp (to Monsanto Co.).
32. U.S. Pat. 2,875,171 (Feb. 24, 1959), S. P. Foster and R. W. Peterson (to du Pont).
33. A. N. Bykov, T. M. Kirillova, and N. P. Lits, *Vysokomolekul. Soedin.* **5,** 428 (1963); *Chem. Abstr.* **59,** 2986g (1963).
34. A. N. Bykov and S. S. Frolov, *Khim. Volokna* **1961** (1), 15; *Chem. Abstr.* **55,** 15985g (1961).
35. A. N. Bykov, E. A. Ermolaeva, N. P. Lits, and T. M. Kirillova, *Khim. Volokna* **1962** (4), 9; *Chem. Abstr.* **58,** 3540b (1963).
36. A. N. Bykov, *Vysokomolekul. Soedin.* **3,** 1307 (1961); *Chem. Abstr.* **57,** 8722a (1962).
37. A. N. Bykov and Z. M. Rudman, *Byul. Isob.* **22,** 44 (1962); *Chem. Abstr.* **58,** 14233e (1963).
38. A. N. Bykov, E. A. Ermolaeva, T. M. Kirillova, and A. N. Golubeva, *Khim. Volokna* **1964** (2), 41.
39. Brit. Pat. 937,798 (Sept. 25, 1963) (to Monsanto).
40. U.S. Pat. 2,784,184 (March 5, 1959), R. Zweidler and E. Keller (to Geigy Chemical Corp.).
41. Ger. Pat. 1,040,555 (Oct. 9, 1958), F. Ackermann, M. Dunnenberger, and A. E. Siegrist (to Ciba Corp.).
42. U.S. Pat. 2,488,094 (Nov. 15, 1949), C. Granacher and F. Ackermann (to Ciba).
43. Brit. Pat. 971,742 (Oct. 7, 1964) (to Allied Chemical).
44. A. Alexander, *Manmade Fiber Processing*, Noyes Development Corp., Parkridge, N.J., 1966, p. 82.
45. *Ibid.*, p. 111.
46. H. Klare, *Synthetic Fibers from Polyamides*, Akademie-Verlag, GmbH, Berlin, 1963.
47. F. Fourné, *Synthetische Fasern*, Wissenschaftlicher Verlag, Stuttgart, 1964, pp. 39–115.
48. H. H. Weinstock, ed., *Nylon 6 Fibers, Technology, Properties, and Applications*, Interscience Publishers, a division of John Wiley & Sons, Inc., New York (in press), sections 10–16.
49. Belg. Pat. 675,294 (Jan. 8, 1964), G. M. Dulin, W. H. Harlacher, and E. A. Swanson (to Allied Chemical).
50. U.S. Pat. 3,257,457 (June 21, 1966), G. M. Dulin (to Allied Chemical).
51. U.S. Pat. 3,311,691 (March 28, 1967), A. N. Good.
52. J. M. McKelvey, *Polymer Processing*, John Wiley & Sons, Inc., New York, 1962.
53. B. T. Hayes, P. V. Papero, and D. C. Prevorsek, *Research Monograph M-12*, Allied Chemical, May 1967. (Presented at the 37th annual meeting of the Textile Research Institute.)
54. H. Mark, *Kolloid Z.* **216–217,** 126–129 (March–April 1967).
55. P. A. Taylor, unpublished literature studies, Allied Chemical.
56. *Man-Made Textiles* **38** (441), 34 (1961).
57. *Man-Made Textiles* **38** (445), 32 (1961).
58. H. Boehringer and F. Bolland, *Faserforsch. Textiltech.* **9,** 405 (1958).
59. K. Greenwood, *Textile Recorder* **78** (62), 113 (1960).
60. G. M. Richardson and H. Stanley, *Mod. Textiles Mag.* **43,** 53 (Feb. 1962).
61. U.S. Pat. 2,891,277 (June 23, 1959), W. L. Sutor (to du Pont).

62. Brit. Pat. 936,729 (Sept. 11, 1963) (to du Pont).

63. *Chem. Eng. News* **43** (5), 34 (1965).

64. M. F. Davis, *ASTME-Electro Metal Removal Seminar, Hartford, Conn., March 10–11, 1964, TP 645.*

65. T. A. Moore, *ASTME-Electro Metal Removal Seminar, Hartford, Conn., Dec. 6–7, 1961, TP 61–15.*

66. Can. Pat. 591,686 (Feb. 2, 1960), R. B. Hayden (to du Pont).

67. Fr. Pat. 1,358,092 (March 2, 1964) (to Snia Viscosa).

68. Brit. Pat. 841,327 (July 13, 1960) (to Snia Viscosa).

69. Fr. Pat. 1,358,093 (March 2, 1964) (to Snia Viscosa).

70. U.S. Pats. 2,939,201 and 2,939,202 (June 7, 1960), M. C. Holland (to du Pont).

71. U.S. Pat. 3,097,416 (July 16, 1963), A. H. McKinney (to du Pont).

72. U.S. Pat. 3,109,220 (Nov. 5, 1963), A. H. McKinney and H. E. Stanley (to du Pont).

73. Brit. Pat. 947,183 (Jan. 22, 1964) (to Farbwerke Hoechst, A.G.).

74. U.S. Pat. 3,138,516 (June 23, 1964), J. G. Sims (to Monsanto).

75. Brit. Pat. 843,179 (Aug. 4, 1960), G. Siemer, H. Laurioch, and W. Stockigt (to VEB Thüringisches Kunstfaserwerk).

76. Fr. Pat. 1,096,943.

77. U.S. Pat. 3,075,242 (Jan. 29, 1963), E. Grafried (to W. C. Heraeus).

78. U.S. Pat. 3,081,490 (March 19, 1963), W. Heynen and W. Martin (to Vereinigte Glanzstoff-Fabriken, A.G.).

79. U.S. Pat. 3,113,369 (Dec. 10, 1963), H. D. Barrett, R. T. Estes, and G. C. Stow (to Monsanto).

80. U.S. Pat. 3,103,448 (Sept. 10, 1963), S. E. Ross (to Allied Chemical).

81. H. C. Speel and E. W. K. Schwarz, *Textile Chemicals and Auxiliaries*, 2nd ed., Reinhold Publishing Corp., New York, 1957, p. 222.

82. R. C. Gunderson and A. W. Hart, *Synthetic Lubricants*, Reinhold Publishing Corp., New York, 1962.

83. A. E. Henshall, *Textil-Rundschau* **14** (1), 28 (1959); *Chem. Abstr.* **53**, 9681f (1959).

84. V. E. Shashoua, *Am. Chem. Soc., Div. Polymer Chem., Preprints* **4** (1), 189 (1963).

85. R. D. Fine, "The Occurrence, Behavior and Elimination of Static on Textiles," *Am. Dyestuff Reptr.* **43**, 405 (June 21, 1954).

86. P. Senner, *Reyon, Zellwolle Chemiefasern* **8**, 666, 744, 807, 865 (1958); *Chem. Abstr.* **53**, 6625e (1959).

87. J. Diemunsch and J. Chabert, *Bull. Inst. Textile France* **102**, 887 (1962); *Chem. Abstr.* **58**, 5822h (1963).

88. Brit. Pat. 963,320 (July 8, 1964) (to du Pont).

89. Brit. Pat. 975,383 (Nov. 18, 1964) (to American Cyanamid Co.).

90. C. Schlatter, R. A. Olney, and B. N. Baer, *Textile Res. J.* **29** (3), (March 1959).

91. H. Klare, E. Fritzsche, and V. Gröbe, *Synthetische Fasern aus Polyamiden*, Akademie-Verlag, Berlin, 1963, p. 272.

92. B. L. Hathorne, *Woven, Stretch and Textured Fabrics*, Interscience Publishers, a division of John Wiley & Sons, Inc., New York, 1964.

93. E. A. Hutton and W. J. Morris, *A Survey of the Literature and Patents Relating to Bulked Continuous Filament Yarns*, Bulletin 81, Shirley Institute, Manchester, July 1963.

94. U.S. Pat. 2,575,781 (Nov. 20, 1951), J. L. Barach (to Alexander Smith).

95. U.S. Pats. 2,575,837, 2,575,838, and 2,575,839 (Nov. 20, 1951), L. W. Rainard (to Alexander Smith).

95a. Spunize Dept., Allied Chemical Corp., New York.

96. G. R. Wray, *Textile Recorder* **78**, 47 (Dec. 1960).

97. J. S. Taylor and D. Bhattacharya, *Textile Recorder* **80**, 58 (1962).

98. *Mod. Textiles Mag.* **42**, 38 (Oct. 1961).

99. U.S. Pat. 2,919,534 (Jan. 5, 1950), E. D. Bolinger and N. E. Klein (to Deering Milliken Research Corp.).

100. U.S. Pats. 3,021,588 (Feb. 13, 1962) and 3,035,328 (June 22, 1962), E. D. Bolinger (to Deering Milliken).

101. U.S. Pats. 3,025,584 (March 20, 1962) and 3,931,089 (April 5, 1960), C. G. Evans (to Deering Milliken).

102. U.S. Pat. 2,019,185 (Oct. 29, 1936), R. H. Kagi (to Heberlein Patent Corp.).

103. U.S. Pats. 2,803,105, 2,803,108, and 2,803,109 (Aug. 20, 1957), N. J. Stoddard and W. A. Seem (to Universal Winding Co.); 3,025,659 (March 20, 1962), N. J. Stoddard and W. A. Seem (to Leesona Corp.).

103a. *Man Made Textiles & Skinners' Record* **44,** 110 (Sept. 1967).

104. J. J. Press, ed., *Man-Made Textile Encyclopedia*, Interscience Publishers, Inc., New York, 1959, p. 241.

105. U.S. Pat. 2,958,112 (Nov. 1, 1960), J. N. Hall (to J. N. Hall).

106. U.S. Pat. 2,884,756 (May 5, 1959), W. I. Head (to Eastman Kodak Co.).

107. U.S. Pats. 2,783,609 (March 5, 1957), 2,852,906 (Sept. 23, 1958), and 2,869,967 (Jan. 20, 1959), A. L. Breen (to du Pont).

108. U.S. Pat. 3,140,525 (July 14, 1964), D. J. Lamb (to Monsanto).

109. U.S. Pats. 3,024,516 and 3,024,517 (March 13, 1962), J. E. Bromley and W. H. Hills (to Chemstrand Corp.).

110. U.S. Pat. 3,137,911 (June 23, 1964), J. E. Bromley (to Monsanto).

111. U.S. Pat. 3,005,251 (Oct. 24, 1961), C. E. Hallden, Jr., and K. Murenbeeld (to du Pont).

112. U.S. Pat. 2,942,402 (June 28, 1960), C. W. Palm (to Celanese).

113. U.S. Pat. 2,884,756 (May 5, 1959), W. I. Head (to Eastman Kodak).

114. U.S. Pat. 2,852,906 (June 23, 1958), A. L. Breen (to du Pont).

115. U.S. Pat. 3,164,882 (Jan. 12, 1965), N. Rosenstein and A. J. Rosenstein (to Spunize Co. of America).

116. U.S. Pat. 3,101,521 (Aug. 27, 1963), A. J. Rosenstein, N. Rosenstein, and T. F. Suggs (to Spunize Co. of America).

117. U.S. Pats. 3,031,734 (May 1, 1962) and 3,037,260 (June 5, 1962), H. J. Pike (to Allied Chemical).

118. U.S. Pat. 2,862,879 (Dec. 2, 1958), H. D. Fardon and H. J. Pike (to Allied Chemical).

119. U.S. Pat. 2,933,771 (April 26, 1960), H. H. Weinstock, Jr., (to Allied Chemical).

120. U.S. Pat. 2,985,995 (May 30, 1961), W. W. Bunting and T. L. Nelson (to du Pont).

121. J. J. Press, ed., *Man-Made Textile Encyclopedia*, Interscience Publishers, Inc., New York, 1959, Chap. 5.

122. F. Fourné, *Synthetische Fasern*, Wissenschaftlicher Verlag, Stuttgart, 1964, Chap. VI.

123. H. Jentgen, *Reyon, Synthetica Zellwolle* **29,** 9 (1951).

124. H. Klare, E. Fritzche, and V. Gröbe, *Synthetische Fasern aus Polyamiden*, Akademie-Verlag, Berlin, 1963, p. 373.

125. P. V. Papero, E. T. Kubu, and L. Roldan, "Fundamental Property Considerations in Tailoring a New Fiber," *Textile Res. J.* **37,** 823–833 (1967).

126. *Technical Bulletin C-3*, Allied Chemical, Oct. 1963.

127. Unpublished data, Allied Chemical.

128. E. B. Grover and D. S. Hamby, *Handbook of Textile Testing and Quality Control*, Interscience Publishers, Inc., New York, 1960, pp. 371, 383.

129. H. D. W. Smith, "Textile Fibers, An Engineering Approach to Their Properties and Utilization," *Am. Soc. Testing Mater. Proc.* **44** (1944).

130. Unpublished data from Allied Chemical (1964 production).

131. J. E. Booth, *Principles of Textile Testing*, Chemical Publishing Co., Inc., New York, 1961, Chap. 8.

132. E. R. Kaswell, *Wellington Sears Handbook of Industrial Textiles*, Wellington Sears Co., New York, 1963.

133. R. Meredith, *Mechanical Properties of Textile Fibers*, Interscience Publishers, Inc., New York, 1956, Chap. 16.

134. W. E. Morton and J. W. S. Hearle, *Physical Properties of Textile Fibers*, Butterworths, London, 1962, Chap. 13.

135. H. Busch, *Z. Ges. Textil-Ind.* **65,** 1014 (1963).

136. Reference 134, p. 333.

137. W. Wegener, *Reyon, Zellwolle Chemiefasern* **32,** 69 (1954).

138. R. Meredith, *Mechanical Properties of Textile Fibers*, Interscience Publishers, Inc., New York, 1956, p. 76.

139. L. F. Beste and R. M. Hoffman, *Textile Res. J.* **20,** 441 (1950).

140. W. E. Morton and J. W. S. Hearle, *Physical Properties of Textile Fibers*, Butterworths, London, 1962, Chaps. 15 and 16.

141. *Technical Bulletin NP-4*, American Enka, July 1960.

142. *Technical Bulletin A4-2*, Perlon-Hoechst.

143. W. Grether, *SVF Fachorgan Textilveredlung* **15** (1), 29 (1960) (from H. U. Schmidlin, *Preparation and Dyeing of Synthetic Fibers*, Reinhold Publishing Corp., New York, 1960, p. 45.

144. *Caprolan Nylon Product Line*, Technical Bulletin C3, Allied Chemical Fibers Division, New York, 1963, p. 11.

145. *Caprolan Nylon, Industrial Rubber Uses*, Bulletin C15, Allied Chemical, 1964.

146. F. Fourné, *Synthetische Fasern*, Wissenschaftlicher Verlag, Stuttgart, 1964, p. 276.

147. *Technical Bulletin A-2*, Perlon-Hoechst, pp. 7, 8.

148. R. W. Moncrieff, *Man-Made Textiles* **41** (481), 34 (1964).

149. R. W. Moncrieff, *Man Made Fibers*, John Wiley & Sons, Inc., New York, 1963.

150. G. A. Nesty, *Textile Res. J.* **29** (10), 765 (1959).

151. H. U. Schmidlin, *Preparation and Dyeing of Synthetic Fibers*, English ed., Reinhold Publishing Corp., New York, 1963, p. 177.

152. W. C. Carter, *Chem. Eng. News* **22**, 44 (May 4, 1944).

153. H. U. Schmidlin, *Preparation and Dyeing of Synthetic Fibers*, English ed., Reinhold Publishing Corp., New York, 1963, p. 26.

154. T. Vickerstaff, *The Physical Chemistry of Dyeing*, 2nd ed., Interscience Publishers, Inc., New York, 1954, p. 451.

155. H. Zahn and H. Spoor, *Z. Anal. Chem.* **168**, 190 (1959).

156. W. E. Beier, V. A. Dorman-Smith, and G. C. Ongemach, *Anal. Chem.* **38** (1), 123–125 (1966).

157. H. H. Schenker, C. C. Castro, and P. W. Mullen, *Anal. Chem.* **29**, 825 (1957).

158. V. V. Korshak and T. R. Frunze, *Synthetic Hetero-Chain Polyamides*, Davy, Daniel & Co., Inc., New York, 1964, pp. 232–233.

159. E A. Tippetts, *Am. Dyestuff Reptr.* **54**, 141–146 (March 1, 1965).

160. R. J. Richardson, *Paper, 9th Canadian High Polymer Symposium, Scarboro, Ont., Oct. 28, 1959.*

161. B. D. Coleman and A. G. Krex, *Textile Res. J.* **27**, 393–399 (1957).

162. T. M. Frunze and V. V. Kurashev, *Izv. Akad. Nauk SSSR Ser. Khim.* **10**, 1860–1866 (1965).

163. R. Notake and T. Kohima, *Sen-i Gakkaishi* **21** (9), 464–470 (1965).

164. V. I. Guikhov, *Dokl. Akad. Nauk SSSR* **166** (4), 901–904 (1966).

165. G. Odian, M. Sobel, A. Rossi et al., *J. Polymer Sci.* **1A**, 639–654 (1963).

166. V. V. Korshak and K. K. Mozgova, *Vysokomolekul. Soedin.* **5** (3), 338–342 (1963).

167. R. J. Ceresa, "Block and Graft Copolymers," in N. Bikales, ed., *Encyclopedia of Polymer Science and Technology*, Vol. 2, Interscience Publishers, a division of John Wiley & Sons, Inc. New York, 1965, pp. 485–528.

168. Brit, Pat. 918,637 (Feb. 13, 1963) (to du Pont).

169. U.S. Pat. 3,242,134 (March 22, 1966), P. V. Papero (to Allied Chemical).

170. S. A. Abramov, *Legkaya Prom.* **18** (12), 23–27 (1958).

171. S. Straus and L. A. Wall, *J. Res. Natl. Bur. Std.* **60**, 39 (1958).

172. *Ibid.*, **63A**, 269 (1959).

173. U.S. Pat. 3,113,120 (Dec. 3, 1963), P. V. Papero and R. L. Morter (to Allied Chemical).

174. F. Fourné, *Synthetische Fasern*, Wissenschaftlicher Verlag, Stuttgart, 1964, p. 276.

175. U.S. Pat. 2,705,227 (March 29, 1955), G. Stamatoff.

176. U.S. Pat. 3,280,053 (Oct. 18, 1966), I. C. Twilley and F. P. Poznik (to Allied Chemical).

177. U.S. Pat. 3,294,735 (Dec. 27, 1966), I. C. Twilley and F. P. Poznik (to Allied Chemical).

178. K. R. Osborn, *J. Polymer Sci.* **38**, 357 (1959).

179. G. A. Nesty, *Textile Res. J.* **29** (10), 763–776 (1959).

180. U.S. Pat. 3,003, 995 (Oct. 10, 1961), E. C. Schule (to Allied Chemical).

181. U.S. Pat. 3,321,436 (May 23, 1967), W. Stilz et al. (to Badische Anilin- und Soda-Fabrik).

182. E. Mikolajewski, J. E. Swallow, and M. W. Webb, *J. Appl. Polymer Sci.* **8**, 2067–2093 (1964).

O. E. Snider and R. J. Richardson
Allied Chemical Corporation

POLYAMIDE PLASTICS

Molding and extrusion compounds based on polyamide polymers have experienced wide acceptance under the generic name of nylon. The list of manufactured grades and types has grown rapidly and products are now available based on many different polyamide polymers.

Initially, nylon plastics, formed from the combination of hexamethylenediamine and adipic acid, were introduced into the United States during 1941 whereas ϵ-caprolactam was the primary raw material to be used in Europe. Since that time other lactams and condensation products of higher molecular weight diacids and diamines have been used to provide special properties not available in the earlier more traditional materials. The presence of the amide group provides a focal point for hydrogen bonding which results in the formation of crystalline structures that are characterized by toughness, resistance to oils and solvents, superior physical strength, a degree of sensitivity to moisture, and high melting points. The number of carbon atoms between the amide groups determines properties by a factor of concentration or dilution of the amide sections.

Polyamide polymers are used in applications where properties such as flame resistance, chemical resistance, toughness, low coefficient of friction, good stiffness, outstanding wear resistance, good electrical properties, and high temperature resistance are required. Because of their general superior properties and relatively high cost per pound, polyamides are considered engineering plastics where they are employed because they perform a needed function that cannot readily be accomplished by the use of any other material. Applications include electrical grommets, bearings, gears, fasteners, valve components, rollers, tubing, pipe, film, monofilaments, wire straps, wire covering, electrical connectors, sports equipment, and many other functional components. As selling prices reach a common level, the polyamides are expected to compete with metals and other materials in many new applications.

Economics

Sales of polyamides have increased steadily since their introduction in the early 1940s, but total volume in the United States is relatively small in comparison to major plastic types and reached a level of approximately 70 million pounds in 1966. This represents a little over 1% of the total plastics consumed, a percentage value that has changed little over the last ten years. The degree of penetration into the total market is expected to increase as special products are developed and price drops to a point where polyamides can compete with more traditional materials of construction.

Pricing remained fairly steady during the more recent years and has had little effect on market growth since the price/unit vol has not dropped to the level where competition with cast metal is attractive. The most recent price is expected to generate new applications solely on the basis of cost whereas previous uses were greatly

Table 1. Price of Nylon Plastics from before 1955 through 1967

Year	Price, $/lb	Year	Price, $/lb
before 1955	1.60	1961	0.98
1955	1.435	1962	0.98
1956	1.33	1963	0.90
1957	1.18	1964	0.90
1958	1.18	1965	0.875
1959	1.18	1966	0.875
1960	0.98	1967	0.75

determined by performance properties alone. The price of general purpose polyamide plastics for the period 1955 through 1967 is shown in Table 1.

The list of producers of polyamides has grown constantly as the use of these materials has achieved worldwide application. Depending upon raw material position, economics, and application, the type of polyamide produced differs greatly.

Table 2 contains a list of some of the major producers of polyamide resins around the world. Basic types only have been shown although most companies offer special compounds, glass filled products, powders, copolymers, and compounded products. Reprocessors and resale agents are not listed.

Manufacture

Polylactam (nylon-6). The polymerization of ϵ-caprolactam for molding compounds, by the batch or continuous process, is usually accomplished by heating the monomer to above 250°C in the presence of catalysts (such as water and phosphoric acid) and chain terminators (such as acetic acid) to a viscous mass. The molecular weight can be varied by the amount and type of polymer initiation and termination, and by the length of polymerization time. Polymerization under these conditions does not go to completion but rather to a point where an equilibrium is established between the monomer and the polymer at approximately 85–90% conversion. At this point the polymer–monomer mixture can be discharged through dies to provide strands or small diameter rods which are cut to short lengths common to pellets normally required by the processes used in the plastics industry. At this point the monomer and low-molecular-weight oligomers may be removed by extraction with water and the pellets then dried. A modification would be to dry the pellets without water washing to make products having some degree of flexibility due to the plasticizing action of the residual monomer. An alternate route is to feed the molten polymer–monomer mixture from the polymerizer into a vacuum stripping chamber where the monomer is removed by evaporation. Pelletizing is then accomplished in the normal manner. High-molecular-weight polymers can also be produced by subjecting pellets of polycaprolactam to temperatures slightly below the melting point for a period of time by a process known as "solid state polymerization." Additives can be incorporated into the polymer during polymerization or in a postextrusion step.

Diacid-diamine (nylon-6,6). The manufacture of nylon-6,6 is accomplished by reacting equal amounts of hexamethylenediamine and adipic acid to provide a high-molecular-weight polymer. A first step in the process is to form the nylon salt by combining the diamine and the adipic acid in a water and alcohol solution. An aqueous

Table 2. Producers of Polyamide Plastics

Country	Polyamide type	Tradename	Country	Polyamide type	Tradename
United States			Germany		
Allied Chemical Corp. Plastics Div. Morristown, N.J.	6	Plaskon nylon	Badische Anilin- und Soda Fabrik, A.G. Ludwigshafen am Rhein	6 6,6	Ultramid
Celanese Plastics Div. of Celanese Corp. Newark, N.J.	6,6	Celanese nylon	Chemische Werke Hüls Kreis Recklinghausen	12	Vestamid
The Chemstrand Corp. Div. Monsanto Co. Greenville, S.C.	6,6	Blue C nylon	Farbenfabriken Bayer A.G. Leverkusen	6	Durethan
E. I. du Pont de Nemours & Co., Inc. Plastics Dept. Wilmington, Del.	6 6,6 6,10	Zytel	Dr. Plate GmbH Bonn	6 6,6 6,10 11 12	Plastamid
Foster Grant Co., Inc. Leominster, Mass.	6	Fosta nylon	Italy		
			Montecatini Edison S.P.A. Milan	6	

Manufacturer and location	Trademark	Type
Gulf Oil Corp. Spencer Chemical Div. Kansas City, Mo.	Gulf nylon	6
England		
Imperial Chemical Industries Ltd. Plastics Div. Welwyn Garden City, England	Maranyl	6 6,6 6,10
France		
Aquitaine-Organico Tour Aquitaine Paris	Orgamide	6 11
Rhodiaceta Plastics Div. Paris	Nylon-Technyl	6 6,6 6,10 soluble grades
Snia Viscosa Milan	Sniamid	6 6,6
Japan		
Tokyo Rayon Co., Ltd. Tokyo	Amilan	6 6,6 6,10
Ube Industries, Ltd. Tokyo		6
Nippon Rayon		6
Netherlands		
Algemene Kunstzijde Unie, N.V. Arnhem	Akulon	6 6,6
Switzerland		
Emser Werke Zürich	Grilon Grilamid	6 12

solution of the salt is subjected to heat and pressure to cause dissociation followed by amide group formation. The pressure is reduced and condensation is promoted to form a high-molecular-weight polymer. The molten, viscous polymer is discharged from the polymerizer and formed into strands or a sheet which is chopped into chips or pellets of suitable size and shape. At this point the chips contain about one percent moisture and a drying operation is required to yield a product that can be processed on standard plastic equipment. The molecular weight of the polymer is normally controlled by use of a chain terminator such as acetic acid.

Acid-amine (nylon-11). Polymerization is relatively simple and consists of heating the monomer (11-aminoundecanoic acid) to slightly above 200°C and removing the water formed by condensation of the acid and the amine. The reaction is normally catalyzed and goes essentially to completion and washing or drying of the product is not necessary. Extrusion from the polymerizer into chips or pellets is performed as in the case of other nylon grades.

Polylactam (nylon-12). The polymerization of lauryllactam is similar to polycaprolactam production in that the lactam ring is opened by heat and a catalyst to form a polymer chain. Temperature of polymerization is somewhat higher. The main point of difference is that the conversion of monomer to polymer is almost complete and it is not necessary to employ a washing step as in the case of some polycaprolactam products.

Additives

Plasticizers. Highly crystalline polymers such as nylon-6 and 6,6 are difficult to plasticize to provide polymers of high flexibility. In the case of nylon-6 an effective additive is caprolactam monomer. In practice, this product is made by not extracting the caprolactam after polymerization has come to equilibrium. The presence of the caprolactam causes a drop in stiffness and a slight increase in impact strength (Table 3).

Table 3. Property Comparison of Nylon-6 and Nylon-6 with 10% Caprolactam

Property	ASTM test method	Nylon-6	Nylon-6 with 10% caprolactam
tensile strength, psi	D638-58T	11,800	11,800
ultimate elongation, %	D638-58T	200	290
flexural strength, psi	D790-58T	16,400	7,600
stiffness, psi	D747-58T	350,000	115,000
Izod impact, ft-lb/in.	D256-56	1.2	1.5

Table 4. Property Comparison of Nylon-11 and Plasticized Nylon-11

Property	ASTM test method	Nylon-11	Nylon-11, plasticized
tensile strength, psi	D638-58T	8,500	6,800
ultimate elongation, %	D638-58T	220	300
flexural modulus, psi	D790-58T	180,000	85,000
Izod impact, ft-lb/in.	D256-56	1.0	4.8

Plasticizers, such as long-chain diols and high-molecular-weight sulfonamides, are highly effective in copolymers and nylon-11 and 12 where lower levels of crystallization are encountered (Table 4).

Plasticizers can be added to the polymerizer by blending with nylon pellets followed by an extrusion step. Major applications for plasticized grades include fishing lines, tubing, gaskets, and adhesives.

Heat and Light Stabilizers. Nylon polymers will degrade and become brittle when exposed to elevated temperatures or sunlight for prolonged periods of time. For practical considerations, continuous exposure of an unstabilized nylon at 150°F is acceptable. Short periods of exposure up to the melting point are possible. However, for long-term use at elevated temperatures heat stabilizers are recommended and used. Antioxidants are effective stabilizers but best results are achieved with combinations of cupric salts and alkali metal halides. These combinations are highly effective and permit continuous use up to 200–250°F. For outdoor exposure the most effective additive is a finely dispersed carbon black in concentration of 1.5–2.5%. Resistance to sunlight exposure is increased by a factor of about 10. Colorless light stabilizers can also be used, but they are less effective. Stabilizers must also be added where long exposure to hot water is required since the amide group undergoes hydrolysis unless properly protected.

Fiber-Reinforcing Agents. The addition of glass fiber to plastic is a common practice when improvements in tensile strength, creep resistance, rigidity, and impact strength are desired. This is particularly true of nylon, where the addition of glass provides a remarkable change in basic properties. Materials of this type are useful in injection molding but cannot be easily extruded because the glass fibers interfere with the melt flow. The content of glass fiber, and the fiber length and the surface

Table 5. Property Changes Due to Variation in Glass Fiber Length

Property	ASTM test method	Unfilled nylon	30% short glass fiber, $<\frac{1}{8}$ in.	30% long glass fiber, $>\frac{1}{4}$ in.
density	D792	1.13	1.34	1.34
water absorption, % per day	D570-57T	1.6	1.1	1.1
tensile strength, psi	D638-58T	11,800	22,000	22,000
ultimate elongation, %	D638-58T	200	2	5
flexural modulus, psi	D790-58T	380,000	1,000,000	950,000
Izod impact, ft-lb/in., notched	D256-56	1.1	1.4	3.6

Table 6. Property Changes Due to Variation in Glass Fiber Content

Property	ASTM test method	Unfilled nylon	30% glass	40% glass
density	D792	1.13	1.34	1.52
water absorption, % per day	D570-57T	1.6	1.1	0.8
tensile strength, psi	D638-58T	11,800	30,000	30,000
ultimate elongation, %	D638-58T	200	5	5
flexural modulus, psi	D790-58T	380,000	950,000	1,200,000
Izod impact, ft-lb/in., notched	D256-56	1.1	3.6	5.0

finish of the glass are important. Typical properties as influenced by fiber length are shown in Table 5.

Compositions of high fiber content possess good injection molding properties and remarkably high strength performance (Table 6).

Colorants. A variety of pigments and dyes can be used to provide a wide color range to nylon products. Clears are not readily obtained except in very thin sections since the crystalline properties that are characteristic of most polyamide polymers cause a slight milky cast to the product which appears opaque in heavy sections. In selecting a particular colorant, special attention should be paid to the relatively high temperatures which are encountered during processing. Therefore, inorganic pigments are more commonly used though organic types such as phthalocyanine blues and greens are perfectly acceptable. Color concentrates are often used to achieve adequate pigment dispersion, and it is more common to use prepigmented pellets for molding rather than dry blended systems. Concentration of colors is kept far below 1% except in special cases where opacity or resistance to sunlight is desired.

Ultraviolet Inhibitors. Nylons will gradually decompose when exposed to intense sunlight or ultraviolet radiation. The mechanism of degradation is apparently associated with oxidation that is catalyzed by the presence of ultraviolet radiation. Temperature has an accelerating effect. Considerable improvement in performance can be achieved by the addition of uv absorbers and other chemicals which reduce the effect of harmful radiation. The greatest benefit is achieved by the presence of finely dispersed carbon black in a concentration of 2–3%. Products of this type are used in piping, wire coverings, and moldings which will be exposed to sunlight for long periods of time.

Molybdenum Disulfide and Graphite. These additives are used to further reduce the low coefficient of friction that is a typical and valuable property of nylon products. In both cases it is believed that particles of molybdenum disulfide and graphite are exposed during wear and plate out on the surface of the nylon to provide

Table 7. Comparison of Unfilled Nylon-6 and Nylon-6 with Molybdenum Disulfide

Property	ASTM test method	Unfilled nylon-6	Nylon-6 with molybdenum disulfide
tensile strength, psi	D638-58T	11,800	13,500
ultimate elongation, %	D638-58T	200	<10
flexural strength, psi	D790-58T	11,800	16,400
flexural modulus, psi	D790-58T	380,000	430,000
Izod impact, ft-lb/in., notched	D256-56	1.1	1.0
Rockwell hardness, R	D785-51	119	120
heat distortion, °F at 264 psi	D648-56	150	155
water absorption, %	D570-57T	1.6	1.5

continuous low friction properties. Because of nylon's low wear characteristics, the result is outstanding abrasion resistance and bearing properties. Molybdenum disulfide has the added advantage of improving physical properties and providing reinforcing action that would not be predicted by its particle size and structure. Physical properties are shown in Table 7.

Concentrations in the range of 1–15% have been used, depending on the type of additive and the intended application.

Fillers. The use of clays, silicates, oxides, and other nonreinforcing fillers is not common in nylon since these products tend to lower the properties even in low concentration and provide little advantage.

Nucleated Nylon. In recent years progress has been made in controlling and altering the basic crystallinity of nylon polymers. This is accomplished by seeding the polymer to produce a more uniform growth in the rate, number, type, and size of the spherulites. The result is the formation of smaller spherulites of more uniform average size. The preferred nucleating agent is one which produces maximum control of crystallinity without causing a reduction in the properties of the plastic. Typical of such products are finely dispersed silicas in concentration of about 0.1% which are introduced into the nylon during the polymerization step.

Nucleation provides nylons of increased tensile strength, flexural modulus, abrasion resistance, and hardness, but often causes some loss in elongation and impact strength. More recent work has resulted in nucleated products where the crystalline type has been altered from the more prominent β form to the α variety.

Table 8 provides a comparison of typical properties of a nucleated and a non-nucleated nylon.

Table 8. Key Property Comparison of Non-nucleated and Nucleated Nylon

Property	ASTM test method	Non-nucleated	Nucleated
tensile strength, psi	D638-58T	11,800	13,200
ultimate elongation, %	D638-58T	200	75
flexural modulus, psi	D790-58T	380,000	460,000
flexural strength, psi	D790-58T	16,400	17,800
Izod impact, ft-lb/in., notched	D256-56	1.1	1.0
deflection temperature, °F, 264 psi	D648	150	180

An important benefit derived from nucleation is improvement in molding cycle time.

Nylon Types, Grades, and Properties

Table 9 compares the properties of the five principal types of nylon. With nylon-6 and 6,6 moisture has a significant effect upon properties related to stiffness and impact. This is not as important with nylon-6,10, nylon-11, and nylon-12 which have low moisture sensitivity. Changes in moisture content are accompanied by a corresponding change in dimension on the order of 1.5% in the case of nylon-6 and 6,6 and below 0.4% for nylon-6,10 at maximum moisture absorption. Temperature has a similar effect on nylon to that produced by moisture absorption. Stiffness decreases and impact strength increases sharply. However, nylons show a high degree of form retention up to their melting points as distinguished from the characteristic distortion associated with other, amorphous thermoplastics. The combined effects of moisture and temperature can be seen in Figure 1, where modulus of elasticity and yield stress of nylon are compared.

Table 9. Comparison of the Physical Properties of the Five Principal Types of Nylon[a]

Property	ASTM test method	Type 6	Type 6,6	Type 6,10	Type 11	Type 12
physical						
relative density	D792	1.13	1.14	1.09	1.04	1.02
water absorption, %						
day	D570	1.6	1.3	0.4	0.2	0.2
saturation		11.0	8.5	3.5	1.5	1.5
mechanical						
tensile strength, psi	D638	11.8×10^3	12.5×10^3	8.5×10^3	7.8×10^3	7.3×10^3
ultimate elongation, %	D638	50–200	40–80	50–200	200–300	200–300
Young's modulus measured over 1% extension at 20°C, psi		3.5×10^5	4.3×10^5	3.0×10^5	1.8×10^5	1.7×10^5
compressive strength, psi	D695	14.0×10^3	16.0×10^3	9.9×10^3	8.0×10^3	8.0×10^3
shear strength, psi	D732	8.5×10^3	9.5×10^3	7.5×10^3	6.1×10^3	5.9×10^3
Izod impact, ft-lb/½ in. of notch	D256	1.1	1.0	1.1	1.8	1.9
thermal						
melting point, °C		225	264	222	185	180
deflection temp under load, °F	D648					
at 66 psi		365	374	302	284	280
at 264 psi		150	167	134	130	130
electrical						
dielectric strength, step by step, V/0.001 in.	D149	280	280	270		
volume resistivity, ohm-cm,	D257					
dry		10^{14}	10^{14}	10^{14}	10^{14}	10^{14}
saturated		10^8	10^9	10^{11}	10^{13}	10^{13}
dielectric constant,	D150					
dry, 10^3 cps		4.0	4.0	3.6	3.7	3.6
dry, 10^6 cps		3.6	3.6	3.5	3.2	3.2
saturated, 10^6 cps		25.0	18.0	5.0		
power factor,	D150					
dry, 10^6 cps		0.03–0.04	0.04	0.03	0.03	0.03
wet, 10^6 cps			0.20	0.11	0.06	0.06

[a] All samples were tested in the dry state (<25% water) unless stated otherwise.

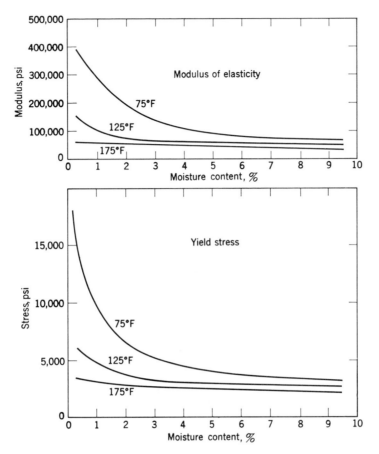

Fig. 1. Flexural properties of nylon-6; effect of moisture content and temperature.

Special grades of nylon have been developed for powder applications. Here, the most success has been achieved by nylon-11, since it possesses a relatively low melting point of 185°C, is low in moisture absorption, and has good chemical resistance.

Nylons can be described as resistant to chemicals and solvents. They are not normally attacked by exposure to pure water and the effects described previously are those where the water acts as a plasticizer. The exception to this is when a nylon is kept in water at high temperatures for prolonged periods of time. In this case, some hydrolysis of the amide groups results in a degradation of the nylon. This effect is less pronounced with low moisture grades. Hot water also contains dissolved oxygen which will cause degradation with time.

Nylons are inert to most inorganic chemicals including sulfur dioxide and liquid ammonia, but are attacked by oxidizing reagents such as chlorine and hydrogen peroxide. Inert solutions of inorganic salts are not harmful although the water will have some plasticizing effect.

The nylons are attacked by concentrated mineral acids at room temperature, but the effect of dilute acids is generally far less. Moisture-resistant nylons, such as 11 and 12, are less sensitive to mineral acids. Resistance to alkalies is good even at elevated temperatures.

Alkyl halides, thiols, esters, glycols, organic solvents, oils, fuels, and aldehydes (except formaldehyde) have little or no effect on nylons. The copolymers are attacked by alcohols and dissolve readily in alcohol–water mixtures. Phenols, cresols, and similar chemicals dissolve all the nylons. Benzyl alcohol will dissolve the nylons at elevated temperatures, as will other materials such as nitrobenzene and nitro alcohols. However, at room temperature there is little effect on nylons by these solvents.

Nylons may be considered good electrical insulators, but are not recommended for high dielectric applications where polyolefin and fluorocarbons are required.

Processing

The most common method for processing of nylon is in the melt state, although fluid-bed powder and solution techniques are also used. A newer method of processing is that of monomer casting where lactam-based nylons can be formed into finished products by direct polymerization of the monomer in the mold.

In melt processing consideration should be made of the fact that nylons are mildly hygroscopic and will pick up excessive amounts of moisture unless properly handled. Most nylons are supplied in sealed metal containers though special moistureproof bags and drums are used. Although it is not necessary, in many cases it has been found beneficial to preheat nylon pellets in the sealed can for a short period of time before adding the nylon to the molding machine hopper. The preheated pellets do not gain moisture as rapidly in the covered hopper and the additional heat aids in obtaining a more rapid melt in the processing equipment.

Injection Molding. Any of the injection presses currently manufactured can be used to mold nylon. The nozzle should be heated with one or more heating bands capable of maintaining an accurate temperature setting. Mold temperature control is preferred since nylon polymers are crystalline in nature and uniformity of properties requires a consistent cooling rate. Most thicknesses of nylon will mold at optimum cycles when the mold temperature is in the range of 70–120°F or 170–220°F. To meet these requirements, a recirculating unit for heating and cooling the mold in this temperature range is suggested. Weigh feeding is important when molding close tolerance parts.

When polyamides are shaped from the melt, the freezing-in of internal stresses is in many cases unavoidable. Major factors contributing to this include high rates of cooling and unfavorable conditions of flow. While such stresses are compensated in molded pieces with thin sections by distortion of a generally negligible extent, they may become so great in very heavy sections as to cause failure of the part when subjected to a load. Such internal stresses can be largely compensated by subsequent heat treatment, a process known as annealing. Annealing is usually carried out in a liquid at temperatures between 130–150°C for periods of from 1 to 24 hr.

As a result of annealing, the pieces undergo some shrinkage. To some degree this is due to a loss in moisture which will be compensated for by renewed take-up of moisture. However, the annealing process does result in a permanent shrinkage as the result of increased molecular crystallization. Proper allowance should be made for this dimensional change when designing the mold in those cases where close tolerances are required. The increase in crystallinity is accompanied by a rise in modulus of elasticity and surface hardness.

In some cases, parts are moisture-conditioned after molding and prior to use.

This can be done by a number of techniques depending on moisture content desired and part thickness. The most important part of this process is to ensure that equilibrium has been established.

Extrusion. Any extruder of sufficient heating capacity to permit continuous operation in the temperature range of 400–800°F is suitable for processing nylon grades. Electrically heated extruders are preferred although the low melting point of some nylon types permits the use of an oil-heated unit.

The general comments which were made concerning the importance of moisture absorption and humidity on the injection molding of nylon also apply to extrusion.

The extruder is essentially a melting device and pump turning out a uniform melt of nylon at a constant rate. The product to be made determines the die geometry required and the posthandling equipment needed to give uniformity and shape to the extrudate during extrusion and cooling. The following sections describe the post-extrusion techniques and equipment used in making the more important extrusion products from nylon.

Tubing. Machine temperatures should be adjusted so that a medium stock temperature is obtained for the extrusion of nylon tubing. A higher temperature level should be used when extruding small (less than $3/16$ in.) diameter tubing.

Nylon tubing can be extruded horizontally in outside diameters up to $1/2$ in. with fairly simple postforming tools. A highly successful cooling and postforming process has been to make small-diameter tubing by using a series of contoured plates immersed in a water-filled cooling tank. The front of the tank has a removable two-piece plate orifice with a diameter about 1.3 times the tubing diameter. The tubing is extruded into the tank through the orifice and then through a series of forming and guide plates which help keep the tube round and submerged in the water. The plates are contoured to diameters slightly larger than the desired diameter of the tubing with the diameters gradually decreasing from the front plate to the back plate. The front orifice is approximately $3/4$–2 in. from the die. The first plate is located about 1–2 in. behind the orifice plate with additional plates located approximately every 1–2 in. for about 8–12 in. Top and bottom plates are alternated.

Pipe. Nylon can be extruded into pipe using both the extended mandrel method and the external sizing technique. The latter is the more popular technique. Crosshead dies can be used but common practice is to use a straight delivery die. Melt stock temperatures are kept about 20–50°F above the melting point and nylons of high melt viscosity are preferred. Nylon has been extruded into pipe with outside diameters up to 5 in. or more.

Wire Coating. Low viscosity nylons are used for coatings over insulated wire in order to improve the mechanical strength, abrasion resistance, and chemical resistance of the wire. Standard equipment commonly used for the insulation of wire with polyethylene and PVC can be used.

Except for magnetic wire, nylon is rarely used as a primary insulation. The most popular use is as a thin outer jacket over another plastic such as vinyl, to increase abrasion resistance and cut-through strength. It is possible to give the wire two coats at once using two extruders and a common head, which directs the plastics in the proper flow pattern. Tandem extrusion is also practical; in this, two extruders and wire covering die heads are placed in line. Dual extrusion offers the advantage that the wire is only handled once. However, the economics of the process are greatly affected by permissible extrusion speeds.

Blow Molding. High melt viscosity nylon resins are suitable for blow molding. Accumulator-type blow molding machines can best handle the more fluid melt of nylon compounds as compared to other plastics, such as polyethylene. The extruder, extruder screw, runners, accumulator, head, and tooling are of conventional design. For nylon, however, this equipment must have sufficient heating capacity to operate continuously and maintain all components at a temperature of 400–600°F. Nylon is not corrosive to metals and no chrome plating or corrosion resistant metals are necessary. Stock temperatures are set for the particular grade of nylon used.

Tape. Nylon tape has found many applications, such as transmission belting, conveyor belts, and stock from which to stamp washers and gasket parts. The tape can be made by extrusion into a waterbath or into a chilled roll stand. The latter is the recommended method for precise tolerances and mirror finish. The head and die design can be adopted to horizontal or vertical extrusion but the former is preferred since chilled roll extrusion is the most commonly used process.

Rod and Slab Extrusion. There are a number of methods for making bar stock from thermoplastic resins. In general, these methods employ various means of maintaining sufficient pressure on the molten extrudate to force additional resin into the center of the newly formed rod, thus preventing large voids occurring in this area as the outer surfaces solidify. If new material was not added, the molten nylon at the center would shrink toward the outer solidified portion causing large voids. Nylon has proved to be successful in the production of continuously extruded rod of up to 8-in. diameters.

Castings. Rod, slab, and tubular bars can be made by continuous extrusion. A market also exists for thick castings of nylon-6 such as rough gear blanks and large-diameter billets which are subsequently machined into a final shape.

Irregular Profiles and Shapes. Extrusion compounds of high molecular weight are now available which offer a high enough melt viscosity to be processed into complicated shapes. Production methods are similar to those used in other thermoplastics provided proper steps are taken to account for the sharp melting point and crystalline nature of the polymer. Applications for extruded profile sections are limited.

Film (see also Film materials). The preparation of nylon film is a more recent development but the applications found for these products make film one of the fastest growing uses for nylon. Flat film is produced by extrusion from a T die onto a cooling drum. The critical part of the process is the temperature of the drum which must be balanced between sticking and too rapid cooling of the film which produces a highly amorphous film that has poor dimensional control and a high degree of blocking. The control of crystallinity is most important to film properties and handling, characteristics. Although the extrusion step is not too critical, the cooling, handling, and winding steps require sophisticated control. The film must be properly moisture-conditioned to yield rolls of good dimensional stability.

Tubular or lay flat film is made by the conventional blown extrusion process. Film gage and bubble diameter control are somewhat more sensitive than polyethylene or flexible polyvinyl chloride.

Monofilament. Bristles, fish lines, and monofilament for fish net are made by extrusion through a multiple-orifice die into cooling water followed by stretching and winding. In the extrusion step, more uniform filaments are obtained by placing a metering pump on the end of the extruder before the point where the melt enters the die. Water cooling is done on a countercurrent or cocurrent technique depending upon filament diameter and cooling rate desired.

Stretch is performed by passing the monofilaments around rolls of increasing surface speed. This is usually done in a steam-heated chamber or by passing the filaments over heated plates to provide easier stretching and lower power requirements on the equipment. Annealing or stress relaxation steps can be achieved by exposure to elevated temperatures under tension or in a relaxed state. Winding is done on spools using constant-torque motors or hydraulic clutches.

The filaments considered here are limited to sizes greater than 0.004-in. diam. Smaller sizes require more highly specialized textile filament spinning equipment and techniques. See Polyamide fibers.

Solution Processes. Soluble polymers of nylon can be made by copolymerization of nylon-6, 6,10, and 6,6 in various proportions. These products have properties of broad fusion temperature, high flexibility particularly in humid or wet conditions, toughness in film form, resistance to abrasion and fatigue, as well as good bonding characteristics.

These polymers are soluble in mixtures of alcohol and water. The best solvents are aliphatic alcohols such as methanol, ethanol, and 1-propanol. The incorporation of water, chlorinated hydrocarbons, and ketones improves the solution characteristics. Solution concentrations of 30–55% are possible depending upon the solvents used and the composition of the copolymer. Typical base solvent would be 80 parts of ethanol and 20 parts of water. To this would be added trichloroethylene to provide a mixture of 65 parts of the base solvent and 35 parts of the trichloroethylene. Plasticizers consist of compounds based on resorcinol esters, toluenesulfonamides, coumarone–indenes, and amides. Compatible resins that can be added to impart special properties are isocyanates, amino plastics, phenolplasts, and polyvinyl acetate.

Solutions are made in stirred autoclaves heated to 50–70°C. The process consists of adding all the solvents and then the polyamide. Dissolution takes about 2–3 hr. The solution is then filtered and stored for use at 40–50°C. The solutions gel upon cooling. The gels can be made fluid again by warming and this cycle can be repeated. The gelation time, however, decreases progressively with each cycle.

When in liquid form, the nylon solutions can be used by normal techniques for coating, dipping, and spraying. Fabric coatings are ready-made by knife spreading and reverse roll coating. See Coated fabrics.

Soluble nylon polymers are excellent in abrasion and oil resistance. Applications include gaskets and seals for gasoline and oil lines, oil resistant finishes for fabrics and hoses, sheaths for insulated cables, abrasion resistant coatings for paper, textiles, and leather, and adhesives for flexible substrates such as fibers and paper.

Powder Processing. Powders can be prepared from nylon polymers by grinding or solution precipitation methods. These materials can then be compressed and heat sintered to form molded parts with varying degrees of porosity. This method is useful in making "self lubricating" bearings and bushings. Additives are easily incorporated into the fine nylon powder before compression molding of the preform. However, the main use for powder nylon is in the coating of metals to impart corrosion resistance, abrasion and wear resistance, or electrical insulation. Coating is performed by first fluidizing the powder, either as a fluid bed or by air spraying. The metal is heated above the melt temperature of the nylon and dipped or coated with the powder which immediately melts and fuses on the metal surface. Sufficient powder is exposed to the metal surface to provide a coating of the desired thickness consistent with the metal preheat temperature. More than one coating is possible. Cooling causes the coating to solidify.

The fluid-bed coating process requires some special techniques. The metal surface should be freed of scale chemically or by sandblasting, degreased, and then primed to produce best results. Parts should be as smooth as possible and sharp angles should be minimized since the nylon coating undergoes a slight shrinkage on solidification. The metal to be coated is then heated to a temperature that is predetermined based on metal thickness and thickness of coating desired. Spray coatings can be achieved by similar preparation. Flame spraying is also possible. Rotational moldings can be made from powdered nylons by methods similar to those used with other powdered resin compounds. A predetermined amount of nylon powder is added to the mold, the part is rotated and heated to above the fusion point, the mold is then cooled while rotating, and the part is removed.

In all cases, considerable care must be exercised in preventing moisture pickup by the fine powder which possesses a large surface area.

Monomer Casting Process. This process, using *anionic polymerization,* is of commercial significance for caprolactam, because of its low cost and availability. The polymerization process can be made to proceed rapidly by the incorporation of a "catalyst accelerator," such as chemicals having active groups of the imide type. Polymerization can be made to occur above the melting point of caprolactam. Most desirable processing temperatures are below 415°F since the polymer that is formed is then in the solid state. In this manner, products can be formed directly in the mold without further processing steps or the need for cooling. The reaction is exothermic and polymerization temperatures must be controlled to prevent melting of the formed polymer if a solid part is desired.

In principle, the process is simple. The caprolactam monomer is melted in a container under an inert atmosphere. The monomer and catalysts are combined at a selected temperature in a mixer and added to a mold where the mixture hardens. The entire process occurs at atmospheric pressure.

The polymer product obtained by the monomer casting process is essentially the same as that obtained from normal molding and extrusion of nylon-6 molding compounds. There are a few important differences in properties, however, which can be attributed to the higher degree of crystallinity and molecular weight which are possible with the anionic method. This can be seen in the comparison of properties shown in Table 10. The chief points to note are the much higher deflection temperatures of the

Table 10. Properties of Regular and Anionic Polymerized Nylon-6

Property	ASTM test method	Injection-molded	Anionic
tensile strength, psi	D638	11,800	13,500
ultimate elongation, %	D638	200	15–30
flexural yield, psi			
at 73°F	D790	17,000	18,000
at 175°F	D790	3,500	5,000–6,000
flexural modulus, psi at 73°F	D790	400,000	470,000
Rockwell hardness, R	D785	119	120
deflection temperature, °F			
at 66 psi	D648	365	428
at 264 psi	D648	152	407
tensile impact, ft-lb/in.²		260	100–210
specific gravity	D792	1.13–1.14	1.15

anionic nylon-6 and the generally higher stiffness and hardness values. The higher specific gravity is an indication of the greater order of crystallinity. Chemically, the polymers are the same and little differences can be found in aging properties or exposure to chemicals and solvents.

The cast monomer method is particularly suited to the preparation of large, thick section parts. Low-cost molds are possible because of the low pressures required and void formation is largely eliminated since solidification occurs as the result of polymerization rather than cooling. The process is therefore suited to the manufacture of large slabs, rods, tubes, and plates which are subsequently machined into finished items. Semifinished castings such as cyclone collectors are produced with no more than minor machining necessary for finishing. Rotational molded parts are well suited to the process since parts are produced rapidly without cyclic heating or cooling of the mold. Commercial quantities of gasoline and fuel tanks are made by this process. Molded-in metal brackets, seals, flanges, and mounting plates can be incorporated. The manufacture of small parts and thin sections is possible by this process but this is not economical in comparison to injection molding or extrusion.

Fillers, reinforcing agents, and additives can be easily incorporated into the monomer prior to polymerization.

Machining, Finishing, and Assembly of Nylon Parts

In addition to as-molded uses, nylons are used in extensive quantities as machined and postformed parts from rod stock and semifinished shapes. For this reason, mention should be made of these finishing operations.

Machining of nylon can be considered to follow the general techniques employed with soft brass. Although the use of coolants, such as water or soluble oils, will permit high machining rates, coolants are not generally required to produce quality work. Since nylons are not as stiff as metals, the stock should be well supported to prevent deflection and associated inaccuracies. Dimensions should be checked after the part has been brought to room temperature.

Annealing procedures are commonly used. One practice is to anneal parts before the final machining to ensure best conformity to desired dimensions. Moisture conditioning should also be considered in postmachining operations.

Some key points are:

Tool Design—sharp tools with sufficient clearance to permit free removal of chips.

Reaming—standard tools of the expansion type are preferred. Because of nylon's resilience, the hole will be smaller than with metal. Final cut should be no less than 0.005 in.

Sawing—standard saws can be used but teeth in all cases should have a slight amount of "set." Good clearance is required and cooling is beneficial.

Drilling—twist drills should have a point angle of 118° with a 10–15° lip clearance angle. A cutting rather than scraping action is required. Coolants are useful.

Threading and Tapping—because of resilience, a cut of 0.005 in. minimum is normal.

Burr Removal—the toughness of nylon presents a problem in burr or flash removal and molds should be machined to keep such conditions to a minimum. In most cases, hand finishing is required. Flame polishing is used along with vapor blasting and honing. Wet abrasive tumbling is used but takes much longer than with metal.

Sanding and Buffing—wet sanding is best. Standard buffing can be used.

Since this is a highly specialized field, the manufacturers of nylons have developed detailed instructions and techniques for machining and finishing purposes. Joining of parts can be accomplished with adhesives based on phenols, resorcinol, and alcohol mixtures. Adhesion to metal surfaces is possible with many commercial products, most based on phenolic and resorcinol polymers. Riveting, snap fits, heat forming, spin welding, and ultrasonic welding are all used commercially.

General References

"Cast Nylon Takes on New Jobs," *American Machinist*, pp. 72–73 (March 2, 1964).

"Cast Nylon Slipper Blocks Outwear Aluminum Bronze on 35 in. Blooming Mill," *Iron and Steel Engineer*, p. 156 (Nov. 1965).

"Nylon Slipper Blocks Performing Well on Weirton Strip Mill," *Iron and Steel Engineer*, p. 159 (Feb. 1966).

"Cast Nylon Tooling, Better Than Metals?," *Tool and Manufacturing Engineer*, pp. 78–80 (Dec. 1962).

"Nylon Coatings, New Protection for Tooling," *Tool and Manufacturing Engineer*, pp. 49–50 (Feb. 1965).

"Nylon Licks Industrial Problems," *Plant Engineering*, pp. 137–139 (June 1963).

"Nylon Parts Smooth Out Materials Handling," *Plant Engineering*, pp. 131–132 (Dec. 1965).

"Use of Nylon in Hydraulic Engineering," *Civil Engineering*, pp. 31–33 (Jan. 1963).

"Non-Metallic Strapping; Now Really Catching On," *Modern Materials Handling*, pp. 48–51 (Aug. 1963).

"Moly-Filled Nylon Extrusions Reduce Conveyor Downtime," *Modern Materials Handling*, p. 67 (March 1966).

"Nylon Cuts 80% from Conveyor Roller Cost," *Modern Materials Handling*, p. 66 (June 1966).

"Vibrating Nylon Finishes Gears," *Steel*, p. 120 (Jan. 27, 1964).

"Plastics Fight Wear Problems with Molybdenum Disulfide," *Iron Age*, pp. 155–157 (June 21, 1962).

"Nylon Sleeve Fittings; Attach Resin to Resin in a Leakproof Joint," *Plastics World*, p. 15 (May 1962).

"Drapery Stay; MoS_2 Nylon Part Used on Motor Operated Rod," *Plastics World*, p. 50 (July 1962).

"Cast Nylon; West German Process Produces Any Size Part," *Plastics World*, p. 9 (Aug. 1962).

"Uses of Large-Sized Pieces of Cast Nylon," *Engineering*, p. 242 (Feb. 16, 1962).

"Uses of Moly-Filled Nylon," *Engineering*, p. 557 (Oct. 26, 1962).

"Nylon Coiled Hoses," *Engineering*, p. 345 (Sept. 10, 1965).

"Firth Cleveland Nylon Nut," *Engineering*, p. 742 (Dec. 10, 1965).

"Nylon Plug for Building Blocks," *Engineer*, p. 537 (Oct. 7, 1966).

"Polyamides," *Machine Design* (Sept. 20, 1962).

"Nylon Zipper," *Plastics World* (Jan. 1962).

"Helmet Protection Plus," *Plastics World* (April 1962).

"Nylon Parts," *Plastics World* (Sept. 1962).

"Nylon Machine Tool Components," *Plastics World* (Nov. 1962).

"Mill Maintenance Costs Cut with Cast Nylon Parts," *Steel* (Aug. 20, 1962).

"Nuts, Bolts and Plastics," *Plastics Technology* (June 1962).

"Impregnated Nylon Bearings for Gas Meters," *British Plastics* (Jan. 1962).

"Better Parts with Nylon Coating," *Modern Plastics* (March 1962).

"Nylon Brushes, Zippers, Fish Lines Win Increasing Customer Acceptance," *Modern Plastics* (July 1962).

"Nylon Parts Solve Design Problem for Air Valve at a Savings," *Modern Plastics* (Sept. 1962).

"High Pressure Nylon Piston," *Review of Scientific Instruments* (Nov. 1962).

"Tiny Nylon Parts Cut Typewriter Wear," *Materials in Design Engineering* (Nov. 1963).

"Gear Finishing," *Product Engineering* (Nov. 25, 1963).

"Nylon Cast into Big Gears," *Iron Age* (Feb. 7, 1963).

"Hardened Gear Teeth Cut With Nylon," *Iron Age* (Nov. 21, 1963).

"Plastic Fasteners Hold, Seal and Insulate Trim," *Steel* (March 25, 1963).

"Cast Slippers," *Plastics World* (Jan. 1963).

"Resin Bushing," *Plastics World* (Jan. 1963).

"Nylon Armor Reduces Building Wire Diameter, Adds Resistance," *Plastics World* (Jan. 1963).

"Nylon Parts," *Plastics World* (Feb. 1963).

"Nylon Gears," *Plastics World* (Nov. 1963).

"Big Possibilities for Improved Nylons," *British Plastics* (May 1963).

"Nylon Strapping Tape Adjusts to Package Shrink," *Modern Plastics* (Oct. 1963).

"Plastics Add New Dimension to Fastener Design," *Modern Plastics* (Oct. 1963).

"Nylon Parts," *Plastics World* (March 1963).

"Nylon Castings Scratch Two Abrasion Problems," *Materials in Design Engineering* (June 1964).

"Castable Nylon Solves Problem Jobs," *Steel* (March 16, 1964).

"Nylon Products Cast Directly From Monomer," *Steel* (June 22, 1964).

"Cast Nylon Parts Resist Wear in Steel Mills and Presses," *Iron Age* (Jan. 23, 1964).

"After Beer Kegs, What?," *Product Engineering* (Aug. 3, 1964).

"Water Removal from Wet Webs by a Porous Nylon Press Roll," *Tappi* (Nov. 1964).

"New Casting Process Makes Large Nylon Parts," *Plastics Technology* (Jan. 1964).

"Fused Nylon Coat," *Plastics World* (Feb. 1964).

"Casting Process," *Plastics World* (April 1964).

"Tiller Cable," *Plastics World* (June 1964).

"Cast Nylon," *Plastics World* (June 1964).

"Two Molded Nylon Insulators Replace 38 Paper Parts," *Modern Plastics* (May 1964).

"Nylon + Asbestos = Strength + Heat Resistance," *Modern Plastics* (June 1964).

"The New Look for Nylon," *Modern Plastics* (Nov. 1964).

"New Building Wire Embodies Important Properties," *Wire and Wire Products* (April 1965).

"Quick-Disconnect Fastener," *Materials in Design Engineering* (May 1965).

"Trim Fastened with Nylon, Stainless," *Steel* (Feb. 15, 1965).

"Nylon Use in Autos is Increasing," *Chemical and Engineering News* (March 1, 1965).

"Nylon Bows as Exterior Building Material," *Chemical and Engineering News* (Dec. 27, 1965).

"Cost Cutting Rollers," *Plastics World* (Feb. 1965).

"Nylon Air Tubing," *Plastics World* (April 1965).

"Nylon Tuneup," *Plastics World* (May 1965).

"Nylon Fabric," *Plastics World* (July 1965).

"Nylon Outlasts Cast Iron," *Plastics World* (Aug. 1965).

"Nylon Seals," *Plastics World* (Aug. 1965).

"What's All This Activity in Nylon Film?," *Modern Plastics* (Aug. 1965).

"Nylon, P.P. Strapping Gets Strong Hold," *Modern Plastics* (Sept. 1965).

"Filled Nylon Solves Tricky Problem—At a Saving," *Modern Plastics* (Oct. 1965).

"Ice-Free Roads, With Nylon/Epoxy," *Modern Plastics* (Nov. 1965).

"Switch to Nylon Brings New Terminal Block Design," *Modern Plastics* (Dec. 1965).

"Friction Weld Bonds Packing Cast Bands," *Machine Design* (July 21, 1966).

"Chain Drives," *Product Engineering* (March 14, 1966).

"Nylon Fittings Join Pneumatic Tubing," *Chemical and Engineering News* (Jan. 1966).

"Surprise-Package Nylon," *Rubber Age* (Nov. 1966).

"Nylon—Tough Strapping that Keeps a Tight Grip," *Plastics World* (May 1966).

"Nylon for Model Racing," *Plastics World* (May 1966).

"Nylon for Precision Components," *British Plastics* (Sept. 1966).

"Nylon—Starring in Detroit and Elsewhere," *Modern Plastics* (Jan. 1966).

"Redesigning in Nylon—By Stages," *Modern Plastics* (April 1966).

"Glass-Reinforced Nylon Replaces Aluminum at Lower Cost," *Modern Plastics* (Dec. 1966).

"Non-Metallic Strapping: Fast Wrap-Up," *Iron Age* (Feb. 2, 1967).

"Extrusion Markets Boost Nylon Sales; Building Applications Look Promising," *Modern Plastics* (Jan. 1967).

"Nylon and Acetal Gears Improve Vertical Blind System," *Modern Plastics* (June 1967).

"Nylon Candles Look Like Wax," *Modern Plastics* (June 1967).

"A Molder's Guide to Nucleated Nylon," *Plastics Technology*, pp. 37–40 (April 1967).

"Glass Spheres in Nylon Mean Lower Cost to Molders," *Materials/Machines/Methods*, pp. 11, 13 (Jan. 1968).

ELMER C. SCHULE
Allied Chemical Corporation

POLYBUTYLENES. For the oligomers, see Vol. 3, pp. 855–857; for the high polymers, see Olefin polymers.

POLYCARBONATES

Polycarbonates are polymers containing the grouping shown below, where the
R's may be aliphatic, aromatic, or mixed.   They are related to the polyesters (qv) for
they may be regarded as polyesters of carbonic acid.

$$\text{H[OROCOR']}_n\text{OH}$$

They can be prepared by reaction of dihydroxy compounds with phosgene, as
illustrated below for ethylene glycol.

$$n\ \text{HOCH}_2\text{CH}_2\text{OH} + (n-1)\ \text{COCl}_2 \rightarrow \text{H[OCH}_2\text{CH}_2\text{OC]}_{n-1}\text{OCH}_2\text{CH}_2\text{OH}$$

They can also be prepared from dihydroxy compounds by transesterification with
dialkyl or diaryl carbonates, or by polymerization of cyclic carbonates of aliphatic
diols.

Although first investigated about the turn of the century, polycarbonates attracted
little interest until Schnell (2) called attention to the exceptional properties of thermoplastic aromatic polycarbonates of the general formula

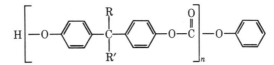

These are the products that have now become commercial.

Production

Most of the polycarbonates of commerce are based on 4,4′-isopropylidene-
diphenol (bisphenol A, see Vol. 1, p. 912), with R = R′ = CH$_3$. One of the routes to
the polycarbonate is transesterification with diphenyl carbonate (see Vol. 4, pp. 391,
392).

In the absence of catalysts, the transesterification of aromatic dihydroxy compounds with diaryl carbonates at temperatures up to 280°C proceeds slowly, accompanied by the formation of volatile aromatic hydroxy compounds. Although the
transesterification is only slightly accelerated by acid catalysts, it is accelerated
markedly by basic catalysts (2,3).

Theoretically, the preparation of aromatic polycarbonate by means of the transesterification process utilizes equimolar quantities of reagents as follows:

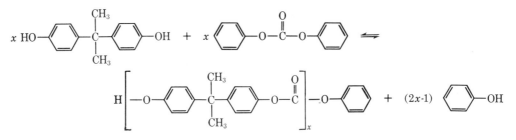

The polycondensation is an equilibrium reaction. To obtain high yields and a high molecular weight, almost complete removal of the aromatic monohydroxy compound from the reaction mixture is required.

The preparation of polycarbonate from bisphenol A (Fig. 1) is usually carried out in the following manner (4): A mixture of 456 g of 4,4'-isopropylidenediphenol, 460 g of diphenyl carbonate, and 0.008 g of lithium hydride is melted under nitrogen at 110–150°C in a round-bottom reactor equipped with a stirrer and a down-flow condenser. The phenol eliminated is removed by distillation at 20 mm Hg and temperatures up to 210°C. At this point the pressure is reduced to 0.2 mm Hg, and the tem-

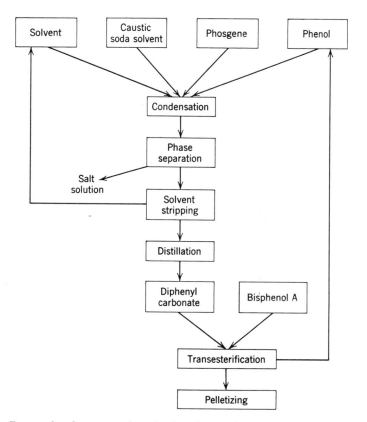

Fig. 1. Process for the preparation of polycarbonate from bisphenol A by transesterification.

perature is raised over a period of 1 hour to 250 and to 280°C during the next 2 hours. Near the end of the polycondensation the catalyst is neutralized by the addition of 0.05 g of dimethyl sulfate, and the excess neutralizing agent is distilled out. The product is a nearly colorless, highly viscous melt which solidifies to a clear, transparent, viscoelastic plastic. The relative viscosity of the polyester, η_{rel}, determined in a 0.5% solution in methylene chloride at 20°C, is 1.32.

The melt viscosity of aromatic polycarbonates is so high at temperatures up to 300°C that polyesters with molecular weights exceeding 50,000 cannot be produced in reactors and agitation systems customarily used in plastic processing; above this molecular weight the melts have rubber-elastic properties.

Properties

Solubility. The following were found to be practical solvents for polycarbonate made from bisphenol A: 1,1,2,2-tetrachloroethane, methylene chloride, *cis*-1,2-dichloroethylene, chloroform, and 1,1,2-trichloroethane.

Compounds having only a very limited dissolving capacity are 1,2-dichloroethane, thiophene, dioxane, tetrahydrofuran, acetophenone, anisole, benzonitrile, cyclohexanone, dimethylformamide, and nitrobenzene.

Swelling effects are observed with benzene, chlorobenzene, 1,2-dichlorobenzene, 1-chloronaphthalene, tetrahydronaphthalene, diphenyl ether, epichlorohydrin, glycol carbonate, acetone, ethyl acetate, carbon tetrachloride, nitromethane, acetonitrile, and 1,1-dichloroethane.

Aliphatic and cycloaliphatic hydrocarbons, ethers, and carboxylic acids neither dissolve nor swell this family of polycarbonates (5).

Melt Viscosity. The bisphenol A polycarbonate retains its stability for many hours in the molten state at temperatures up to 320°C (2). For short periods it will withstand temperatures up to 330–350°C. Above 350°C decomposition sets in, evidenced by discoloration, chain degradation, a release of carbon dioxide, and the formation of unspecified decomposition products. Since even small amounts of water in the polycarbonate melt will cause degradation accompanied by a release of CO_2, it is imperative that solid polycarbonate be dried to a moisture content below 0.01% before melting. The absence of atmospheric oxygen is also a requirement, since oxygen causes dis-

Table 1. Mechanical Properties of Injection-Molded Bisphenol A Polycarbonate

Property	DIN method	Value	Property	ASTM method	Value
density, g/ml	53 479	1.20			
yield strength in flexure, kp/cm²	53 452	900	flexural strength, psi	D-790	11,000–13,000
			deformation under load, %	D-621	0.14
impact strength, (cm)(kp)/cm² notched	53 453	100% unbroken >20	impact strength (Izod), notched ft-lb/in.	D-256[a] D-256[b]	2–3 12–16
compressive strength, kp/cm²	53 454	790–840	compressive strength at yield point, psi	D-695	12,000
ball indentation hardness of plastics, kp/cm²	53 456[c]		Rockwell hardness	D-785	R-115
10 s		900–1050			
60 s		870–1000			
kp/mm²	53 456[d]	Hc 10.6			
tensile yield strength, kp/cm²	53 455	625	tensile yield strength, psi	D-638	8000–9000
elongation, %	53 455		elongation, %	D-638	
at yield		5–7	at yield		5–7
ultimate		>80–120	ultimate		>80–120
modulus of elasticity, kp/cm²		22,000–25,000	modulus of elasticity tension, psi	D-638	2.8–3.2 × 10⁵

NOTE: Kilopond, kp, means the same as kilogram force, kgf.
[a] For ½ in. × ¼ in.   [c] DIN-Entwurf.
[b] For ½ in. × ⅛ in.   [d] DIN-Vornorm.

coloration and perhaps promotes crosslinking reactions. The entire relatively wide temperature range from 230 to 320°C is available for thermoplastic processing.

Injection molding of bisphenol A polycarbonate is rendered somewhat difficult by the high melt viscosity. It is necessary to take full advantage of the high thermal stability of the material if, in the interest of favorable mechanical properties, polycarbonates of sufficiently high molecular weights are to be processed by this method.

Crystal Structure. The crystallizability of bisphenol A polycarbonate varies with molecular weight and also to some extent with molecular-weight distribution. Low-molecular products will crystallize more easily and completely than those of high molecular weight. Polycarbonate copolymers obtained by replacing the bisphenol A in part with a 4,4'-dihydroxydiphenylalkane of unsymmetrical structure, or one with bulky substituents introduced on the central C atom, display a reduced tendency to crystallize. Partially replacing the carbonic acid residues with residues of unsymmetrical aromatic dicarboxylic acid has the same effect.

Parts made from bisphenol A polycarbonates having molecular weights above 25,000, either by cooling from the melt or by rapid evaporation of the solvent from a solution, are clear and transparent. x-Ray examination (6), however, reveals that these clear and transparent articles, produced commercially by thermoplastic methods (eg, injection-molded parts) or solution casting (eg, film) are not entirely amorphous. They have a structure comparable to that of a subcooled liquid (glass state), by which short-range order begins to be supplemented with regularity extending over larger distances. Since the ordered regions are considerably smaller than the wavelengths of visible light, the parts appear optically clear.

Mechanical and Thermal Properties. The usefulness of plastic parts is, for a variety of applications, determined by a large number of properties, only few of which can be characterized by well-defined physical values. The mechanical properties of finished parts as determined or effected by exposure conditions, eg, temperature and humidity, method of manufacture, shape, and possibly size of the individual item, are always of great importance in screening potential areas of application for a new product. Particularly in the United States and Germany, these have been extensively studied for commercial bisphenol A polycarbonates, using established methods and standardized specimens (2,5,7–21). Almost all test work has been done on injection molded pieces or on extruded or solvent-cast film. Only exploratory data are available for stretched and crystallized polycarbonate fibers. Standard material specifications for injection molding-grade polycarbonate (type 300) exist (22).

Table 1 summarizes the mechanical properties of injection-molded commercial bisphenol A polycarbonates as determined by United States and German standard methods (11,19).

The mechanical properties of bisphenol A polycarbonate are dependent on the molecular weight. Materials having an average mol wt below 10,000, are brittle, and will not form films. If mol wt is between 10,000 and about 25,000, low-strength parts are obtained (23). The strength values given in Table 1 are all measured on specimens having a mol wt between 32,000 and 35,000. A further increase in molecular weight no longer is accompanied by a significant improvement in mechanical properties, and at the same time thermoplastic processing on injection-molding equipment becomes increasingly difficult because of the rapid rise in melt viscosity with increasing molecular weight (5). In general, the values summarized in this table present the picture of a hard and tough plastic material with very desirable mechanical properties.

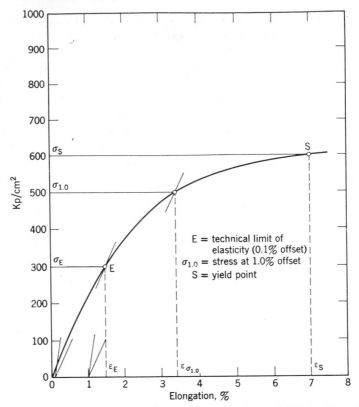

Fig. 2. Stress-strain diagram from the tensile test conducted (as per DIN 53 455) on Makrolon 3000.

Moisture content, which in the open atmosphere reaches a maximum value of 0.20%, does not affect the mechanical properties.

The toughness of the material is maintained even in the face of extremely fast acting external forces. This is well documented by the fact that the impact of a bullet does not shatter polycarbonate plate as it does many other plastics (11). The stress-strain curve of a test specimen (Fig. 2) shows essentially linear reversible elongation up to high stress values, the type of behavior common to most metals (11). As a result, the dimensional stability of the polycarbonate is excellent; its tendency to cold flow is very low.

A sample held under 220 kp/cm² tensile stress for a one-year period showed no measurable plastic deformation (11).

The glasslike structure of molded parts together with their strongly inhibited crystallization and high second-order transition temperature allow this polycarbonate to maintain its toughness over an unusually wide temperature range of about −150 to +150°C (12).

Parts injection-molded from bisphenol A polycarbonate display favorable mechanical properties and high dimensional stability over a temperature range of more than 200°C.

As a result of the fact that the crystallization tendency of bisphenol A polycarbonate is very low indeed, mechanical properties of parts stored at room temperature remain unchanged indefinitely.

Electrical Properties. Bisphenol A polycarbonate, in accordance with its largely nonpolar character, displays favorable electrical properties at room temperature, particularly along the lines of high insulating value and low dielectric loss at frequencies between 50 cps and 1 Mc/sec. Water absorption, as a result of immersion or exposure to more or less humid air, changes the electrical properties very little because of the low moisture pickup of the polymer. Molecular weight has essentially no effect on electrical properties.

The dielectric constant shows no significant change between 10 and 10^8 cps. The dissipation factor, tan δ, increases with frequency until it reaches a flat-topped maximum at 10^7 cps, then decreases again with a further increase in frequency.

Since much of the equipment utilizing polycarbonate as a dielectric is called upon to perform at elevated temperatures, the variations of the dielectric values with temperature, particularly the dissipation factor, are of great practical importance. They are also of scientific interest, since they supply detailed evidence with respect to molecular mobility phenomena within the solid material.

A plot of dissipation factor tan δ versus temperature, measured on bisphenol A polycarbonate at 20 kc/sec over a range from -120 to $+190°C$, is shown in Figure 3 (24).

The curve, which is in agreement with experimental results reported by Krum, Müller, and Huff (25–27), displays a high- as well as a low-temperature peak.

Both peaks are shifted toward higher temperatures by an increase in frequency. A summary of the temperatures associated with the tan δ peaks at various frequencies is given in Table 2. The corresponding data for the mechanical loss factor at a frequency of 1 cps have been included in the table for the purpose of comparison.

Table 2. Locations of the tan δ Peaks as a Function of Frequency for Bisphenol A Polycarbonate

Measuring frequency, cps	Low-temperature peak at °C, approx	High-temperature peak at °C, approx	Reference
1	-97	155	
10^3	-80	175	25
10^4	-60	180	25
2×10^4	-40	174	24
10^5	-30	190	25
3.16×10^5	-20		25

The low-temperature peak is attributed to the mobility of the CO-group (carbonyl dipole) in the alternating electric field. The high-temperature peak is ascribed to the mobility of segments of larger molecules in the alternating electric field.

Figure 4 shows the *light transmittance* curve in the visible and ultraviolet range for bisphenol A polycarbonate (11). For this polycarbonate the light transmittance in the visible spectrum of a 100-μ solvent-cast film varies between 85 and 90%. In the ultraviolet range, transmittance drops off rapidly.

At the present time it is possible to obtain nearly colorless parts from commercial bisphenol A polycarbonates. As sections increase in thickness, a yellowish color becomes apparent. This color, however, is not an inherent quality of the material but is

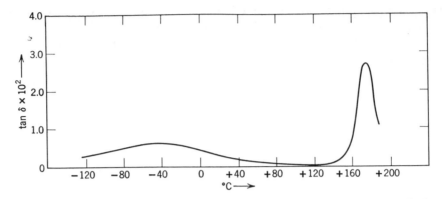

Fig. 3. Dissipation factor versus temperature of bisphenol A polycarbonate at 20 kc/sec.

the result rather of impurities introduced with the intermediates, manufacturing methods, and, to some extent, the processing of the material. Further development of all the processes involved to the point at which essentially colorless polycarbonates will be available is definitely within the realm of possibility.

Aging and Chemical Resistance. The resistance of bisphenol A polycarbonate to environmental factors, such as temperature, water, moisture, air, oxygen, light, acids, alkalies, solvents, and chemicals (28–30), is influenced by the crystallinity and orientation as well as by the shape, size, and past history of any given sample. Oriented and crystallized fibers or film, for instance, will stand up successfully to a number of solvents which are capable of dissolving or swelling highly amorphous material.

Internal stresses set up during manufacturing operations or tensile stress may cause stress cracking, especially under the influence of elevated temperature, water, or swelling agents (31,32).

Data presented further on in this section on aging properties and chemical resistance of bisphenol A polycarbonate are true for largely amorphous resin in the form of film or injection-molded parts.

At or below room temperature the polymer is fully resistant in contact with water or water vapor; physical properties and dimensions remain unchanged indefinitely.

The effects of boiling water and steam are somewhat related to the processing history of the parts as well as to the purity of the polycarbonate used. Essentially stressfree, solvent-cast film changes its physical properties no more on long-term exposure to boiling water than it does with annealing in 100°C air (2). Molded parts containing residual stresses, on the other hand, will show roughening of the surface, stress cracking, and turbidity after extended boiling (5), without evidence of appreciable chemical degradation.

Impurities in the resin, particularly those capable of an alkaline reaction, are known to reduce the resistance to steam and boiling water. Articles injection-molded from commercial bisphenol A polycarbonate, however, have ample stability to withstand the conditions normally encountered by tableware and household utensils for many years. They can also be repeatedly sterilized with steam up to 120°C in conventional equipment.

Molten polycarbonate is not stable in the presence of water vapor, which causes degradation by hydrolysis. Thorough drying of polycarbonate resins to a very low moisture content before thermoplastic processing is therefore mandatory.

The aromatic polycarbonates have good resistance to air, oxygen, and light. Annealing of solvent-cast film in air at temperatures up to and above 150°C for extended periods reduces only the elongation, without a noticeable decrease in molecular weight (7).

Solvent-cast film made from uncontaminated bisphenol A polycarbonate has shown only very slight yellowing after extended exposure to temperatures in excess of 150°C. In actual installations the maximum-continuous-service temperature for parts made from this resin has been found to be about 135 to 140°C.

Bisphenol A polycarbonate displays remarkable resistance to ultraviolet radiation, and is combustible. However, although thin films and fibers will support combustion, larger parts will not because of the material's high ignition temperature (above 500°C), poor thermal conductivity, and probably the fact that thermal decomposition releases carbon dioxide (33). Thus the polymer is classified as self-extinguishing in accordance with ASTM D 635 (5).

The stability of bisphenol A polycarbonate in aqueous solutions of inorganic and organic acids, salts, and oxidizing agents is very good. This polycarbonate is also fully resistant to aqueous solutions of weak alkalies, such as sodium carbonate and sodium bicarbonate. Organophilic bases, on the other hand, such as ammonium hydroxide and amines, are capable of saponifying the polycarbonate rapidly and completely back to bisphenol A (7). Aqueous solutions of strong alkalies will attack the surfaces of specimens and systematically break them down by saponification.

The resistance of highly amorphous bisphenol A polycarbonate parts to organic solvents is rather limited. It is indifferent to aliphatic and cycloaliphatic hydrocarbons, mono- and polyfunctional alcohols with the exception of methanol, and vegetable and animal fats and oils. Most other organic solvents either swell or dissolve it (7).

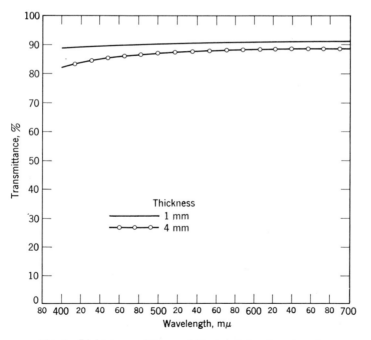

Fig. 4. Light transmittance of bisphenol A polycarbonate.

Very important for many commercial applications is the full resistance of this polymer to aqueous solutions of soaps, detergents, and bleaches, fruit juices, alcoholic beverages, animal and vegetable fats, oils and waxes, photographic chemicals, all varieties of foodstuffs, and many disinfectants. Of particular advantage is its complete indifference to aqueous solutions of natural and synthetic dyes and pigments, which precludes the discoloration of parts by coffee, tea, fruit juices, ink, lipstick, etc.

Physiological Properties. Parts made from commercial bisphenol A polycarbonate have found many applications where they are used in contact with food items, eg, kitchen appliance components, dinnerware, milking-machine parts, packaging film, and bottles. The material is also used for dentures and artificial teeth, plasma containers, and in the packaging of pharmaceuticals. A necessary requirement common to all such applications is the absence of any biological activity of the plastic itself or any components extractable from it.

In accordance with the rules of "Gesundheitsblatt 1960," No. 26, p. 416, there are no reservations under German food law with regard to articles manufactured from 4,4'-isopropylidenediphenol and 1,1-bis(4-hydroxyphenyl)cyclohexane polycarbonates.

The U.S. Department of Health, Education, and Welfare—Food and Drug Administration—has ruled polycarbonates safe for use in direct contact with all types of solid, liquid, fatty, and nonfatty foodstuffs. The classification covered by the listing numbered 121 2574 includes food containers and packages as well as components for food dispensers, processing equipment, and serving utensils (34).

Uses

The largest portion by far of the commercially produced bisphenol A polycarbonate is converted into parts and finished products by thermoplastic processing methods (5,11,35–45). Thermoplastic processing of the material utilizes the conventional equipment of the plastics industry, such as injection-molding machines and extruders.

Molding-grade bisphenol A polycarbonates have average molecular weights (calculated from solution viscosity) between 32,000 and 35,000. The melt viscosities of higher-molecular products exceed the limits of economical processing methods.

The temperature range available for processing extends from 240 to 330°C. In this range the polycarbonate will not suffer any noticeable degradation so long as it contains less than approximately 0.01% moisture.

Injection-molded bisphenol A polycarbonate parts have proved themselves in actual service in many fields (46–53). The most important applications are in the electrical industry (radio, phono, TV, communications), where they have been used as enclosures, guards, safety shields for TV tubes, components, such as printed circuit boards, coil forms, plugs, terminal boards, telephone housings, accessories, battery cases and lids, terminal covers, acid level gages, distributor covers; in the industrial equipment line, as precision parts for instruments and controls, typewriters, calculators, and fans; in the home, as components of kitchen appliances, refrigerators, freezers, and domestic heaters, as well as in dishes and camping utensils; on the farm, as parts of milking equipment; in the medical supply field, as Petri dishes, blood filters, and cases for dental drills; in the office, as drafting equipment, slide rules, and templates; in industrial safety equipment, as safety helmets and parts of mine helmets; in the lighting industry, as street-light lenses and neon-tube sockets; in the photographic industry, as camera and lightmeter housings; and in the automotive industry, as transparent covers, indicator lights, directional-signal-light lenses, distribution boxes, instrument housings, and guards.

Simple injection-molding equipment has been developed for use in the dental laboratory. In these units bisphenol A polycarbonate can be melted and injected under pressure into plaster molds of teeth and associated supporting structures, such as clasps. Dentures made from this polycarbonate are distinguished by excellent dimensional stability, regardless of variations in temperature and moisture, good mechanical properties, and high elasticity. They will not discolor, and they can be underlined and repaired with any one of the cold- or hot-curing poly(methyl methacrylate) base plastics commonly used in denture work (54,55).

Conventional techniques and equipment are used in the production, by extrusion, of bisphenol A polycarbonate pipe, rods, shapes, sheets, and various tubular products. Every type of extruder developed for thermoplastic material is suitable. The wall thickness of bisphenol A polycarbonate tubing and pipe can be kept lower than those conventionally used with other plastics, thanks to the superior mechanical strength and better cold-flow properties of the material. Finished pipe can be cemented and welded (heat-sealed).

Bisphenol A polycarbonate pipe has been successfully used in food applications for conveying fruit juices, beer, wine, milk, etc, for which its sterilizability, absence of taste and odor, biological inertness, and resistance to color pickup make it eminently suitable.

With properly designed dies and take-up equipment, no undue difficulties are encountered in the continuous extrusion of shapes and profiles or in the continuous and discontinuous extrusion of semifinished goods, such as bar stock and block material.

Bisphenol A polycarbonate is used as a film material (qv).

U.S. production of polycarbonate for 1966 was of the order of 20 million lb, at a unit price of 90¢/lb.

Bibliography

1. L. Bottenbruch, "Polycarbonates," in H. F. Mark, N. G. Gaylord, and N. Bikales, eds., *Encyclopedia of Polymer Science and Technology*, Vol. 10, Interscience Publishers, a division of John Wiley & Sons, Inc., New York, (in preparation); H. Schnell, *The Chemistry and Physics of Polycarbonates*, Interscience Publishers, Division of John Wiley & Sons, Inc., New York, 1964.
2. H. Schnell, *Angew. Chem.* **68,** 633 (1956).
3. Ger. Pat. 971,790 (1959), Belg. Pat. 532,543 (1954), H. Schnell, L. Bottenbruch, and H. Krimm, (to Farbenfabriken Bayer A.G.).
4. Ger. Pat. 1,031,512 (1958), H. Schnell and G. Fritz (to Farbenfabriken Bayer A.G.).
5. W. F. Christopher and D. W. Fox, *Polycarbonates*, Reinhold Publishing Corp., New York, 1962.
6. A. Prietzschk, *Kolloid-Z.* **156,** 8 (1958).
7. H. Schnell, *Ind. Eng. Chem.* **51,** 157 (1959).
8. H. Schnell, *Plastics Inst. (London), Trans. and J.* **28,** 143 (1960).
9. W. F. Christopher, *SPE J.* **14,** 31 (1958).
10. R. I. Thompson and K. B. Goldblum, *Modern Plastics* **35,** 131 (1958).
11. W. Hechelhammer and G. Peilstöcker, *Kunststoffe* **49,** 3, 93 (1959).
12. G. Peilstöcker, *Kunststoffe* **51,** 509 (1961).
13. *Brit. Plastics* **31,** 112 (1958).
14. K. B. Goldblum, *Corrosion* **14,** 90 (1958).
15. H. Gadd, K. B. Goldblum, and W. R. Christopher, *Canad. Plastics* **34** (1959).
16. *Modern Plastics* **37,** 10 (1959).

17. E. E. Hardy, in R. E. Kirk and D. F. Othmer, eds., *Encyclopedia of Chemical Technology*, 2nd Suppl. Vol., Interscience Publishers, Inc., New York, 1960, p. 587.
18. V. E. Yarsley, *Kunststoff-Rundschau* **8**, 165 (1961).
19. *Modern Plastics* **37**, 164 (1960).
20. I. P. Locev, O. V. Smirnova, and E. V. Smurova, *Plasticheskie Massy* **9**, 10 (1962).
21. C. A. Brighton and S. J. Skinner, *Plastics Inst. (London), Trans. and J.* **31**, 70 (1963).
22. *Polycarbonatspritzgussmassen*, DIN 7744, Aug. 1961.
23. J. V. Roslov, L. Makavuk, V. N. Fonin, and V. N. Olchovskij, *Vysokomolekul. Soedin.* **2**, 770 (1960).
24. G. P. Michailov and M. P. Eidelnant, *Vysokomolekul. Soedin.* **2**, 287 (1960).
25. F. Krum and F. H. Müller, *Kolloid-Z.* **164**, 81 (1959).
26. F. M. Müller and K. Huff, *Kolloid-Z.* **164**, 34 (1959).
27. F. Krum, *Kolloid-Z.* **165**, 77 (1959).
28. B. M. Kovarskaja, *Plasticheskie Massy* **10**, 11 (1962).
29. B. G. Achhammer, M. Tryon, and G. M. Kline, *Modern Plastics* **37**, 131 (1959); *Kunststoffe* **49**, 600 (1959).
30. *Chem. Eng. News*, **40** (38), 60 (1962).
31. M. L. Huggins, *J. Am. Chem. Soc.* **64**, 2716 (1942).
32. O. K. Spürr, Jr., and W. D. Niegisch, *J. Appl. Polymer Sci.* **6**, 585 (1962).
33. M. Tomikawa, *Chem. High Polymers (Tokyo)* **20**, 102 (1963); (through) *Makromol. Chem.* **65**, 252 (1963).
34. *Chemical Horizons* **2** (23), 91 (1963); *J. Commerce* **9** (1963); *Federal Register* **28**, 5083 (May 22, 1963).
35. *Makrolon*, Tech. Bull., Farbenfabriken Bayer A.G. (1960).
36. W. Backofen, *Kunststoffe* **49**, 664 (1959).
37. W. Backofen, *Kunststoffe* **52**, 98 (1962).
38. E. F. Fiedler, W. F. Christopher, and T. R. Calkins, *Modern Plastics* **36**, 115 (1959).
39. W. Backofen, *Ind. Plastiques Mod. (Paris)* **12**, 61 (1960).
40. H. W. Streib, *Brit. Plastics* **33**, 406 (1960).
41. W. Backofen, *Plastverarbeiter* **12**, 1, 55, 105 (1961).
42. W. Backofen, *Kunststoffe* **51**, 728 (1961).
43. W. Backofen, *Plastics* **26**, 71 (1961).
44. W. Woebecken, *Kunststoffe* **51**, 547 (1961).
45. W. Backofen and W. Schröder, *Kunststoffe* **52**, 29 (1962).
46. H. W. Streib, *Chem. Ind.* **11**, 463 (1959).
47. B. Waeser, *Kunststoffe—Plastics* **6**, 57 (1959).
48. *Modern Plastics* **37**, 172 (1959).
49. R. P. Sonderman, *Mod. Plastics* **36**, 136 (1959).
50. Anon., *Modern Plastics* **37**, 102 (1960).
51. H. W. Streib, *Gummi, Asbest, Kunststoffe* **14**, 304 (1961).
52. *Modern Plastics* **38**, 87 (1961); **39**, 84 (1961); **39**, 179 (1961).
53. A. D. Thomas and C. V. Leunig, *SPE J.* **18**, 1464 (1962).
54. Ger. Pat. 1,046,254 (1959), H. Schnell, H. J. Rehberg, and W. Hechelhammer (to Farbenfabriken Bayer A.G.).
55. H. Ritze, G. Franz, and W. Kühl, *Deut. Zahnärztl. Z.* **17**, 106 (1962).

H. Schnell
Farbenfabriken Bayer AG

POLYELECTROLYTE COMPLEXES

Polyelectrolyte complexes (PEC) are ionically crosslinked hydrogels formed by the coreaction of two highly, but oppositely, charged polyelectrolytes. Whereas the individual polyelectrolytes are water soluble, the PEC undergoes only limited swelling in water and electrolyte solutions. PEC hydrogels, ranging from clear rigid solids to opaque spongy materials, can be prepared by controlling the reaction conditions, ionic stoichiometry, and the chemistry of the individual polyelectrolytes. These hydrogels possess unique properties that have led to a variety of applications. The distinguishing properties to be emphasized are: (1) high permeability to water and microsolute; (2) controllable selectivity between micro- and macrosolutes; (3) high electrical conductivity (ionic); (4) excellent biological compatibility; (5) excellent chemical stability; and (6) controllable ion-exchange capacity.

Physical Chemistry

Polyelectrolyte complexes are a special class of ionically interacting polymers. Life scientists have long been interested in ionic interactions of proteins (1), but it was not until the work of Bungenberg de Jong and co-workers (2) in the 1930s and 1940s that interactions of reasonably pure and chemically stable polyelectrolytes of opposite charge were investigated in detail. They found that certain water-soluble polymers of natural origin (gums, gelatin, etc), containing ionic moieties of opposite sign, coreacted in aqueous solutions to form what they called "complex coacervates." The complex coacervate was a liquid phase, rich in the two oppositely charged polyions, in equilibrium with a second liquid phase lean in polyelectrolytes. Gelatin–gum arabic coacervates were extensively studied under pH conditions where the gelatin was positively charged (a polycation with $-NH_3^+$ functionality) and the gum arabic was negatively charged (a polyanion with $-COO^-$ functionality). Because of the amphoteric nature of gelatin and the weakly acidic nature of gum arabic, the complex coacervate could readily be destroyed (a single liquid phase being formed) by raising or lowering the pH. In addition, the coacervates were unstable in the presence of even minute concentrations of indifferent electrolytes.

In spite of their both being interaction products of oppositely charged polyelectrolytes, coacervates and polyelectrolyte complexes are distinctly different. Coacervates are liquids, unless caused to gel by temperature-controlled secondary valence interactions; polyelectrolyte complexes are thermally stable gels from the time they are formed. PEC hydrogels are characterized by complete stoichiometric interaction of the two polyelectrolytes in aqueous solution; this is not true of complex coacervates. A PEC is prepared from polyelectrolytes where the individual polyions contain ionizable groups of one charge only; a complex coacervate contains at least one polyampholyte. Complex coacervation is generally restricted to polyelectrolytes with equivalent weights (g-mol wt/ionic group) in the 1000 to 3000 range; the preferred range for PEC formation is under 500. Although a PEC may undergo some swelling or shrinking in the presence of high concentrations of indifferent electrolytes, it will not dissolve as will complex coacervates.

Concerning complex coacervates, it may be pointed out that their environmental instability has not detracted from their utility as novel microencapsulating resins. The activities of National Cash Register Company in this field are based in part on the work of Green and his associates on the in situ complex coacervation and gelation of polyelectrolytes at the surfaces of emulsified oil droplets (3). See also Micro-encapsulation.

Under certain pH conditions, weak acid–weak base polyelectrolytes can be made to interact stoichiometrically (4), and thus they are potentially capable of forming polyelectrolyte complexes. However, the resulting hydrogels are not as strong mechanically, their degree of hydration is more difficult to control, and they are thermally and chemically less stable than PEC hydrogels prepared from polymeric salts of strong acids and strong bases. Emphasis has, therefore, been placed on the latter materials for the development of commercial products. The most stable PEC hydrogels are made from polyelectrolytes whose derivative acids and bases have a pK of less than 2.0. This has focused attention on sulfonated polymers such as sodium poly(styrene sulfonate), sodium poly(vinyl sulfonate), etc as the polyanion, and quaternary nitrogen-bearing polymers such as poly(vinylbenzyltrimethylammonium) chloride, poly(vinylpyridinium) chloride, etc as the polycation. The hydrolytic instability of sulfated organic polymers and inorganic polyphosphates makes them undesirable for many applications in spite of their low pK's. Presumably sulfonium or phosphonium polymers would make satisfactory polycations, but none are available as a commercial product.

The first reported study of an interaction between a strongly acidic polyanion, sodium poly(styrene sulfonate), and a strongly basic polycation, poly(vinylmethylpyridinium) chloride, in aqueous solution was by Fuoss and Sadek in 1949 (5). They found that the PEC rapidly precipitated out of solution and was essentially a stoichiometric reaction product of the polyelectrolytes. It was not until 1961 that extensive examination of the physical properties of PEC hydrogels began under Michaels and co-workers (6–10). This group concentrated their attention on the reaction of sodium poly(styrene sulfonate) (NaSS) with poly(vinylbenzyltrimethylammonium) chloride (VBTAC) to give a complex which will be denoted as VBTA-SS, ie, poly(vinylbenzyltrimethylammonium) poly(styrene sulfonate). Initial work by this group confirmed the stoichiometric colloidal precipitation of PEC in dilute solutions, but they also observed that at higher polyelectrolyte concentrations (above 0.6 % by wt or approx 0.03N) a thin interfacial film of PEC about 200 Å thick rapidly formed between the two polyelectrolyte solutions when they were brought together. This film was also stoichiometric in polyanions and polycations. Because of the impermeability of this PEC film to the two polyions, the reaction stopped after the initial thin-film formation. These stoichiometric PEC hydrogels (both the colloidal precipitate and the interfacial film) could, with careful washing, be freed of all the microcounterions (Na$^+$ and Cl$^-$) originally associated with the individual polyelectrolytes.

Neither the detailed molecular structure of these polysalts, nor the rapid and complete reaction from which they are formed is completely understood. The apparent high free energy of interaction must be entropic in origin since the reaction is nearly athermal (estimated heat of reaction is 1.9 kcal/mole (11)). The high positive entropy of reaction appears to come from the microcounterions (eg Na$^+$ in NaSS and Cl$^-$ in VBTAC). The thermal motion of microcounterions in the individual polyelectrolyte solutions is restricted because of being site- or chain-bound to the polymer ion (12). After a polyelectrolyte complex is formed, however, the simple salt (eg NaCl from the VBTA–SS complex) ions are no longer restricted in their thermal motion by association with polymer ions, and their entropy is thereby increased as a result of the reaction.

The most probable structure of a PEC is that of a so-called "scrambled polysalt" shown in Figure 1. In this figure, electrostatic interactions between the two polyions are depicted as "diffuse field interactions" taking place randomly between groups of ionic sites of opposite sign; this is to be contrasted with a "ladder" structure resulting from the orderly interaction of each charged site with one of opposite sign. As might be expected from this scrambled salt model, the hydrogels are completely amorphous. They are network polymers in the sense that all polymer hydrogels involve three-dimensional interactions between mer units or chain segments. However, in this case the "crosslinking" interactions (interpolymer attraction between covalently bonded

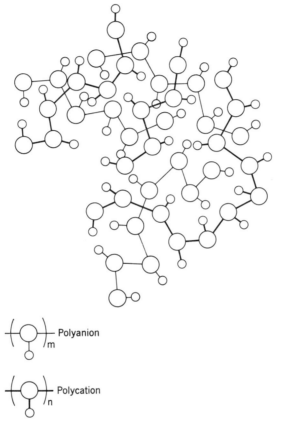

Fig. 1. "Scrambled salt" structure of a polyelectrolyte complex.

chains) are ionic in contrast to the covalent—or hydrogen—bonding normally encountered in conventional hydrogels. This unique network structure has a strong effect on the physical properties of a PEC, and is given further consideration below.

Polyelectrolyte complexes in the dry or partially hydrated states are infusible, and therefore, manipulation into useful shapes has generally been accomplished by solution casting. It was found by Michaels and co-workers that a PEC could be dissolved in a ternary solvent consisting of water, a strongly ionized simple electrolyte, and a polar organic solvent, miscible with the electrolyte solution, even though a PEC is insoluble in single-component or binary solvents composed of these ingredients. The solubilizing activity of these so-called "shielding solvents" is believed to result from the ion-shielding activity of the electrolyte (which "discharges" the polyelectro-

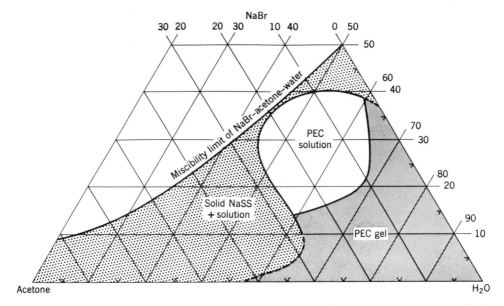

Fig. 2. Phase diagram for a ternary solvent system for poly(vinylbenzyltrimethylammonium)–poly-(styrene sulfonate).

lytes), and the solvating action of the organic component of the solvent on the organophilic backbones of the polyelectrolytes.

Figure 2 shows a phase diagram of a typical shielding solvent for the VBTA–SS complex at room temperature. The enclosed region marked "PEC solution" denotes the range of solvent compositions which give homogeneous, transparent viscous solutions of the complex. Outside of this region, either NaSS is preferentially precipitated, or a homogeneous PEC hydrogel is formed. To make homogeneous films, fibers, coatings, etc of PEC, a dope of the complex is prepared using a solvent whose composition is within the solution range. The solid hydrogel then is formed by evaporating or washing out shielding solvent components.

The discovery of PEC solvents led to an additional degree of freedom in their composition. It became possible to make shielded solutions of the two polyelectrolytes that were nonstoichiometric in polyion equivalents. When hydrogels were made from these solutions by solvent removal, they were also nonstoichiometric, but nonetheless, compositionally stable. Presumably the excess polyanion or polycation could not be leached from the hydrogel, because all polymer chains participate to some degree in the ionic crosslinking reaction. Therefore, hydrogels with ion-exchange capacities (anion or cation) could be prepared in this manner. Stable gels with ion-exchange capacities up to 1 meq excess polyion/meq neutralized polyion, or about 2 meq exchange capacity/dry g of resin, have been prepared from the VBTA–SS complex.

Properties

Polyelectrolyte complexes have general physical properties akin to those of other hydrogels eg uncoated cellophane, ethylene glycol dimethacrylate crosslinked with 2-hydroxyethyl methacrylate, and glyoxal-crosslinked polyvinyl alcohol. They are hard, brittle solids when bone-dry, and leathery or rubbery when saturated with

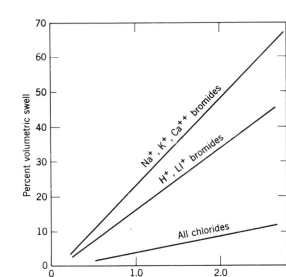

Fig. 3. Swelling of neutral polyelectrolyte complex in salt solutions.

moisture. Hydrogels are usually employed in the moisture-swollen state, and attention has been focused on PEC properties in this condition.

Unlike conventional hydrogels, moisture sorption by a PEC is not uniquely defined by chemical composition. Depending on the manner in which the PEC is gelled from solution, the stable moisture content, when it is immersed in water, will vary. For a stoichiometric or "neutral" PEC, the stable, room-temperature moisture or gel water content can be varied at will from a low of 20% to over 90%. The ability to control the stable gel water content of a PEC presumably depends on the ability to control the morphology of ionic crosslinking; for non-neutral complexes (those with ion-exchange capacity), the minimum stable gel water content increases as the ion-exchange capacity increases, reflecting the lower ionic crosslink density of these resins.

The minimum water sorbed by a neutral complex corresponds to approximately three water molecules per ionic site (anionic and cationic) within the gel, indicating that virtually all of this water is site-bound as water of hydration. Gels containing more than approx 20% of moisture presumably contain free or unbound water.

In spite of the presence of free water in most gels, a given PEC with a particular gel water content will be remarkably stable to changes in ambient conditions. For instance, changing the temperature from 4 to 60°C will not change the room temperature gel water content significantly. Likewise, immersion in dilute solutions of simple monovalent electrolytes will produce only a slight effect on the gel water content.

Moderate, or even very low concentrations of specific electrolytes will "plasticize" the PEC. For a neutral PEC of low water content, this plasticizing action is manifested as a softening and swelling of the hydrogel; for a non-neutral PEC of high gel water content, it results in network collapse and hydrogel shrinkage. Figure 3 shows a typical correlation of the swelling of a neutral, low-gel-water PEC with concentration and type of electrolyte (9). Weaker swelling by chlorides than bromides, and by lithium than other alkali cations, reflects the relative site-binding capacity of these

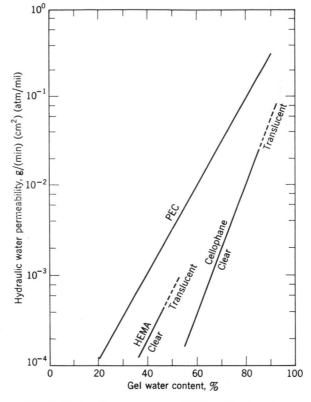

Fig. 4. Hydraulic water permeabilities of hydrogels.

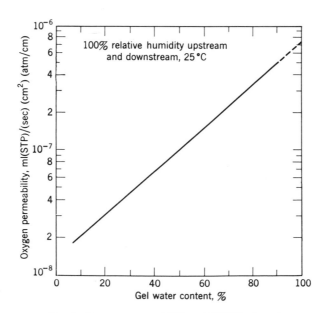

Fig. 5. Oxygen permeabilities of PEC hydrogels.

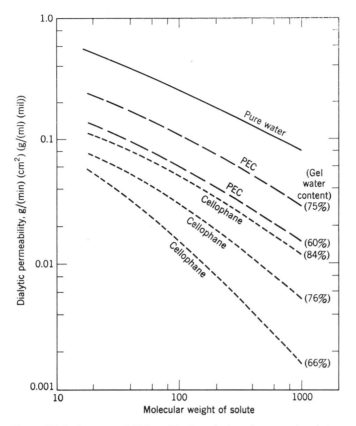

Fig. 6. Dialytic permeabilities of hydrogels to polar organic solutes.

microions to polyions (13,14).   Calcium and other polyvalent cations also interact strongly with PEC hydrogels for apparently the same reasons.   Strong microion site-binding reduces the strength of PEC crosslinks, and this promotes swelling.   In addition, the effect of concentrated electrolytes on the PEC polyion hydration, and the effect of Donnan exclusion in non-neutral gels, must be considered in analyzing the swelling and shrinking action of electrolytes.

The most remarkable and useful properties of polyelectrolyte complexes are their extremely high and controllable water (and microsolute) permeability (see Dialysis). High permeability is a manifestation of the ionic network structure of a PEC, and permselectivity stems from the above-mentioned ability to control gel water content and ionic crosslink topology.   Figure 4 shows the low-pressure (<100 psi) hydraulic water permeability of clear membranes of homogeneous PEC, cellophane, and cross-linked 2-hydroxyethyl methacrylate (HEMA) as a function of gel water content (16–18).   It can be seen that a PEC is at least ten times more water permeable than cellophane at the same gel water content and is also considerably more permeable than the HEMA hydrogel.   This apparently reflects the water-destructuring action of the ionic matrix of a PEC which greatly enhances water mobility within the gel. The more uniform and diffusely crosslinked PEC also makes it possible to retain optical clarity in the hydrogel over a wider range of gel water contents than for covalently bonded gels.

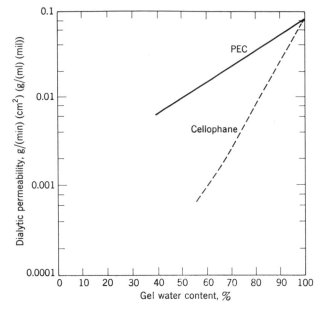

Fig. 7. Dialytic permeabilities of hydrogels to 1000 mol wt polysaccharide.

The correlation in Figure 4 holds for hydrogels made from non-neutral as well as neutral complexes. It might, therefore, be expected that conventional ion-exchange membranes would behave similarly. However, a PEC is much more permeable to water than is a covalently crosslinked sodium poly(styrene sulfonate) ion-exchange membrane. The latter has a hydraulic water permeability of about 10^{-5} g/(min)(cm²)-(atm/mil) at 50% gel water content (15). This is less than one one-hundredth of that of a PEC of comparable water content. The microheterogeneity associated with co-valent crosslinking in ion-exchange membranes causes a nonuniformity in swelling which more than offsets any permeability-enhancing influence of water destructuring by the ionic matrix.

The high and controllable permeability of PEC to microsolutes is illustrated in Figures 5, 6, and 7. In Figure 5, the oxygen permeability of these hydrogels is seen to be a unique function of gel water content. Their oxygen permeability is not as high as for a nonpolar, amorphous low modulus polymer such as silicone rubber, but nonetheless it is high enough to render PEC well suited for several biomedical applications requiring materials of high oxygen permeability, especially when other attributes of the resins are considered (see below). Figure 6 shows the dilute solution permeabilities of PEC hydrogels and cellophane (16) to various solutes correlated with solute molecular weight. These correlations would apply to dilute aqueous solutions of alcohols, sugars, polysaccharides, and other nonionic water soluble solutes in the molecular-weight range shown. For comparison, the dialytic permeabilities of a 1-mil film of pure water are shown for the same range of solutes. These have been calculated by dividing reported diffusion constants in water by the film thickness (16). Again, a PEC is considerably more permeable than cellophane at the same gel water content, presumably because of the greater micro-uniformity of gel water dispersion in the former hydrogels. Figure 7 shows that gel water content is a unique correlating parameter for nonionic solute permeabilities in a manner identical to that shown for oxygen in

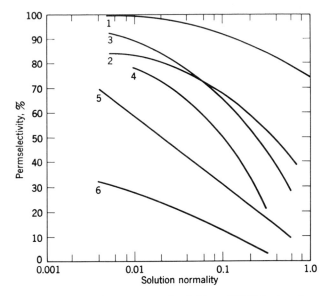

Fig. 8. Electrodialytic permselectivities of PEC hydrogels.

Curve	1	2	3	4	5	6
salt	$CaCl_2$	KCl	KCl	KCl	KCl	KCl
pEC	neutral	anionic	cationic	anionic	neutral	neutral
exchange capacity, meg/g	0	2.0	2.0	1.0	0	0
gel H₂O, %	40	50	50	70	40	80
permselectivity	anion	cation	anion	cation	anion	anion

Figure 5. In this figure dialytic permeabilities for a 1000-molecular-weight polysaccharide (eg, cyclohexamylose) have been used for illustration, but a similar result would now be expected for virtually any solute in dilute aqueous solution.

A correlation such as that shown in Figure 6 could be used in the absence of data to predict the permeabilities of PEC hydrogels to high-molecular-weight solutes such as synthetic water soluble polymers and proteins. It would appear as if PEC were impermeable, for all practical purposes, to polymers with a molecular weight greater than 10,000 when the gel water content is less than 50%. On the other hand, it would appear as if polymers in the range 100,000 mol wt would have some measurable mobility within PEC hydrogels containing approx 95+% gel water.

The transport of ionic solutes in PEC hydrogels is controlled not only by gel water content but also by ionic site-binding, and in non-neutral gels, Donnan exclusion. Very little work has been done on dialytic transport of electrolytes through PEC hydrogels, but electrodialytic transport has been examined. Figure 8 is a plot of electrodialytic permselectivities for KCl in stoichiometric neutral and non-neutral PEC and for $CaCl_2$ in neutral PEC (see also Electrodialysis). The non-neutral PEC's show expected permselectivities based on the sign of charge on the resin, the charge density, and the water content (19). The anion selectivity of neutral PEC to KCl and $CaCl_2$ solutions is probably due to restricted mobility of the larger cations in these hydrogels. As would be expected if diffusion of the cations were the controlling factor in the observed selectivity, the anion permselectivity increases markedly with decreasing gel water content.

Table 1.   Reverse Osmosis Percent Retention for Neutral VBTA–SS PEC[a]

Salt	Percent retention
MgSO₄	99.5
MgCl₂	96.9
CaCl₂	97.5
NaCl	80
KCl	76
NaBr	59
NaCNS	46

[a] Gel water content, 40%; salt conc, 0.1M; pressure, 1500 psi; water permeability, approx 10^{-4} g/(min)(cm²)(atm/mil).

Further confirmation of the restricted mobility of specific ions in these hydrogels is obtained from reverse osmosis measurements (20). In these experiments, 0.1M solutions of individual salts were placed in contact with a neutral VBTA–SS polyelectrolyte complex of approx 40% gel water content at 1500 psi hydrostatic pressure. Percent retention for the various salts are shown in Table 1. In general, the percent

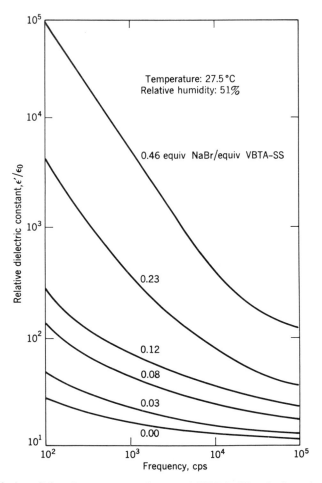

Fig. 9. Relative dielectric constants of neutral VBTA–SS polyelectrolyte complex.

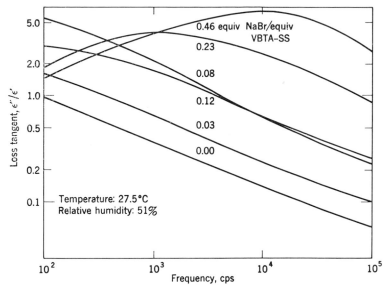

Fig. 10. Loss tangents of neutral VBTA–SS polyelectrolyte complex.

retention decreases with decreasing size of the hydrated salt (cation plus anion(s)); however, the specific interaction of certain anions such as Br⁻ and CNS⁻ with the polyanion matrix has a stronger influence than size alone on the percent retention. The high pressure used in these experiments significantly compresses the PEC matrix since the recorded water permeability is about one order of magnitude lower than the predicted value from Figure 4.

The electrical properties of PEC hydrogels are more closely related to those of biologically-derived solids than they are to conventional synthetic polymers. Figures 9 and 10 show the relative dielectric constants and loss tangents for a neutral PEC doped with various levels of NaBr. For the saltfree polyelectrolyte complex, these properties are comparable to those of leather—a microcrystalline fibrous polyampholyte (21). Like leather, the low-frequency (100 cps) dielectric constant varies from about 5 in the dry state to about 50 when saturated with water. The extremely high relative dielectric constants and the dispersion properties of salt-doped PEC are equaled only by those of raw beefsteak which is a similar complex composite of structured polyampholytes and saline solutions (21). This dielectric behavior has been ascribed to the polarizability of electrolyte sorbed into isolated, microscopic domains within the PEC matrix (8).

The low-frequency electrical (ionic) conductivities of neutral and nonneutral PEC hydrogels equilibrated with electrolyte solutions are comparable to those of con-

Table 2. Ionic Conductivities of VBTA–SS PEC at 20°C[a]

Gel water content, %	Conductivity, $\times 10^{-3}$ mho/cm
40	4.5
68	20.7
80	38.4
100[b]	50.0

[a] Equilibrating solution: 0.5M KCl.   [b] Conductivity of 0.5M KCl.

ventional ion-exchange membranes (22). Table 2 contains conductivity data for neutral gels equilibrated with 0.5M KCl.

It can be seen from Table 2 that the gel conductivity is very close to that of the equilibrating solution for gels with water content in excess of 80%. Such highly swollen gels still retain good mechanical properties. In the absence of salt, the conductivities of the gels range from 10^{-8} mho/cm when equilibrated at 50% relative humidity to 10^{-6} mho/cm at 95% relative humidity.

The tensile strength, modulus, and elongation-to-break of a medium gel water content PEC are compared in Table 3 with those of a cellophane and a lightly crosslinked HEMA hydrogel having comparable water contents. The PEC is seen to be stiffer than the other two hydrogels and intermediate in strength. Dynamic mechanical properties of PEC have been examined (9). The master stress-relaxation curve for

Table 3. Room Temperature Tensile Properties of Hydrogels

Hydrogel	Tensile strength, psi	Modulus, psi	Elongation, %
PEC (55% H_2O)	800	8000	18
cellophane (55% H_2O)	4100	4400	92
HEMA (45% H_2O)	60	<1000	140

PEC is surprisingly similar to those for conventional glassy amorphous polymers. As would be expected, the presence of water and electrolyte solution together with temperature promotes the onset of rubbery behavior.

The refractive index for a series of homogeneous VBTA–SS polyelectrolyte complexes of different gel water contents has been measured (18). In the range of 40–80% gel water, the refractive index at 22°C is given by:

$$n = 1.294 + 0.336(1 - \alpha)$$

where α is the gel water content expressed as a weight fraction.

Applications and Uses

The major commercial applications of polyelectrolyte complexes are in ultrafiltration and dialysis membranes, battery separators, and biomedical prosthetic materials and device components. The unusual properties of these materials also suggest a number of potential applications that will be considered in a brief summary at the end of this section.

Ultrafiltration and Dialysis Membranes. Ultrafiltration has long been considered a potentially attractive means of separating molecules in solution on the basis of size and shape (23,24). The process has never been widely used because of the unavailability of membranes which combine high permeability with high permselectivity. The inherently high water permeability of polyelectrolyte complexes, plus their controllable permselectivity to water-soluble solutes, has led to the development of the first practical ultrafiltration membranes (25). Amicon Corporation of Lexington, Mass. markets a series of PEC ultrafiltration membranes under the trade name Diaflo. These membranes possess water permeabilities in excess of 200 gal/(day)(ft²) at 100 psi operating pressure and are capable of preventing the passage of molecules

Table 4. Diaflo Ultrafiltration Membranes

Membrane	Water permeability at 10 psi		Approx mol wt cutoff[a]
	gal/(day)(ft²)	ml/(min)(cm²)	
UM-05	25	0.07	500
UM-2	70	0.2	1000
UM-10	180	0.5	10,000
UM-50	250	0.7	20,000

[a] Smallest molecule to be substantially retained on the membrane.

as small as sucrose. Table 4 lists the important physical properties of four of these membranes.

Uncoated cellophane, suitably hydrated to approach UM-10 cutoff characteristics, has a water permeability of about 0.007 ml/(min)(cm²) at 100 psi, only about one one-hundredth that of the UM-10. The high permeabilities of the Diaflo membranes are achieved not only because they are fabricated from PEC, but also because of their anisotropic geometry. The permselective barrier layers on these membranes are in the range of 0.1–1 μ thick, the bulk of the complete membrane being an open-celled foam of gross porosity. In addition to high permeability this membrane geometry substantially eliminates membrane fouling.

The highly selective retention characteristics of these membranes are illustrated in Figure 11 where % retention on the membrane is plotted vs solute mol wt. These retention characteristics apply to relatively unstructured, flexible-chain molecules. For more highly structured molecules such as hormones, proteins, and polypeptides, the retention is generally higher than indicated in this figure.

The UM-3 membrane demonstrates another degree of freedom in tailoring PEC ultrafilters. This membrane, in contrast to the others listed above, is made from non-neutral resin which carries a net negative charge (anionic). This charge can be used to effect separation of zwitterions by Donnan exclusion through suitable pH adjustment of the solution being ultrafiltered. Thus, low-molecular-weight amino acids will pass through this membrane when held in solution at their isoelectric points, but they will be retained when the pH of the solution is maintained above their isoelectric points.

These membranes are being employed in pharmaceutical, chemical, and food processing, life science research, and waste-water treatment. Specific applications include nondestructive concentration of labile natural products (26,27), desalting of protein solutions (28), fractionation of proteins (29), clinical differentiation of aberrant metabolites (30), membrane osmometry (31), and purification of industrial and municipal waste waters (32).

Homogeneous PEC membranes have already been shown to possess superior dialytic capability when compared with cellophane—presently the most widely used dialysis membrane. Amicon fabricates this version of PEC membrane under the trade name Biolon, and Table 5 lists the properties of those which are commercially available.

Many of the applications for these membranes are in the biomedical field and will be discussed below. However, they do possess the potential for being used in selected industrial dialytic separations where ultrafiltration for one reason or another is not applicable. The permselectivities of the non-neutral membranes are not adequate for use in electrodialytic desalination of brines, but could be used where separation of organic ions is of interest. The anion permselectivity of the neutral complex has also created interest for use in a so-called cation/neutral electrodialyzer for brackish water desalination.

Battery Separators. Polyelectrolyte complexes possess three outstanding properties which have led to their development as battery separators (see Vol. 3, p. 217 and p. 262): (*1*) low resistivity when saturated with electrolytes, (*2*) controllable permeability and/or porosity, and (*3*) ability to solidify or gel normally low-viscosity liquid electrolytes at low solids levels. Low resistivity (<2 ohm-cm above that of the electrolyte) is essential to control the internal resistance of a battery contributed by the separator. Controlled permeability of a battery separator is the key to long battery life, especially as more esoteric electrode reactions are being considered in primary energy cells. Solid electrolytes are preferred in batteries to prevent leakage and spillage, and to permit the battery to operate if it is slightly sloping. Polyelectrolyte complexes can be used as unsupported films or as saturants for the pores of fibrous sheets in fabricating battery separators. They also have the advantage of being sufficiently stable to oxidation and reduction to be incorporated directly onto electrode surfaces.

Table 5. Biolon Dialysis Membranes

Membrane	Ionic charge	Ion-exchange capacity, meq/dry g	Gel water content, %
BN-40	neutral	0.0	40
BN-60	neutral	0.0	60
BN-80	neutral	0.0	80
BA-50	anionic	1.5	50
BA-70	anionic	1.5	70
BC-50	cationic	1.5	50
BC-70	cationic	1.5	70

Medical and Surgical Applications. In many ways, polyelectrolyte complexes possess colloidal properties similar to body protein structures. These include their ionic charge characteristics, their hydrogel structure, and their controllable permeabilities to water and solutes found in body fluids. As a result of these combined properties, they have displayed unusually good biocompatibility for materials derived solely from synthetic polymers. Subcutaneous implants have shown no deterioration or adverse reaction with surrounding tissue for periods up to a year (33). Likewise, a PEC hydrogel containing 0.5 meq/dry g of excess anionic charge was the first totally synthetic polymer not to induce blood clotting when used in vivo as a blood conduit (34). The fact that body proteins are not denatured when brought into contact with PEC hydrogels accounts in part for this unusually good biocompatibility (26).

Polyelectrolyte complex membranes show considerable promise in dialytic-type artificial kidneys because of their antithrombogenic properties and their high dialysis coefficients for blood toxins. A new type of artificial kidney, based on ultrafiltration of blood rather than dialysis, employs PEC membranes (35). This new extracorporeal blood purifier offers the advantage of more complete detoxification of uremic patients. The need for an antithrombogenic membrane in blood oxygenators (required for open heart surgery) has stimulated the development of PEC membranes for this purpose.

PEC hydrogels are also being evaluated and promoted for use as prosthetic materials for body repair. Included in the list of applications in this field are blood vessel and body fluid duct prostheses, in-swelling catheters, coatings and components of heart valves and artificial hearts, sutures, burn and wound dressings, and adhesive for tissue repair. The optical clarity of these hydrogels, combined with the properties mentioned above, has prompted their use in contact lenses, as well as repair materials in ophthalmic surgery (18).

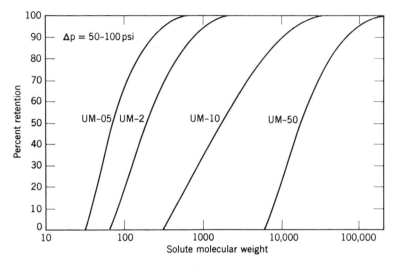

Fig. 11. Retention characteristics of Diaflo ultrafiltration membranes for flexible, linear molecules

Miscellaneous Applications. The potential utility of these materials in a number of relatively new technologies remains to be exploited. PEC hydrogels can be prepared in the form of pigmentlike microporous powder. When these powders are incorporated in conventional plastics such as vinyls and urethans, they greatly enhance the moisture "breathability" of the resulting film or sheet. Improved breathability of these plastics is essential in the development of rugged, yet comfortable, leather substitutes for shoes and upholstery and various other outer garments such as rainwear (see Poromeric substances). Table 6 indicates the improvements in moisture transmission that can be imparted to vinyl and urethans by incorporation of PEC hydrogels in particulate form.

Table 6. Moisture Vapor Transmission through PEC Composites

Composite	MVT, g/(day)(100 in.^{2})[a]
vinyl control (54% dioctyl phthalate + 46% poly(vinyl chloride))	20
vinyl + 18% PEC powder	150
urethan control (Estan)	50
urethan + 30% PEC powder	250

[a] Measured on 1-mil films at 73°F and a relative humidity driving force of from 100% to 50%.

The moisture permeabilities of these thin-film composites compare favorably with those of finished shoe uppers (approx 75 g/(day)(100 in.²)) and the normal rate of sweat production by the human body (approx 100 g/(day)(100 in.²)). These improvements in MVT are not the result of introducing through-porosity into the plastic sheeting since the gas and hydraulic permeabilities of the filled and unfilled materials are identical. A novel application of these composites has been reported in the aerospace literature in which they are used to cool the inside of an extravehicular space suit by pervaporation of water through the suit wall (36).

The unusual electrical properties of polyelectrolyte complexes could be employed in a number of interesting applications. The relatively high conductivities of the gels at low relative humidities suggest their use as antistatic coatings for textiles and plastics. The sensitivity of the dielectric and dc conductive properties of PEC to moisture content and ion content, coupled with their ability to equilibrate with their surroundings rapidly, make them ideal candidates for moisture and specific ion detectors. The use of these resins to form solid electrolytes in batteries has already been mentioned; it can be extended to electrolytic capacitors.

The emerging field of enzyme technology, where these highly specific natural catalysts can be used industrially to promote desired reactions without the formation of unwanted by-products, offers a unique opportunity for PEC hydrogels. These hydrogels are ideally suited as matrices to which enzymes can be "tethered," thus localizing and concentrating their activity without destroying it.

Economics. The raw materials for forming polyelectrolyte complexes are generally specialty chemicals with 1968 prices in the $2–$3/lb range. A finished PEC, therefore, falls in the range of $3–$5/lb. For many of the sophisticated applications noted above, this material cost is tolerable, but for other applications to develop, a lower-cost PEC is required. There is now reason to believe that before 1970 PEC resins will be produced for under $1/lb.

Bibliography

1. A. Kossel, *The Protamines and Histones*, Longmans, Green & Co., London, 1928.
2. H. G. Bungenberg de Jong, "Complex Colloid Systems" in H. Kruyt, ed., *Colloid Science*, Vol. II, Elsevier Publishing Co., Inc., New York, 1949, Chap. X.
3. U.S. Pat. 2,800,457 (July 23, 1957), B. K. Green and L. Schleicher (to National Cash Register Co.).
4. H. Deuel, J. Solms, and A. Dengler, *Helv. Chim. Acta* **36,** 1671–1680 (1953).
5. R. M. Fuoss and H. Sadek, *Science* **110,** 552–554 (1949).
6. A. S. Michaels and R. G. Miekka, *J. Phys. Chem.* **65,** 1765 (1961).
7. A. S. Michaels, L. Mir, and N. S. Schneider, *J. Phys. Chem.* **69,** 1447–1455 (1965).
8. A. S. Michaels, G. L. Falkenstein, and N. S. Schneider, *J. Phys. Chem.* **69,** 1456–1465 (1965).
9. C. A. Gray, *The Mechanical Properties of Polyelectrolyte Complexes*, Sc.D. Thesis, M.I.T., September, 1965.
10. A. S. Michaels, *Ind. Eng. Chem.* **57,** 32–40 (1965).
11. R. D. Falb, G. A. Grode, M. T. Takahashi, and R. I. Leininger, "Characteristics of Heparinized Surfaces" in R. Gould, ed., *Advan. Chem. Ser.* **87,** (1968).
12. S. Rice and M. Nagasawa, *Polyelectrolyte Solutions*, Academic Press, Inc., New York, 1961, Chap. VIII.
13. U. Strauss and Y. Leung, *J. Am. Chem. Soc.* **84,** 1476–1480 (1965).
14. F. Helfferich, *Ion Exchange*, McGraw-Hill Book Co., Inc., New York, 1962, Chap. 5.
15. S. Tuwiner, *Diffusion and Membrane Technology*, Reinhold Publishing Corp., New York, 1962, Chap. 16.
16. E. Renkin, *J. Gen. Physiol.* **38,** 225–243 (1954).

17. M. F. Refojo, *J. Appl. Polymer Sci.* **9**, 3417–3426 (1965).
18. M. F. Refojo, *J. Appl. Polymer Sci.* **11**, 1991–2000 (1967).
19. A. Despic and G. J. Hills, *Trans. Faraday Soc.* **51**, 1260 (1955).
20. R. F. Baddour, W. R. Vieth, A. S. Douglas, and A. S. Hoffman, *Expanded Glassy Polymers and Polyelectrolyte Complexes as Reverse Osmosis and Ion Selective Membranes*, Massachusetts Institute of Technology, Desalination Lab. Rept. No. 624-1, Cambridge, Mass., 1961.
21. A. von Hippel, *Dielectric Materials and Applications*, John Wiley & Sons, Inc., New York, 1954, Chap. 5.
22. F. Helfferich, *Ion Exchange*, McGraw-Hill Book Co., Inc., New York, 1962, Chap. 7.
23. J. D. Ferry, *Chem. Rev.* **18**, 373–455 (1935).
24. L. Ambard and S. Trautman, *Ultrafiltration*, Charles C Thomas, Springfield, Ill., 1960.
25. A. S. Michaels, "Ultrafiltration" in E. S. Perry, ed., *Advances in Separations and Purifications*, John Wiley & Sons, Inc., New York, 1968.
26. W. F. Blatt, M. P. Feinberg, H. B. Hopfenberg, and C. A. Saravis, *Science* **150**, 224–226 (1965).
27. D. I. C. Wang, T. Sonoyama, and R. I. Mateles, "Enzyme and Bacteriophage Concentration by Membrane Filtration," accepted for publication in *Anal. Biochem.* (1968).
28. W. F. Blatt, S. M. Robinson, F. M. Robbins, and C. A. Saravis, *Anal. Biochem.* **18**, 81–87 (1967).
29. W. F. Blatt, B. G. Hudson, S. M. Robinson, and E. M. Zipilivan, *Nature*, **216**, 511–513 (1967).
30. E. C. Adams and M. J. Rozman, "Differentiation of Hemoglobinuria and Myoglobinuria in Renal Diseases," *Applied Seminar on Laboratory Diagnosis of Kidney Diseases, Sec. 14, Association of Clinical Scientists, Philadelphia, Pa., 1967.*
31. J. R. H. Wake and A. M. Posner, *Nature* **213**, 692–693 (1967).
32. R. W. Okey and P. L. Stavenger, "Reverse Osmosis Applications in Industrial Waste Treatment," *Symposium on Membrane Processes for Industry, Southern Research Institute, Birmingham, Ala., 1966.*
33. L. L. Markley, H. J. Bixler, and R. A. Cross, to be published in *J. Biomed. Materials Res.* (1968).
34. L. M. Nelsen, R. A. Cross, H. J. Bixler, M. Fadali, M. M. Ameli, and V. L. Gott, to be published in *Surgery* **64**, (1969).
35. L. W. Henderson, A. Besarab, A. Michaels, and L. W. Bluemle, Jr., *Trans. Amer. Soc. Artif. Int. Organs* **13**, 216–222 (1967).
36. H. J. Bixler, A. S. Hoffman, and L. A. Spano, *Space Aeronautics* **48**, 107–113 (1967).

ALAN S. MICHAELS AND HARRIS J. BIXLER
Amicon Corporation

POLYENE ANTIBIOTICS

The polyene-macrolide antifungal antibiotics constitute a large and varied group of substances produced by the *Streptomycete* species of microorganisms. They are highly active against fungi (see also Vol. 3, pp. 34–35), including numerous human pathogens, and many of them exhibit some antiprotozoal activity. They do not possess significant antibacterial activity.

Several polyene antibiotics (nystatin, amphotericin B, and trichomycin) are important therapeutic agents. Their characteristic ultraviolet absorption spectra (examples shown in Fig. 1) make it possible to detect their presence readily in fermentation broths; 15–30% of all *Streptomycete* species examined have been reported to produce such substances. The task of individually characterizing each product is, however, a difficult one, and of the sixty or seventy such antibiotics which have been given names and which have been examined chemically and biologically only a comparative few have been characterized by full structural elucidation.

History and Classification. In 1950, Drs. Elizabeth Hazen and Rachel Brown of the Division of Laboratories, New York State Department of Health, in Albany,

Table 1. Physical and Chemical Properties

Compound[a]	Chromophore	Empirical formula (mol wt)	Specific rotation[b]	Amino sugar	Structure of the aglycone or functional groups present
nystatin (fungicidin, Mycostatin)	tetraene	$C_{47}H_{75}O_{18}N$ (942.08)	−10 AcOH +12 DMF +21 pyr −7 0.1N HCl in MeOH	mycosamine	
rimocidin	tetraene	$C_{38}H_{63}O_{13}N$ (741.89)	+116 pyr	mycosamine	
pimaricin (tennecetin, Myprozine)	tetraene	$C_{33}H_{47}O_{13}N$ (665.72)	+180 DMSO	mycosamine	
tetrin A tetrin B	tetraene	$C_{34-35}H_{53-55}O_{13-14}N$ (684–714)	A, +28 pyr B, not reported	mycosamine	

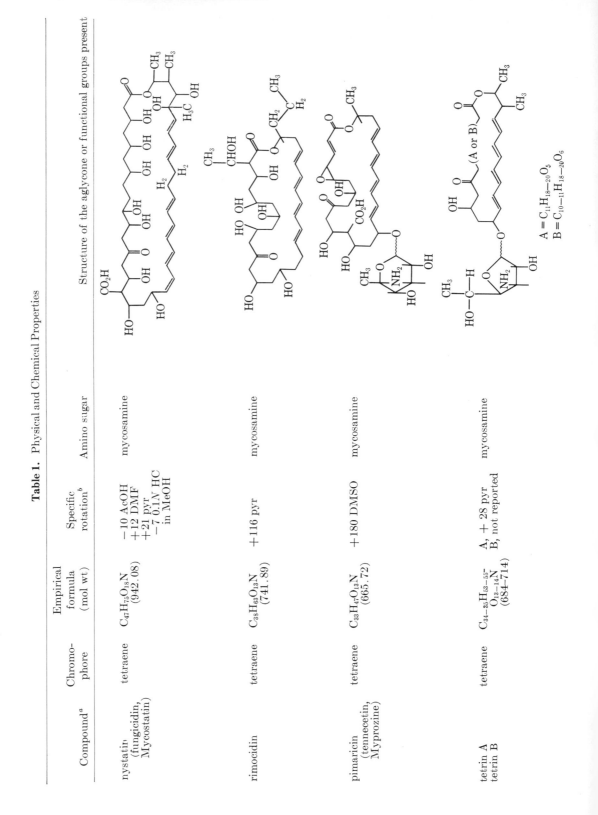

$A = C_{11}H_{18-20}O_5$
$B = C_{10-11}H_{18-20}O_6$

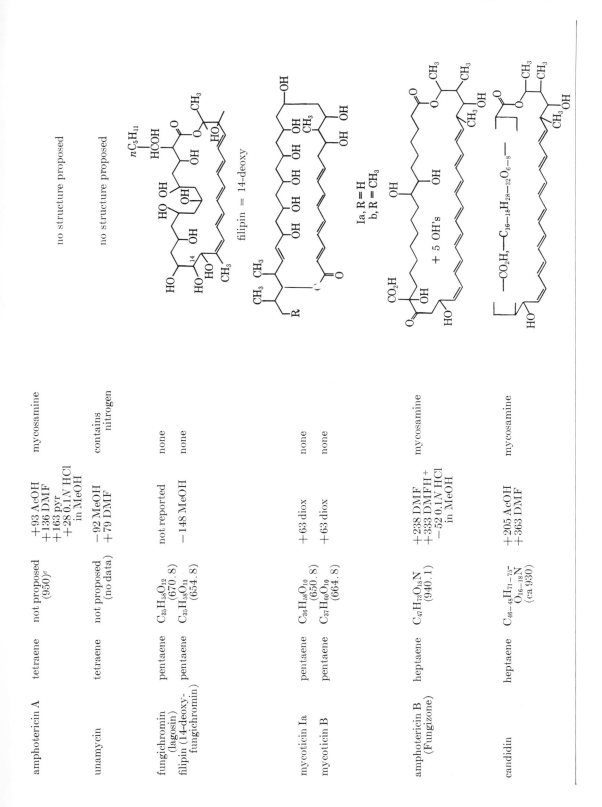

amphotericin A	tetraene	not proposed (950)[c]	+93 AcOH +136 DMF +163 pyr +28 0.1N HCl in MeOH	mycosamine	no structure proposed
unamycin	tetraene	not proposed (no data)	−92 MeOH +79 DMF	contains nitrogen	no structure proposed
fungichromin (lagosin)	pentaene	$C_{35}H_{58}O_{12}$ (670.8)	not reported	none	
filipin (14-deoxy-fungichromin)	pentaene	$C_{35}H_{58}O_{11}$ (654.8)	−148 MeOH	none	filipin = 14-deoxy
mycoticin Ia	pentaene	$C_{36}H_{58}O_{10}$ (650.8)	+63 diox	none	
mycoticin B	pentaene	$C_{37}H_{60}O_{10}$ (664.8)	+63 diox	none	
amphotericin B (Fungizone)	heptaene	$C_{47}H_{73}O_{18}N$ (940.1)	+238 DMF +333 DMFH+ −52 0.1N HCl in MeOH	mycosamine	
candidin	heptaene	$C_{46-48}H_{71-75}$-$O_{16-18}N$ (ca 930)	+205 AcOH +363 DMF	mycosamine	

Table 1 (*continued*)

Compound[a]	Chromophore	Empirical formula (mol wt)	Specific rotation[b]	Amino sugar	Structure of the aglycone or functional groups present
candicidin group	heptaenes	provisional			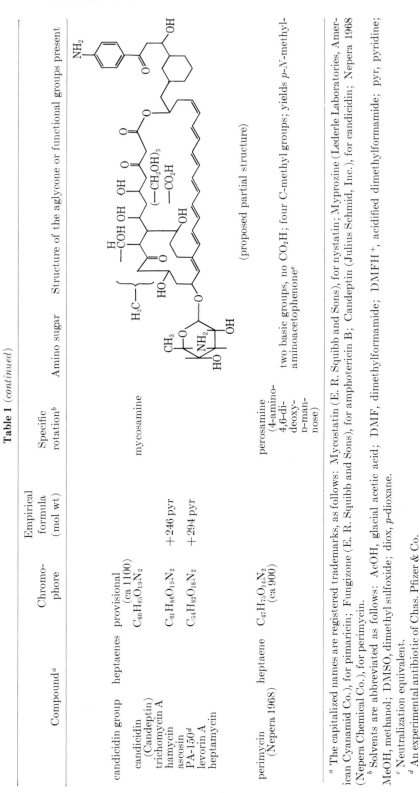
candicidin (Candeptin)		(ca 1100) $C_{60}H_{85}O_{19}N_2$		mycosamine	
trichomycin A					
hamycin		$C_{61}H_{86}O_{19}N_2$	+246 pyr		
ascosin		$C_{54}H_{82}O_{18}N_2$	+294 pyr		
PA-150[d]					
levorin A					
heptamycin					
					(proposed partial structure)
perimycin (Nepera 1968)	heptaene	$C_{47}H_{75}O_{14}N_2$ (ca 900)		perosamine (4-amino-4,6-di-deoxy-D-man-nose)	two basic groups, no CO_2H; four C-methyl groups; yields p-N-methyl-aminoacetophenone[e]

[a] The capitalized names are registered trademarks, as follows: Mycostatin (E. R. Squibb and Sons), for nystatin; Myprozine (Lederle Laboratories, American Cyanamid Co.), for pimaricin; Fungizone (E. R. Squibb and Sons), for amphotericin B; Candeptin (Julius Schmid, Inc.), for candicidin; Nepera 1968 (Nepera Chemical Co.), for perimycin.

[b] Solvents are abbreviated as follows: AcOH, glacial acetic acid; DMF, dimethylformamide; $DMFH^+$, acidified dimethylformamide; pyr, pyridine; MeOH, methanol; DMSO, dimethyl sulfoxide; diox, p-dioxane.

[c] Neutralization equivalent.

[d] An experimental antibiotic of Chas. Pfizer & Co.

[e] The aromatic amine obtained by alkaline retroaldol reaction (retrograde aldol condensation) from perimycin has been identified as p-N-methylaminoacetophenone (2a) rather than p-aminophenylacetone (2), as reported initially.

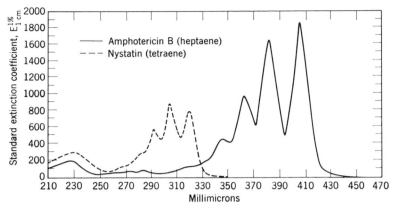

Fig. 1. Ultraviolet absorption spectra of two polyene antibiotics (1,3).

reported the discovery, in the culture of an organism which they named *Streptomyces noursei*, of an antibiotic that had marked antifungal activity (1a). The unique biological properties of this substance, initially called fungicidin but later given the name nystatin (N.Y. State-in), stimulated workers at The Squibb Institute to explore its potential for use in human fungal infections. Prior to this time there existed no clinically effective antifungal antibiotics. The properties of nystatin, as well as of the subsequently discovered polyenes, are such as to make production, isolation, and purification very difficult. The polyenes are bound to the mycelium of the culture; they are quite insoluble in water and the usual organic solvents; they are unstable compounds, being sensitive to acids and alkalis, and decomposed by light and oxygen. Nevertheless, within five years, methods of production had been developed, bioassay procedures devised, and clinical studies carried out. In 1955 it was possible to hold an international symposium to discuss this valuable new drug for fungus diseases (2). The chemical characterization of nystatin had also been undertaken but it was to be fifteen years before the structure of this complex substance was completely elucidated (see Table 1).

Subsequent to the discovery of nystatin there has been reported the isolation of some sixty-odd members of this family of compounds. The ultraviolet absorption spectrum of nystatin possesses a well-resolved triplet of absorption bands (Fig. 1), indicative of the presence in the molecule of a conjugated polyene system. The wavelength and spacing of these bands are those of a chromophore with four conjugated double bonds, a *tetraene*. The additional antibiotics of this group which have been discovered have been found to possess either tetraene, pentaene, hexaene, or heptaene chromophores. This makes a convenient basis for classifying the group. Additional features which serve to classify the various individual antibiotics are (*1*) the presence or absence of a glycosidically bound amino sugar, and (*2*) the presence or absence of an aldolically bound aromatic grouping (3–6). These properties are described in Table 1, which lists some of the representative and better-characterized polyene-macrolide antifungal antibiotics. Attempts at complete tabulation of this group have been published in review articles (7–9a). In several cases, the further purification of a preparation and the direct comparison with other members have demonstrated that compounds initially thought to be different substances actually are identical products. Thus, tennecetin and pimaricin were found to be identical; lagosin and fungichromin are the same compound; and, recently, evidence has been published demonstrating the probable identity of trichomycin, candicidin, and hamycin (10–11).

Because of the difficulties involved in purification, analytical characterization, and structure elucidation of these substances, some of the empirical compositions listed in Table 1 are only approximate. The same degree of uncertainty applies to the comparison of their biological activities and toxicity. These properties have been determined in a great variety of ways, frequently with material of undefined purity.

Several members of the heptaene group were discovered a few years after the discovery of nystatin: candicidin at Rutgers University, trichomycin in Japan, and amphotericin B at The Squibb Institute. Their medical usefulness was soon demonstrated. The principal uses of nystatin and trichomycin are as topically applied agents against superficial mycoses such as candidiasis and vaginal trichomoniasis (see the discussion of medical uses, under Biological activities); in the case of amphotericin B, its utility as a therapeutic agent for the treatment of systemic mycoses such as blastomycosis, cryptococcosis, many cases of coccidiomycosis, and histoplasmosis was quickly recognized. For a while amphotericin B became the only effective drug for these infections; more recently, hamycin (administered orally) has been acclaimed to be equally, if not more, effective (12). Only one or two of the other polyenes have shown potential medical usefulness. At present, the annual commercial production of nystatin in the U.S. is approx 100,000 lb, and that of amphotericin B, 20,000 lb.

Physical and Chemical Properties

In view of the considerable variation in molecular size and the nature and number of functional groups present, it is to be expected that the physical properties of the polyenes would vary widely. Nevertheless, most of the polyenes can be described as difficultly soluble substances—both in aqueous solvents and in organic solvents such as methanol, ethanol, acetone, ether, chloroform, and benzene. The structural feature common to all polyenes, in addition to the conjugated polyenic chromophore, is the presence of a many-membered lactone ring. The size varies from a 26-atom ring in pimaricin to a 38-atom ring in nystatin and amphotericin B. This fact alone serves to place these antibiotics in a category with other large-ring lactone antibiotics, eg erythromycin (see Macrolide antibiotics). In addition, most of them possess a carboxyl group and one or more amino groups. Although they can be brought into solution with acids or bases, they are not generally stable in solution at the pH required to dissolve them. Pyridine, glacial acetic acid, dimethylformamide, and dimethyl sulfoxide are the best solvents. When sufficiently purified, several members have been crystallized, either as salts of their functional groups or as zwitterions.

The considerable number of oxygen atoms are present as secondary alcohol groups. The nitrogen atom present in many of the polyenes is there as a primary amino group. Hydrolysis results in the liberation of an amino sugar, mycosamine, the structure of which was shown to be 3-amino-3,6-dideoxy-D-mannose (13,14). As seen in Table 1, this amino sugar is obtained from many of the polyenes. A second unique amino sugar has been obtained from the hydrolysis of perimycin and has been named perosamine. Its structure is 4-amino-4,6-dideoxy-D-mannose (15).

Several of the polyenes (heptaenes) contain in addition to the amino sugar an aromatic amine grouping which is cleaved by retroaldol reaction. The candicidin group has yielded p-aminoacetophenone under such conditions, whereas perimycin has yielded p-N-methylaminoacetophenone (2a). The presence of this aromatic amine

Table 2. In Vitro Antifungal Activity of Typical Polyenes, Shown as Inhibitory Concentration,[a] μg/ml

Microorganism	Nystatin	Pimaricin	Filipin	Amphotericin B	Candicidin group[b]	Perimycin
Candida tropicalis	0.17 (17)	3–12 (25)	1.2 (17)	0.005–0.02 (17)		0.3 (27)
Candida albicans	3.0 (18,19) 1.2 (20)	3–5 (25,26) 2.5 (24)	7.7 (28)	0.6–2.5 (18) 0.5 (27) 0.2 (20)	C: 0.02–0.04 (20,27) T: 0.03 (27) H: 0.01 (21)	0.06–0.1 (27)
Saccharomyces cerevisiae	3.0 (18,23) 0.8 (20)	3–15 (26)	5.0 (28)	0.5 (18,27) 0.2 (20)	C: 0.03 (27) T: 0.03 (27) C: 0.01 (20)	0.07 (27)
Blastomyces dermatitidis	0.8 (18)	1.0 (24) 3–15 (26)	31.0 (28)	0.1 (19)	H: 0.005 (21)	
Cryptococcus neoformans	1.6 (18)	5–10 (24,25) 15–30 (26)	1.0 (28)	0.2–0.4 (18)	H: 0.005 (21)	
Trichophyton ubrum	12–14 (18)	3–15 (26)	7.7 (28)	7.0–8.0 (18)	H: 1.0–5.0 (21)	
Trichophyton mentagrophytes	12–14 (18)	10 (24)		2.4 (18)		
Histoplasma capsulatum	1.6 (18)	1.0 (24)	7.7 (28)	1.0 or less (22) 0.04 (18)	H: 0.1–0.5 (21)	
Aspergillus niger	2.0 (20)	1–10 (24) 1.8 (25)	4.0 (28)	0.12 (20) 0.09 (27)	C: 0.3 (20) C: 0.83 (27)	0.01–0.06 (27)

[a] References for details of assay methods given in parentheses.
[b] C, candicidin; T, trichomycin; H, hamycin.

grouping also serves as a means of classifying the polyenes (16). This additional moiety contributes quantitatively to the biological activity of the polyenes, as may be seen in Table 2 (17–28a). Although the position of the linkage of this grouping has been suggested in the structure proposed for trichomycin (29), the evidence for this assignment, as well as that for the position of the glycosidic linkage of the amino sugar to the polyenes, is still not conclusive.

The elucidation of the complex chemical structure of nystatin and the other polyenes listed in Table 1 was a task which enlisted many research groups and which required the utilization of many diverse chemical and biological techniques. The initial chemical studies and degradative reactions (30) revealed both the nature of the chromophore groupings and the presence of the functional groupings such as the carboxyl and lactone ring, and established the presence and structure of the amino sugar moiety, mycosamine. Further systematic degradations (31) yielded oxidative fragments such as tiglic aldehyde, succinic acid, and the long-chain, singly branched dicarboxylic acid, 2-methylheptadecanedioic acid. Insight into the sequence of the carbon skeleton was achieved by the ingenious procedures of biogenesis studies (32). These revealed that the nystatin molecule, excluding the mycosamine, was assembled from three propionate and sixteen acetate residues. By varying the position in the substrate of the radioactively labeled carbon atom and then locating this atom in the degradation products of the assembled antibiotic, it was possible to derive the arrangement of the carbon skeleton of the aglycone. For other members of the polyene group, the nature of the carbon skeleton was established by means of exhaustive reductive procedures which yielded complex branched hydrocarbons as major products (33,34). The identification of these products was accomplished by the use of the contemporary techniques of organic chemistry: vapor phase chromatography, nuclear magnetic resonance studies, and mass spectrometry (34,35). The remaining task was the location of the numerous hydroxyl functions that are characteristic of these molecules, and here the characterization of the products of mild acid- or alkaline-retroaldolization reactions served the purpose (32,36). To complete the structure elucidation of these unique substances there still remains the formidable job of clarification of their stereochemistry and spatial conformation. A start on this problem has been made through efforts at correlating and systematizing the stereochemistry of the entire macrolide group of antibiotics (37), but the ultimate answer probably awaits a successful x-ray analysis.

Biological Activities

The polyenes are primarily inhibitors of the growth of fungal species. The spectrum of activity of all members is especially broad and includes most of the pathogens and the filamentous fungi (see Microorganisms). Antiprotozoal activity has also been found for most of the polyenes tested, and this activity extends from the trichomonads, which are especially sensitive, to the *Leishmania* and *Trypanosoma* species (see also Therapeutic agents, protozoal infections). None of the polyenes possesses significant antibacterial activity, a fact which finds explanation in the light of studies regarding the mode of action of these substances (see below).

Antifungal Activity. The differences in antifungal activity among the various members, as may be seen in Table 2, are quantitative rather than qualitative. The lower-molecular-weight polyenes (tetraenes and pentaenes) without sugar moieties, eg filipin, are broadly inhibitory but require relatively high concentrations. The tetraenes and heptaenes which contain mycosamine as a substituent, eg nystatin, pimaricin, amphotericin B, are inhibitory at concentrations about one-third to one-tenth that of the former, whereas those polyenes (heptaenes) that contain an aromatic substituent in addition to the amino sugar moiety, eg the candicidin group and perimycin, are the most active on a weight basis.

The development of fungal species resistant to the action of the polyenes is not marked. In those cases where some resistance has been produced in vitro the order of magnitude is only three- or fourfold (38). The detection of resistant species arising during the clinical use of the polyenes has not been reported.

Much interesting work has been done and is still in progress concerning the mechanism of the antifungal activity of the polyenes. The site of action has been established as the cell membrane and has been shown to involve the binding of the polyene to this sterol-containing material. The rearrangement of or damage done to this structure leads to changes in ion permeability and ultimately to metabolic failure and loss of viability of the organism (39–42). The absence of a sterol component in bacterial cell membranes appears to account for the lack of inhibitory activity of the polyenes for these microorganisms.

Because of the variable solubilities of the polyenes the determination of their animal toxicity is dependent upon the mode of administration and the physical form of the antibiotic. There also appears to be considerable variation in the toxicity among the animal species tested. The LD_{50} for orally administered pimaricin in rats is 1.5 g/kg body weight. For guinea pigs this value is 0.45 g/kg. A solubilized form of pimaricin had an LD_{50} for rats of 0.25 g/kg (43). Orally administered nystatin is tolerated in laboratory animals up to 5.0 g/kg, and oral doses of amphotericin B up to 8.0 g/kg show no toxic effects. The LD_{50} of intravenously administered amphotericin B depends upon the species of animals studied. In mice and rabbits it is about 6 mg/kg. For therapeutic use in man, therefore, a total daily intravenous dose of less than 1.5 mg/kg is used (44). Topical application of the polyenes has not resulted in any development of drug sensitivities of the allergic type. Very little, if any, absorption of these substances from the gastrointestinal tract occurs. For this reason it has been possible to use them for suppressing fungal overgrowth of the gastrointestinal tract during medication with broad spectrum antibacterial antibiotics. At present, only amphotericin B is administered systemically by intravenous infusion for the treatment of disseminated mycoses. Some impairment of renal function is observed during such treatment (45).

Nystatin has found laboratory use for the control of fungal contaminants in tissue-culture studies and amphotericin B, similarly, has low cytotoxicity in vitro and is used together with antibacterial antibiotics to isolate cells or viruses from naturally infected tissues (46).

Antiprotozoal Activity. The inhibitory effect of the polyenes on protozoa was first observed with *Endamoeba histolytica* (47), and with *Trichomona vaginalis* (48). Subsequently it was found that the growth of *Leishmania donovanii* (49) was inhibited to a high degree by nystatin, as was also *L. brasiliensis*, *L. tropicalis*, *Trypanosoma cruzii*, and *T. congolense* (50). Trichomycin inhibits *T. vaginalis* at 1 mg/ml concentration (51). *L. brasiliensis* is destroyed by concentrations of amphotericin B as low as 0.01 µg/ml (52).

Bibliography

1. J. Vandeputte, J. L. Wachtel, and E. T. Stiller, in H. Welch and F. Marti-Ibañez, eds., *Antibiotics Annual, 1955–1956*, Medical Encyclopedias, Inc., New York, 1956, p. 587.

1a. E. L. Hazen and R. Brown, *Science* **112**, 423 (1950).

2. T. H. Sternberg and V. D. Newcomer, eds., *Therapy of Fungus Diseases, An International Symposium*, Little, Brown and Co., Boston, 1955.

2a. L. Falkowski, private communication.

3. J. D. Dutcher, *Monographs on Therapy* **2**, 87 (1957) (The Squibb Institute).

4. W. Oroshnik, L. C. Vining, A. D. Mebane, and W. A. Taber, *Science* **121**, 147 (1955).

5. J. D. Dutcher, M. B. Young, J. H. Sherman, W. E. Hibbits, and D. R. Walters, *Antibiotics Annual 1956–1957*, Medical Encyclopedia, Inc., New York, 1956, p. 866.

6. H. Nakano and K. Hattori, *J. Antibiotics (Tokyo)*, Ser. A. **9**, 172 (1956).

7. L. C. Vining, *Hindustan Antibiot. Bull.* **3**, 37 (1960).

8. W. Oroshnik and A. D. Mebane, *Progress in the Chemistry of Natural Products*, Vol. 21, Springer-Verlag, Vienna, 1963, p. 17.

9. H. Umezawa, *Recent Advances in Chemistry and Biochemistry of Antibiotics*, Microbial Chemistry Research Foundation, Tokyo, Japan, 1964, p. 44.

9a. S. A. Waksman, H. A. Lechevalier, and C. P. Schaffner, *Bull. World Health Organ.* **33**, 219 (1965).

10. Y. M. Khokhlova, A. I. Korenyako, N. I. Nikitana, A. V. Puchnina, and N. O. Blinov, *Z. Allgem. Mikrobiol.* **3**, 195 (1963).

10a. P. V. Divekar, V. C. Vora, and A. W. Khan, *J. Antibiotics (Tokyo)*, Ser. A. **19**, 63 (1966).

11. E. Borowski, M. Malyshkina, S. Soloviev, and T. Ziminski, *Chemotherapia* **10**, 176 (1965–1966).

12. John P. Utz, H. Jean Shadomy, and S. Shadomy, "Hamycin: Clinical Laboratory Studies in Systemic Mycoses in Man," *Abstr. 7th Intersci. Conf. Antimicrobial Agents and Chemotherapy, Chicago, Ill., Oct. 25–27, 1967*.

13. J. D. Dutcher, D. R. Walters, and O. Wintersteiner, *J. Org. Chem.* **28**, 995 (1963).

14. M. von Saltza, J. D. Dutcher, J. Reid, and O. Wintersteiner, *J. Org. Chem.* **28**, 999 (1963).

15. Chi-Hang Lee and C. P. Schaffner, *Tetrahedron Letters* **1966**, 5837.

16. E. Borowski and C. P. Schaffner, *5th Intern. Congr. Biochem., Moscow, 1961*, Pergamon Press, Ltd., London, 1961, p. 3.

17. J. R. Gerke and M. E. Madigan, *Antibiot. Chemotherapy* **11**, 227 (1961).

18. G. Hildick-Smith, H. Blank, and I. Sarkany, *Fungus Diseases and Their Treatment*, Little, Brown and Co., Boston, 1964, pp. 372, 388, 476.

19. H. I. Winner and R. Hurley, *Candida Albicans*, Little, Brown and Co., Boston, 1964, p. 190.

20. *Antibiotics Annual 1959–1960*, Medical Encyclopedia, Inc., New York, 1960 (H. Lechevalier, p. 614).

21. M. J. Thirumalachar, *Antimicrobial Agents Chemotherapy* **1965**, 1123.

22. D. Artis and G. L. Baum, *Antibiot. Chemotherapy* **11**, 373 (1961).

23. J. F. Pagano and H. Stander, in ref. 2, p. 186.

24. V. D. Newcomer, T. H. Sternberg, E. T. Wright, R. M. Reisner, E. G. McNall, and L. J. Sorensen, *Ann. N.Y. Acad. Sci.* **89**, 240 (1960).

25. A. P. Struyk, J. Hoette, G. Drost, J. M. Waisvisz, T. van Eek, and J. C. Hoogerheide, *Antibiotics Annual 1957–1958*, Medical Encyclopedia, Inc., New York, 1958, p. 878.

26. A. L. Welsh, *Ann. N.Y. Acad. Sci.* **89**, 267 (1960).

27. E. Borowski, C. P. Schaffner, H. Lechevalier, and B. S. Schwartz, *Antimicrobial Agents Annual 1960*, Plenum Press, New York, 1961, p. 532.

28. A. Amman, D. Gottlieb, T. D. Brock, H. E. Carter, and G. B. Whitfield, *Phytopathology* **45**, 559 (1955).

29. H. Nakano, *J. Antibiotics (Tokyo)*, Ser. A. **14**, 72 (1961); Ser. B. **15**, 41 (1962).

30. J. D. Dutcher, G. Boyack, and S. Fox, *Antibiotics Annual 1953–1954*, Medical Encyclopedia, Inc., New York, 1954, p. 191.

31. A. J. Birch, C. W. Holzapfel, R. W. Rickards, C. Djerassi, M. Suzuki, J. W. Westley, J. D. Dutcher, and R. Thomas, *Tetrahedron Letters* **1964**, 1485.

32. A. J. Birch, C. W. Holzapfel, R. W. Rickards, C. Djerassi, P. C. Seidel, M. Suzuki, J. W. Westley, and J. D. Dutcher, *Tetrahedron Letters* **1964**, 1491.

33. A. C. Cope, R. K. Bly, E. P. Burrows, O. J. Ceder, E. Ciganek, B. T. Gillis, R. F. Porter, and H. E. Johnson, *J. Am. Chem. Soc.* **84**, 2170 (1962).

34. O. J. Ceder, J. M. Waisvisz, and M. G. Van Der Hoeven, *Acta Chem. Scand.* **18**, 83 (1964).

35. M. Ikeda, M. Suzuki, and C. Djerassi, *Tetrahedron Letters*, **1967** (38), 3745–3750.

36. E. Borowski, W. Mechlinski, L. Falkowski, T. Ziminski, and J. D. Dutcher, *Roczniki Chem.* **41**, 61 (1967).

37. W. D. Celmer, *Antimicrobial Agents Chemotherapy* **1965**, 144 (1966).

38. *Antibiotics Annual 1955–1956*, Medical Encyclopedia, Inc., New York, 1956, (H. A. Stout and J. F. Pagano, p. 704).

39. J. O. Lampen, P. M. Arnow, Z. Borowska, and A. I. Laskin, *J. Bacteriol.* **84**, 1152 (1962).

40. J. O. Lampen, "Biochemical Studies of Antimicrobial Drugs," *16th Symp. Soc. General Microbiology 1966*, Cambridge University Press, London, 1966.

41. S. C. Kinsky, G. R. Gronau, and M. M. Weber, *Mol. Pharmacol.* **1**, 190 (1965).

42. S. C. Kinsky, *Antimicrobial Agents Chemotherapy* **1963**, 387 (1964).

43. G. J. C. Korteweg, K. L. H. Szabo, A. M. G. Rutten, and J. C. Hoogerheide, *Antibiot. Chemotherapia* **11**, 261 (1963).

44. Reference 18, p. 395.

45. *Ibid.*, p. 406.

46. D. Perlman, N. A. Guiffre, and S. A. Brindle, *Proc. Soc. Exptl. Biol. Med.* **106**, 880 (1961).

47. H. Seneca, in ref. 38, p. 697.

48. M. Magara, E. Yokouti, T. Senda, and E. Amino, *Antibiot. Chemotherapy* **4**, 433 (1954).

49. B. K. Ghosh, D. Holdar, J. C. Ray, and A. N. Chatterjee, *Ann. Biochem. Exptl. Med.* **21**, 25 (1961).

50. P. Actor, S. Wind, and J. F. Pagano, *Proc. Soc. Exptl. Biol. Med.* **110**, 409 (1962).

51. M. Magara, H. Nittono, and T. Senda, *Antibiot. Med.* **394** (1955).

52. T. A. Furtado, E. O. Cisalpino, and U. M. Santos, *Antibiot. Chemotherapy* **10**, 692 (1960).

JAMES D. DUTCHER
The Squibb Institute for Medical Research

POLYESTER FIBERS

The Federal Trade Commission defines a polyester fiber (1) as "a manufactured fiber in which the fiber forming substance is any long chain synthetic polymer composed of at least 85% by weight of an ester of a dihydric alcohol and terephthalic acid (p-HOOCC$_6$H$_4$COOH)."

The most common polyester in use throughout the world is that derived from the linear polymer poly(ethylene terephthalate) (PET) (**1**).

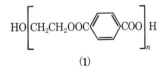

(**1**)

The first recognition of the useful fiber-forming properties of PET, made by Whinfield in 1941 in the laboratories of Calico Printers Ltd. in England, resulted in a patent dominant in the field until its expiration in the early 1960s. E. I. du Pont de Nemours & Co., Inc., acquired the U.S. patent rights in 1948 and Imperial Chemical Industries Ltd. (ICI) of Great Britain obtained patent rights for the rest of the world (1). Earlier, Carothers and Hill, as part of the classical work of Carothers in the early 1930s, had produced fiber-forming aliphatic polyesters (2), but these products had low melting points and were unsuitable for commercial use.

Polyester fibers became available commercially in the U.S. in 1953 and their production has expanded at an ever-increasing rate so that they now constitute the fastest-growing fiber on the North American continent. The fiber has a great diversity of end uses, but blends with cotton easily comprise the largest single end use and the recent development of "permanent-press" (often referred to as "durable-press") garments has boosted this application further.

Chemical Composition. Unlike the acrylic fibers which vary quite widely in their chemical composition, polyester fibers are generally derived from the linear homopolymer PET, which, on paper, is contrived from terephthalic acid (see Phthalic acids) and ethylene glycol (see Glycols). Other derivatives have been investigated extensively (3) but this material still remains dominant. The only other homopolymer to achieve any commercial significance is poly(1,4-cyclohexylenedimethylene terephthalate) (**2**) (Kodel II, Eastman Chemical Products, Inc.) in which ethylene glycol is replaced by 1,4-cyclohexanedimethanol (4). This results in a fiber with a higher melting point, and some advantages and disadvantages over PET.

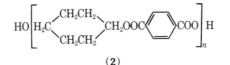

(**2**)

Molecular weights in the region of 15,000 are required for useful textile-fiber properties from these condensation polymers but can be reduced on the one hand to give staple fibers of low tendency to pilling (this is the formation of little "pills" of the fiber on the surface of the fabric) (5), and increased on the other hand to give improved fibers for industrial end uses (6). Many products contain a delusterant in varying amounts (usually TiO_2 in quantities up to 2%). Optically brightened polymers are quite common. Furthermore, there are commercial fibers containing minor amounts of copolymer or noncombined additive in order to confer specific properties such as basic dyeability (7).

Manufacture

Polymerization. The older batch process simply uses the catalyzed ester exchange reaction between molten dimethyl terephthalate (DMT) and glycol to give a mixture of monomer, very low molecular weight polymer, and methyl alcohol which distills off at approx 150°C. The monomer is then polymerized, usually in the presence of a catalyst, of which many are available (8). Additives such as TiO_2 are added at this stage; then, with carefully controlled agitation and a progressive reduction of pressure to about 1.5 mm, the excess glycol is removed at a temperature of about 280°C. Heating is continued at this temperature until the desired degree of condensation is obtained (9). Control of molecular weight is usually exercised by determinations of melt viscosity, frequently using the power input to the agitator as an indicator.

For large-scale operation there are advantages in using a continuous polymerization, direct-spinning system and most of the large new installations now use such a process. The continuous polymerization system has shown cost savings because it eliminates the steps of forming chips of polymer, followed by blending and remelting, but the equipment needs to be of large capacity in order to reduce capital investment per annual pound produced. Higher-molecular-weight products also are produced

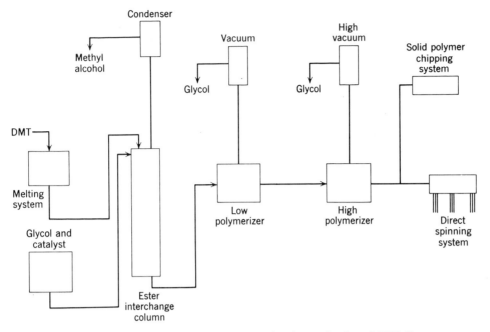

Fig. 1 Continuous polymerization system for the production of PET fibers.

more easily (10). Interruptions to the process need to be minimized, otherwise much raw material can be lost. Furthermore, the equipment cannot produce the large variety of different items possible with the batch system. A typical continuous polymerization system (Fig. 1) comprises a DMT melter, ester interchange column, glycol flash vessel, low polymerizer, high polymerizer, and a molten-polymer manifold system feeding several banks of spinning heads.

An alternative system employs terephthalic acid (TA) rather than DMT and involves a direct esterification process rather than ester exchange. With both systems, the design of the high polymerizer is quite critical and it usually comprises a high-vacuum, horizontal cylindrical vessel with a horizontal rotating shaft to which are attached discs or shallow flight screws that give large surface areas so that glycol may escape from the polymerizing mass (11,12). The agitator also moves the material slowly through the vessel from the inlet to the screw that extracts the polymer from the high-vacuum vessel. Control of the degree of polymerization is done usually by some measurement of melt viscosity and deviations from a set value are corrected automatically by a change in the degree of vacuum applied. Quite sophisticated instrumentation is required particularly in controlling the flow of material through the various stages, and due to the considerable inertia of the system, it is difficult to make substantial changes in throughputs quickly.

Spinning. Filaments are formed by forcing the molten polymer at about 290°C through a sand-bed filter to a stainless-steel spinneret containing many cylindrical holes which are traditionally 0.009 in. in diam. Control of polymer throughput is normally achieved by use of a special gear pump of low slip characteristics which generates the pressure required (1500–2000 psi) to force the polymer through the filter/spinneret assembly. Hydrolytic degradation of molten PET is very high, so it must be conveyed to the spinneret under extremely dry conditions (12). The ex-

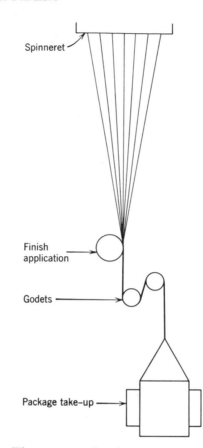

Fig. 2. Filaments extruding from the face of a spinneret.

truded filaments cool mainly by air convection, and uniform cooling is assisted by a carefully controlled forced-air quench system which must be free from turbulence (13). Solidification of the filaments occurs about 2 ft below the extrusion point and the threadline (that is, all the filaments from one spinneret) is converged lower down, passed over a spin finish applicator, (Fig. 2) and then, for staple, several threadlines, each containing 250–1000 filaments, are brought together, passed over capstans through an air ejector, and coiled in a large can or wound up as bobbins for subsequent drawing. For continuous-filament yarns the spun threadline, comprising 15–50 filaments, is either wound up on bobbins for subsequent draw-twisting or drawn directly at high speed and wound up on the final salable package.

At this stage the filaments have been attenuated to 0.001 in. in diam. They are in the amorphous stage but show a very small degree of orientation along the fiber axis as measured by optical birefringence (14). This contrasts with nylon-6,6 where the filaments are crystalline but the crystallites are not well oriented. This molecular orientation in polyester is an important parameter as, together with the stretch applied at drawing, it defines the physical properties of the final yarn. A number of studies of the spinning of PET fibers have been reported (15–17).

Processing. In order to produce the oriented crystalline structure that gives the fiber its characteristic properties of strength, modulus, recovery, abrasion resistance, etc, the amorphous spun filaments are drawn to about four times their original length. The theory of the drawing of synthetic fibers has been discussed with special reference to PET (18,19).

In staple manufacture, very large tows, comprising about a quarter of a million filaments, of undrawn yarn are made by plying together several "ends" (that is, several lines) of spun yarn and then drawing them on a heavy-duty drawing frame at speeds around 250–500 ft/min. The draw is brought about by leading the tow between two sets of rolls operating at different speeds. In order to ensure that no slip occurs, the rolls are highly polished (this effectively increases the coefficient of friction) and there may be additional nip rolls which grip the tow. It is necessary to heat the spun yarn above the second-order transition temperature of approx 80°C in order to obtain uniform drawing, and heating can be done in a variety of ways, using steam, hot water, hot rolls, infrared heat, etc. The drawn tow so made is then crimped, usually employing a crimper of the stuffer-box type; dried and heat-set; and either packaged as tow or cut into the required staple lengths, commonly 1.5–6 in., and baled for sale.

The continuous-filament yarn usually is made on a draw-twister, the draw again being achieved by stretching the yarn between two rolls, the second or draw roll operating at about three and a half times the speed of the feed roll. The draw-twister can operate on about 150 ends at the same time. Slippage is minimized by taking several turns around the highly polished rolls which normally have associated with them smaller idler rolls canted so that the "turns" do not run together. In order to obtain uniformity, the draw point is localized either by taking the yarn around a heated mat chrome pin or onto some other form of heated surface (20). The drawn yarn is wound up at speeds up to 4000 ft/min on a cylindrical tube using a conventional ring and traveller mechanism, and the package, which contains about 2–6 lb of yarn and has a small amount of base twist, is then either packed for sale or sent forward to a beaming operation. In order to obtain the higher stretch, which gives high-strength industrial yarn, a second stage of drawing at a high temperature (approx 200°C) is usually necessary (21). Normally, a slightly curved hot plate is inserted between the feed and draw rolls, the actual additional incremental draw ratio being determined naturally depending upon total draw ratio and the temperature employed. More recently, high-speed drawing processes which are integrated with spinning (spin-draw) have been developed (22,23). Here, spun yarn is passed directly over a series of rolls, heated, stretched, and wound up at high speed. Advantages of these processes are lower labor costs and elimination of several handling steps, but it is necessary to develop much more highly sophisticated machinery in order to run them effectively.

Products

A wide range of polyester fibers are manufactured for textile, industrial, and carpet end uses.

Staple. *Blends with cotton* form polyester's major end use in the U.S., and the cut staple is capable of being handled on fairly conventional textile-yarn-making equipment. The material is sold in bales of about 500 lb in wt; the fiber is in the range of 1.5–3 den/filament; the cut length is 1.5–3 in.; the crimp frequency is approx 10–15 crimps/in.; and the tenacity is about 5 g/den (the denier of a fiber is the weight in grams of 9000 m). Blend ratios with cotton are commonly 65% for light-weight and 50% for heavier-weight fabrics, the latter being particularly useful for permanent-press goods. Currently, du Pont offers a fiber that can be dyed with basic dyes in order to obtain styling effects. Fiber Industries, Inc. has recently introduced a high-modulus staple which gives advantages in mill processing and yields light-weight fabrics of high strength (24).

Blends with wool are also important, and fabric containing 65 or 50% of polyester are commonly used for men's suiting. Staple length is 3–4 in. and den/filament is usually 3 or 4.

Use of polyester staple in *sewing threads* is increasing rapidly. The fiber used is above 6 g/den in tenacity, and 1.25 den/filament. High-tenacity continuous-filament yarns are also used for this purpose with deniers between 45 and 440.

Recently, 6–16 den/filament staple has been used as a *carpet fiber* and this end use is developing rapidly. The staple of lower den/filament is used in throw rugs and tufted area rugs, the staple of higher den/filament is used in broadloom carpeting. Eastman offers Kodel II for carpet end use. The future could also see the advent of continuous-filament polyester yarns specially engineered for carpet end uses.

Filament. The total consumption of filament yarn only comprises about 18% of the present market for polyester fibers in the U.S. Applications are in such items as curtain nets, ties, dress fabrics, etc. In Europe and Japan, there has been a rapidly expanding business in textured polyester filament yarns for the knitting trade. In particular Crimplene, the textured set form of Terylene (the polyester of ICI), has achieved an ever-growing share of the market in double jersey fabrics in the United Kingdom (25) and the end uses are expanding for this type of product. In the U.S. there is a livening interest in this area and it seems safe to predict that textured polyesters will become a familiar part of the scene on this side of the Atlantic. They offer durability, ease of care, and excellent esthetics.

A wide variety of deniers is already offered ranging from 30 to 250, with individual filament deniers in the region of 1.5–5. Tenacities are in the range 4.5–5.0 g/den.

High-strength continuous-filament yarns are made for automobile tires (see Tire cord), seat belts, fire hose, V-belts, etc, where strength, high modulus, and low creep are important. The deniers are in the range 840–1680, with den/filament at about 6. Tenacities are in the range 8.0–9.5 g/den.

Properties

Polyester fibers have a number of desirable properties which by themselves are worthwhile and in combination with natural fibers such as cotton and wool enhance performance in many end uses. One obvious attribute of PET is its property of crease retention, whereby creases (eg, pleats) set in garments above 125–135°C, ie, above the second-order transition temperature in the drawn state, are virtually permanent (augmented by crosslinking the cotton in blends with durable-press resins). In addition, fabrics exhibit remarkable wrinklefree properties and possess good hand characteristics.

Structural. From a very simplified standpoint, drawn polyester fibers may be considered to be composed of crystalline and noncrystalline regions. The structural unit (unit cell) has been deduced both for PET (26) and poly(1,4-cyclohexylenedimethylene terephthalate) (Kodel II) (27), the latter existing both in cis and trans forms. These findings were made by the use of x-ray diffraction techniques. From a knowledge of the dimensions of the unit cell, the theoretical density of pure crystalline material can be calculated. Then, if the noncrystalline density can be deduced by suitable means (for example, by quenching the polymer very rapidly), it becomes possible, using interpolation, to calculate a "percentage crystallinity." This is considered to be a most important parameter in a fiber (for example, it relates to shrinkage) but the various methods of measurements are subject to pitfalls (28). Other structural information has been derived by the use of many other techniques ranging from infrared through to solution-viscosity measurements.

Mechanical. PET fibers may be produced with different physical properties. These are dependent on the method of manufacture and upon the molecular weight of the polymer. To generalize, as the degree of stretch is increased so are properties such as tensile strength and initial Young's modulus. At the same time, ultimate extensibility normally shows a downward trend. Typical physical and mechanical properties of polyester fibers are summarized in Table 1 and some representative stress strain curves for a number of polyester fibers, including one for regular-tenacity nylon-6,6 filament for comparative purposes, are given in Figure 3. Thus it can be seen that the polyester depicted in curve C (regular-tenacity) has a much higher initial modulus than the regular-tenacity nylon-6,6 shown in curve B. On the other hand, the latter exhibits a greater tenacity and elongation. High-tenacity polyester (curve A) has a very high breaking strength and modulus but relatively low elongation. Plots such as these are readily determined on a number of commercially available instruments (29).

Table 1. Physical Properties of Polyester Fibers

	PET			Kodel II
Property	Regular-tenacity filament	High-tenacity filament	Staple and tow	Staple and tow
breaking tenacity, g/den				
std[a]	2.8–5.2	6.0–9.5	2.2–6.9	2.5–3.0
wet[b]	2.8–5.2	6.0–9.5	2.2–6.0	2.5–3.0
std loop[c]	2.5–4.9		2.0–4.8	2.0–2.6
breaking elongation, %				
std[a]	19–40	10–13.5	18–65	24–34
wet[b]	19–40	10–13.5	18–65	24–34
elastic recovery, %	88–93 at 5%	90 at 5%	75–85 at 2%	85–95 at 2%
specific gravity	1.38	1.39	1.38	1.22
moisture regain,[d] 70°F, 65% rh	0.4	0.4	0.4	0.4
melting temperature, °C	258–263	258–263	258–263	290

[a] Standard measurements are conducted in air at 65% rh and 72°F.

[b] Measurements conducted in water at ambient temperature.

[c] One fiber is bent to a U and another fiber is threaded through to form an interlocking U. Each U is then attached to the appropriate jaw of the measuring device.

[d] The equilibrium moisture content of the fibers at 70°F and 65% rh.

The shrinkage of the fibers varies as does the mode of treatment. If relaxation is allowed to occur, the initial modulus is normally reduced. Yarns held to a fixed length during heat treatment are less affected with respect to changes in modulus, etc. Shrinkage values will, however, be reduced. This latter aspect has great importance in fabric stabilization treatments (30).

Like most textile fibers, PET shows nonlinear and time-dependent elastic behavior. Creep occurs under load with subsequent delay in recovery on removal of the load.

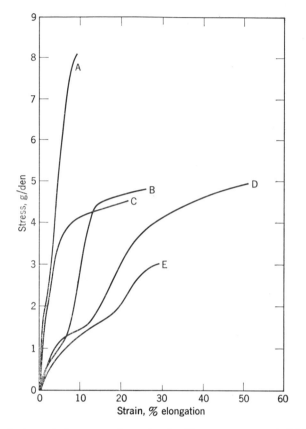

Fig. 3. Typical stress-strain curves for polyester fibers. LEGEND: A, high-tenacity filament; B, regular-tenacity nylon-6,6 filament; C, regular-tenacity filament; D, regular staple (A, C, and D are PET); and E, staple from Kodel II.

Chemical. Polyesters have good resistance to most mineral acids but are dissolved with partial decomposition by concentrated sulfuric acid. Hydrolysis is a most important reaction, but is highly dependent on temperature. Thus, on standing conventional fibers in water at 70°C for several weeks, there is no measurable loss in strength, but after one week at 100°C the strength is reduced by about 20% (31).

Basic substances attack the fiber in two ways. Strong alkalies, such as caustic soda, only assail the surface of the fiber. Any reduction in strength, therefore, comes about by the dissolution of the surface. In contrast, ammonia and other organic bases, such as methylamine, penetrate the structure initially by means of the non-crystalline regions (32), causing degradation and a general loss in physical properties.

The polyesters display excellent resistance to conventional textile bleaching agents and in addition are most resistant to cleaning solvents and surfactants. It should be pointed out, however, that most of these effects are conditioned by the degree of crystallinity and molecular orientation present in the specimens.

Other. PET fibers display good resistance toward sunlight and are surpassed only by the acrylics. Modern light stabilizers are also available, which can be used to enhance the performance in this respect, if required. The resistance to mildew, aging, and abrasion is generally considered excellent.

Dyeing and Finishing

Dyeing. Polyester fibers are almost exclusively dyed with disperse dyes (see also Dyes—application and evaluation) because of the lack of chemical dye sites in the fiber. These dyes act primarily through controlled diffusion with only relatively weak hydrogen bonding of the dye molecule to the fiber (33–37). The rate of dyeing polyester fibers is slower than that of dyeing cellulose triacetate and considerably below that of dyeing cellulose acetate. Trade names for disperse dyes commonly used are given in Table 2. Other classes of dyes which have been used to a significant degree are the following:

azoic dyes	limited shades by special high-temperature process
vat dyes	a few selected dyes, mainly for Thermosol dyeing (see Vol. 2, pp. 517, 894; Vol. 7, p. 554)
leuco ester dyes	few pale shades (see Vol. 2, p. 529; Vol. 7, p. 561)
resin-bonded pigments	pale to medium shades and printing
cationic dyes	only for modified polyester fiber variants

Table 2. Disperse Dyes for Polyester

Trade name	Supplier	Trade name	Supplier
Amacron	American Aniline Products, Inc.	Foron	Sandoz Inc.
		Genecron	Geigy Chemical Corp.
Artisil	Sandoz Inc.	Harshaw Ester	Harshaw Chemical Co.
Calcosperse	American Cyanamid Co.	Latyl	E. I. du Pont de Nemours & Co., Inc.
Cekryl	Althouse Chemical Co.		
Celliton	General Aniline & Film Corp.	Palanil	Badische Anilin- & Soda- Fabrik Colors & Chemicals
Dispersol	ICI Organics, Inc.		
Duranol	ICI Organics, Inc.	Polydye	Interchemical Corp.
Eastman Polyester	Eastman Chemical Products, Inc.	Resolin	Verona Dyestuffs
		Samaron	American Hoechst Corp.
Esterophile	Cie. Française des Matières Colorantes S.A.	Setacyl	Geigy Chemical Corp.
		Terasil	Ciba Chemical & Dye Co.

The rate of dyeing polyester is dependent on the temperature, time, and thermal history of the fiber. A temperature-time plot for a typical disperse dyeing is given in Figure 4. It will be seen that exhaustion of the dye shown in Figure 4 does not take place below 120°C within practical limits of time. For this reason, pressure-dyeing equipment or addition of dyeing accelerants is often needed for optimum dye utilization and economical dyeing times. Heat-setting polyester before dyeing markedly affects dyeability, as can be seen in Figure 5. The dye uptake is decreased with increasing setting temperature, going through a broad minimum between 160 and 200°C. Above 200°C, dye uptake increases, exceeding the dye capacity of the nonheat-set fiber and reflecting changes in crystalline structure of the polyester fiber.

Because of the hydrophobic nature of polyester and its lack of dye sites, dyeing from an aqueous bath for practical considerations requires temperatures above 100°C or the use of a dyeing accelerant (commonly called a carrier). Carriers are generally aromatic organic compounds which have some ability to swell the polyester fiber so that the monomolecular disperse dye can penetrate more rapidly into the fiber. Carriers most frequently used are biphenyl, *o*-phenylphenol, phenyl salicylate, chlori-

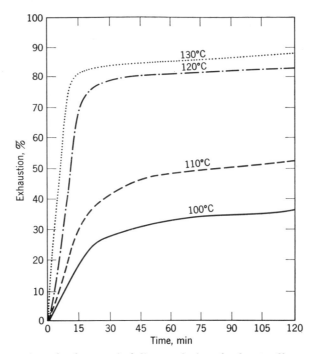

Fig. 4. A temperature-time plot for a typical disperse dyeing of polyester fibers.   (The dye used was
Palanil Navy Blue RE.)

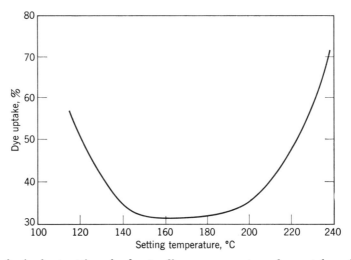

Fig. 5. Effect of prior heat setting of polyester fibers on percentage dye uptake.   (Terylene fiber
treated with 2.0% Dispersol Fast Scarlet B 150 Powder Fine at 100°C for 90 min.)

nated aromatics, and aromatic ethers.   Ideally, a carrier should have low volatility in
steam, be easily removed after dyeing, and cause no impairment of the lightfastness of
the dye.   A carrier will increase dye uptake up to an optimum concentration;   then
stripping of the dye from the fiber begins to occur because of the solvent action on the
dye.   For this reason, carriers are often used at higher concentrations to achieve
partial stripping of the dyed fabric (38–41).

Heat fixation of disperse dyes can be carried out by a continuous dyeing system called Thermosol dyeing. This process involves padding the fabric with a dispersion of suitable dyes, drying, and then subjecting the fabric to temperatures of 400–450°F for 30–60 sec. This process has advantages in that large yardages can be dyed economically, no carrier is required, dye utilization is excellent, and dyeing is not affected by preheat-setting. Fabrics most commonly dyed by this procedure are 50/50 and 65/35 blends of polyester/cellulosic fibers. Disperse dyes must be carefully selected for Thermosol dyeing in order that their diffusion into the fiber is rapid. This depends on molecular size and shape, volatility, and solubility of the dye in the polyester fiber. The application of heat opens up the polymer structure which allows the dye molecule to diffuse into the fiber (42–45).

The dyeing of polyester is very often complicated by its combination with other fibers in fabric blends. Blends of polyester/cotton, a primary fabric in both men's and women's clothing, can be dyed with disperse/vat, disperse/direct, and disperse/reactive dye systems. The important consideration in these systems is minimizing the staining of disperse dye on the cotton since cellulosic dyes do not stain polyester. In heavy shades, it is often necessary to include an intermediate clearing step after dyeing with disperse dye and before dyeing the cotton. In another system commonly used on polyester/cotton, resin-bonded pigments, which can be used for pastel shades, are held to the surface of the fiber by a polymeric binder and do not penetrate the fiber.

In the dyeing of polyester/wool blend yarns, it is again important to reduce staining on wool by disperse dye selection. A one-bath method using carriers at 100°C is favored because of damage to the wool at higher temperatures and longer dyeing times. Since rapid exhaustion of disperse dye from the bath will reduce staining on wool, a type of polyester fiber that dyes faster is frequently used.

Nylon or triacetate are sometimes combined with polyester and can be dyed with disperse dyes along with the polyester.

The modification of polyester fiber for changes in dyeability or performance properties is becoming more important. Dacron 64, because it contains sulfonic acid groups, can be dyed with both disperse and cationic dyes (7). When it is used in blends with regular polyester and cotton, unique multicolor effects can be obtained. Type 405 polyester fiber of Fiber Industries, Inc. is modified to dye more rapidly with disperse dyes, and when it is blended with regular polyester in carpets, tone-on-tone color effects are achieved.

Finishing. In the finishing of polyester, the most important development is called permanent press (46,47). This is not truly a finish for polyester but a system where cotton in 50/50 or 65/35 polyester/cotton blends is given a crosslinking treatment. A well-known system involves the following steps:

1. Dyed polyester/cotton fabric is impregnated with a urea–formaldehyde derivative resin.
2. Fabric is dried.
3. Garments are cut and sewn.
4. Creases are pressed into the garments.
5. Garments are placed in an oven and the resins are cured.

Permanent press has created new problems because dyes tend to migrate into the resin finish during curing and cause reduced fastness. Dyes of high sublimation fastness need to be selected to withstand the temperatures which are used to cure the garments (48,49). In addition, the resin-treated fabrics are more hydrophobic than nonresinated polyester/cotton fabrics. For this reason, they exhibit greater soiling tendency and additional finishes (many are in the process of development) are needed to change the surface characteristics of permanent-press fabrics. A finish of particular interest for 100% polyester fabrics, known as Cirrasol PT (ICI Organics, Inc.) has recently made its advent. It imparts durable antistatic protection and outstanding resistance to pickup of soil during laundering.

Analysis and Testing Methods

Both chemical and physical methods which are applicable to most fibers can be used for PET. Physical (and mechanical) methods have been aptly described (50). PET fibers can be identified by microscopic tests, such as the measurements of birefringence, combined with measurements of specific gravity and softening point. Many of the producers identify their own products by the use of tracer elements or from the catalyst residues remaining in the polymer. These are usually rapidly and accurately determined using x-ray fluorescence methods. Recourse to spectroscopic data can be invaluable. Detailed structures of the infrared spectra of PET have been reported (51,52) together with that for Kodel II (53). Nuclear-magnetic-resonance data can be useful (54) and provide one means, amongst others, of determining second-order transition temperatures both on polymer and oriented fibers. Differential

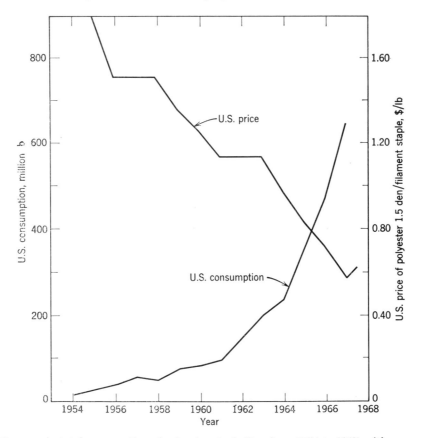

Fig. 6. Increase in total consumption of polyester staple fiber from 1954 to 1967, with corresponding change in price of 1.5 den/filament staple over the same period of time.

thermal analysis is yet another method of detecting heat-energy transitions such as the melting point, etc. This is now extensively used for the examination of polymers and fibers (55).

With respect to wet methods, solution viscosity is widely used to measure molecular weight, a most important parameter. Powerful solvents such as phenol, o-chlorophenol, tetrachloroethane, and dichloroacetic acid are needed to dissolve polyester fibers. A number of correlations have been made between number average molecular weight (M_n) and the intrinsic viscosity $[\eta]$ (see Vol. 4, p. 623). These are set down in mathematical form. The normal equation has the form

$$[\eta] = KM_n{}^a$$

where K and a are constants. For quality control purposes, relative viscosities are commonly used. This is the ratio of the solution viscosity to solvent viscosity at a fixed concentration.

Economic Aspects

Since the beginnings of polyester fibers (in the 1940s), when terephthalic acid was a rare and expensive chemical, world production of these fibers has risen (1966) to

Table 3. Major U.S. Polyester Fiber Producers

Trademark	Grades available	
	Staple and tow[a]	Filament[b]
Blue "C" (Monsanto Co.)	semidull, bright; variety of deniers and cut lengths	
Dacron (E. I. du Pont de Nemours & Co., Inc.)	semidull, bright; large variety of deniers and cut lengths	dull, semidull, bright; large variety of deniers (up to 1300) and filament counts
Encron (American Enka Corp.)		semidull, bright; variety of deniers and filament counts
Fortrel (Fiber Industries, Inc.)	semidull, clear; large variety of deniers and cut lengths	dull, semidull, bright; large variety of deniers (up to 1300) and filament counts
Kodel (Eastman Chemical Products, Inc.)	type II: semidull, bright type IV: semidull, bright; large variety of deniers and cut lengths	
Quintess (Phillips Fibers Corp., subsidiary of Phillips Petroleum Co.)	semidull, bright; variety of deniers and cut lengths	
Trevira (Hystron Fibers, Inc.)	semidull, bright; variety of deniers and cut lengths	
Vycron (Beaunit Fibers Division of Beaunit Corp.)	semidull, bright; variety of deniers and cut lengths	semidull, bright; variety of deniers (up to 1300) and filament counts

[a] Used in blends with rayon and cotton for all types of apparel fabrics. Also used in blends with wool for all types of apparel fabrics, especially men's wear fabrics.

[b] Used in fabrics for apparel (blouses, dresses, and tricot); thread for high-pressure hose, tapes, ropes, tire cord, and sail cloth; and filled products.

1300 million lb (56), the U.S. share being around 600 million lb and expected to rise sharply. Pushing polyester staple and filament growth to these estimated highs are a number of factors which include recent hefty declines in prices of staple, expanding end uses, and new producers. These factors are illustrated in Figure 6 for 1.5 den/filament staple. Staple fiber currently holds 80% of the polyester market in the U.S. but is a

Table 4. Selected List of World Producers of Polyester Fibers

Location	Producer	Trademark
Austria		
Lenzing	Austria Faser GmbH	Trevira
Canada		
Millhaven, Ontario	Millhaven Fibers Ltd.	Terylene
France		
Besançon (Doubs)	Société Rhodiaceta	Tergal and Tralbé
German Democratic Republic (East)		
Premnitz	VEB Chemiefaserwerk	Grisuten
German Federal Republic (West)		
Uentrop/Kreis Unna	E. I. du Pont de Nemours GmbH	Dacron
Bad Hersfeld/Hessen and		
Bobingen/Augsburg-Land	Farbwerke Hoechst AG	Trevira
Marl	Faserwerke Hüls GmbH	Vestan
Oberbruch and Obernburg	Glanzstoff AG	Diolen
Ostringen	ICI (Europa) Fibres GmbH	Terylene
Italy		
Cesano Maderno and Varedo	Snia Viscosa	Wistel
Casoria and Pallanza	Societá Rhodiatoce	Terital
Japan		
Tamashima	Kurashiki Rayon KK	Kuraray
Okazaki	Nippon Ester Co. Ltd.	Nitiray
Matsuyama (Shikoku)	Teijin Ltd.	Teijin-Tetoron
Iwakuni	Toyobo Co. Ltd.	Toyobo
Ehime and Mishima	Toyo Rayon KK	Toray-Tetoron
Switzerland		
Widnau	Société de la Viscose Suisse	Tersuisse
U.S.S.R.		
number of plants	Government	Lavsan and Okson
United Kingdom		
Wilton and Kilroot	ICI Fibres Ltd.	Terylene

Table 5. Estimated Domestic Consumption of Various Types of Polyester Fibers, million lb

Type of fiber	1964	1965	1966	1967
industrial filament yarn[a]	11.7	19.2	30.5	80.5
textile filament yarn[b]	39.0	47.3	46.4	55.0
staple and tow[c]	146.5	280.0	471.0	650.0
fiberfill[d]	30.0	35.0	40	45.0

[a] Industrial filament yarn covers such end uses as tire cord, V-belts, fire hose, thread, and others.

[b] Textile filament yarn goes into dresses, lingerie, uniforms, sport shirts, rainwear, home furnishings, and other items.

[c] Staple and tow also goes into many of the apparel outlets listed above plus such things as carpets, sheets, pillowcases, and scatter rugs.

[d] Fiberfill is a filling material and is used in pillows, sleeping bags, mattresses, cushions, and like products.

smaller proportion of the total consumption in the rest of the world. The deterioration of prices of textile filament yarn over the last decade has been much less dramatic. For example, the average price of 70-den yarn was \$2.01 in 1957 and \$1.67 in 1967, whereas over the same period of time, 1.5-den staple dropped from \$1.51 to \$0.58/lb. (It has recently (1967) risen to \$0.61/lb.)

Producers in the U.S. are listed in Table 3. A selected list of world producers and their trademarks is given in Table 4. Table 5 shows U.S. consumption of polyester fibers in the years 1964–1967 (57).

Uses

Polyester fibers have found their outlets in a large number of end uses which are continuing to grow and expand at a very rapid rate. The biggest penetration has been in the apparel field with staple fiber, where the fabrics used are primarily 50/50 polyester/cotton blends of the durable-press variety. Women's dress goods, blouses, and sportswear account for the largest usage in broadcloths, batistes, and poplins. In men's wear, slacks, shirts, and suits have been the major uses for polyester fiber; polyester/cotton broadcloth for shirting, polyester/worsted for suits, and polyester/cotton and polyester/rayon twills and poplins for slacks. Children's clothing has been an ideal area for durable-press, polyester/cotton blends. Fabrics made in this manner are hard wearing, easily washed, and require no ironing if the manufacturers' simple instructions are adhered to.

New growth areas are seen already in broadloom carpeting, and the home furnishings market is one of great potential. Durable-press sheets, pillowcases, bedspreads, drapery fabrics, and tablecloths are receiving rapid acceptance.

In the industrial end-use market high-tenacity filament yarn is gaining rapidly as a material for tire cord (qv). In strength it is as high as nylon yarn but without the attendant flatspotting problem. This makes the fiber ideal for reinforcing tires on automobiles where rayon has been king due to the above problem with nylon yarns. Goodyear Tire & Rubber Co., Inc. is the leading proponent of polyester tire cord. Other areas of use are V-belts, sewing threads, coated fabrics, fire hose, sail cloths, and ropes.

The development of textured circular-knit fabrics to date, particularly in Europe, has given a new look to women's outerwear and has resulted in the first major end use of polyester textile filament (25). Fiberfill applications are continuing to show a steady increase in items such as mattresses, sleeping bags, pillows, and so on.

Bibliography

"Textile Fibers (Polyester)" in *ECT* 1st ed., Vol. 13, pp. 840–847, by S. A. Rossmassler, E. I. du Pont de Nemours & Co., Inc., Textile Fibers Department.

1. "Polyester Fibers," in N. M. Bikales, ed., *Encyclopedia of Polymer Science and Techology*, Vol. 10, Interscience Publishers, a division of John Wiley & Sons, Inc., New York (in press).
2. W. H. Carothers and J. W. Hill, *J. Am. Chem. Soc.* **54**, 1577, 1579 (1932).
3. I. Goodman and J. A. Rhys, *Polyesters*, Vol. I, Iliffe Books Ltd., London, 1965.
4. U.S. Pat. 2,917,549 (Dec. 15, 1959), R. Hasek and M. B. Knowles (to Eastman Kodak Co.).
5. U.S. Pat. 3,104,450 (Sept. 24, 1963), J. M. Christens and D. Gintis (to E. I. du Pont de Nemours & Co., Inc.).
6. U.S. Pat. 3,051,212 (Aug. 28, 1962), W. W. Daniels (to E. I. du Pont de Nemours & Co., Inc.).
7. U.S. Pat. 3,018,272 (Jan. 23, 1962), J. M. Griffing and W. R. Remington (to E. I. du Pont de Nemours & Co., Inc.).

8. U.S. Pat. 2,647,885 (Aug. 4, 1953), H. R. Billica (to E. I. du Pont de Nemours & Co., Inc.).
9. R. Hill, *Fibres from Synthetic Polymers*, Elsevier Publishing Co., Amsterdam, 1953, p. 149.
10. U.S. Pat. 2,933,476 (April 14, 1960), W. F. Fisher (to E. I. du Pont de Nemours & Co., Inc.).
11. U.S. Pat. 2,758,915 (Aug. 14, 1956), J. L. Vodonik (to E. I. du Pont de Nemours & Co., Inc.).
12. U.S. Pat. 3,118,739 (Jan. 21, 1964), W. G. Atkinson and J. L. Thomas (to E. I. du Pont de Nemours & Co., Inc.).
13. U.S. Pat. 3,135,811 (June 2, 1964), T. R. Barrett and H. E. Warner (to Imperial Chemical Industries Ltd.).
14. Reference 9, p. 269.
15. A. B. Thompson, in J. W. S. Hearle and R. Peters, eds., *Fibre Structure*, Butterworth & Co. Ltd., London, 1963.
16. A. Ziabicki, *Kolloid-Z.* **171,** 51 (1960); **175,** 14 (1961).
17. B. C. Sakiadis, *AIChEJ.* **7,** 26, 221, 467 (1961).
18. I. Marshall and A. B. Thompson, *Proc. Roy. Soc. (London), Ser. A* **221,** 541 (1954).
19. A. B. Thompson, *J. Polymer Sci.* **34,** 741 (1959).
20. Reference 9, p. 375.
21. U.S. Pat. 2,942,325 (Sept. 15, 1961), F. E. Spellman (to E. I. du Pont de Nemours & Co., Inc.).
22. U.S. Pat. 3,216,187 (Dec. 27, 1963), W. A. Chantry and A. E. Molini (to E. I. du Pont de Nemours & Co., Inc.).
23. Brit. Pat. 874,652 (Aug. 10, 1961), J. G. Gillet, R. Lipscomb, and R. B. Macleod (to Imperial Chemical Industries Ltd.).
24. K. C. McAlister, *Mod. Textiles Mag.* **48,** 77 (1967).
25. E. Sharpe, *Textile Ind.* **130,** 93 (1966).
26. R. Daubeny, C. W. Bunn, and C. J. Brown, *Proc. Roy. Soc. (London), Ser. A* **226,** 531 (1954).
27. C. A. Boye, *J. Polymer Sci.* **55,** 275 (1961).
28. G. Farrow and I. M. Ward, *Polymer* **1,** 330 (1960).
29. H. Hindman and G. S. Burr, *J. Eng. Ind.* **71,** 789 (1949).
30. D. N. Marvin, *J. Soc. Dyers Colourists* **70,** 16 (1954).
31. *Chemical Properties of "Terylene": The Effect of Water and Steam*, Tech. Bull. ICI Fibres Ltd., Harrogate, England.
32. G. Farrow, D. A. S. Ravens, and I. M. Ward, *Polymer* **3,** 17 (1962).
33. H. U. Schmidlin, *Preparation and Dyeing of Synthetic Fibers*, Reinhold Publishing Corp., New York, 1963.
34. *The Dyeing of Terylene Polyester Fiber*, Imperial Chemical Industries Manual, 1955.
35. L. Hughes, *Textile Mfr.* **89,** 117 (1963).
36. R. E. Pomfret, *Can. Textile J.* **80,** 52 (Sept. 1963).
37. *Dyeing and Finishing of Polyester Fibers and Blends with Other Fibers*, Badische Anilin- & Soda-Fabrik Manual, 1964.
38. E. Balmforth et al., *J. Soc. Dyers Colourists* **82,** 405 (1966).
39. C. R. Jin and D. M. Cates, *Am. Dyestuff Reptr.* **53,** 64 (1964).
40. J. H. Lemons, S. K. Kakar, and D. M. Cates, *Am. Dyestuff Reptr.* **55,** 76 (1966).
41. Anon., *Knitted Outerwear Times* **33** (35), 21 (1964).
42. W. J. Wygand, *Am. Dyestuff Reptr.* **53,** 1066 (1964).
43. S. H. W. Buchholz, *Am. Dyestuff Reptr.* **54,** 545 (1965).
44. V. Tullio, *Am. Dyestuff Reptr.* **55,** 412 (1966).
45. W. Beckmann, *Can. Textile J.* **83,** 43 (March 1966).
46. U.S. Pat. 2,974,432 (March 14, 1961), W. K. Warnock and F. G. Hubener (to Koret of California).
47. Anon., *Textile Ind.* **129,** 121 (Jan. 1965); **130,** 133 (Sept. 1966); **130,** 167 (April 1966); **131,** 147 (March 1967).
48. J. J. Porter et al., *Am. Dyestuff Reptr.* **55,** 115 (1966).
49. J. Price et al., *Am. Dyestuff Reptr.* **54,** 13 (1965).
50. J. W. S. Hearle and R. Meredith, eds., *Physical Methods of Investigating Textiles*, Interscience Publishers, Inc., New York, 1959.
51. D. Grime and I. M. Ward, *Trans. Faraday Soc.* **54,** 959 (1958).
52. A. Miyake, *J. Polymer Sci.* **38,** 479, 497 (1959).
53. C. A. Boye, *J. Polymer Sci.* **55,** 263 (1961).

54. C. A. Boye and V. W. Goodlett, *J. Appl. Phys.* **34**, 59 (1963).
55. B. Ke, ed., *Newer Methods of Polymer Characterization*, Interscience Publishers, a division of John Wiley & Sons, Inc., New York, 1964, Chap. IX.
56. *Textile Organon* **38** (6), 93 (1967).
57. *America's Textile Reporter* **81**, 75 (1967).

ACKNOWLEDGMENT: The authors would like to express their appreciation to Dr. P. Weinle of the Application and Product Development Laboratories of the Celanese Fibers Marketing Company for the section on Dyeing and Finishing.

G. FARROW AND E. S. HILL
Fiber Industries, Inc.

POLYESTERS

Polyesters (1) may be classed as heterochain macromolecular compounds that possess a plurality of carboxylate ester (—CO.O—) groups as components of their skeletal structures. By this definition they are distinguished from other ester-containing polymers such as the cellulose esters, polyacrylates, and poly(vinyl esters) in which the carboxylate groups form part of substituent entities pendant from the backbone structure. Materials of polyester character have long been known, through sporadic researches extending back well over 100 years, but their proper nature was only recognized with the evolution of the macromolecular concept of polymer structure, towards which polyester studies made an important contribution. Their first significant technical application occurred with the introduction of the glyceryl phthalate coating and impregnating materials ("Glyptal") during World War I, though at that time the preparation and handling of such substances was still empirical in nature. The growth of general scientific and technical interest in polyesters stems from the researches of Kienle and of Carothers in the late 1920s. Kienle's investigations of the course of the glycerol–phthalic anhydride reaction and of the effects of its modification by unsaturated fatty acids forms the basis of alkyd resin technology, whilst Carothers' studies on the preparation and properties of the linear polyesters and the discovery of their fiber-forming character represented a major advance in the understanding of the structural dependence of polymer properties and created the pattern of ideas that led to the discovery of the fibrous polyamide nylon-6,6 (in 1935) and thence to the establishment of the modern synthetic textiles industry.

Carothers' researches in the polyester field were mainly concerned with the aliphatic members which, although fiber-forming, were too low-melting and solvent-sensitive to find direct use as textile materials, but the underlying structural concepts were later extended to crystalline ring-containing polyesters by Whinfield and Dickson who (in 1941) discovered the fiber- and film-forming material poly(ethylene terephthalate) (PET) which, by production volume and sales value, is now the most important member of the polyester group. The aliphatic polyesters subsequently found use in a variety of applications, eg as intermediates for polyurethan elastomers, foams, and spandex fibers, and as plasticizers. In the late 1930s, important observations on the crosslinking properties of the polyesters of maleic acid, and its acceleration by the incorporation of vinyl monomers, were made by Bradley, Kropa, and Johnston, and by Ellis. This work led to the development from 1941 onwards of the polyester laminating and casting resins. Polyesters of varied structure have also been proposed for use as coating enamels, peroxide-curable elastomers, and adhesives, but the most significant of the later developments occurred in the mid-1950s with the discovery by Schnell and by Fox and Goldberg of the high-softening polycarbonates of alkylidene-bisphenols and their analogs as impact-resistant thermoplastic molding resins.

Related polymers that have been studied intensively during the past twenty years include the poly(ester amides), the poly(ether esters), and the poly(ester urethans); many of these are fiber-forming. In the past few years attention has also been paid to the high-melting all-aromatic polyesters (polyarylates) and their structural analogs, the polysulfonates; members of both groups have been suggested to have potential as rigid heat-resistant polymers but they have not yet entered commercial production. By variations in molecular composition, polyesters have thus proved to be a versatile family of materials of widespread utility. The relative status of the more important varieties in the U.S. market during 1964–1966 is indicated by the figures given in Table 1.

Table 1. U.S. Production and Typical Prices of Polyester Products

Class of product	Production, 10^6 lb			Unit price, 1966, ¢/lb
	1964	1965	1966	
alkyd resins	570	592	642	26
unsaturated polyesters	275.1	326	461	22
polycarbonate	11	15.2	20.8	90
polyester fibers	245	450	500	72–90
polyester films	45	50	55	54–73
polyester plasticizers	43.3	40.3[a]	47.9	39–40
polyurethan intermediates[b]	90	100	100	34

[a] The apparent reduction from the previous year is due to classification changes in the U.S. Tariff Commission statistics.

[b] The available statistics for these products are generally consolidated with those for polyether–polyols, now increasingly used for polyurethan formation; the figures given in the table should therefore be regarded only as indicative estimates.

This article deals in the main with those members that are film- and fiber-forming, or which find use as plasticizers or as intermediates for elaboration to polyurethans. See also Polyester fibers; Film materials; Laminated and reinforced plastics; Unsaturated polyesters.

The linear homopolymeric polyesters are of two main types—those derived, whether actually or notionally, from hydroxycarboxylic acids by self-esterification and conforming to structure (**1**), and those analogously derived from the interaction of diols with dicarboxylic acids, resulting in the general structure (**2**):

$$n \text{ HORCOOH} \rightleftharpoons n \text{ H}_2\text{O} + [\text{—ORCO—}]_n \tag{1}$$

$$(\mathbf{1})$$

$$n \text{ HOR'OH} + n \text{ HOOCR''COOH} \rightleftharpoons 2n \text{ H}_2\text{O} + [\text{—OR'OCOR''CO—}]_n \tag{2}$$

$$(\mathbf{2})$$

For the reasons implied by the above equations, polyesters are commonly regarded as condensation polymers, but many can only be obtained (or are obtained equally satisfactorily) by chain-growth addition reactions, so that the conventional classification is mainly of historical significance. It is sometimes convenient to distinguish polyesters of types (**1**) and (**2**) as A—B and A—A/B—B polymers, but the distinction is more apparent in synthesis than in their properties. By structural variations in the groups denoted as R, R', and R'', literally hundreds of homopolyesters have been prepared, and since mixtures of reactants can generally readily be used to produce copolymers with almost any desired ratio of co-units, the number of known copolyesters amounts to thousands.

The nomenclature of polyesters is usually adapted from that used for simple esters. Thus, analogously with *methyl acetate*, the polyester (**3**) is termed *poly(ethylene adipate)*. Recent recommendations of the Committee on Nomenclature of the American Chemical Society Division of Polymer Chemistry (2) provide an alternative structure-based nomenclature which is particularly convenient for polyesters since

$$[\text{—O(CH}_2)_2\text{OCO(CH}_2)_4\text{CO—}]_n \quad [\text{—O(CH}_2)_4\text{CO—}]_n \quad [\text{—OCHRCO—}]_n$$
$$(\textbf{3}) \qquad\qquad\qquad (\textbf{4}) \qquad\qquad (\textbf{5})$$

these always contain at least one chain-oxygen atom per repeating-unit which is assigned seniority in writing the unit structure from left to right. On this basis, polymer (**3**) is also named *poly(oxyethyleneoxyadipoyl)*, and the system is specially useful for polymers of type (**1**) for which euphonic "ester-type" names are not always available. In the past, such substances have been named trivially by reference to their precursors, eg *poly(δ-valerolactone)* for (**4**), and *polyglycolide* or *polylactide* for (**5**) (R = H and Me, respectively); the self-explanatory expressions *poly(oxypentanoyl)*, *poly(oxyacetyl)*, and *poly(oxy(methylacetyl))* will now describe these structures, and use will be made of both logical systems throughout this article. In accordance with common practice, formulas such as (**1**) and (**2**) do not specify the chain end-groups which are often important in polyesters, and these will be discussed where appropriate.

Synthesis

Many reactions can be used for the synthesis of polyesters (3–5) but the most valuable, because of their range and utility, comprise (a) the polyesterification of dicarboxylic acids or certain of their functional derivatives with diols or their functional derivatives, yielding A—A/B—B type polyesters, and the analogous self-polyesterification reactions of hydroxycarboxylic acids and their derivatives to A—B type polyesters, and (b) the ring-opening polymerization reactions of lactones and cyclic esters. The ring-opening reactions are most useful for the preparation of aliphatic A—B type polyesters of the lower hydroxy-acids which are not readily obtained by polyesterification methods, but they are by no means restricted to this group. All of these reactions can be applied to a very wide range of starting materials but each has certain structural limitations that will be discussed below. Finally, whilst the following account deals primarily with the synthesis of homopolymers, many of the methods described are equally well able to produce copolyesters from mixtures of the appropriate reactants and, despite some exceptions (for which reason analytical confirmation should always be sought), it can be assumed as a first approximation that the molar ratios of the units in copolyesters made by the normal reactions are about the same as in the reactant mixtures.

SYNTHESIS BY POLYESTERIFICATION AND ALLIED REACTIONS

Under this general heading we discuss a range of polyesterification procedures in which dicarboxylic acids are employed directly or as the esters, carbonyl chlorides, salts, anhydrides, etc for reaction with aliphatic, alicyclic, or aralkylene diols (glycols) and dihydric phenols, or with certain of their derivatives such as the diacyl esters, dihalides, or cyclic ethers. Correspondingly, hydroxycarboxylic acids and their analogous derivatives may be employed. With few exceptions—mainly represented by the formation of polyarylates from the anions of dihydric phenols and dicarbonyl chlorides—these reactions require the use of relatively high temperatures and long reaction times. They are therefore not suitable for use with thermally unstable materials. Moreover, the use of such conditions frequently results in the establishment of an equilibrium between the polyester product and its cyclic oligoesters. The occurrence of such events is independent of the type of polyesterification reaction involved, and although these and some related matters are discussed, for convenience, with the following account of direct esterification methods, the reader should note their general validity.

Direct Esterification Methods. The simplest method of polyester synthesis consists in heating a hydroxycarboxylic acid, or a mixture of a glycol with a dicarboxylic acid, to temperatures (commonly in the range of 150–250°C but sometimes as high as 280°C) at which condensation occurs with the production of molecules of water and a polyester. According to the general theory of step-growth reactions of which polyesterification processes are typical (6,7), the degree of polymerization ($\overline{\text{DP}}$) of a linear polymer formed by the interaction of A—B, or of equimolecular amounts of A—A with B—B reactants is given by $1/(1-p)$, where p is the extent of reaction; and the number average (M_n) and weight average (M_w) molecular weights of the products are given by

$$M_n = M_o/(1-p)$$

and

$$M_w = M_o(1+p)/(1-p)$$

where M_o is the molecular weight of the structural repeating-unit. Values for p of 0.50, 0.90, 0.95, and 0.99 (ie 50, 90, 95, and 99% conversion of reactive groups) thus correspond to $\overline{\text{DP}}$'s of 2, 10, 20, and 100, respectively, which indicates (a) that a high degree of chemical conversion is needed to produce a high-molecular polymer, and (b) that the main increase in molecular weight occurs during the later stages of reaction. The polyesterification reaction is an equilibrium process (see eqs. 1 and 2), and its progress—and hence the polymer molecular weight—is determined by the efficiency with which water is removed from the reaction zone. For the production of the lower-molecular-weight polyesters of the plasticizer or polyurethan-precursor type which have $\overline{\text{DP}}$'s in the range of 5–20, it is normally sufficient to allow the liberated water to be driven off at the temperature of reaction, preferably in a stirred reactor system and with the passage of a current of dry inert gas such as nitrogen or carbon dioxide which assists in the removal of water. Products of high molecular weight are rarely obtained by this simple mode of operation, but can be obtained either by carrying out the reaction in a boiling inert organic solvent, eg xylene, chlorobenzene, or kerosene, with azeotropic entrainment of the liberated water and recycle of the separated and dried liquid or addition of fresh solvent to the condensation vessel, or by precondensation at moderate temperatures followed by performing the later stages of reaction under reduced pressures. Polymerization to high conversions requires that equal numbers of the reacting groups be present at all stages of reaction. Provided that there are no side-reactions which might cause adventitious loss of functionality, this condition is satisfied in the self-polycondensation of hydroxycarboxylic acids, but in the reaction of dicarboxylic acids with glycols the latter are often relatively volatile and some portion of the initial charge may be lost by distillation of the glycol with liberated steam or in the carrier gas or under reduced pressure, with consequent limitation of molecular weight in the product. It is therefore usual to employ an excess of glycol (eg 10–20 mole % excess with respect to dicarboxylic acid) to compensate for physical losses and to provide hydroxyl-terminated macromolecules at whose chain ends further polymerization can be promoted by interchain alcoholysis.

The rationale of the situation is as follows: At temperatures up to about 150°C and when there are no sensitive groups prone to degradative side-reactions, the principal reaction to be considered is the esterification-hydrolysis equilibrium (eq. 2) where, if the reactants fall out of balance so that B—B is in excess, the $\overline{DP}$ of the product is given by

$$\frac{1 + r}{2r(1 - p) + 1 - r}$$

where r is the ratio of A—A to B—B molecules and p is the extent of reaction. For complete conversion of reactive groups (ie when $p = 1$), this reduces to

$$\overline{DP} = (1 + r)/(1 - r)$$

An excess of either glycol or dicarboxylic acid thus regulates the molecular weight of the polymer as well as the nature of the end-groups—a feature that is particularly important when hydroxyl-terminated materials are required. Similarly, the introduction (whether intentionally, or as an impurity, or by side-reactions), of a monofunctional acid or alcohol limits the chain length according to the relation (applicable at $p = 1$) $\overline{DP}$ = number of molecules of bifunctional compounds/(1 + number of molecules of monofunctional compound). This emphasizes the need for the use of pure starting materials when high-molecular products are required. At higher temperatures (>200°C) and in the presence of catalysts, the simple reaction of equation 2 is supplemented by ester–ester exchange reactions between molecules (which do not, however, affect the number of end-groups and are therefore not relevant in this context) and, more importantly, by alcoholysis or acidolysis reactions at the chain ends which involve the liberation of glycol or dicarboxylic acid molecules with concurrent linking of chain units (eqs. 3, 4). These reactions are also reversible but, in practice, the dicarboxylic acids produced according to equation 4 are invariably too involatile to be lost from the system so that this reaction does not contribute significantly to chain growth, whereas the alcoholysis reaction (eq. 3) can be driven to the right, especially by working under reduced pressure which removes the liberated diol from the system and provides an efficient way of obtaining polyesters of high molecular weight.

$$\text{\tiny\textasciitilde\textasciitilde\textasciitilde}OCR'COOROH + HOROOCR'CO\text{\tiny\textasciitilde\textasciitilde\textasciitilde} \rightleftharpoons HOROH + \text{\tiny\textasciitilde\textasciitilde\textasciitilde}OCR'COOROOCR'CO\text{\tiny\textasciitilde\textasciitilde\textasciitilde} \quad (3)$$

$$\text{\tiny\textasciitilde\textasciitilde\textasciitilde}OROOCR'COOH + HOOCR'COORO\text{\tiny\textasciitilde\textasciitilde\textasciitilde} \rightleftharpoons HOOCR'COOH + \text{\tiny\textasciitilde\textasciitilde\textasciitilde}OROOCR'COORO\text{\tiny\textasciitilde\textasciitilde\textasciitilde} \quad (4)$$

The direct polyesterification reaction is self-catalyzed by carboxyl groups of the acid components but because of the reduction in concentration of these groups with increasing conversion, other catalysts are often employed to maintain the rate of reaction; such catalysts include sulfonic acids (eg *p*-toluenesulfonic or camphorsulfonic acid in amounts of 1–2.5% by wt of reactants), antimony pentafluoride, phosphoric acid, titanium alkoxides, or dialkyltin oxides (0.2–0.5% by wt of reactants). The strongly acidic catalysts are disadvantageous, however, because of their tendency to promote discoloration and hydrolysis unless removed from the polyester product. Illustrative examples of the preparation of high-molecular-weight polyesters by direct esterification procedures are given in the literature for (a) poly(10-oxydecanoyl) (mol wt 25,000) by direct polycondensation in vacuo at 200–230°C (3), (b) various A—A/B—B type polyesters (mol wt up to 82,000) by acid-catalyzed reaction in the azeotropic system with special provisions for drying the recycled solvent and optionally with the additional use of anhydrous copper sulfate as an internal drying agent (8), (c) similar polyesters (mol wt up to 100,000) by the use of basic catalysts and reduced pressures (9), and (d) poly(hexamethylene terephthalate) by azeotropic reaction in high-boiling kerosene (10).

The foregoing methods are most suitable for the formation of polyesters from aliphatic dicarboxylic acids. Ring-containing acids can also be used, but on account of their high melting points and slight solubilities it is often preferable to prepare their polyesters by the alternative reactions described below. The direct procedure is generally applicable to glycols containing primary or secondary hydroxyl groups, but it is not effective with tertiary hydroxylic diols which are readily prone to dehydration, or with phenols which are normally too unreactive to be esterified directly; an exception occurs with *p*-hydroxybenzoic acid whose polyesterification occurs when the material is dissolved in excess of trifluoroacetic anhydride (11).

It is characteristic of many polyesters that an equilibrium exists between the linear macromolecules and their cyclic oligo-esters or lactones, favoring the production of the cyclic low-molecular species at higher temperatures. The investigations of Carothers on the depolymerization of aliphatic polyesters (3), of Stoll and Rouvé on the lactonization of aliphatic ω-hydroxyacids (12,13), and of other workers in the field (14–20) have delineated the relationships between polyester structure and proneness to cyclization, and on the stabilities of cyclic esters of various ring sizes with respect to the polymers. The essential conclusions relative to this discussion are that (a) when the structures of the reactants are such that cyclization can occur with the formation of 5- or 6-membered cyclic esters, this reaction will seriously compete with and may predominate over linear polymerization, (b) 7- to 9-membered rings will be produced in normal polyesterification reactions in small to moderate amounts, and (c) 10-membered or larger rings will be formed in significant amounts only in forced (ie nonequilibrium) conditions that are rarely important in polymer synthesis. The cyclic products are believed to be formed mainly by exchange processes between the segments of polyester molecules, though some proportion may also arise by end-group reactions or directly from the starting materials; their formation is therefore broadly independent of the type of polyesterification reaction used but is strongly influenced by temperature. For these reasons polyesters cannot be formed satisfactorily by the high-temperature polycondensation of glycolic or lactic acids which yield the cyclic dimeric esters, glycolide and lactide; of 4-hydroxybutyric acids which yield the very stable γ-butyrolactones; or of 5-hydroxypentanoic or 6-hydroxycaproic acids which also give significant amounts of lactones. Polyesters of these acids are best obtained by way of the lactones (see below), but linear aliphatic hydroxycarboxylic acids whose functional groups are separated by chains of 9 or more carbon atoms can be polyesterified without difficulty.

Side-reactions may occur during the high-temperature polyesterification of thermally sensitive substances with effects on the yields and molecular weights, or structures of the products. Examples of such limitations occur in the case of readily decarboxylated acids such as oxalic or malonic acids (21); with the readily dehydrated 3-hydroxypropionic acid and certain of its derivatives which yield mainly acrylic acid compounds; with unstable acetylenic compounds which yield low-molecular polyesters (22,23); and with compounds containing *cis*-vinylene or *cis*-alicyclic rings which may be isomerized partly or wholly to trans isomers (24,25).

A number of studies have been made of the kinetics of direct esterification polymerization reactions (4,26–28). Despite some discrepancies of observation and interpretation, the main features appear to be as follows: (a) In the polycondensation of hydroxycarboxylic acids, or of diols with dicarboxylic acids, the terminal functional groups have reactivities that are independent of the lengths of the molecular chains to which they are attached. (b) The rate of reaction in the self-catalyzed process (ie catalyzed by carboxyl groups of the acidic reactants) follows a third-order law corresponding to $k[COOH]^2[OH]$, at least over the later stages from $p = 0.8$ up to 0.98, but when the reaction is catalyzed by strong acids whose concentration can be regarded as constant, the reaction is second order, with a rate given by $k'[COOH][OH]$. In the early stages of reaction, p tends to increase nonlinearly with time, and this deviation has been ascribed to changes in the character of the environment as the major proportion of reactive groups is consumed. Activation energies of 12 to 23 kcal/mole have been reported for a number of polyesterifications of aliphatic compounds, but discordant results have been obtained in separate investigations of particular reaction systems. A recent study of the polycondensation of neopentylene glycol with different acids gives reactivities in the order: maleic (as anhydride) > succinic > adipic = sebacic > o-phthalic acid, and all of these reactions had activation energies of 15 ± 0.5 kcal/mole (29).

Ester-Exchange Methods. This title covers a group of reactions of outstanding practical importance in which polyesters are synthesized by exchange reactions of alcoholysis or acidolysis between paired reactants comprising diols + dicarboxylic acid diesters, and diol-diesters + dicarboxylic acids, respectively. Double ester-exchange reactions of diol-esters with dicarboxylic acid diesters also yield polyesters but have lesser practical value. The reactions are expressed stoichiometrically in equations 5–7 which represent the formation of A—A/B—B type polyesters, and each procedure can also be adapted to the preparation of A—B type products from the corresponding hydroxycarboxylic acid derivatives which will not be separately discussed.

$$n \text{ HOROH} + n \text{ R''OOCR'COOR''} \rightleftharpoons [-\text{OROOCR'CO}-]_n + 2n \text{ R''OH} \qquad (5)$$

$$n \text{ R''COOROOCR''} + n \text{ HOOCR'COOH} \rightleftharpoons [-\text{OROOCR'CO}-]_n + 2n \text{ R''COOH} \qquad (6)$$

$$n \text{ R''COOROOCR''} + n \text{ R'''OOCR'COOR'''} \rightleftharpoons [-\text{OROOCR'CO}-]_n + 2n \text{ R''COOR'''} \qquad (7)$$

The alcoholysis reaction (which here also includes the use of phenolic hydroxyl) has the greatest importance and will be discussed first. By proper choice of the groups represented as R'' in equation 5, the process can be applied to a very wide range of starting materials, the main distinctions being that aliphatic and alicyclic glycols, arylenedialkanols and arylenedi(oxyalkanols) are best reacted with dialkyl esters of the acid components, whereas phenolic hydroxyl compounds require the use of the diaryl esters, or of diaryl carbonates when polycarbonates are being prepared. Compounds with tertiary aliphatic hydroxyl groups cannot normally be polyesterified by ester-exchange, but virtually all polyesters that can be made by direct esterification methods can be equally well, and often advantageously, prepared in this way. The choice between the methods is primarily one of convenience and of the availability of starting materials. In particular, high-melting and poorly soluble aromatic acids which are neither readily purified nor easily polymerized directly, are usually readily converted to polyesters by way of their simple esters whose lower melting points permit the production of homogeneous melts of the reactants. Any easily purified lower alkyl ester may be used, and methyl esters are often preferred because of the ease of removal of the liberated methanol and the higher effective proportion of acid units; similarly, when aryl esters are employed for polyarylate or polycarbonate formation, the phenyl esters are preferred. The commercial manufacture of PET is mainly by the reaction of ethylene glycol with dimethyl terephthalate.

The simplest method of ester-exchange polycondensation is to heat a mixture of a dicarboxylic acid ester and a diol (used in 10–50 mole % excess over the requirement of equation 5 in order to force completion of the displacement of alkyl group from the carboxylic ester and to provide hydroxyl-ended chains) with a polyesterification catalyst, preferably with stirring, in an inert atmosphere at temperatures of 150–200°C until the evolution of alcohol is complete, and then to continue the reaction at higher temperatures and reduced pressures (down to 0.5 mm Hg) when further polymerization proceeds by the elimination of glycol from the chain ends. The choice of final working temperature is governed by the properties of the product which must ordinarily be kept molten, but it is usually in the range of 230–280°C. The viscosity of the product increases with conversion, and the reaction conditions are maintained until this has reached a value corresponding with the desired molecular weight; the total reaction time is usually a few hours. This basic technique can be modified in various ways. When the diol component is a bisphenol or a higher glycol of low volatility, equivalent proportions of the reactants can be employed to give polymers directly according to equation 5. Conversely, polyesterification of the lower, more volatile glycols is commonly effected in two stages—the dicarboxylic ester is first reacted at atmospheric pressure and about 150–200°C with a considerable excess (eg 2.2 molar equivalents) of glycol to give the bishydroxyalkyl ester (**6**) which is then polycondensed in vacuo at higher temperatures (eqs. 8,9). Compounds of type (**6**) may also be obtained by independent reactions, eg from dicarboxylic acids and oxiranes, and polycondensed as shown. Monofunctional molecular-weight regulators may also be used. Lastly, the high melting points of some polyesters involve the risk of degradation if attempts are made to complete the reaction in the melt, and it is usual in such cases to use the melt-phase only for the primary alcohol-elimination reaction and the formation of a low-molecular-weight polyester which is then allowed to solidify and, after grinding finely, is polymerized further in the solid state in vacuo or under a current of inert gas at temperatures (eg 220–250°C) where the material is thermally stable. It will be appreciated that ester-exchange processes are inherently reversible, and that their development to give high-molecular-weight products depends on the removal of a volatile reaction product; the reverse reaction of alcoholysis or glycolysis of a polyester is used technically for the removal of polymer residues from manufacturing equipment or for the recovery of intermediates from waste polyesters.

$$2 \text{ HOROH} + \text{R}''\text{OOCR}'\text{COOR}'' \rightleftharpoons 2 \text{ R}''\text{OH} + \text{HOROOCR}'\text{COOROH} \tag{8}$$
$$\textbf{(6)}$$

$$n \text{ HOROOCR}'\text{COOROH} \rightleftharpoons n \text{ HOROH} + [\text{—OROOCR}'\text{CO—}]_n \tag{9}$$

Many substances act as catalysts for the ester-exchange polycondensation of glycols and bisphenols with dicarboxylic acid esters. They are generally weak bases typified by the carbonates, alkanoates, hydrides or alkoxides of sodium, lithium, zinc, calcium, magnesium, aluminum and titanium, organomagnesium halides, and complex alkoxides such as NaHTi(OBu)_6, MgTi(OBu)_6, and CaTi(OBu)_6, used in amounts of 0.05–0.5% by wt of the total reactants (9,30–40). It has been suggested that the initial action of the catalysts is with the diol component giving an ionized glycoloxide which is capable of nucleophilic attack on the carbonyl group of the ester as shown below (M represents the catalyst metal atom); the simple metal alkoxide is then eliminated and regenerates the active species by contact with further glycol (41).

$$\text{wwwCH}_2\text{CH}_2\text{O}^-\text{M}^+ + \overset{\text{OCH}_3}{\underset{\text{O}}{\overset{|}{\underset{\parallel}{\text{C}}}}}\text{—Rww} \rightleftharpoons \text{wwCH}_2\text{CH}_2\text{O}\overset{\text{OCH}_3}{\underset{\text{O}^-\text{M}^+}{\overset{|}{\underset{|}{\text{C}}}}}\text{—Rww} \rightleftharpoons \text{wwCH}_2\text{CH}_2\text{O}\overset{}{\underset{\text{O}}{\overset{}{\underset{\parallel}{\text{C}}}}}\text{—Rww} + \text{CH}_3\text{O}^-\text{M}^+$$

The subject of catalysis will be considered further in connection with the manufacture of PET, but it is convenient to give some references here for polyester formation by the alcoholysis ester-exchange method as exemplified for polymeric alkylene tereph thalates (30) and substituted terephthalates (42); cyclopentane- and cyclohexane dimethylene alkanedicarboxylates and terephthalates (31,34,43); alkylene sulfonyl-4,4'-dibenzoates (44–46) and sulfonylalkanedicarboxylates (47); polyoxalates (48,49); polyarylates (50–52); and various A—B type polyesters (41,53–59).

The acidolysis ester-exchange method of polyesterification (eq. 6) is particularly useful for preparing polyarylates of aliphatic (58,60–64) and ring-containing (65–70) dicarboxylic acids. It is performed by heating a diester (usually the diacetate) of a dihydric phenol or bisphenol with the dicarboxylic acid and a catalyst (eg p-toluene-sulfonic acid, antimony oxide, magnesium metal, titanium butoxide, zinc, or sodium acetate) either in the melt or in a high-boiling inert liquid medium. Acetic acid is eliminated at about 200°C, and the reactions are continued with the melts under reduced pressure and at temperatures up to 280°C, or by solid-state polymerization. Acetoxyalkyl- or aryl- carboxylic acids can be converted analogously to A—B type polyesters (71–73). A prerequisite for successful reaction is that the ester groups of the phenol acetates should be freely accessible to the attacking carboxylic acid; the acetates of o,o'-bisphenols or of p,p'-bisphenols having large substituent groups adjacent to the phenolic function are sterically hindered and do not yield polyesters in this way (62). The mechanism of the acidolysis reaction has been suggested (74) to involve an initial hydrogen-bonding association of the phenolic ester with a carboxylic acid group which increases the electrophilic character of the ester carbonyl-oxygen atom. This favors attack by the carboxylate anion, producing a 4-membered transition state intermediate in which exchange occurs with formation of (volatile) acetic acid and an arylate ester bond:

$$\text{CH}_3\text{—}\overset{-\text{O}\cdots\text{H}\cdots\text{OCOAr}'\text{—}}{\underset{-\text{O—COAr}'\text{—}}{\overset{|}{\underset{|}{\text{C}}}}}\text{—O—Ar—} \longrightarrow \left[\text{CH}_3\text{—}\overset{\text{O—H}}{\underset{\text{O—COAr}'\text{—}}{\overset{|}{\underset{|}{\text{C}}}}}\text{—O—Ar—}\right] \longrightarrow \text{CH}_3\text{COOH} + \text{—Ar}'\text{COOAr—}$$

As already mentioned, polyesters can also be prepared by double exchange reactions in which the eliminated species is itself an ester. The reaction conditions resemble those of the other methods of ester-exchange polymerization. PET has thus been obtained from the reaction of dimethyl terephthalate and 1,2-diacetoxyethane with magnesium as catalyst (75), and poly(p-phenylene terephthalate) from diphenyl terephthalate and p-diacetoxybenzene with zinc acetate (76); the eliminated esters are methyl and phenyl acetates, respectively. Correspondingly, methyl p-acetoxybenzoate gives methyl acetate and poly(p-oxybenzoyl) (77). Mixed esters can also be used, as in the formation of PET and 1,2-dibenzoyloxyethane from di(2-benzoyloxyethyl) terephthalate (78), and of a variety of polycarbonates from diol-bis(alkyl carbonates) according to the following scheme (33,79–81):

$$n \text{ R'OOCOROCOOR'} \rightarrow [\text{—OROCO—}]_n + n \text{ (R'O)}_2\text{CO}$$

Methods Involving the Use of Acid Chlorides. The polycondensation of diols with dicarbonyl chlorides can be effected in a number of ways of which the simplest is the direct reaction of the components at elevated temperatures, yielding the polyester and hydrogen chloride (4,82):

$$n \text{ HOROH} + n \text{ ClOCR'COCl} \rightarrow [\text{—OROOCR'CO—}]_n + 2n \text{ HCl}$$

When the reactants and polymeric product are low-melting and capable of providing a homogeneous mixture no solvent is required, but it is usually more convenient to employ a boiling inert solvent through which a current of nitrogen is passed to remove the liberated hydrogen chloride. The choice of solvent is determined by the reactivities of the components and hence by the required temperature of reaction which may range from 100 to 300°C. Commonly used solvents are chlorobenzene, o-dichlorobenzene, and the chlorinated biphenyls, and the progress of reaction can conveniently be followed titrimetrically by passing the effluent gas through an alkali solution. To obtain high-molecular-weight products it is essential that the reagents, solvent, and carrier gas be well dried since traces of moisture will hydrolyze the acid chlorides and thus block the reaction. Because of the side-reactions that may be induced by hydrogen chloride at high temperatures, this method of polymerization cannot be used with the lower glycols which are prone to acid-catalyzed rearrangements or to etherification, but it is effective with neopentylene glycol (83); with the linear C_6 or higher glycols and fluoroglycols (84–87); and with many dihydric phenols (63,67,88–90). By the use of an excess of acid chloride, polyesters with terminal —COCl groups can be obtained and subsequently used for block copolymer formation with diamines, etc.

A more satisfactory procedure—limited, however, to use with dihydric phenols—is to carry out polyesterification at moderate temperatures in the presence of a basic substance which combines with the liberated hydrogen chloride, ie by a polymeric variant of the classical Schotten-Baumann reaction. Whilst this can be done by allowing the dicarbonyl chloride and the phenol to react in the presence of a tertiary amine, with or without a solvent, the method of choice is by interfacial polycondensation which makes use of the virtually instantaneous reaction of phenolate anions with carbonyl chlorides:

$$n \text{ }^-\text{OArO}^- + n \text{ ClCOR'COCl} \rightarrow [\text{—OArOOCR'CO—}]_n + 2n \text{ Cl}^-$$

The theory and practice of this reaction has been studied intensively (4,65,66,82, 91–97) and the general procedure is as follows: The bisphenol is dissolved in aqueous sodium hydroxide to form a solution of the phenolate di-anion which is treated, with vigorous stirring, with a solution of the dicarbonyl chloride in a water-immiscible solvent. The condensation, which is diffusion-controlled, takes place at the boundary between the two liquid phases (which is constantly renewed by mechanical agitation) and the liberated chloride ions are neutralized by the alkali in the aqueous phase. It is helpful to employ small amounts of (a) a surfactant to assist in the dispersion of the organic liquid phase, and (b) a reaction accelerator—usually a tetraalkylammonium, phosphonium, or sulfonium salt—which is believed to provide its corresponding phenolate which is more soluble at the organic phase boundary than the sodium phenolate. The esterification reaction liberates the tetraalkyl ammonium or analogous ion which returns to the aqueous phase and assists further reaction. For sensitive bisphenols, a small amount of antioxidant or an inert gas atmosphere may also be used to counteract aerial oxidation.

Optimum reaction conditions must be sought for each particular case, but the formation of high-molecular-weight products is generally favored by the use of water-immiscible liquids that dissolve, or at least highly swell, the polyester (methylene chloride, 1,2-dichloroethane, and 1,1,2-trichloroethane are widely used since they dissolve many polyarylates), and of low temperatures (0–25°C) where the risk of hydrolysis of dicarbonyl chloride to nonreactive compounds is minimized. Because the reaction is molecularly localized at the phase boundary it is not essential to maintain exact equivalence of reactants in the system as a whole, and polyesters can be made with one component in excess. Monofunctional acid chlorides or phenols can also be used as molecular-weight regulators. In contrast to high-temperature polycondensations, the interfacial reaction is irreversible and no exchange reactions occur between the macromolecules so that the molecular-weight distributions of the products may differ markedly from those of the previously discussed processes. The polymer yields are generally 80 to 100% of theoretical, and in favorable cases molecular weights as high as 80,000–90,000 can be attained—considerably in excess of those accessible by most melt-polymerization procedures.

Apart from the inadmissibility of aliphatic diols (which cannot give an effective concentration of alkoxide ions in the presence of water) the structural range of the interfacial procedure is very wide. It forms the basis for a method of commercial production of polycarbonates by the use of phosgene as a dichloride, or can be used with most aliphatic, alicyclic, aromatic, and heterocyclic dicarbonyl chlorides though, on account of their greater tendency to hydrolysis, the aliphatic chlorides tend to give lower-molecular-weight products. The usual bisphenols (and also the more acidic aliphatic dithiols (98)) are all conveniently reactive, and mild reaction conditions can thus be used to prepare many polyarylates whose high melting or softening points would preclude a melt-condensation process. In addition, polyarylates can be prepared from bisphenols containing other reactive centers that would interfere with the normal high-temperature reactions; examples of such substances are phenolphthalein, phenolphthalimidine, fluorescein and o-carboxy-α,α-bis(4-hydroxyphenyl)toluene (96,99,100), as well as alkylene di(4-hydroxybenzoates) which give alternating copolyesters (101). Lastly, the interfacial polycondensation method is equally applicable to the formation of polysulfonates, polyphosphonates and polyphosphorates by the use of acid chloride compounds of the types $R(SO_2Cl)_2$, $RPOCl_2$, and $ROPOCl_2$.

Miscellaneous Polycondensation and Allied Reactions. A brief description will now be given of some further polycondensation and related reactions that have been used in polyester synthesis. Some of these involve the use of diol or dicarboxylic acid derivatives different from those already mentioned; others use such derivatives for the intermediary production of diesters of type (6) which are then further polymerized, and a third category employs anhydro derivatives of the diol or acid components in reactions that are really addition polymerizations but are conveniently dealt with here.

Terephthalic acid as the diammonium or bistriethylammonium salt reacts readily with ethylene glycol in high-temperature polycondensation conditions, giving PET by way of di(2-hydroxyethyl) terephthalate (102). Its saltlike complex with N-methylpyrrolidone reacts similarly (103) as does the dicarboxamide (104) and dinitrile (105). Dicarbonitriles can also be converted to polyesters by the hydrogen chloride-promoted reaction with diols, giving first polymeric iminoether hydrochlorides which are then hydrolyzed with water (106–108). Another variation yields polyesters together with sodium or potassium halide when an alkylene dihalide is heated with the sodium or potassium salt of a dicarboxylic acid, or analogously from the salt of a halogenocarboxylic acid (109–112); but on account of the heterogeneous character of the reaction system such syntheses are not easily controlled and, like the dicarbonitrile routes, they tend to give low-molecular-weight products.

An unusual type of ester-exchange reaction is found in the polycondensation of diisopropenyl sebacate with cyclohexanedimethanol to polyester and acetone (113). Other variations involve the hydroxylic reaction component: Cyclic carbonates or sulfites of 1,2-diols thus react with aliphatic and aromatic dicarboxylic acids to give polyesters and carbon or sulfur dioxides (114,115). When ethylene carbonate is reacted with phenolic compounds etherification occurs, and its reaction with methyl p-hydroxybenzoate in polyesterification conditions thus gives poly(p-oxyethoxybenzoyl) directly, whilst a similar reaction with hydroquinone and dimethyl terephthalate yields poly(ethylene 4,4′-ethylenedioxydibenzoate) (116). A surprising etherification also occurs when p-hydroxybenzoic acid or its alkyl esters is heated with ethylene glycol in the presence of cobalt acetate; a mixture of the hydroxyacid with glycol and dimethyl terephthalate thus gives directly an ethylene terephthalate copolyester containing p-oxyethoxybenzoyl groups, and this reaction is the basis of manufacture of the copolyester fiber Grilene (117,118). Two other polyesterification processes involve interesting acyl-oxygen fission reactions: 9,10-Dimethoxymethylanthracene is claimed to react with dicarboxylic acids in the presence of protonic catalysts to give polyesters (119), and the di-2-$tert$-butoxyethyl esters of dicarboxylic acids, t-BuOCH$_2$CH$_2$OOCR′-COOCH$_2$CH$_2$Ot-Bu, are cleaved in the presence of acid catalysts to give isobutene and di-2-hydroxyethyl esters which can be polycondensed in situ to polyesters (120).

A number of polyester-forming reactions make use of the anhydro derivatives of the dicarboxylic acid and/or the diol moiety. This is seen most simply in the reaction of epoxides with dicarboxylic acids to give intermediary esters of type (6), and more directly when phthalic, maleic, succinic, and similar anhydrides are reacted with diols in normal polyesterification conditions. A detailed study of the reaction between succinic anhydride and 1,6-hexanediol has been made by Kern and co-workers (121,122), who obtained hydroxyl-ended polyesters of high molecular weight (up to 80,000); these were converted to carboxyl-ended materials by further reaction with succinic anhydride in mild conditions. Polymeric anhydrides of dicarboxylic acids have also been used to prepare polyesters with glycols (123) and bisphenols (124), and a related reaction is the polyaddition of carbon suboxide (C$_3$O$_2$) and glycols, giving polymalonates (125), and of bisketenes with diols, yielding other polyesters (126,127). Lastly, polyesters are produced by alternating step-polyaddition reactions of the cyclic anhydrides of dicarboxylic acids with 1,2- (128–133), 1,3- (131,134), and 1,4- (135) epoxides, as well as by their reaction with cyclic carbonates or sulfites (131,136) and 1,3-dioxans (137). Of these reactions, that of cyclic anhydrides with 1,2-epoxides has been the most studied (128,131). It is an irreversible base-catalyzed reaction induced at temperatures of 70–150°C by catalytic amounts of sodium phthalate or trichloroacetate or by tertiary amines, and favored by polar solvents. The molecular weights of the products can be quite high (up to 93,000 in some cases), and the nature of the end-groups as OH or COOH can be regulated by using an excess of either epoxide or anhydride. The alternating pattern of reaction is very specific and essentially of zero order with an activation energy (in the case of phthalic anhydride + phenyl glycidyl ether) of 17.3 kcal/mole. According to Fischer (128), the initial step comprises the ring-opening of the anhydride by the catalyst, giving a carboxylate anion that adds to the epoxide with formation of a second anion at which alternating addition continues as shown below:

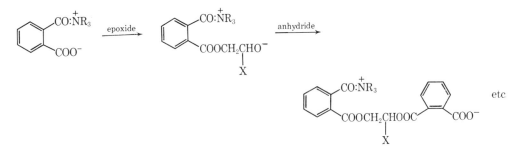

SYNTHESIS BY THE POLYMERIZATION OF CYCLIC ESTERS AND LACTONES

The ability of certain lactones such as δ-valerolactone and glycolide to be transformed more or less easily into higher-molecular-weight compounds has been known for many years (138,139) but the identification of this change as a step-polymerization reaction was essentially due to Carothers (3), who instituted the systematic study of lactone polymerizability in relation to structure—a topic that has since been extended considerably, notably by Hall and co-workers (140,141), by Cherdron, Ohse, and Korte (142–146), and by Tsuda and Yamashita (147–154). In this article the term *lactone* is used to distinguish the internal mono-, di-, or higher esters of hydroxycarboxylic acids from the *cyclic esters* of diols with dicarboxylic acids or carbonic acid; the polymerization of lactones thus yields A—B type polyesters whereas that of cyclic esters or carbonates gives A—A/B—B polyesters or polycarbonates. The general scheme of the reaction can be expressed thus:

$$R \overset{CO}{\underset{O}{\diagdown \vert \diagup}} \rightleftharpoons [-ORCO-]_n \tag{10}$$

where R represents a divalent hydrocarbon group in the simple lactones, or an ester-containing group in the di- or higher lactones and cyclic esters. In the following general review of the subject, the reader should also consider the earlier remarks on the cyclization side-reactions of polyesterification processes.

Although a few lactones and cyclic esters polymerize with great ease, apparently spontaneously on standing or when heated (3,15,16,155), most do so only under the influence of catalysts or initiators which include cationic and anionic species; organic tertiary bases; alkali and alkaline earth metals, hydrides, alkoxides, and alkyls; certain coordination-complexes and complex compounds resulting from the reaction of zinc or aluminum alkyls with alcohols or water; and hydrogen-donor compounds such as carboxylic acids, alcohols, glycols, primary and secondary amines, and alkanolamines. The practical conditions of reaction vary greatly with monomer and catalyst. Many of the compounds polymerize in the temperature range of -20 to $100°C$ but some require temperatures of $200°C$ or higher, and the reactions can be performed in bulk, or with melts, or solutions of the monomers in inert solvents. It is advisable to work with well-dried materials, and the prior distillation of lactones from isocyanates has been recommended for this purpose (142).

Except in the cationic polymerization of some substituted β-propiolactones, the reaction is believed to involve fission of the acyl–oxygen bond in the monomers, viz:

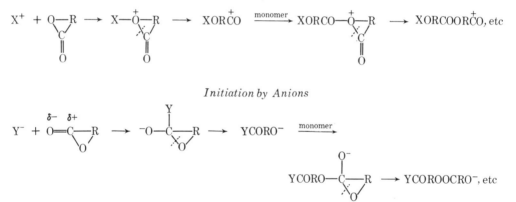

The polymerization initiated by hydrogen-donating compounds such as alcohols and amines is thought to proceed by nucleophilic attack of the initiator on the carbonyl group of the monomer, giving intermediate products of the type HORCOOR′ and HORCONHR′ through which the reaction is continued, but when such initiators are used together with acids or bases as catalysts the normal ionic reactions occur (156). Initiation by tertiary amines has been suggested to yield active betaine intermediates, $R'_3\overset{+}{N}RCOO^-$, which then cause propagation by the usual anionic mechanism, resulting in chains of the type $R'_3\overset{+}{N}-[RCOO]_n-R-COO^-$ (148). The character of the termination step depends on the particular system used, and considerable control can be exercised on the nature of the end-groups—an acid-catalyzed reaction in the presence of ethylene glycol may thus be completed as follows:

$$\text{\textasciitilde\textasciitilde\textasciitilde ORCO} + HO(CH_2)_2OH \rightarrow \text{\textasciitilde\textasciitilde\textasciitilde ORCOO}(CH_2)_2OH + H^+$$

It will be noted that the polymerization formulated in equation 10 was represented as an equilibrium reaction. The tendency of different cyclic esters and lactones to polymerize, and correspondingly of their polymers to depolymerize, is greatly affected by the details of monomer structure, particularly the ring size and the presence of substituents. Monocyclic ester compounds containing 5-membered rings, eg γ-butyrolactone and ethylene carbonate, have long been regarded as unpolymerizable, and theoretical arguments have been developed suggesting that, in contrast to lactones with 4-, 6- and 7-membered rings, the free energy of polymerization of γ-butyrolactone is positive (157,158). However, this substance has recently been shown to polymerize at 160°C under a pressure of 20,000 atm, and the polymer—although of rather low molecular weight ($\overline{DP}$ in the range 14–40)—showed no tendency to depolymerize at 80°C (159). It is also interesting that the mechanistic pathway to depolymerization of poly(oxypentanoyl)—normally regarded as a material of low stability with respect to its monomer—can be blocked by acetylation of the end-groups (156). The relative tendencies of lactones to polymerize are affected by the nature of the reactions employed: thus, cationic initiation with acetyl perchlorate gave the reactivity order δ-valerolactone $>$ ϵ-caprolactone $>$ β-propiolactone whereas anionic initiation with sodium naphthalene gave the order ϵ-caprolactone $>$ δ-valerolactone $>$ β-propiolactone (142,143). In each case, β-propiolactone which, for reasons of strain in the 4-membered ring, might have been expected to show exceptional reactivity was, in fact, the least reactive. The presence of substituents on a lactone ring frequently, but not invariably, reduces the ease of polymerization.

Theoretical understanding of the reactivity differences in the polymerization of ester monomers is, as yet, very incomplete. Factors that may be involved in different degrees for various monomers include ring strain, conformational strain, strain due to hydrogen crowding, differences in the configuration of the ester group, differential reactivities towards different classes of initiators, and stereochemical influences on the ease of approach of the activating reagent to the relevant part of the ester group. A number of studies of lactone structure and reactivity in simple reactions have been made in attempts to elucidate these factors. Huisgen and Ott (160) inferred from dipole moment measurements that the —COO— group in the smaller ring (4–7 membered) lactones exists in the energy-rich cis planar form whereas that in 10–16 membered rings possesses the trans form that is characteristic of open-chain esters; in 8- and 9-membered ring lactones there is a mixture of both forms. The general correctness of these conclusions is supported by x-ray investigations on 5- and 6-membered ring lactones and by conformational studies on cyclic esters and lactones with rings of up to twenty-four members (14,161–164) but no clear correlation has been established between ester-group configuration and polymerization behavior. There is similarly no correlation between skeletal ring strain, as deduced from the C=O infrared stretching frequencies, and the polymerization behavior (141). The rates of hydrolysis of lactones by hydroxyl ion were also examined by Huisgen and Ott as a measure of the susceptibility to nucleophilic attack, but whilst those members with cis ester groups were the most rapidly hydrolyzed, the detailed pattern of reactivities was not parallel with the polymerization behavior. Hall, Brandt, and Mason (165) have commented that hydrolysis by hydroxyl ion does not involve ring cleavage as a rate-determining step; they suggest that a better measure of reactivity in polymerization is given by the comparative equilibrium constants for the hydrolysis of lactones by water, but relatively few values are available for comparison. Yamashita and co-workers (153) have attempted to correlate the reactivities of lactones in cationic polymerization with their basicities as determined by the shift in the O-D frequency in the infrared spectrum of methanol-d solutions of the lactones. This approach gave pK_b values in the order: δ-valerolactone $<$ ϵ-caprolactone $<$ γ-butyrolactone $<$ β-propiolactone, which is again inconsistent with the abnormal stability of the 5-membered ring lactone towards polymerization. Attempts to estimate the degree of hydrogen crowding in lactones from the infrared C—H bending frequencies have also been inconclusive (166,167), and further work is clearly required to promote understanding in this field.

In practice, the formation of polyesters by the polymerization of cyclic esters and lactones is limited mainly by the relative inaccessibility of more than a few monomers, but where these are available the method has considerable advantages. Thus, the relatively low temperatures usually involved permit avoidance of cyclization and other side-reactions that sometimes complicate or even prohibit the use of high-temperature polyesterification reactions; it is therefore possible to obtain polyesters from monomers containing secondary reactive centers such as vinyl or epoxy groups that would not survive the conditions of conventional polycondensation (168). Secondly, as a polyaddition reaction, this method of polymerization eliminates the problems of removing substances such as water, glycols, hydrogen chloride, etc, which are liberated in normal condensation processes, and thirdly it provides a convenient means of controlling the nature of polyester end-groups by the use of suitable reaction initiators and terminators, as in the production of the hydroxyl-ended Niax polyols (see p. 181) by the glycol-initiated polymerization of ϵ-caprolactone.

Copolymerization Reactions of Lactones. As in polyesterification reactions, mixtures of lactones or cyclic esters may be copolymerized to copolyesters (151,153,169–175). Information on the compositions of the copolymers relative to that of the monomer mixtures is, however, very meager except for the interesting case of the copolymerization of β-propiolactone with γ-butyrolactone in methylene chloride at 0°C, catalyzed by a 1:1 complex of triethylaluminum with water, when the normally unreactive butyrolactone is incorporated to the extent indicated by the copolymerization parameters r_1 (propiolactone) $= 18 \pm 2$, r_2 (butyrolactone) $= 0.36 \pm 0.10$; an initial butyrolactone concentration of 80 mole % thus gives a copolyester containing 29.5 mole % of oxybutyryl units. Ethylene carbonate (though not γ-butyrolactone) is also claimed to copolymerize to some extent with glycolide. Lactones are also reported to copolymerize with other classes of compounds, eg oxiranes (130,145,176,177), oxetanes (149,151,178), 1,3,5-trioxane (179–181), aziridine (182,183), vinyl monomers (150,152,154,184–188), and isocyanates (189), and with lactams, amino acids, and nylon salts (190–192).

Manufacturing Processes

In general, reactions for this preparation of the relatively low molecular weight aliphatic polyesters are carried out batchwise in stirred glass-lined or stainless-steel vessels with capacities of 0.5–25 tons, furnished with the usual ancillary equipment for metering, mixing and introducing the reactants, purging with inert dry gas, heating, condensing volatile by-products such as water or glycols, and, where required, operating under reduced pressures. The course of polymerization is followed by measuring the volume of distillate and from the measurement of end-groups and viscosity in samples drawn from the reaction mixture. The reaction is interrupted when the product has attained the required molecular weight (24).

Until recently PET was always manufactured batchwise by the primary reaction of dimethyl terephthalate with ethylene glycol to give a precondensate composed mainly of di(2-hydroxyethyl) terephthalate with some proportion of higher linear oligomers. This was then polycondensed in the melt to the polyester, which was then recovered, quenched, and chipped for subsequent conversion to fibers and films. In the last few years continuous processes have been developed for the ester-exchange and polymerization steps, and the latter can now be integrated directly with the spinning process.

In the batch procedure, a mixture of dimethyl terephthalate with 2.1–2.2 molar proportions of ethylene glycol and a catalyst is heated at temperatures rising from 150 to about 210°C. Methanol is evolved and is removed through a fractionating column; the slight excess of ethylene glycol assists the complete removal of methanol at this stage. The temperature is then increased and vacuum applied to remove excess glycol and induce polymerization by the alcoholysis-interchange reaction. The reactants must be kept molten so that reaction can proceed and the polymer be eventually discharged from the vessel. The second stage of reaction is therefore carried out at about 270–280°C with pressures of 0.5–1 mm Hg. The course of polymerization can be followed by torque meters connected with the stirrers which indicate increases in the melt viscosity of the material, and reaction is interrupted when this reaches the required value. The PET is then extruded through a bottom valve of the autoclave under positive pressure of dry inert gas.

The properties of polyester fibers are intimately dependent on the fine chemical structure of the polymer as well as on the details of the spinning and drawing processes. Rigorous attention must therefore be paid to every aspect of the polymerization reaction since deviations in its chemistry, eg by thermal degradation, can influence the color, dye uptake, and thermal or photostability of the fibers. An important aspect of this control is the choice of catalyst that will promote the desired ester-exchange and polymerization reactions with minimal tendency to cause side-reactions. Originally, PET was prepared using a single catalyst (commonly lead oxide) for both stages of the reaction but it is now usual to employ mixed catalysts, one component of which is specially active for ester-exchange and the other for the polymerization stage. Commonly used ester-exchange catalysts include the oxides, carbonates, or acetates of zinc, calcium, magnesium, manganese, or cobalt, and antimony trioxide is widely employed as a polymerization catalyst; the quantities of catalyst used are in the range of 0.05–0.1% by wt of dimethyl terephthalate. These substances are by no means the only effective catalysts: Wilfong's review (193) lists twenty-two classes that had been described in the literature up to 1961, and later publications disclose many others including compounds of indium, thallium, gallium, and germanium, and specially complexed forms of the higher valence states of antimony, titanium, and other elements which are claimed to give PET of superior whiteness. Tetramethylguanidine has also been recommended as an organic catalyst for ester-exchange in conjunction with antimony pentoxide for the second step, and compounds such as benzil, benzophenone, and biacetyl are said to catalyze polymerization after ester-exchange with zinc acetate. The comparative efficiencies of various substances as catalysts for PET synthesis have been investigated (194–199) but the mechanism of their action is poorly understood, though Yoda and co-workers have suggested that catalytic efficiency can be correlated with the electronegativity and electron affinity of the metal atom (198). According to these workers, the diacetate of a divalent metal M reacts with glycol at the ester-exchange stage, giving an intermediate compound $HO(CH_2)_2OMAc$ which assists the polarization of the ester-carbonyl group by coordination, and then transfers its glycol residue to the carbonyl-carbon atom, as follows:

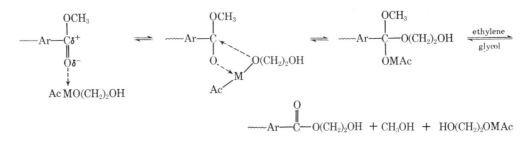

A number of investigations have been made on the kinetics of the ester-exchange and polymerization reactions and on the so-called redistribution reaction,

$$\sim R'COO(CH_2)_2OOCR''\sim + HO(CH_2)_2OOCR'''\sim \rightarrow$$

$$\sim R'COO(CH_2)_2OOCR'''\sim + HO(CH_2)_2OOCR''\sim$$

which makes an important contribution to the equilibration of molecular weights in PET. There are, however, serious disagreements between the conclusions of various workers. Thus, Griehl and Schnock considered the ester-exchange to be a first-order reaction (194,200), whereas Peebles and Wagner (201) and Sumoto (202,203) found it to be second-order. There are also discrepant views on the molecularity of the polymerization reaction and on the activation energies of the reactions, for which values have been given in the range of 9.5–32 kcal/mole for ester-exchange and 25–35 kcal/mole for polymerization (194,200,204–206). There is clearly need for further work in this field.

In addition to the obvious constituents of the reaction mixture, it is common to add stabilizers or color improvers such as triaryl phosphites or phosphates (197,207, 208), and monofunctional chain-terminators can be used to control the molecular weight (209,210). Fiber-grade PET is also normally delustered with titanium dioxide (as anatase), introduced as a slurry with glycol at an early stage of the reaction; the quantity used depends on the degree of dullness required, being normally around 0.5% but as little as 0.02% for "micro-dull" and as much as 1–2% for "extra-dull" grades. Phenolic additives can be used to improve the thermal and photostability of the polymer (211–214).

Side-Reactions in the Synthesis of PET. The usual synthesis of PET does not lead entirely to the linear poly(ethylene terephthalate) structure. In common with most other polyesters there is equilibration with cyclic oligomers, and PET made by melt polymerization therefore contains 1.5–1.7% of cyclic ethylene terephthalates, principally the trimer with small amounts of tetramer and pentamer (18,20,215). A second structural aberration arises with the formation of 3-oxapentamethylene terephthalate units, $\sim OCC_6H_4COO(CH_2)_2O(CH_2)_2OOCC_6H_4CO\sim$, by the in-situ etherification of ethylene glycol or perhaps of hydroxyethyl end-groups. Representative commercial PET's contain about 2.5 mole % of ether groups (216–218), of which a small proportion is present as a mixed cyclic dimeric ester (215).

The pattern of thermal decomposition in PET has been carefully studied (219–223). At temperatures around 280°C, which are technically important in synthesis and fabrication, the primary reaction is the scission of an ethylene–ester grouping to vinyl ester and carboxyl, which participate in subsequent reactions as follows:

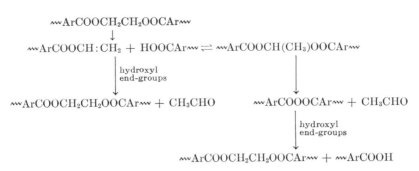

The most important net effects are to produce (a) carboxyl end-groups which formally should not result from ester-polycondensation but which, in practice, may constitute 20–60% of all the end-groups in the polymer, (b) acetaldehyde which is mainly removed in the vacuum cycle of polymerization but part of which, like the vinyl ester intermediate, can become involved in subsidiary reactions that may contribute to coloration in the polymer. Since carboxyl end-groups can affect the long-term stability of polyesters by autocatalyzing hydrolysis, manufacturing conditions in polymerization and fabrication aim to keep their production to a minimum, and chemical treatments (eg with copper compounds, diazomethane, epoxides, and pyrocarbonates) have been recommended to convert them to innocuous derivatives (224–227).

Continuous Polymerization and Other Techniques for the Manufacture of PET. Although the batchwise manufacture of PET, refined by many years of development, remains the main source of world production of the polymer, technical and economic advantages are expected from the continuous polymerization processes which have become operational since the mid-1960s (228–235). The fullest description of these processes has been given for the Vickers-Zimmer 12 tons/day installation at Taipei (Formosa) where a molten mixture of dimethyl terephthalate and ethylene glycol (in the molar ratio 1:1.7) is fed to a horizontal precondenser at 160–180°C. Ester-exchange takes place during 4 hr and is complete at 245°C. The precondensate then passes through two successive horizontal polymerization reactors, each divided into cells which are individually stirred, the first operating at 270°C/15–25 mm Hg and the second at 280–285°C/0.5–1 mm Hg, to give normal fiber-grade polymer ($[\eta]$ = approx 0.7) which can either be extruded and quenched for chipping or fed to an integrated multicell spinning plant. The production of higher-molecular-weight PET ($[\eta] \geqslant 1.0$), required nowadays for the higher-tenacity industrial yarns, is difficult to achieve in conventional batch reactions owing to competitive reactions of thermal degradation but it can be realized in continuous polymerization plants or by solid-state polymerization in static or fluid-bed reactors (236). Another recent development in PET manufacture arises from the growing availability of polymer-grade terephthalic acid which can be polyesterified with glycol in multistage continuous reactors, giving PET directly.

Characterization of Polyesters

Because of the multiplicity of types, grades, and uses of polyester products there are no uniformly accepted specification and testing standards, and the materials are mostly sold on the basis of suitability for particular end-uses determined, as required, from such properties as the melting and/or brittle temperature, viscosity, color, haze, moisture content, storage life, unsaturation, and end-group content. For scientific purposes, especially with new materials, much more extensive characterization is required and this may include the study of chemical structure; molecular weight and molecular-weight distribution; optical, electrical, and mechanical properties; thermal transitions; crystallinity and crystal structure; rheological properties; and studies of the chemical, thermal, and photochemical stability. For the most part this calls on the general technique of polymer science, and the only aspects that will be discussed here are those specifically directed to the determination of structure and molecular weight in polyesters.

Chemical Structure.   The chemical structure of polyesters is usually apparent from the method of synthesis but on occasions, eg in using a new synthetic reaction or when there is a possibility of side-reactions or isomerization, independent confirmatory evidence may be required. This can sometimes be gained directly by infrared or other spectroscopic examination of the polymer, but more often by its alkaline hydrolysis or methanolysis to simple compounds (diols, dicarboxylic acids or esters, or hydroxy acids) that are identified in the usual way. Other degradative reactions of structure-diagnostic value are (a) the complete reduction of a polyester to simple diols by use of lithium aluminum hydride (237), and (b) scission of the ester linkages by hydrazine, benzylamine, or ethanolamine to give corresponding amide derivatives of the original carboxyl function (3,238–241).

Chemical analysis is also often required with copolyesters, particularly those made from mixtures of diols by ester-exchange methods (where one component may be preferentially removed in the volatile products), or for the determination of 3-oxapentamethylene ("diethylene glycol") residues in PET. This may be done by alcoholysis followed by vapor-phase chromatographic analysis of the reaction products (216,218, 242,243). Quantitative determination can be made in some cases from the depression of melting point relative to that of the homopolymer; diethylene glycol units in PET thus depress T_m by 2.2°C per mole % of co-unit (217). 1,2-Diols such as ethylene glycol can also conveniently be determined in polyester hydrolyzates by oxidation with periodic acid, and recent publications indicate that nuclear magnetic resonance techniques will provide a useful means of studying the relative amounts and the sequential distribution of co-units in copolyesters (25,30,244,245).

End-Group and Molecular-Weight Determination.   The molecular weights of linear polyesters are most conveniently determined by end-group analysis or by viscometry. The latter, of course, requires calibration with samples of known molecular weight determined independently by end-group analysis, osmometry, or light-scattering. Knowledge of end-group contents in polyesters is also required for the formulation of polyurethan compositions. End-group analysis is thus an important method of characterization whose utility extends up to $\bar{M}_n$ values of about 50,000 beyond which their decreasing concentration renders analysis very difficult in the majority of cases (246–248).

From the chemistry of polyester-forming reactions, the end-groups whose analysis is most frequently required are carboxyl and hydroxyl. The carboxyl group is readily determined by alkalimetric titration, the end-points being determined with visual indicators or potentiometrically. The titration is invariably carried out in solution, the choice of solvent depending on the nature of the polyester. The more soluble members can be titrated in chloroform, chloroform—methanol, or methanol—dioxan with alcoholic solutions of sodium or potassium hydroxide or sodium ethoxide (159,

246,249,250), whilst less soluble ones such as PET are best dissolved in hot benzyl alcohol, diluted with chloroform to give solutions that are sufficiently stable at room temperature, and titrated with sodium hydroxide in benzyl alcohol (251); aniline has also been used as a solvent for the titration of carboxyl end-groups in PET with ethanolic sodium hydroxide (252). In an alternative method, carboxyl-ended polyesters have been reacted with phenyl isocyanate, using pyridine as catalyst, followed by acid hydrolysis which liberates aniline that was determined colorimetrically by diazotization and coupling with naphthylethylenediamine (121,122).

The determination of hydroxyl end-groups in low-molecular-weight (<5000) polyesters can be effected by adaptations of the Verley-Bölsing procedure (253, 254), in which the substance to be analyzed is treated with an excess of acetic anhydride, usually in pyridine, when the hydroxyl groups are acetylated with liberation of an equivalent amount of acetic acid:

$$\text{\textasciitilde OH} + (CH_3CO)_2O + C_5H_5N \rightarrow \text{\textasciitilde OCOCH}_3 + CH_3COOH \cdot C_5H_5N$$

Water is then added to hydrolyze the residual excess anhydride, and the whole of the liberated acetic acid (as pyridinium acetate) is determined by titration with alkali. A blank titer must also be obtained in the absence of the polyester, and the difference between the two values gives the quantity of acetyl group used in reaction with the hydroxyl. The titration value must be corrected for the contribution of any carboxyl groups that may have been originally present in the polyester, or these may be neutralized before acetylation.

This method is not sufficiently accurate for higher-molecular-weight polyesters where the hydroxyl-group content is small, and a convenient variation in these cases involves reaction of the polymer with succinic anhydride which liberates new carboxyl groups equivalent to the original hydroxyl content:

$$\text{\textasciitilde OH} + H_2C\text{---}CH_2 \rightarrow \text{\textasciitilde OCO(CH}_2)_2COOH$$

The polyester is recovered after treatment, washed free of residual succinic anhydride, and the total carboxyl-group content determined by alkalimetry with correction for any carboxyl groups initially present in the material. The conditions of succinoylation are chosen with regard to the properties of the polymer: Aliphatic members can be reacted at relatively low temperatures in benzene (122) or pyridine (159) whilst PET is reacted in 1-methylnaphthalene at 175°C (252,255).

Several other reactions have been used for the determination of hydroxyl end-groups in polyesters. Reilly and Orchin treated a toluene solution of poly(ethylene adipate) with excess phenyl isocyanate and determined the residual excess by addition of dibutylamine and titration of the residual amine with hydrochloric acid (256). The reaction of PET with chloroacetyl chloride or bromoacetyl bromide gives products containing terminal chloro- or bromoacetoxy groups which can be determined by hydrolysis or fusion with sodium peroxide followed by the argentometric titration of halide ion (257,258); alternatively, PET is treated with an excess of a 3,5-dinitrobenzoyl chloride–pyridine reagent in nitrobenzene and the residual reagent is determined by hydrolysis and alkalimetric titration without the need to recover the acylated polymer (259). Phosgene has also been recommended for the conversion of hydroxyl end-groups to chlorocarbonate groups which can be hydrolyzed and determined as chloride ion (260). Lastly, isotope methods can be used to give the sum of [OH] + [COOH] by exchange of the active hydrogen atoms with D_2O (261,262) or T_2O (263), and infrared and nuclear-magnetic-resonance analysis permits the identification and determination of these groups in polyesters (264,265).

From the molecular weights determined by end-group or other methods it is possible to derive the constants relating the limiting viscosity number ([η]) to number-average molecular weight in the Mark-Houwink-Sakurada equation, $[\eta] = KM^{\alpha}$. The viscosity of molten polyesters varies with the weight-average molecular weight according to the relation $\ln \eta = A + CM_w^{1/2}$ where A and C are constants (249,266); this provides a useful basis for studying changes in molecular weight during polymerization or thermal degradation but it is not normally used for the direct determination of molecular weights.

A number of studies have been made of the distribution of molecular weights in polyesters, particularly PET (257,258,262,267–271). For polyesters prepared in conditions that are conducive to structural randomization, eg melt polymerization, the polydispersity appears to correspond closely with the predictions of the Flory distribution function (272), but PET prepared by solid-state polymerization displays a considerably wider distribution owing to the immobility of the chain segments (273).

Uses of Polyesters in Relation to Structure

For the reasons already given, the typical aliphatic polyesters cannot be used directly as structural materials but advantage is taken of their low T_g's in applications as plasticizers and as components of polyurethans. Both purposes require materials of freely flexible molecular character with little or no tendency to crystallize in the conditions of actual use, a requirement which is satisfied in some cases by polyesters of asymmetric repeating-unit structure and more often by the employment of copolyesters. The many proprietary brands available in both groups cover a considerable range of structures, and correspondingly of prices and properties.

Polyester plasticizers are employed mainly to prepare poly(vinyl chloride) and poly(vinyl acetate) speciality products, where their low volatility, resistance to extraction by solvents, and nonmigrating character offer advantages in comparison with conventional low-molecular-weight plasticizers. However, the relatively high price of the polyester plasticizers (see Table 1) which is approximately double that of the conventional materials, and technical difficulties in processing and plasticizer efficiency restricts them at present to only a minor part (approx 4.5% in 1964) of the whole U.S. plasticizer market. The detailed structures of the commercial polyester plasticizers are not generally disclosed by the manufacturers, but the patent and technical literature indicates that they are usually homo- or copolyesters of the A—A/B—B type, typified by poly(1,2-propylene glutarate, adipate, azelate, or sebacate) and including formulations based on the polyesterification of diethylene glycol (3-oxapentamethylene glycol), 1,3-butanediol, and neopentylene glycol. They commonly have molecular weights in the range of 1000–2000, but some varieties extend up to 6000–8000. Most of these materials result from the polycondensation of diols with dicarboxylic acids which yields chains mainly terminated by hydroxyl groups, but in some cases monofunctional fatty acids or higher alcohols have been incorporated to control the molecular weights by chain-blocking with terminal alkyl groups, and acetyl-terminated poly(oxypentanoyl) (**4**), an A—B type polyester, has also been recommended as a plasticizer. Polyester plasticizers are marketed in many grades and under a variety of trade names, eg Parapiex (Rohm and Haas Co.), Reoplex (Geigy Ltd.), Hexaplas (ICI Ltd.), Ultramoll (Bayer), Santicizer (Monsanto Co.). Further details of their structures and use can be gained from the specialist literature (24,274–276). See also Plasticizers.

Polyesters for urethan-polymer manufacture are essentially hydroxyl-ended macromolecular polyols that are reactive towards polyisocyanates. The properties of polyurethans employed in such diverse applications as coatings, adhesives, cast elastomers, spandex fibers, and flexible or rigid foams are governed by the structures of both reacting components, and the types of polyesterpolyols in commercial use include (a) simple linear compounds such as poly(ethylene adipate) (**3**) and its copolymers with units derived from 1,2-propanediol, diethylene glycol, and 1,3-butanediol, (b) linear copolymers containing o-phthalate units, (c) branched polyols made by incorporating units from glycerol, trimethylolethane, trimethylolpropane, or pentaerythritol. The branched polyols are used when a degree of crosslinking is required in the final product, and the phthalate copolyesters are used to give polyurethans of higher T_g than those from the acyclic intermediates. These materials are sold under such trade names as Multron and Multrathane (Mobay Chemical Co.), Desmophen (Bayer), Daltocel and Daltolac (ICI Ltd.), Foamrez (Witco Chemical Co.), and Selectrofoam (Pittsburgh Plate Glass Co.). Hydroxyl-terminated poly(oxyhexanoyl) compounds, made by the polymerization of ε-caprolactone, have recently been introduced under the name of Niax polyols (Union Carbide Corp.) as urethan cast-elastomer precursors; they are claimed to give products with very low brittle points (−70°C) and superior hydrolytic stability, similar to that of the polyether–polyols that are increasingly used for polyurethan manufacture. As with the plasticizers discussed above, the polyester urethan-precursors are generally of low molecular weight, in the range of 500–3000 depending on type. For further details see references 275 and 277–279. See also Urethan polymers.

High-melting aliphatic polyesters such as poly(oxyacetyl) (**5**) (R = H) (280,281), the stereoregular forms of poly(oxy(methylacetyl)) (**5**) (R = CH₃) (169,282–285), and poly(oxy-2,2-dimethylpropionyl) [—OCH₂C(CH₃)₂CO—]ₙ (286–288) have been proposed as self-supporting materials suitable for use as fibers, films, and thermoplastic molding resins but none has yet acquired commercial importance; the reasons undoubtedly include the lowered thermal and hydrolytic resistance of these materials as compared with the aromatic polyesters and polycarbonates that satisfy these purposes. Detailed accounts of the molecular basis of fiber-forming character in polymers are available elsewhere (289,290) and it will suffice to note here that useful fiber properties require that the polymer should combine (a) high melting or softening points (preferably above 200°C), (b) linear and symmetrical structure and high molecular weight, (c) a measure of molecular flexibility allied to the capacity to retain induced molecular orientation, (d) considerable resistance to environmental degradative influences, and (e) the capability of synthesis from economically available raw materials. In distinction to the polyesters discussed above, the fiber-forming polyesters of present or potential commercial interest are therefore normally crystalline, with molecular weights of 20,000 or more. They are mostly homopolymers, modified—if at all—with only minor proportions (<5 mole %) of copolymeric units, generally to improve dyeability or surface properties.

The basic molecular requirements for useful film-forming character are substantially the same as for fibers, and the dominant polyester for both applications is poly-

(ethylene terephthalate).   Various other ring-containing polyesters have been considered for commercial use, and one such polymer—poly(1,4-cyclohexanedimethylene terephthalate) with a 30:70 ratio of cis to trans units in the alicyclic moiety—has been manufactured as an apparel fiber under the names Kodel (Eastman Kodak Co.) and Vestan (Chemische Werke Hüls).   Other fiber-forming polyesters that have received detailed study include poly(p-oxymethylenebenzoyl) (54,55,291), poly(p-oxyethoxybenzoyl) (292,293), and alkylene polyesters of 4,4'-sulfonyldibenzoic (44,45), 4,4'-bibenzoic (294), and 4,4'-ethylenedioxydibenzoic acids (295–298) but none of these has yet been manufactured commercially.   The patent literature contains many claims to the suitability of ring-containing homo- and copolyesters as molding plastics, but apart from the polycarbonates the only member of this class that has appeared on the market is poly(ethylene terephthalate).   The polyarylates and polysulfonates must still be regarded as experimental materials; recent Russian work in this field (299) suggests that the iso- and terephthalate polyesters of phenolphthalein may prove to be interesting as moldable heat-resistant electrical insulators.

Other applications which have been considered for linear polyesters include uses as wire coating enamels (300) and as oil-resistant peroxide-curable elastomers (301). Aromatic copolyesters such as poly(tetramethylene isophthalate-co-terephthalate) and poly(ethylene-co-neopentylene terephthalate) have also acquired interest as hot-melt adhesives suitable for shoemaking and for the fabrication of laminates, and are believed to be manufactured for this purpose though on a rather small scale (302–304).

Bibliography

1. I. Goodman, "Polyesters" in H. F. Mark, N. G. Gaylord, and N. M. Bikales, eds., *Encyclopedia of Polymer Science and Technology*, Vol. 10, Interscience Publishers, a division of John Wiley & Sons, Inc., New York, in press.
2. *Polymer Preprints* **8** (2), (1967).
3. H. F. Mark and G. S. Whitby, eds., *Collected Papers of Wallace Hume Carothers*, Interscience Publishers, Inc., New York, 1940.
4. V. V. Korshak and S. V. Vinogradova, *Polyesters*, Pergamon Press, Ltd., Oxford, 1965.
5. I. Goodman and J. A. Rhys, *Polyesters*, Vol. 1: *Saturated Polyesters*, Iliffe Books, Ltd., for The Plastics Institute, London, 1965.
6. R. J. W. Reynolds, Chap. 5 in R. Hill, ed., *Fibers from Synthetic Polymers*, Elsevier Publishing Co., Amsterdam, 1953.
7. R. W. Lenz, *Organic Chemistry of Synthetic High Polymers*, Interscience Publishers, a division of John Wiley & Sons, Inc., New York, 1967.
8. H. Batzer, H. Holtschmidt, F. Wiloth, and B. Mohr, *Makromol. Chem.* **7**, 82–103 (1951).
9. E. A. Zavaglia, W. A. Mosher, and F. W. Billmeyer, Jr., *Offic. Dig.* (*J. Paint Technol. Eng.*) **37**, 229–234 (1965).
10. French Pat. 1,457,711 (1966), M. J. Hurwitz and E. W. Miller (to Rohm and Haas Co.).
11. E. J. Bourne, M. Stacey, J. C. Tatlow, and J. M. Tedder, *J. Chem. Soc.* **1949**, 2976–2979.
12. M. Stoll and A. Rouvé, *Helv. Chim. Acta* **17**, 1283–1288 (1934).
13. M. Stoll, A. Rouvé, and G. Stoll-Comte, *Helv. Chim. Acta* **17**, 1289–1308 (1934).
14. J. Dale, *J. Chem. Soc.*, **1965**, 72–78.
15. S. Sarel and L. A. Pohoryles, *J. Am. Chem. Soc.* **80**, 4596–4599 (1958).
16. V. Stannett and M. Szwarc, *J. Polymer Sci.* **10**, 587–591 (1953).
17. C. E. Berr, *J. Polymer Sci.* **15**, 591–592 (1955).
18. I. Goodman and B. F. Nesbitt, *Polymer* **1**, 384–396 (1960).
19. H. Zahn and G. Valk, *Makromol. Chem.* **64**, 37–48 (1963).
20. S. Hashimoto and S. Jinnai, *Chem. High Polymers* (*Japan*) **24** (261), 36–41 (1967).
21. V. V. Korshak and S. V. Rogozhin, *Izvest. Akad. Nauk SSSR, Otdel. Khim. Nauk* **1954**, 541–549.

22. H. Batzer and G. Weissenberger, *Makromol. Chem.* **12,** 1–19 (1954).
23. B-A. Feit, D. Raucher, and A. Zilkha, *J. Appl. Polymer Sci.* **9,** 2379–2391 (1965).
24. B. Parkyn, F. Lamb, and B. V. Clifton, *Polyesters,* Vol. 2: *Unsaturated Polyesters and Polyester Plasticisers,* Iliffe Books Ltd., for The Plastics Institute, London, 1967.
25. J. C. W. Chien and J. F. Walker, *J. Polymer Sci.* **45,** 239–242 (1962).
26. P. J. Flory, *Principles of Polymer Chemistry,* Cornell University Press, Ithaca, N.Y., 1913, pp. 79–83.
27. M. Davies and D. R. J. Hill, *Trans. Faraday Soc.* **49,** 395–404 (1953).
28. M. T. Pope and R. J. P. Williams, *J. Chem. Soc.* **1959,** 3579–3582.
29. C. Y. Huang, Y. Simono, and T. Onizuka, *Chem. High Polymers (Japan)* **23** (254), 408–414 (1966).
30. J. G. Smith, C. J. Kibler, and B. J. Sublett, *J. Polymer Sci. A-1* **4,** 1851–1859 (1966).
31. C. J. Kibler, A. Bell, and J. G. Smith, *J. Polymer Sci. A-2,* 2115–2125 (1964).
32. Brit. Pat. 979,401 (1965), E. I. du Pont de Nemours & Co., Inc.
33. U.S. Pat. 2,789,509 (1957), D. D. Reynolds and J. van den Berghe (to Eastman Kodak Co.).
34. Brit. Pat. 818,157 (1959), C. J. Kibler, A. Bell, and J. G. Smith (Kodak Ltd.).
35. U.S. Pat. 2,843,567 (1958), J. L. R. Williams and K. R. Dunham (to Eastman Kodak Co.).
36. Belg. Pat. 546,376 (1956), Farbenfabriken Bayer A. G.
37. Brit. Pat. 842,759 (1960), Farbenfabriken Bayer A. G.
38. French Pat. 1,278,284 (1961), E. U. Elam, J. C. Martin, and R. Gilkey (to Kodak-Pathé).
39. U.S. Pat. 2,720,503 (1955), J. W. Wellman (to Eastman Kodak Co.).
40. U.S. Pat. 2,727,881 (1955), J. R. Caldwell and J. W. Wellman (to Eastman Kodak Co.).
41. M. Horio, I. Imamura, T. Seizo, and T. Takegoshi, *Kyoto Daigaku Nippon, Kagaku Sen-i-Kenkusho Koenshii* **19,** 43–55 (1965).
42. Brit. Pat. 968,403 (1964), I. Goodman, R. C. Russell, and J. W. Stimpson (to Imperial Chemical Industries Ltd.).
43. U.S. Pat. 3,198,769 (1965), A. R. Macon (to E. I. du Pont de Nemours & Co., Inc.).
44. U.S. Pats. 2,744,088–2,744,095 (1956), J. R. Caldwell (to Eastman Kodak Co.).
45. U.S. Pat. 3,228,913 (1966), G. A. Nesty and L. J. Spillane (to Allied Chemical Corp.).
46. U.S. Pat. 2,921,052 (1960), J. R. Caldwell and J. W. Wellman (to Eastman Kodak Co.).
47. C. F. Horn, *Makromol. Chem.* **30,** 123–153 (1959).
48. Belg. Pat. 585,556 (1960), Gevaert Photo-Producten N. V.
49. Brit. Pat. 857,378 (1960), Farbenfabriken Bayer A. G.
50. Brit. Pat. 956,206 (1964), W. J. Jackson and J. R. Caldwell (to Eastman Kodak Co.).
51. Brit. Pat. 924,607 (1963), B. E. Jennings (to Imperial Chemical Industries Ltd.).
52. U.S. Pat. 3,254,061 (1966), J. C. Martin and R. Gilkey (to Eastman Kodak Co.).
53. C. G. Overberger, S. Ozaki, and D. M. Braunstein, *Makromol. Chem.* **93,** 13–23 (1966).
54. Z. Zámorský and R. Veselý, *Chem. Prumysl* **6** (33), 106–108 (1958).
55. H. Ludewig, H. Ramm, and K. Wiegand, *J. prakt. Chem.* **6** (4), 103–114 (1958).
56. U.S. Pats. 2,692,248–2,692,249 (1954), British Celanese Ltd.
57. I. Tachi and K. Murakami, *Mokuzai Gakkaishi* **5,** 177–181 (1959); (through) *Chem. Abstr.* **54,** 16001 (1960).
58. French Pat. 1,220,725 (1960), Inventa A. G. für Forschung und Patentverwertung.
59. Brit. Pat. 985,611 (1965), M. K. McCreath and I. Goodman (to Imperial Chemical Industries Ltd.).
60. Brit. Pat. 636,429 (1950), E. R. Wallsgrove and R. Reeder (to Courtaulds Ltd.).
61. M. Levine and S. C. Temin, *J. Polymer Sci.* **28,** 179–184 (1958).
62. S. C. Temin, *J. Org. Chem.* **26,** 2518–2521 (1961).
63. Brit. Pat. 989,552 (1965), I. Goodman, J. E. McIntyre, and J. W. Stimpson (to Imperial Chemical Industries Ltd.).
64. U.S. Pat. 2,595,343 (1952), J. G. N. Drewitt and J. Lincoln (to Celanese Corporation of America).
65. A. Conix, *Ind. Chim. Belge* **22,** 1457–1462 (1957).
66. A. Conix, *Ind. Eng. Chem.* **51,** 147–150 (1959).
67. U.S. Pats. 3,036,990–3,036,992 (1962) and 3,160,604 (1964), F. F. Holub and S. W. Kantor (to General Electric Co.).
68. Brit. Pat. 883,312 (1961), A. J. Conix (to Gevaert Photo-Producten N.V.).
69. U.S. Pat. 3,225,003 (1965), A. R. Macon (to E. I. du Pont de Nemours & Co., Inc.).

70. U.S. Pat. 3,219,627 (1965), A. A. D'Onofrio (to Union Carbide Corp.).
71. R. Gilkey and J. R. Caldwell, *J. Appl. Polymer Sci.* **2,** 198–202 (1959).
72. U.S. Pat. 2,728,747 (1955), D. Aelony and M. M. Renfrew (to General Mills Inc.).
73. U.S. Pat. 3,179,636 (1965), R. J. Convery (to Sun Oil Co.).
74. D. F. Loncrini, *J. Polymer Sci. A-1* **4,** 1531–1541 (1966).
75. Brit. Pat. 590,417 (1947), J. G. Cook and Imperial Chemical Industries Ltd.
76. French Pat. 1,163,702 (1958), H. Gudgeon and F. G. Jeffers (to Imperial Chemical Industries Ltd.).
77. U.S. Pat. 3,039,994 (1962), W. K. T. Gleim (to Universal Oil Products Co.).
78. Brit. Pat. 760,125 (1956), W. R. Burton and D. S. Davies (to Imperial Chemical Industries Ltd.).
79. M. Gawlak, R. P. Palmer, J. B. Rose, D. J. H. Sandiford, and A. Turner-Jones, *Chem. Ind. (London)* **1962,** 1148–1149.
80. U.S. Pat. 2,799,666 (1957), J. R. Caldwell (to Eastman Kodak Co.).
81. U.S. Pats. 2,789,965–2,789,971 (1957), D. D. Reynolds, et al. (to Eastman Kodak Co.).
82. V. V. Korshak and S. V. Vinogradova, *Russ. Chem. Rev. (English transl.),* **30,** 171–192 (1961).
83. Brit. Pat. 1,034,194 (1966), Borg-Warner Corporation.
84. Brit. Pat. 627,270 (1949), Wingfoot Corp.
85. G. C. Schweitzer and P. Robitschek, *J. Polymer Sci.* **24,** 33–41 (1957).
86. U.S. Pat. 3,016,360 (1962), G. C. Schweitzer and P. Robitschek (to Hooker Chemical Corp.).
87. U.S. Pat. 3,240,800 (1966), W. A. Severson (to Minnesota Mining and Manufacturing Co.).
88. Brit. Pat. 993,272 (1965), I. Goodman, J. E. McIntyre, and D. H. Aldred (to Imperial Chemical Industries Ltd.).
89. Brit. Pat. 1,000,200 (1965), I. Goodman and D. H. Aldred (Imperial Chemical Industries Ltd.).
90. Brit. Pat. 863,704 (1961), Farbwerke Hoechst A. G.
91. H. Schnell, *Chemistry and Physics of Polycarbonates,* Interscience Publishers, a division of John Wiley & Sons, Inc., New York, 1964.
92. W. M. Eareckson, *J. Polymer Sci.* **40,** 399–406 (1959).
93. U.S. Pat. 3,256,242 (1966), P. W. Morgan (to E. I. du Pont de Nemours & Co., Inc.).
94. E. L. Wittbecker and P. W. Morgan, *J. Polymer Sci.* **40,** 289–297 (1959).
95. P. W. Morgan and S. L. Kwolek, *J. Polymer Sci.* **40,** 299–327 (1959).
96. P. W. Morgan, *J. Polymer Sci. A* **2,** 437–459 (1964).
97. P. W. Morgan, *Condensation Polymers by Interfacial and Solution Methods,* Interscience Publishers, a division of John Wiley & Sons, Inc., New York, 1965.
98. A. S. Astakhova and L. B. Sokolov, *Geterotsepnye Vysokomol. Soedin.* **1964,** 64–67.
99. Japan. Pat. 14846/1962, Y. Matsuda, Y. Nakahara, T. Yasue, H. Sawada, and S. Suzuki (Dai-Nippon Celluloid Co.).
100. V. V. Korshak, S. V. Vinogradova, S. N. Salazkin, and T. A. Sidorov, *Izvest. Akad. Nauk SSSR, Otdel. Khim. Nauk* **1962,** 1416–1423.
101. Brit. Pat. 968,390 (1964), I. Goodman and E. Haddock (to Imperial Chemical Industries Ltd.).
102. Brit. Pat. 590,451 (1947), J. T. Dickson, H. P. W. Huggill, and J. C. Welch.
103. U.S. Pat. 2,719,835 (1955), The Chemstrand Corporation.
104. Brit. Pat. 805,855 (1958), E. J. Gasson, D. J. Hadley, and B. Wood (to The Distillers Co. Ltd.).
105. French Pat. 1,365,841 (1964), Toyo Rayon Co. Ltd.
106. E. N. Zil'berman and A. E. Kulikova, *Zh. Obshch. Khim.* **29,** 1694–1699 (1959).
107. E. N. Zil'berman and N. M. Teplyakov, *Vysokomol. Soedin.* **2,** 133–135 (1960).
108. M. V. Prokof'eva, S. R. Rafikov, and B. V. Suvorov, *Zh. Obshch. Khim.* **32,** 1318–1323 (1962).
109. S. Bezzi, *Gazz. Chim. Ital.* **79,** 219–233 (1949).
110. Belg. Pat. 538,255 (1956), Vereinigte Glanzstoff Fabriken.
111. Brit. Pat. 815,852 (1959), Pittsburgh Plate Glass Co.
112. U.S. Pat. 3,177,180 (1965), J. D. Doedens and E. H. Rosenbrock (to The Dow Chemical Co.).
113. Brit. Pat. 1,037,898 (1966), Albright and Wilson Ltd.
114. U.S. Pat. 2,799,667 (1957), J. G. N. Drewitt and J. Lincoln (to British Celanese Ltd.).

115. Brit. Pat. 769,700 (1957), The Chemstrand Corporation.
116. Brit. Pat. 742,793 (1956), J. Lincoln (to British Celanese Ltd.).
117. Brit. Pat. 933,448 (1963), Inventa A. G. für Forschung und Patentverwertung.
118. W. Griehl, *Lenzinger Berichte* **22**, 55–63 (1966).
119. U.S. Pat. 2,722,555 (1955), R. W. Amidon (to U.S. Rubber Co.).
120. Brit. Pat. 1,043,671 (1966), Sinclair Research Inc.
121. W. Kern, R. Munk, A. Sabel, and K. H. Schmidt, *Makromol. Chem.* **17**, 201–218 (1956).
122. W. Kern, R. Munk, and K. H. Schmidt, *Makromol. Chem.* **17**, 219–230 (1956).
123. Brit. Pat. 801,412 (1958), Gevaert Photo-Producten N. V.
124. Brit. Pat. 898,301 (1962), Monsanto Chemical Co.
125. V. V. Korshak, S. V. Rogozhin, and V. I. Volkov, *Vysokomol. Soedin* **1**, 804–808 (1959).
126. U.S. Pat. 2,533,455 (1950), H. J. Hagemeyer (to Eastman Kodak Co.).
127. U.S. Pat. 3,002,024 (1961), A. T. Blomquist (to B. F. Goodrich Co.).
128. R. F. Fischer, *J. Polymer Sci.* **44**, 155–172 (1960).
129. R. F. Fischer, *Ind. Eng. Chem.* **52**, 321–323 (1960).
130. U.S. Pat. 2,975,149 (1961), W. S. Port, L. L. Gelb, and W. C. Ault (to U.S. Secretary of Agriculture).
131. E. Schwenk, K. Gulbins, M. Roth, G. Benzing, R. Maysenhölder, and K. Hamann, *Makromol. Chem.* **51**, 53–69 (1962).
132. T. Tsuruta, K. Matsuura, and S. Inoue, *Makromol. Chem.* **75**, 211–214 (1964).
133. Brit. Pat. 996,248 (1965), Allied Chemical Corp.
134. Brit. Pat. 729,487 (1955), Henkel et Cie.
135. U.S. Pat. 2,811,512 (1957), P. R. Austin and O. W. Cass (to E. I. du Pont de Nemours & Co., Inc.).
136. Brit. Pat. 955,514 (1964), Fabriek van Chemische Producten Vondelingenplaat, N. V.
137. Brit. Pat. 999,403 (1965), M. Lerer (to Inst. Français du Pétrole, des Carburants et Lubrifiants).
138. C. A. Bischoff and P. Walden, *Ber.* **26**, 262–265 (1893).
139. F. Fichter and A. Beisswenger, *Ber.* **36**, 1200–1205 (1903).
140. H. K. Hall and A. K. Schneider, *J. Am. Chem. Soc.* **80**, 6409–6412 (1958).
141. H. K. Hall and R. Zbinden, *J. Am. Chem. Soc.* **80**, 6428–6432 (1958).
142. H. Cherdron, H. Ohse, and F. Korte, *Makromol. Chem.* **56**, 179–186 (1962).
143. *Ibid.*, 187–194 (1962).
144. H. Ohse, H. Cherdron, and F. Korte, *Makromol. Chem.* **86**, 312–315 (1965).
145. H. Cherdron and H. Ohse, *Makromol. Chem.* **92**, 213–223 (1966).
146. H. Ohse and H. Cherdron, *Makromol. Chem.* **97**, 139–145 (1966).
147. Y. Yamashita, T. Tsuda, Y. Ishikawa, and T. Shimizu, *Kogyo Kagaku Zasshi* **66**, 1493–1497 (1963).
148. Y. Yamashita, Y. Ishikawa, and T. Tsuda, *Kogyo Kagaku Zasshi* **67**, 252–255 (1964).
149. T. Tsuda, T. Shimizu, and Y. Yamashita, *Kogyo Kagaku Zasshi* **67**, 1661–1664 (1964).
150. *Ibid.*, 2145–2149 (1964).
151. *Ibid.*, 2150–2153 (1964).
152. T. Tsuda and Y. Yamashita, *Makromol. Chem.* **86**, 304–307 (1965).
153. Y. Yamashita, T. Tsuda, M. Okada, and S. Iwatsuki, *J. Polymer Sci. A-1* **4**, 2121–2135 (1966).
154. Y. Yamashita, K. Umchara, K. Ito, and T. Tsuda, *J. Polymer Sci. B* **4**, 241–243 (1966).
155. K. W. Rosenmund and H. Bach, *Chem. Ber.* **94**, 2401–2408 (1961).
156. K. Saotome and Y. Kodaira, *Makromol. Chem.* **82**, 41–52 (1965).
157. P. A. Small, *Trans. Faraday Soc.* **51**, 1717–1720 (1955).
158. F. S. Dainton and K. J. Ivin, *Quart. Revs.* **12**, 61–92 (1958).
159. F. Korte and W. Glet, *J. Polymer Sci. B* **4**, 685–689 (1966).
160. R. Huisgen and H. Ott, *Tetrahedron* **6**, 253–267 (1959).
161. J. F. McConnell, A. McL. Mathieson, and B. P. Schoenborn, *Tetrahedron Letters* **1962**, 445–448.
162. A. McL. Mathieson, *Tetrahedron Letters* **1963**, 81–84.
163. K. K. Cheung, K. H. Overton, and G. A. Sim, *Chem. Communs.* **1965**, 634–635.
164. G. A. Jeffrey and S. H. Kim, *Chem. Communs.* **1966**, 211–212.

165. H. K. Hall, M. K. Brandt, and R. M. Mason, *J. Am. Chem. Soc.* **80,** 6420–6427 (1958).

166. H. K. Hall, *J. Am. Chem. Soc.* **80,** 6412–6420 (1958).

167. R. Zbinden and H. K. Hall, *J. Am. Chem. Soc.* **82,** 1215–1218 (1960).

168. H. Ohse and H. Cherdron, *Makromol. Chem.* **95,** 283–295 (1966).

169. U.S. Pat. 2,703,316 (1955), A. K. Schneider (to E. I. du Pont de Nemours & Co., Inc.).

170. Brit. Pat. 1,086,314 (1967), Union Carbide Corp. (F. Hostettler and E. F. Cox).

171. R. Chujo, H. Kobayashi, J. Suzuki, S. Tokahura, and T. Tanabe, *Makromol. Chem.* **100,** 262–266 (1967).

172. French Pat. 1,425,333 (1965), R. A. Fouty (E. I. du Pont de Nemours & Co., Inc.).

173. Brit. Pats. 859,639–859,645 (1961), Union Carbide Corp.

174. French Pat. 1,341,074 (1963), Shell International Research Maatschappij N. V.

175. Brit. Pat. 977,230 (1964), Farbenfabriken Bayer A. G.

176. S. Inoue, Y. Tomoi, T. Tsuruta, and J. Furukawa, *Makromol. Chem.* **48,** 229–233 (1961).

177. Belg. Pat. 639,062 (1964), Shell International Research Maatschappij N. V.

178. U.S. Pat. 3,140,274 (1964), H. A. Kantor, J. A. Vona, and B. S. Ainsworth (to Celanese Corp. of America).

179. Brit. Pat. 926,904 (1963), Celanese Corp. of America (R. J. Kray and C. A. De Fazio).

180. German Pats. 1,152,818 (1963), 1,190,189 (1965), and 1,202,492 (1965), Deutsche Gold- und Silber-Scheideanstalt.

181. Brit. Pat. 998,479 (1965), W. Wilson and H. May (to British Industrial Plastics, Ltd.).

182. T. Kagiya, S. Narisawa, K. Manabe, and K. Fukui, *Kogyo Kagaku Zasshi* **68,** 1741–1747 (1965).

183. Brit. Pat. 1,020,617 (1966), Sumitomo Chemical Co. Ltd.

184. German Pat. Appln. K. 18022, 39c, 25/01 (1955) and German Pat. 929,875 (1955), J. Kleine.

185. U.S. Pat. 2,835,658 (1958), J. L. Lang (to Dow Chemical Co.).

186. U.S. Pat. 2,856,376 (1958), M. A. McCall and H. W. Coover, Jr. (to Eastman Kodak Co.).

187. Japan. Pat. 17696/62, Japanese Association for Radiation Research on Polymers (S. Okamura, K. Hayashi, and Y. Kitanishi).

188. K. Ito, K. Baba, and Y. Yamashita, *Kogyo Kagaku Zasshi* **68,** 703–706 (1965).

189. Japan. Pat. 1499/63, Toyo Rubber Industry Co. Ltd. (J. Furukawa, S. Yamashita, and H. Okamoto).

190. Japan. Pat. 20522/64, Asahi Chemical Co. Ltd. (R. Wakoda, K. Saotome, and N. Kawamoto).

191. French Pat. 1,473,724 (1967), I. Goodman and N. R. Hurworth (to Imperial Chemical Industries Ltd.).

192. Brit. Pat. 1,099,184 (1968), I. Goodman and N. R. Hurworth (to Imperial Chemical Industries Ltd.).

193. R. E. Wilfong, *J. Polymer Sci.* **54,** 385–410 (1961).

194. W. Griehl and G. Schnock, *J. Polymer Sci.* **30,** 413–422 (1958).

195. V. V. Korshak, V. A. Zamyatina, and N. I. Bekasova, *Izvest. Akad. Nauk SSSR, Otdel. Khim. Nauk* **1958,** 482–485; (through) *Chem. Abstr.* **52,** 17167 (1958).

196. G. Torraca and R. Turriziani, *Chim. Ind.* (*Milan*) **44**(5), 483–488 (1962).

197. H. Zimmermann, *Faserforsch. u. Textiltech.* **13,** 481–490 (1962).

198. K. Yoda, K. Kimoto, and T. Toda, *Kogyo Kagaku Zasshi* **67,** 909–914 (1964).

199. F. Pochetti and R. Turriziani, *Ann. Chim.* (*Rome*) **55,** 1242–1251 (1965).

200. W. Griehl and G. Schnock, *Faserforsch. u. Textiltech.* **8,** 408–416 (1957).

201. L. H. Peebles and W. S. Wagner, *J. Phys. Chem.* **63,** 1206–1212 (1959).

202. M. Sumoto, *Kogyo Kagaku Zasshi* **66** (12), 1867–1870 (1963); (through) *Chem. Abstr.* **61,** 3198 (1964).

203. M. Sumoto, A. Kito, and R. Inoue, *Kobunshi Kagaku* **15,** 664–670 (1958); (through) *Chem. Abstr.* **54,** 16001 (1960).

204. V. V. Korshak, N. I. Bekasova, and V. A. Zamyatina, *Izvest. Akad. Nauk SSSR, Otdel. Khim. Nauk* **1958,** 486–491.

205. G. Challa, *Rec. Trav. Chim.* **79,** 90–100 (1960).

206. G. Challa, *Makromol. Chem.* **38,** 105–146 (1960).

207. Brit. Pat. 802,921 (1958), E. Isaacs and N. Munro (to Imperial Chemical Industries Ltd.)

208. Brit. Pat. 886,966 (1962), N. D. Scott and N. Munro (to Imperial Chemical Industries Ltd.).

209. U.S. Pat. 2,758,105 (1956), F. P. Alles and W. R. Sauer (to E. I. du Pont de Nemours & Co., Inc.).

210. Brit. Pat. 838,663 (1960), N. Fletcher (Imperial Chemical Industries Ltd.).
211. Brit. Pat. 1,033,999 (1966), W. M. Corbett (to Imperial Chemical Industries Ltd.).
212. Brit. Pat. 1,034,014 (1966), W. M. Corbett and D. Harrison (to Imperial Chemical Industries Ltd.).
213. U.S. Pat. 3,227,680 (1966), J. W. Tamblyn, C. J. Kibler, and A. Bell (to Eastman Kodak Co.).
214. Belg. Pat. 676,491 (1966), Monsanto Co.
215. I. Goodman and B. F. Nesbitt, *J. Polymer Sci.* **48**, 423–433 (1960).
216. R. Janssen, H. Ruysschaert, and R. Vroom, *Makromol. Chem.* **77**, 153–158 (1964)
217. J. R. Kirby, A. J. Baldwin, and R. H. Heidner, *Anal. Chem.* **37**, 1306–1309 (1965).
218. D. R. Gaskill, A. G. Chasar, and C. A. Lucchesi, *Anal. Chem.* **39**, 106–108 (1967).
219. R. J. P. Allan, R. L. Forman, and P. D. Ritchie, *J. Chem. Soc.* **1955**, 2717–2725.
220. H. V. R. Iengar and P. D. Ritchie, *J. Chem. Soc.* **1956**, 3563–3570.
221. E. P. Goodings in *High Temperature Resistance and Thermal Degradation of Polymers*, Monograph No. 13, Society of Chemical Industry, London, 1961, pp. 211–228.
222. A. Mifune, S. Ishida, A. Kobayashi, and S. Sakajiri, *Kogyo Kagaku Zasshi* **65**, 992–995 (1962).
223. R. B. Rashbrook and G. W. Taylor, *Chem. Ind. (London)* **1962**, 215–216.
224. Brit. Pat. 889,851 (1962), E. I. du Pont de Nemours & Co., Inc.
225. Brit. Pat. 1,048,068 (1966), E. I. du Pont de Nemours & Co., Inc.
226. Neths. Pat. Appln. 67,02845 (1967), E. I. du Pont de Nemours & Co., Inc.
227. U. S. Pat. 3,300,447 (1967), W. Thoma and H. Rinke (to Farbenfabriken Bayer A. G.).
228. Brit. Pats. 1,039,231–1,039,233 (1966), Monsanto Co.
229. Brit. Pat. 1,041,853 (1966), Eastman Kodak Co. (J. S. Perlowski, R. D. Coffee, and R. B. Edwards).
230. Brit. Pat. 1,045,343 (1966), Farbwerke Hoechst A. G.
231. Brit. Pat. 1,046,526 (1966), Inventa A. G.
232. *Chem. Eng. News* **44**, 56–57 (April 4, 1966).
233. H. Scheller, *Chemiefasern* **1965** (12), 923–928.
234. *European Chem. News* (May 19, 1967), 28–30.
235. P. Ellwood, *Chem. Eng.* **74**, 98–100 (Nov. 20, 1967).
236. Brit. Pat. 1,066,162 (1967), T. Davies, G. E. Head, and K. Porter (to Imperial Chemical Industries Ltd.).
237. G. Natta, G. Mazzanti, G. Pregaglia, M. Binaghi, and M. Peraldo, *J. Am. Chem. Soc.* **82**, 4742–4743 (1960).
238. R. Huisgen and J. Reinertshofer, *Ann.* **575**, 174–216 (1952).
239. W. Funke, W. Gebhardt, H. Roth, and K. Hamann, *Makromol. Chem.* **28**, 17–57 (1958).
240. W. Funke, H. Gilch, and K. Hamann, *Makromol. Chem.* **31**, 93–111 (1959).
241. J. Haslam and D. C. M. Squirrell, *Analyst* **82**, 515–516 (1957).
242. K. Tada, Y. Numata, T. Saegusa, and J. Furukawa, *Makromol. Chem.* **77**, 220–228 (1964).
243. A. Mifune and S. Ishida, *Kogyo Kagaku Zasshi* **65**, 824–826 (1962).
244. M. Murano, Y. Kaneishi, and R. Yamadera, *J. Polymer Sci.* [A] **3**, 2698–2700 (1965).
245. R. Yamadera and M. Murano, *J. Polymer Sci. A-1* **5**, 2259–2268 (1967).
246. G. F. Price, Chap. 7 in P. W. Allen, ed., *Techniques of Polymer Characterization*, Butterworth & Co., Ltd., London, 1959.
247. M. Hellmann and L. A. Wall, Chap. 5 in G. M. Kline, ed., *Analytical Chemistry of Polymers*, Part III, Interscience Publishers, Inc., New York, 1962.
248. S. R. Rafikov, S. A. Pavlova, and I. I. Tverdokhlebova, *Determination of Molecular Weights and Polydispersity of High Polymers*, Academy of Sciences of the U.S.S.R. (1963); English translation by Israel Program for Scientific Translations, Jerusalem, 1964.
249. W. O. Baker, C. S. Fuller, and J. H. Heiss, *J. Am. Chem. Soc.* **63**, 2142–2148 (1941).
250. P. Fijolka, I. Lenz, and F. Runge, *Makromol. Chem.* **23**, 60–70 (1957).
251. H. A. Pohl, *Anal. Chem.* **26**, 1614–1616 (1954).
252. J. Majewska and J. Warzywoda, *Melliand Textilber.* **43**, 480–481 (1962).
253. A. Verley and Fr. Bölsing, *Ber.* **34**, 3354–3358 (1901).
254. E. A. Emelin and Ya. A. Tsarfin, *Plasticheskie Massy*, **1961** (3), 75–76.
255. A. Conix, *Makromol. Chem.* **26**, 226–235 (1958).
256. C. B. Reilly and M. Orchin, *Ind. Eng. Chem.* **48**, 59–63 (1956).
257. W. Griehl and S. Neue, *Faserforsch. u. Textiltech.* **5**, 423–429 (1954).

258. K. Ueberreiter and T. Götze, *Makromol. Chem.* **29,** 61–69 (1959).

259. H. Zimmermann and A. Tryonadt, *Faserforsch. u. Textiltech.* **18,** 487–490 (1967).

260. D. G. Bush, L. J. Kunzelsauer, and S. H. Merrill, *Anal. Chem.* **35,** 1250–1252 (1963).

261. I. M. Ward, *Trans. Faraday Soc.* **53,** 1406–1412 (1957).

262. H. M. Koepp and H. Werner, *Makromol. Chem.* **32,** 79–89 (1959).

263. C-Y. Cha, *J. Polymer Sci. B* **2,** 1069–1073 (1964).

264. D. Patterson and I. M. Ward, *Trans. Faraday Soc.* **53,** 291–294 (1957).

265. T. F. Page and W. E. Bresler, *Anal. Chem.* **36,** 1981–1985 (1964).

266. P. J. Flory, *J. Am. Chem. Soc.* **62,** 1057–1070 (1940).

267. E. V. Kuznetsov, A. O. Vizel', I. M. Shermergorn, and S. S. Tyulenev, *Vysokomol. Soedin.* **2,** 205–209 (1960).

268. E. Turska, T. Skwarski, and S. Szapiro, *J. Polymer Sci.* **30,** 391–398 (1958).

269. K. Gehrke and G. Reinisch, *Faserforsch. u. Textiltech.* **17,** 201–207 (1958).

270. F. Pailhes, M. Alliot-Lugaz, N. Dueau, and J. Kyritsos, *J. Polymer Sci. C*, **16,** 1177–1190 (1967).

271. M. J. R. Cantow, ed., *Polymer Fractionation*, Academic Press, Inc., New York, 1967.

272. G. J. Howard, "The Molecular Weight Distribution of Condensation Polymers," in J. C. Robb and F. W. Peaker, eds., *Progress in High Polymers*, Vol. 1, Heywood and Co., London, 1961.

273. C-Y. Cha, *Polymer Preprints* **6,** 84–89 (1965).

274. Brit. Pat. 1,032,648 (1966), Asahi Kasei Kogyo Kabushiki Kaisha.

275. *Modern Plastics Encyclopedia 1967*, McGraw-Hill Book Co., Inc., New York, 1966.

276. D. A. Lannon and E. J. Hoskins, Chap. 7 in P. D. Ritchie, ed., *Physics of Plastics*, Iliffe Books Ltd. for The Plastics Institute, London, 1965.

277. L. N. Phillips and D. B. V. Parker, *Polyurethanes: Chemistry, Technology and Properties*, Iliffe Books Ltd., for The Plastics Institute, London, 1964.

278. B. A. Dombrow, *Polyurethanes*, 2nd ed., Reinhold Publishing Corp., New York, 1965.

279. R. Vieweg and A. Höchtlen, eds., *Polyurethane*, Vol. 7 of *Kunststoff-Handbuch*, Carl Hauser Verlag, Munich, 1966.

280. K. Chujo, H. Kobayashi, J. Suzuki, and S. Tokahura, *Makromol. Chem.* **100,** 267–270 (1967).

281. U.S. Pat. 2,585,427 (1952), M. L. Beck (to E. I. du Pont de Nemours & Co., Inc.).

282. U.S. Pat. 2,758,987 (1956), P. L. Salzberg (to E. I. du Pont de Nemours & Co., Inc.).

283. J. Kleine and H-H. Kleine, *Makromol. Chem.* **30,** 23–28 (1959).

284. Brit. Pats. 1,040,168 and 1,048,088 (1966), E. I. du Pont de Nemours & Co., Inc.

285. T. Asahara and S. Katayama, *Kogyo Kagaku Zasshi* **67,** 956–961 (1964); **68,** 983–986 (1965).

286. Brit. Pat. 766,347 (1957), R. J. W. Reynolds and E. J. Vickers (to Imperial Chemical Industries Ltd.).

287. U.S. Pat. 2,658,055 (1953), T. Alderson (to E. I. du Pont de Nemours & Co., Inc.).

288. Brit. Pat. 1,046,944 (1966), E. I. du Pont de Nemours & Co., Inc.

289. J. W. S. Hearle and R. H. Peters, eds., *Fibre Structure*, Butterworths and The Textile Institute, London, 1963.

290. I. Goodman, "Synthetic Fibre-Forming Polymers," *Royal Institute of Chemistry* (*London*), *Lecture Series, 1967*, No. 3.

291. Brit. Pat. 604,985 (1948), J. G. Cook, J. T. Dickson, A. R. Lowe, J. R. Whinfield, and Imperial Chemical Industries Ltd.

292. M. Korematsu, H. Masuda, and S. Kuriyama, *Kogyo Kagaku Zasshi* **63,** 884–888 (1960).

293. U.S. Pats. 2,686,198 (1954) and 2,755,273 (1956), L. H. Bock (to Rayonnier Inc.).

294. U.S. Pats. 3,008,930–3,008,935 (1961), E. A. Wielicki and R. D. Evans (to American Viscose Corp.).

295. Brit. Pat. 579,462 (1946), J. T. Dickson.

296. Brit. Pat. 1,047,978 (1966), E. F. Harris, R. J. B. Marsden, and J. F. Ll. Roberts (Imperial Chemical Industries Ltd.).

297. Brit. Pat. 1,082,330 (1967), R. B. Rashbrook and J. F. Ll. Roberts (Imperial Chemical Industries Ltd.).

298. R. Imamura, T. Kiyotsukuri, Y. Yamamoto, O. Sangen, and M. Horio, *Sen-i-Gakkaishi*, **23** (2), 51–57 (1967); (through) *Chem. Abstr.* **67,** 44675 (1967).

299. S. V. Vinogradova, V. V. Korshak, E. I. Fridman, M. A. Andreeva, and L. N. Baraboshkina, *Soviet Plastics* **9,** 20–22 (1966).

300. Brit. Pat. 676,372 (1952), O. B. Edgar, B. Jacob, and Imperial Chemical Industries Ltd.

301. B. S. Biggs, R. H. Erickson, and C. S. Fuller, *Ind. Eng. Chem.* **39**, 1090–1097 (1947).

302. Brit. Pats. 962,853 (1964) and 998,654 (1965), Bostik Ltd.

303. French Pat. 1,436,992 (1966), Farbwerke Hoechst A. G. vormals Meister Lucius u. Brüning.

304. Brit. Pat. 1,043,313 (1966), The Goodyear Tire and Rubber Co.

General References

R. Hill and E. E. Walker, *J. Polymer Sci.* **3**, 609–630 (1948).

H. Batzer, *Angew. Chem.* **66**, 513–519 (1954).

R. E. Wilfong, *J. Polymer Sci.* **54**, 385–410 (1961).

E. Müller, *Polycarbonsäure Ester*, Chap. 1 in Part 2 of Vol. XIV/2, *Makromolekuläre Stoffe*, of E. Müller, ed., *Methoden der Organischen Chemie (Houben-Weyl)*, Georg Thieme Verlag, Stuttgart, 1963.

J. Hacquard, *Bull. Assoc. Franç. Tech. Pétrole* **172**, 559–579 (1965).

H. Mark and G. S. Whitby, eds., *Collected Papers of Wallace Hume Carothers*, Interscience Publishers, Inc., New York, 1940.

R. Hill, ed., *Fibres from Synthetic Polymers*, Elsevier Publishing Co., Amsterdam, 1953.

J. W. S. Hearle and R. H. Peters, eds., *Fibre Structure*, Butterworths and The Textile Institute, London, 1963.

V. V. Korshak and S. V. Vinogradova, *Polyesters*, Pergamon Press, Oxford, 1965.

H. Schnell, *Chemistry and Physics of Polycarbonates*, Interscience Publishers, a division of John Wiley & Sons, Inc., New York, 1964.

H. V. Boenig, *Unsaturated Polyesters: Structure and Properties*, Elsevier Publishing Co., Amsterdam, 1964.

I. Goodman and J. A. Rhys, *Polyesters, Vol. 1: Saturated Polyesters*, Iliffe Books Ltd. for The Plastics Institute, London, 1965.

I. GOODMAN
Imperial Chemical Industries, Ltd.;
and University of Manchester
Institute of Science and Technology

POLYETHERS. See Glycols; Resins, water-soluble.

POLYETHYLENE. See Olefin polymers.

(POLYHYDROXY)BENZENES

The dihydroxybenzenes (pyrocatechol or catechol (1,2-), resorcinol (1,3-), and hydroquinone (1,4-)) are discussed under Hydroquinone. This article discusses the tri- and higher (polyhydroxy)benzenes. (The parentheses show that the meaning of "poly" applies to "hydroxy" but not to "benzene"; in other words, more than one hydroxyl group on one benzene nucleus.)

The names of the trihydroxybenzenes are as follows:

	Systematic names	
Trivial names	Preferred	Alternative
pyrogallol	1,2,3-benzenetriol	1,2,3-trihydroxybenzene
hydroxyhydroquinone	1,2,4-benzenetriol	1,2,4-trihydroxybenzene
phloroglucinol	1,3,5-benzenetriol	1,3,5-trihydroxybenzene

The three isomeric benzenetetrols, and benzenepentol and benzenehexol, do not have trivial names (except for the name "apionol," which has been applied to 1,2,3,4-benzenetetrol).

Derivatives of these compounds or their corresponding quinones are of widespread occurrence in nature. They are abundant in plants and fruits as glucosides, chromones, coumarin derivatives, flavonoids, essential oils, lignins, tannins, and alkaloids; they are also found in microorganisms and animals.

The biochemical activity of the benzenepolyols is at least in part based on their oxidation-reduction potential. Many biochemical studies of these compounds have been made, eg, of enzymic glycoside formation, enzymic hydroxylation and oxidation, biological interactions with biochemically important compounds such as the catechol amines, and humic acid formation. Doubtless, the range of biochemical function of these compounds and their derivatives is not yet fully understood.

The chemistry of the benzenepolyols is generally similar to that of phenol, but is characterized by enhanced reactivity in electrophilic (eg, alkylation, halogenation, nitration) and nucleophilic substitution (eg, hydroxylation and amination) reactions. The benzenepolyols that have two hydroxyl groups in ortho or para position to each other are readily oxidized to quinones, particularly in alkaline solution. Those having two hydroxyl groups meta to each other, are, like resorcinol or 2-naphthol, capable of reacting in the tautomeric keto form to yield carbon- instead of oxygen-substitution products, and capable of keto-group reactions. In these cases, the greater stability of the keto than the phenolic (enol) forms makes up for the loss of resonance stabilization (aromaticity).

The uses of the benzenepolyols are generally based on their high reactivity and functionality in certain reactions such as aldehyde condensations and coupling with diazonium salts, or on their ease of oxidation. Thus, they are used mainly in resins, dyestuffs, photographic and duplicating processes, antioxidants, and stabilizers. Some important drugs are derived from the benzenepolyols. Medicinal and agricultural chemical applications of derivatives of benzenepolyols appear to be receiving increasing attention.

Of the eight benzenepolyols covered in this article, only two (pyrogallol and phloroglucinol) are manufactured on a sizable scale. Even for these two, the known production methods are relatively costly. Larger-volume uses and broader applications of the benzenepolyols seem probable if new low-cost syntheses could be developed.

Pyrogallol

Pyrogallol (1,2,3-benzenetriol, 1,2,3-trihydroxybenzene) was first observed by Scheele in 1786 as a product of the dry distillation of gallic acid (3,4,5-trihydroxybenzoic acid). In 1832, Braconnot noted that pyrogallol rapidly reduced metallic silver from silver nitrate solutions while gallic acid reduced it only gradually. Pyrogallol, of widespread occurrence in nature, is incorporated in tannins, anthocyanins, flavones, and alkaloids.

Physical and Chemical Properties. Pyrogallol forms colorless (graying on contact with air or light) needles or leaflets. Some of its other properties are as follows: mp, 133–134°C; bp at atmospheric pressure with partial decomposition, 309°C; bp at 100 mm pressure, 232°C, and at 10 mm pressure, 168°C; when heated slowly pyrogallol sublimes without decomposition; sp gr at 4°C, 1.453; heat of combustion, 639 kcal/mole; solubility in parts per 100 parts solvent, 40 in water at 13°C, 62.5 in water at 25°C, 100 in alcohol at 25°C, 83.3 in ether at 25°C; slightly soluble in benzene, chloroform, and carbon disulfide.

Pyrogallol is the strongest reducing agent among the benzenepolyols. Therefore, it is oxidized rapidly in air; its aqueous alkaline solution absorbs oxygen from the air and darkens fast; sodium sulfite retards such oxidation.

"Pyrogallol oxidized," obtained by the action of air and ammonia on pyrogallol, is a brownish-black to black lustrous powder which is almost insoluble in water, alcohol, or ether, but is soluble in alkalies. It was formerly used to dye furs. Hexahydroxydiphenyl (biphenylhexol), $(HO)_3C_6H_2C_6H_2(OH)_3$, is formed by shaking pyrogallol with barium hydroxide solution while air is passed through. In solutions of hydrogen peroxide, pyrogallol is oxidized rapidly in the presence of such catalysts as colloidal suspensions of metals or metallic oxides, and luminescence occurs.

Purpurogallin (**5**), a red-brown to black mordant dye, results from electrolytic and other mild oxidations of pyrogallol (**1**). The reaction is believed to proceed through 3-hydroxy-*o*-benzoquinone (**2**) and 3-hydroxy-6-(3,4,5-trihydroxyphenyl)-*o*-benzoquinone (**3**). The latter, in the form of its tautomeric triketonic structure, represents the vinyl analog of a β-diketone, and acid hydrolysis leads to (**4**), followed by cyclization and loss of formic acid to yield purpurogallin (**1**).

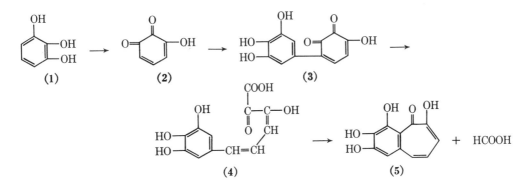

Pyrogallol undergoes all the reactions characteristic of phenols. Methylation with methyl iodide or dimethyl sulfate in the presence of alkali gives 3-methoxy-1,2-benzenediol, 2,3-dimethoxyphenol, or 1,2,3-trimethoxybenzene (2). On heating with aqueous potassium bicarbonate, pyrogallol-4-carboxylic acid (**6**) and a lesser amount of gallic acid (**7**) are formed (3).   Reaction of pyrogallol with phosgene in the presence of pyridine (4) gives pyrogallol carbonate (**8**).

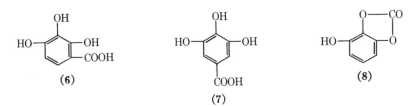

Bromination of this carbonate yields both 4-bromopyrogallol and 4,6-dibromo-pyrogallol.   The direct bromination of pyrogallol in carbon tetrachloride (5) produces 4,5,6-tribromopyrogallol, and with more bromine 1,2,6,6-tetrabromocyclohexene-3,4,5-trione (**9**) is obtained.   The formation of the latter compound is evidence for the ability of pyrogallol to react in keto forms.   However, in contrast to phloroglucinol, pyrogallol does not react as a ketone with hydroxylamine.

Stereoisomeric 1,2,3-cyclohexanetriols were first obtained by Sabatier by hydro-genation of pyrogallol in the presence of a nickel catalyst.   In more recent studies, the hydrogenation of pyrogallol in ethanol at 100°C and 2400 psig, using a moist Raney nickel catalyst, was found to give up to a 60% yield of *cis,cis*-1,2,3-cyclohexanetriol (the γ isomer) with only minor amounts of the *cis,trans*-(β) and *trans,trans*-(α) (6); the hydrogenation of pyrogallol in water in the presence of 1 mole of alkali at 60°C and 1000 psig, again using a Raney nickel catalyst, gave dihydropyrogallol (**10**), an ene-diol (7).

Pyrogallol forms salts or chelates with many metals, some of which are used for identification in analysis, as pigments or lakes (eg in inks), or for medicinal purposes.

Analysis.   The *National Formulary* test for pyrogallol is as follows: 1 ml freshly prepared aqueous solution of pyrogallol (1 in 20) is colored brownish red by a few drops of ferric chloride test solution.   Freshly prepared ferrous sulfate test solution produces a blue color in an aqueous solution of pyrogallol (8).

Pyrogallol can be detected in amounts on the order of 0.5 μg by the violet to orange color which results from the addition of phloroglucinol to an ammoniacal solution of pyrogallol.   Ammonium molybdate in the presence of acetic acid gives a reddish-brown color with pyrogallol, as well as with other *o*-hydroxyphenols.

Pyrogallol combines with osmium tetroxide to form a compound which is reddish violet in dilute solution and almost black in concentrated solution.   This reaction is extremely sensitive and is capable of detecting as little as 1 part pyrogallol in 2 million parts water (9).   Various other color tests for pyrogallol have been reported (10,11).

Derivatives used for the identification of pyrogallol are as follows: tri(phenyl-urethan), mp 173°C;   tri(3,5-dinitrobenzoate), mp 205°C;   tribenzoate, mp 90°C.

Manufacture and Synthesis.   The commercial manufacturing process is based on Scheele's original procedure starting with crude gallic acid (see under Derivatives) extracted from nutgalls or tara powder.   It proceeds according to the following equation:

$$C_6H_2(OH)_3COOH \rightarrow C_6H_3(OH)_3 + CO_2$$

Gallic acid is heated with about half its weight of water in a copper autoclave until the pressure reaches 12 atm and the temperature is 175°C. Steam and carbon dioxide are then allowed to escape, leaving sufficient water to keep the pyrogallol liquid. The cooled solution is decolorized with animal charcoal and evaporated until the volatile pyrogallol has distilled over into iron receivers. The solidified material is purified by repeated distillation or sublimation.

If crude gallic acid, or dried gall mash, is distilled in vacuum at about 300°C, virtually pure pyrogallol is obtained (12).

There are two U.S. manufacturers (Harshaw and Mallinckrodt) who make pyrogallol by extraction and decarboxylation of gallic acid from nutgalls or tara powder. It has been claimed that the decarboxylation of gallic acid is improved by carrying it out at 130–140°C in the presence of a tertiary amine such as N,N-dimethylaniline (13).

As long as adequate supplies of plant materials for the extraction of gallic acid have been available, alternate sources and synthesis have received relatively little attention.

Pyrogallol derivatives occur in certain creosote fractions, from which pyrogallol can be obtained by digestion with hydrochloric acid under pressure. Pyrogallol, its monomethyl ether, and dialkyl ethers of 5-alkylpyrogallols can be separated from wood-tar distillates by extraction with water or aqueous alkali-metal borate solution (14).

An old patent describes the synthesis of pyrogallol from 2,6-dichlorophenol-4-sulfonic acid by alkali fusion, followed by desulfonation with hot dilute mineral acid under pressure (15). Similarly, the synthesis of pyrogallol from 2,6-dichloro-4-*tert*-butylphenol by hydrolysis and debutylation has been patented (16).

A most interesting synthesis of pyrogallol triacetate (**12**) in 90% yield by treating 6,6-diacetoxy-1,3-cyclohexadien-5-one (**11**) with boron trifluoride in acetic anhydride has been described (17).

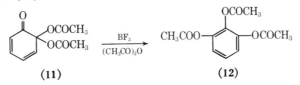

(11)   (12)

Another interesting patented (18) synthesis of substituted pyrogallols consists of the γ-irradiation of a dihydric phenol containing one electron-withdrawing substituent with water or hydrogen peroxide in the presence of oxygen; β-resorcylic acid (**13**) gave, in this manner, a 26% yield of 2,3,4-trihydroxybenzoic acid (pyrogallol-4-carboxylic acid (**6**)).

(13)   (6)

Table 1. Specifications for Different Grades of Pyrogallol

Grade	Appearance	Solubility in water	Ash, wt %	Mp, °C	Purity, %
technical	gray granular powder	soluble			>90
NF X	white to pale yellow crystals	clear and colorless to slightly yellow solution	0.02 max to 0.1 max	130–133 to 132–134	
reagent[a]	white, lustrous crystals	clear, colorless solution	0.005 max	132–134	

[a] Additional specifications: heavy metals (eg Pb), 0.0005% max; iron (Fe), 0.001% max; chloride (Cl), 0.001% max; sulfate (SO_4), 0.005% max.

The U.S. Tariff Commission does not publish statistics on the production of pyrogallol.

Grades, Specifications, and Prices. Three grades of pyrogallol are commercially available: technical, NF, and reagent grade. Packaging is in 25-, 50-, or 100-lb drums. Manufacturers' specifications for these products are given in Table 1.

USP XVII specifies for reagent-grade pyrogallol a melting range of 131.5–134.5°C, not more than 0.01% residue on ignition, and a colorless, or at most slightly yellow, solution of 1.0 g in 20 ml freshly boiled water.

In May 1967, the sales price of pyrogallol was $3.91/lb for technical grade and $4.29/lb for the NF grade, both in 1000-lb lots; the list price was $7.77/lb for the reagent-grade material in 25-lb drums.

Toxicity. Although there are few recorded cases of actual deaths from pyrogallol, it is recognized as being extremely poisonous. Extensive exposure of the skin may cause discoloration, local irritation, eczema, or even death due to absorption. In addition, repeated contact with the skin may lead to sensitization. Proper care in handling is necessary.

The principal symptom of poisoning attributable to pyrogallol is its effect on the red blood corpuscles, which break down and lose their hemoglobin. The tremendous affinity of pyrogallol for the oxygen of the blood has been shown in experimental animals, where complete removal of the oxygen from the blood occurred (with resulting death) as well as fragmentation and destruction of the erythrocytes.

Severe pyrogallol poisoning also leads to degeneration of the liver and kidneys, and symptoms exhibited in such cases include urinary disturbance, headache, cyanosis, chills, vomiting, and diarrhea (19). The subcutaneous MLD in rats is 700 mg/kg and the oral MLD in dogs is 25 mg/kg (20).

Uses. The main commercial applications of pyrogallol depend on either its ease of oxidation, or its ability to form metal salts, or its nuclear reaction with electrophilic reagents.

Pyrogallol is the oldest of the photographic developing agents still in general use. It was introduced by Scott-Archer in the wet collodion process in 1852, but was not used in alkaline solution until 1862, nor was sodium sulfite used as a preservative until 1882.

Pyrogallol is a very versatile developing agent, much more capable of modification than some of the agents that have largely replaced it. Strong contrasts are possible with concentrated solutions, and soft delicate shades are achieved with more dilute solutions and lower alkali concentrations.

However, pyrogallol has a number of disadvantages which have caused a decrease in its use. Since it oxidizes readily, the yellow oxidation product stains the gelatin so that the useful life of a pyrogallol developer is short. The oxidation taking place during development and the consequent reduction of the exposed silver halide to metallic silver produce a stain image with most developers. The stain image formed with pyrogallol is more intense than with other developers and in addition shows wide variations, depending on such factors as the amount of sodium sulfite or other preservative used, the amount of solution exposed to the air, the temperature, and the degree of agitation. Since the density and contrast of the negative vary with the stain image, it is difficult to secure as uniform results with pyrogallol as with other developing agents (21).

It has been claimed that alkaline developer solutions of pyrogallol can be stabilized against oxidation by the addition of boric acid, sodium sulfite, or potassium metabisulfite (22). The addition of 7,8-dihydroxycoumarin, a water-soluble salt of ascorbic acid borate, or alkali-metal sulfites in the presence of magnesium sulfate at pH 7–8, to improve the storage stability of pyrogallol developers has been patented (23). Esters (triethoxalate, carbonate, benzoate, oxalate, acetate) of pyrogallol were reported to be improved developers for silver halide emulsions, preventing fogging, staining, and desensitization (24). 4-*tert*-Butylpyrogallol has been reported to be a useful developer for lithographic plates (25).

Photothermographic reproduction processes, based on the formation of dark-colored reaction products of ferric stearate with pyrogallol (or its condensation product with acetone) under the influence of heat, have been patented (26). Similarly, an electrolytic recording paper based on the reaction of pyrogallol with ferric tartrate in the presence of an activating electrolyte has been disclosed (27). Pyrogallol has also been claimed to be an adhesion promoter in composite photographic films (28).

The uses of pyrogallol, its antimonyl derivative, its isoamyl ether, or its alkyl derivatives as antioxidants (29) for nylon, synthetic rubber, hydraulic transmission fluids, lubricants, motor fuel containing paraldehyde, and foods, and as nonstaining antiozonants for rubber (14) have been patented. Pyrogallol and its alkyl derivatives were claimed to be stabilizers for vinyl aromatics and poly(trifluorochloroethylene) (30). The decomposition of cellulose by ionizing radiation was reported to be prevented by soaking in a solution of pyrogallol (31). Reportedly, a mixture of cyclohexanone oxime with a minor amount of pyrogallol is an effective antiskinning agent for paints and varnishes (32). Dialkyl ethers or 5-alkyl ethers, extracted from wood-tar distillates, have been described to be useful antiozonants for rubber (14).

A composition obtained by vulcanizing a polychloroprene rubber with pyrogallol and sodium sulfide has been patented as an adhesive (33). Alkali salts of pyrogallol have been used as vulcanizing agents for nitroso rubber made by copolymerization of perhalonitrosoalkanes and perhaloalkenes (34). Encapsulation of pyrogallol in polyethylene has been reported to give an accelerator composition for neoprene which allows delayed vulcanization; the encapsulated accelerator does not become active until the melting point of the polyethylene is reached (35).

The adhesion of polyamide fibers to synthetic rubber has been improved by the treatment of the fibers with a mixture of pyrogallol and zinc salts; the adhesion of regenerated cellulose or mineral fiber to vulcanized rubber has been effected by the addition of a pyrogallol–aldehyde resin and a substituted chlorobenzene (36).

Pyrogallol–formaldehyde resins have good oxidation-reduction properties and are useful for removing traces of oxygen from solution; such resins can also be used for the preparation of anion-permeable membranes (37).

Silicate, phosphite, phosphate, and borate polymers prepared from pyrogallol are reported to be useful because of their high heat stability (38). Pyrogallol is a useful agent for the hardening of polyepoxides (39).

Condensation products of pyrogallol with sulfonated catechol, or of 7-hydroxy-2, 4-dimethylbenzopyrylium chloride with pyrogallol and formaldehyde, have been claimed for the surface dyeing or tanning of leather (40). Hair-dyeing compositions are obtained by oxidizing pyrogallol either in combination with amines or complexed with metal salts (41).

Pyrogallol has been used externally in the form of an ointment or a solution in the treatment of skin diseases such as psoriasis, ringworm, and lupus erythematosus. Gallamine triethiodide (14) is an important muscle relaxant in surgery; it is also used in

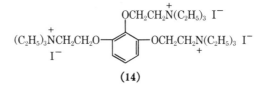

(14)

convulsive shock therapy. 4-(2-Amino-1-hydroxyethyl-)pyrogallol, 4-hydrazino-methylpyrogallol, and antimony salts of pyrogallol have been reported to have therapeutic value, for example, pressor activity (42).

Several important alkaloids contain pyrogallol moieties; this fact has prompted increasing pharmaceutical investigations and uses in this area. Examples are given under derivatives of pyrogallol.

Esters of pyrogallol with chlorinated acids (eg α,α-dichloropropionic acid) have herbicidal properties (43). Ammoniacal alcoholic solutions of pyrogallol are claimed to be useful in preparing palladium articles for soldering (44).

Derivatives. *Gallic acid* (3,4,5-trihydroxybenzoic acid, pyrogallol-5-carboxylic acid) (**7**), $C_6H_2(OH)_3COOH$, is the most important derivative of pyrogallol. It is a colorless solid, crystallizing from water as the monohydrate (begins to dehydrate at about 100°C); the anhydrous compound melts at 253°C (with decomposition); its sp gr at 4°C is 1.694; dissociation constant at 25°C is 3.8×10^{-5}. It is soluble in alcohol and acetone, sparingly soluble in water, insoluble in chloroform and benzene. It is manufactured by the chemical or enzymic hydrolysis of tannins from nutgalls (gallnuts, Aleppo galls) or tara powder (the ground seed pod of the Peruvian tree, *Coulteria tinctoria*, family caesalpiniaceae). Gallic acid is sold as the monohydrate in technical, NF, and reagent grades.

(7)   (15)

Gallic acid is used medicinally as a urinary astringent and internal antihemor-rhageant, and in veterinary medicine for the treatment of diarrhea by its astringent action on the bowel. It is also used to manufacture pyrogallol by decarboxylation. Esters of gallic acid, such as propyl gallate (**15**) (45), are useful as antioxidants or stabilizers, particularly for oils, fats, and ethers; the esters have also been reported as shortstopping agents in the emulsion polymerization of styrene–butadiene rubber (46); bismuth subgallate is useful as a medicinal agent. Gallic acid has traditionally been used with ferrous sulfate to make various types of inks, particularly the blue-black, permanent-type writing inks. It is also used in photothermographic reproduction processes (47); as a process chemical in engraving and lithography; as a developer in photography; and in tanning, and fur- and hair-dyeing preparations. Miscellaneous applications of gallic acid include its use as a deflocculating, thickening, and sizing agent in the manufacture of wallboard; as a mordant in the manufacture of colored paper and fiberboard; as an analytical reagent for alkaloids, metals, and mineral acids; and in the manufacture of alizarin, thioflavine, and gallocyanine dyes. Thus, oxida-tion of gallic acid with air in alkaline solution yields Galloflavine W (CI 1017); oxida-tion with potassium ferricyanide gives purpurogallic acid; oxidation with potassium permanganate in cold sulfuric acid gives ellagic acid (Alizarin Yellow, CI 1016) (**16**);

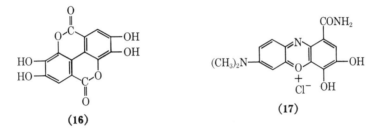

(16)   (17)

these are yellow to red to brown mordant dyes. Heating gallic acid or gallamide with *p*-nitroso-*N*,*N*-dimethylaniline hydrochloride gives the oxazine dyes Gallocyanine (CI 883) and Gallamine Blue (CI 894) (**17**), respectively.

In addition to gallic acid esters, the following products derived from gallic acid are available commercially: 3,4,5-trimethoxybenzoic acid (**18**), colorless crystals, mp 170–173°C; 3,4,5-trimethoxybenzaldehyde (**19**), colorless to pale yellow flakes, melting range of 3° within 72–78°C; and 3,4,5-trimethoxycinnamic acid (**20**), colorless powder,

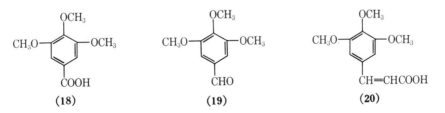

(18)   (19)   (20)

melting range of 3° within 124–129°C. They are being used in the synthesis of com-mercial therapeutics and experimental drugs with hypotensive, sedative, antispasmodic, or tranquilizer activity (48). Hexobendin (**21**) is being marketed in Europe as a heart muscle energizer. 3,4,5-Trimethoxy-*N*-(*β*-diethylaminoethyl)benzamide has anti-pyretic activity (49). The important drug reserpine (see Psychopharmacological agents), contains the 3,4,5-trimethoxybenzoate nucleus.

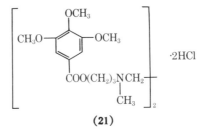

(21)

Pyrogallol monoacetate (monoacetylpyrogallol, eugallol), is a white or brownish liquid, bp$_{23}$ about 185°C; it is soluble in water, alcohol, chloroform, ether, and acetone. It is a mixture of isomers made from pyrogallol and acetic anhydride and is marketed only as a 67% solution in acetone, which is a reddish-brown sirupy liquid. The mono-acetate has been recommended for the treatment of chronic dermatitis.

Pyrogallol triacetate (acetpyrogall, NNR 1951, Lenigallol), is a white crystalline powder, mp 164–165°C. It is very slightly soluble in water, but is soluble in alcohol and ether. The triacetate is commercially available, and is used in medicine as a substitute for pyrogallol. However, it also is somewhat toxic since it gradually liberates pyrogallol.

Gallein (pyrogallolphthalein, 4,5-dihydroxyfluorescein, tetrahydroxyfluoran CI 45445), C$_{20}$H$_{12}$O$_7$ (**22**), forms greenish-yellow crystals when anhydrous and red crystals with one and a half molecules of water. The water of crystallization is driven off at about 180°C and the compound decomposes above this temperature. Gallein is only very slightly soluble in hot water, and almost insoluble in benzene or chloroform. It is slightly soluble in hot ether, and soluble in alcohol, acetone, and alkalies. It is obtained by heating 1 part of phthalic anhydride with 2 parts of pyrogallol or gallic acid.

Gallein is used as a sensitive indicator for acids, alkali hydroxides, and ammonia, but not for carbonates. Gallein (dilute solution in 50% alcohol) also is used as a colorimetric reagent for determining phosphates in urine; monophosphates give a yellow color, dibasic phosphates give red, and tribasic phosphates give violet (49a).

Gallacetophenone (4-acetylpyrogallol, 2,3,4-trihydroxyacetophenone, Alizarin Yel-low C), C$_8$H$_8$O$_4$ (**23**), forms gray leaf crystals or a powder of a yellow or brown tint, mp 173°C. It is slightly soluble in water, soluble in alcohol and in ether, and very slightly soluble in benzene. It is used medicinally as an antiseptic for skin diseases. It and other 4-acylpyrogallols have been claimed to be useful protective agents against harm-ful radiation (50). Derivatives of gallacetophenone, such as 3-morpholino-3′,4′,5′-trimethoxyacrylophenone (**24**), are useful as central nervous system depressants (51).

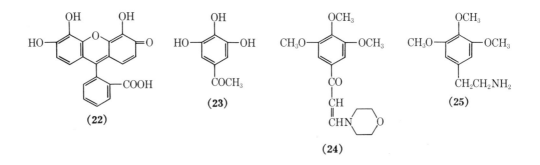

Alkyl Ethers. (See also Phenolic ethers.) Both the monomethyl ether and the monoethyl ether have been suggested as starting materials in making photographic developers having no tendency to become oxidized.

The 1,3-dimethyl ether (2,6-dimethoxyphenol), is a white, monoclinic crystalline material, mp 55–56°C, bp 262.7°C. It is soluble to the extent of 1.75 parts per 100 parts water at 13°C, and it is very soluble in alcohol and in ether. A number of methylated, ethylated, or other substituted pyrogallols have been patented for photographic use (16).

Mescaline, 2-(3,4,5-trimethoxyphenyl)ethylamine, $(CH_3O)_3C_6H_2CH_2CH_2NH_2$ (**25**), is the active ingredient in "mescal buttons" ("peyotl," "peyote"), the dried tops of the Mexican dumpling cactus *Lophopora williamsi,* which produces visual hallucinations on ingestion. Its possible use as a psychotomimetic drug in the field of mental health has been under study. (See also Psychopharmacological agents.)

Colchicine (**26**) is a toxic substance occurring in *Colchicum autumnale;* it contains the nucleus of pyrogallol trimethyl ether. Colchicine has been used in the treatment of acute gout.

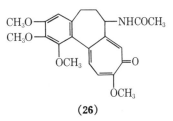

(**26**)

Hydroxyhydroquinone

Hydroxyhydroquinone (1,2,4-benzenetriol, 1,2,4-trihydroxybenzene) forms colorless plates (from diethyl ether) when freshly prepared. It occurs in many plants and trees in the form of ethers, quinonoid pigments, and coumarin derivatives. It has strong reducing properties. Applications have been suggested in hair dyes, agricultural and photographic chemicals, and stabilizers.

Physical and Chemical Properties. *Constants.* Hydroxyhydroquinone forms platelets or prisms; its mp is 140.5°C. The compound is easily soluble in water, ethanol, diethyl ether, and ethyl acetate; very sparingly soluble in chloroform, carbon disulfide, benzene, and ligroin.

Reactions. Hydroxyhydroquinone reacts as a typical, oxidizable polyhydric phenol, but it also gives certain keto group reactions. In aqueous alkaline solution, it is said to absorb oxygen as effectively as pyrogallol; these solutions, under the action of oxygen, hydrogen peroxide, or potassium peroxysulfate, darken rapidly and produce a dark, humic acid-type precipitate. On mixing with excess bromine, 2-hydroxy-3,5,6-tribromobenzoquinone-1,4 (**27**) is produced (52). Reduction with sodium amalgam produces dihydroresorcinol (**28**) (53). Condensation with aldehydes, RCHO, in the presence of sulfuric acid, leads to 9-substituted 2,6,7-trihydroxyfluorones (**29**) (54).

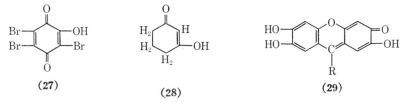

(**27**)   (**28**)   (**29**)

The condensation of hydroxyhydroquinone with ethyl acetoacetate (55) gives 6,7-dihydroxy-4-methylcoumarin (**30**). Condensation with phthalic anhydride (56) gives hydroxyhydroquinone–phthalein (**31**). Mild oxidants, such as silver oxide, produce

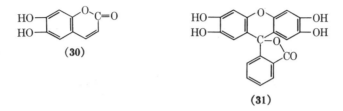

(**30**)   (**31**)

2-hydroxy-*p*-benzoquinone. With ammonia or amines in aqueous solution at room temperature in the absence of air, the corresponding 2,4-dihydroxyanilines are formed. On prolonged heating with sodium bisulfite, an adduct containing 2 moles of sulfite is formed (57). Catalytic hydrogenation of hydroxyhydroquinone in water or alcohol, using a nickel catalyst, gives a mixture of stereoisomeric 1,2,4-cyclohexanetriols. Ethers or esters can be formed in the usual manner with alkylating and acylating agents.

Analysis. Dilute aqueous solutions of hydroxyhydroquinone give a temporary blue-green color with ferric chloride which darkens upon addition of a little sodium carbonate and turns red with larger amounts of this reagent. In ethereal solution, hydroxyhydroquinone gives a blue color with phosphomolybdic acid which does not change when ammonia is added.

Derivatives used for identification are the picrate, with orange-red needles and a mp of 96°C, and the triacetate, mp 96–97°C.

Synthesis. Hydroxyhydroquinone is not produced on a sizable commercial scale, but is available from laboratory-reagent manufacturers. The most convenient preparation of hydroxyhydroquinone is the reaction of *p*-benzoquinone (**32**) with acetic anhydride in the presence of sulfuric acid or phosphoric acid; the triacetate (**33**) obtained (58) can be hydrolyzed to hydroxyhydroquinone (58,59).

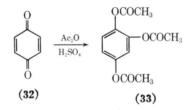

(**32**)   (**33**)

Hydroxyhydroquinone was first synthesized by the caustic fusion of hydroquinone (52,60). The oxidation of aqueous alkaline solutions of 2,4- or 3,4-dihydroxybenzaldehyde or 2,4- or 3,4-dihydroxyacetophenone with hydrogen peroxide yields hydroxyhydroquinone (61); the oxidation of vanillin in this manner gives 2-methoxyhydroquinone. 5-*tert*-Alkyl-2-hydroxy-1,4-benzoquinone can be obtained in good yield by the oxidation of 4-*tert*-alkylcatechol with oxygen in methanolic potassium hydroxide (62); reduction of the quinone should lead to the corresponding alkylhydroxyhydroquinone.

Toxicology and Handling Precautions. The LD_{50} of 1,2,4-trihydroxybenzene in mice after intracutaneous injection was reported to be 371 γ/g (63). In handling hydroxyhydroquinone, care should be observed since contact leaves a black stain on skin and fingernails.

Uses. Several patents cover the use of hydroxyhydroquinone and certain of its derivatives, or 2,4-hydroxyanilines made from it by amination, as hair dyes to give brownish shades. The compounds are applied to hair or other keratinous material in aqueous solution, then heated with ammonia and an oxidant such as hydrogen peroxide or perborate (64).

The use of hydroxyhydroquinone and certain of its 5-substituted derivatives for the acceleration of wound healing in harvested plant products has been reported; for example, the corking of cut pieces of seed potatoes was said to be promoted (65).

Friedel-Crafts condensation of hydroxyhydroquinone with phthalic anhydride gives the mordant dye, purpurin (**34**), CI 58205 (66). This dye also occurs as the glycoside in the madder root.

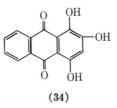

(34)

Hydroxyhydroquinone has been reported to inhibit the corrosion of ferrous metal by chlorinated unsaturated hydrocarbons, such as trichloroethylene, in the presence of amine stabilizers (67).

Neoprene adhesive solutions can be stabilized with hydroxyhydroquinone (or other benzenepolyols) in the presence of zinc oxide or a zinc salt and an aliphatic poly-carboxylic acid (68).

Derivatives. *Rotenone* (see Vol. 11, p. 687), a natural product containing a hydroxyhydroquinone moiety, occurring in many leguminous plants of the tropics and subtropics, is used as an insecticide.

Phloroglucinol

Phloroglucinol (1,3,5-benzenetriol, 1,3,5-trihydroxybenzene, *sym*-trihydroxybenzene) (**35**) is a colorless and odorless solid which is only sparingly soluble in cold water. It was found by Hlasiewitz in 1855 in the hydrolysis products of the glucoside phloretin, which he obtained from the bark of fruit trees. Because of its sweet taste, he called it phloroglucine (from the Greek for "sweet bark"). The name was eventually changed to phloroglucinol to show the phenolic character of the compound. Phloroglucinol occurs in many other natural products, in the form of derivatives such as flavones, catechins, coumarin derivatives, anthocyanidins, xanthins, and glucosides.

Although most of its physical and chemical properties characterize phloroglucinol as a polyhydric phenol, in many cases it reacts in a tautomeric keto form or even as the β-triketone, 1,3,5-cyclohexanetrione (**36**). This tautomeric triketone has never

(35)   **(36)**

been isolated.   However, phloroglucinol dianion has been shown by proton magnetic resonance spectroscopy to exist as the ketone (**37**) (69).   Also, the rapid nuclear hydrogen–deuterium exchange of phloroglucinol in weakly alkaline solutions may be evidence for this ketone–enolate tautomerism (70).

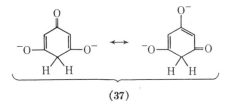

(**37**)

The major users of phloroglucinol are the dye and reproduction process industries.

Physical and Chemical Properties.   Phloroglucinol forms odorless, colorless, sweet-tasting, rhombic crystals which tend to discolor on exposure to air or light;   the dihydrate (mp 113–116°C on quick heating) loses its water of crystallization at about 110°C; the anhydrous material melts at 217–219°C when heated rapidly.   It can be sublimed at higher temperatures with partial decomposition.   The heat of combustion of phloroglucinol is 618 kcal/mole; $K_1 = 4.5 \times 10^{-10}$ at 25°C.   It is soluble to the extent of 1 part in 100 parts water at 25°C, 10 parts in 100 parts ethanol at 25°C, and 296 parts in 100 parts pyridine;   it is soluble in ether.   Phloroglucinol is a mild reducing agent.   It will reduce Fehling's solution;   in aqueous alkali it is slowly oxidized by air.

Phloroglucinol can undergo the special reactions of certain phenols, such as 2-naphthol and resorcinol, that are based on the ease of formation of tautomeric keto forms;   these reactions are most pronounced for phloroglucinol and are favored under certain conditions.   Thus, phloroglucinol forms a trioxime with hydroxylamine (71); it forms mono, di, and tri addition compounds with sodium bisulfite (72);   it undergoes the Bucherer reaction with ammonia at room temperature (73) to give at first phloramine (5-amino-1,3-dihydroxybenzene) and eventually 3,5-diaminophenol; similarly, displacement of the hydroxyl groups with aromatic amines is possible at higher temperatures (74);   alkylation with a methyl halide in alkaline media leads to 2,2,4,4,6,6-hexamethylcyclohexane-1,3,5-trione (**38**)   (75);   cyanoethylation   in   the presence of sodium methylate gives 2-(2-cyanoethyl)phloroglucinol (**39**) (76);   sodium

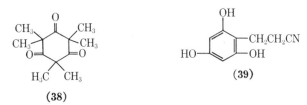

(**38**)   (**39**)

borohydride reduces phloroglucinol to 1,3-benzenediol (resorcinol) (77); halogenation in anhydrous solvents yields halogenated cyclohexane-1,3,5-triones; and the reaction of phloroglucinol with potassium cyanide in the presence of sulfuric acid yields the cyanohydrin of dihydrophloroglucinol which gives γ-resorcylic acid (3,5-dihydroxybenzoic acid) on treatment with concentrated hydrochloric acid (78).

Under the proper conditions, phloroglucinol can participate in all the reactions typical of phenols.   Some examples follow.

Etherification with diazomethane gives phloroglucinol trimethyl ether (79). With dimethyl sulfate at pH 8–9, the mono-, di-, or trimethyl ether can be obtained

(80). Friedel-Crafts acylation with acid chlorides and aluminum chloride in carbon disulfide gives the nuclear monoacylated phloroglucinols in good yield (81). The reaction of phloroglucinol with excess acetyl chloride yields phloroglucinol triacetate. The Gatterman reaction of phloroglucinol with hydrogen cyanide and hydrochloric acid gives 2,4,6-trihydroxybenzaldehyde; similarly, with zinc cyanide the dialdehyde of phloroglucinol can be formed (82). The Hoesch reaction of phloroglucinol with nitriles yields the corresponding ketones; eg with benzonitrile in the presence of hydrochloric acid, phlorobenzophenone (see under Derivatives) is produced. Phloroglucinol couples readily with aryldiazonium salts to give di- and triazo compounds. Phloroglucinol reacts readily in the presence of alkaline or acid catalysts with aliphatic and aromatic aldehydes to give various condensation products, often colored. The reaction of phloroglucinol with phthalic anhydride gives phloroglucinol phthalein (83). Both the Perkin condensation of 2,4,6-trihydroxybenzaldehyde with sodium acetate and acetic anhydride, and the Pechmann reaction of phloroglucinol with ethyl acetoacetate in the presence of sulfuric acid yield coumarin derivatives. The Lewis acid-catalyzed reaction of phloroglucinol with olefins or alkyl halides gives nuclear alkylation products; for example, the reaction with ethylene catalyzed by $FeF_2.BF_3$ and HF gives triethylphloroglucinol (84). Alkylphloroglucinols can also be prepared by the Clemmensen reduction of acylphloroglucinols. The catalytic hydrogenation of phloroglucinol gives a mixture of the stereoisomeric phloroglucinols (cyclohexane-1,3,5-triols). Aqueous alkali bicarbonate or carbonate reacts with phloroglucinol even at 20°C to give phloroglucinolcarboxylic acid (85). 2,4,6-Trinitrosophloroglucinol is obtained by reaction of phloroglucinol with nitrous acid in acetic acid (86).

Analyses. USP XVII gives the following tests for reagent-grade phloroglucinol: (1) insolubles in alcohol—dissolve 1 g in 20 ml alcohol and a clear and complete solution results; (2) melting range—between 215 and 219°C; (3) residue on ignition—ignite 1 g with 0.5 ml sulfuric acid; the residue weighs not more than 1 mg (0.1%); (4) diresorcinol—heat to boiling a solution of 100 mg in 10 ml acetic anhydride, cool the solution, and superimpose it upon 10 ml sulfuric acid: no violet color appears at the zone of contact of the liquids.

With ferric chloride, phloroglucinol in aqueous solution gives a bluish-violet color which reddens on addition of a few drops of ammonia. With furfuryl alcohol and hydrochloric acid, phloroglucinol gives a greenish-black precipitate.

Derivatives of phloroglucinol used for identification are tri(phenylurethan), mp 190–191°C; tri(3,5-dinitrobenzoate), mp 162°C; tribenzoate, mp 173–174°C; picrate, mp 101–103°C.

Manufacture and Synthesis. Although phloroglucinol occurs in the bark of fruit trees and in numerous plants and fruits, usually in the form of glucosides, these plant sources have never been used as a commercial source of phloroglucinol.

The only commercial preparation that has been used for many years is the reduction and decarboxylation of 2,4,6-trinitrobenzoic acid (obtained from 2,4,6-trinitrotoluene by oxidation with dichromate) to 1,3,5-triaminobenzene followed by hydrolysis to phloroglucinol. Whereas tin and hydrochloric acid are used in laboratory preparations (84), iron and hydrochloric acid (Béchamp reaction (87)) are used in the commercial process in the United States.

The substitution of iron for tin was made possible by determining the extremely close limits of temperature and acidity within which the reaction would take place with iron. In addition to eliminating the necessity for expensive tin, the modification proved to have other advantages. In the old tin reduction process it was necessary to remove most of the dissolved tin from the reaction solution before the hydrolysis step could be accomplished. The ferrous chloride produced in the newer process does not inhibit the hydrolysis. Furthermore, it stabilizes the triaminobenzene formed in the reduction and reduces the number of partial-reduction products, partial-hydrolysis products, polymers, and decomposition products formed as by-products during the reduction. The presence of ferrous chloride in the product of the hydrolysis tends to reduce the solubility of phloroglucinol, thus decreasing the product loss in the centrifugate. The process now used may be represented by equations 1–3.

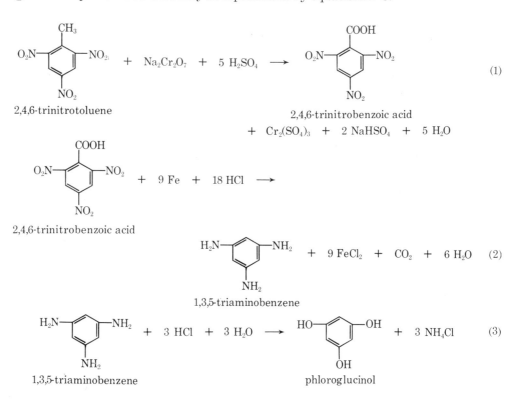

$$+ \ Na_2Cr_2O_7 \ + \ 5 \ H_2SO_4 \ \longrightarrow \tag{1}$$

2,4,6-trinitrotoluene

2,4,6-trinitrobenzoic acid

$$+ \ Cr_2(SO_4)_3 \ + \ 2 \ NaHSO_4 \ + \ 5 \ H_2O$$

$$+ \ 9 \ Fe \ + \ 18 \ HCl \ \longrightarrow$$

2,4,6-trinitrobenzoic acid

$$+ \ 9 \ FeCl_2 \ + \ CO_2 \ + \ 6 \ H_2O \tag{2}$$

1,3,5-triaminobenzene

$$+ \ 3 \ HCl \ + \ 3 \ H_2O \ \longrightarrow \qquad + \ 3 \ NH_4Cl \tag{3}$$

1,3,5-triaminobenzene   phloroglucinol

The first step, the oxidation of trinitrotoluene to trinitrobenzoic acid, is conducted in jacketed steel pots. Sulfuric acid (500 lb, 98%) is pumped into the pots with constant agitation, and trinitrotoluene (50 lb) is added. Sodium dichromate (75 lb) is then stirred into the mixture at such a rate that the temperature of the reaction is kept at 50–60°C. The oxidation is considered to be complete when the temperature begins to drop (usually about 4 hr after the dichromate addition has begun). The charges from five reactors are dumped into a lead-lined drownout tub containing 2400 lb crushed ice. The trinitrobenzoic acid is then recovered in 82% yields by centrifuging. The acid, which contains approximately 2–4% impurities, largely unreacted trinitrotoluene, is not dried but is used directly in the reduction step.

The reduction step is carried out in glass-lined kettles. Hydrochloric acid (250 gal, 21° Bé) is run into the kettle and the 2,4,6-trinitrobenzoic acid (432 lb) is then slowly added. Iron powder (700 lb) is introduced in small portions throughout the entire reduction. Decarboxylation occurs simultaneously with the reduction so that the product from the reduction is 1,3,5-triaminobenzene. The yield is approximately 95%, the side reaction products being polymers of triaminobenzene.

For the hydrolysis, the reduction mixture from two of the reactors is decanted from the iron sludge and pumped to a large glass-lined vessel. One hundred gallons water is added to ensure complete solution of the 1,3,5-triaminobenzene hydrochloride and the ferrous chloride formed in the reduction step. Additional hydrochloric acid is added to lower the pH. The mixture is heated to 108°C and held at that temperature for 20 hr. At the end of this period the hydrolysis is complete. The hydrolyzed solution is filtered hot through a filter press to remove the residual iron sludge and small amounts of carbon and tar produced in the reduction and hydrolysis. The filtrate is then cooled to 10°C to precipitate the crude phloroglucinol. The yield of the centrifuged and dried product (phloroglucinol dihydrate) is 70–75% (about 400 lb) of the theoretical. The material can be recrystallized from water to obtain purer and lighter-colored material. This process for the manufacture of phloroglucinol affords a major waste-disposal problem. The filtrates are highly acidic and contain considerable quantities of chromium and iron salts, which must be eliminated from the waste before it can be run into any public water source.

The only step in the phloroglucinol process which may be considered hazardous is the oxidation of 2,4,6-trinitrotoluene to 2,4,6-trinitrobenzoic acid. It is important that no overheating occurs, and therefore care should be taken to keep the cooling system in the best condition at all times. It is also necessary that the dichromate be added in small increments, determined by experience. Furthermore, after each series of runs the oxidation pots must be carefully inspected for pits in their inner surface, since a leak of water from the water jacket into the oxidation mixture could lead to overheating.

Improvements in certain steps of this process have been claimed; eg the reduction of 2,4,6-trinitrobenzoic acid with iron and hydrochloric acid is said to be smoother when carried out in a solvent such as acetone (88). The hydrolysis of 2,4,6-trinitrobenzoic acid is said to be improved by using a copper catalyst (89).

Modifications of the commercial process have been described and several other routes to phloroglucinol are known which are interesting laboratory syntheses but probably are not of commercial value (90–97).

The U.S. Tariff Commission does not publish statistics on the production of phloroglucinol.

Grades, Specifications, and Prices. The following three grades of phloroglucinol are commercially available: phloroglucinol dihydrate, commercial; phloroglucinol dihydrate, technical; and phloroglucinol dihydrate, chemically pure (cp).

The manufacturer's specifications (98) for the three grades of phloroglucinol are given in Table 2.

Table 2. Phloroglucinol Dihydrate: Grades and Specifications

Property	Commercial	Technical	cp
appearance	tan to chocolate-brown crystals	white to light-cream crystals	white to cream-white crystals
melting point,[a] °C	200 min	214 min	214 min
melting range, °C	3 max	2 max	3 max
ash, %	2.0 max	0.2 max	0.1 max
moisture, %	21.5–22.5	21.7–22.5	21.5–22.5

[a] Sample air-dried 1 hr at 110°C.

In May 1967, the sales price of phloroglucinol dihydrate was $8.75/lb for technical grade and $5.75/lb for commercial grade, both in 100-lb drum lots, and $16.00/lb for cp grade in 50-lb drum lots.

Toxicity. Phloroglucinol does not have antiseptic properties nor does it precipitate proteins; it has anticoagulant action on the blood. Phloroglucinol is relatively nontoxic. Cases of human poisoning by phloroglucinol appear to be unknown (99). The subcutaneous MLD in rats is 1500 mg/kg and the intravenous MLD in dogs is 1000 mg/kg (100).

Uses. Two of the principal commercial applications of phloroglucinol, in the diazotype-copying process and in textile-dyeing processes, are based on the ability of each mole of phloroglucinol to couple rapidly with 3 moles of diazo compound. The azo dyes thus produced give fast, superior black shades. See Azo dyes.

Phloroglucinol is listed in the *Colour Index* as CI Developer 19. It is particularly valuable in the dyeing of acetate fiber, but has been used also as a coupler for azoic colors on viscose, Orlon, cotton, rayon, or nylon fibers, or union fabrics containing these fibers (101). For example, cellulose acetate fabric is treated with an aromatic amine such as *o*-dianisidine or a disperse dye such as *p*-hydroxyphenylazo-2-naphthylamine and the amine is diazotized on the fiber; the fabric is then rinsed, freed of excess nitrite, and the azo color is developed in a phloroglucinol bath at pH 5–7. Depending on the diazo precursor used, intense blue to jet-black shades can be obtained with excellent light-, bleach-, and rubfastness.

The condensation on the fabric of 1-amino-3-imino-isoindolenines or 2-amino-5-iminopyrrolenines with phloroglucinol, preferably in the presence of metal salts and solvents, was reported to yield fast dyeings in brownish shades (102). Metalized azo dyes derived from phloroglucinol have been reported to yield fast dyeings on leather and/or silk (103).

The diazotype duplicating and copying processes (eg "white printing" process) are methods for making positive, direct copies of written, drawn, or typed material. A light-sensitive diazonium compound is coated onto a sheet of supporting material such as paper. The tracing to be copied is placed on this light-sensitive sheet and exposure to a suitable light source is made. Where not protected by the lines of the tracing or drawing the diazonium compound is decomposed with loss of nitrogen and loss of the ability to form azo compounds by coupling. The copy is developed by coupling the remaining diazonium compound with, eg, phloroglucinol. Two processes are used. In the dry process the paper is coated with both the light-sensitive diazo compound and phloroglucinol in the presence of an acid to prevent reaction; after exposure, the paper is developed with ammonia and water vapor to neutralize the acid and to form the azo dye. In the wet process, the sensitized paper contains only the diazo compound and, after exposure, development is effected by means of a dilute aqueous solution of phloroglucinol. The subject has been exhaustively described in a book by Kosar (104); literature quotations to 1964 are included. See also Reprography.

A dry diazo process in which heat replaces ammonia as the developer has been patented (105); it is based on a light-sensitive arylazo sulfone component which, after exposure, reacts with a fast coupler such as phloroglucinol when heated. A thermographic copying process has been described in which the original or an intermediate sheet is covered with a sublimable compound such as phloroglucinol, brought in contact with a paper sheet coated with a stabilized diazonium salt, submitted to infrared radiation, and developed by ammonia or alkali (106).

There are many patents on the use of phloroglucinol in various resins, but the higher cost of phloroglucinol vs resorcinol makes its application in resins less attractive.

Thus, the use of amine–epoxy–phenol (eg phloroglucinol) compositions has been claimed in the preparation of varnishes, coatings, and molded articles (107). Epoxy resins in part derived from phloroglucinol have been described as useful for the treatment of wool to obtain higher strength and chemical resistance (108). The cure of epoxy resins with phloroglucinol has been patented (109).

Paperboard adhesives with long pot lives, curable to form water-resistant bonds, are prepared by treating an aqueous solution of partially gelatinized starch at pH 8–11 with phloroglucinol and formaldehyde (110). Mixtures of phloroglucinol–formaldehyde reaction product with vinyl resins, useful as adhesives for laminated metal products, have been patented (111). Cation-exchange resins have been obtained by reacting 4-(sulfomethyl)phenol in acid solution with formaldehyde, phloroglucinol, and resorcinol (112). The coagulation of rubber latexes with phloroglucinol–formaldehyde resins has been described (113). The condensation product of methylolated formamide with phloroglucinol was reported to have tanning activity (114). A method of forming sealing deposits in wells with a resinous partial condensate of an aldehyde and phloroglucinol has been invented (115).

"Polyarylates" (polyesters from aromatic polyols and aromatic dibasic acids) prepared in part from phloroglucinol, useful for the preparation of films and shaped articles, have been reported (116). Polycarbonates crosslinked by the addition of paraformaldehyde and phloroglucinol were said to have improved dimensional and heat stability (117). The condensation of alkenyl chloroformate with phloroglucinol and cure of the products with peroxide at 80°C to give hard, transparent polymers with low shrinkage was patented (118).

Hexamethylenetetramine-cured polymers with high heat-stability were prepared by reacting mixtures of tri- and tetrameric phosphonitrilic chlorides with phloroglucinol in the presence of acid acceptors (119). Flame-resistant polymers for the impregnation of textiles, made by condensation of phloroglucinol and tris(1-aziridinyl)phosphine oxide or sulfide, have been patented (120). Useful resins were said to be obtained by the condensation of aryl dichlorophosphate with dihydric phenols, the softening point of the resin being raised by the addition of phloroglucinol (121). Hydraulic fluids and lubricants useful at elevated temperature have been obtained by reacting a mixture of phloroglucinol and ethylene glycol with phosphorus oxychloride (122). The preparation of polyurethans by treating organic polyisocyanates with propylene oxide–phloroglucinol condensates has been patented (123).

The vulcanization of synthetic rubber with phloroglucinol has been patented (124). The use of the adduct of magnesium oxide with di-o-tolylguanidine/phloroglucinol for the vulcanization of natural or synthetic rubber is said to minimize scorching (125). An adhesive made from polychloroprene rubber by vulcanizing it with phloroglucinol and sodium sulfide has been proposed (126).

There is no lack of suggested uses for phloroglucinol outside the resin field. The addition of phloroglucinol to control the hardening and fogging of photographic (gelatin) emulsions has been the subject of several patents (127). The thermal stabilization of alkyl cellulose by incorporation of a small amount of phloroglucinol has been described (128).   Formylated and acetylated amines have been found to be stabilized by trace amounts of phloroglucinol; thus N,N-dimethylformamide containing 0.01 to 0.1% phloroglucinol can be distilled at atmospheric pressure without decomposition (129).   The hydration of acrylonitrile to acrylamide in concentrated sulfuric acid is improved by the addition of phloroglucinol and ferrous salts as polymerization inhibitors (130).   The addition of small amounts of phloroglucinol to polyisocyanates has been reported to inhibit their discoloration (131).   The addition of small amounts of phloroglucinol to inhibit the corrosion of ferrous metals by amine-stabilized, chlorinated olefins has been patented (132).

A priming composition for percussion and friction fuses, containing hydrated lead trinitrophloroglucinate, has been disclosed (133).   An ignition composition for electric detonators, incorporating a lead salt of trinitrosophloroglucinol, has been reported (134).

The incorporation of a condensation product of phloroglucinol was reported to impart prolonged activity to vitamin B_{12} preparations (135).   Phosphorylation products of phloroglucinol having antienzymic and anticoagulant activity, capable of precipitating protamines and histones, have been patented (136).

Fibers of polyacrylonitrile and its copolymers have been found to be delustered by successive treatments with chlorine bleach, phloroglucinol (reducing agent), and then with titanium dioxide in the presence of a nonionic emulsifier (137).   The reaction of phloroglucinol with polyalkoxyacetals was reported to yield bisphenols useful as stabilizers for polymers as well as components suitable for resins with antistatic properties (138).

Phloroglucinol has been used in place of silver iodide for cloud seeding to modify weather conditions (139).

Reagent-grade phloroglucinol is used as a sensitive analytical reagent for the detection and estimation of aliphatic and aromatic aldehydes, and carbohydrates (pentoses, pentosans, glycuronic acids, galactoses, and galactans).

Derivatives. *Phloroacylophenones* are prepared by the Friedel-Crafts acylation of phloroglucinol.   The simplest example is 2,4,6-trihydroxyacetophenone (**40**) (phloroacetophenone, acetophloroglucinol), needles from water, mp 219°C (anhydrous). Many derivatives of acylated phloroglucinols, bearing a benzene ring substituent or an ether or glycoside linkage, occur in nature.   Examples are cotoin (**41**) in coto bark (from a tree native to northern Bolivia), and conglomerone (**42**) found in *Eucalyptus conglomerata.*

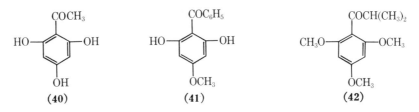

(40)   (41)   (42)

Phloroglucinolcarboxylic acid (2,4,6-trihydroxybenzoic acid) is prepared by the reaction of sodium or potassium bicarbonate solution with phloroglucinol.   It decomposes to phloroglucinol at approx 100°C.

Phloroglucide (**43**) (2,3',4,5',6-pentahydroxybiphenyl), a pale-yellow solid, darkening at 250°C and decomposing at 285°C, is formed on heating phloroglucinol above its melting point, or (better) by refluxing phloroglucinol with concentrated hydrochloric acid (140). Its use as a coupling component in diazotype processes has been patented (141).

Griseofulvin (**44**) contains the phloroglucinol nucleus. It is an important oral antifungal agent both in man and animals, elaborated by certain strains of *Penicillium*. A synthetic route to griseofulvin, starting from the appropriately substituted phloroglucinol, has been patented (142).

5,7-Dihydroxy-4-methylcoumarin (5-hydroxy-4-methylumbelliferone) (**45**), mp (monohydrate) 280–286°C, H₂O content 9%, crystallizes in free-flowing crystals. The compound is fluorescent and absorbs ultraviolet radiation. It has been used as a whitening agent in dyes, soaps, and plastics. See Brighteners, optical. It has a structural similarity to coumarin derivatives used pharmaceutically as anticoagulants. It is prepared by condensing phloroglucinol with acetoacetic ester, $CH_3COCH_2COOC_2H_5$, in the presence of acid catalysts such as sulfuric acid or phosphorus pentoxide.

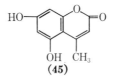

Benzenetetrols

There are three possible isomers, 1,2,3,4-, 1,2,3,5-, and 1,2,4,5-benzenetetrol, of these tetrahydric phenols, all of them known. They occur in nature in essential oils, quinones found in the plant and animal kingdoms, flavones, and coumarin derivatives.

1,2,3,4-BENZENETETROL

1,2,3,4-Benzenetetrol (1,2,3,4-tetrahydroxybenzene, apionol) forms needles (from benzene); its mp is 161°C. It is easily soluble in water, diethyl ether, ethanol, and glacial acetic acid, sparingly soluble in benzene. It gives a blue color with ferric chloride in aqueous solution. Surprisingly, 1,2,3,4-benzenetetrol in alkaline solution does not absorb oxygen.

It reacts in alkaline solution with dimethyl sulfate to give the tetramethyl ether, mp 89°C; with acetic anhydride in the presence of sulfuric acid as the catalyst, the tetraacetate is obtained (mp 139°C).

1,2,3,4-Benzenetetrol is best prepared by the hydrolysis of 4-aminopyrogallol hydrochloride (**46**) (143), which in turn can be prepared by the reduction of 4-nitropyrogallol. Its 1,2-dimethyl ether (48), bp 160–170°C at 20 mm pressure, can be prepared by the oxidation of gallacetophenone-3,4-dimethyl ether (47) with hydrogen

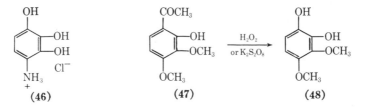

(46)   **(47)**   **(48)**

peroxide (144) or with potassium peroxysulfate (145). The oxidation of pyrogallol 1,2-dimethyl ether with potassium peroxysulfate gives the 2,3-dimethyl ether of 1,2,3,4-benzenetetrol (1,4-dihydroxy-2,3-dimethoxybenzene), mp 84–85°C (146). The γ-irradiation of gallic acid (49) in aqueous solution in the presence of hydrogen perox-

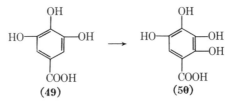

(49)   **(50)**

ide and oxygen to give 2,3,4,5-tetrahydroxybenzoic acid (50) in good yield, and the similar treatment of 5-nitropyrogallol (51) to give 2,3,4,5-tetrahydroxynitrobenzene (52) have been patented (147).

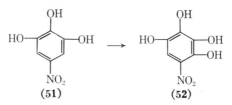

(51)   **(52)**

Derivatives. The most important derivatives of 1,2,3,4-benzenetetrol are the ubiquinones (coenzyme Q) which are dimethoxytoluquinones with a polyisoprenoid side chain (53); they occur in both plants and animals. The biological function of coen-

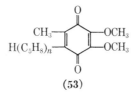

(53)

zyme Q is in the mitochondrial electron-transfer chain and in oxidative phosphorylation; it is possibly involved in photosynthetic reactions. Coenzyme Q may have hematological activity in an anemia in children caused by a protein-deficient diet. Broad studies of its activity and possible therapeutic use are continuing (148).

1,2,3,5-BENZENETETROL

1,2,3,5-Benzenetetrol (1,2,3,5-tetrahydroxybenzene) forms needles (from water); its mp is 165°C. The compound is easily soluble in water, alcohol, and ethyl acetate, and insoluble in chloroform and benzene. In aqueous solution, this tetrol gives a fugitive reddish color with ferric chloride.

1,2,3,5-Benzenetetrol is very sensitive to air and decomposes easily; therefore, it is stored preferably as the tetraacetate. In aqueous potassium bicarbonate solution sparged with carbon dioxide, 1,2,3,5-benzenetetrol yields 2,3,4,6-tetrahydroxybenzoic acid (54), mp 308–310°C (with decomposition).

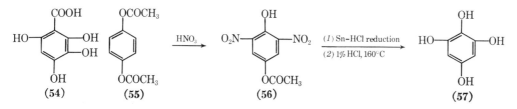

1,2,3,5-Benzenetetrol has been prepared by the hydrolysis of 2,4,6-triaminophenol with dilute hydrochloric acid (149,150); reportedly, this hydrolysis is improved in the presence of copper (151). Similarly, it has been prepared in 46% overall yield by the nitration of hydroquinone diacetate (55) at low temperature to 2,6-dinitrohydroquinone acetate (56) followed by reduction to the corresponding diamine hydrochloride with tin and hydrochloric acid; finally the diamine hydrochloride is hydrolyzed to the tetrol (57) with 1% hydrochloric acid at 155–160°C (150).

1,2,4,5-BENZENETETROL

1,2,4,5-Benzenetetrol (1,2,4,5-tetrahydroxybenzene) forms leaflets from glacial acetic acid; mp 215–220°C. It is easily soluble in water, ethanol, and diethyl ether, not quite as soluble in concentrated hydrochloric acid and glacial acetic acid. The aqueous solution of this tetrahydric phenol turns brown quickly when exposed to air. Ferric chloride produces a precipitate of 2,5-dihydroxy-1,4-benzoquinone (58); the

(58)

same compound is produced by aeration of the alkaline solution. On the other hand, aeration of its acid solutions precipitates a black quinhydrone.

1,2,4,5-Benzenetetrol is obtained by the reduction of 2,5-dihydroxy-1,4-benzoquinone (58) (readily made by the oxidation of hydroquinone dissolved in strong aqueous sodium hydroxide with hydrogen peroxide) with stannous chloride and hydrochloric acid or by hydrogenation using a platinum catalyst (152). On treatment with acetic anhydride in the presence of a catalytic amount of sulfuric acid, the tetraacetate of 1,2,4,5-benzenetetrol is obtained, mp 226–227°C. Etherification with methyl iodide in the presence of base gives the tetramethyl ether of 1,2,4,5-benzenetetrol, mp 103°C. Several partial ethers, halo, and amino derivatives of 1,2,4,5-benzenetetrol have been obtained by reduction of the appropriately substituted 1,4-benzoquinones.

1,2,4,5-Benzenetetrol has been co-condensed with catechol and formaldehyde to give oxidation-reduction resins (153). The use of 1,2,4,5-benzenetetrol as a component of heat-sensitive copying materials has been patented (154). Polyquinone ethers prepared by condensation of the tetrol with chloranil in N,N-dimethylformamide at reflux were said to be useful as black pigment dyes for polypropylene, polystyrene, and polyamides (155).

Benzenepentol

Benzenepentol (pentahydroxybenzene) (**60**) seems to be the most obscure of the benzenepolyols. The compound has been prepared by boiling 2,4,6-triaminoresorcinol diethyl ether (**59**) with water, followed by ether cleavage with HI (156); the product

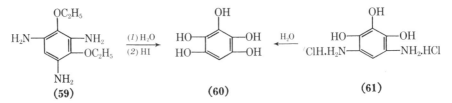

is said to be very soluble in water but very sparingly soluble in organic solvents. On the other hand (157) benzenepentol prepared by hydrolysis of 4,6-diaminopyrogallol hydrochloride (**61**), was said to be sparingly soluble in water, easily soluble in ether, alcohol, and ethyl acetate, and insoluble in benzene; the compound formed pale-violet needles which blackened on heating; in aqueous solution it gave a dark reddish-brown color with ferric chloride; with acetic anhydride in the presence of concentrated sulfuric acid it gave a pentaacetate, mp 165°C (with decomposition).

Ethers of benzenepentol have been obtained by the Dakin oxidation of the appropriately substituted acetophenone. Thus, the oxidation of 2-hydroxy-3,4,6-trimethoxyacetophenone and 2-hydroxy-3,4,5-trimethoxyacetophenone with hydrogen peroxide in the presence of alkali gave 1,2-dihydroxy-3,4,6-trimethoxybenzene and 1,2-dihydroxy-3,4,5-trimethoxybenzene, respectively; further methylation of these ethers gave the pentamethyl ether of benzenepentol, mp 58–59°C (158).

Benzenehexol

Benzenehexol (hexahydroxybenzene), $C_6(OH)_6$ (**62**), forms snow-white crystals when freshly prepared and collected in an inert atmosphere.

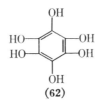

It is readily oxidized; its solution turns red-violet quickly on exposure to air; it reduces cold silver nitrate solutions. Its hexahydro derivatives are biologically important carbohydrates, found in microorganisms, plants, and animals. It is also useful for the preparation of quinonoid derivatives which are employed as analytical reagents.

Physical and Chemical Properties. Benzenehexol of good purity does not melt up to at least 310°C. It is sparingly soluble in water, ethanol, diethyl ether, and benzene. It readily reduces silver nitrate solution and is oxidized by air in sodium carbonate solution to tetrahydroxy-p-benzoquinone (**63**). By oxidation with concentrated nitric acid, triquinoyl (**64**) is obtained. Benzenehexol is readily converted to esters

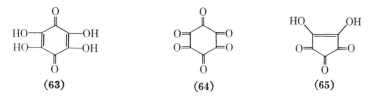

(63)   **(64)**   **(65)**

such as the hexaacetate by the usual methods. Catalytic hydrogenation (160) gives inositols (stereoisomeric cyclohexanehexols) and quercitols (cyclohexanepentols), although the hydrogenation of benzenehexol with platinum oxide catalyst at 50–55°C reportedly yields phloroglucinol (159). On evaporation with potassium carbonate, the potassium salt of croconic acid (**65**) is formed by a benzilic acid-type rearrangement via quinonoid intermediates.

Analysis. Benzenehexol gives a violet color with ferric chloride. Derivatives which can be used for its identification are the hexaacetate, mp 205°C, and the hexabenzoate, mp 313°C.

Synthesis. Benzenehexol is available only from laboratory reagent suppliers. The simplest laboratory preparation (161) involves the aeration of the glyoxal–bisulfite addition product in sodium carbonate solution at 40–80°C, isolation of the sodium salt of tetrahydroxybenzoquinone, followed by acidification to obtain the free tetrahydroxy-*p*-benzoquinone in about 8% yield (eq. 4); the latter is reduced with stannous chloride in boiling dilute hydrochloric acid solution to benzenehexol (eq. 5) in 77% yield.

$$\text{(4)}$$

$$\text{(5)}$$

The oldest method of preparation of benzenehexol involves the reaction of molten potassium with carbon monoxide to give the potassium salt of the hexol; the free phenol is obtained by neutralization of the salt with dilute acid (162). This reaction has been reinvestigated and improved (163). Sodium metal containing 1% potassium was heated at 340°C under an initial 90 atm carbon monoxide pressure to give a 77.5% yield of the sodium salt of benzenehexol after 7.5 hr reaction time.

Bibliography

"Phloroglucinol" in *ECT* 1st ed., Vol. 10, pp. 386–391, by J. F. Kaplan, The Edwal Laboratories, Inc.; "Pyrogallol" in *ECT* 1st ed., Vol. 11, pp. 315–320, by Desmond M. C. Reilly, Midwest Research Institute.

Pyrogallol

1. A. Critchlow, R. D. Haworth, and P. L. Pauson, *J. Chem. Soc.* **1951**, 1318.
2. E. Chapman, A. G. Perkin, and R. Robinson, *J. Chem. Soc.* **1927**, 3028.
3. O. Widmer, *Z. Physik. Chem.* (*Leipzig*) **140A**, 175 (1929).
4. A. Einhorn and J. Cobliner, *Ber.* **37**, 106 (1904).

5. F. J. Moore and R. M. Thomas, *J. Am. Chem. Soc.* **39,** 987 (1917).

6. W. R. Christian, C. J. Gogek, and C. B. Purves, *Can. J. Chem.* **29,** 911 (1951).

7. B. Peacherer, L. M. Jampolsky, and H. M. Wuest, *J. Am. Chem. Soc.* **70,** 2587 (1948).

8. National Formulary X, American Pharmaceutical Association, Washington, D.C., 1955, p. 479.

9. M. B. Jacobs, *Analytical Chemistry of Industrial Poisons, Hazards, and Solvents,* 2nd ed., Interscience Publishers, Inc., New York, 1949, pp. 707–708.

10. F. Feigl, *Qualitative Analysis by Spot Tests,* 3rd ed., Elsevier, New York, 1946, pp. 329–332.

11. L. S. Malowan, *Mikrochemie ver. Mikrochim. Acta* **38,** 212 (1951).

12. Krannich et al., "Bibliography of Scientific and Industrial Reports," *U.S. Dept. Comm. Office Tech. Serv. PB Rept. 30161* (1947), p. 668.

13. U.S.S.R. Pat. 105,427 (April 25, 1957), P. N. Zemenko.

14. U.S. Pat. 2,908,719 (Oct. 13, 1959), H. S. Bloch and R. C. Wackler; U.S. Pat. 2,934,567 (April 26, 1960), J. G. Gatsis; U.S. Pat. 2,964,569 (Dec. 13, 1960), J. A. Chemicek and W. L. Cox (all to Universal Oil Products Co.).

15. Ger. Pat. 207,374 (Jan. 12, 1907), (to Agfa).

16. U.S. Pat. 2,603,662 (July 15, 1952), D. R. Stevens (to Gulf Research and Development Co.).

17. H. Budzikiewicz, W. Metlesics, and F. Wessely, *Monatsh.* **91,** 117 (1960).

18. Ger. Pat. 1,228,258 (Nov. 10, 1966), F. Merger and D. Graesslin (to Gesellschaft für Kernforschung G.m.b.H.).

19. F. A. Patty, ed., *Industrial Hygiene and Toxicology,* 2nd ed., Vol. 2, Interscience Publishers, a division of John Wiley & Sons, Inc., New York, 1963, pp. 1386–1387.

20. W. S. Spector, ed., *Handbook of Toxicology,* Vol. 1, W. B. Saunders Co., Philadelphia, 1956.

21. C. B. Neblette, *Photography, Its Principles and Practice,* 4th ed., D. Van Nostrand Company, Inc., New York, 1942, pp. 323–324.

22. Ger. Pat. (East) 37,764 (May 5, 1965), R. Goldbecker.

23. U.S.S.R. Pat. 162,421 (April 16, 1964), E. F. Rul, M. S. Khaikin, and G. V. Derstuganov (to All-Union Scientific Research, Motion Picture and Photographic Institute Kazan); U.S. Pat. 2,967,772 (Jan. 10, 1961), J. F. Willems and A. E. van Hoff (to Gevaert Photo Producten N.V.); Fr. Pat. 1,395,367 (April 9, 1965), VEB Filmfabrik Wolfen.

24. U.S. Pat. 2,751,295 (June 19, 1956), I. F. Salminen, J. A. Van Allen, and E. C. Yackel (to Eastman Kodak Co.); Belg. Pat. 559,465 (Nov. 16, 1957), J. F. Willems and A. E. van Hoff (to Gevaert Photo Producten N.V.); U.S.S.R. Pat. 162,422 (April 14, 1964), M. S. Khaikin, E. F. Rul, L. G. Fedorina, G. V. Derstuganov, and V. A. Kukhtin (to All-Union Scientific Research, Motion Picture and Photographic Institute Kazan).

25. Belg. Pat. 549,431 (Jan. 13, 1961), Kodak Soc. Anon.

26. U.S. Pats. 2,663,654-7 (Dec. 22, 1953), C. S. Miller and B. L. Clark (to Minnesota Mining & Manufacturing Co.); Belg. Pat. 591,479 (June 30, 1960), Kodak Soc. anon.; Ger. Pat. 1,145,-643 (March 21, 1963), E. W. Grieshaber (to Minnesota Mining and Manufacturing Co.); Brit. Pat. 958,962 (May 27, 1964), H. C. Yutzy and E. C. Yackel (to Kodak Ltd.).

27. Ger. Pat. 1,029,662 (May 8, 1959), M. Staud (to Air Associates, Inc.).

28. U.S. Pat. 3,201,249 (Aug. 17, 1965), G. W. Pierce, G. F. Nadeau, and C. B. Thompson (to Eastman Kodak Co.).

29. Japan. Pat. 2187 (1961), H. Kobayashi, M. Aoki, and H. Hattori (to Toyo Rayon Co., Ltd.); Can. Pat. 553,787 (March 4, 1958), B. A. Hunter (to Dominion Rubber Co., Ltd.); Brit. Pat. 859,438 (Jan. 25, 1961), Office national d'étude et de recherches aéronautiques (O.N.E.R.A.); Swiss Pat. 232,831 (Sept. 1, 1954), Lonza Elektrizitätswerke und Chemische Fabriken A.-G.; Japan. Pat. 23,467 (1961), T. Matsuda and R. Ueno.

30. U.S. Pat. 2,561,915 (July 24, 1951), E. R. Erickson (to Mathieson Chemical Corp.); Ger. Pat. 1,010,733 (June 19, 1957), H. H. Frey and R. Huth (to Farbwerke Hoechst A.-G.).

31. Japan. Pat. 9598 (1961), I. Sakurada, N. Okada, and Y. Akiyama (to Japan Radioactive High Polymer Research Institute).

32. Pol. Pat. 47,840 (Dec. 30, 1963), A. Gomulka and Z. Jedlinski (to Politechnika Slaska, Katedra Technologii Powlok Ochronnych).

33. U.S.S.R. Pat. 161,840 (April 1, 1964), S. K. Zherebkov, V. A. Orlov, and L. N. Efremov.

34. Fr. Pat. 1,434,310 (April 8, 1966), Thiokol Chemical Corp.; Brit. Pat. 1,040,352 (Aug. 24, 1966), J. Green, N. B. Levine, and R. C. Keller (to Thiokol Chemical Corp.).

35. U.S. Pat. 3,179,637 (April 20, 1965), B. P. Brodt and S. G. Smith (to E. I. du Pont de Nemours & Co.).
36. Ger. Pat. (East) 2,645 (Aug. 4, 1961), F. Kanis and H. Bigga; Brit. Pat. 933,952 (Aug. 14, 1963), Continental Gummi-Werke A.-G.
37. H. P. Gregor and M. Beltzer, *J. Polymer Sci.* **53**, 125 (1961); Ger. Pat. 972,626 (Aug. 20, 1959), H. Lauth (to Farbenfabriken Bayer A.-G.); U.S. Pat. 2,767,135 (Oct. 16, 1956), W. Juda and W. A. McRae (to Ionic Inc.).
38. Belg. Pat. 565,569 (March 31, 1958), Union chimique Belge S.A.; Fr. Pat. 1,391,765 (March 12, 1965), Albright & Wilson (Mfg.) Ltd.; Brit. Pat. 925,105 (May 1, 1963), M. Apley and J. R. Alexander (to Walker Chemical Co.).
39. Fr. Pat. 1,364,456 (June 19, 1964), Consortium für Elektrochemische Industrie G.m.b.H.; U.S. Pat. 2,890,195 (June 9, 1959), B. Phillips, F. C. Frostick, Jr., C. W. McGary, Jr., and C. T. Patrick, Jr. (to Union Carbide Corp.).
40. Ger. Pat. 935,604 (Nov. 24, 1955); Ger. Pat. 1,061,466 (July 16, 1959), M. Meister (to Farbenfabriken Bayer A.-G.).
41. Brit. Pat. 993,923 (June 2, 1965), Revlon, Inc.; U.S. Pat. 2,875,769 (March 3, 1959), P. F. Rosmarin and M. Pautzer (to Apod Corp.); Japan. Pat. 4350 (1955), T. Shigenuki and T. Ueno; Fr. Pat. 1,135,232 (April 25, 1957), Yamashatsu Sangyo Kaisha Ltd.; Japan. Pat. 5599 (1957), T. Kinoshita (to Tsuneyoshi Ishiguro).
42. Austrian Pat. 226,220 (March 11, 1963), G. Zoelss, O. Schmid, and K. Wismayer (to Österreichische Stickstoffwerke A.-G.); Belg. Pat. 619,015 (Dec. 11, 1962), F. Hoffmann-La Roche & Co.; U.S. Pat. 2,466,019 (April 5, 1949), E. A. H. Friedheim.
43. U. S. Pat. 2,815,365 (Dec. 3, 1957), H. O. Senkbeil and H. F. Brust; U.S. Pats. 2,815,366 and 2,815,365 (Dec. 3, 1957), H. F. Senkbeil (all to Dow Chemical Co.).
44. Austrian Pat. 226,495 (March 25, 1963), S. Radai, S. Varga, and G. Polereczky (to Budavox Budapesti Hiradas-technikai Vallalat).
45. *Propyl Gallate*, Fine Chemicals Data Sheet, The Harshaw Chemical Co.
46. U.S. Pat. 2,848,443 (Aug. 19, 1958), L. R. Sperberg (to Phillips Petroleum Co.).
47. Ger. Pat. 1,086,719 (Appl. April 1, 1957), C. S. Miller and C. A. Kuhrmeyer (to Minnesota Mining and Manufacturing Co.).
48. *Gallic Acid Derivatives*, Data Sheet, Mallinckrodt Chemical Works.
49. Ger. Pat. 1,230,032 (Dec. 8, 1966), R. Y. Mauvernay.
49a. *The Merck Index*, 7th ed., Merck & Co., Rahway, N.J., 1960, p. 470.
50. Fr. Pat. 1,204,793 (Jan. 28, 1960), J. C. Seailles.
51. Belg. Pat. 670,495 (April 4, 1966), S. R. Safir and R. P. Williams (to American Cyanamid Co.).

Hydroxyhydroquinone

52. L. Barth and J. Schreder, *Monatsh.* **5**, 595 (1884).
53. J. Thiele and K. Jaeger, *Ber.* **34**, 2837 (1901).
54. C. Liebermann and S. Lindenbaum, *Ber.* **37**, 1176 (1904).
55. E. v. Pechmann and E. v. Krafft, *Ber.* **34**, 423 (1901).
56. W. Feuerstein and M. Dutoit, *Ber.* **34**, 2637 (1901).
57. W. Fuchs and B. Elsner, *Ber.* **57**, 1228 (1924).
58. J. Thiele, *Ber.* **31**, 1248 (1898); Ger. Pat. 101,607 (Dec. 31, 1897); Ger. Pat. 107,508 (Dec. 31, 1897) (both to Farbenfabriken Bayer).
59. U.S. Pat. 2,118,141 (May 24, 1938), F. R. Bean (to Eastman Kodak Co.).
60. L. Barth and J. Schreder, *Monatsh.* **4**, 176 (1883).
61. H. Dakin, *Am. Chem. J.* **42**, 495 (1909); W. Baker, *J. Chem. Soc.* **1934**, 1684.
62. J. Pospišil and V. Ettel, *Chem. Listy* **52**, 939 (1958); *Collection Czech. Chem. Commun.* **24**, 729 (1959).
63. P. Marquardt, R. Koch, and J. P. Aubert, *Z. Ges. Inn. Med. Ihre Grenzgebiete* **2**, 333 (1947).
64. Austrian Pat. 203,635 (May 25, 1959); Fr. Pat. 1,189,619 (Oct. 5, 1959); Brit. Pat. 824,519 (Dec. 2, 1959) (all to Société Monsavon-l'Oréal); U.S. Pat. 3,214,472 (Oct. 26, 1965), R. Charle and R. Lantz (to Société Monsavon-l'Oréal).
65. Ger. Pat. 1,114,360 (Jan. 6, 1960), G. Johnson (to Schering A.-G.).
66. O. Dimroth and R. Fick, *Ann.* **411**, 321 (1916).
67. U.S. Pat. 3,031,412 (April 24, 1962), W. H. Petering and W. A. Callahan (to Detrex Chemical Industries, Inc.).

68. Brit. Pat. 913,478 (Dec. 19, 1962), M. Dollhausen and E. Bock (to Farbenfabriken Bayer A.-G.).

Phloroglucinol

69. R. J. Highet and T. J. Batterham, *J. Org. Chem.* **29,** 475 (1964).
70. E. S. Hand and R. M. Horowitz, *J. Am. Chem. Soc.* **86,** 2084 (1964).
71. A. Bayer, *Ber.* **19,** 159 (1886).
72. W. Fuchs, *Ber.* **54,** 245 (1921).
73. J. Pollak, *Monatsh.* **14,** 419 (1893).
74. G. Minunni, *Ber.* **21,** 1984 (1888).
75. A. R. Stein, *Can. J. Chem.* **43,** 1493 (1965) (and refs. therein).
76. G. S. Misra and R. S. Asthana, *Ann.* **609,** 240 (1957).
77. G. I. Fray, *Tetrahedron* **3,** 316 (1958).
78. W. T. Gradwell and A. McGookin, *Chem. Ind. (London)* **1956,** 377.
79. J. Herzig and F. Wenzel, *Monatsh.* **27,** 785 (1906).
80. H. Bredereck, I. Hennig, and W. Rau, *Ber.* **86,** 1085 (1953).
81. Ger. Pat. 941,372 (April 12, 1956), W. Riedl.
82. W. Gruber, *Ber.* **75,** 29 (1942).
83. G. Link, *Ber.* **13,** 1652 (1880).
84. Ger. Pat. 1,144,727 (March 7, 1963), C. B. Linn (to Universal Oil Products Co.).
85. R. Mayer and A. Melhorn, *Z. Chem.* **3** (10), 390 (1963).
86. A. G. Perkin, *J. Chem. Soc.* **71,** 1154 (1897).
87. M. L. Kastens and J. F. Kaplan, *Ind. Eng. Chem.* **42,** 402 (1950); U.S. Pat. 2,614,126 (Oct. 14, 1952), J. Krueger (to Edwal Laboratories; later this became Ringwood Chemical Co., and is now Morton Chemical Co.).
88. Brit. Pat. 1,022,733 (March 16, 1966), E. Vero and J. N. Vickers (to Whiffen & Sons, Ltd.).
89. Ger. Pat. 1,195,327 (June 24, 1965), S. Pietzsch (to Kalle A.-G.).
90. P. M. Heertjes, *Rec. Trav. Chim.* **78,** 452 (1959).
91. Brit. Pat. 1,012,782 (Dec. 8, 1965), (to Farbwerke Hoechst A.-G.).
92. Brit. Pat. 751,598 (June 27, 1956), A. F. Shepard (to Hooker Electrochemical Co.); Ger. Pat. (East) 12,239 (Oct. 16, 1956), F. Seidel, M. Schulze, and H. Baltz (to VEB-Farbenfabriken Wolfen); U.S. Pat. 2,799,698 (July 16, 1957), M. A. Taves (to Hercules Powder Co.); U.S. Pat. 3,028,410 (April 3, 1962), W. F. Zimmer (to Hooker Chemical Co.).
93. L. C. Borell, M.S. Thesis, University of Pittsburgh, Pa., 1932, and references therein.
94. U.S. Pat. 2,773,908 (Dec. 11, 1956), W. R. Cake (to Heyden Chemical Corp.).
95. Ger. Pat. (East) 24,998 (March 26, 1963), D. Ullrich and J. Seiffert.
96. U.S. Pat. 3,230,266 (Jan. 18, 1966), A. A. Baldwin and J. Miyashiro (to Morton International, Inc.).
97. R. Kuhn, G. Quadbeck, and E. Roehm, *Ann.* **565,** 1 (1949).
98. Data sheets on phloroglucinol dihydrate, technical, commercial and cp grade, Morton Chemical Co., Chicago, Ill.
99. W. F. von Oettingen, "Phenol and its Derivatives. The Relation Between Their Chemical Constitution and Their Effects on the Organism," *Natl. Inst. Health Bull. 190,* U.S. Gov. Printing Office, Washington, D.C., 1949.
100. W. S. Spector, ed., *Handbook of Toxicology,* Vol. 1, W. B. Saunders Co., Philadelphia, 1956.
101. U.S. Pat. 2,546,861 (March 27, 1957), C. S. Maher; P. F. Pascoe, *Chem. Prod.* **18,** 454 (1955); Ger. Pat. 917,991 (Sept. 16, 1954), R. Fleischhauer (to Cassella Farbwerke Mainkur A.-G.); Ger. Pat. 946,976 (Oct. 9, 1956), Farbwerke Hoechst A.-G.; Brit. Pat. 823,446 (Nov. 11, 1959), J. G. Kennedy (to Whiffen & Sons, Ltd.).
102. Ger. Pat. 1,012,406 (July 18, 1957), A. Tartter and O. Weissbarth (to Badische Anilin- und Soda-Fabrik A.-G.); Ger. Pat. 1,051,242 (Sept. 3, 1959), H. A. Dortmann, P. Schmitz, and J. Eibl (to Farbenfabriken Bayer A.-G.).
103. Brit. Pat. 668,474 (March 19, 1952), J. R. Atkinson and D. A. Plant (to Imperial Chemical Industries, Ltd.); Ger. Pat. 760,951 (March 30, 1953), E. Fellmer (to I. G. Farbenindustrie A.-G.).
104. J. Kosar, *Light Sensitive Systems,* John Wiley & Sons, Inc., New York, 1965.
105. U.S. Pat. 3,113,865 (Dec. 10, 1963), J. J. Sagura and J. A. Van Allen (to Eastman Kodak Co.).

106. Belg. Pat. 615,436 (Sept. 24, 1962), Ozalid Co. Ltd.

107. U.S. Pat. 2,510,885-6 (June 6, 1950), S. O. Greenlee (to Devoe & Raynolds Co., Inc.).

108. Japan. Pat. 6648 (1961), C. Yotsuyanagi and Y. Murayama (to Hamano Textile Industrial Co., Ltd.).

109. U.S. Pat. 3,021,304 (Feb. 13, 1962), S. O. Greenlee (to Devoe & Raynolds Co., Inc.).

110. U.S. Pat. 2,884,389 (April 28, 1959), J. F. Corwin and F. Person (to Koppers Co., Inc.).

111. Ger. Pat. 805,721 (May 27, 1951), F. J. Nagel (to Westinghouse Electric Corp.).

112. Ger. Pat. 968,543 (March 6, 1958), H. Wassenegger (to Farbenfabriken Bayer A.-G.).

113. Fr. Pat. 961,294 (May 9, 1950), Société auxiliaire de l'institut français du caoutchouc.

114. Ger. Pat. 1,020,985 (Dec. 19, 1957), E. Honold and A. Miekely (to Cassella Farbwerke Mainkur A.-G.).

115. U.S. Pat. 2,485,527 (Oct. 17, 1949), P. H. Cardwell (to Dow Chemical Co.).

116. Brit. Pat. 907,647 (Oct. 10, 1962), B. E. Jennings (to Imperial Chemical Industries Ltd.).

117. Span. Pat. 269,023 (Oct. 26, 1961), A. H. Lopez.

118. Brit. Pat. 611,529 (Nov. 1, 1948), J. A. Bralley and F. B. Pope (to B. F. Goodrich Co.).

119. U.S. Pat. 3,121,704 (Feb. 18, 1964), R. G. Rice, B. H. Geib, and L. A. Kaplan (to General Dynamics Corp.).

120. U.S. Pat. 2,912,412 (Nov. 10, 1959), W. A. Reeves, J. D. Guthrie, and L. H. Chance (to U.S. Dept. of Agriculture).

121. Ger. Pat. 843,753 (July 14, 1952), B. Helferich and H. G. Schmidt (to Dynamit A.-G. vorm. Alfred Nobel & Co.).

122. U.S. Pat. 2,978,478 (April 4, 1961), W. J. Sandner and W. L. Fierce (to the Pure Oil Co.).

123. Brit. Pat. 849,405 (Sept. 28, 1960), A. V. Mercer (to Petrochemicals Ltd.).

124. Austrian Pats. 162,570 (March 10, 1949), 162,572 (March 19, 1949), and 165,035 (Jan. 10, 1950), H. Deutsch and H. P. Franck (to "Semperit" Österreichische-Amerikanische Gummiwerke A.-G.).

125. Fr. Pat. 1,352,678 (Feb. 14, 1964), R. A. Patton (to Morton Salt Co.).

126. U.S.S.R. Pat. 161,840 (April 1, 1964), S. K. Zherebkov, V. A. Orlov, and L. N. Efremov.

127. Ger. Pat. 1,040,778 (Oct. 9, 1958), E. v. Pechmann (to C. F. Boehringer & Soehne G.m.b.H.); U.S.S.R. Pat. 129,483 (June 15, 1960), S. M. Levi, Y. B. Vilenskii, T. N. Veretenova, S. N. Kochnevna, and O. V. Popova; Belg. Pat. 631,556 (Aug. 16, 1963), Gevaert Photo Producten N.V.; Belg. Pat. 635,753 (Feb. 3, 1964), W. Saleck and R. Koslowsky (to Agfa A.-G.); Brit. Pat. 981,470 (Jan. 27, 1965), Agfa A.-G.

128. U.S. Pat. 2,547,141 (April 3, 1951), J. H. Sharphouse and J. Downing (to Celanese Corp. of America).

129. Ger. Pat. 880,298 (June 22, 1953), R. Zoller and J. H. Schmidt (to Phrix-Werke A.-G.).

130. U.S. Pat. 3,130,229 (April 21, 1964), R. E. Friedrich, G. D. Jones, and S. N. Heiny (to Dow Chemical Co.).

131. U.S. Pat. 3,035,078 (May 15, 1962), R. C. DeLong, M. Kaplan, and C. R. Wagner (to Allied Chemical Corp.).

132. U.S. Pat. 3,031,412 (April 24, 1962), W. H. Petering and W. A. Callahan (to Detrex Chemical Industries, Inc.).

133. Brit. Pat. 940,649 (Oct. 30, 1963), Dynamit-Nobel A.-G.

134. Japan. Pat. 6298 (Dec. 7, 1953), S. Takenaka (to Nippon Chemical & Drug Co.).

135. Belg. Pat. 608,915 (April 6, 1962), N. V. Organon.

136. U.S. Pat. 3,008,951 (Nov. 14, 1962), O. B. Fernö, H. J. Fex, T. O. E. Linderot, E. T. Rosenberg, and K. B. Högberg, (to Aktiebolaget Leo); Brit. Pat. 773,495 (April 24, 1957), R. J. Boscott (to National Research Development Corp.).

137. Ger. Pat. 870,542 (Mar. 16, 1953), R. Zoller and E. Bubek (to Phrix-Werke A.-G.).

138. U.S. Pat. 3,061,650 (Oct. 30, 1962), R. Steckler, J. Werner, and F. A. Hessel (to General Aniline & Film Corp.).

139. T. E. Hoffer and M. L. Ogne, *J. Geophys. Res.* **70**, 3857 (1965).

140. J. Herzig and J. Pollak, *Monatsh.* **15**, 703 (1884); W. Riedl and F. Linhof, *Ann.* **597**, 153 (1955).

141. U.S. Pat. 2,432,593 (Dec. 15, 1947), J. M. Straley (to General Aniline and Film Corp.).

142. U.S. Pat. 3,190,824 (June 22, 1965), D. Taub, N. L. Wendler, and C. H. Kuo (to Merck & Co., Inc.).

Benzenetetrols

143. A. Einhorn, J. Cobliner, and H. Pfeiffer, *Ber.* **37,** 119 (1904).
144. W. Baker, E. H. T. Jukes, and C. A. Subrahmanyam, *J. Chem. Soc.* **1934,** 1681.
145. G. Bargellini, *Gazz. Chim. Ital.* **46** (1), 249 (1916).
146. W. Baker and R. I. Savage, *J. Chem. Soc.* **1938,** 1604.
147. Ger. Pat. 1,228,258 (Nov. 10, 1966), F. Merger and D. Graesslin (to Gesellschaft für Kernforschung G.m.b.H.).
148. R. A. Morton, ed., *Biochemistry of Quinones,* Academic Press, Inc., New York, 1965; *Chem. Eng. News* **45,** 94 (March 20, 1967).
149. K. Oettinger, *Monatsh.* **11,** 248 (1895); M. Nierenstein, *J. Chem. Soc.* **111,** 5 (1917).
150. G. Zemplén and J. Schwartz, *Acta Chim. Acad. Sci. Hung.* **3,** 487 (1953).
151. Ger. Pat. 1,195,327 (March 10, 1966), S. Pietzsch (to Kalle A.-G.).
152. R. Nietzki and F. Schmidt, *Ber.* **21,** 2377 (1888); J. Pospišil and V. Ettel, *Chem. Listy* **52,** 939 (1958); *Collection Czech. Chem. Commun.* **24,** 729 (1959).
153. U.S. Pat. 2,927,096 (March 1, 1960), S. Soloway.
154. Brit. Pat. 927,895 (June 6, 1963), T. V. Crevling, D. J. Haag, and T. I. Abbott (to Kodak Ltd.).
155. Ger. Pat. 1,179,716 (Oct. 15, 1964), H. Naarmann (to Badische Anilin- und Soda-Fabrik A.-G.).

Benzenepentol

156. F. Wenzel and H. Weidel, *Chem. Zentr.* **1903** (II), 829.
157. A. Einhorn, J. Cobliner, and F. Pfeiffer, *Ber.* **37,** 132 (1904).
158. W. Baker, *J. Chem. Soc.* **1941,** 662.

Benzenehexol

159. H. Wieland and R. S. Wishart, *Ber.* **47,** 2082 (1914); S. J. Angyal and D. J. McHugh, *Chem. Ind.* (*London*) **1955,** 947.
160. R. Kuhn, G. Quadbeck, and E. Röhm, *Ann.* **565,** 1 (1949).
161. A. J. Fatiadi and W. F. Sager, *Org. Syn.* **42,** 66, 91 (1962) and references therein.
162. J. Liebig, *Ann.* **11,** 182 (1834); R. Nietzki and T. Benkiser, *Ber.* **18,** 1834 (1885).
163. W. Buechner and E. Weiss, *Helv. Chim. Acta* **47,** 1415 (1964); U.S. Pat. 2,736,752 (Feb. 28, 1956), U. Hoffmann, O. Schweitzer, and K. Rinn (to Deutsche Gold- und Silber-Scheideanstalt).

H. Dressler
Koppers Company, Inc.

POLYIMIDES. See Polyamides, p. 42.

POLYMERIZATION MECHANISMS AND PROCESSES

A polymerization reaction is the conversion of a particular compound to some large multiple of itself. See Polymers. In the chemical literature of fifty years ago or more, the mere act of physical association was termed polymerization, but today we restrict the usage of the term to chemical multiplication. There is still some confusion, however, resulting from the use of the word for reactions which form small cyclic compounds containing two or more molecules of the same low-molecular-weight (lmw) material and, from the point of view of the polymer chemist, it would be desirable if the term polymerization was confined to describing reactions in which linear or branched chains of substantial molecular weights are formed from specific lmw materials. The term oligomerization should then be applied to reactions yielding either cyclic compounds or very low molecular weight products.

Classically, polymerization reactions which yield linear, high-molecular-weight (hmw) products have been divided into two main groups on the basis of a comparison of the structure of the repeating unit of the polymer formed with the structure of the monomer from which the polymer is derived. These two general divisions are *addition polymerization* and *condensation polymerization*, but such has been the rate of growth of polymer chemistry that classic definitions are only about forty years old. The original classification into addition and condensation polymers was suggested by Carothers in 1929 (1). Carothers proposed essentially the following definitions which, although now too inflexible, are still widely used.

Addition Polymerization. An addition polymerization is a polymerization reaction yielding a polymeric product in which the molecular formula of the repeating unit is identical with that of the monomer, and the molecular weight of the polymer so formed is a simple summation of the molecular weights of all combined monomer units in the chain. For example, polystyrene (**2**), having the molecular formula $(C_8H_8)_n$, is obtained by the addition polymerization of styrene (**1**), which also has the molecular formula C_8H_8.

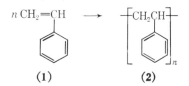

$$n \ CH_2{=}CH \longrightarrow \text{\small$-$}CH_2CH\text{\small$-$}$$

(1)   (2)

Condensation Polymerization. A condensation polymerization is a polymerization reaction yielding a polymeric product in which the repeating unit contains fewer atoms than the monomer or monomers, and, necessarily, the molecular weight of the polymer so formed is less than the sum of the molecular weights of all the original monomer units which were combined in the reaction to form the polymer chain. For example, poly(hexamethylene adipamide) (**5**), which has the molecular formula $(C_{12}H_{22}N_2O_2)_n$, is obtained by the condensation polymerization of hexamethylenediamine (**3**), $C_6H_{16}N_2$, and adipic acid (**4**), $C_6H_{10}O_4$; the secondary product of the condensation is water.

$$n \ H_2N(CH_2)_6NH_2 \ + \ n \ HOOC(CH_2)_4COOH \longrightarrow \text{\small$-$}\!\!\begin{bmatrix} & & O & & O \\ & & \| & & \| \\ NH(CH_2)_6NHC(CH_2)_4C \end{bmatrix}_{\!n}\!\! + \ 2n \ H_2O$$

(3)   (4)   (5)

For the majority of polymerization reactions encountered, this classification is sufficient, but in many important cases it is of little value or even misleading. The major weakness of this system of nomenclature is that, as far as the structure of the repeating unit is concerned, many polymers can be made by either addition or condensation polymerization reactions. That is, chemically, a polymer with a particular molecular structure and elemental analysis could be prepared by either route, but the physical properties of the polymer will almost always depend on the route chosen because the molecular weight of the polymers obtained will differ considerably for the two routes. In general, for polymers which can be prepared by either route, addition polymerization reactions yield polymers of significantly higher molecular weight than condensation polymerization reactions, and therefore, produce polymers with significantly better physical or mechanical properties. For example, polyethylene (**6**),

$$n \; CH_2{=}CH_2 \rightarrow {-}[CH_2CH_2]{-}_n$$

$$(6)$$

is usually prepared by the addition polymerization of ethylene. A polymer (**7**), with

$$n \; Br(CH_2)_{10}Br + 2n \; Na \rightarrow {-}[CH_2CH_2]{-}_{5n} + 2n \; NaBr$$

$$(7)$$

virtually the identical empirical formula, has also been prepared by the condensation polymerization of decamethylene bromide and sodium by the Wurtz reaction (2). Furthermore, a polymer (**8**), with essentially the same chemical analysis, has been

$$n \; CH_2N_2 \rightarrow {-}[CH_2CH_2]{-}_{n/2} + n \; N_2$$

$$(8)$$

prepared by the polymerization of diazomethane (3), and, according to the definitions above, this reaction would have to be termed a condensation polymerization.

The polymeric products obtained by these three routes are chemically equivalent, but the appearance and physical properties of two of the three are notably different from the third. Polymer (**6**), obtained from the self-addition of ethylene, is a comparatively hard, tough solid which melts between 115 and 135°C to form an extremely viscous liquid. Polymer (**7**), obtained by the Wurtz condensation of decamethylene bromide, is a brittle wax which melts between 87 and 105°C to form a free-flowing liquid. Finally, polymer (**8**), obtained by the self-condensation of diazomethane, is almost identical in properties to addition polymer (**6**) instead of being related to the condensation polymer (**7**) as the formal definitions would indicate. The difference between polymers (**6**) and (**8**) on the one hand and polymer (**7**) on the other is one of physical size or molecular weight, (**7**) having a very much lower molecular weight than either (**6**) or (**8**). The molecular weight of (**7**) is reportedly less than 1000 compared to greater than 1,000,000 for both (**6**) and (**8**).

The controlling factor, not recognized in the above definitions, is the difference in the growth mechanisms of the polymerization reactions, and, in the example above, it is this difference which determines the attainable molecular size of the polymer. The polymerization reactions of ethylene to form (**6**) and of diazomethane to form (**8**) both involve chain reactions capable of permitting the growth of polymer molecules of remarkably extended lengths. In comparison, the Wurtz reaction of decamethylene bromide to form (**7**) is a haphazard and tedious step reaction, inherently incapable of building up large polymer molecules. Therefore, a more meaningful classification, from the point of view of physical properties, is one based on the characteristics of the propagation or growth reactions producing the polymers, and in a system of nomenclature based on the mechanism of the growth reaction in a polymerization, the two major classifications are *chain-growth polymerization* and *step-growth polymerization* (4).

Taking as another example the synthesis of a polyester, polythioglycolide, it has been found, as expected, that two physically different polymers are obtained, depending on the polymerization mechanisms involved (5). The self-esterification reaction of thioglycolic acid (**9**) yields a typical step-growth polymer, while the ring-opening transesterification reaction of dithioglycolide (**10**) yields a typical chain-growth polymer.

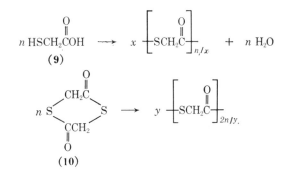

From previous experience, it is to be expected that the step-growth polymerization reaction of (**9**) will produce a greater number of polymer molecules, x, with a lower average degree of polymerization, n/x, than will the chain-growth polymerization reaction, y and $2n/y$; that is, $x > y$ and $n/x < n/y$. Discounting the negligible influence of end groups, it will generally be found in a case of this type that the elemental composition, infrared spectra, and other methods of analysis which depend only upon the structure of the repeating unit will be identical for the polymeric products of the step-growth reaction of (**9**) and the chain-growth reaction of (**10**). However, physical properties, such as melting point, solubility, and melt viscosity, which depend upon the size of the polymer molecule, will differ markedly, the chain-growth polymer having the higher melting point, the lower solubility, and the higher viscosity, as expected for a higher-molecular-weight polymer. This contrast in properties was found to occur for these two polyglycolides.

This example and the previous one of the preparation of polyethylene should serve to indicate the general nature of the terms *step-growth polymerization* and *chain-growth polymerization*. A detailed definition and discussion of each is presented in the two following sections.

Step-Growth Polymerization (4)

The general character of step-growth and chain-growth polymerization reactions is that for the former each polymer chain grows at a relatively slow rate over a much longer period of time than for the latter. In step-growth polymerization there is generally only one type of reaction, and the same basic mechanism is involved in the reactions of two monomer units with each other, a monomer with the end group on a polymer chain, and two polymer-chain end groups with each other. In contrast, a chain-growth polymerization generally consists of three different types of reactions: an initiation reaction which creates a highly active species, a propagation reaction in which the only reaction possible is the addition of monomer to active polymer-chain end groups, and termination in which the activity of the end group is destroyed and the polymer chain can no longer add new monomer units.

To illustrate this distinction in more detail, consider the example above of the two approaches to preparing polythioglycolide. In the step-growth polymerization of thioglycolic acid (**9**), every polymer chain will contain, exactly like the monomer, one thiol and one carboxylic acid end group. Hence, it can be assumed that each successive addition of a monomer unit to a polymer chain will involve an esterification reaction essentially identical in rate to the reaction between any two monomer units. As a result, because the monomer, thioglycolic acid, can react with equal facility either with another monomer or with a polymer-chain end group, the initial stage of this polymerization reaction of (**9**) will consist largely of random combinations of two monomer units to form dimer molecules. Dimer molecules will then combine, again with equal facility, either with a monomer or with another dimer to form trimers or tetramers, respectively. In this manner, all polymer chains will start growing at approximately the same time and will continue to grow at the same relatively slow steady rate, one step at a time, as indicated by the following schematic representation of the reactions occurring in a small region of the polymerization medium:

$$
\begin{array}{llll}
M_1 & M_1 & M_1 & M_1 \\
M_1 & M_1 & M_1 & M_1 \\
M_1 & M_1 & M_1 & M_1 \\
M_1 & M_1 & M_1 \text{---} M_1
\end{array}
\longrightarrow
\begin{array}{lll}
& M_1 & M_1 & M_1 \\
M_2 & & M_1 & M_1 \\
M_1 & & M_2 & M_1 \\
M_2 & M_1 & & M_2
\end{array}
\qquad 25\% \text{ reacted, } \overline{DP} = 2
$$

$$
\begin{array}{lll}
& M_1 & M_1 & M_1 \\
M_2 & & M_1 \text{---} M_1 \\
M_1 & & M_2 & M_1 \\
M_2 \text{---} M_1 & & M_2
\end{array}
\longrightarrow
\begin{array}{ll}
& M_1 & M_1 \\
M_3 & & M_2 \\
M_1 & & M_1 \\
M_3 & M_4
\end{array}
\qquad 50\% \text{ reacted, } \overline{DP} = 3
$$

$$
\begin{array}{ll}
& M_1 & M_1 \\
M_3 & & M_2 \\
M_1 & & M_1 \\
& M_3 \text{-----} M_4
\end{array}
\longrightarrow
\quad M_4 \begin{array}{l} M_3 \\ M_1 \\ M_8 \end{array}
\qquad 75\% \text{ reacted, } \overline{DP} = 5
$$

$$
\begin{array}{l}
M_4 \quad M_3 \\
\quad M_1 \\
\quad M_8
\end{array}
\longrightarrow
\quad M_{13} \; M_3
\qquad 87.5\% \text{ reacted, } \overline{DP} = 8
$$

In this schematic representation, the notation $\overline{DP}$ signifies the average degree of polymerization, of the collection of polymer molecules only, in the products at each point in the reaction as indicated by the percent conversion. The subscript attached to the symbol M indicates the degree of polymerization of that particular molecule; for example, M_1 is a monomer unit and M_4 is a tetramer. The reaction conversion is equal to the percentage of the original number of molecules remaining at that stage in the reaction because each molecule remaining, regardless of size, contains only two terminal functional groups; each reaction, as indicated by the dotted line, consumes two of these terminal groups.

As can be seen by this schematic representation, the random or haphazard growth of the polymer permits only a very gradual increase in molecular size. After 50% of the functional groups have reacted, the average degree of polymerization of the remaining molecules, other than monomer molecules, is still only equal to a value of three. After the reaction has gone to 75% of completion, the average degree of polymerization has only progressed to a value of five. This schematic presentation is, of course, an over-simplified representation of the reaction in a highly localized area, and in this case, the maximum degree of polymerization attainable would be only 16 at a conversion of 93.75%, assuming that intramolecular, ring-forming reactions do not occur. To attain quantitative conversions and thereby high polymers, the products of each of the localized areas would, of course, have to combine. For the overall polymerization reaction, the relationship between $\overline{DP}$ and reaction conversion, p, for the preparation of linear polymers is the following: $\overline{DP} = 1/(1 - p)$ (4).

This simple equation derived by Carothers dictates the rigorous requirements which must be met by the basic reaction of the step-growth polymerization in order to attain a reasonable degree of polymerization. According to this limiting equation, a step-growth polymerization reaction which has gone to 95% of completion will have formed a polymer with only twenty repeating units in the average chain. Very rare indeed is the linear polymer which even begins to show interesting physical properties at an average degree of polymerization of 20. Even a $\overline{DP}$ of 50 is a bare minimum, for all but the most polar of repeating units, for a polymer to show promise. Nevertheless, the achievement of a $\overline{DP}$ of 50 requires a reaction conversion of 98%. Very few reactions are known to the organic chemists that can be forced to and beyond 98%, and yet this requirement is the first characteristic that should be considered when it is proposed to make use of a step-growth polymerization. Furthermore, this requirement is no more important than several others which must also be considered, because a reaction in which 98% of the functional groups are consumed is not necessarily one in which a 98% yield of product is formed. The other requirements must also be met within very narrow limits, particularly (1) an exact equivalence of functional groups, (2) an absence of side reactions, (3) high monomer purity, (4) reasonably high reaction rates, and (5) little or no tendency toward ring formation by the bifunctional monomers involved.

There are two notable exceptions to this relationship between degree of polymerization and conversion; one is for step-growth polymerization reactions carried out by a process termed interfacial polycondensation and the other is for polymerization reactions involving monomers whose average functionality is greater than two. In both cases, very high molecular weight polymers can be obtained at relatively low conversions.

Interfacial polycondensation involves polymer formation at or near the interface between two immiscible monomer solutions under very mild reaction conditions; so, to be successful, this technique requires an extremely fast reaction. The step-growth polymerization reaction which has been found to satisfy this requirement best is the Schotten-Baumann reaction of an acid chloride with a functional group containing an active hydrogen atom, especially amines, alcohols, and thiols; for example, a diacyl chloride and a diamine can be used. The acid chloride is generally a carboxylic acid chloride, but other closely related functional groups, such as sulfonyl chlorides, have also been used, and a number of different polymers have been prepared by this route in addition to polyesters and polyamides. In general, this type of polymerization reaction is particularly useful where the polymer formed would normally decompose, isomerize, or crosslink at the elevated temperatures required for preparation in the melt or in solution.

In interfacial polycondensation the polymerization reaction occurs very close to the interface between an aqueous solution of one monomer and an immiscible organic solvent solution of the other, generally just within the organic solvent layer which contains the diacid chloride. The adjacent aqueous phase generally contains, in addition to the reactive hydrogen monomer, a basic reagent capable of neutralizing hydrogen chloride liberated in the reaction. The reaction rate of the two monomer functional groups is so fast that the polymerization reaction becomes diffusion-controlled, and after the polymer molecules begin to grow, incoming monomer units of both types react so rapidly with polymer-chain end groups that the monomer molecules are unable to diffuse all the way through the layer of polymer. As a result, two different monomer molecules cannot react with each other to start new polymer chains, and the number of growing chains is limited. For this reason, polymers with much higher molecular weights are formed than are obtained in a normal step-growth polymerization reaction, in which any two species are capable of reacting with each other, and these high molecular weights are achieved far below quantitative conversion. Furthermore, because the polymerization reaction is diffusion-controlled, there is no need to start with an exact balance of the two monomers in the two phases, and for the same reason, monomer purity is not critical except for the presence of reactive, monofunctional impurities which will still cause chain termination.

For step-growth polymerization reactions of polyfunctional monomers, the relationship between $\overline{DP}$ and p as originally derived by Carothers contained a factor, f, to account for the effect of monomers containing more than two functional groups on the degree of polymerization. The modified Carothers equation is given below, and it can be seen that when the average degree of functionality is 2 for the preparation of linear polymers, this equation reverts to the previous form. When the functionality is greater than 2, the products formed from the step-growth polymerization reaction will be nonlinear, branched, or network polymers.

$$\overline{DP} = 2/(2 - pf)$$

This equation shows how sensitive polymer growth is to the presence of small amounts of polyfunctional monomers which act as branching or crosslinking sites in the growing chain. For example, in a step-growth polymerization reaction involving two different difunctional monomers (A—A and B—B) and a trifunctional monomer related to one of these, $\left(A-\!\!\!\!<\begin{smallmatrix}A\\A\end{smallmatrix}\right)$, if there is one trifunctional monomer in every ten original monomer molecules containing functional groups A, then $f = 2.1$. In this case, a reaction conversion of 90% will yield a $\overline{DP}$ of approximately 18 instead of 10 for strictly linear growth. Remarkably, a conversion of 95% will result in a polymer having a $\overline{DP}$ of 200 instead of 20. Rearranging the equation above to the one below

$$p = 2/f - 2/f\overline{DP}$$

reveals that for this type of system a polymer having an infinite average degree of polymerization will be formed at the comparatively low reaction conversion of about 95.2%.

The reason for this vastly accelerated growth is that a polymer chain containing a multifunctional repeating unit is capable of growing by reactions at more than just two end groups. The more multifunctional units incorporated in the chain, the more reactive it becomes, and the more probable is the inclusion of additional multifunctional units. Therefore, the growth of such a polymer molecule takes on the characteristics of an autoaccelerating reaction and can be almost explosive in nature. As the polymerization reaction proceeds, large multifunctional molecules coalesce, forming a polymer molecule with tens of hundreds of growth sites, and this explosive growth continues until the entire reaction mixture becomes enmeshed within a network of a single, giant macromolecule of infinite molecular weight. At this point, the reaction mixture becomes immobilized into an insoluble, infusible gel, although polymer molecules of finite and even quite low molecular weights are still present.

Typical examples of step-growth polymerization reactions of importance are collected below for the formation of both linear and network polymers:

Linear Step-Growth Polymers

polyamides

$$n \; \text{HOC(CH}_2)_4\text{COH} \; + \; n \; \text{H}_2\text{N(CH}_2)_6\text{NH}_2 \; \longrightarrow \; \left[\text{C(CH}_2)_4\text{CNH(CH}_2)_6\text{NH} \right]_n \; + \; 2n \; \text{H}_2\text{O}$$

nylon-6,6

polyesters

$$n \; \text{CH}_3\text{OC} - \bigcirc - \text{COCH}_3 \; + \; n \; \text{HOCH}_2\text{CH}_2\text{OH} \; \longrightarrow \; \left[\text{C} - \bigcirc - \text{COCH}_2\text{CH}_2\text{O} \right]_n \; + \; 2n \; \text{CH}_3\text{OH}$$

poly(ethylene terephthalate)

polyurethans

$$n \; \text{OCN(CH}_2)_6\text{NCO} \; + \; n \; \text{HO(CH}_2)_4\text{OH} \; \longrightarrow \; \left[\text{CNH(CH}_2)_6\text{NHCO(CH}_2)_4\text{O} \right]_n$$

poly(alkylene polysulfides)

$$n \; \text{Cl(CH}_2)_6\text{Cl} \; + \; n \; \text{Na}_2\text{S}_x \; \longrightarrow \; \left[(\text{CH}_2)_6\text{S}_x \right]_n \; + \; 2n \; \text{NaCl}$$

Network Step-Growth Polymers

glyptal resins

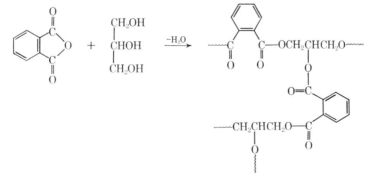

phenol–formaldehyde resins

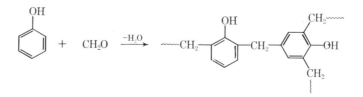

urea–formaldehyde resins

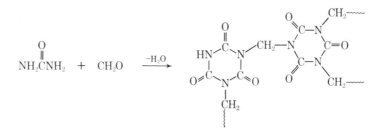

Chain-Growth Polymerization (4)

Unlike a step-growth polymerization in which the polymer chains continue to grow from both ends throughout the course of the overall reaction, a chain-growth polymerization generally creates long polymer chains in a very short time compared to the overall reaction time. That is, each polymer chain, once initiated, grows at an extremely rapid rate and, once terminated, is, barring side reactions, generally incapable of further growth from either end. This type of polymerization reaction occurs through a series of reactions in which the rates and mechanisms of the initiation, propagation, and termination steps are generally different, and the propagation or growth reaction always predominates if a hmw polymer is to be obtained.

Chain-growth polymerization is initiated either by some form of external energy, which is supplied to the normally unreactive monomer to produce a reactive species, or by the addition of a highly reactive compound. Both the reactive species prepared in situ and the reactive compound added are capable of reacting with the monomer to initiate the propagation reaction, and both of these species are generally much more reactive than the original monomer molecule. The growing polymer molecule, once initiated in this manner, remains active until a reaction occurs which transforms the end group to an inactive species. This termination reaction in many cases is also much faster than the propagation reaction, but, in order to obtain hmw polymers, the frequency of the termination reaction must be much less than that of the growth reaction.

Referring again to the example of the preparation of polythioglycolide, the formation of this polymer from dithioglycolide (10) is a ring-opening polymerization reaction preferably initiated by addition of catalytic quantities of a strong base, B:⁻, which in this case constitutes the reactive species. The base reacts with dithioglycolide in the initiation step, presumably to form a reactive mercaptide anion (11), which is capable of rapidly reacting with still another cyclic monomer unit to regenerate essentially the same reactive species (12). Once started, therefore, the polymer

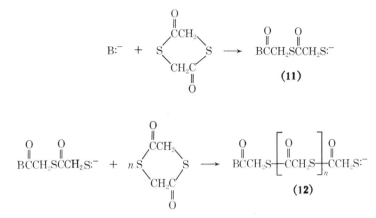

$$B:^- + S\overset{\overset{O}{\|}}{\underset{CH_2C\underset{\|}{O}}{\overset{CCH_2}{\diagup}}}S \longrightarrow \overset{O\quad O}{\underset{\|\quad\|}{BCCH_2SCCH_2S:^-}}$$

(11)

$$\overset{O\quad O}{\underset{\|\quad\|}{BCCH_2SCCH_2S:^-}} + n\,S\overset{\overset{O}{\|}}{\underset{CH_2C\underset{\|}{O}}{\overset{CCH_2}{\diagup}}}S \longrightarrow \overset{O}{\underset{\|}{BCCH_2S}}\left[\overset{O}{\underset{\|}{CCH_2S}}\right]_n\overset{O}{\underset{\|}{CCH_2S:^-}}$$

(12)

molecule will grow by a chain of reactions emanating from a particular initiator molecule, as indicated in the following schematic representation:

$$
\begin{array}{cccc}
M_1 & M_1 & M_1 & M_1 \\
M_1 & M_1 & M_1 & M_1 \\
M_1 & M_1 & M_1 & M_1 \\
M_1 & M_1 & M_1 & M_1 \\
\end{array}
$$

$$B:^- +$$

$$\longrightarrow$$

$$
B
\begin{array}{cccc}
M_1\text{---}M_1 & M_1\text{---}M_1 \\
M_1 & M_1 & M_1 & M_1 \\
M_1 & M_1 & M_1 & M_1 \\
M_1 & M_1\text{---}M_1 & M_1 \\
\end{array}
$$

$$\longrightarrow \quad BM_{11}M:^- + 4\,M_1$$

75% reacted, $\overline{DP} = 12$

In the absence of termination or secondary reactions, the number of polymer molecules formed will be identical to the number of initiator molecules reacted. Therefore, the kinetic chain length of the reaction, which is the average number of monomer molecules caused to react by a given initiator molecule, will be equal to the chain length of the polymer which is given by the average degree of polymerization. It is seen that in this polymerization reaction a conversion of 75% of the monomer units in the localized reaction region results in the formation of a single polymeric molecule with a degree of polymerization of twelve. The polymer still retains the active mercaptide anion as an end group and is capable of further growth into other regions. Only complete reaction of all monomer units or the occurrence of some adventitious side reaction can terminate the growth of the chain. Significantly, the reaction of monomer molecules with each other is either virtually impossible or very much slower than their reaction with the end of a growing polymer chain.

In most, but far from all, cases, chain-growth polymerization reactions are based on the application of a free-radical or ionic reaction to a polymerization scheme in such a manner that the primary growth of a single polymer chain or macromolecule results from the propagation of one kinetic chain reaction. As stated above, a kinetic chain reaction is a series of closely related reactions caused by one, and only one, initiator (not catalyst) molecule, but chain reactions generally consist of at least three basic types of reactions: (*1*) an initiation step, which may involve more than one reaction; (*2*) a propagation step, which involves a long sequence of identical reactions repeated many times; and (*3*) a termination step, which kills the kinetic chain reaction.

It often happens, however, that a single kinetic chain reaction may cause the formation of more than one polymer chain molecule through a reaction in which the active site is transferred without loss of activity from the end of a growing polymechain molecule to another molecule from which a new polymer chain molecule can grow. This type of reaction is termed a chain-transfer reaction. The net effect of this reaction is to terminate the growth of one polymer chain molecule and to initiate the growth of another, but the continuity of that kinetic chain reaction endures. These reactions are illustrated schematically in equations 1–4, in which an asterisk is used to denote the location of an active species, either a radical or an ion, and symbols

$$\text{Initiation} \qquad A \longrightarrow A^* \qquad\qquad\qquad\qquad (1)$$
$$A^* + B \longrightarrow AB^*$$

$$\text{Propagation} \quad AB^* + B \longrightarrow AB_2^* \overset{B}{\longrightarrow} AB_3^* \qquad (2)$$

$$AB_3^* + n\ B \ \underset{\longrightarrow}{\overset{\longrightarrow}{\longrightarrow}} \ AB_{n+3}^* $$

$$\text{Transfer} \qquad AB_n^* + C \longrightarrow AB_n + C^* \qquad\qquad (3)$$

$$\text{Termination} \quad AB_n^* \longrightarrow AB_n \qquad\qquad\qquad\qquad (4)$$

A, B, and C refer to an initiator, a monomer, and a molecule with a chain transfer site, respectively (4).

Most examples of chain-growth polymerization reactions are either multiple-bond addition reactions or ring-opening reactions. At present, the most important type of organic polymerization reaction is the addition reaction of a radical or an ion to a carbon–carbon double bond such as in the preparation of polystyrene (2), or polyethylene (6), discussed in the introductory section. The next general type in importance is the ring-opening reaction of a number of different types of heterocyclic monomers including principally cyclic ethers, equation 5; lactams, equation 6; and lactones, equation 7. Other than addition reactions to a carbon–carbon double bond, the only multiple-bond addition reaction presently receiving much attention is the addition polymerization of the carbon–oxygen double bond in aldehydes, equation 8.

$$n\ (CH_2)_xO \longrightarrow \ +\!(CH_2)_xO\!+\!_n \qquad\qquad (5)$$

$$n\ (CH_2)_x\overset{NH}{-\!\!\!\!\overset{|}{C}}\!\!=\!\!O \longrightarrow \left[\!(CH_2)_x\overset{O}{\overset{\|}{C}}NH\!\right]_n \qquad (6)$$

$$n\ (CH_2)_x\overset{O}{-\!\!\!\!\overset{|}{C}}\!\!=\!\!O \longrightarrow \left[\!(CH_2)_x\overset{O}{\overset{\|}{C}}O\!\right]_n \qquad (7)$$

$$n\ RCHO \longrightarrow \ +\!CHRO\!+\!_n \qquad\qquad\qquad (8)$$

Specific examples of important chain-growth polymerization reactions applied to the preparation of linear and network polymers are the following:

Linear Chain-Growth Polymers

vinyl polymers

$$n\ CH_2\!\!=\!\!\overset{}{\underset{R}{\overset{|}{CH}}} \longrightarrow \left[CH_2\overset{}{\underset{R}{\overset{|}{CH}}}\right]_n \qquad R = Cl,\ \bigcirc,\ \overset{O}{\overset{\|}{C}}OCH_3,\ CN,\ \text{etc}$$

polyamides

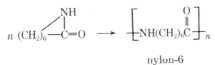

nylon-6

polyacetals

$$n \ CH_2{=}O \ \longrightarrow \ {+}CH_2O{+}_n$$

polyoxymethylene

polyethers

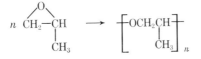

poly(propylene oxide)

Network Chain-Growth Polymers

crosslinked polystyrene

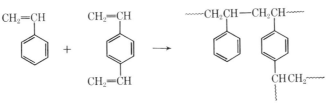

alkyd resins

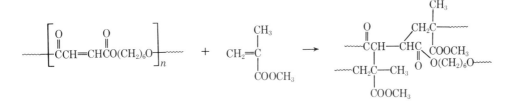

siloxane elastomers

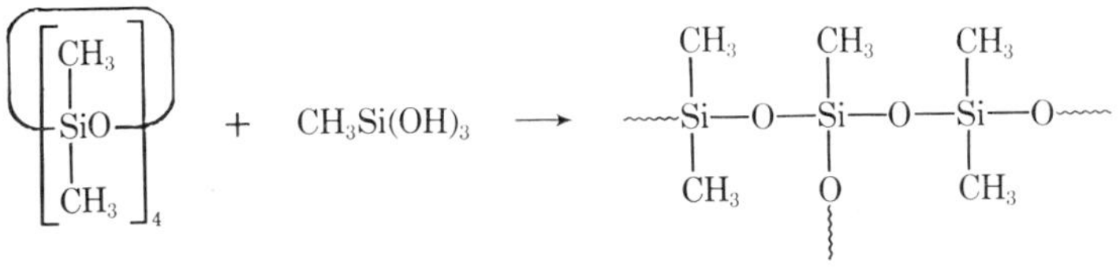

Reaction Mechanisms. In some of the specific examples of chain-growth polymers illustrated above, the polymers can be prepared by both free-radical and ionic polymerization reactions. The applicability of more than one type of reaction mechanism is particularly characteristic of olefin monomers. The chain-growth polymerization of aldehydes and cyclic monomers is generally restricted to only anionic or cationic reaction mechanisms. The types of mechanism available to most of the important monomers undergoing chain polymerizations are indicated in Table 1 (6).

Each of these three types of reaction mechanism (radical, ionic, heterogeneous) has its own distinctive characteristics in the initiation, propagation, and termination

Table 1. Applicability of Various Types of Reaction Mechanism to Chain-Growth Polymerization[a]

Monomer	Monomer structure	Homogeneous initiation			Heterogeneous initiation (solid catalyst)
		Radical	Anionic	Cationic	
ethylene	$CH_2\!=\!CH_2$	+	−	+	+
propene	$CH_2\!=\!CHMe$	−	−	−	+
1-butene	$CH_2\!=\!CHEt$	−	−	−	+
isobutylene (methyl propene)	$CH_2\!=\!CMe_2$	−	−	+	−
1,3-butadiene	$CH_2\!=\!CH\!-\!CH\!=\!CH_2$	+	+	−	+
isoprene	$CH_2\!=\!C(Me)\!-\!CH\!=\!CH_2$	+	+	−	+
styrene	$CH_2\!=\!CHPh$	+	+	+	+
vinyl chloride	$CH_2\!=\!CHCl$	+	−	−	+
vinylidene chloride	$CH_2\!=\!CCl_2$	+	+	−	−
vinyl fluoride	$CH_2\!=\!CHF$	+	−	−	−
tetrafluoroethylene	$CF_2\!=\!CF_2$	+	+	−	+
vinyl ethers	$CH_2\!=\!CHOR$	−	−	+	+
vinyl esters	$CH_2\!=\!CHOCOR$	+	−	−	−
acrylic esters	$CH_2\!=\!CHCOOR$	+	+	−	+
methacrylic esters	$CH_2\!=\!C(Me)COOR$	+	+	−	+
acrylonitrile	$CH_2\!=\!CHCN$	+	+	−	+
formaldehyde	$CH_2\!=\!O$	−	+	+	+
acetaldehyde	$CH_3CH\!=\!O$	−	+	+	+
ethylene oxide	$\overline{CH_2CH_2O}$	−	+	+	+
propylene oxide	$\overline{CH_3CHCH_2O}$	−	+	+	+
tetrahydrofuran	$\overline{CH_2CH_2CH_2CH_2O}$	−	−	+	+
ethyleneimine	$\overline{CH_2CH_2NH}$	−	−	+	−
caprolactam	$\overline{HN(CH_2)_5CO}$	−	+	+	−
caprolactone	$\overline{O(CH_2)_5CO}$	−	+	+	−

[a] Symbols: +, monomer can be polymerized to hmw polymer by this form of initiation; −, no polymerization reaction occurs or only lmw polymers or oligomers are obtained with this type of initiator.

steps. In general cationic-polymerization (eq. 9) and anionic-polymerization (eq. 10) reactions have more in common with each other than with radical-polymerization reactions (eq. 11), because of the presence of a counterion associated with the active end group of a growing polymer chain in both types of ionic chain-growth polymerization reaction (4).

$$P^+ X:^- + CH_2 \!=\! \underset{\underset{R}{|}}{CH} \rightarrow PCH_2\overset{+}{\underset{\underset{R}{|}}{CH}} X:^- \tag{9}$$

$$P:^- X^+ + CH_2 \!=\! \underset{\underset{R}{|}}{CH} \rightarrow PCH_2\overset{..}{\underset{\underset{R}{|}}{CH}}{}^- X^+ \tag{10}$$

$$P\cdot + CH_2 \!=\! \underset{\underset{R}{|}}{CH} \rightarrow PCH_2\underset{\underset{R}{|}}{CH} \tag{11}$$

For ionic-chain reactions the degree of association between the end-group ion and the counterion is a very important variable; and how tightly associated the counterion is to the ionic site in the end group depends upon such factors as the stability of the ionic end group, the type of counterion, the polarity of the reaction medium, the temperature, the presence of extraneous salts, and other factors. Tight ion-pair formation between the polymer-chain end group and the counterion (as opposed to ion solvation) has a considerable effect on the course of the polymerization reaction, particularly on such factors as the rate of polymerization, the rate of termination (and consequently the molecular weight of the polymer formed), the stereospecificity of monomer incorporation into the polymer chain, and the reactivity ratios in copolymerization reactions. In radical propagation, solvent polarity generally exerts no influence on either rate or stereospecificity of homopolymerization or on reactivity ratios in copolymerization.

Radical, anionic, and cationic polymerization reactions also show distinctly different termination mechanisms, but the behaviors of radical and cationic polymerization reactions in this respect are, in general, more closely related than are the behaviors of cationic and anionic polymerization reactions.

Radical and most cationic polymerization reactions have two types of facile kinetic chain-termination reactions, namely, *combination* and *disproportionation*. In a radical polymerization reaction, both combination (eq. 12) and disproportionation (eq. 13) reactions involve two growing polymer chains:

$$
P_mCH_2\overset{\cdot}{\underset{\underset{R}{|}}{CH}} + P_nCH_2\overset{\cdot}{\underset{\underset{R}{|}}{CH}}
\begin{cases}
\rightarrow P_mCH_2\underset{\underset{R}{|}}{CH}\!-\!\underset{\underset{R}{|}}{CH}CH_2P_n & (12) \\
\rightarrow P_mCH_2\underset{\underset{R}{|}}{CH_2} + P_nCH\!=\!\underset{\underset{R}{|}}{CH} & (13)
\end{cases}
$$

In a cationic polymerization reaction, on the other hand, a type of combination (eq. 14) and disproportionation (eq. 15) reaction occurs between the end group and the counterion of a single active polymer chain; anion capture and proton release are more appropriate terms.

$$
P_nCH_2\overset{+}{\underset{\underset{R}{|}}{CH}}\cdot[XY]^=
\begin{cases}
\rightarrow P_nCH_2\underset{\underset{R}{|}}{CHX} + Y & (14) \\
\rightarrow P_nCH\!=\!\underset{\underset{R}{|}}{CH} + HX + Y & (15)
\end{cases}
$$

In contrast, most anionic and possibly some cationic polymerization reactions are considered to have no facile or inherent termination step, excluding of course, secondary reactions between a carbanion or carbonium ion end group and an active solvent or an impurity, which can also occur in all types of polymerization reactions. For this reason, the active polymeric products of an anionic polymerization reaction, before quenching, have been termed *living polymers*. Free-radical and cationic polymerization reactions are also alike in the extent to which chain-transfer reactions occur (that is, polymer termination without kinetic termination), while chain transfer in anionic polymerization is again of negligible importance.

Because the termination reactions in a free-radical polymerization reaction are bimolecular and of such high rates as compared to the unimolecular termination reactions in ionic polymerization reactions, it is possible to maintain a much higher concentration of growing polymer chains in an ionic reaction. That is, because termination in a free-radical polymerization reaction occurs by the reaction of the active end groups of two growing polymer chains, in order to prepare hmw polymers, the concentration of growing polymer chains must be maintained at a very low level, approx 10^{-8} to 10^{-9} M. In anionic or cationic polymerizations, on the other hand, there is no tendency for two polymer-chain end groups of like ionic charge to react, and much higher concentrations of growing polymer chains may be maintained without penalty to the molecular weights produced. For this reason, the concentration of carbanion or carbonium ion end groups in homogeneous polymerization reactions may easily reach 10^{-2} to 10^{-9} M, and because of these high concentrations, the rates of ionic polymerization reactions can be 10^4–10^5 times higher than that of a free-radical polymerization reaction of the same monomer, even though the activation energies for propagation are comparable.

An important practical difference between radical and ionic polymerization reactions which will be discussed in more detail below under Polymerization processes is the greater versatility of physical methods available for carrying out a polymerization reaction by radical initiation and growth. Radical polymerization reactions can be initiated effectively in gas, solid, and liquid phases, and for the latter, procedures involving bulk, solution, and several other techniques have been applied. Ionic polymerization reactions, in contrast, are limited experimentally almost entirely to solution or bulk methods, although crystalline, solid-state polymerization reactions have been observed in a number of cases. A wider variety of physical procedures is available for radical polymerization reactions in part because of the unreactivity of water toward free radicals. Suspension and emulsion systems are generally based upon the use of water as the continuous phase and a hydrophobic monomer as the discontinuous phase.

Copolymerization (7)

The previous discussion on reaction types and mechanisms has made no mention of the fact that more than one type of monomer may be involved in the polymerization reaction, or more than one type of repeating unit may be generated in the polymer. Nevertheless, the simultaneous polymerization of two or more monomers, termed copolymerization, is a common occurrence and one very important to both step-growth and chain-growth polymerization.

In step-growth polymerization reactions, different monomers of the same general class with a given type of functional group generally show only minor differences in reactivity. In a broad series of diester monomers to be used for preparing polyesters, for example, the difference in reactivities between ester functions is negligible compared to the differences in reactivities generally encountered for double bonds in a series of olefins. As a result, most copolymers prepared by step-growth copolymerization reactions contain essentially random placements of repeating units, the proportion of each monomer incorporated into the copolymer being essentially the same as the proportions in the original monomer mixture.

In contrast, strong selective effects are often encountered in chain-growth copolymerization reactions, and the compositions of the copolymers formed may be greatly different from the composition of the monomer mixture. For example, it is known that in a radical polymerization reaction vinyl acetate monomer is converted to homopolymer at a rate approximately twenty times faster than that of the homopolymerization of styrene monomer, but in contrast, an attempted radical copolymerization of a mixture of vinyl acetate and styrene yields, instead of the copolymer, almost pure polystyrene containing less than 2% vinyl acetate. Even more striking is the fact that vinyl acetate containing 1 or 2% of styrene shows essentially no tendency to polymerize under conditions used for the radical homopolymerization of this monomer. That is, styrene acts as an inhibitor rather than as a comonomer when present in small amounts in the radical polymerization of vinyl acetate.

To understand this behavior one must consider the four possible propagation reactions involved in the chain-growth copolymerization of two monomers, M_1 and M_2, as shown below.

$$P_1{}^* + M_1 \xrightarrow{\ k_{11}\ } P_1{}^*$$

$$P_1{}^* + M_2 \xrightarrow{\ k_{12}\ } P_2{}^*$$

$$P_2{}^* + M_2 \xrightarrow{\ k_{22}\ } P_2{}^*$$

$$P_2{}^* + M_1 \xrightarrow{\ k_{21}\ } P_1{}^*$$

Four different rate constants, k, must be considered for the combination of each active radical or ionic polymer chain end group, P^*, with its own or the other monomer. From these equations and certain simplifying assumptions, a quantitative relationship has been derived between the mole fraction, m_1, of each monomer in the copolymer, and the concentration, $[M_1]$, of each monomer in the polymerization reaction mixture, as follows:

$$\frac{m_1}{m_2} = \frac{[M_1]}{[M_2]} \cdot \frac{r_1[M_1] + [M_2]}{[M_1] + r_2[M_2]}$$

In this equation the symbol r, termed the *reactivity ratio*, represents the ratio of rate constants for addition of a given radical or ion to its own and to the other monomer:

$$r_1 = \frac{k_{11}}{k_{12}} \qquad\qquad r_2 = \frac{k_{22}}{k_{21}}$$

Therefore, the tendency of two monomers to copolymerize is reflected in values of $0 < r < 1$, while values of $r > 1$ indicate that the monomer would tend to homopoly-

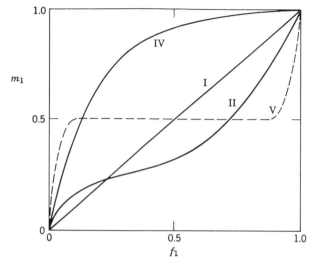

Fig. 1. Copolymer composition as a function of monomer ratio in the feed for various types of reactivity ratio combinations.

merize. For olefin monomers copolymerized by radical or ionic initiators, five different types of reactivity ratio combination are possible (4), as follows:

$$\text{Type I:} \quad r_1 \simeq r_2 \simeq 1.0$$

In this case, $k_{11} \simeq k_{12}$ and $k_{22} \simeq k_{21}$ so that little or no selectivity is exhibited by an active polymer end group for either monomer, and monomer insertion into the co-polymer chain is random. The composition of the copolymer is approximately equal

$$-M_1-M_1-M_2-M_1-M_2-M_2-M_2-M_1-M_2-$$

to the composition of the monomer feed mixture as idealized in Figure 1, in which m_1 is the mole fraction of monomer M_1 in the copolymer, and f_1 is the mole fraction of monomer M_1 in the feed. Examples of this type of radical copolymerization reaction are methyl acrylate ($r_1 = 0.84$) with vinylidene chloride ($r_2 = 0.99$) and styrene (0.78) with 1,3-butadiene (1.4).

$$\text{Type II:} \quad r_1 \text{ and } r_2 < 1$$

In this case, $k_{11} < k_{12}$ and $k_{22} < k_{21}$, so that there is a decided tendency to form an alternating copolymer. The copolymer composition plot of Figure 1 for Type II contains a point at which the curve crosses over the diagonal line. At this point,

$$-M_1-M_1-M_2-M_1-M_2-M_1-M_2-M_2-M_1-M_2-$$

termed the azeotropic copolymerization composition, the copolymer has the same com-position as the monomer feed mixture, and a polymeric product of constant composi-tion is formed throughout the copolymerization reaction. Examples of this type of radical copolymerization are methacrylonitrile (0.15) with α-methylstyrene (0.21) and acrylonitrile (0.04) with styrene (0.40).

$$\text{Type III:} \quad r_1 \text{ and } r_2 > 1$$

This combination of reactivity ratios would produce either a block copolymer or a physical mixture of two homopolymers. Such a combination has never been observed experimentally in radical copolymerization reactions but has been reported for ionic copolymerization.

Type IV: $r_1 \gg 1$ and $r_2 \ll 1$

In this case, the copolymer consists mostly of monomer M_1, and, at high feed compositions of M_1, essentially a homopolymer of this monomer is formed. Examples of this case are the radical copolymerization reactions of acrylonitrile (4.1) with vinyl acetate (0.06) and the extreme case of styrene (55) with vinyl acetate (0.01) discussed previously.

Type V: $r_1 \simeq r_2 \simeq 0$

In this case, there is virtually no tendency for either type of active end group to react with its own monomer, and reactivity is almost entirely with an unlike monomer. As a result, a highly regular, alternating copolymer is formed. Examples of this case are the radical copolymerization reactions of styrene (0.01) with maleic anhydride (0.0) and α-methylstyrene (0.022) with fumaronitrile (0.0).

Much less is known about the detailed copolymerization behavior of olefins in anionic and cationic systems and of other types of chain-growth monomers than for the radical copolymerization of olefins, so few generalizations can be made in these cases. In ionic chain-growth copolymerization reactions, as mentioned previously, reactivity ratios are very sensitive to conditions which affect the ion-pair structure of the active end group, so widely different values of this parameter can be obtained for the same monomer pair under different reaction conditions.

Stereochemistry of Polymerization

The chain-growth polymerization reaction of monomers containing carbon–carbon double bonds involves the formation of two new bonds at tetravalent carbon atoms as each new monomer is added onto the end of a growing polymer chain. The spatial arrangement of covalent bonds, or configuration, of the carbon–carbon bonds formed at the active terminal carbon atom of the growing polymer chain is permanently established during the reaction and two distinguishable diastereomeric configurations are possible (8). During the growth of the polymer, the regularity with which the two different configurations are established in the addition of each successive repeating unit will have a marked effect on the long-range order in the macromolecule.

For example, in the chain-growth polymerization of propylene to form polypropylene as depicted in this equation, the opening of the double bond of the incoming

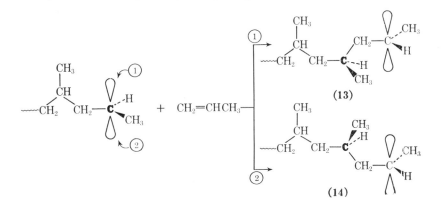

236   POLYMERIZATION MECHANISMS AND PROCESSES

monomer molecule and formation of a new single bond at the active carbon atom (indicated by boldface type) on the end of the polymer chain will result in the formation of either one of two possible, mirror-image configurations, (13) or (14), at this carbon atom. The active terminal carbon atom in the equation for this reaction is represented in an sp^2 hybridization, which is believed to be the case for the structure of the active species in either a radical or a cationic polymerization reaction. However, the same type of equation applies to an anionic polymerization reaction involving an sp^3 carbon atom if it is assumed that either rapid inversion of the carbanion or rapid rotation around the terminal carbon–carbon bond can occur. In either case, when the tetragonal carbon atom is firmly established in space as a result of the addition reaction, the substituents bonded to the previously active carbon atom will be set in one of two configurations, (13) or (14), as mentioned.

It may appear in this example that, after the addition of the next repeating unit, structures (13) and (14) will become equivalent, because two of the substituents on the tetragonal carbon atoms in question will be identical, as indicated by structures (15) and (16) in the equation below. That is, simple rotation of (15) through 180° in the plane of the paper seems to generate a structure identical in stereochemistry to (15),

but, in fact, the difference between these two configurations is real and a point of true dissymmetry is introduced into the polymer chain. The basis fo rthis distinction is that, while structures (15) and (16) are neither asymmetric nor pseudoasymmetric because no asymmetric atom exists on either side of the carbon atom in boldface type, the structures are dissymmetric because a set of three successive repeating units in the middle of a polymer chain (a triad) may exist in at least three possible combinations of configurations. This point is best illustrated graphically by depicting the carbon–carbon backbone of the polymer chain as existing in an extended zigzag conformation in the plane of the paper, and the pendant substituents will then lie either above or below the plane of the paper as shown for polypropylene by structures (17)–(19) with the equiv-

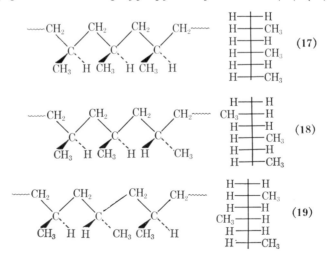

alent Fischer projections (9–10). The three basic triads for polypropylene in this example are those with (*1*) all methyl groups on one side, either above or below (**17**); (*2*) two neighboring substituents above and the third below (**18**), or vice versa; and (*3*) the first and third substituents above and the second below (**19**), or vice versa.

If more than one of these triads are present in significant amounts and are randomly dispersed along the polymer chain, the polymer will not contain long-range order and will generally be incapable of packing into a regular crystalline lattice. On the other hand, if one of the triads is repeated for extended lengths along the polymer chain, then groups of chains having these blocks of the same triad will be capable of packing into an ordered alignment in the solid state. These crystalline high polymers, like their lmw counterparts, will exhibit crystalline melting points and well-defined x-ray diffraction patterns and, most important, considerably different physical properties than those of the same polymer in an amorphous state.

Most crystalline polyolefins have ordered chain structures consisting of either the triad of structure (**17**) or the triad of structure (**19**). A polymer containing principally repeating units with identical configurations, triad structure (**17**), is termed an *isotactic* polymer, while a polymer containing principally units of exactly alternating configurations, triad structure (**19**), is termed a *syndiotactic* polymer. A chain showing no regular order of repeating unit configurations is termed an *atactic* polymer.

Not all polymerization reactions involve the type of bond formation in which specific configurations are unequivocally established. Reactions in which only divalent or trivalent atoms are involved in bond formation generally do not have to lead to this stereochemical situation, and polymers formed by such reactions are free of structural complexity arising from the formation of dissymmetric centers occurring in the polymerization reaction. As an example, an amidation reaction (see eq. 16) involves bond formation between a trigonal active carbon atom and a trivalent nitro-

$$n\ H_2NRNH_2\ +\ n\ HOOCR'COOH\ \longrightarrow\ \left[\begin{array}{c} -NH \quad NH \quad R' \\ R \qquad C \quad C \\ \qquad\qquad \| \quad \| \\ \qquad\qquad O \quad O \end{array}\right]_n\ +\ 2n\ H_2O \quad \textbf{(16)}$$

gen atom, and although apparently either of two configurations, (**20**) or (**21**), may be formed at the nitrogen atom, these two configurations are equivalent because of the ease of racemization by inversion of the trivalent nitrogen atoms in such molecules. The absence of configurational complexity is one of the most valuable assets of this

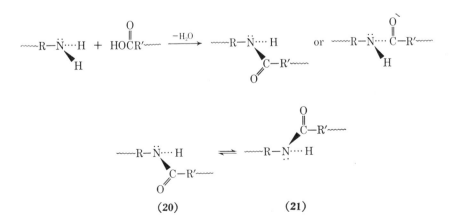

(20)   (21)

type of polymerization reaction. The resulting simplicity in polymer stereochemistry is the reason why step-growth polymerization reactions and many ring-opening chain-growth polymerization reactions which produce linear polymers, generally produce crystalline, or at least crystallizable, polymers.

Polymerization Processes (11–12)

Most step-growth polymerization reactions are carried out in homogeneous systems by simple combination of two or more monomers in the melt, in the absence of solvent. In contrast, a wide variety of methods are used experimentally and industrially for the preparation of chain-growth polymers, and in many important cases the reaction requires the presence of a solid catalyst or is complicated by the formation of a two-phase reaction system. In almost all cases for both step-growth and chain-growth polymerizations, the reactions are conducted in an inert atmosphere, but for different reasons in the two cases. An inert atmosphere is used in step-growth polymerization reactions primarily to prevent oxidation of the polymer when high reaction temperatures are involved. On the other hand, the absence of oxygen is much more critical in almost all chain-growth polymerization reactions because, in general, oxygen reacts directly with the highly reactive radicals or ions involved in these polymerization reactions.

At present, radical chain-growth polymerization reactions are considerably more important industrially than either cationic or anionic chain-growth reactions, but the latter two are used to some extent and will continue to grow in importance. Similarly, chain-growth polymerization reactions involving the presence of solid catalysts (and, therefore, termed heterogeneous polymerizations) have recently become very important industrially, particularly for the polymerization of olefin monomers to form linear, hmw polyolefins.

Radical chain-growth polymerization reactions of olefin monomers can be carried out in a number of different types of reaction systems, including the following: bulk polymerization, solution polymerization, suspension polymerization, emulsion polymerization, and precipitation polymerization. Each of these methods is used industrially, and each has its own peculiar characteristics, advantages, and special applications. Two other general methods are of experimental interest; these are gas-phase polymerization and solid-state polymerization.

Bulk Polymerization. Bulk polymerization is the direct conversion of liquid monomer to polymer in a reaction system in which the polymer remains soluble in its own monomer. In the application of this method to the polymerization of olefin monomers, the most important problem is the removal of the high exothermic heat of polymerization, which is common to most monomers of this type. This problem can become very serious at high viscosities of the reaction mixture in large batch preparations, and localized overheating can often lead to runaway reactions or degradation and discoloration of the polymer. To minimize this problem, the bulk polymerization may either be terminated at relatively low conversions of 40–60% and excess monomer distilled off or the polymerization reaction may be carried out in two steps. In the first step, a large batch of monomer is polymerized to an intermediate conversion and then, for ease of heat dissipation, the polymerization reaction is completed in thin layers. The final reaction may be carried out in a mold to form a finished plastic piece directly or the polymerization reaction may be carried to completion while the monomer-polymer mixture flows either through a small-diameter tube or down the walls of a column, or moves simply by free fall in thin streams. Completion of polymerization in a mold, for example, is used commercially for the production of sheets, rods, and tubes of acrylic polymers. In addition to minimizing the problem of overheating, the use of monomer–polymer syrups for this purpose is advantageous because shrinkage in the mold is lowered by the amount corresponding to the degree of preconversion of monomer to polymer and also curing times are shortened, the danger of leakage is lessened because of the higher viscosity of the syrup, and the problem of inhibition due to oxygen dissolved in the monomer is averted.

Bulk polymerization reactions have been applied to both radical and ionic chain-growth polymerization. In either case the initiator is dissolved in the monomer and dissolved gases, particularly oxygen, are removed either by placing the monomer under a partial vacuum or by purging with a nitrogen stream. In some unusual cases, styrene and methyl methacrylate are examples, the polymerization reaction may be initiated simply by heating the monomer alone in the absence of initiator through a process termed *thermal polymerization*. The principal advantage of a bulk polymerization reaction is that the product obtained is essentially free of diluent or impurities and can be used directly.

Solution Polymerization. In solution polymerization a solvent is used which is capable of dissolving the monomer, the polymer, and the polymerization initiator. Diluting the monomer with the solvent causes a direct reduction in the rate of polymerization and in the viscosity of the product mixture at a given degree of conversion. These characteristics plus the ability of the solvent to act as an inert heat-transfer medium virtually eliminate the serious heat-dissipation problem characteristic of bulk polymerizations. The disadvantage of this method, however, is that the solvent may show some reactivity with the active species of the polymerization reaction and undergo chain-transfer reactions and also that the solvent must be removed at the end of the polymerization to isolate the solid polymer. On the other hand, in applications such as coatings, impregnating fluids, adhesives, and laminating resins, the polymer solution can be used directly, eliminating the expensive solvent removal and recovery step, and in many cases the chain-transfer reactions are desirable to limit the molecular weight of the product.

Suspension Polymerization. For reasons of cost and nonreactivity, water is a much more desirable diluent and heat-transfer medium than organic solvents. Two types of polymerization systems based on water as the reaction medium are widely used industrially; these are suspension polymerization and emulsion polymerization. In both methods the monomer is dispersed rather than dissolved in the medium, but the two methods differ considerably because of the degree of dispersion attained and because of the manner by which initiation occurs in each.

In suspension polymerization the initiator is dissolved in the monomer, the monomer is dispersed in water, and a dispersing agent is incorporated to stabilize the suspension formed. The monomer droplets are generally on the order of approx 0.1–1 mm in size, and each droplet behaves as though it were a small bulk polymerization system. That is, the polymerization rates and molecular weights obtained in a suspension polymerization reaction are essentially identical to those for a bulk polymerization of the same monomer. A major advantage of this method is that the polymeric products are obtained in the form of small beads, which are easily filtered, washed and dried to form molding powders. In some cases, such as in the manufacture of ion-exchange resins, the beads are used directly. Because water is used as the reaction medium in both suspension and emulsion polymerization, and water reacts readily with both anions and cations, these methods are utilized only in radical polymerization reactions.

Emulsion Polymerization. In emulsion polymerization the locus of the polymerization reaction is a particle of colloidal size varying from 50 to 1500 Å in diam, and the initiator radical is formed in the aqueous phase, not directly in the monomer droplet. These two characteristics lead to the formation of much higher molecular weight polymers at considerably enhanced polymerization rates.

An emulsion polymerization is actually a three-phase reaction system consisting of large droplets of the monomer (approx 15,000 Å in diam), the aqueous water phase containing the dissolved initiator, and the colloidal particles of monomer-swollen polymer (generally 500–1500 Å in diam). Because of the much greater number of monomer–polymer particles compared to monomer droplets, essentially all the polymerization reaction occurs in the former, and monomer in the droplets is gradually transferred to the colloidal particles by dissolving in and diffusing through the aqueous phase. For this reason, monomers applicable to emulsion polymerization must have a finite water solubility, but still not so high a solubility as to cause a substantial amount of polymerization to occur in the aqueous phase itself. The monomer droplets and the swollen monomer–polymer particles are stabilized in the aqueous medium by absorbed surface-active agents incorporated into the reaction mixture before the start of the polymerization. Because the initiator must be present only in the aqueous phase, generally inorganic peroxides, which are highly soluble in water, are used for this purpose. Hydrogen peroxide and ammonium peroxysulfate are examples of such initiators, and the rates of radical formation by these initiators are often enhanced by the addition of inorganic, water-soluble reducing agents to the reaction mixture. The combination of peroxide and reducing agent is termed a *redox initiator*. Because an inherent characteristic of this method of polymerization is the formation of unusually high molecular weight polymers, chain-transfer agents, termed modifiers, are often added to the reaction mixture to limit the molecular weight without reducing the rate of the polymerization reaction.

Precipitation Polymerization. If a polymer is insoluble in its own monomer or in a particular monomer–solvent combination, it will precipitate out as it is formed. If in a radical polymerization reaction, the growing polymer chains precipitate out in the form of small compact spheres while still containing live radical end groups, an increase in the rate of polymerization and in the molecular weight of the product will be observed. The reason for these increases is that the live end groups become buried inside the spheres, and termination between two active polymer chains becomes extremely difficult or improbable. This phenomenon is termed precipitation polymerization, and as in emulsion polymerization, the rate of polymerization follows kinetic relationships considerably different from those for homogeneous bulk or solution polymerization reactions.

Vapor-Phase Polymerization. The term vapor-phase polymerization is to some extent a misnomer in that it refers only to a polymerization reaction initiated on monomer vapors. High-molecular-weight polymer molecules are not volatile, so a fog of polymer particles containing growing polymer chains quickly forms, and the major portion of the polymerization reaction occurs in the condensed state. Vapor-phase polymerization, in this sense, is very similar in mechanism to emulsion and precipitation polymerization because the polymer particles in the fog contain isolated growing polymer chains which are capable of very long lifetimes, and therefore, capable of exhibiting unusually high rates of polymerization and molecular weights.

Solid-State Polymerization. Chain-growth polymerization reactions have been carried out on a large number of olefin and cyclic monomers in the crystalline solid state. The reaction is generally initiated by irradiating the crystals with ionizing radiation, and as a result, the exact mechanism of the polymerization is unknown. That is, whether the polymerization reaction follows an ionic or radical course or both cannot be ascertained directly because of the wide variety of reaction types which can be induced by ionizing radiation. In many cases the crystalline monomer will convert directly to the polymer without any obvious change in appearance of the solid. Again, the polymer chains are often isolated, and the rates of termination in these polymerization reactions can be markedly reduced.

Table 2. Some Olefin Monomers Polymerized with Ziegler-Natta Catalysts

Monomer	Product
ethylene	linear polyethylene
propylene	isotactic polypropylene
	syndiotactic polypropylene
1-butene	isotactic polybutene
3-methyl-1-butene	isotactic polymer
2-butene	monomer isomerized to 1-butene, which polymerizes
(+)(S)-3-methyl-1-pentene	optically active polymer
racemic 4-methyl-1-pentene	optically active polymer prepared with a TiCl$_3$ plus (+)-tris((S)-2-methylbutyl)Al etherate catalyst
styrene and substituted styrenes	isotactic styrene and ring-substituted polymers
acetylenes	essentially completely conjugated polymers
vinyl chloride	tetrahydrofuran is used to prevent reaction of Al(C$_2$H$_5$)$_3$ with chlorine atoms in monomer and polymer and permit polymerization
vinyl acetate, acrylonitrile	polymerization in a polar solvent without an active hydrogen (ethyl acetate) to prevent reaction of aluminum alkyl with monomer

Heterogeneous Polymerization (13). Polymerization processes involving the use of insoluble, solid catalysts, termed heterogeneous polymerization, have been developed for the preparation of stereoregular chain-growth polymers. It is possible to achieve some degree of regularity in radical and ionic homogeneous chain-growth polymerization reactions carried out at very low temperatures, but heterogeneous processes are much more effective for this purpose. For olefin monomers the most versatile of these are the Ziegler-Natta catalysts. The polymerization reaction systems involving Ziegler-Natta catalysts usually consist of the reaction products of an organometallic compound (for example, triethylaluminum) and a transition metal compound (for example, titanium tetrachloride) slurried in a dry, oxygenfree, inert hydrocarbon solvent (for example, heptane) along with the monomer or monomers to be polymerized. The polymerization reactions are usually carried out at temperatures up to about 90°C and at monomer pressures up to about 5 atm. Some olefin monomers polymerized with Ziegler-Natta catalysts and the products obtained are listed in Table 2 (4).

The polymerization of 1-olefins with Ziegler-Natta catalysts is generally assumed to involve initially adsorption and complexing of the monomers. The resulting stereoregularity in the polymers produced with these and other heterogeneous catalysts may be due to steric hindrance at the catalyst site which prevents the adsorption of monomer except in one orientation relative to the site.

Bibliography

1. W. H. Carothers, *J. Am. Chem. Soc.* **51**, 2548 (1929).
2. W. H. Carothers, J. W. Hill, G. E. Kirby, and R. A. Jacobson, *J. Am. Chem. Soc.* **52**, 5279 (1930).
3. G. D. Buckley, L. H. Cross, and N. H. Ray, *J. Chem. Soc.* **1950**, 2714.
4. R. W. Lenz, *Organic Chemistry of Synthetic High Polymers*, Interscience Publishers, a division of John Wiley & Sons, Inc., New York, 1967.
5. A. Schöberl, *Makromol. Chem.* **37**, 64 (1967).
6. B. Vollmart, *Grundriss der makromolekulären Chemie*, Springer-Verlag, Berlin, Germany, 1962, p. 35.
7. G. Ham, ed., *Copolymerization*, Interscience Publishers, a division of John Wiley & Sons, Inc., New York, 1964.
8. M. Farina, M. Peraldo, and G. Natta, *Angew. Chem. Intern. Ed.* **4**, 107 (1965).
9. C. L. Arcus, *Progr. Stereochem.* **3**, 264 (1962).
10. M. L. Huggins, G. Natta, V. Desreux, and H. Mark, *J. Polymer Sci.* **56**, 153 (1962).
11. C. E. Schildknecht, ed., *Polymer Processes*, Interscience Publishers, Inc., New York, 1956.
12. W. M. Smith, ed., *Manufacture of Plastics*, Vol. I, Reinhold Publishing Corp., New York, 1964.
13. L. Reich and A. Schindler, *Polymerization by Organometallic Compounds*, Interscience Publishers, a division of John Wiley & Sons, Inc., New York, 1966.

ROBERT W. LENZ
University of Massachusetts

POLYMERS

Polymers (or macromolecular substances) are of great fundamental importance for our existence and our culture. The human body, all animal and plant tissues, and most building substances in organic nature, such as proteins, wood, and chitin, consist of polymeric or macromolecular materials. Many minerals, such as silica and feldspar, are inorganic polymers, and numerous products of ancient and modern industry, such as porcelain, glass, textiles, paper, rubbers, and plastics, are either entirely or substantially polymeric. It was, however, only recently clearly recognized that all these substances possess one essential common feature, namely, that they consist of very large molecules. See also Polymerization mechanisms and processes.

Definition and Classification

A polymer (Greek *polys*, many; *meros*, part or unit) is a substance consisting of molecules which are, at least approximately, multiples of low-molecular-weight (lmw) units. The lmw unit is the *monomer*. As long as the polymer is strictly uniform in molecular weight and molecular structure, its degree of polymerization is indicated by the Greek word for the number of monomers which it contains; thus we speak of a *dimer, trimer, tetramer, pentamer,* and so on. The term *polymer* designates a combination of an unspecified number of units. For example, trioxymethylene is the (cyclic) trimer of formaldehyde, and polystyrene is the polymer of styrene,

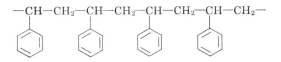

The term *oligomer* (ŏ·lĭ′·gŏ·mer), meaning "few units," can be applied where the number of units is not greater than about ten. If the number of units becomes very large, one uses the term *high polymer*.

According to present-day usage, a polymer need not consist of individual molecules which all have the same molecular weight, nor is it necessary that they all have the same chemical composition and molecular structure as each other or as the monomer unit. Natural polymers may exist in their native state, such as certain globular proteins or polysaccharides, in which the individual molecules all have the same molecular weight and molecular structure, but most synthetic and natural high polymers are obtained and investigated in a state where significant differences occur in the molecular weight of the individual macromolecules so that the material must be considered as a mixture of *homologous polymeric constituents*. The existence of a lesser or wider weight distribution is caused by our present inability to prepare polymers of exactly uniform character and by the lack of methods of resolving a homologous polymeric mixture into completely homogeneous fractions. The slight variability in chemical composition and molecular structure results from the presence of end groups, occasional branches, variations in the orientation of the monomeric units, and irregularity in the sequence of different types of these units in copolymers. A more rigorous definition and nomenclature, conforming to the practice in the domain of ordinary organic molecules, whould be impracticable because the above variations always occur and their elimination, or even the quantitative determination of their nature or amount, is not possible by methods now available. The present usage of the words polymer and high polymer may further be justified on the basis that the above-mentioned variations often do not significantly affect the physical and chemical properties of the substance.

Isomeric polymers are polymers which have essentially the same percentage composition, but differ with regard to the arrangement of the individual atoms or atom groups in the molecules. Isomeric vinyl-type polymers may differ in the relative orientations (head to tail, head to head and tail to tail, or random mixtures of the two) of consecutive mers (monomeric units):

head to tail: $-CH_2-CHX-CH_2-CHX-CH_2-CHX-CH_2-CHX-$

head to head and tail to tail: $-CH_2-CHX-CHX-CH_2-CH_2-CHX-CHX-CH_2-$

or in the orientation of substituents or side chains with respect to the plane of the hypothetically extended backbone chain:

$$\begin{array}{cccccccc} H & H & X & H & H & H & X & H \\ -C{-}C{-}C{-}C{-}C{-}C{-}C{-}C{-} \\ X & H & H & H & X & H & H & H \end{array}$$

Cis-trans isomerism may and probably does occur for any polymer containing double bonds other than those in pendent vinyl groups (those attached to the main chain):

cis: (structure with $C=C$ double bonds)   trans: (structure with $C=C$ double bonds)

Isomeric linear polymers from dienes, such as polybutadiene, polyisoprene, and polychloroprene, may and do result from different amounts of 1,2 and 1,4 addition.

Isomeric copolymers may and probably do differ with respect to the way in which the different monomers are distributed along the chain even though their overall composition is the same:

regular alternation: —A—B—A—B—A—B—A—B—A—B—A—B—

random alternation: —A—B—B—A—A—A—B—A—B—B—A—B—

A *homopolymer* consists of macromolecules which are formed either by a single type of unit or by two (or more) chemically different types in regular sequence. Homopolymers may and do contain irregularities in minor amounts at the chain ends and at branch junctions.

Copolymers are macromolecules containing two or more chemically different monomeric units in a more or less irregular sequence. Normally, the relative numbers of the different types of units are not the same in different individual macromolecules or even at different points in a single macromolecule. A mixture of macromolecules containing essentially only one type of monomeric unit with other macromolecules containing essentially only another type of monomeric unit is called a *polyblend* or a mixture of homopolymers. A *block copolymer* is a copolymer which contains longer stretches of two or more monomeric units linked together by chemical valences in one single chain,

—A—A—A—A—A—B—B—B—B—A—A—A—A—

A *graft copolymer* contains branches of varying length made up of different monomeric units, on a common backbone or trunk chain,

B—B—B—B—B—B—B—B—B—B—
|
—A—A—A—A—A—A—A—A—A—A—A—A—A—A—

Graft and block copolymers represent in their structure and in their properties a transition between normal copolymers and polyblends.

The detailed structure of copolymers depends essentially on the relative reactivity ratios of the various building units, which in turn are determined by the polarity and donor-acceptor characteristics of the individual monomers. See Polymerization mechanisms and processes.

A *tactic polymer* consists of macromolecules whose monomeric units follow one another along the chain with steric configurations ordered according to some rule. The rule, or *tacticity*, may be simple or composed of a few simple elements, but in any case it must not have a random or statistic character.

More complex tacticities can be originated not only by steric configuration of a few units, but also by programmatic arrangements of monomeric units having a different configuration along the macromolecular chain.

A *eutactic polymer* is a tactic polymer whose monomeric units are *completely* ordered, so that it is devoid of any element of structural disorder. By way of example, a butadiene polymer is eutactic when all the monomeric units have the same *trans*-1,4 configuration or all have the *cis*-1,4 configuration.

An *atactic polymer* is a polymer whose macromolecules, although they have positional or structural arrangements, do not possess a steric order of the units. By way of example, a vinyl polymer, obtained by conventional radical processes, is generally atactic; it may possess a head-to-tail arrangement, but it is disordered with regard to the steric configurations of the tertiary carbon atoms which follow each other along the main chains.

An *isotactic polymer* is one whose monomeric units are asymmetric, ordered in such a way that, when passing along a single chain from one monomeric unit to the next, one finds repetition of the unit configuration. Isotactic polymers are usually eutactic.

A *syndiotactic polymer* consists of macromolecules whose monomeric units are asymmetric and ordered in such a way that, when passing along the chain from one unit to the next, one finds a repetition of position and of structure, but an *inversion* of the steric configuration. For example, a butadiene polymer formed through 1-2, head-to-tail enchainment, the successive monomeric units of which have alternately right and left configuration along the chain in respect of a selected direction, is a syndiotactic polymer.

Stereocopolymers are polymers with macromolecules which are formed by monomeric units which are chemically identical, and which are ordered through positional and structural arrangements, but which do not have a unitary steric structure.

Stereoblock polymers are stereocopolymers with molecules which are formed either by tactic blocks of at least two types, or by tactic and atactic blocks.

Polyelectrolytes are substances which, on dissolving in water or other ionizing solvents, dissociate to give polyions together with an equivalent amount of counterions (ions of small charge and opposite sign). Polyelectrolytes can be polyacids, polybases, polysalts, or polyampholytes.

Under certain conditions the possibility exists for the establishment of chemical bonds between individual growing polymer chains. Such *cross links* can be formed during polycondensation reactions whenever tri- or tetrafunctional monomers are used, and during addition polymerization whenever dienes or trienes are involved. The initial result of a *crosslinking reaction* is the formation of small domains, within which the macromolecules consist of a random three-dimensional network of chemically linked chains; such domains are called *microgels*. They can be discovered by dynamic viscosity measurements, by turbidity, and by microfiltration. If a crosslinking reaction extends over macroscopic dimensions and if the polymerizing system is imbibed by a solvent or by the monomer, there results a gel which, after drying, is converted into an insoluble and infusible three-dimensional network, such as thermosetting resins like phenol– or urea–formaldehyde or copolymers of styrene and divinylbenzene. Similar insoluble and infusible systems are obtained if a vinyl derivative is polymerized in the presence of a small amount of a divinyl compound in such a manner that a local excess of free radicals prevails. The materials thus obtained are called *popcorn* polymers; their exact structure and properties are still being investigated.

Measurement of High Molecular Weights

The outstanding property of all polymers is that they have molecules of high molecular weights; as a consequence, methods for measuring high molecular weights are of special interest in polymer research. Of the four methods to be mentioned, three permit the absolute determination of the various molecular weight averages of dissolved macromolecules; the fourth permits only relative molecular weight determinations but is frequently applied because of its experimental simplicity.

Up to molecular weights of 4000–5000, conventional cryoscopic, ebullioscopic, and vapor-pressure measurements are applicable. The results can be evaluated by equations based on Raoult's law and van't Hoff's law; lmw impurities have a falsifying effect on the measurements and their interpretation. No general experimental techniques exist for measuring molecular weights between 5000 and 15,000.

Osmotic Pressure. Above 15,000 the direct measurement of the osmotic pressure with the aid of semipermeable membranes is applicable. Special types of osmometer have been developed for the purpose of working in the temperature range from -20 to 120°C, using different types of solvents. The most useful membranes are denitrated cellulose nitrate, gel cellophane, and crosslinked polyvinyl alcohol. The method is limited at the lmw end by noticeable diffusion of the solute through the membrane and at high molecular weight by the small magnitude of the osmotic pressure. No really reliable determinations can be made above molecular weights of about 1.5 million.

Solutions containing macromolecules with molecular weights above 15,000 do not obey van't Hoff's law and must be evaluated by the Huggins-Flory equation,

$$P/c = RT/M_n + Bc \qquad (1)$$

where P = osmotic pressure, c = solute concentration, R = gas constant (in appropriate units), T = absolute temperature, M_n = *number-average molecular weight* of the solute, and B = an empirical constant, characterizing the solubility of the particular polymer in the particular solvent.

In order to arrive at numerical values for M_n and B, it is necessary to carry out individual osmotic-pressure measurements at four or five different concentrations within the range of 0.1–0.5% and to plot P/c versus c. If the measurements are properly made and no disturbing influences interfere, the points are arranged on a straight line, whose slope is B and whose intercept is RT/M_n. A great deal of important information has been accumulated by this method. See Osmosis.

Light Scattering. According to Einstein, Raman, and Debye, it is possible to determine the osmotic pressure of a solution from its capacity to scatter light. The total amount of laterally scattered intensity is measured by the turbidity, τ, of a system, which is defined by

$$\tau = (1/l) \ln I/I_0 \qquad (2)$$

where l = length of the scattering system, and I_0 and I = intensity of the beam as it enters and leaves the scattering system, respectively.

Turbidity and molecular weight of a polymer solution are related by the equation

$$Hc/\tau = RT/M_w + 2\,Bc \qquad (3)$$

where τ = turbidity as defined in equation 2, c, R, and T have the same meaning and B the same value as in equation 1, M_w = *weight-average molecular weight* of the solute, and H = a constant which depends on the wavelength of the scattered light and on the refractive indexes of the solvent and the solution; it has to be determined by a measurement independent of these quantities. To use equation 3 it is necessary to carry out individual turbidity measurements at four or five different concentrations within the range of 0.02–0.10% and to plot Hc/τ versus c. If the measurements are properly made and no disturbing influences interfere, the points are arranged on a straight line, whose slope is $2B$ and whose intercept is RT/M_w. With sufficiently sensitive instruments it is possible to measure molecular weights as small as 3000–4000; in the domain of molecular weights above 300,000–400,000, the application of equation 3 is not permissible any more because the dimensions of the scattering particles become comparable with the wavelength of the scattered light. As soon as this is the case, a more complicated analysis is necessary which involves measurements of the scattered intensity at different concentrations and different angles. Debye, Doty, and Zimm have expanded the theory and the experimental techniques so that molecular weights up to several million can be successfully measured by the turbidity method.

Ultracentrifuge. Svedberg has originated the use of this instrument for the determination of the molecular weight of macromolecules. Two approaches can be used:

1. *Sedimentation and Diffusion Velocities.* The molecular weight of a solute can be expressed as follows:

$$M_w = \frac{RTs}{D(1 - V\rho)} \tag{4}$$

where M_w = weight-average molecular weight of solute, R and T have the same meaning as in equation 1, V = partial specific volume of solute, ρ = specific gravity of solvent, D = diffusion rate constant, and s = sedimentation rate constant.

In the case of globular macromolecules, such as certain proteins, D and s do not depend noticeably on concentration and can be obtained from a single measurement of the rates of diffusion and sedimentation at an arbitrary concentration in the range between 0.05 and 0.25%. For linear polymers with long flexible chains, D and s depend noticeably on solute concentration; four or five measurements of the rates of diffusion and sedimentation have to be carried out and the intrinsic values of D_0 and s_0 must be determined by extrapolation to infinite dilution. These values are then used in equation 4. The weight-average molecular weights thus obtained, in general, agree well with those computed by equation 3.

2. *Sedimentation Equilibrium.* The rate of concentration during sedimentation and back diffusion in a high-speed centrifuge establishes a final stationary state of solute concentration which permits determination of the moecular weight of the solute according to the following equation:

$$M_z = \frac{2RT \ln c/c_0}{(1 - V\rho)\omega^2(x^2 - x_0^2)} \tag{5}$$

where ω = angular speed of rotation; R, T, V, and ρ have the same meaning as in equations 1 and 4; c_0 and c are the equilibrium solute concentrations at the distance x_0 and x from the axis of rotation, respectively; and M_z is the z-average molecular weight of the solute. This method has been greatly improved and expanded by Williams and Wales; it permits the determination of all three averages of the molecular weight of the solute and establishes valuable knowledge concerning the molecular-weight distribution of a given material.

Viscosity. Berl, Biltz, and Ostwald pointed out that a relation exists between the molecular weight of a polymer and its capacity to produce solutions of high viscosity, and Staudinger formulated a quantitative relation between the relative thickening power of a polymer on solution and its molecular weight. Kramer has expressed this relation in the form

$$[\eta] = K_m M_w \qquad (6)$$

where $[\eta]$ = *limiting viscosity number* (or *intrinsic viscosity*), K_m = Staudinger constant, and M_w = weight-average molecular weight of the solute; $[\eta]$ is obtained by extrapolating to zero concentration the Huggins equation for the *viscosity number* (or *specific viscosity*)

$$\frac{\eta_c - \eta_0}{\eta_0} \cdot \frac{1}{c} = [\eta] + k' \, [\eta]^2 c \qquad (7)$$

where η_c = viscosity of a solution of concentration c (in g/100 ml of solvent), η_0 = viscosity of the pure solvent, and k' = empirical constant describing the influence of concentration on the thickening power of the polymer.

Having first determined $[\eta]$ from four or five individual viscosity measurements according to equation 7, and having calibrated the empirical constant k_m by any of the absolute methods previously described, the Staudinger equation 6 purportedly permits the determination of the molecular weight of a polymer by viscosity measurements. It has been shown, however, by subsequent, more detailed studies that equation 6 only holds for a few solute–solvent systems and has to be replaced in general by the relation

$$[\eta] = KM^a \qquad (8)$$

known as the Mark-Houwink equation, where two constants, K and a, are necessary to convert limiting viscosity numbers into molecular weights. Equation 8 holds for all previously known polymer solutions over a considerable molecular-weight range and is therefore widely used to obtain molecular weights of macromolecules from viscosity

Table 1. Constants for Calculating Viscosity-Average Molecular Weights

Polymer	Solvent	Temperature, °C	K	a
cellulose acetate	acetone	25	1.9×10^{-5}	1.03
cellulose nitrate	acetone	25	3.8×10^{-5}	1.0
nylon-6,6	90% formic acid	25	11.0×10^{-4}	0.72
poly(vinyl acetate)	acetone	20	2.76×10^{-4}	0.66
polystyrene	benzene	30	1.7×10^{-4}	0.72
polyisobutylene	benzene	20	3.6×10^{-4}	0.64
natural rubber	toluene	25	5.02×10^{-4}	0.67
GR-S	toluene	25	5.3×10^{-4}	0.67
neoprene	toluene	25	5.0×10^{-4}	0.62

measurements. The expression "viscosity-average molecular weight" is used for the value arrived at by this equation; it is somewhat lower than the weight-average molecular weight. The characteristic constants K and a have been determined for many solute-solvent combinations. A few particularly important cases are listed in Table 1. To apply them it is necessary to measure the solute concentration in grams of solute per 100 ml of solvent, and to carry out the viscosity measurements in a concentration range below 2 g/100 ml.

Molecular Heterogeneity of Polymers

Most polymers, natural or synthetic, are nonhomogeneous as far as their molecular weight is concerned; they represent a mixture of macromolecules with different degrees of polymerization. Several methods exist for determining the molecular-weight distribution in a given sample; some are of only analytical character, whereas others actually permit separation of the various molecular-weight fractions from each other in a preparative manner.

The relatively simplest way to get a first impression of the molecular heterogeneity of a polymer sample is to determine the different modes or averages of the molecular-weight distribution function. The first mode or number-average molecular weight is defined by

$$\bar{M}_n = \frac{\int f(M)M\,dM}{\int f(M)\,dM} \tag{9}$$

where $f(M)$ represents the fraction of the material having a molecular weight M as a function of M. Experimentally, $\bar{M}_n$ can be obtained by all those methods which count the individual molecules in a solution of the sample, such as the analytical determination of end groups, the direct measurement of the osmotic pressure, the vapor-pressure lowering, the boiling-point elevation, or the melting-point lowering.

The second mode or weight-average molecular weight is defined as

$$\bar{M}_w = \frac{\int f(M)M^2\,dM}{\int f(M)M\,dM} \tag{10}$$

It can be obtained experimentally by measurement of the turbidity of a macromolecular solution, or by the combination of sedimentation and diffusion (see p. 247).

The third mode or z-average molecular weight is represented by

$$\bar{M}_z = \frac{\int f(M)^3 M\,dM}{\int f(M)M^2\,dM} \tag{11}$$

It can be determined by sedimentation equilibrium.

In order to illustrate the significance of the three averages $\bar{M}_n$, $\bar{M}_w$, and $\bar{M}_z$, let us assume that we have a mixture of four molecules having a molecular weight of 2 and four molecules having a molecular weight of 4. Then the three averages are given by

$$\bar{M}_n = \frac{(4 \times 2) + (4 \times 4)}{4 + 4} = \frac{24}{8} = 3$$

$$\bar{M}_w = \frac{(4 \times 2^2) + (4 \times 4^2)}{(4 \times 2) + (4 \times 4)} = \frac{80}{24} = 3.33$$

$$\bar{M}_z = \frac{(4 \times 2^3) + (4 \times 4^3)}{(4 \times 2^2) + (4 \times 4^2)} = \frac{288}{80} = 3.6$$

From this it can be seen that for any nonuniform polymer the z-average is largest and the n-average is smallest.

For a completely homogeneous material the three average molecular weights are identical; growing nonuniformity causes the ratios $\bar{M}_z : \bar{M}_w : \bar{M}_n$ to increase. If the

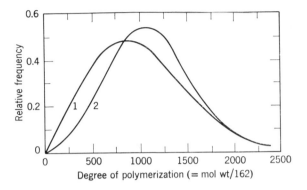

Fig. 1. Characteristic molecular-weight distribution curves of natural cellulose. 1, a sulfite pulp; 2, cotton linters.

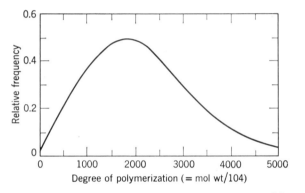

Fig. 2. Characteristic molecular-weight distribution curve of a commercial sample of polystyrene.

molecular-weight distribution function is caused by complete randomness in the building up or degradation of linear macromolecules, the "normal" ratios are simply

$$\bar{M}_z : \bar{M}_w : \bar{M}_n = 3 : 2 : 1$$

By experimental determination of the values for $\bar{M}_z$, $\bar{M}_w$, and $\bar{M}_n$ one can therefore arrive at a conclusion whether a given material is "normal" in its distribution or whether it has a narrower or wider distribution.

More quantitative statements as to the shape of $f(M)$ can be obtained by an analysis of the concentration gradient in the meniscus of a sedimentation-equilibrium run or in a series of sedimentation-velocity or diffusion experiments. If the macromolecules carry electric charges, electrophoresis experiments can be used for the same purpose.

Another analytical method is the turbidity titration, which involves measurement of the turbidity increase of a dilute polymer solution on the gradual addition of a precipitant and fractional precipitation of the different molecular-weight species. The most accurate results are obtained when the individual fractions are separated by centrifugation or filtration. Particularly practical and important is the filtration of a dilute polymer solution through a swollen gelatinous network which contains cavities of different sizes. This method has been very useful in the form of gel permeation chromatography. In this way these fractions are obtained in a pure state and their weight and molecular weight can be determined by independent measurements. Plotting the percentage weights of the individual fractions against their molecular weights, a differential molecular-weight distribution curve of the investigated material is obtained, which gives a fairly complete insight into the molecular heterogeneity of the sample. Figures 1 and 2 represent characteristic molecular-weight distribution curves of some important polymers as obtained by fractionation experiments.

General Properties of High Polymers in Bulk

The most important property of organic polymers as compared with ordinary organic substances is that they exhibit considerable mechanical strength in their bulk state. Hence they can be used to make fibers, films, plastics, rubbers, or coatings with commercially valuable properties. The degree to which mechanical properties are exhibited depends upon several factors, the cooperation of which determines the most appropriate utilization of a given polymer and characterizes it as a typical material to form a fiber, a plastic, or a rubber.

One decisive factor for mechanical resistance is the *degree of polymerization* (or molecular weight) of the material under consideration. Extensive experiments with many polymers have shown that for each polymer there exists a certain critical molecular weight below which the material shows no mechanical strength at all. Above this critical value, mechanical strength is rapidly developed with increasing molecular weight, as shown by the relatively steep rise of the curve in Figure 3. In the domain of higher degrees of polymerization, the increase of mechanical resistance with molecular weight becomes less pronounced, as represented by the flatter part of the curve in Figure 3. An industrially useful material must, therefore, have a molecular weight somewhat above the inflection point of this curve. In principle, and as a matter of safety, it is advisable to choose a molecular weight well above this inflection point, but it has been found that materials having too high a degree of polymerization exhibit exorbitant viscosities in solution or in the molten state, which render such important processes as filtration, spinning, casting, and molding unduly difficult. A proper compromise between easy processability and desirable ultimate properties must therefore be established by choosing an optimum molecular-weight range in each individual case. Another important factor for the development of characteristic mechanical properties is the *magnitude of the intermolecular forces between the individual macromolecules* of a given material. It the intermolecular attraction is small and the chains

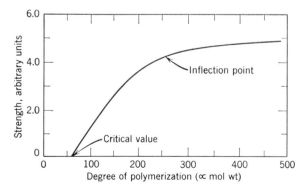

Fig. 3. Dependence of mechanical strength upon degree of polymerization (molecular weight).

are difficult to fit laterally into a lattice-like structure, then at a given temperature and stress the material will show a distinct tendency to return to its curled-up, relaxed state. Such conditions are typical for *rubbers* (see Rubber, natural; Elastomers, synthetic). On the other hand, if the molar cohesion is strong and the fine structure of the chains provides for easy lateral fitting into a lattice-like arrangement, a state of high external crystallinity is favored and the material is a typical *fiber* (see Fibers, manmade). In intermediate cases, in which the forces are moderate and the geometry of the chains is moderately favorable for crystallization, the behavior of the material will depend greatly upon external conditions such as temperature and external mechanical forces. Such systems are typical *plastics*.

These qualitative considerations show that rubbers, plastics, and fibers are not intrinsically different materials. Their difference is rather a matter of degree and is produced by the way in which the intermolecular forces between the long chains and their general tendency to curl and fold cooperate in forming a certain mixture of crystallized and disordered portions in a given sample of the material. In general, it can be said that under given conditions, such as temperature and external forces applied to the sample, the tendency to crystallize is brought about by two different factors, which to a certain extent conflict with each other:

1. The forces between the individual macromolecules. This influence corresponds to the ΔH term in the expression for the free-energy change during crystallization. If the forces are strong (above 5000 cal/mole of the group involved), then at ordinary temperatures they will preponderantly determine the behavior and the material can be expected to behave more or less as a typical fiber. This seems to be true for the following fibers: cellulose, protein, polyamide, polyester, acrylics, etc.

2. The geometrical bulkiness of the chains. This influence corresponds to the $T\Delta S$ term in the expression for the free-energy change during crystallization. Chains that fit easily into a crystal lattice (polyethylene, *trans*-polydiolefins) crystallize under the influence of comparatively weak forces and hence, in general, have a tendency to appear more fiberlike than would be expected if the forces alone were considered. On the other hand, materials which have bulky and irregular chains do not crystallize even if the intermolecular forces are quite strong. Hence they will be more rubberlike than would be expected on the basis of only the intermolecular forces (vinyl copolymers, cellulose mixed esters, etc).

From the point of view of thermal behavior polymeric materials are characterized by two important temperatures. One is the *melting point*, T_m, of the crystalline phase of a solid polymer; it is usually a rather sharp temperature at which the material passes from a hard solid to a viscous liquid. The other is the *glass transition point*, T_g, of amorphous polymers, or of the amorphous domains in partly crystalline polymers. It is usually a somewhat broader temperature range through which the material passes from a rigid and somewhat brittle solid to a soft and rubbery mass.

Bibliography

"Polymers" in *ECT* 1st ed., Vol. 10, pp. 957–971, by Herman Mark, Polymer Research Institute, Polytechnic Institute of Brooklyn.

C. E. H. Bawn, *The Chemistry of High Polymers*, Butterworth & Co., Ltd., London, and Interscience Publishers, Inc., New York, 1948.

F. W. Billmeyer, *Textbook of Polymer Science*, John Wiley & Sons, Inc., New York, 1962.

P. J. Flory, *Principles of Polymer Chemistry*, Cornell University Press, Ithaca, N.Y., 1953.

R. W. Lenz, *Organic Chemistry of Synthetic High Polymers,* Interscience Publishers, a division of John Wiley & Sons, Inc., New York, 1967.

H. Mark, *Physical Chemistry of High Polymeric Systems,* Interscience Publishers, Inc., New York, 1940.

H. Mark and R. Raff, *High Polymeric Reactions* (Vol. III of *High Polymers*), Interscience Publishers, Inc., New York, 1941.

H. Mark and G. S. Whitby, eds., *Collected Papers of Wallace Hume Carothers on High Polymeric Substances* (Vol. I of *High Polymers*), Interscience Publishers, Inc., New York, 1940.

C. S. Marvel, *Organic Chemistry of Polymers,* John Wiley & Sons, Inc., New York, 1959.

K. H. Meyer, *Natural and Synthetic High Polymers* (Vol. IV of *High Polymers*), Interscience Publishers, Inc., New York, 1942.

K. H. Meyer and H. Mark, *Der Aufbau der hochpolymeren organischen Naturstoffe,* Akademische Verlagsgesellschaft, Leipzig, Germany, 1930.

H. Staudinger, *Die hochmolekularen organischen Verbindungen,* Springer-Verlag, Berlin, Germany, 1932.

J. K. Stille, *Introduction to Polymer Chemistry,* John Wiley & Sons, Inc., New York, 1962.

HERMAN MARK
Polytechnic Institute of Brooklyn

POLYMERS CONTAINING SULFUR

POLYSULFIDES

The polysulfide elastomers, first commercialized in 1929, have carved out a modest but significant niche as specialty polymers because of solvent resistance, good low-temperature performance, and good weathering and ozone resistance properties.

The solid elastomers have a limited market and are used in printing rolls, paint spray hose, and gaskets and diaphragms where resistance to aromatic and ester solvents is required.

The most important commercial products are the thiol-terminated liquid polymers. These were originally developed as plasticizers for the solid elastomers, but the convenience of room-temperature in situ cure led to major markets in sealants and adhesives. In fact, this cure feature led to the development of the case-bonded solid-propellant rocket motor.

The polysulfide polymers are prepared in a condensation process involving organic polyhalides with inorganic polysulfides in aqueous suspension. The principal monomer is bis-2-chloroethyl formal, $H_2C(OCH_2CH_2Cl)_2$. Modest amounts of ethylene dichloride are used in special polymers. Most products contain some crosslink precursor derived from the trihalide, 1,2,3-trichloropropane. The alkali polysulfide used is primarily sodium disulfide although some special polymers contain monosulfide or tetrasulfide structures.

Many of the unique performance characteristics of these polymers are derived from the presence of the polysulfide linkages. The solvent resistance is in direct proportion to the sulfur content. Interchange at the sulfur bonds is the basis for the reactions leading to high molecular weight in the condensation polymerization. Interchange chemistry is deeply involved in the heat-aging and stress-relaxation properties of these polymers.

Nomenclature. The expression "mercaptan" has been used, and often still is used, in the literature on these polymers. However, the name "thiol" is now recommended for "mercaptan," is used by Chemical Abstracts, and will be used here. It brings the expression into line with so many other names beginning with "thi-" (derived from the Greek) and connected with sulfur.

Monomers

Table 1 gives some properties of the monomers.

1,2,3-Trichloropropane is available as a by-product from the manufacture of glycerol (qv) from allyl chloride.

Table 1. Physical Properties of Monomers

Monomer	Bp, °C/mm	n_D^{20}	d_4^{20}
ethylene dichloride (see Vol. 5, p. 149), $C_2H_4Cl_2$	83.6	1.4443	1.257
1,2,3-trichloropropane, $C_3H_5Cl_3$	156	1.4835	1.386
bis-2-chloroethyl formal, $C_5H_{10}Cl_2O_2$	105–106[14]	1.4557	1.225
bis-4-chlorobutyl ether, $C_8H_{16}Cl_2O$	125–128[12]	1.4589	1.075
bis-4-chlorobutyl formal, $C_9H_{18}Cl_2O_2$	154–156[3]	1.4066	1.103

The bis-2-chloroethyl formal is prepared by condensation of ethylene chlorohydrin (see Vol. 5, p. 306) with anhydrous formaldehyde in the presence of an appropriate azeotroping agent. This is an acid-catalyzed reaction but there is usually sufficient residual acidity in the chlorohydrin to obviate the need for added catalyst. The formation of the formal proceeds very readily and is driven to completion by elimination of the water formed in the process.

$$2 \ ClCH_2CH_2OH + CH_2O \rightarrow ClCH_2CH_2OCH_2OCH_2CH_2Cl + H_2O$$

The monomer can be purified by distillation but this may not be necessary if the initial ethylene chlorohydrin is of sufficient purity. The principal source of chain-stopping impurity would be the presence of trace amounts of ethylene glycol. The formal group is susceptible to oxidation as well as hydrolysis in the presence of acid. Neutralization of residual acidity with gaseous ammonia is usually sufficient to stabilize the monomer. If very long-term storage is contemplated, a small amount of conventional phenolic antioxidant may be added. These stabilizers do not have to be removed prior to polymerization.

The bis-2-chloroethyl formal has no unusual chemical properties. The chlorine terminals are fairly reactive. This, of course, is the basis for the use of this monomer in the principal polysulfide polymers. The terminals are reactive to all the conventional nucleophilic displacement agents such as amines and salts of weak acids, including the sodium salts of the hydrogen polysulfides, such as sodium disulfide. At elevated temperatures, particularly over high surface catalyst, hydrogen chloride may be eliminated by pyrolysis, yielding divinyl formal.

Bis-4-chlorobutyl formal and bis-4-chlorobutyl ether are used in minor amounts where improved low-temperature performance is necessary.

The formal is synthesized from tetrahydrofuran, paraformaldehyde, and anhydrous HCl (1); the ether from tetrahydrofuran and phosphorus oxychloride (2).

Alkali Polysulfides. Sodium hydrosulfide and sodium monosulfide are readily available commercially (see Sodium compounds).

A number of techniques can be used to prepare sodium polysulfides: the reaction of anhydrous sodium sulfide with molten sulfur; the reaction of the sulfide with sulfur in aqueous or alcoholic solution; and the reaction of aqueous caustic with sulfur (3). The most widely used process for the commercial production of inorganic polysulfide solutions is the last. The process may be visualized as taking place in two steps,

$$6\ NaOH + (2x + 1)S \rightarrow 2\ Na_2S_x + 3\ H_2O + Na_2SO_3 \tag{1}$$
$$\text{sodium sulfite}$$

$$S + Na_2SO_3 \rightarrow Na_2S_2O_3 \tag{2}$$
$$\text{sodium thiosulfate}$$

The value of x in the first equation may vary from one to five and this value is generally designated as the *rank* of the polysulfide, both in the ionic species and in the polymer sulfur bonds. Ordinarily, the reaction converting the sulfite to thiosulfate takes place very rapidly and the amount of sulfite remaining is very small. However, by working with concentrated caustic solutions at higher temperatures, the sodium sulfite formed crystallizes out of the reaction mixture and only small amounts of thiosulfate remain in the aqueous sulfide solution. In addition to the trace amounts of thiosulfate, the product is contaminated with small amounts of potentially reactive anions such as sulfite and hydroxide. Fortunately, these are so much less reactive than the polysulfide that their presence does not cause any difficulty.

An excess of caustic is used in order to consume all the sulfur. Since excessive hydroxide ion can hydrolyze the halogen terminals, it is usually neutralized with sodium hydrosulfide,

$$NaOH + NaSH \rightarrow Na_2S + H_2O$$

This procedure is well suited for the preparation of the various sodium sulfides, ranging from the monosulfide to the pentasulfide.

The reaction of a solution of sodium sulfide with sulfur is a convenient laboratory technique. However, even by this process the aqueous polysulfide is contaminated with other anions since the monosulfide ion is almost completely hydrolyzed in water and the hydroxide ion formed reacts with sulfur (eq. 1) in competition with the desired direct polysulfide formation.

$$S_x^{2-} + H_2O \rightleftharpoons HS_x^- + OH^- \tag{3}$$
$$HS_x^- + H_2O \rightleftharpoons H_2S_x + OH^- \tag{4}$$

The hydrolysis occurs with all the polysulfide ion species, the extent of hydrolysis being a function of the concentration and the polysulfide rank. The higher the dilution or the lower the rank, the greater the hydrolysis. A further complication in defining the exact nature of the sodium polysulfide species is that the polysulfide anions in an aqueous solution are in a dynamic equilibrium mixture. For example, nominal sodium trisulfide solution is a mixture containing sodium monosulfide through sodium pentasulfide with an average rank value of three. This may have an effect on the rank of the polymer formed from this solution since the different polysulfide anions have different reactivity toward the halogen terminals of the monomer. In commercial practice, only a small excess of the polysulfide is used and the final product rank is quite similar to that of the polysulfide since the various species are ultimately consumed.

Polymerization

The polysulfide polymers are prepared as suspensions by polycondensation of the dihalide monomer with aqueous polysulfide solution. Bis-2-chloroethyl formal is the monomer usually used and 0.1–4.0% of trichloropropane is added as a crosslinking agent. Commercial polymers today are primarily disulfide polymers but in the production process the rank of the aqueous polysulfide used is 2.25 rather than 2.00 since the higher rank ensures that the products will be closer to the desired disulfide structure after the product is worked up. Since most of the commercial production consists of thiol-terminated products, the high-molecular-weight (hmw) dispersions are reduced with sodium hydrosulfide and sodium sulfite to give the desired lower-molecular branched thiol-terminated product.

The polymerization and the reduction processes proceed quite readily with the lower-molecular-weight dihalide monomers but with monomers of limited water solubility such as bis-4-chlorobutyl formal or decamethylene dichloride, it is generally necessary to use an aqueous alcoholic reaction medium.

The polymerization is carried out in a suspension rather than an emulsion. Standard practice is to feed the monomer into the aqueous polysulfide solution containing appropriate suspending agents. The suspending agents of choice are a combination of a sodium alkylnaphthalenesulfonate with a magnesium hydroxide sol prepared in situ. A relatively coarse suspension is desired since the heavy polymer formed can then be readily washed by decantation. If a fine-particle latex is prepared, the elimination of salts and excess alkali polysulfide is greatly slowed because of the slower rate of settling.

Stainless-steel equipment is used in large-scale production. Glass-lined reactors are attacked by the strongly alkaline inorganic polysulfide solution, while ordinary steel equipment results in dark polymer because of the solubilization of iron.

Chemistry. In conventional condensation polymerization by functional monomers it is normally essential to have close to perfect stoichiometry in order to achieve high molecular weight. If an excess of one of the reagents is used, it rapidly serves to limit the degree of polymerization. In addition, if side reactions cause loss of one of the functional terminals, the chain-stopping action also serves to limit the degree of polymerization.

The polysulfide polymers are unique in that very high molecular weight products can be obtained without the need to observe super precautions. In fact, an excess of the alkali polysulfide is always used, the excess serving to drive to completion the conversion of the halogen terminals to the desired alkyl polysulfide groups. Some hydrolysis does occur in the strongly alkaline solution and hydroxyl terminals are formed as chain stoppers. The basic polysulfide chemistry is described in the equations below:

$$-\text{SRSSRSSRSSRS}- + S_2{}^{2-} \rightleftharpoons -\text{SRSSRSS}^- + {}^-\text{SSRSSRS}-$$

$$-\text{SRSSRSSRSSROH} + S_2{}^{2-} \rightleftharpoons -\text{SRSSRSS}^- + {}^-\text{SSROH}$$

$$-\text{SRSSRS}^- + -\text{SRSSRSSRSSRS}- \rightleftharpoons -\text{SRSSRSSRSSRS}- + {}^-\text{SRSSRS}-$$

$$-\text{SRSSRS}^- + -\text{SRSSROH} \rightleftharpoons -\text{SRSSRSSRS}- + {}^-\text{SROH}$$

The polysulfide ion present in solution can interchange with the intermediate-molecular-weight polysulfide polymer formed; if the interchange occurs in the middle of the polymer chain, then two lower-molecular-weight still insoluble fragments are formed. On the other hand, if the interchange occurs near the terminal, then water-soluble hydroxyalkyl polysulfide ions are released to the aqueous reaction liquor. Similarly, interchange is possible by the thiol-terminated intermediate-molecular-weight product with the backbone of other chains present. Again, if the interchange takes place in the middle of the chain, little or no effect is observed, while if the change occurs near a terminal, the chain stopper is solubilized.

The hydroxyl-terminated segments accumulate in the aqueous phase and on completion of the reaction, the polymer dispersion is settled and the supernatant mother liquor containing the chain stoppers and excess polysulfides is decanted. The remaining intermediate-molecular-weight polymer, essentially free of chain stopper, is brought to the hmw stage by further washing and decantation treatments. These serve to reverse the equilibrium described in the first equation. The polysulfide ion formed is removed with recombination of the lower-molecular-weight segments to form the hmw product. If the reaction with excess polysulfide and the washing process does not yield a product of high enough molecular weight, the polymer suspension can be treated again with fresh alkali polysulfide solution to complete the conversion of any remaining halogen terminals and to solubilize any remaining hydroxyl group. In general practice, molecular weights on the order of half a million or better can be readily obtained.

The following is a typical laboratory procedure for the preparation of polymers: Place 4.8 moles of sodium polysulfide solution of the required polysulfide rank (about $2M$ concentration) in a 5-l flask. Add, while stirring and heating, 20 ml of 5% Nekal BX-78 (65% sodium alkylnaphthalenesulfonate, General Aniline & Film Corp.) solution and 17 ml of 50% sodium hydroxide. Then add 117 ml of 25% magnesium chloride hexahydrate dropwise from the addition funnel.

Continue heating until the temperature of the reaction mixture reaches 200°F. At this point remove the heat and start adding slowly 4 moles of halide. The rate of addition should be such that the entire amount will be added in about 1 hr. The temperature of the reaction is controlled partly by the rate of halide addition. The reaction is completed by heating for an additional hour at 200°F. The reaction mixture is allowed to settle and the supernatant mother liquor decanted from the heavy polymer latex. Hot water is added, the suspension is stirred and allowed to settle, and the wash water is removed by decantation. If the latex is not to be toughened, continue washing in this manner until the supernatant liquid shows no discoloration of lead acetate test paper.

If the latex is to be toughened, stir and heat the latex after removal of the second wash liquid. When the temperature reaches 210°F, add 1 mole of sodium polysulfide solution (rank 2.25), and maintain the temperature at 200°F for 30 min. At the end of this time, dilute the reaction mixture with cold water and wash the latex clean as described above.

Preparation of Thiol-Terminated Liquid Polymers. The polymerization technique described previously covers the preparation of hmw crosslinked products. These are converted to commercially useful materials by a process that corresponds to reduction of some of the disulfide groups present to thiol terminals. They result in a range of products varying in molecular weight from 500 to about 100,000, which contain various amounts of branching derived from the proportions of trichloropropane added to the monomer feed and carrying thiol terminals which are used as the cure site to convert these products back to the original hmw crosslinked structure.

The reduction process involves a treatment of the polymer dispersion with sodium hydrosulfide and sodium sulfite. The reaction of the disulfide groups in the polymer with sodium hydrosulfide generates thiol and hydrodisulfide terminals. As can be seen in the equations below, recovery of the product at this stage by the washing and decantation process will result in regeneration of the original hmw polymer. Even acidification and washing will give the same result, since H_2S is water soluble as well as volatile and the reversal will occur. It is necessary, as indicated below, to treat the suspension with the sodium sulfite. Sulfite ion reacts with the extra sulfur present to form the stable thiosulfate ion and this serves to force the reaction in the desired direction to give a suspension of stable thiol-terminated product. This is then recovered by acidification and the washing process.

$$—SRSSRSSRSSRS— + SH^- \rightleftharpoons —SRSSRS^- + HSSRSSRS—$$

$$—SRSSRSSH + SO_3{}^{2-} \rightarrow —SRSSRSH + S_2O_3{}^{2-}$$

The molecular weight can be controlled to any desired level by the use of suitable proportions of the hydrosulfide together with the necessary sulfite. Commercial polymers range in molecular weight from as low as 500 to crude rubber in the 100,000 range.

A typical laboratory procedure is as follows: Two liters (2.0 moles is 332 g on a dry-solids basis) of the high-molecular-weight latex prepared as described previously is treated with two-tenths of a mole (18.4 g) of sodium hydrosulfide dihydrate and 2.2 moles (252 g) of sodium sulfite for 60 min at 85°C. The liquid polymer is recovered by adjusting the aqueous suspension to a pH of 6 by addition of acetic acid. The coagulated polymer is washed by decantation with fresh water to remove the last traces of acid. The polymer is then dried at 100°C in a vacuum using a rotating evaporator. The viscosity of the liquid polymer will be approx 300 P. Doubling the sodium hydrosulfide added yields product with a viscosity of 75 P.

Preparation of Copolymers. Random copolymers are fairly readily prepared by using mixed dihalide monomer feed in a conventional polymerization process. Even if there is considerable differential reactivity of the halides, the interchange processes described previously in the homopolymerization section result in a randomization of the polymer structure. Even if there were some tendency to block copolymer formation, under the conditions of the polymerization the rapid interchange processes result in a formation of a completely random polymer. Incidentally, this random polymer also carries the molecular-weight distribution predicted by Flory for interchange in condensation polymerization, that is, the ratio of the weight-average to number-average molecular weight is 2.0.

There is one difficulty in the preparation of copolymers of exact composition from mixed halide feed; it is that if the segment derived from one of the monomers is substantially more soluble than the other, there will be some tendency for this segment to be solubilized into the reaction liquor with consequent minor modification of the copolymer ratio. This problem is circumvented by blending dispersions of the individual homopolymers in the desired ratio, adding a small amount of sodium disulfide to act as interchange catalyst, and heating at 90°C for half an hour to bring about the interchange. Equilibrium in most systems is fairly readily achieved and since minimal amounts of polysulfide ion are used, there is relatively little solubilization. Workup of the copolymer dispersion would be as is conventional for the homopolymers.

If a block copolymer is desired, it cannot be prepared by stepwise addition of the monomers. Interchange during the course of the polymerization results in randomization. The best way to achieve block copolymers is to prepare individual thiol-terminated liquid polymers of the desired molecular weight, blend these in an appropriate proportion, and then co-cure the blended system by conventional techniques. Little or no randomization occurs in the cure process.

Polymer Properties

General Properties. The tensile properties of unreinforced polysulfide polymers are relatively poor. However, in the presence of suitable reinforcing pigments, quite adequate tensile and elongation properties can be obtained. In the case of the thiol-terminated liquid polymers, their molecular weight before cure also affects the resulting physical properties. However, it is difficult to make a direct comparison on the effect of molecular weight on physical properties since the oxidative cure used is different for the various molecular weights. This arises from the nature of the oxidation reaction in which the hmw solid elastomer has a relatively low thiol content and requires rather active curing agents and elevated temperatures for cure, while the intermediate-molecular-weight polymers (about 4000 mol wt) can be cured with a very wide variety of oxidizing agents. The lower-molecular-weight polymers (mol wt about 1000) are so active because of the high concentration of thiol groups so that relatively sluggish oxidizing agents are needed to minimize side reactions from the cure exotherm.

As can be seen from Table 2, the higher tensile strength is obtained with the higher-molecular-weight materials. This is probably because the reduction of the initial hmw disulfide polymer to the thiol-terminated product may introduce small amounts of inert terminals and the proportion of these would logically be greater, the greater the ex-

Table 2. Effect of Molecular Weight on Physical Properties

	Polymer type[a]		
	ST	LP-2	LP-3
polymer	100	100	100
quinone dioxime	1.5		
PbO$_2$		7.5	
MnO$_2$			3
m-dinitrobenzene			1
zinc oxide	0.5		
stearic acid	3		
SRF black (see Carbon black)	60	60	60
cure time	30 min at 287°F	24 hr at RT	24 hr at RT
Physical properties of cured sheets			
tensile strength, psi	1250	900	600
elongation, %	310	450	450
hardness, Shore A	70	65	45

[a] All polymers have the basic structure H-(SCH$_2$CH$_2$OCH$_2$OCH$_2$CH$_2$S-)$_n$H and contain 2 mole % of trichloropropane. ST is a high-molecular-weight elastomer, LP-2 and LP-3 are thiol-terminated liquid polymers having number-average molecular weights of 4000 and 1000, respectively.

tent of reduction.   Furthermore, in the oxidation process the efficiency of the cure
reaction is probably less than 100% and the side reactions would be greater for the
lmw materials with the highest thiol content and, therefore, the greatest effect would be
observed on the properties of these products.

The effect of crosslink density is as expected; the higher the proportion of trifunctional monomer the higher the polymer modulus and the lower the elongation.
Table 3 lists the results obtained with a series of ethyl formal disulfide polymers of
constant molecular weight of approx 4000, in which the percent crosslink is varied.

Table 3. Effect of Crosslinking Agent on the Physical Properties of Polysulfide Liquid Polymers

	Polymer					
	1	2	3	4	5	6
polymer	100	100	100	100	100	100
crosslink, %	4.0	2.0	1.5	1.0	0.5	0.1
SRF black	30	30	30	30	30	30
stearic acid	1	1	1	1	1	1
C-5 catalyst (based on PbO$_2$)	15	15	15	15	15	15
Physical properties of molded sheet						
tensile strength, psi	550	500	550	625	575	500
300% modulus	500	375	350	375	250	200
elongation, %	310	420	700	850	930	1000
hardness, Shore A	55	53	53	53	45	40

The effect of reinforcing filler is quite significant.   Thus, the polymer indicated in
column 5 of Table 3 cured with the same formulation but omitting the SRF carbon
black yields a product with tensile strength of 100 psi and elongation of 250%.   Increasing the filler content from the 30 parts indicated in Table 3 to a 50-part level
results in improvement in properties to a tensile strength of 700 psi and an elongation
of 700%.   There is a limit to the amount of filler that can be incorporated since the
more effective reinforcing agents have a substantial effect on the liquid polymer viscosity and only limited amounts can be added before the system becomes too viscous to
handle properly.

Solvent Resistance.   The first commercially produced elastomer was Thiokol A
(Thiokol Chemical Corp.), ethylene tetrasulfide.   This had outstanding resistance to
most solvents; for example, no more than 5% swell in benzene.   The relatively unpleasant odor combined with poor physical properties limited the growth of this polymer.   Small quantities are still manufactured today but these are used primarily as
plasticizers for sulfur in acid-resistant sulfur cements.   See Sulfur (special uses).

It was found that the polymers of bis-2-chloroethyl formal had greatly improved
odor and this led to the development of a copolymer of ethylene dichloride with bis-2-
chloroethyl formal, Thiokol FA.   This is a linear hmw elastomer plasticized with
benzothiazyl disulfide to control processability.   This still finds a significant market in
hose, printing rolls, and gaskets.   However, the lack of crosslink in the backbone results in a product with no resistance to compression set.

Thiokol ST is the latest product in the evolutionary scale.   This is essentially a
bis-2-chloroethyl formal polymer containing 2% of crosslink derived from 1,2,3-tri-

Table 4. Solvent Resistance of Cured Polysulfide Polymers[a]

Solvent	Vol increase, %			
	LP-2	LP-32	ST	FA
hydrocarbons				
benzene	195	315	110	95
toluene	95	140	70	55
xylene	40	60	40	30
motor oil	<5	<5	<5	<5
diesel oil	<5	<5	<5	<5
aromatic aviation SR-6 gasoline	10	20	15	10
aliphatic aviation SR-10 gasoline	<5	10	<5	<5
esters				
ethyl acetate	40	65	35	20
dibutyl phthalate	30	55	10	7
tricresyl phosphate	10	15	7	5
linseed oil	<5	<5	<5	<5
alcohols and ketones				
ethyl alcohol	<5	<5	<5	<5
n-butyl alcohol	<5	<5	<5	<5
ethylene glycol	<5	<5	<5	<5
ethyl Cellosolve	15	25	15	10
acetone	40	50	35	20
methyl ethyl ketone	55	90	35	30
halogenated compounds				
ethylene dichloride	440	600	230	210
carbon tetrachloride	55	80	45	35
trichloroethylene	275	400	160	
perchloroethylene	30	45	30	
chlorobenzene	270	475	160	150
inorganic systems				
sulfuric acid, 10%	<5	<5	<5	<5
sulfuric acid, 50%	nr	nr	nr	nr
nitric acid, 10%	nr	nr	nr	nr
acetic acid, 10%	15	50	10	50
acetic acid, 50%	25	50	25	40
acetic acid, 100%	25	30	20	20
sodium hydroxide, 10%	<5	<5	<5	<5
sodium chloride, 10%	<5	<5	<5	<5
copper sulfate, 10%	<5	<5	<5	<5
zinc chloride, 10%	<5	<5	<5	<5
water	<5	<5	<5	<5

[a] Immersion for 30 days at 80°F.
NOTE: nr—not recommended. Polymer disintegrates or loses all physical properties.

chloropropane in which the molecular weight has been brought to 75,000–100,000, which is appropriate for mill processing, by reduction of the hmw disulfide latex. This still retains solvent resistance and has good low-temperature properties as well. The compression set performance has been improved because of the network structure but the maximum operating temperature limits are about 100°C. The polymer can be used intermittently at temperatures up to 150°C.

The liquid polymers obtained by more intensive reduction of the formal disulfide suspension yield products with solvent resistance very similar to that of Thiokol ST. This is what would be expected because of the essentially identical backbone. There are differences which arise because the cure of the lower-molecular-weight liquid polymer is usually less efficient than with the crude rubber and this results in a lower effective crosslink in the final product. Therefore, Thiokol LP-2, which contains 2% of crosslink, has about 50–100% greater swell than Thiokol ST.

Table 4 compares the properties of the various polysulfide polymers cured with conventional filled systems. The data are not absolute since results will be somewhat dependent on the efficiency of the cure. Systems that are not properly compounded will show somewhat poorer solvent resistance. If solutions of these polymers are needed, the aromatics, which are among the most effective swelling agents, are commonly used. However, the lower the molecular weight, the better the solubility in less potent solvents. For example, ethyl acetate, which is only a moderate swelling agent, is quite compatible with LP-2; 175 pts of the ester can be added to 100 pts of the liquid polymer.

Low-Temperature Properties. The second-order transition temperature is dependent on the nature of the hydrocarbon moiety and the polysulfide rank. The effect of crosslink density is minor since the proportion of crosslinking monomer used is less than a few percent. Table 5 lists the glass-transition temperatures of the elastomeric polysulfide polymers. The greater the hydrocarbon proportion, the lower the glass-transition temperature; the higher the polysulfide rank, the higher the glass-transition temperature.

Table 5. Glass-Transition Temperatures (T_g)

Polymer	T_g, °C	Polymer	T_g, °C
poly(ethylene disulfide)	−27	poly(pentamethylene disulfide)	−72
poly(ethylene tetrasulfide)	−24	poly(hexamethylene disulfide)	−74
poly(ethyl ether disulfide)	−53	poly(butyl formal disulfide)	−76
poly(ethyl ether tetrasulfide)	−40	poly(butyl ether disulfide)	−76
poly(ethyl formal disulfide)	−59		

The first-order transition is more difficult to pinpoint since the crystallization rate of these polymers is usually very slow. Prolonged storage at low temperatures can bring about density and hardness changes corresponding to partial crystallization. The monomer units containing relatively high proportions of hydrocarbon and having the most regular structures are the most easily crystallized.

Gobran and Berenbaum (4) reported the crystallization behavior of poly(butyl formal disulfide) and poly(butyl ether disulfide) polymers. At −30°C, the crystallization rate of these polymers appeared to be at an optimum. The changes in specific volume with time were studied for the homopolymers as well as for random and block copolymers of the aforementioned monomers with poly(ethyl formal disulfide). The random polymers were prepared by redistributing blends of homopolymer latexes in the desired molar proportions. This procedure is preferred to random copolymerization with the dihalide polymers since differential solubility of the monomer intermediates may result in enrichment of a monomer component in the final polymer. The block copolymers were prepared by co-curing thiol-terminated liquid polymers of about 1000 mol wt as described in the following equation:

$$\text{HSRSH} + \text{HSR'SH} \xrightarrow{[O]} -\text{SRSSR'SSR'SSRSSRSS}\ldots$$

Poly(ethyl formal disulfide) does not give any indication of crystallization in 160 hr at $-30°C$, but poly(butyl formal disulfide) and poly(butyl ether disulfide) show fairly rapid changes in specific volume, up to 1–1.2% shrinkage in 30 hr. The more regular poly(butyl ether disulfide) shows a significantly higher crystallization rate than the corresponding butyl formal polymer containing the relatively flexible formal structure.

A random copolymer containing a 75/25 mole ratio of the poly(butyl formal disulfide) and poly(ethyl formal disulfide) polymers shows no indication of crystallization in the 160-hr test period. Some crystallization will still occur in a block copolymer of this composition, but this small degree of crystallization can be eliminated by increasing the proportion of the second comonomer to a 64/36 mole ratio.

The crystallization rate of the polymers can be accelerated by maintaining the polymer in a stretched condition at low temperature. The principal effect is on the rate of crystallization although some evidence of crystallization will occur with the poly(ethyl formal disulfide) polymer in a temperature retraction test at $-30°C$. In the compositions normally used in practical formulations containing the residues of the curing agents and other compounding ingredients there is little evidence of crystallization with the poly(ethyl formal disulfide) polymers, although the crystallization rate of the polymers derived from monomers containing a greater proportion of CH_2 groups is still quite substantial.

High-Temperature Properties. The thermal stability of the polysulfide polymers is a function both of the polymer backbone as well as the cure used to convert the polymer to the final vulcanized state. Since the commercially available polymers are based on the poly(ethyl formal disulfide) backbone, the characteristics of the ethyl formal structure govern the upper temperature limits for utility (5). The initial attack on this structure is an acid-catalyzed hydrolytic attack on the formal group by trace amounts of water. This reaction releases free formaldehyde which in turn acts as a reducing agent on the polymer disulfide bonds to bring about reduction to thiol with formation of formic acid. Formic acid further catalyzes the hydrolysis at the formal group. The thiol terminal in turn can react with the hydroxyl group to yield a monosulfide bond with the evolution of water which is then available for additional hydrolysis. These reactions are described in the following equations:

$$-SCH_2CH_2OCH_2OCH_2CH_2S- + H_2O \xrightarrow{H^+} -SCH_2CH_2OH + CH_2O + HOCH_2CH_2S-$$

$$-CH_2CH_2SSCH_2CH_2- + CH_2O \xrightarrow{H^+} 2 -CH_2CH_2SH + HCOOH$$

$$-CH_2CHSH + HOCH_2CH_2S- \xrightarrow{H^+} -CH_2CH_2SCH_2CH_2S- + H_2O$$

The consequences of these processes is a weight loss together with a hardening of the polymer which is a result of the formation of the monosulfide structure and loss of the flexibilizing action available through free rotation at the disulfide and the formal bonds. It was shown that in model compounds addition of calcium oxide would stabilize the liquid polymers at temperatures of about 150°C for extended periods of time. The calcium oxide was particularly effective since it was capable of both neutralizing any acid and absorbing any water present in the polymer. This information has not been of practical value since the elimination of water affects the curing systems used with the thiol-terminated liquid polymers. Practical cure rates cannot be achieved in anhydrous systems with any of the metal dioxide curing agents conventionally used with these polymers.

The acidity required to initiate the polymer hydrolysis reaction is believed to arise from the peroxidation of the formal bond and the subsequent breakdown of this intermediate to formic acid and water. This is a free-radical process and can be inhibited in model systems by exclusion of air or by addition of conventional antioxidants. Again, in practical systems there has been no significant effect observed by addition of these antioxidants since the effect of oxygen attack tends to be swamped out by the attack on the polymer backbone of the excess amounts of oxidizing agents that are used in order to bring about commercially useful cure rates. Twice the stoichiometric amount of oxidizing agent may be needed for practical cure systems.

Additional study is needed to develop oxidizing agents which will convert the thiol to disulfide in the desired cure process without attacking either the formal or the disulfide bonds present in the polymer. The substantially improved high-temperature performance of polysulfide polymers converted to the hmw state by reaction with diepoxides or diisocyanates is confirmation of this hypothesis. Unfortunately, these materials are not as fully elastomeric as the disulfide polymer and these addition cures cannot be used in many applications.

Work has been done with hydrocarbon- or ether-containing monomers and these do give somewhat higher temperature operating limits, perhaps as much as a $25°C$ improvement. However, at these higher temperatures, reactions involving the excess oxidizing agent take place and limit further improvement.

One other source of thermal instability arises from incorporation of salt bonds in the polymer backbone from reaction of the thiol terminals with metal oxides. The metal oxides arise as a consequence of the redox processes occurring in the cure with metal dioxides. Reactions for lead dioxide, the most commonly used oxidizing agent, are described below.

$$2 \text{ --CH}_2\text{CH}_2\text{SH} + \text{PbO}_2 \rightarrow \text{--CH}_2\text{CH}_2\text{SSCH}_2\text{CH}_2\text{--} + \text{PbO} \qquad (5)$$

$$2 \text{ --CH}_2\text{CH}_2\text{SH} + \text{PbO} \rightarrow \text{--CH}_2\text{CH}_2\text{SPbSCH}_2\text{CH}_2\text{--} + \text{H}_2\text{O} \qquad (6)$$

$$\text{--CH}_2\text{CH}_2\text{SPbSCH}_2\text{CH}_2\text{--} \xrightarrow{\text{heat}} \text{--CH}_2\text{CH}_2\text{SCH}_2\text{CH}_2\text{--} + \text{PbS} \qquad (7)$$

$$\text{--CH}_2\text{CH}_2\text{SPbSCH}_2\text{CH}_2\text{--} + \text{S} \rightarrow \text{--CH}_2\text{CH}_2\text{SSCH}_2\text{CH}_2\text{--} + \text{PbS} \qquad (8)$$

The lead thiolate structure indicated in equation 6 is responsible for a number of the deficiencies of improperly cured commercial sealants based on this cure. Thiolate–disulfide interchange, which occurs as a consequence of the presence of these groups, has a profound effect on the compression-set characteristics of the product.

Reaction 7, the conversion of the thiolate bond to a monosulfide linkage, is brought about by heat or light. The principal effect of this phenomenon is loss of adhesion although there is some weight loss as well. Equation 8 indicates one way of minimizing the formation of thiolate groups by the incorporation of small amounts of molecular sulfur. Larger proportions aggravate the stress relaxation problem, contribute to thermal instability by the attack of the free sulfur on the hydrocarbon backbone, and adversely affect the adhesion properties of the sealant.

Presence of the thiolate also contributes to weight loss by cyclodepolymerization as in the next equation. Since the thiolate group is generated, the interchange can continue until a major part of the polymer is volatilized.

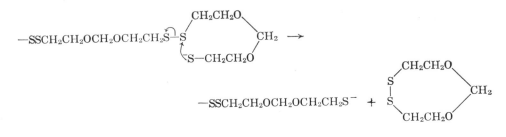

A good many compounding studies have been carried out to find oxidizing agents with fewer side reactions than lead dioxide. Particularly useful are tellurium dioxide, manganese dioxide, and the various chromate salts. Systems formulated with these curing agents will provide continuous service at 250°F and intermittent service at 300°F.

Viscoelastic Properties. The viscoelastic properties of polysulfide polymers have been extensively studied by Professor A. V. Tobolsky, to whom we owe almost everything published on the subject. In his book, *Polymeric Sulfur and Related Polymers* (6), Professor Tobolsky devoted two chapters to a detailed review of viscoelastic properties and chemical stress relaxation of polysulfide rubbers.

The viscoelastic properties of the polysulfide polymers are governed by the interchange chemistry of the polysulfide linkages in the polymer chain. On rapid application of stress, the crosslinked rubbers behave as conventional elastomers. Under fixed strain, interchange processes set in to relieve the stresses. Disulfide–disulfide exchange is relatively slow at temperatures below 150°C or in the absence of ultraviolet radiation. Trace amounts of sulfur, thiolate, or alkaline agents capable of generating thiolates by reaction with the disulfide bonds catalyze the exchange and bring about a relaxation of stress at moderate temperatures.

In addition to the effect caused by ionic mechanisms, polymers containing polysulfide bonds of rank higher than two are particularly susceptible to chemical flow. Tobolsky, MacKnight, and Takahashi (7) have studied poly(ethylene tetrasulfide) crosslinked with 10% of trichloropropane prepared directly as the hmw polymers. It was concluded that the relaxation process in these polymers probably occurs by the exchange of the tri- and tetrasulfide bonds present. Only 6% of the polysulfide linkages need be present as high-rank linkages to explain the observed relaxation times. Work at Thiokol Chemical Corporation confirms the presence of approximately this proportion of higher-rank linkages in polymers with a nominal rank of two.

Processing of Polymers

The solid elastomers are handled in the same fashion as conventional large-volume elastomers. Mill or Banbury (Farrel Corp.) mixing with reinforcing agents and accelerators is straightforward with minor modifications. For Thiokol FA rubber, relatively small batches are used. The rolls are kept warm, at about 65°C, and are set as tightly as possible. After the rubber has been passed through the mill to form a loose sheet, the peptizers are added until the batch sheets out. After the pigments are fully incorporated and when the batch is banding well on the mill, the rolls are opened slightly to keep the stock running smoothly. If blends with other elastomers are being prepared, the latter should be added as a masterbatch at the end of the mix. Thiokol ST rubber is started on a cool mill (35–45°C). No breakdown is required with

Thiokol ST. The compounding ingredients are added as soon as the crude is banded. In extruding both ST and FA, a cool tubing machine with a hot die is recommended. Open steam cure of extruded ST rubber products is recommended, but in the case of FA stocks it is necessary to use pressure wrapping to avoid surface blistering and porosity in the stock. Press cures of products molded from ST can be dropped hot without danger of porosity or pock marking. However, because of the greater thermoplasticity of FA, it is necessary to cool the mold to avoid deforming the product. In the case of ST, postcure for 24 hr at 100°C will improve compression set resistance. Since FA does not contain a true crosslink network after cure, posttreatment cannot improve compression set performance.

Techniques appropriate to the processing of fluids are used with the polysulfide liquid polymers, the procedure depending on the polymer viscosity. Because of the loss in physical properties with decrease in molecular weight, the lower-molecular-weight liquid polymers through the Thiokol LP-3 and LP-33 range (1000 mol wt) are usually used where low viscosity is a primary requirement. For this reason, processing of these polymers is generally relatively simple. In some applications such as leather impregnation or epoxy modification, simple mixing with light-to-medium-duty agitators is all that is required. In casting systems where fluidity is important, the fillers are usually added to the base polymer on a paint mill. The curing agents, such as manganese dioxide or tellurium dioxide, can be predispersed into a curing paste and then added to the polymer in a simple mixing operation.

Processing of the higher-molecular-weight sealant-grade polymers is more complex. Formulations for the Thiokol LP-2 and LP-32 and higher molecular polymers indicated in the section on Physical properties are considerably simplified from practical sealant compounds. A typical sealant will contain as many as three different kinds of fillers, including reinforcing agents, pigments for improved color, and fillers to reduce cost. Similarly, there may be plasticizers to improve low-temperature properties and viscosity characteristics as well as extenders to reduce cost. Viscosity modifiers, thixotropic agents, and adhesion additives are necessary in a properly formulated compound. Careful mixing of the various ingredients is necessary in order to get proper dispersion. In addition, optimum reinforcing properties and thixotropic performance require high-shear continuous-feed units such as colloid mills; the Frenkel mixer or the Marco homogenizer can be used but care is required to avoid excessive heat buildup since it is difficult to get the required degree of cooling in production-scale operations. For heat-sensitive compounds this can be a problem which can best be handled on the more effectively cooled three-roll paint mill. For production economies and greater throughput it is adequate to prepare a preliminary mix of the various ingredients in a change can mixer or some similar piece of blending equipment before final passage through the high shear step. The curing agents to be added to the base sealant compound are usually dispersions of the metal dioxides such as PbO_2, MnO_2, ZnO_2, or CaO_2 with cure rate modifiers in a plasticizer. These cure pastes are usually homogenized on a paint mill or in a ball mill.

With the current trend to one-part systems activated by water in the atmosphere, the processing of sealants has become somewhat more complex. Since humidity will trigger the cure which can then proceed in a chain reaction, it is essential to exclude moisture from the environment during processing or to react all traces of water in the compound before the cure reaction is initiated. Since addition of desiccants to a system to tie up any free water frequently results in a reduction of cure rate, it is preferable to use closed mixing equipment for fast-curing systems.

Field application equipment of sealant depends on the end market. In the building trade, the conventional practice has been to mix two-part systems consisting of the sealant base and curing paste on the job using something like a modified propeller driven by a half-inch electric drill. A few gallons are mixed at a time and then loaded into standard calking cartridges. It is also possible to mix larger quantities of two-part systems at a more convenient location off the building site, load the calking cartridges, and then store these in a freezer. The shelf life at −20 to −40°C is three to six months. The frozen cartridges are delivered to the job, stored in a small ice cream type of freezer and single cartridges are taken out as needed, thawed for a few moments and then handled in a normal fashion (see also Calking and sealing compositions).

With the trend to one-part systems, the mixing and storage problems have been greatly simplified but at some loss of initial performance on the job. Two-part systems cure quite rapidly and will achieve a substantial proportion of their final properties in a few hours. One-part systems which rely on activation by environmental humidity are generally much slower curing, requiring a week or more to achieve a significant proportion of the final properties.

In smaller industrial applications, the manual two-part mixing techniques are used. However, in larger volume production as in automotive windshield sealing, continuous mixing equipment has been successfully used. Similarly, highway and airfield joint sealants require very rapid cures in order to return the job area to traffic service as quickly as possible. This also requires continuous mixing in order to get the necessary cure rate. Heavy-duty positive displacement metering pumps are required to maintain the necessary proportioning. Provision must be made for solvent flushing the mixing head and feed nozzle to prevent the sealant from setting up in the head.

Specifications

Different types of specifications and corresponding test methods are used for the solid rubbers and for the liquid polymers. Specifications on the latex are very simple and relate to percent solids and freedom from extraneous matter. The specifications for the solid elastomers are in Table 6, for the liquid polymers in Table 7, and for the latexes in Table 8.

Table 6. Specifications for Polysulfide Crude Rubbers

Type	Bulk viscosity	Modulus, psi	Min tensile strength, psi	Min elongation, %	Hardness, Shore A	Compression set
Thiokol A	0.130–0.170[a]	450 min at 100% extension	700	200	75–79	
Thiokol FA	0.118–0.150[a]	1000–1250 at 300% extension	1300	400	71 min	
Thiokol ST	25–35[b]	750–1100 at 200% extension	1050	250	70–75	50% max[c]

[a] Williams plasticity (ASTM D926-76).　　[b] Mooney viscosity ML-1 and -3 at 212°F.
[c] ASTM method B.

Table 7. Specifications for Polysulfide Liquid Polymers

Polysulfide polymer	pH	Moisture, %	Viscosity, cP	Sp gr at 25/25°C	Thiol, %	Color (Helige), max	Compounded polymer properties[a]			
							Modulus, psi	Min tensile strength, psi	Min elongation, %	Hardness, Shore A
LP-8	6.5–7.5	0.2 max	290–440[b]	1.10–1.30	as reported					25 min
LP-33	6.0–8.0	0.1 max	1400–1650[c]	1.260–1.280	5.0–6.5	11	170–230 at 300%	350	600	32–38
LP-3	6.0–8.0	0.1 max	700–1200[c]	1.260–1.283	5.9–7.7	12	100–200 at 100%	250	200	30–50
LP-5	6.0–8.0	0.2 max	75–125[c]	1.28–1.30	2.0–4.0	13		300	350	45 min
LP-12	6.5–7.5	0.2 max	350–450[c]		1.3–2.3	12	100 min at 300%	150	650	35 min
LP-32	6.5–7.5	0.1–0.2	375–425[c]			12	150–300 at 300%	225	675	48 min
LP-2	6.5–7.5	0.1–0.2	375–425[c]			14	270–410 at 300%	350	400	50 min
LP-31	6.5–7.5	0.1–0.2	800–1400[c]			12	175–325 at 300%	250	600	48 min
LP-205	6.0–7.5	0.10 max	1300–1810[b]	1.125–1.139	3.5–5.5		80–180 at 300% / 100–300 at 500%	180	600	
LP-370	6.0–8.0	0.10 max	1300–1810[b]	1.110–1.120	4.0–8.0		115–215 at 300% / 150–260 at 500%	180	500	

[a] LP-33 and LP-3 cured for 20 hr at 170°F; LP-32, LP-2, and LP-31 cured for 20 hr at 80°F.
[b] At 25°C.
[c] At 80°F.

Table 8. Specifications for Polysulfide Latexes

Polymer	Dihalide component composition	Particle size, μ	Odor	Solvent resistance	Water resistance
MX	ethylene dichloride propylene dichloride	2–6	very poor	excellent	good
WD-6	ethylene dichloride propylene dichloride	2–6	very poor	excellent	good
MF	ethylene dichloride dichloroethyl formal	4–8	poor	very good	good
WD-2	dichloroethyl formal trichloropropane	8–15	very slight	good	good

Analytical and Test Methods

Most of the test procedures for the determination of properties indicated in the product specifications are straightforward. Only two measurements are at all unusual. The moisture analysis cannot be carried out by the Karl-Fischer method since the thiol terminals of the polymers interfere. Azeotropic analysis using the Dean-Stark trap, while not too sensitive, is adequate for this measurement. The thiol analysis requires some modification from literature methods since the oxidation of the thiol terminals which is the basis for most analyses results in chain extension with precipitation of hmw polysulfide polymer. Polymer formation can foul the electrodes used unless appropriate precautions are taken. The procedure used at Thiokol Chemical Corp. involves the iodometric oxidation of the thiol terminals to disulfide. The end point is detected by a deadstop procedure using as titrant a solution of iodine in benzene. A solvent system of pyridine–benzene is used to dissolve the sample and maintain the polymer formed in solution as long as possible. A small amount of potassium iodide solution in water is added to initiate the electrode response.

Health and Safety Factors

The older crude rubbers based on ethylene tetrasulfide presented some difficulties because of the evolution of lacrimatory fumes during the milling and compounding steps. Inadequate removal of residual traces of lmw sulfur-containing halogenated compounds can cause vesiccant reactions. Neither of these phenomena presents problems in the products now being manufactured.

It might be expected that the lower-molecular-weight thiol-terminated liquid polymers would be more likely to cause difficulty since more intimate contact and a higher diffusion rate are inherent in the fluid. However, toxicological studies have been carried out on LP-32, the 4000-molecular-weight ethyl formal disulfide polymer in greatest commercial use, to ascertain its safety in use with respect to the Federal Hazardous Substances Act. No cautionary labeling is required since the product passes the requirements for acute oral toxicity, eye irritation, and primary skin irritation. Prolonged contact should be avoided and precautionary devices such as protective gloves should be worn by people working intimately with these materials.

Polysulfide-based sealants have been evaluated for their toxicity hazards under catastrophic conditions such as thermal breakdown in a confined space in government-sponsored studies for the nuclear submarine program. The principal gases evolved on thermal degradation are hydrogen sulfide, ethylene sulfur dioxide, and carbon dioxide. However, the rate of evolution of these various compounds was far below the level considered hazardous.

Properly compounded and cured polysulfide systems present little toxicity hazard. For example, dental molding impression compounds are based on LP-2 cured with lead dioxide. Despite the possible toxicity of the lead compound, the short contact time and low solubility of the reagents makes use in the mouth quite feasible. Similarly, the low rate of abrasion of polysulfide–epoxide systems passing Federal Drug Administration (FDA) requirements permits use in coatings coming in contact with dry foods.

Uses and Economic Factors

Solid Elastomers.   Total sales of solid polysulfide elastomers are approx 1.5 million lb a year. Thiokol FA, a copolymer of ethylene dichloride and bis-2-chloroethyl formal selling for $0.71/lb in truckloads, is the largest-volume product. This goes into three principal markets: printing rollers, and hose and gaskets in applications where solvent resistance is critical and where the relatively poor compression-set properties can be tolerated.

Thiokol ST is a disulfide polymer of bis-2-chloroethyl formal containing 2% of branching to improve compression set. This polymer has an excellent combination of low-temperature performance and solvent resistance offset by only fair compression-set and high-temperature properties. The present high price of $1.12/lb (1968) in truckload quantities is a consequence of the limited volume; the price could drop substantially if major new outlets could be developed. The principal market today is in gas-meter diaphragms.

Thiokol A, ethylene tetrasulfide, was the first polysulfide polymer manufactured but is presently used in negligible quantities. The outstanding solvent resistance does not make up for the mediocre physical properties, poor compression set, and unpleasant odor. About the only significant commercial use today is as a plasticizer for sulfur in acid-resistant cements.

Liquid Polymers.   About a dozen or so thiol-terminated liquid polymers are in current production with U.S. sales of more than 10 million lb a year. The principal liquid polymers used in sealant and adhesive applications cost $0.85/lb in truckload quantities and $0.88/lb in less-than-truckload quantities, and range up to $3.48 for LP-370 used as a binder in solid-propellant rockets. Foreign sales are modest but are growing at a somewhat higher rate than in the U.S., as market uses standard here are becoming more widely accepted overseas.

One of the early and more glamorous outlets for the polysulfide liquid polymer was as a fuel in case-bonded solid-propellant rockets. Ability to cast a polymer–oxidizer mix into special configurations designed to control combustion characteristics led to dramatic growth in the volume and in the reputation of the polysulfide polymers. This market has since declined considerably since hydrocarbon binders of greater fuel value have been developed specifically for the rocket market. LP-33 is the workhorse polymer which still finds some application because of the relatively low cost of the rocket fuel, excellent shelf life, and the ease of motor production. LP-205 and LP-370 are special polymers used in limited volume where low-temperature performance in the fuel is necessary.

Polysulfide building sealants are another well-established market. The outstanding aging properties have been an important factor in the penetration of this market. Properly formulated sealant has an expected lifetime of better than twenty years as indicated by sealant installed in the Lever Building in 1954 still looking excellent after fourteen years of exposure in the potent New York City environment. See Calking and sealing compositions.

The increase in curtain-wall construction with greater demands for sealant performance has helped the polysulfide products capture 80% of the high-performance sealant market. The relatively fluid sealants have the advantage over elastomeric gaskets because of the ability to fill the irregularities due to the usual dimensional variations in the structural components of the building. As polysulfide sealant cures to a fairly good elastomer, excellent adhesion is obtained to a number of substrates with bond retention under most weather conditions. The elastomeric properties are essential to withstand the joint dimension changes arising from the thermal expansion–contraction cycle. Polysulfide-base sealants are recommended for joints with movements of up to $\pm 25\%$. The stress relaxation characteristics of the polysulfide polymers may be an advantage where more extensive joint movement takes place such as that arising from settling of a building, since the resulting stresses can be relieved before sealant failure.

The building sealant market is relatively mature and growth now parallels the rate of new construction of institutional and office buildings. Most sealants are still based on two-component formulations but there is a strong trend to the more convenient one-part systems despite the slower cure rate.

Industrial sealant applications are broadening steadily. One of the earliest and still important developments was the use of polysulfide polymers in the sealant for integral aircraft-wing fuel tanks. The elimination of the fuel bladder by converting the entire wing structure to a fuel reservoir necessitated a high-performance solvent-resistant sealant. Polysulfide-based systems are being used today in all major passenger and military aircraft manufactured in the United States. Since they can be easily applied to fill channels, joints, and seams and then set up at room temperature to a solvent-resistant elastomer with good adhesion, polysulfide sealant has been able to capture this market.

The industrial market is a rapidly growing part of the polysulfide sealant business. Automotive windshield sealant is the largest-volume single application. Substantial economies over the old hand-installed solid-rubber gasket can be obtained by automated application of the fluid sealant. Extra benefits are in the better seal achieved by the ability to compensate for the structural variations inherent in production-line dimensional variations and in the structural stiffening derived from bonding the windshield to the frame.

Other important original equipment markets for sealants are truck trailer, marine, and insulating-glass assemblies.

Use of coal tar as an extender has resulted in lower-cost systems with retention of many of the desirable sealant properties. The color and odor have limited its application to heavy construction as in highways, canals, airfield runways, and highway expansion joints. Addition of the polysulfide polymer to the coal tar imparts rubbery characteristics and improved compression-set properties. A number of new applications as coatings or membranes are under development because they are favored by the economics of this low-cost extender.

272 POLYMERS CONTAINING SULFUR

A host of other specialty markets as adhesives and as coating and potting compounds add up to significant but heavily fragmented business.

Bibliography

1. U.S. Pat. 2,532,044 (Nov. 28, 1950), J. F. Walker and T. J. Mooney (to E. I. du Pont de Nemours & Co., Inc.).
2. K. Alexander and H. V. Towles, in A. C. Cope, ed., *Organic Syntheses*, Vol. 30, John Wiley & Sons, Inc., New York, 1950, p. 27.
3. U.S. Pat. 2,796,325 (June 18, 1957), E. R. Bertozzi (to Thiokol Chemical Corp.).
4. R. H. Gobran and M. B. Berenbaum, *Papers Meeting Am. Chem. Soc., 133rd, San Francisco, Cal., April 13–18, 1958.*
5. N. A. Rosenthal and M. B. Berenbaum, *Papers Meeting Am. Chem. Soc., 131st, Miami, Fla., April 7–12, 1957.*
6. A. V. Tobolsky and W. J. MacKnight, *Polymeric Sulfur and Related Polymers*, Interscience Publishers, a division of John Wiley & Sons, Inc., New York, 1965.
7. A. V. Tobolsky, W. J. MacKnight, and M. Takahashi, *J. Phys. Chem.* **68,** 787 (1964).
8. M. B. Berenbaum, "Polysulfide Polymers. I. Chemistry," in N. G. Gaylord, ed., *Polyethers*, Part 3, Interscience Publishers, a division of John Wiley & Sons, Inc., New York, 1962, Chap. XIII.
9. J. R. Panek, "Polysulfide Polymers. II. Applications," in N. G. Gaylord, ed., *Polyethers*, Part 3, Interscience Publishers, a division of John Wiley & Sons, Inc., New York, 1962, Chap. XIV.
10. E. R. Bertozzi, *Rubber Chem. Technol.* **41** (1), (1968).

The reviews by Berenbaum (8) on polysulfide chemistry and by Panek (9) on polymer compounding are the best general references available. The review by Bertozzi (10) is less detailed but more current. See also M. B. Berenbaum, "Polysulfide Polymers," in N. M. Bikales, ed., *Encyclopedia of Polymer Science and Technology*, Interscience Publishers, a division of John Wiley & Sons, Inc., New York (in press).

M. B. BERENBAUM
Thiokol Chemical Corporation

POLYSULFONE RESINS

Sulfones are compounds of the formula RSO_2R'. See Sulfur compounds. Polysulfones contain the sulfone group,

Aliphatic polysulfones can be prepared by radical-induced copolymerization of olefins and sulfur dioxide. These polymers do not have commercial significance, and will not be dealt with here. This article deals with high-molecular-weight (hmw) polyaryl ethers, derived from dihydric phenols, typically 4,4′-isopropylidenediphenol (bisphenol A, see Vol. 1, p. 912) and dihalosulfones, typically 4,4′-dichlorodiphenyl sulfone, DCDPS. These polymers are available from Union Carbide Corporation under their trademark Bakelite.

The Bakelite polysulfones are clear, rigid, tough thermoplastics with glass transitions in the 180–250°C range. Chain rigidity is derived from the relatively inflexible and immobile phenyl and SO_2 groups and toughness from the connecting ether oxygens. These groupings also impart the excellent thermal stability and chemical inertness that characterize these resins. Coupled with the high glass-transition temperatures, continuous use temperatures in the 150–200°C range are realized.

Good thermal stability allows the usual spectrum of thermoplastic processing operations in spite of the high melting temperatures encountered. Both molded objects and extrusions where good thermal stability as well as good electrical properties are required are applications which are particularly suited for the Bakelite polysulfones.

Chemistry of Polymerization. Bakelite polysulfone is prepared (1) according to the following equation, where *n* has values between 50 and 80:

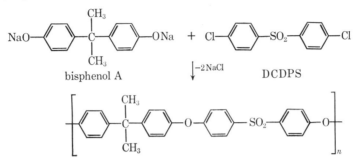

The disodium salt is prepared in situ by reaction of bisphenol A with exactly 2 moles of aqueous caustic soda. A solvent is required for this polymerization and dimethyl sulfoxide, CH_3SOCH_3, is best. Very few others are effective. The reaction must be carried out at 130–160°C, primarily because of the poor solubility of the disodium salt at lower temperatures. Polymerization is, however, very rapid at these temperatures, leading to molecular weights as high as 250,000 in an hour's time. As these molecular weights are too high for commercial processing, chain growth must be

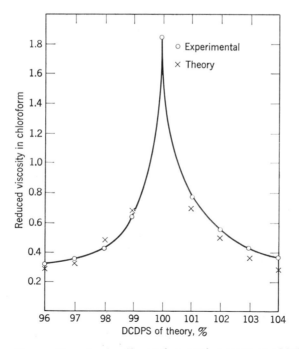

Fig. 1. Preparation of polysulfone using varying amounts of DCDPS.

regulated by the addition of terminators. A variety of monohydric phenolic salts or monohalogen compounds have been found to be effective.

The effect of these terminators is an illustration of the principle of functionality as developed by Carothers (2) in the late 1920s at the Du Pont Company. Thus, in the polysulfone polymerization, the highest molecular weights will be obtained when the mole ratio of comonomers approaches unity. Any deviation results in lowered molecular weights. This is illustrated (Fig. 1) for the plot of reduced viscosity (chloroform solution) for the polymers produced versus the mole percent of DCDPS of theory. The cut-off point for useful mechanical properties is considered to be 0.4 reduced viscosity (reduced viscosity $= (\eta - \eta_0)/\eta_0 c$).

Since the comonomers contain two functional groups per molecule as is required for this type of polycondensation, addition of a compound with only one functional group per molecule will result in an overall imbalance in functionality. The molecular-weight-limiting effect of the terminator depends on its relative reactivity as well as on the amount added.

All but traces of water must be removed from the reaction mixture before polymerization. Hydrolysis (3) of the dihydric phenol salt otherwise occurs, resulting in the formation of sodium hydroxide, which reacts very rapidly with the DCDPS, forming the monosodium salt of 4-chloro-4'-hydroxydiphenyl sulfone,

$$ClC_6H_4SO_2C_6H_4Cl + 2\ NaOH \rightarrow ClC_6H_4SO_2C_6H_4ONa + NaCl + H_2O$$

Two moles of caustic soda (from 2 moles of disodium salt) are used up per mole of DCDPS, which creates an imbalance in functionality between the comonomers. It then becomes impossible to attain high molecular weight.

Another, somewhat less important, side reaction may occur (3) if caustic soda is present during polymerization. Cleavage of polymer chains para to the sulfone groups results in the formation of two phenoxides as shown below for polysulfone:

In this example the sulfone moiety is considerably less reactive toward DCDPS than that from bisphenol A. Also the ratio of available phenoxide to halogen functional groups increases. Both of these factors contribute to lowered molecular weights.

Gross contamination with air must also be avoided. This point has not been investigated in detail but there is little doubt that besides the gross discoloration of the polymer that results, the ability to reach the highest molecular weights would certainly be impaired.

Other aromatic polysulfones are prepared by using the sodium salts of other dihydric phenols, and other aromatic dihalides (1,3).

Other Methods of Synthesis. Until relatively recently the synthesis of aromatic polyethers of truly high molecular weight eluded the efforts of the synthetic organic polymer chemist (4).

In 1959, it was disclosed (5) by scientists at General Electric Co. that 2,6-disubstituted phenols, such as 2,6-xylenol, polymerize to hmw polyethers by the "oxidative-coupling" technique. This discovery is the basis of the polyphenylene oxide (PPO) family of plastics. Shortly after the original disclosure by the General Electric group, Union Carbide scientists discovered a way for making polyaryl ethers containing sulfone groups by a different chemical reaction, aromatic nucleophilic substitution. Another way to make aryl polysulfones has been announced by scientists with ICI Ltd. (6,7), in Great Britain, and at the 3M Company (8) in the United States. These aryl polysulfones are prepared by means of the Friedel-Crafts reaction. Thus, a chlorosulfonated aromatic, such as 4-chlorosulfonyldiphenyl, when mixed with ferric chloride and heated, yields the hmw polysulfone where a sulfone group alternates with the diphenyl rings in the repeat unit. Other examples have been published.

Polymer Properties

Physical and Mechanical Properties (9). Bakelite polysulfone is a rigid, strong thermoplastic which can be molded, extruded, or thermoformed into a variety of shapes. It is both stable and self-extinguishing in its natural form. Polysulfone offers useful properties which are maintained to a high degree over a temperature range from −150 to above 300°F and over extended periods of time. This results in higher use temperatures than are available with other true melt-processable thermoplastics. This is illustrated by the list of maximum service temperatures for some representative engineering materials (Table 1). The physical properties of polysulfone are presented in Table 2.

Table 1. Recommended Maximum Service Temperatures of Typical Structural Materials

Material	Temp, °F	Material	Temp, °F
general-purpose phenolic molding material	300–350	polyphenylene oxide	225–250
polysulfone	300–340	polypropylene	225
polycarbonate	250	polyamides	170–240
zinc die-cast alloy	250	polyacetals	185–220

Table 2. Physical Properties of Polysulfone, at 72°F unless otherwise noted

Property	ASTM method	Av value
color		amber
clarity	D-1003	transparent; 5% haze
refractive index		1.633
odor		none
density, g/cm³	D-1505	1.24
bulk factor (pellets)	D-1895	1.8
flammability	D-635	self-extinguishing
glass transition temp, °C		190
deflection temp (264 psi), °C	D-648	174
Rockwell hardness	D-785	M 69 (R 120)
water absorption (24 hr), %	D-570	0.22
water absorption (equil), %	D-570	0.62
water absorption (equil), %	D-570	0.85 at 212°F
melt flow, g/10 min	[a]	
P-1700		6.5
P-3500		3.5
mold shrinkage, in./in.		0.007

[a] Similar to melt-index test (ASTM D-1238) for lower-melting thermoplastics. Number indicates rate of flow from 0.0825-in.-diam orifice under 44 psi at 650°F.

Polysulfone may be obtained in a variety of colors by compounding techniques or by dry blending where organic soluble dyes are used. Polysulfone is self-extinguishing, as tested in conformance with ASTM D-635, and is classified self-extinguishing group II by the Underwriters' Laboratories. Polysulfone tested for flame resistance according to Federal Test Method Standard No. 406 (method 2023) yielded the following representative values:

ignition time, sec   100   weight loss, %   7.5
burning time, sec   65

The results of mechanical property tests are presented in Table 3. These data describe the behavior of polysulfone under loads applied for relatively short periods of time. Polysulfone has a high tensile strength of 10,200 psi at yield, a high modulus of

Table 3. Typical Polysulfone Mechanical Properties, at room temperature[a]

Property	ASTM method	Value
tensile strength, yield, psi	D-638	10,200
tensile modulus of elasticity, psi	D-638	360,000
tensile elongation, yield, %	D-638	5–6
tensile elongation, break, %	D-638	50–100
flexural strength, yield, psi	D-790	15,400
flexural modulus of elasticity, psi	D-790	390,000
compressive strength, break, psi	D-695	40,000
compressive strength, yield, psi	D-695	13,900
compressive modulus of elasticity, psi	D-695	374,000
shear strength, yield, psi	D-732	6,000
shear strength, ultimate, psi	D-732	9,000
Poisson's ratio, at 0.5% strain		0.37
modulus of rigidity, G, psi		133,000
Izod impact strength,	D-256	
notched, ft-lb/in.		
¼-in. specimen		1.2
⅛-in. specimen		1.3
at −40°F		1.2
unnotched, ft-lb/in.		
⅛-in. specimen		>60 (no breaks)
tensile impact, short specimen, ft-lb/in.^{2}	D-1822	200
falling dart impact,[b] ft		4–5
Rockwell hardness	D-785	M 69 (R 120)

[a] Unless otherwise stated.

[b] Max height required to produce cracks in a 3 × 4 × ⅛ in. specimen on impact by a falling 10-lb cylinder with a ½-in. diam tip.

elasticity in tension, about 360,000 psi, and a 390,000-psi modulus of elasticity in flexure. More rigidity may be obtained by reinforcement with glass fibers. This modification of polysulfone, for example, Sulfil (Fiberfil Inc.), has a flexural modulus of 950,000 psi and an Izod impact of 2.5 at 23°C.

The high strength and ductility of polysulfone impart good toughness and impact resistance to fabricated products. Polysulfone ranks well with other engineering thermoplastics in tensile impact. Impact resistance will be reduced by the presence of sharp radii and abrupt changes in cross section, giving rise to a difference in notched versus unnotched Izod impact. At below room temperature polysulfone retains its toughness. For example, tensile impact is 100 ft-lb/in.^{2} at $-150°$F. As is found for polycarbonates and polyhydroxy ethers, polysulfone exhibits a low-temperature glass transition (minor) at about $-100°$C, in addition to the major transition at $190°$C. Rigid glassy polymers which possess good mechanical properties at room temperature all show this minor transition at low temperatures.

The fatigue endurance limit (10^6 cycles at 1800 cycles/min) at room temperature for polysulfone is about equivalent to the performance of polycarbonate resin but lower than that for acetal or nylon resins. Representative data are given below:

Fatigue endurance, psi		*Fatigue endurance, psi*	
nylon (2.5% moisture)	6000	polycarbonate	1000
acetal (homopolymer)	7000	polysulfone	1000

Thermal Properties. The thermal properties of polysulfone are listed in Table 4. At 264 psi outer fiber stress, polysulfone has a deflection temperature of $345°$F.

Table 4. Thermal Properties of Polysulfone

Property	ASTM method	Value
heat-deflection temp at 264 psi, °F (°C)	D-648	345 (174)
heat-deflection temp at 66 psi, °F (°C)	D-648	358 (181)
coefficient of linear expansion, per °F	D-696	3.1×10^{-5}
thermal conductivity, Btu/(hr)(ft^2)(°F/in.)		1.8
specific heat, at 72°F		0.24
at 320°F		0.37
Vicat softening temp, °F		405
brittle temp, °F		-150

This changes little with stress ($385°$F at 66 psi), showing the ability of this material to remain rigid under load at high temperatures.

For continuous or long-term intermittent operation at high temperatures, it is essential that a material retain a high proportion of its initial properties. Polysulfone does this at $300°$F.

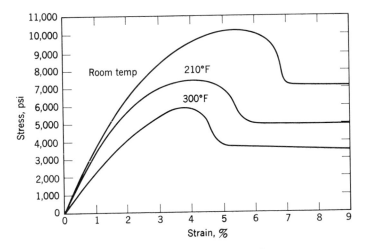

Fig. 2. Polysulfone tensile stress-strain curves.

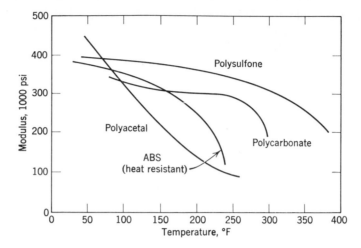

Fig. 3. Flexural modulus vs temperature. NOTE: ABS is acrylonitrile–butadiene–styrene.

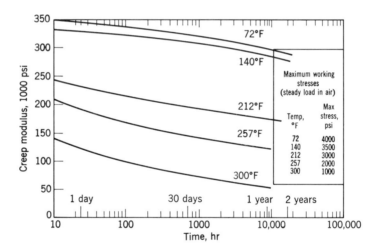

Fig. 4. Creep modulus of polysulfone. Data are obtained from tensile and flexural creep tests in air at the indicated temperatures.

In general, tensile properties such as modulus, tensile strength, and heat deflection increase, and toughness decreases over the period of the aging. These changes are mainly physical in nature as the aged specimens show only minor changes in molecular weight.

The stress-strain behavior at 72, 210, and 300°F is shown in Figure 2. The behavior is typical for a rigid, ductile material.

Flexural modulus of elasticity versus temperature is plotted for polysulfone and some other engineering thermoplastics in Figure 3.

For a thermoplastic material the creep of polysulfone is unusually low, even at elevated temperatures. For design use, it is convenient to express creep data in terms of creep modulus versus time and temperature so that engineering equations may be used to predict long-term behavior. From tensile creep data, creep modulus is determined by dividing the applied stress by the total strain at any time. The creep modulus merely provides a means of taking into account anticipated creep under load and does not mean stiffness is changing. In Figure 4 the plot of creep modulus versus time at various temperatures is given.

Polysulfone can easily be molded to precise dimensions and will retain these dimensions within narrow tolerances.

Electrical Properties. Polysulfone exhibits good electrical properties under a wide variety of conditions as shown in Table 5. These properties are stable up to

Table 5. Electrical Properties of Polysulfone

Properties	ASTM method	Conditions		
		At 72°F and 50% rh	At 72°F after 48 hr immersion in water of	
			122°F	*350°F*
dielectric constant	D-150			
60 cycles		3.07	3.31	2.82
10^3 cycles		3.06	3.29	2.80
10^6 cycles		3.03	3.23	2.73
dissipation factor	D-150			
60 cycles		0.0008	0.0008	0.006
10^3 cycles		0.0010	0.0012	0.003
10^6 cycles		0.0034	0.0073	0.003
			At 95°F and 90% rh after 96 hr at these conditions	
surface resistivity, Ω	D-257	3×10^{16}	2.7×10^{11}	
vol resistivity, Ω-cm	D-257	5×10^{16}	1.6×10^{12}	
arc resistance, sec	D-495			
tungsten electrodes		122		
stainless-steel strip electrodes		22		

Properties	ASTM method	At 72°F after 48 hr immersion in water of		
		122°F	*212°F*	*320°F*
dielectric strength, short time, V/mil	D-149			
130-mil thickness		425	380	530
10-mil thickness		2200		2250 1600
1-mil thickness		7500		8600 6200

350°F. In addition, they are virtually unchanged after exposure to 300 or 340°F for 1½ years' aging.

Chemical and Solvent Resistance. Polysulfone is not soluble in or attacked by aqueous acids or alkalies. Polysulfone dissolves in concentrated sulfuric acid; sulfonation and chain degradation occur upon dissolving. Solubility in aliphatic media is low but some attack by polar compounds will occur. Polysulfone is soluble in most polar aromatic solvents and highly chlorinated compounds in general.

Fabrication of Polysulfone

Rheology of Polysulfone. Unlike many polymers, the melt viscosity of polysulfone is relatively insensitive to shear rate. At low shear rates, low-density polyethylene and polystyrene are considerably more viscous at 210°C than polysulfone is at 375°C. However, as shear rate is increased, the molecules of these polymers tend to orient in the direction of flow, thus permitting easier slippage between the molecules and hence reducing melt viscosity. As a result polyethylene and polystyrene are less viscous than polysulfone at the high shear rates encountered in most polymer processing equipment.

Although the low degree of shear sensitivity gives polysulfone a relatively high melt viscosity under processing conditions, this same phenomenon produces beneficial effects in important properties. For example, the low degree of molecular orientation during flow results in molded parts with uniform physical properties which vary little with the direction of flow. Variation in the strength, toughness, and dimensions of molded parts according to the direction of flow are frequent problems with shear-sensitive polymers. The low shear sensitivity of polysulfone also tends to minimize die swelling in extrusion and blow molding. This can be helpful in the control of size and shape in contour extrusions and in the control of parison dimensions in blow molding (see Plastics technology).

As in other polymers, the melt viscosity of polysulfone is highly temperature-sensitive. A 50°F increase in temperature results in a 50% decrease in melt viscosity. Because of its high heat-distortion temperature and relative insensitiveness to shear rate polysulfone requires relatively high temperatures for processing. Melt stability must be and is excellent in commercial processing equipment at the temperatures found necessary. Polysulfone can be heated in a limited air atmosphere to 400°C for 30 min without appreciable change in melt flow. Polysulfone has flow characteristics similar to those of polycarbonate. Because of this behavior, it has been found that extruders, molding machines, dies, and molds which are used successfully for the processing of polycarbonate usually also give proper processing of polysulfone.

Drying of Polysulfone Before Melt Processing. Polysulfone must be dried before it is molded or extruded. The material absorbs up to 0.3% atmospheric moisture in storage. The moisture content must be reduced to about 0.05% by drying. Otherwise surface streaks, or splash marks will appear on injection-molded parts and extruded forms will exhibit severe bubbling. Moisture, however, does not hydrolyze polysulfone or in any way react with it to cause discoloration, chemical degradation, or deterioration of its physical properties. Parts formed from undried resin will only be unsatisfactory in appearance or in some cases may be weak due to formation of internal bubbles.

Polysulfone may be dried in a circulating hot-air oven or in a dehumidifying hopper dryer. Usually a drying time of 4 hr at 275°F or 2 hr at 325°F suffices.

Molding Methods. Polysulfone can be readily molded in most modern *injection-molding* equipment (10). A high injection pressure is usually required. Stock temperatures required will generally range between 625 and 750°F.

Most commercial *blow-molding* equipment, including constant extrusion, intermittent extrusion, and extrusion-ram accumulator types, is suitable for polysulfone provided they are capable of obtaining the 575–675°F melt processing temperatures.

Polysulfone can be processed on all well-designed conventional *extrusion* equipment (11). It can be extruded as sheet and thin film, as pipe, and as wire coating. Depending on the specific extrusion operation, melt temperatures of the extruded stock will run in the range of 600–700°F.

Polysulfone sheet can be easily *thermoformed* by any of the conventional techniques such as vacuum, pressure, and plug-assist. When using a plug-assist, a temperature of approx 345°F for the plug is recommended.

Annealing. Improvements in thermal (physical) aging properties and solvent crazing or cracking resistance of molded polysulfone parts are afforded by annealing. Annealing relieves molded-in stresses but increases the stiffness properties somewhat. Overannealing can result in a deterioration of impact. Annealing is best performed by immersion in hot (330°F) glycerin for a short time (1–5 min depending on thickness) or in air at 330°F for 3–4 hr. Use of hot molds in injection molding results in less stressed parts.

Joining. Polysulfone sheets or molded parts may be adhered to one another or to metals by direct heat sealing or by solvent fusion. Where applicable, ultrasonic sealing and hot-gas welding are recommended. Heat sealing is done at 700°F. Solvent fusion is done with a 5% solution of polysulfone in methylene chloride as the dope, followed by pressing the parts at 500 psi.

Bibliography

1. R. N. Johnson, A. G. Farnham, R. A. Clendinning, W. F. Hale, and C. N. Merriam, *J. Polymer Sci., Sect. A* **1** (5), 2375 (1967).
2. W. Carothers, *J. Am. Chem. Soc.* **51,** 2548 (1929).
3. R. N. Johnson and A. G. Farnham, *J. Polymer Sci., Sect. A* **1** (5), 2415 (1967).
4. N. G. Gaylord, "Polyacetals and Other Polyethers," in N. G. Gaylord, ed., *Polyalkylene Oxides, High Polymers,* Vol. 13, Part 1, Interscience Publishers, a division of John Wiley & Sons, Inc., New York, 1963, Chap. 7.
5. A. S. Hay et al., *J. Am. Chem. Soc.* **81,** 6335 (1959).
6. M. E. A. Cudby et al., *Polymer* **6,** 589 (1965).
7. S. M. Cohen and R. H. Young, *J. Polymer Sci., Sect. A* **1** (4), 722 (1966).
8. U.S. Pat. 3,321,449 (1967), H. A. Vogel (to 3M Co.); Brit. Pat. 1,060,546 (1967).
9. T. E. Bugel and R. K. Walton, *Machine Design* **37,** 195 (1965).
10. H. D. Bassett, A. M. Fazzari, and R. B. Staub, *Plastics Technol.* **11** (9), 50 (1965).
11. *Ibid.,* **11** (10), 49 (1965).

NOTE: See also R. N. Johnson, "Polysulfone Resins," in N. M. Bikales, ed., *Encyclopedia of Polymer Science and Technology,* Interscience Publishers, a division of John Wiley & Sons, Inc., New York (in press).

R. N. JOHNSON
Union Carbide Corporation

POLYMETHINE DYES

Polymethine dyes are characterized by compounds in which two polar atoms are connected by a chain of "methine" or "methylidene" groups (1) (see also Cyanine dyes; Color and constitution of organic dyes):

$$[Y—(CH)_n{=}Y]^{+ \text{ or } -}$$

(1)

Further, there is an odd number of atoms in the chain. (NOTE: Compounds are known which have even numbers of carbons in the chain, ie, where n is 2, 4, etc; however, they absorb in the ultraviolet region of the spectrum even where values of n are quite large.) (See ref. 1.) Thus, the individual polymethine dyes are members of a vinylogous series (2), differing only by the number of vinyl residues in the chain. In this case,

$$[Y—(CH{=}CH)_n—CH{=}Y]^{+ \text{ or } -}$$

(2)

n is zero or a small whole number (strictly speaking, when n is zero the compound is not a polymethine dye).

The compounds defined by (2) are resonance hybrids which have a high degree of degeneracy (3):

$$\begin{bmatrix} Y—CH{=}CH—CH{=}Y \\ \updownarrow \\ Y{=}CH—CH{=}CH—Y \end{bmatrix}^{+ \text{ or } -}$$

(3)

If Y is nitrogen, (3) becomes an amidinium ion (4):

$$\begin{bmatrix} N—CH{=}CH—CH{=}CH—CH{=}N \\ \updownarrow \\ N{=}CH—CH{=}CH—CH{=}CH—N \end{bmatrix}^{+}$$

(4)

When Y is oxygen, (3) becomes a carboxylate system (5):

$$\begin{bmatrix} O{=}CH—CH{=}CH—O \\ \updownarrow \\ O—CH{=}CH—CH{=}O \end{bmatrix}^{-}$$

(5)

Absorption Characteristics. The vinylogs of (3) have relatively narrow absorption bands of high intensity. The peaks of absorption may be in the near ultraviolet, visible, or near infrared regions of the spectrum, dependent on the values of n and individual structural features. Data from (6)—an example of (2) in which the heterocyclic nitrogen atoms of benzothiazole nuclei represent Y (in (6) and similar examples the value of "n" is one less than the value of "n" in (2))—show that with each increase in the value of n the absorption peak moves successively to longer wavelengths. In

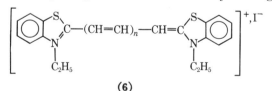

(6)

(**6**), where $n = 1$, the compound is 3-ethyl-2-[3-(3-ethyl-2-benzothiazolinylidene)-propenyl]benzothiazolium iodide (see also Vol. 5, p. 777). Other names for this compound (see below under Nomenclature), found variously in Beilstein, patents, and other literature, are bis[3-ethylbenzothiazole(2)]carbocyanine iodide; bis[3-ethyl-benzothiazole(2)]trimethine cyanine iodide; and, 3,3'-diethylthiacarbocyanine iodide.

	Absorption, maxima
n	*(in methanol)*, $m\mu$
0	423
1	555
2	654
3	756

The 100-$m\mu$ shift with increasing values of n is general. Also, the extinction coefficients usually increase somewhat with the increase of n (2). However, if the terminal groups are not identical (ie, in the case of an unsymmetrical molecule), the shifts become progressively less as values of n increase. Also, the greater the differences between the terminal groups the smaller the shifts with successive values of n. Such vinylogs are of a convergent series.

Solubility. Dyes of the type of (**6**) are usually prepared with iodide as the anion. As iodide salts, the dyes are insoluble in ether and are very sparingly soluble in water. Their solubility in the lower alcohols at room temperature is also low but adequate for application (see below under Uses). Some water solubility can be attained by preparing the dye with a different anion, for example, as the chloride. Dyes as perchlorates, on the other hand, have lower solubilities.

History. In 1856, Williams (3) accidentally prepared (**7**) in experiments with the amyl iodide quaternary salt of crude quinoline:

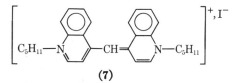

(**7**)

The blue color led to the use of the term "cyanine" (from the Greek *kyanos*, dark blue) in reference to the dye. Since then, "cyanine" has become the general name of the group of related dyes even though they may be obtained in many colors (4) (see Cyanine dyes). This compound, (**7**), is a true cyanine (see below), a subclass of polymethine dyes. Often, the term cyanine is used loosely to refer to other subclasses which have the same heterocyclic nuclei.

SUBCLASSES OF POLYMETHINE DYES

Some of the other nitrogen-containing nuclei whose nitrogen atoms may be substituted for Y in (**2**), as illustrated by the benzothiazole moiety in (**6**), are shown in Figure 1.

True Cyanines. By definition, (**2**) becomes a cyanine when the polar atom, Y, is a member of a cyclic group. Also, at least the first and last carbons of the carbon chain, ie, those adjacent to the nitrogens, are members of the cyclic groups. See (**6**) and (**7**). The cyanine class of dyes as illustrated by (**6**) and (**7**) is very important and is perhaps the most widely investigated of polymethine dyes.

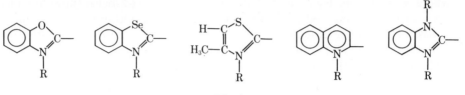

Fig. 1

Pyranines (**8**) represent another cationic series. An example is 4-[3-(2-phenyl-4H-1-benzopyran-4-ylidene)propenyl]flavylium perchlorate (CA), where $n = 1$. Other names for this compound include (bis-4-flavylo)trimethinecyanine perchlorate;

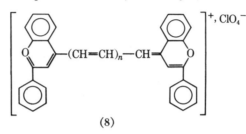

(**8**)

bis(2-phenylbenzopyran)trimethinepyranine perchlorate; and, 2,2′-diphenylbenzo-pyranocarbocyanine perchlorate. Absorption data (6) show the higher vinylogs of (**8**) (**5**) to absorb in the near infrared.

n	Absorption, maxima (in acetic acid), $m\mu$
0	600
1	703
2	812
3	920

Oxonols, as illustrated by dyes (**9**) and (**10**), are examples of the carboxylate system as defined by (**5**). The term "oxonol" for this series was coined by Brooker (7). Structure (**9**) ($n = 1$) is a typical oxonol: the sodium derivative of 2-[3-(3-hydroxy-2-

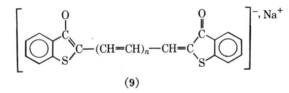

(**9**)

thianaphthenyl)allylidene]-3(2)-thianaphthenone (CA). Members of this particular series were described in early patents (8) for use as sensitizing dyes in photographic emulsions. Oxonols of type (**10**) were patented by Gasper as photographic antihala-tion dyes (9). Often dyes of this class are written in the keto form (**10a**) instead of the preferred enol form (**10b**). Where $n = 0$, (**10a**) is 4,4′-methylidenebis(1-phenyl-3-methyl-5-pyrazolone) (10).

Examples of other "active methylene" compounds which may be used to form oxonols are shown in Figure 2, where W may be O, S, Se, or $>$N–R groups; and R may be H, alkyl, aryl, etc.

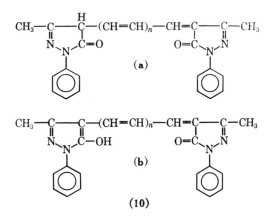

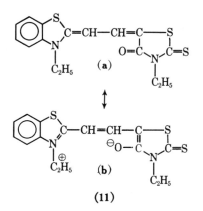

Merocyanines. Dyes which are essentially half cyanine and half oxonol, such as (**11**), were discovered independently in the U.S., England, and Japan in about 1933 (**11**). Hamer of Great Britain named the series "merocyanine" (from the Greek *meros*, part) (**11**).

Sometimes the term merocyanine has been loosely used to refer to the subclass hemioxonols (**12**) shown below. In 3-ethyl-5-[2-(3-ethyl-2-benzothiazolinylidene)-ethylidene]rhodanine (**11**) ($n = 1$), one of the extreme (resonance) structures, (**11a**), is a neutral form—an amide vinylog; the other, (**11b**), is a charge-separation form. In (**11b**) the nitrogen in the benzothiazole moiety has become "quaternary" and cationic in nature and the 4-oxo group of the rhodanine ring has become anionic in character. As opposed to the preceding series, the absorption maxima are materially affected by the solvent. The peaks of absorption in methanol, for example, lie toward the red region of the spectrum with respect to the peaks in acetone. The real molecule (**11**), ie, the resonance hybrid, has properties more like those expected of a structure

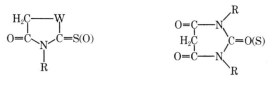

Fig. 2

like (**11a**) than like (**11b**).   Also, in the merocyanine series, the shifts in the absorption peaks with increases of n are less than 100 mμ and get progressively smaller as n increases unless the terminal nuclei can attain resonance stabilization in the charge-separation form.   The nuclei of Figures 1 and 2 are used to prepare merocyanines.

A number of other combinations of groups and heterocyclic compounds can yield polymethine dyes.   The **hemioxonols (12), hemicyanines (13), styryls (14)**, and *p*-**dialkylaminobenzylidenes** (**15**) are typical examples.   (See also the description of rhodacyanines below, p. 288.)

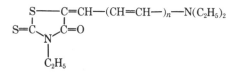

5-(3-diethylaminopropenylidene)-3-ethylrhodanine ($n = 1$)

(**12**)

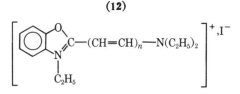

2-(2-diethylaminovinyl)-3-ethylbenzoxazolium iodide ($n = 1$)

(**13**)

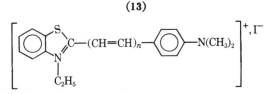

2-*p*-dimethylaminostyrylbenzothiazole ethiodide ($n = 1$)

(**14**)

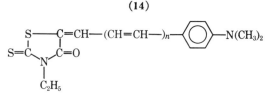

5-*p*-(dimethylaminobenzylidene)-3-ethylrhodanine ($n = 0$)

(**15**)

Of the last four dyes, only the name of (**12**) is free of some form of "common" usage terminology.   "Vinyl" is found in the name of (**13**).   It is used more often than "ethenyl" by polymethine dye chemists.   The term styryl in the common name of (**14**) is used because of the general relationship to the large group of compounds containing the styryl group.   The same custom with regard to benzylidene led to the use of this term in the name of (**15**).   If the values of n are changed in (**14**) and (**15**) and the new compounds are named, the close similarities of (**14**) and (**13**) as well as of (**15**) and (**12**) will become more apparent.

NOMENCLATURE

The first dyes known in the "cyanine" series were made up of quinoline nuclei as in (**17**), (**18**), and (**19**). They were named cyanines with the *N*-substituted groups and the

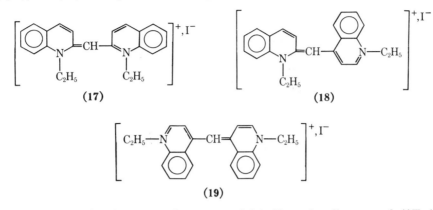

(17)   **(18)**

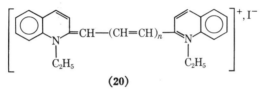

(19)

positions of connection between the two nuclei indicated. Compound (**17**) is 1,1'-diethyl-2,2'-cyanine iodide. In the same manner, (**18**) is 2,4'-cyanine and (**19**) is 4,4'-cyanine.

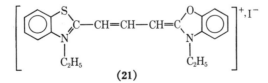

(20)

When there is a three-carbon chain between the nuclei, as in (**20**) ($n = 1$), the prefix "carbo" is added (12). Thus, (**20**) becomes 1,1-diethyl-2,2'-carbocyanine iodide. When n is two (five-carbon chain), "dicarbo" is used (13); when n is three (seven-carbon chain), "tricarbo" (14); etc.

When the chemistry and structures of the above series became better understood, other nuclei (see Figure 1) were used to prepare analogous dyes. The same system of nomenclature was used with the addition of, for example, "thia" for the benzothiazole moiety and "oxa" for the benzoxazole nucleus to give thiacyanines or oxacarbocyanines, respectively, as well as other combinations. Since nuclei such as these are always connected in the 2-positions the 2,2'- is dropped from the names. Thus, (**21**) becomes

(21)

3,3'-diethyloxathiacarbocyanine iodide. This system of nomenclature is very widely followed (15).

Beilstein (16) used a system in which the nuclei are named as in the uncombined condition. In this system (**21**) is [3-ethylbenzoxazole(2)][3-ethylbenzothiazole(2)]-trimethinecyanine iodide. This system is also widely used. The subject indexes of *Chemical Abstracts* list many dyes according to this nomenclature. However, the greater number is listed as follows (using (**21**) as an example): 3-ethyl-2-[3-(3-ethyl-2-benzoxazolinylidene)propenyl]benzothiazolium iodide. This compound can also be named as the benzoxazolium derivative.

The merocyanine (**11**) was named as a rhodanine derivative. The Beilstein system is often used with this class of dyes, and *Chemical Abstracts* lists many in this manner. The name of (**11**) in this system is [3-ethylbenzothiazole(2)][3-ethylrhodanine(5)]dimethinemerocyanine.

Compound (**22**) is a combination of cyanine and merocyanine. Dyes of this type are sometimes called *rhodacyanines*, or *rhodacarbocyanines*, but can be named in

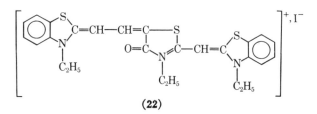

(**22**)

several ways without including rhodacyanine as a part of the name: as two different benzothiazolium salts; as a thiazolidine derivative; or, as a merocyanine. The latter is as follows: [3-ethylbenzothiazole(2)]{[2-[3-ethylbenzothiazole(2)]methyl]-3-ethyl-4-oxothiazoline(5)}dimethinemerocyanine iodide. *Chemical Abstracts* lists such dyes as thiazolidine (thiazolinium) derivatives and as merocyanine salts.

Certain cyanine, hemicyanine, and styryl dyes, relatively lightfast and developed for textile use, are often referred to as *Astrazon* dyes. These are discussed separately (see p. 292).

SYNTHESIS

A number of reactions is available for the preparation of dyes of or related to the cyanine series (see under True cyanines, p. 283). The synthesis of symmetrical dyes, with carbon chains of three or more carbons, can be achieved by the use of ortho esters, diphenylformamidine, 1,1,3,3-tetraethoxypropane (in pyridine), or 3-anilinoprop-2-enanil (in acetic anhydride). Under controlled conditions diphenylformamidine or 3-anilinoprop-2-enanil can be used to prepare intermediates leading to unsymmetrical dyes illustrated by the 3-ethylbenzothiazolium derivative (**23**),

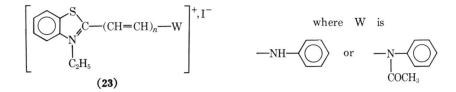

or where W may also be other groups, prepared by other methods, such as $—SCH_3$ or $—Cl$ as specific examples. Compounds analogous to (**23**) can be reacted with active methyl or methylene compounds to yield symmetrical as well as unsymmetrical dyes. The unsymmetrical dye (**24**), 3,3'-diethylselenathiacarbocyanine iodide, is an example of this synthesis route.

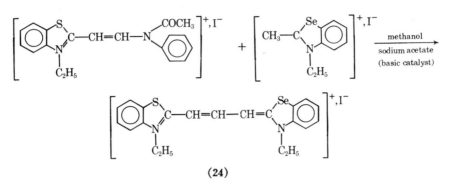

(24)

With certain exceptions (eg, Astrazon dyes, see p. 293) polymethine dyes range from modestly expensive to very expensive. Compounds listed as photographic sensitizing dyes can be purchased as fine chemicals from about $5 to well over $100 per gram. Very small amounts of dye are used in photographic systems (see below). Should there be a need for a dye even in kilogram amounts the costs can be reduced very substantially.

USES

Much of the knowledge related to cyanine and merocyanine dyes was derived through their synthesis and study for spectral sensitization in silver halide photography. Gelatin–silver halide emulsions have an intrinsic sensitivity only to blue light. Hence, sensitivity to longer wavelengths of light must be imparted to them for the design of color films and for superior materials for black- and-white photography. This sensitivity is brought about by incorporating cyanine or merocyanine or certain other dyes in the photographic emulsion. Some members of yet other series of dyes impart an added sensitivity to silver halide emulsions; in general, however, they are comparatively inefficient. Sensitizing dyes are not to be confused with the dyes responsible for the color observed in color prints or transparencies.

The mechanism of optical or spectral (the preferred term) sensitization of silver halide emulsions is not fully understood. From an energy point of view, the longer the wavelength of the radiation the lower the energy per quantum or photon. To be effective as sensitizing dyes, the dyes must be on the silver halide crystals, absorb the desired radiation, and transfer the energy or photon to the crystal. The dye on the crystal (17) absorbs photons having less energy than the photons absorbed by the crystal itself, yet where these photons or their equivalent energy absorbed by the dye become available within the crystal they bring about the same photochemical reaction as that produced by photons of blue light absorbed by the silver halide with or without dye.

A color film is basically put together as a sandwich of at least three emulsion layers (Fig. 3).

Since the green- and red-sensitive layers are also sensitive to blue light, precautions must be taken so that blue light does not get to these layers (see Fig. 3). The spectral sensitizing dyes for the green- and red-sensitive layers (in a suitable solvent, usually methanol for cyanine and acetone for merocyanine dyes) are added to the silver halide emulsion in the liquid state before the emulsion is spread on the support.

Relatively small amounts of dye, which must be of the highest purity, are used. From about 0.005 to 0.050 g will suffice for a kilogram of emulsion as it is spread upon

_____ Blue-sensitive layer

_____ A yellow filter to remove blue light

_____ Green-sensitive layer

_____ Red-sensitive layer

// Support

Fig. 3

the support (a kilogram of emulsion may contain from less than 30 to more than 90 g of silver halide, dependent on the halide, ratio of halides as in a bromo–iodide emulsion, and application of the emulsion). The emulsion layers in color films are approx 3- to 5-μ thick. In black-and-white camera films the layers are generally somewhat thicker.

Most photographic papers, especially materials to make "prints" or "snapshots," are relatively much less sensitive than films used in cameras. The emulsions of such photographic papers usually contain sensitizing dyes but the latter extend the sensitivity to only slightly beyond 500 mμ. Most papers for black-and-white photography can be prepared and processed in "dark-rooms" illuminated with yellow light, ie, illumination containing no blue light.

Some negative films commonly used to make snapshots are made with sensitizing dyes which extend their sensitivity to about 600 mμ. These films can be handled in red light. Materials having this range of sensitivity are referred to as "orthochromatic" films. Black-and-white films sensitive to beyond 600 mμ are "panchromatic" films. The latter as well as color materials must be handled in complete darkness or under very special conditions of lighting.

Almost any desired peak of maximum absorption can be attained by variation in the value of n and by the selection of a heterocyclic nucleus for Y in (2). However, absorption maxima (and peaks of sensitivity) in photographic emulsions lie 25–40 mμ (18) toward longer wavelengths compared to absorption peaks in solution. Dye (6) absorbs at 555 mμ in methanol and sensitizes a silver halide emulsion with a peak of sensitivity at about 595 mμ. Dye (25), 3,3',9-triethylthiacarbocyanine iodide (or (CA) 3-ethyl-2-[2-ethyl-3-(3-ethyl-2-benzothiazolinylidene)propenyl]benzothiazolium iodide), a compound closely related to (6), absorbs at 545 mμ in methanol and, in

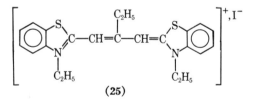

(25)

many emulsions, imparts a peak of sensitivity at about 590 mμ, when absorbed on the silver halide crystals. In certain silver halide systems (usually silver bromoiodide emulsions), however, compound (25) has a peak of sensitivity at about 645 mμ. This sensitization is attributed to the dye absorbed in the form of a J-aggregate (19) on the latter type of silver halide crystals. When a dye responds well in this aggregated state the sensitivity imparted to the emulsion is usually noticeably greater than that of dyes that have the same sensitization maxima but that do not form the J-aggregate.

The formation of J-aggregates may occur in aqueous solutions of certain cyanines, carbocyanines (those substituted on the center of the trimethine chain), and merocyanines. It appears that these planar molecules (planarity is required of efficient spectral sensitizing dyes) form long threadlike crystals by coming together in a close-packed arrangement with their molecular planes parallel to each other. The relationship of the molecules resembles that of the cards in a deck of cards. J-Aggregation is frequently facilitated in gelatin solution, and frequently by adsorption, especially to silver halides (20).

Polymethine dyes are excellent also for the spectral sensitization of other photosensitive systems such as zinc oxide electrostatic materials. The application of dyes to such materials is similar to that in silver halide systems. A noticeable exception is that the coating of the "photosensitive" layer on a support need not be done in darkness; strong light, however, should be avoided. The material becomes sensitive when given an electrical charge in darkness. The exposure is usually made immediately.

Bibliography

"Polymethine Dyes" in *ECT* 1st ed., Vol. 10, pp. 972–976, by E. J. Van Lare and G. H. Keyes, Eastman Kodak Company.

1. L. G. S. Brooker, "Resonance and Organic Chemistry" in *Advances in Nuclear Chemistry and Theoretical Organic Chemistry*, Vol. III in R. E. Burk and O. Grummitt, eds., *Frontiers of Chemistry*, Interscience Publishers, Inc., New York, 1945, p. 99.
2. *Ibid.*, p. 126.
3. C. C. Williams, *Trans. Roy. Soc. Edinburgh* **21**, 377 (1857).
4. C. E. K. Mees, ed., *The Theory of the Photographic Process*, rev. ed., The Macmillan Company, New York, 1954, p. 381 footnote.
5. R. Wizinger and H. V. Tobal, *Helv. Chim. Acta* **40**, 1305 (1957).
6. *Ibid.*, p. 1308.
7. Reference 1, p. 98.
8. U.S. Pat. 2,032,506 (1936), W. Schneider (to Agfa Ansco Corp.); Brit. Pat. 418,561 (1934), W. Schneider (to I. G. Farbenindustrie A.G.).
9. Brit. Pats. 506,385 (1939) and 515,998 (1939), B. Gaspar.
10. A. A. Morton, *The Chemistry of Heterocyclic Compounds*, The McGraw-Hill Book Company, Inc., New York, 1946, p. 445.
11. Frances M. Hamer, *The Cyanine Dyes and Related Compounds*, Interscience Publishers, a division of John Wiley & Sons, Inc., New York, 1964, p. 511.
12. W. H. Mills and F. M. Hamer, *J. Chem. Soc.* **1920** (Vol. 117), 1550.
13. S. Beattie, I. M. Heilbron, and F. Irving, *J. Chem. Soc.*, **1932**, 260.
14. N. I. Fisher and F. M. Hamer, *J. Chem. Soc.*, **1933**, 189.
15. W. West and B. H. Carroll, in T. H. James, ed., C. E. K. Mees, *The Theory of the Photographic Process*, 3rd ed., The Macmillan Company, New York, Collier-Macmillan Ltd., London, 1966, p. 203.
16. F. K. Beilstein, *Handbuch der organischen Chemie*, 4th ed., Springer, Berlin, Vol. 27, 1938.
17. Reference 15, p. 238.
18. *Ibid.*, p. 243.
19. E. E. Jelley, *Nature* **138**, 1009 (1936); **139**, 631 (1937); G. Scheibe, *Z. Angew. Chem.* **49**, 563 (1936); **50**, 51, 212 (1937); reference 15, p. 244.
20. Reference 15, p. 246.

Lee C. Hensley
GAF Corporation

Cyanine, Hemicyanine, and Styryl Dyes

Shortly before World War II, I. G. Farbenindustrie produced certain dyes specifically for printing on acetate rayon (1). They were marketed under the trademark "Astrazon," which included (a) some blue and turquoise dyes (not in the polymethine class at all, but belonging to the triphenylmethane (2) and the oxazine series of dyes) (see Triphenylmethane and related dyes; Vol. 2, p. 864) and (b) orange, red, pink, and violet water-soluble polymethine dyes of the following types: cyanine—see structures (2) and (3) (see also Cyanine dyes); hemicyanine—see (4) and (5) (3); and styryl—see (6), (7), and (8). (See also pp. 282–288.) Some fifteen years later, in the early 1950s, the impact of this type of dye on the dyeing of synthetic fibers could not yet be anticipated.

Only those Astrazon dyes which are in the polymethine class (see group (b) above) are discussed in this article. All of these have the 3H-indole nucleus (1) in common. (Well-known synonyms for 3H-indole are 3-pseudoindole and indolenine.)

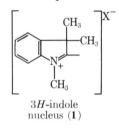

3H-indole
nucleus (1)

The original polymethine-type Astrazon dyes produced had the following structures:

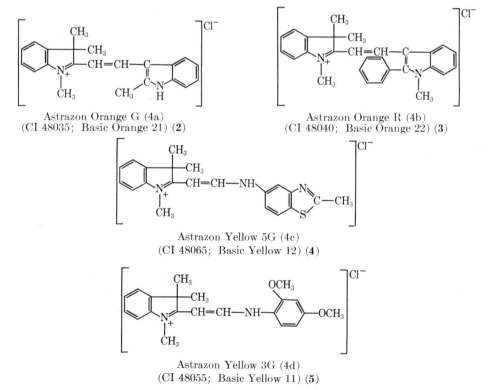

Astrazon Orange G (4a)
(CI 48035; Basic Orange 21) (2)

Astrazon Orange R (4b)
(CI 48040; Basic Orange 22) (3)

Astrazon Yellow 5G (4c)
(CI 48065; Basic Yellow 12) (4)

Astrazon Yellow 3G (4d)
(CI 48055; Basic Yellow 11) (5)

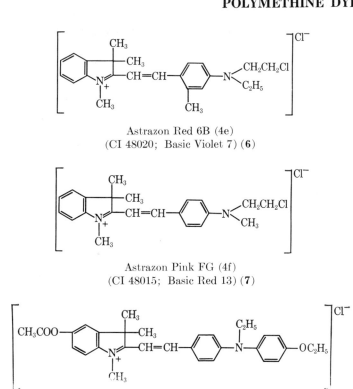

Astrazon Red 6B (4e)
(CI 48020; Basic Violet 7) (**6**)

Astrazon Pink FG (4f)
(CI 48015; Basic Red 13) (**7**)

Astrazon Violet R (5)
(CI 48030; Basic Dye) (**8**)

Although these dyes are outstanding in their brilliancy of shade, they have only moderate fastness on acetate. Thus, they never did achieve any great technical importance as acetate dyes in the past, although lately they have been used increasingly for bright prints, where brilliancy was considered more significant than durability.

However, about 1955, Du Pont brought out several of these dyes for the dyeing of acrylic fibers, on which their fastness properties are considerably better than on acetate. Since then they have continued to grow in use, primarily for the dyeing of acrylic fibers.

Production. Figures reflecting the growing importance of this class of dyestuffs are given in Table 1.

They range in price from $3.50 to $5.50/lb.

Table 1. U.S. Production for Typical Astrazon Dyes,[a] lb

Dye	1962	1963	1964	1965	1966
Basic Yellow 11			332,000	482,000	612,000
Basic Orange 21	135,000	236,000	367,000	358,000	268,000

[a] From U.S. Tariff Commission Reports on Synthetic Organic Chemicals, 1963–1967.

The fact that an increasing number of large dyestuff manufacturers have gone into production of these dyes gives further evidence of their importance. Table 2 lists a number of such manufacturers and their identifying trademarks.

Table 2. Some Manufacturers and Trademarks of Astrazon-Type Polymethine Dyes

Manufacturer	Trademark
Allied Chemical Corporation	Nabor
American Cyanamid Company	Calcozine
Atlantic Chemical Corporation	Atacryl
Badische Anilin- & Soda-Fabrik AG	Basacryl
Ciba Chemical and Dye Company, a Division of Ciba Corporation	Deorlene
E. I. du Pont de Nemours & Co., Inc.	Sevron
Geigy Dyestuffs, Division of Geigy Chemical Corporation	Maxilon
GAF Corporation	Genacryl
L. B. Holliday & Co., Ltd.	Panacryl
Verona Dyestuffs, Division of Verona-Pharma Chemical Corporation	Astrazon

Historically the oldest representative of this class of dyes was prepared in 1924 by W. König, who condensed Fischer's base, 1,3,3-trimethyl-2-methyleneindoline (**9**) (indoline is 2,3-dihydroindole), with ethyl orthoformate in the presence of acetic anhydride (**6**):

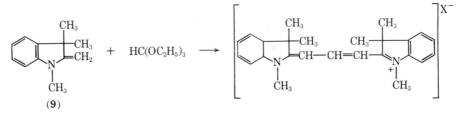

(**9**)

Although this bluish-red dye, known as Astraphloxin FF (CI 48070; Basic Red 12), is outstanding in its brilliancy of shade on animal and vegetable fibers it never achieved any great technical importance because of its relatively poor fastness properties (see also Vol. 6, p. 605).

König's method involving the use of Fischer's base still forms, at present, one of the basic schemes for the manufacture of this class of dyestuffs having the indolenine nucleus. This intermediate warrants more than passing mention because of its importance for that purpose.

Fischer's Base. In 1887 Fischer and his co-workers methylated 2-methylindole with methyl iodide, under pressure, and obtained predominantly what they believed to be a quinoline derivative (**7**). This product became known as Fischer's base. Ten years later, however, Brunner proved the true structure of Fischer's base as follows (**8**): Methyl isopropyl ketone was reacted with 1-methyl-1-phenylhydrazine and the resulting hydrazone was cyclized. Treatment of this product with alkali gave a base which, on addition of hydriodic acid, resulted in a product identical with the corresponding salt of Fischer's base (**9a**):

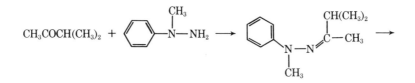

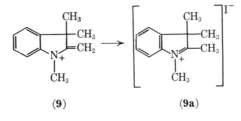

(9)   (9a)

1,3,3-Trimethyl-2-methyleneindoline (**9**) is a colorless oil when first distilled (bp 120°C/20 mm) but rapidly turns to a rose-red color on exposure to air.   Its odor resembles that of quinoline.   It is not soluble in water but dissolves readily in alcohol, ether, chloroform, and benzene.   It dissolves readily in dilute acids to give well-defined salts (9).   On oxidation with a potassium permanganate solution made alkaline with sodium hydroxide or with a sulfuric acid solution of dichromate, it is converted to 1,3,3-trimethyloxindole (**10**).

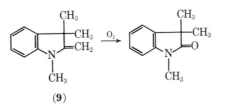

(9)

Recent investigations have shown that prolonged exposure of Fischer's base to air results in its decomposition into 1,3,3-trimethyloxindole and formaldehyde (11):

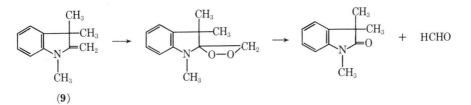

(9)

Fischer's base represents the oldest of the heterocyclic compounds having an active methylene group.   In its properties, it parallels those of acetoacetic ester, malonic ester, and cyanoacetic ester.   For example, it couples with diazonium salts (12),

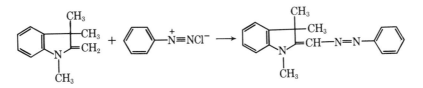

and reacts with acid chlorides (13),

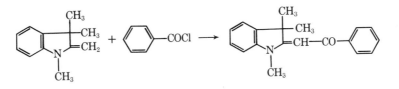

For a more complete review of its reactions, one should refer to Coenen's excellent article on reactions of heterocyclic compounds having a reactive methylene group (14).

PREPARATION OF ASTRAZON–TYPE POLYMETHINE DYES

Intermediates used in the manufacture of the original Astrazon dyes included Fischer's base (**9**), Fischer's aldehyde (**10**), various aromatic amines such as 6-amino-2-methylbenzothiazole (**11**), 2,4-dimethoxyaniline (**12**), the heterocyclic amine 2-methylindole (**13**), as well as the following aromatic aldehydes: 1-methyl-2-phenyl-3-indolcarboxaldehyde (**14**), p-[(2-chloroethyl)methylamino]benzaldehyde (**15**), and p-[(2-chloroethyl)ethylamino]-o-tolualdehyde (**16**).

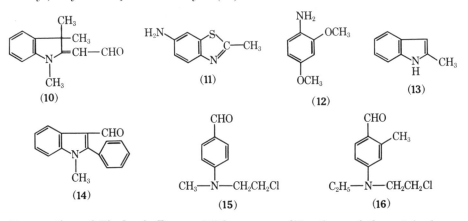

Preparation of Fischer's Base. With some modifications of the original process for the formation of Fischer's base, I. G. Farbenindustrie first manufactured this product by preparing 2,3-dimethylindole and then treating this with methyl bromide (reaction 1).   The 2,3-dimethylindole obtained in this manner was converted into Fischer's base by reaction 2.

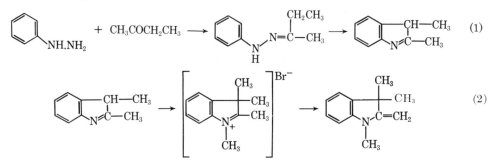

Reaction 1. Briefly, their process was as follows (15): 110 kg of 98.5% phenylhydrazine was added to a 2400-liter lead-lined vessel containing 1350 liters of water and 126 kg of 60° Bé sulfuric acid.   Then, at 85–88°C, under agitation and under the surface, 74 kg of methyl ethyl ketone (2-butanone) was added during the course of 5 hr. During this period, the temperature was maintained at 90–92°C and then held there for another half hour.   The reaction mass was cooled to 60°C and, after addition of 100 liters of cold water, cooled further to 20°C.   Then it was filtered and the cake washed first with 100 liters of cold water, then with 50 liters of sodium carbonate solution and finally washed neutral with water.   The paste of 2,3-dimethylindole then

was dehydrated by heating in a 500-liter enamel vessel. After all the water had been removed, the product was vacuum-distilled, giving 266 kg of indole derivative equivalent to 93% of theory. The product had a setting point of 104.5°C and possessed a very disagreeable odor.

Reaction 2. Into a 400-liter-capacity, lead-lined steel autoclave were charged 109 kg of 2,3-dimethylindole and 54 kg of methanol. The mass was cooled to 5°C, and 100 kg of liquid methyl bromide was added during the course of 3 hr. After all the bromide had been added, the charge was heated as follows: 3 hr at 70°C, 4 hr at 90°C, and finally 24 hr at 100–105°C. At the end of this time, the pressure in the autoclave was about 24–25 atm. The autoclave was cooled to 40–50°C and its contents transferred to a vessel containing 140–150 kg of 30% sodium hydroxide. After heating to 60°C and filtering, the aqueous bromide layer was separated from the oily crude base which then was vacuum-distilled. The fraction boiling at 114–119°C/10 mm was collected, giving about 112 kg of Fischer's base having a purity of 98–99%.

Alternate Methods. It is also possible to treat 2-methylindole with methyl bromide to give Fischer's base, but 2-methylindole is more difficult to methylate than is 2,3-dimethylindole.

Fischer's base may also be manufactured by an application of the Fischer synthesis of indoles utilizing phenylhydrazine and methyl isopropyl ketone. In this process the resulting 2,3,3-dimethylindole was treated with dimethyl sulfate which, on reaction with sodium hydroxide, ultimately gave Fischer's base (Plancher's reaction) (16,17):

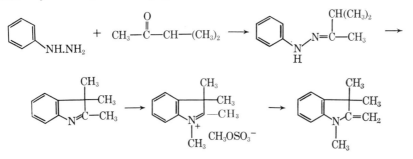

Preparation of Fischer's Aldehyde (10). The I. G. prepared Fischer's aldehyde from Fischer's base by reaction with *N*-methylformanilide and phosphorus oxychloride (Vilsmeier's reaction) (18,19):

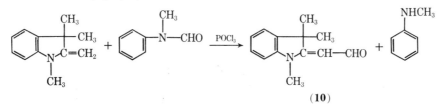

(10)

Procedure. Into a lead-lined iron vessel of 3000-liter capacity, containing 312 kg of Fischer's base (100%), 360 kg of *o*-dichlorobenzene, and 243 kg of *N*-methylformanilide, there was added 280 kg of phosphorus oxychloride. During this addition, the temperature was maintained at 20–25°C, then held for 20 hr, and finally raised to 60–65°C where it was held for 3 to 4 hr. After this, the reaction mass was pumped into a brick-lined iron vessel, having a capacity of 7000 liters, which contained 4000 kg of ice and 990 kg of 45% sodium hydroxide (equal to 446 kg of 100%).

During this period, the temperature was not allowed to rise over 25°C. Then the charge was stirred at 20–25°C for 3 hr, heated to 60°C and allowed to stand for a while. The lower layer thus formed was separated to a copper vessel having a 3000-liter capacity. Here the mass was steam-distilled until no more oil came over. In this manner, 330–340 kg of o-dichlorobenzene and 70–75 kg of N-methylaniline were obtained. The residue, consisting of Fischer's aldehyde, was cooled to 25°C, filtered, and washed with 800 liters of water. The resultant paste was either consumed as such or vacuum-distilled. Thus, 360 kg of a 75% paste was obtained equivalent to a yield of 270 kg of 100% material.

Preparation of Other Aldehydes. N,N-Disubstituted aminoaryl aldehydes, (**14**) to (**16**), also were prepared by the Vilsmeier reaction. However, in more recent times, considerable improvement has been made in the manufacture of such aldehydes by substituting dimethylformamide for the N-methylformanilide (**20**).

I. G. Methods for Astrazon Dyes. Two general schemes were employed by I. G. Farbenindustrie for the manufacture of polymethine-type Astrazon dyes. One involved the use of Fischer's base, the other Fischer's aldehyde.

With Fischer's Base. Typical of the first method is the manufacture of Astrazon Red 6B (**21**):

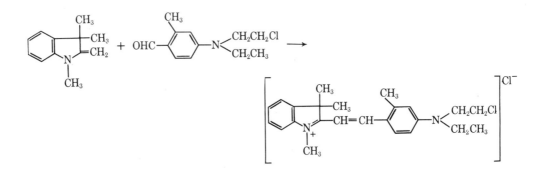

To a 2000-liter enamel kettle were added 500 kg of glacial acetic acid and 250 kg of the aldehyde. The mass then was heated to 80–85°C and 192 kg of Fischer's base added rapidly under agitation. The temperature of the reaction rose to 95–100°C where it was held for half an hour. Then it was added to 8500 liters of cold water contained in a 10,000-liter wooden vat, 2600 kg of salt added, and the precipitated, crystalline dyestuff stirred overnight. The following morning the dye was filtered off and redissolved in 8500 liters of water at 70°C. Then 2600 kg of salt was added to reprecipitate the dye and the reaction mass allowed to cool to 30–35°C. After filtration, the crystalline dyestuff was dried at 30–40°C. In this manner, there was obtained 435 kg of dry dyestuff equivalent to 1450 kg of standardized dye.

In the above reaction, involving the condensation of Fischer's base with an aromatic aldehyde, an improvement in the process results if the reaction is carried out in a water-soluble alcohol, ketone, or ether, all containing from 5–40% of water, and if phosphoric acid instead of glacial acetic acid is used (**22**).

With Fischer's Aldehyde. The manufacture of Astrazon Yellow 3G illustrates the use of Fischer's aldehyde (**23**):

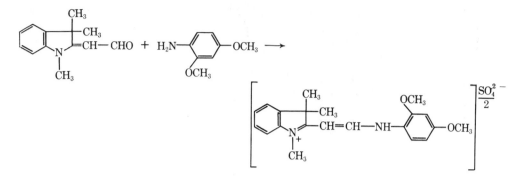

On a lead-lined wooden vessel of 1200-liter capacity, there were added 210 kg of 60% sulfuric acid and 820 kg of 20% sulfuric acid. Then 158 kg of Fischer's aldehyde was added at room temperature and the reaction mass was stirred until all the aldehyde had dissolved. At this point, the amine was added and the mass stirred for 24 hr at room temperature. The crystalline dyestuff that precipitated was filtered off and washed with 3100 liters of 10% salt solution. Then the crude dye was redissolved in a lead-lined vessel containing 11,000 liters of water at 90–95°C. The reaction mass was stirred at 90–95°C with 16 kg of decolorizing charcoal, filtered, 120 kg of 30% hydrochloric acid added to the filtrate, and the charge allowed to cool slowly to 20–25°C with slow agitation. The dye was filtered off, washed with about 100 liters of ice water and dried at 40°C. The yield of dried material amounted to 217 kg which gave 720 lb of standardized dye.

Instead of using sulfuric acid as the condensing agent (as in the above procedure), other acidic reagents such as phosphorus oxychloride or thionyl chloride may be employed (24,25).

A variety of other arylamines have also been condensed with Fischer's aldehyde (26). In general, the resulting shades are all in the yellow to red range.

Bibliography

1. *U.S. Dept. Comm. Office Tech. Serv. PB Rept. 2461*, Appendix 37, 1 (M. A. Dahlen Rept., 1945).
2. K. Venkataraman, *The Chemistry of Synthetic Dyes*, Vol. 2, Academic Press Inc., New York, 1952, p. 713. (The two volumes of this work belong to a series of monographs, "Organic and Biological Chemistry," ed. by Louis F. Fieser and Mary Fieser.)
3. *Ibid.*, pp. 1173–1174.
4. *U.S. Dept. Comm. Office Tech. Serv. PB Rept. 60946* (Aug. 7, 1945), (a) Frame 2408; (b) F. 2409; (c) F. 2407; (d) F. 2406; (e) F. 2410; (f) F. 2411.
5. Reference 1, Appendix 37, p. 7.
6. W. König, *Ber. Deut. Chem. Ges.* **57**, 685 (1924).
7. E. Fischer and A. Steche, *Ann. Chem.* **242**, 353 (1887).
8. K. Brunner, *Ber. Deut. Chem. Ges.* **31**, 612 (1898).
9. *Beilstein's Handbuch der organischen Chemie*, Vol. 20, 4th ed., Springer-Verlag, Berlin, p. 235.
10. G. Giamician and A. Piccinini, *Ber. Deut. Chem. Ges.* **29**, 2467 (1896).
11. B. Robinson, *Chem. Ind.* **1962**, 1291.
12. W. König, *Ber. Deut. Chem. Ges.* **57**, 146, 892 (1924).
13. Brit. Pat. 498,012 (Dec. 30, 1938), M. Coenen (to I. G. Farbenindustrie).
14. M. Coenen, *Z. Angew. Chem.* **61**, 11 (1949).
15. *U.S. Dept. Comm. Office Tech. Serv. PB Rept. 74197*, Frame 751 (Dec. 11, 1945).
16. Reference 1, Appendix 37, p. 1.
17. G. Plancher, *Gazz.* **28**, 405 (1898).
18. Reference 15, Frame 754.

19. A. Vilsmeier and A. Haack, *Ber. Deut. Chem. Ges.* **60,** 119 (1927); Ger. Pats. 614,325 (June 6, 1935) and 615,130 (June 27, 1935), P. Wolff (to I. G. Farbenindustrie).

20. U.S. Pats. 2,437,370 (Mar. 9, 1948) and 2,558,285 (June 26, 1951), C. D. Wilson (to E. I. du Pont de Nemours & Co., Inc.).

21. Reference 15, Frame 170.

22. U.S. Pat. 2,734,901 (Feb. 14, 1956), C. F. Belcher (to E. I. du Pont de Nemours & Co., Inc.).

23. Reference 15, Frame 167.

24. U.S. Pat. 2,126,852 (Aug. 16, 1938), P. Wolff and A. Sieglitz (to Agfa Ansco Corp.).

25. U.S. Pat. 2,164,793 (July 4, 1939), C. Winter and N. Roh (to General Aniline Works, Inc.).

26. U.S. Pat. 2,155,459 (Apr. 25, 1939), C. Winter, N. Roh, P. Wolff, and G. Schaefer (to General Aniline Works).

General References

K. Venkataraman, *op. cit.*

H. A. Lubs, ed., *The Chemistry of Synthetic Dyes and Pigments*, ACS Monograph 127, Reinhold Publishing Corp., New York, 1955, p. 250.

H. R. Schweizer, *Künstliche organische Farbstoffe und ihre Zwischenprodukte*, Springer-Verlag, Berlin-Wilmersdorf (West), 1964, p. 287.

R. C. Elderfield, ed., *Heterocyclic Compounds*, Vol. 3, John Wiley & Sons, Inc., New York, 1952, p. 83.

A. J. Cofrancesco
GAF Corporation

(POLYMETHYL)BENZENES

This article discusses the trimethylbenzenes (hemimellitene, pseudocumene, mesitylene), the tetramethylbenzenes (prehnitene, isodurene, and durene), and penta- and hexamethylbenzene. See also Toluene; Xylenes and ethylbenzene. The parentheses in "(polymethyl)benzenes" indicate that the word does not denote a polymer, but a molecule in which more than one methyl group is attached to a benzene nucleus.

Table 1. Physical Properties

Compound	Specific gravity, 60/60°F	Refractive index (77°F), n_D	Boiling point, °F	dt/dp, °F/(in. Hg) at 1 atm	Freezing point, °F (in air at 1 atm)
benzene	0.8846	1.49792	176.18	1.954	+41.96
toluene	0.8719	1.49414	231.12	2.117	−138.98
o-xylene	0.8848	1.50295	291.94	2.272	−13.33
m-xylene	0.8687	1.49464	282.39	2.242	−54.17
p-xylene	0.8657	1.49325	281.03	2.248	+55.87
hemimellitene	0.8987	1.51150	348.95	2.406	−13.68
pseudocumene	0.8802	1.50237	336.83	2.372	−46.84
mesitylene	0.8696	1.49684	328.49	2.332	−48.50
prehnitene	0.9094	1.5181	401.07	2.51	+20.75
isodurene	0.8946	1.5107	388.40	2.51	−10.63
durene	0.8918[a]	1.5093[a]	386.24	2.47	+174.63
pentamethylbenzene	0.921[a]	1.525[a]	449.2	2.6	+129.7
hexamethylbenzene[b]			506.8		+329.5

[a] For the undercooled liquid below the normal freezing point.

[b] From ref. 1. All other data shown in this table are from ref. 2.

The trivial names and the systematic names of the tri- and tetramethylbenzenes are as follows:

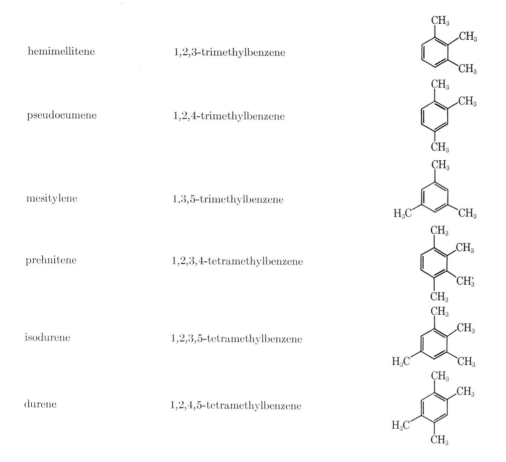

hemimellitene	1,2,3-trimethylbenzene
pseudocumene	1,2,4-trimethylbenzene
mesitylene	1,3,5-trimethylbenzene
prehnitene	1,2,3,4-tetramethylbenzene
isodurene	1,2,3,5-tetramethylbenzene
durene	1,2,4,5-tetramethylbenzene

Properties. Some of the physical properties of benzene and its twelve methyl homologs are given in Tables 1 and 2. Table 3 gives research method octane numbers of some of these compounds. Figure 1 gives the vapor pressure–temperature relationship for all the methylbenzenes, and Figures 2 and 3 illustrate the calculated solubility–temperature relationships for the C_8 aromatics (xylenes plus ethylbenzene) and the tetramethylbenzenes, respectively.

Solubility Curves. The solubility curves shown in Figures 2 and 3 were established from the following relationship:

$$\log_{10} p = 2.00000 - \left(\frac{A}{2.30259}\right)(t_1 - t)[1 + B(t_1 - t)]$$

where A and B are the cryoscopic constants, p is the mole percent of the major component in the mixture, t_1 is the freezing point in °C of the major component when pure in air at 1 atm, and t is the freezing point in °C of the mixture.

From inspection of the above equation, it is somewhat surprising to see that the freezing point depends only on the molar quantities present and not on the nature of the components present. However, it is to be emphasized that the above equation re-

Table 2. Critical Properties (2)

Compound	Temperature, °C	Pressure, atm	Density, g/ml	PV/RT
benzene	289.45	48.6	0.300	0.274
toluene	320.8	40.0	0.29	0.26
o-xylene	359.0	36.0	0.28	0.26
m-xylene	346.0	35.0	0.27	0.27
p-xylene	345.0	34.0	0.29	0.25
hemimellitene	395.0	31.0	0.28	0.26
pseudocumene	381.5	32.0	0.28	0.26
mesitylene	369.0	32.0	0.28	0.26

lating composition of the liquid phase in the solid-liquid equilibrium requires that all the solute (minor component(s)) remain in the liquid phase during crystallization and form with the major component an ideal solution or a dilute real solution.

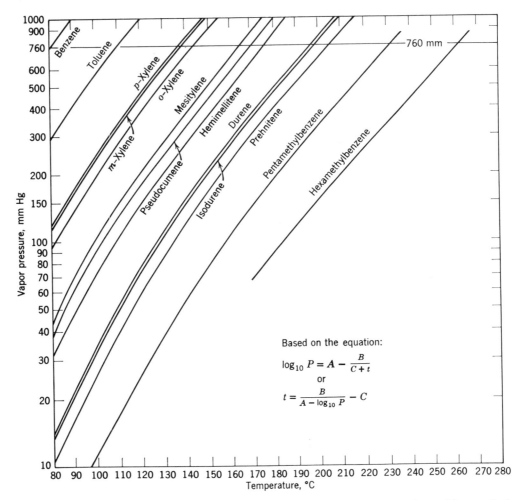

Based on the equation:

$$\log_{10} P = A - \frac{B}{C + t}$$

or

$$t = \frac{B}{A - \log_{10} P} - C$$

Fig. 1. Vapor pressure of the (polymethyl)benzenes. SOURCE OF DATA: penta- and hexamethylbenzene, ref. 1; all others, ref. 2.

Table 3. Octane Data (3)

Aromatic	Research method[a] blending octane number (no TEL added)
benzene	98
toluene	124
o-xylene	120
m-xylene	145
p-xylene	146
hemimellitene	118
pseudocumene	148
mesitylene	170
prehnitene	146
isodurene	154
durene	

[a] Calculated for pure aromatic, based on data obtained with 20% of indicated aromatic in admixture with an 80% mixture of isooctane and n-heptane.

The way in which Figures 2 and 3 can be employed can be illustrated by the following example. Consider a mixture of C_8 aromatics consisting of 15, 20, 25 and 40 mole % ethylbenzene, p-xylene, o-xylene and m-xylene, respectively. From Figure

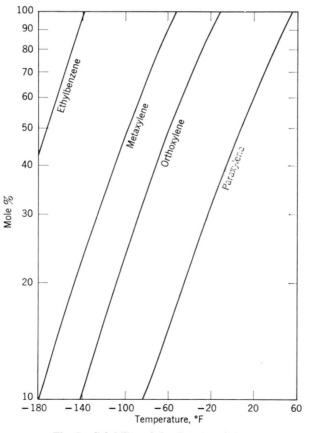

Fig. 2. Solubility of the C_8 aromatics.

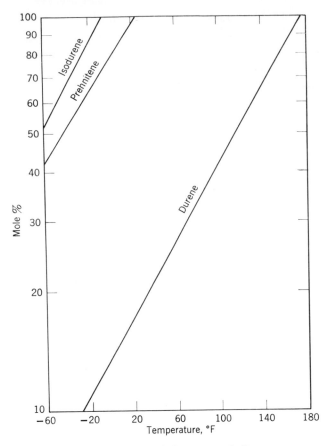

Fig. 3. Solubility of the tetramethylbenzenes.

2, it can be seen that p-xylene will first commence to crystallize from the solution at about $-44°$F. Assume now that the solution is cooled to $-80°$F. The freezing point curve shown in Figure 2 for p-xylene indicates that about 11 mole % of p-xylene is left in solution at $-80°$F. By calculation, the complete composition of the liquid phase at $-80°$F can be ascertained by normalizing the original component concentrations to a value of 89 mole % $(100 - 11)$. Hence 89/80 multiplied by 15.25 and 40 gives 16.7, 27.8 and 44.5 for the concentrations of ethylbenzene, o-xylene, and m-xylene, respectively, at $-80°$F.

One additional piece of information can be obtained by the use of a set of solubility curves such as shown in Figure 2; namely, at what temperature eutectic formation occurs. This is done by a trial and error calculation as carried out above. In the above illustration, for example, if one reads the temperatures from Figure 2 corresponding to the concentrations of 16.7, 27.8 and 44.5, the values are approximately < -180, -88, and $-104°$F, respectively. Hence, it can be concluded that a eutectic is not formed at $-80°$F, since no other component had a concentration sufficiently large to crystallize out at this temperature. By a trial and error procedure, it can be shown that by lowering the temperature to about $-86°$F, eutectic formation is encountered (o- and p-xylene both commence freezing out of solution together). Curves such as shown in Figures 2 and 3 can be employed with a surprising degree of accuracy for appraising crystallization processes. For extreme accuracy, however, the freezing point–composition curve should be obtained experimentally.

Availability and Manufacture. Aromatics in general are present in some crudes, but are more readily available from the products of catalytic reforming and catalytic cracking. Table 4 estimates the amounts available (4).

Table 4. Availability of C_9 and C_{10} Aromatics, Potential from 1000 bbl/CD^a of Crude Oil Processed, gal/year

Aromatic	Virgin	Catalytic reformate	Catalytic cracking	Total potential
C_9's	115,000	145,000	155,000	415,000
C_{10}'s	115,000	90,000	110,000	315,000

^{a} CD = calendar day.

Of the C_9 reformate the percentages of trimethylbenzenes were estimated to be as follows: 1,2,3-, 8.2%; 1,2,4-, 41.3%; 1,3,5-, 7.6%. Among the C_{10}'s, 1,2,3,4-, 5.3%; 1,2,3,5-, 12.7%; 1,2,4,5-, 8.0%.

Pseudocumene can be manufactured from the C_9 reformate by distillation, but durene requires a combination of fractionation plus crystallization. Disproportionation of xylenes may be available for some of the (polymethyl)benzenes. A number of synthetic methods have been considered (5).

Commercial Status. Pseudocumene and durene are produced on a scale of some millions of pounds annually, as raw materials for, respectively, trimellitic anhydride (anhydride of 1,2,4-benzenetricarboxylic acid, see Vol. 15, p. 473) and pyromellitic dianhydride (dianhydride of 1,2,4,5-benzenetetracarboxylic acid, see Vol. 15, p. 480). As of 1968 none of the other (polymethyl)benzenes had achieved significant commercial status (6).

Bibliography

"Polymethylbenzenes" in *ECT* 1st ed., Suppl. 2, pp. 610–655, H. W. Earhart, Humble Oil and Refining Company.

1. T. E. Jordon, *Vapor Pressure of Organic Compounds*, Interscience Publishers, Inc., New York, 1954.
2. *Selected Values of Physical and Thermodynamic Properties of Hydrocarbons and Related Compounds*, API Research Project No. 44, American Petroleum Institute, 1953.
3. *Knocking Characteristics of Pure Hydrocarbons*, ASTM Special Technical Publication No. 225, American Society for Testing Materials, 1958.
4. H. W. Earhart, R. L. Heinrich, E. W. Lewis, T. M. Newsom, and E. F. Wadley, "Manufacture and Utilization of Aromatics from Petroleum," *Paper, 5th World Petroleum Congress, New York, May 30–June 5, 1959.*
5. H. E. Cier and H. W. Earhart, "The Polymethylbenzenes" in K. A. Kobe and J. J. McKetta, eds., *Advances in Petroleum Chemistry and Refining*, Vol. 8, Interscience Publishers, a division of John Wiley & Sons, Inc., New York, 1964.
6. *Oil, Paint Drug Reptr.* **189**(5), 3, 30, 47 (Jan. 31, 1967).

POLYOLS. See Alcohols, polyhydric.

POLYPEPTIDE ANTIBIOTICS

Although numerous antibiotics derived from bacteria, actinomycetes, and fungi (see Microorganisms) have been recorded since the discovery of penicillin in 1929, only about thirty such metabolites have attained any real therapeutic significance. (See also Antibiotics; Bacterial infections, chemotherapy; Chloramphenicol; Macrolide antibiotics; Penicillins; Polyene antibiotics; Streptomycin and related antibiotics; Tetracyclines.) The remainder either proved to be less effective than existing antibiotics or their toxicities were too high for safe medication. Many have been only partially characterized and the purity of others is still open to question.

In this large group of natural products a variety of chemical structures is encountered and one logical approach to their classification is based on biogenetic derivation, as suggested by Abraham and Newton (1). These authors define three major groups, dependent on whether the antibiotics are derived from (a) amino acids, (b) acetates or propionates, or (c) sugars. The members of group (a) can be subdivided according to the number of amino acids involved in their structures, as illustrated in Table 1.

Table 1. Antibiotics Derived from Amino Acids (qv)

From a single amino acid	From two amino acids	From several amino acids	
		Polypeptides	
D-cycloserine	penicillins	tyrocidines	circulins
chloramphenicol	cephalosporin C	gramicidins	thiostrepton
azaserine		bacitracins	actinomycins
alanosine		polymyxins	viomycin, etc

This section deals with the polypeptide subgroup, but even a cursory examination of the literature reveals that a large and growing number of members are involved. Further subclassification becomes essential and this can be based conveniently on structural types, as depicted in Figure 1.

LINEAR PEPTIDES

Relatively few natural antibiotics are linear peptides and exceptions such as gramicidins A, B, and C form a small independent group. Attention of the reader is, however, drawn to the antimicrobial activity of certain synthetic poly-α-amino acids such as poly-L-lysine (207), poly-L-α,γ-diaminobutyric acid (208), and poly-L-aspartic acid (209).

CYCLIC PEPTIDES

Most antibiotic polypeptides possess cyclic structures, distinct however from those involving disulfide bridges such as are found in insulin (qv) and oxytocin (see

Linear peptides — Gramicidins A, B, C.

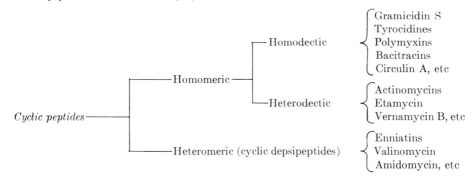

Fig. 1. Structural types of polypeptide antibiotics.

Hormones, posterior-pituitary). In these former structures the terminal carboxyl group of an otherwise linear peptide participates in the cyclization by condensation with an amino or a hydroxyl function at some position along the peptide chain.

An appropriate classification of cyclic peptides has now been adopted, presenting two main groups (2). These are the *homomeric* cyclic peptides, embodying a ring constructed entirely from amino acids, and the *heteromeric* cyclic peptides, in which at least one component of the ring is not an amino acid.

Homomeric Cyclic Peptides. These may be of the *homodectic* type, in which the amino acids in the ring are joined only through amide bonds, or of the *heterodectic* type, in which two or more amino acids present in the ring are joined through bonds other than amide bonds. Thus, in peptide lactones such as the actinomycins, vernamicin B, etc, the "hetero" bond is an ester bond involving the alcoholic hydroxyl function of the amino acid threonine.

Heteromeric Cyclic Peptides. Typical members of this group are the enniatins, valinomycin, and amidomycin, so-called depsipeptides or peptolides, in which the "hetero" units contributing to the formation of the ring are α- or β-hydroxyaliphatic acids.

Other Distinguishing Characteristics. In addition to the presence of these specific cyclic structures, the polypeptide antibiotics differ in other respects from the proteins and polypeptides having hormonal and other functions in higher animals (see Hormones). They may contain an uncommon amino acid, ie, one not found in proteins (eg, α,γ-diaminobutyric acid in the polymyxins) or a nonamino acid component (eg, ethanolamine in certain gramicidins). The presence of one or more amino acids having the D-configuration appears to be a prerequisite in promoting antibiotic activity (see Vol. 2, pp. 175–176, 187). Many of these antibiotics are complex mixtures of related polypeptides, forming mixed crystals or aggregates and requiring elaborate methods of separation, such as countercurrent distribution, which may be prohibitively expensive or even impracticable on a large scale. A number of antibiotics are therefore unresolved mixtures of a number of biologically active components, purified to the extent of removing toxic or inert contaminants.

ESTABLISHED ANTIBIOTICS—SCOPE OF THE DISCUSSION

The peptide antibiotics are produced by fermentation, the basic principles of which are described in more general articles (see Antibiotics; Fermentation). Certain

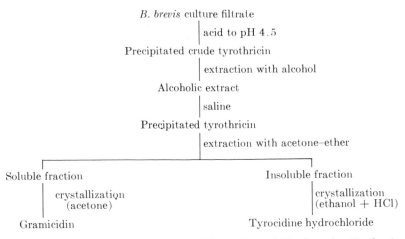

Fig. 2. Flowsheet of the extraction of tyrocidine and gramicidin from *Bacillus brevis*.

details pertaining to the production in culture and methods of isolation and purification are given, but the reader is referred to the original literature and patents for the more exacting details.

Only those antibiotics which have established applications as antibacterial or antifungal agents in human and veterinary medicine will be discussed in any great detail. Thus, the actinomycins are referred to only briefly, for present interest lies essentially in their cytostatic activity.

Bacitracin, tyrothricin, the polymyxins, viomycin, pristinamycin, and thiostrepton are probably the most important members of the group and are produced commercially. They have narrow spectra of antibiotic activity (see Table 2) and are

Table 2. The Source and Biological Activity of the More Important Polypeptide Antibiotics

Antibiotic	Biological source	Antibiotic spectrum
tyrothricin	*Bacillus brevis*	Gram-positive bacteria, some fungi
bacitracin	*Bacillus subtilis*	Gram-positive bacteria, Gram-negative cocci
subtilin	*Bacillus subtilis*	Gram-positive bacteria
polymyxins	*Bacillus polymyxa*	Gram-negative bacteria
viomycin	*Streptomyces puniceus*	mycobacteria
thiostrepton	*Streptomyces azureus*	Gram-positive bacteria
etamycin	*Streptomyces* spp	Gram-positive bacteria, mycobacteria
pristinamycin[a]	*Streptomyces* spp	Gram-positive bacteria

[a] See also Table 11.

often incorporated with other antibiotics and chemotherapeutic agents to provide polyantibiotic therapy of wider antibacterial range. Tables of compatible mixtures can be found in *The Dispensatory of the U.S.A.* (3). A number of such formulations are included at the end of each section dealing with the individual antibiotics, but it should be borne in mind that trade names tend to change as improvements are made in the prescriptions and the examples serve only to illustrate the types of medications available. Constant perusal of the literature is essential to keep such information up to date.

An important aspect of the use of bacitracin is its addition to the feed of poultry and pigs to produce an increased growth response and more economical use of the feed (4). On the other hand, the application of polypeptide antibiotics in the control of plant diseases has not been encouraging, particularly as the result of poor absorption and phytotoxicity. The reader is referred to the review by Dekker (5) for further details of agricultural applications.

In the discussion of the individual antibiotics which follows, methods of bioassay have been referred to only briefly, but can be found, collectively, and in detail, in such textbooks as *Analytical Microbiology*, edited by Kavanagh (6). Attention is however drawn to the chemical syntheses of a number of these antibiotics and their analogs which have been carried out in recent years. Although probably of no immediate commercial significance, they have provided both absolute proof of structure and valuable insight into structural-biological relationships. Note should also be made of the marked effect of variations in strain of a microorganism on the nature of the antibiotic metabolite it produces. This is particularly emphasized in the sections dealing with the polymyxins and with substances derived from *Bacillus subtilis*.

Antibiotics Derived from *Bacillus brevis*

Tyrothricin was the first antibiotic to be discovered as the result of planned investigations of the metabolic products of microorganisms found in soil. It was extracted by Dubos (7) from cultures of *B. brevis*, a member of the Tyrothrix group of bacteria. Substrates for the biosynthesis of tyrothricin have been reviewed by Lewis and co-workers (8).

It is produced in aerated submerged culture using synthetic media consisting essentially of glucose, amino acids, and mineral salts, or natural media such as corn steep with added glucose and mineral salts. Maximum antibiotic titers of the order of 3 g tyrothricin/liter of filtrate are obtained after fermentation periods of 6–8 days, but the yields vary with different strains of *B. brevis* and changes of cultural conditions. Isolation usually involves adjusting the culture filtrate to pH 4.5–4.8 with hydrochloric acid, when the crude antibiotic is precipitated. The dried solid is extracted with alcohol and the tyrothricin is precipitated from the solution by addition of saline. The product is not homogeneous but separable by extraction with an acetone–ether mixture into a soluble neutral fraction, *gramicidin*, and an insoluble basic fraction, *tyrocidine* (9) (see Fig. 2).

The separation of tyrothricin into gramicidin and tyrocidine marked only the beginning of the work on the metabolites of *B. brevis*. Both these fractions were found to be complex mixtures of polypeptides, and additional antibiotics were isolated from different strains of the same microorganism (see Fig. 3).

Properties. Commercial tyrothricin, a purified unresolved mixture of these two components, with a gramicidin content of about 20%, is a white amorphous powder, practically insoluble in water but soluble in pyridine, methanol, ethanol, acetic acid, and ethylene glycol. Solubility figures for these and other organic solvents have been determined by Weiss et al. (9a). Clear aqueous solutions can be obtained by using formaldehyde or cationic surface-active agents as solubilizers. The solubility of tyrothricin in alcohol and ethylene glycol makes it feasible to prepare stable emulsions for clinical use by adding the requisite amount of the stock solution to isotonic saline or distilled water.

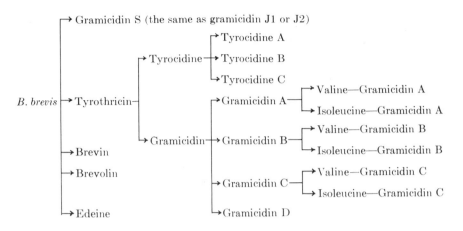

Fig. 3. Antibiotic polypeptides derived from *Bacillus brevis*.

Both dry tyrothricin powder and solutions or emulsions are stable. Thus the dry powder withstands heating at 100°C for 1 hr but the sterilization of solutions and emulsions by heating is not recommended.

The antibiotic gives positive Hopkins-Cole and biuret reactions. Proprietary standards require that the loss of weight on drying for 3 hr at 105°C should be no more than 5% and the sulfated ash no more than 3.5% of the weight of tyrothricin examined.

Clinical Applications. Tyrothricin is very effective in vitro and in experimental infections against many Gram-positive pathogens (9). Unfortunately it has a hemolytic action, due mainly to the tyrocidine, and is therefore not suitable for systemic chemotherapy. The lower but persistent hemolytic action of gramicidin can be further reduced without loss of antibiotic activity by treatment with formaldehyde, which produces a methylol derivative. However, the antibacterial activities of both gramicidin and tyrocidine are inhibited in the presence of plasma, hence fractionation appears to offer little advantage in efforts to obtain a preparation acceptable for parenteral administration. The clinical application of tyrothricin (alone or admixed with other antibacterial agents) is restricted, in general, to local and topical uses. It is readily tolerated by skin and mucous membrane.

A variety of pharmaceutical formulations, emulsions, powders, ointments, troches, lozenges, and dentifrices are available. Special interest lies in the treatment of wounds, ulcers, and upper respiratory tract infections. Ocular infections due to Gram-positive organisms respond satisfactorily to tyrothricin ointments and suspensions. In dermatology, superficial infections due to sensitive organisms may be treated with tyrothricin ointments. When considerable amounts of pus are present, the inclusion of a wetting agent helps to increase the penetration but in extreme cases irrigation may be necessary. Vasoconstrictors are added to suspensions of tyrothricin to provide concomitant decongestion and antibiotic action.

Customary Dosage Levels in Prescriptions

Topically—0.02–0.1% solutions in ointments or creams, 2–4% wt/vol solutions in alcohol or ethylene glycol.

Lozenges and troches—1–2 mg.

Intravaginal suppositories—5 mg.

Some Available Products

Soluthricin (Merck Sharp & Dohme, Ltd.): (Solubilized tyrothricin 25 mg/ml to be diluted with sterile distilled water or isotonic saline.) Used locally—as dressings, drops, spray, irrigation, or instillation into cavities not directly connected to the blood stream.

Unioptal (Unipharma, Ltd.): (Each milliliter containing, in a buffered base, polymyxin B sulfate 6000 units (USP), neomycin sulfate 2 mg, and tyrothricin 0.02 mg.) For superficial bacterial infection of the eye, including conjunctivitis, blepharitis, etc.

Sigatricin (Siegfried S.A.): (Pastilles, containing tyrothricin 1 mg, ethyl *p*-amino-benzoate 3 mg, oil of menthol 2 mg, and benzethonium chloride 0.5 mg.)

Tyrozets (Merck Sharp & Dohme, Ltd.): (Lozenges, containing, in a flavored base, tyrothricin 1 mg and benzocaine 5 mg.) For throat and mouth infections and following tonsillectomy and surgical procedures of throat and mouth.

Pyracord (Lemmon Pharmaceutical Co.): (Hydrocortisone acetate 0.02%, tyrothricin 0.02%, phenylephrine hydrochloride 0.25%, and methapyrilene hydrochloride 0.2%.) Nasal suspension for rhinitis, sinusitis, and common cold.

Tyroderm (Merck Sharp & Dohme, Ltd.): (In a washable cream base, tyrothricin 0.25 mg/g.) Treatment of skin infections caused by Gram-positive bacteria, varicose ulcers, and minor burns.

Tyromist (British Schering, Ltd.): (In an aqueous vehicle, tyrothricin 0.02%, cetrimide 0.05%, and amethocaine hydrochloride 0.05%.) A spray for the relief of common sore throat, laryngitis, and allied conditions.

Veterinary Uses. Tyrothricin has a useful place in veterinary practice and is applied locally in such infectious conditions in animals as bovine mastitis, metritis, infected wounds and burns, superficial skin infections, and infections of the external ear. Intramammary and intrauterine infusions are available for treatment of cattle.

Gramicidin (the gramicidins A, B, C, and D). Gramicidin, the insoluble neutral fraction isolated by treating tyrothricin with a mixture of acetone and ether, was obtained as colorless platelets by crystallization from acetone or dioxan. This so-called gramicidin (Dubos) melted at 228–231°C, had $[\alpha]_D^{25}$ of + 5° (c = 0.17 in 95% ethanol) (9), and in the uv spectra three maxima were observed at 281.5, 290.5 and 271 mμ (ethanol).

Its uses are restricted to those already listed under tyrothricin. There are certain advantages in dispensing gramicidin rather than the unfractionated tyrothricin. A crystalline material is obviously more readily defined and its standardization more precise. In addition, gramicidin is more active biologically than tyrocidine and has therefore replaced tyrothricin to a limited extent in some pharmaceutical preparations.

Some Available Products

Neosporin (Burroughs Wellcome & Co., Ltd.): (Polymyxin B 5000 units (USP), neomycin 2.5 mg, and gramicidin 0.025 mg/ml.) A sterile solution for ophthalmic use.

Biomydrin (Warner-Chilcott Laboratories): (Neomycin sulfate, gramicidin, thonzylamine hydrochloride, and phenylephrine hydrochloride.) A nasal spray with bactericidal, mucolytic, and decongestant action.

Sofradex (Roussel Laboratories, Ltd.): (Framycetin 5 mg, gramicidin 0.05 mg, and dexamethasone 0.5 mg/ml.)   Solution or unguent for ophthalmic use.

Gromidin (Bengué and Co., Ltd.): (Tablets containing 0.25 mg gramicidin.)

Soframycin (Roussel Laboratories, Ltd.): (Nebulizer containing, in isotonic saline, framycetin 12.5 mg, gramicidin 0.005%, and phenylephrine 0.25%.)   Nasal spray.

Spectrocin (E. R. Squibb & Sons, Inc.): (In ointment base, neomycin 2.5 mg and gramicidin 0.25 mg/g.)   Ophthalmic ointment.

The Chemistry of the Gramicidins.   Gregory and Craig (10) first demonstrated that gramicidin was heterogeneous.   By countercurrent distribution, the complex was fractionated into gramicidins A, B, C, and D (11–13).   Gramicidin A was found to be the major component, with B and C each approximating to one-tenth the amount of A. Gramicidin D was a very minor constituent.   Crystallization of gramicidin effects no separation of the components but simply results in the formation of mixed crystals.

Again, although gramicidins A, B, and C were isolated in apparently pure crystalline forms, each has been resolved by additional methods of countercurrent distribution and by partition chromatography into two closely related polypeptides (12,14,15). By sequential analyses of their fragments of partial hydrolysis, these six gramicidins were shown to be linear pentadecapeptides, differing only in the nature of the amino acids at positions 1 and 11 (see Table 3).   Although these peptides possess neither free

Table 3.   The Structures of the Gramicidins A, B, and C

```
                                     15      14     13     12
        CHO                 HOCH₂.CH₂.NH—Try—D-Leu—Try—D-Leu
         |                                                  |
        X—Gly—Ala—D-Leu—Ala—D-Val—Val—D-Val—Try—D-Leu—Y
        1    2    3     4     5    6     7    8    9    10  11
```

	X	Y	Reference
valine–gramicidin A	Val	Try	(16)
isoleucine–gramicidin A	Ileu	Try	(16)
valine–gramicidin B	Val	Phe	(15)
isoleucine–gramicidin B	Ileu	Phe	(15)
valine–gramicidin C	Val	Tyr	(17)
isoleucine–gramicidin C	Ileu	Tyr	(17)

amino nor free carboxyl groups, they are not cyclic peptides, the terminal amino group being formylated and the carboxyl blocked as the ethanolamide.   The valine and isoleucine gramicidins A have been synthesized (18).

Gramicidin S (Soviet gramicidin).   Gramicidin S was isolated in 1955 from a Russian strain of *B. brevis* (19).   The term gramicidin S is an unfortunate misnomer and has given rise to some confusion.   Structurally the antibiotic is completely different from gramicidins A, B, and C and is related to the tyrocidines.   Ideally it should be renamed and included in this latter group of antibiotics.

Gramicidin S is produced in submerged culture and precipitated from the filtrate by addition of hydrochloric acid to pH 4.7.   The dried solid is extracted with alcohol; the solution is treated with activated charcoal, filtered, and concentrated.   Recrystallization from alcohol gives gramicidin S as colorless needles, mp 268–270°C, $[\alpha]_D^{20}$ $= -295°$ ($c = 1.5$ in ethanol).   The antibiotic is insoluble in water, soluble in ethanol and methanol but less so in acetone.   Its structure as the cyclic decapeptide (**1**), formed

$$Val \rightarrow Orn \rightarrow Leu \rightarrow D\text{-}Phe \rightarrow Pro$$
$$Pro \leftarrow D\text{-}Phe \leftarrow Leu \leftarrow Orn \leftarrow Val$$

gramicidin S (**1**)

by the union of two identical pentapeptides, was deduced by analyzing the products of total and partial acid hydrolyses (20). The total synthesis by Schwyzer and Sieber (21) was the first example of the synthesis of a cyclic polypeptide. The two gramicidins J1 and J2, isolated by Otani et al. (22) from two Japanese strains of *B. brevis*, are now recognized as being identical with gramicidin S (23).

Gramicidin S is considered to be more active against staphylococci than tyrothricin (19,24) but suffers equally from the defect of having a hemolytic action. Its comparatively simple structure has led to the synthesis of many analogs (25) and the reader is referred to the original papers for details of the relationship between structure and biological activity.

Tyrocidine (the tyrocidines A, B, and C). Tyrocidine, isolated by fractionation of tyrothricin, crystallizes as a monohydrochloride from ethanol containing hydrochloric acid. Recrystallization from methanol–hydrochloric acid or ethanol–hydrochloric acid gives colorless needles, mp, 240°C; $[\alpha]_D^{25} = -101°$ ($c = 1$ in 95% ethanol).

$$Val \rightarrow Orn \rightarrow Leu \rightarrow D\text{-}Phe \rightarrow Pro$$
$$Tyr \leftarrow Glu \leftarrow Asp \leftarrow D\text{-}Phe \leftarrow Phe$$
$$\qquad | \qquad |$$
$$\qquad NH_2 \quad NH_2$$

tyrocidine A (**2**)

$$Val \rightarrow Orn \rightarrow Leu \rightarrow D\text{-}Phe \rightarrow Pro$$
$$Tyr \leftarrow Glu \leftarrow Asp \leftarrow D\text{-}Phe \leftarrow Try$$
$$\qquad | \qquad |$$
$$\qquad NH_2 \quad NH_2$$

tyrocidine B (**3**)

$$Val \rightarrow Orn \rightarrow Leu \rightarrow D\text{-}Phe \rightarrow Pro$$
$$Tyr \leftarrow Glu \leftarrow Asp \leftarrow D\text{-}Try \leftarrow Try$$
$$\qquad | \qquad |$$
$$\qquad NH_2 \quad NH_2$$

tyrocidine C (**4**)

As in the case of gramicidin, this material, although crystalline, is not homogeneous and Battersby and Craig (26) found that it was separable by countercurrent distribution into three major components, tyrocidines A, B, and C. The structures of these antibiotics have been elucidated (27). They are cyclic decapeptides, very closely related, as seen in formulas (**2**), (**3**), and (**4**). The presence in the tyrocidines and gramicidin S of the common fragment Val–Orn–Leu–D-Phe–Pro suggests a biogenetic relationship. Tyrocidine A has been synthesized (28).

Brevolin (29), a basic polypeptide, was isolated from the culture filtrate of a strain of *B. brevis* by adsorption on activated charcoal at pH 6.8, followed by elution with methanol containing hydrochloric acid. It gives a crystalline reineckate, mp 165°C. On hydrolysis, ornithine, arginine, glutamic acid, histidine, serine, glycine, valine, tyrosine, and leucine were liberated (30).

The antibiotic is nonhemolytic and is active in vitro against *Escherichia coli*, *Staphylococcus aureus*, *Bacillus subtilis*, *Salmonella*, *Shigella*, *Diplococcus*, *Proteus*, *Neisseria*, and *Mycobacteria*.

Brevin (31) is a polypeptide antibiotic containing aspartic acid, glycine, serine, tyrosine, and an unidentified basic substance. It is active in vitro against Grampositive bacteria and mycobacteria.

Edeine is a mixture of basic peptides isolated from cultures of a mutant of *B. brevis* (206). It is a broad-spectrum antibiotic which has been separated by column chromatography into four components, A, B, C, and D, of which edeines A and B are the major components.

Antibiotics Derived from *Bacillus subtilis*

Some twenty different antibiotic polypeptides have been isolated from the bio-synthetic products elaborated by different strains of *B. subtilis* (see Table 4) but only

Table 4. Antibiotics Produced by Strains of *Bacillus subtilis*

Antibiotic	Activity (in vitro)	Properties, etc	Ref.
aterrimins	Gram-positive bacteria	lactones	32
bacilipin A	*Mycobacterium phlei, Streptococcus pyogenes, Corynebacterium diphtheriae, Salmonella typhi, Escherichia coli*	thermolabile	33
bacilipin B	same as bacilipin A	thermolabile	33
bacillin	streptococci, *E. coli, Diplococcus pneumoniae, Salmonella schottmuelleri*	amorphous, water-soluble	34
bacillomycin A	pathogenic fungi and yeasts	polypeptide	35, 36
bacillomycin B	pathogenic fungi and yeasts	polypeptide	35, 36
bacillomycin C	*Aspergillus niger*	polypeptide	35, 36
bacilysin	mycobacteria, *Streptococcus pyogenes*	amorphous, polypeptide	33
bacitracins	see below		
endosubtilysin	*Streptococcus pyogenes, E. coli,* mycobacteria, *Salmonella typhi*	organic acid	37
eumycin	*C. diphtheriae*		38
fluvomycin	pathogenic fungi, Gram-positive and Gram-negative bacteria	polypeptide	39
fungistatin	pathogenic fungi	amphoteric polypeptide	40
globicin	mycobacteria, Gram-positive bacteria	polypeptide	41
iturins	*Penicillium notatum,* Gram-positive bacteria	polypeptide	42
licheniformins	Gram-positive and Gram-negative bacteria, very toxic in vivo	polypeptides	43
mycobacillin	pathogenic fungi	polypeptide	44
mycosubtilin	pathogenic fungi and yeasts, very toxic in vivo	crystalline polypeptide	45
neocidine	*Streptococcus pyogenes, Bacillus anthracis, Mycobacterium avium*	thermolabile, water-soluble	46
petrin	Gram-negative bacteria		47
subtenolin	*Streptococcus pyogenes, Salmonella typhi, E. coli, Pasteurella pestis*	amorphous, water-soluble	48
subtilin	see p. 000		
subtilysine	*E. coli, Pasteurella, Clostridium septicum*	amorphous, water-soluble	49
toximycin	pathogenic fungi and plant fungi	polypeptide	50
xanthellin	Gram-positive bacteria	thermolabile acid	51
B. 456	pathogenic fungi, produces hemolysis in vivo	polypeptide	52

subtilin, bacitracin, and possibly mycobacillin have stimulated any commercial interest.

Subtilin is a mixture of basic polypeptides produced by a particular strain of *B. subtilis* (NRRL No. B-543) (53). The main component, *subtilin A*, was isolated as an amorphous powder ($[\alpha]_D^{23} = -29$ to $-35°$, $c = 1\%$ in acetic acid) by chromatography on silica gel (54). It is sparingly soluble in water but readily soluble in dilute mineral acids. It is salted out of solution on addition of sodium chloride.

Subtilin A is a cyclic polypeptide of approximate molecular weight 3200, producing on hydrolysis the sulfur-containing amino acids lanthionine and β-methyllanthionine, in addition to the common amino acids glycine, alanine, valine, leucine, isoleucine, proline, phenylalanine, tryptophan, lysine, asparagine, glutamic acid, and sarcosine (54).

The antibacterial activity of subtilin is surpassed by that of other antibiotics and principal applications have been in the canning industry, against heat-resistant spore-forming organisms (55), and in agriculture, to prevent seed rot.

Mycobacillin. This antibiotic (44) was found to be highly active against skin fungi and plant pathogens.

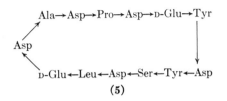

$$(5)$$

Its structure has been given as a *cyclotridecapeptide* (5) (56) in which four of the five aspartic acid residues are of the D-configuration (57).

The Bacitracins. Bacitracin is a complex mixture of water-soluble polypeptides originally isolated from culture fluid of *B. subtilis* var. Tracy (58) and from certain strains of *Bacillus licheniformis* (59). The antibiotic from the latter microorganism was first referred to as ayfivin but the common name bacitracin was adopted (60) when the major components of the antibiotics from the two sources were found to be identical.

It is produced in submerged culture (61) in media consisting essentially of sources of carbohydrate (glucose, starch, or dextrin) and protein (soya flour or peanut flour) and maintained at a pH between 6 and 8. Maximum titers of bacitracin of the order 5 mg/ml are obtained after about 24 hr. The antibiotic is recovered from the culture filtrate by procedures such as countercurrent centrifugal extraction with 1-butanol (62), by precipitation with basic dyestuffs (64), zinc chloride (65), or methylene-disalicylic acid (66), or by adsorption on cationic exchange resins, from which it is eluted with dilute ammonia solution (63). Although bacitracin is considered to have an inherent nephrotoxicity, several methods of purification have been introduced which reduce this toxicity considerably by removing impurities and particularly bacitracin F (67), the nature of which is discussed under The chemistry of the bacitracins (see p. 317).

Properties. Commercial bacitracin is a white amorphous powder, neutral in reaction and somewhat hygroscopic. It is soluble in water, ethanol, methanol, 2-propanol, and 1-butanol but insoluble in acetone, ether, and chloroform. Solubilities have been determined by Weiss et al. (9a).

Bacitracin gives Hopkins-Cole and biuret reactions. Standard specifications require that the loss of weight on drying in vacuo at 60°C for 3 hr be no more than 5% and that the pH of a solution containing 10,000 units of bacitracin per milliliter should be between 5.5 and 7.5. The USP unit of bacitracin is defined as the bacitracin activity given by 26 μg of the dried FDA master standard; commercial medicinal-grade material contains 42–50 units/mg. Biological standardization is based on plate assay, using cultures of *Micrococcus flavus* or *Sarcina subflava* (6,6a).

Bacitracin is stable at temperatures between 25 and 37°C, provided that its moisture content is less than 1%. Maximum temperature of drying appears to be 56°C, after which there is a rapid loss of potency. Aqueous solutions adjusted to pH 5.7 deteriorate rapidly at room temperature and somewhat more slowly when refrigerated. Bacitracin has been stated to be relatively stable in acid solution and to decompose in solution above pH 9. Craig et al. (72,73) have, however, reported changes of stereochemical configuration at pH 4.0 or less, resulting in the formation of products having different antibacterial activities.

Bacitracin is inactivated by oxidizing agents and should not be compounded with such materials. It is incompatible in solution with organic acids such as tannic acid, benzoic acid, and salicylic acid; high concentrations of saline will precipitate the antibiotic.

Insoluble salts such as zinc bacitracin and bacitracin methylenedisalicylate are more stable when dry than the parent antibiotic. Moreover, they are less bitter in taste and hence, being more palatable, are often compounded in oral preparations. Bacitracin methylenedisalicylate contains two moles of methylenedisalicylic acid per mole of bacitracin and has a potency of about 18 bacitracin units/mg. Its solubility in water is about 50 mg/ml and the pH of its saturated solution is 3.5–5.0. Zinc bacitracin contains about 7% zinc and its potency lies between 50–60 units/mg of bacitracin activity; its solubility in water is about 5 mg/ml.

Clinical Applications. Bacitracin is active against most cocci, Gram-positive rods, and some spirochetes. By routes of administration other than parenteral it is virtually nontoxic. Although methods of purification have vastly reduced the nephrotoxicity, intramuscular injections of average or large doses may frequently be followed by renal damage; hence such methods of administration are still regarded with suspicion and restricted, if used at all, to hospitalized cases, with contraindication when preexisting renal damage exists. As measures of precaution, fluid intake is increased to at least 2.5 liters per day in patients receiving parenteral bacitracin, and progressive renal damage with diminished renal output requires prompt withdrawal of the antibiotic. For intestinal amebiasis the oral route is perfectly safe, as bacitracin is not absorbed from the gastrointestinal tract, but the drug is used more widely either topically or locally. Alone, or as an adjunct to therapy with other antibacterial agents, vasoconstrictors, etc, it is dispensed in a wide variety of formulations for dermatological, ophthalmic, dental, otorhinological and surgical uses. It is incorporated in the dressing of adhesive absorbent bandages.

Customary Dosage Levels in Prescriptions

Topically in ointments or solution: 250–1000 USP units/g or ml.

Ophthalmic ointments and drops: 500 units/g or 500–1000 units/ml.

Intramuscularly (im): The safe range for a single dose is 10,000–20,000 units with a maximum total daily dose of 100,000 units. For children the dose should be reduced according to the recognized principles.

Intrathecally, intracisternally, and intracerebrally: a solution of concentration 1000 units/ml in isotonic saline with a total daily dose of 10,000 units.

Intraperitoneally: 20,000 units in 20 ml of sterile isotonic saline.

Some Available Products

Bacidrin (The Upjohn Co.): (Bacitracin 200 units and phenylephrine hydrochloride 2.5 mg/15 ml when dissolved as directed.) Powder for solution. Nasal decongestant, etc.

Baci-troches (The Upjohn Co.): (Bacitracin 1000 units, benzocaine 3 mg/troche.) Acute infections of mouth and throat.

Bacimycin (Walker Laboratories, Inc.): (Neomycin undecylenate 8.7 mg, bacitracin 500 units, hydrocortisone 10 mg, and benzocaine 10 mg/g.) Otic suspension.

Canelettes (Chas. Pfizer & Co., Inc.): (Bacitracin 50 units, polymyxin B sulfate 1000 units, benzocaine 5 mg/troche.) Antibiotic troches for minor throat and mouth irritations.

Tracinets (Merck Sharp & Dohme, Ltd.): (Zinc bacitracin 50 units, tyrothricin 1 mg, and benzocaine 5 mg/troche.) Antibiotic troches for minor throat and mouth infections.

Bacillets (Abbott Laboratories): (Penicillin G potassium 20,000 units and bacitracin 50 units/troche.) Superficial infections of oral cavity.

Mycitracin (The Upjohn Co.): (Bacitracin 500 units, neomycin base 3.5 mg, polymyxin B sulfate 5000 units/g.) Ophthalmic ointment.

Polybactrin (Calmic, Ltd.): (In a spray under pressure, zinc bacitracin 37,500 units, neomycin 750 mg, and polymyxin B sulfate 150,000 units.) Prophylaxis and treatment of sepsis.

Polyfax (Burroughs Wellcome & Co. (U.S.A.), Inc.): (In either topical or ophthalmic ointment, zinc bacitracin 500 units and polymyxin B sulfate 10,000 units.)

Cortisporin (Burroughs Wellcome & Co. (U.S.A.), Inc.): (Zinc bacitracin 400 units, polymyxin B sulfate 5000 units, neomycin sulfate 5 mg, and hydrocortisone 10 mg/g.) Ophthalmic ointment.

Framspray (Fisons Pharmaceuticals, Ltd.): (Zinc bacitracin 10,000 units, polymyxin B sulfate 165,000 units, and framycetin 1 g, as 110 g of pressurized aerosol.)

Fortracin (S. P. Penick & Co.): (Bacitracin methylenedisalicylate.) Veterinary product.

Veterinary Uses. Bacitracin has a wide range of veterinary uses, for instance, as a feed additive (to which reference has been made) and in the treatment of respiratory and enteric infections. It is less effective in mastitis than are other antibiotics.

The Chemistry of the Bacitracins. Commercial bacitracin was separated by countercurrent distribution into a number of components referred to as bacitracins A, B, C, D, E, F, and G (68). Bacitracin F was shown later to be an artifact of low antibacterial activity and high nephrotoxicity, derived from bacitracin A, the major component (69), the structure of which has received most attention and embodies some very interesting features.

On the basis of the amino acid analysis of the total acid hydrolyzate and the sequential analyses of the fragments obtained by partial hydrolysis, the structure (**6**) was first postulated for bacitracin A (70).

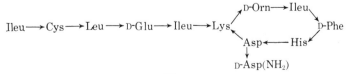

(6)

This cyclic dodecapeptide structure accounted for the detection of only three basic centers, the liberation of 1 mole of ammonia on hydrolysis, and the location of isoleucine as the *N*-terminal amino acid. However, it was not consistent with the absence of a free thiol group in bacitracin and the presence of certain peptides containing the sequence Phe–Ileu in the partial hydrolyzates.

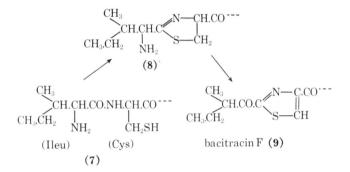

Further evidence was presented which indicated that the isoleucine–cysteine fragment (7) was condensed, as seen in the partial structure (8), to give a thiazoline ring, thereby accounting for the absence of a free thiol group in bacitracin and appearance of this group only after treatment with hot dilute acid (68–70). The conversion of bacitracin A to bacitracin F under mild alkaline conditions was the result of the oxidative deamination of thiazoline (8) to the thiazole analog (9) (69,70).

The phenylalanine–isoleucine-containing peptides present in the hydrolyzates were more difficult to explain, and an "undefined bond" between the D-phenylalanine and the *N*-terminal isoleucine was postulated (71). More recent data (72) suggest an interaction of the thiazoline grouping with the ring phenylalanyl peptide linkage, producing a type of tautomeric or resonating system of linkages. Additional lability in the structure has been demonstrated, when, at pH 4 or less, epimerization of the terminal isoleucine residue occurs, resulting in stereoisomers having different antibacterial activity (73).

The D-aspartic acid was found to be present as the α-amide and the β-carboxyl group of the L-aspartic acid was found to be linked to the ϵ-amino group of lysine (74). The structure of *bacitracin A* is therefore best presented as seen in structure (10) in which the undefined bond is indicated by the dotted line.

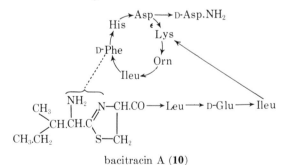

bacitracin A (10)

Although *bacitracin B* is also considered to be a true metabolite, it is not yet certain if bacitracins C, D, and E exist as such in situ or are modified components arising during the extraction and purification procedures (71a). Bacitracin B contains one more L-valine residue than does bacitracin A, but its structure is as yet unknown (70a).

Antibiotics Derived from *Bacillus polymyxa*—the Polymyxins

In 1947, Ainsworth et al. (75) announced the isolation of an antibiotic, aerosporin, from cultures of a soil isolate and simultaneously two American groups, Shepherd et al. (76) and Benedict and Langlykke (77) described an antibiotic, "polymyxin," again derived from soil isolates. A series of cooperative studies (78) revealed that the antibiotics were not identical but closely related chemically and practically indistinguishable biologically. The organisms involved were identified as different strains of *B. polymyxa*.

By mutual agreement, the generic name polymyxin was adopted (79). "Aerosporin" was renamed polymyxin A and "polymyxin" became polymyxin D. Both these antibiotics were nephrotoxic, which excluded their use parenterally. This clinical defect led to the search for other antibiotic-producing strains of *B. polymyxa*, and to the development of three new polymyxins, B, C, and E, of which polymyxins B and E produced negligible toxic effects within the limits of the therapeutic dosage range (80).

In 1950, Koyama (81) isolated an antibiotic from cultures of a soil bacterium of Japanese origin. The microorganism, initially referred to as *Bacillus colistinus*, is now recognized as *Bacillus polymyxa* var. *Garyphalus*. The antibiotic was called colistin but it has also been examined extensively under the name colimycin. It should not be confused with the Russian colimycin, which is a member of the neomycin group isolated from a *Streptomyces* sp (82).

In 1958, a strain of *B. polymyxa* from a soil sample taken in Moscow yielded an antibiotic which is now marketed by the Russians as polymyxin M (83).

Polymyxins B and E are produced in aerated submerged culture in a medium consisting essentially of glucose, autolyzed yeast, and diammonium phosphate. As indicated in Tables 5 and 6, strain selection is of fundamental importance in obtaining

Table 5. Distribution of Polymyxin A-, B-, C-, and E-producing Strains Among Soil Isolates Examined

polymyxin A-producing strains	10
polymyxin B-producing strains	14
polymyxin C-producing strains	4
polymyxin E-producing strains	3
strains not classified	15
total	46

Table 6. Variations of Antibiotic Titer with the Strain (Polymyxin B)

Number of strains	Range of antibiotic titer, units/ml
1	>800
5	600–800
10	400–600
15	200–400
17	<200

satisfactory titers.   In the biosynthesis of polymyxins B and E, two colchicine-treated variants, resistant to bacteriophage, have yielded titers of the order of 3500–4500 units/ml (ca 500 mg polymyxin/l) after a fermentation time of 48 hr.

A high proportion of gummy polysaccharide is produced simultaneously and is broken down by a short period of hydrolysis with dilute acid (preferably sulfuric acid) prior to filtration.   The polymyxin is isolated from the culture filtrate by procedures such as precipitation with acidic dyestuffs, by extraction, or by adsorption using either charcoal or cationic exchange resins (78).

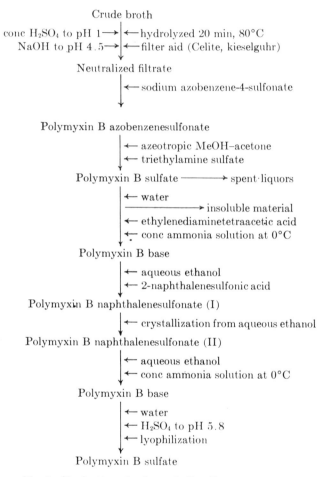

Fig. 4.   Production of polymyxin B sulfate.

In a typical extraction (see flowsheet, Fig. 4), polymyxin B is precipitated from the neutralized hydrolyzed filtrate as the azobenzene-4-sulfonate and recovered by centrifugation.   Treatment of the dried salt with triethylamine sulfate in an azeotropic mixture of methanol and acetone gives the crude polymyxin sulfate.   This is purified first by precipitation of the base (84) and then by recrystallization of the naphthalene-2-sulfonate (85).   The base is regenerated, converted to the neutral sulfate, and lyophilized.

All the polymyxins are basic polypeptides whose basicities are associated with the uncommon dibasic amino acid, α,γ-diaminobutyric acid. They form water-soluble salts with mineral acids, of which only the phosphates have been isolated in crystalline form. The neutral sulfates, the normal form of pharmaceutical presentation, the acid sulfates, and the hydrochlorides are amorphous solids. The water-insoluble naphthalene-2-sulfonates and azobenzene-4-sulfonates can be obtained in well-defined crystalline forms from aqueous alcohol. The picrates, reineckates, helianthates, Polar Yellow, and other acid dyestuff salts, long-chain alkyl sulfates, etc, are very insoluble in water and have, in the course of development of the polymyxins, been employed at various stages of isolation and purification.

The individual polymyxins can be distinguished by a combination of several criteria, including behavior on paper and thin-layer chromatography, the qualitative amino acid composition, and the specific optical rotation. Moreover, whereas the free bases of polymyxins A, C, D, and M are water-soluble, polymyxins B and E and colistin are precipitated on neutralizing aqueous solutions of their salts. The data are summarized in Table 7.

Table 7. Qualitative Amino Acid Compositions and Physical Constants of the Polymyxins

Polymyxin	Dab	Thr	Phe	Leu	Ser	R_f value PC[a]	TLC[b]	$[\alpha]_D$, °	$[\alpha]_{5461}$, °	Solubility of base in water
A	+	+		+		0.58	0.47	-37.0^c		+
B	+	+	+	+	+	0.54	0.57	-80.4^d	-106.3^c	−
C	+	+	+							+
D	+	+		+	+			-40^c		+
E	+	+		+		0.51	0.57	-59^c	-98.7^c	−
M	+	+		+		0.58	0.47	-37.5^c		+
colistin	+	+		+		0.51	0.57	-59.2^e	-98.5^c	−

^{a} Paper chromatography, Whatman No. 1 solvent system—1-butanol:pyridine:acetic acid:water (30:20:6:24).

^{b} Thin-layer chromatography, silica gel G solvent system—1-butanol:pyridine:acetic acid:water (30:20:6:24). See also reference 213.

^{c} Hydrochloride in water.

^{d} Hydrochloride in 85% ethanol.

^{e} Phosphate in water.

The polymyxins are irreversibly inactivated in alkaline solution or by treatment with acetic anhydride or other acylating agents. Accompanying the alkaline inactivations are characteristic changes in the specific optical rotations and the optical rotatory dispersion curves, which can be observed, even in the case of the water-insoluble polymyxin bases, by the use of the nickel complexes of the antibiotics and measurements determined at pH 9.3 (86).

All the polymyxins are painful on intramuscular injection and, in common with many polypeptides, tend to cause inflammatory reactions at the site of injection. However, by treatment with formaldehyde and sodium bisulfite, they are converted into their sodium N-sulfomethyl derivatives, which are relatively free from causing pain on injection whilst still retaining their antibacterial activities. Because the potencies of these derivatives ultimately depend on regeneration in vivo to the parent antibiotics, nephrotoxicity is not reduced. The degree of N-sulfomethylation in relation to therapeutic response has been discussed by Barnett et al. (87) and by Petersdorf and Plorde (88).

Chemistry of the Polymyxins. Following the original observation by Hausmann and Craig (89) that commercial samples of polymyxin B were not homogeneous but separable by countercurrent distribution into two components, a major fraction, polymyxin B1, and a lesser fraction, polymyxin B2, the other members of this group of antibiotics have similarly been shown to be composite. Each consists essentially of a pair of related polypeptides but trace amounts of a third peptide may also be found.

On acid hydrolysis, each unfractionated polymyxin yields, in addition to a characteristic series of amino acids, a mixture of saturated aliphatic acids. Gas-chromatographic analysis of the mixed acids reveals a major proportion of the optically active (+)-6-methyloctanoic acid, a smaller amount of the optically inactive isooctanoic (6-methylheptanoic) acid, and a trace of octanoic acid. These free fatty acids arise from three respective polypeptides in each of the polymyxins. Those components giving (+)-6-methyloctanoic acid on hydrolysis are referred to as polymyxins A1, B1, etc, whilst those which yield isooctanoic acid are named polymyxins A2, B2, etc. Quantitative analyses have shown that the ratios of the individual fatty acids, ie, the ratios of amounts of the respective polypeptides, are not constant in the various polymyxins (see Table 8).

Table 8. Relative Proportions of the Component Antibiotics in the Polymyxins

Polymyxin	I (+)-6-Methyloctanoic acid components, %	II Isooctanoic acid components, %
polymyxin A	86	14
polymyxin M	91	9
polymyxin B	83	17
polymyxin E	95	5
colistin	77	23

The presence of aliphatic acid residues in the polymyxins is not a unique example of their occurrence in antibiotics. Similar examples have been found in the antibiotic glumamycin (90), in which the terminal aspartic acid is acylated with 3-isotridecanoic acid, and in visconin (91), in which the terminal valine is acylated with (−)-3-oxy-decanoic acid.

The structures of the individual pairs of the two major components have been shown to differ only in the nature of the accompanying aliphatic acid. By a combination of partial acid and enzymic hydrolyses, all these antibiotics have proved to be basic decapeptides having a common type of structure. A chain of three amino acids is attached to a cyclic heptapeptide via the α-amino group of an α,γ-diaminobutyric acid residue. The terminal α-amino group of the chain is acylated with one or other of the two major fatty acid components described above. The structures of the individual antibiotics are depicted in Table 9.

Certain points pertaining to this table require elaboration. The production of polymyxin C was never pursued because of the high nephrotoxicity of this antibiotic. Although the qualitative amino acid composition of polymyxin C was established as threonine, α,γ-diaminobutyric acid, and D-phenylalanine (80), no further characterization was carried out. Included in the list of structures is that of circulin A, an antibi-

Table 9. The Structures of the Members of the Polymyxin Group of Antibiotics[a]

$$\text{R} \xrightarrow{\alpha} \underset{\underset{NH_2(\gamma)}{|}}{Dab} \longrightarrow Thr \xrightarrow{\alpha} X \xrightarrow{\alpha} \underset{\underset{Thr \leftarrow \underset{\underset{NH_2(\gamma)}{|}}{Dab}}{\nwarrow}}{Dab} \begin{array}{c} NH_2(\gamma) \\ | \\ Dab \rightarrow Y \\ \searrow Z \\ \downarrow \\ Dab\text{-}NH_2(\gamma) \end{array}$$

Polymyxin	R	X	Y	Z	Reference
A1 (= M1)	MOA	D-Dab	D-Leu	Thr	92
A2 (= M2)	IOA	D-Dab	D-Leu	Thr	92
B1	MOA	Dab	D-Phe	Leu	93
B2	IOA	Dab	D-Phe	Leu	94
D1	MOA	D-Ser	D-Leu	Thr	95
D2	IOA	D-Ser	D-Leu	Thr	95
E1 (or colistin A)	MOA	Dab	D-Leu	Leu	96, 97
E2 (or colistin B)	IOA	Dab	D-Leu	Leu	96, 97
circulin A	MOA	Dab	D-Leu	Ileu	98

[a] All the amino acids shown are of the L-configuration unless stated otherwise.

LEGEND: Dab = α,γ-diaminobutyric acid; MOA = (+)-6-methyloctanoic acid; IOA = isooctanoic acid.

otic isolated in 1948 from a strain of *Bacillus circulans* (99). It has long been suspected of being related to the polymyxins and its recently established structure is now conclusive proof of this relationship.

The structures of the components of the Japanese antibiotic colistin (see p. 319) and of polymyxin E were found to be identical (96,97). Similarly, identical structures were established for the components of polymyxin A and the Russian polymyxin M (92). Consequently the original five polymyxins, A, B, C, D, and E, still remain the only known polypeptide antibiotics derived from strains or variants of *B. polymyxa*.

In contrast to polymyxins B and E, which possess only one D-amino acid, polymyxins A and D each contain two such amino acids. This fundamental difference may account for the considerably higher degree of nephrotoxicity encountered with polymyxins A and D. The higher proportions of hydroxyamino acids also found in the antibiotics A and D are reflected in the water solubility of the bases of these polymyxins, as contrasted with that of polymyxins B and E and circulin A, which readily precipitate on neutralizing aqueous solutions of their salts.

Although total syntheses of polymyxins B1 and E1 (colistin A), and of circulin A have been completed by Vogler et al. (100), and of polymyxin A1 by Wilkinson (101), the procedures nevertheless appear to be too long and expensive, particularly because of poor yields obtained at the cyclization stage, to offer any serious competition to the microbiologically produced antibiotics. The methods used are modifications of a common theme, exemplified in the synthesis of polymyxin B1, shown in Figure 5.

The three protected peptides (a), (b), and (c) were synthesized by classical methods, invariably using the azide procedure to avoid racemization. By treatment with trifluoroacetic acid, the BOC residue was removed from (a), which was then treated with the azide derived from peptide (b). The resulting octapeptide ester was in turn converted via the hydrazide to the azide and coupled with peptide (c) to give the protected open-chain decapeptide ester (d). The substituent Bu^t and BOC residues were removed with trifluoroacetic acid and the product was cyclized in highly dilute solution in a mixture of dioxan and dimethylformamide, using a large excess of dicyclohexyl carbodiimide. The *N*-protecting benzyloxycarbonyl residues were removed by reduction with sodium in liquid ammonia and the product was purified by counter-current distribution to give a 10–15% yield of polymyxin B1 at the cyclization–reduction stage. Even lower yields were encountered at the cyclization stage during the syntheses of circulin A and polymyxin A1.

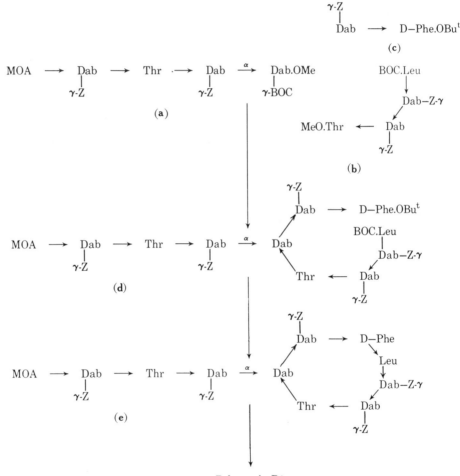

LEGEND: MOA = (+)-6-methyloctanoic acid;   Z = benzyloxycarbonyl;   BOC = 3^t-butyloxy-carbonyl;   Bu^t = 3^t-butyl.

Fig. 5. The synthesis of polymyxin B1.

During their earlier work on the synthesis of polymyxin B1, Vogler and co-workers inadvertently prepared a number of analogs (86), based on the assumption of an incorrect structure for the antibiotic (102). Nevertheless, these have provided valuable information on the relationship between structure and antibacterial activity in this group of antibiotics.

The Antibacterial Activity of the Polymyxins. The polymyxins are active against a number of Gram-negative organisms (*Pseudomonas*, *Escherichia*, *Klebsiella*, *Enterobacter*, *Salmonella*, *Shigella*, and *Haemophilus* spp) but not against *Proteus* and Gram-positive bacteria. Preparations of the sulfates of polymyxin and of colistin (polymyxin E) are available for local, topical, oral, and intravenous medication, whilst the sodium *N*-sulfomethyl derivatives are presented for intramuscular and intrathecal administration. A wide range of mixed antibiotic formulations is marketed.

The sulfates of polymyxin B and colistin may be used orally for gastrointestinal infections or sterilization prior to surgery but not for systemic infections, because of poor absorption. Toxic effects by this route are minimal except in newborn infants, when appreciable blood levels can be obtained. Dose rates are of the order of 75–100 mg daily for adults, reducing to 3–5 mg/kg body weight, given in divided doses, for infants and children.

For local or topical use, for example, in otic solutions or ointments, 0.1–0.25% wt/vol or wt/wt preparations of the sulfates are available.

Ophthalmic ointments contain 0.2% wt/vol of the sulfate.

Intrathecally, 5 mg sulfate in 1 ml isotonic saline is administered.

Sterile, pyrogenfree polymyxin B sulfate is available for slow intravenous infusion in cases of severe systemic infections requiring hospitalization.

Although the acute intravenous toxicity of the polymyxins is reduced by sulfomethylation with formaldehyde and sodium metabisulfite, this toxicity is of no therapeutic importance because the sulfates have a satisfactory therapeutic index. The advantage of using the sulfomethyl derivatives is the reduction of pain at the site of intramuscular injection, making parenteral therapy tolerable to the patient.

Barnett et al. (87) have discussed the relationship between the degree of sulfomethylation and therapeutic response and have correlated the acute intravenous LD_{50} values of various preparations with their therapeutic efficiency. Results have indicated that detoxification by sulfomethylation should be minimal and sufficient only to abolish the pain of injection and that derivatives with LD_{50} (iv in mice) of the order of 100 mg/kg are the best compromise. It has been emphasized that Thiosporin (sodium sulfomethyl polymyxin B, Burroughs Wellcome & Co.), and the various preparations of sodium sulfomethylcolistin which are marketed (eg, Sodium Colistimethate, Warner Chilcott Laboratories; Colimycine Intramusculaire, Laboratoire Roger Bellon, S.A.) are products with distinctly different LD_{50} values and should be considered as completely individual products, each exhibiting characteristic properties. Since the activity of the sodium sulfomethyl derivatives ultimately depends on the regeneration in vivo of the parent antibiotic, these products are contraindicated for topical or local use. More specifically, they are administered intramuscularly or intrathecally to combat acute enteritis, urinary and respiratory tract infections, bacteremia, peritonitis, and meningitis associated with *Pseudomonas* spp, *E. coli*, *Enterobacter aerogenes*, and *Klebsiella* spp.

Methods of Assay. Potency of polymyxin B sulfate is expressed in terms of a master standard assigned the arbitrary value of 10,000 units/mg of polymyxin B sulfate.

Potency of colistin sulfate is expressed in terms of a master standard assigned the arbitrary value of 30,000 units/mg of colistin base, ie, 20,000 units/mg of colistin sulfate (201).

Strict tests for pyrogens are required for injectable products.

Table 10. Polypeptide Antibiotics from *Streptomyces* spp

Streptomyces sp	Antibiotic	Activity (in vitro)	Ref.
antibioticus	actinomycins	see p. 330	
arsitensis	arsimycin	mycobacteria	103
bobiliae	mycospocidin	Gram-positive, mycobacteria, fungi	104
bottropensis	bottromycin	Gram-positive	105
canus	amphomycin	Gram-positive, trypanosomes	106
canus	antibiotic C 159	Gram-positive	107
candidus	telomycin	Gram-positive	197
capreolus	capreomycins I and II	mycobacteria	108
carcinomycicus	carcinomycin	Gram-positive	109
carzinostaticus	neocarzinostatin	antitumor	200
chrysomallus	actinomycins	antitumor	110
cinnamoneus f. *azacoluta*	duramycin	Gram-positive, mycobacteria, phytopathogens	111
cinnamoneus	cinnamycin	Gram-positive, mycobacteria, phytopathogens	112
cremoris	nisins	see p. 330	159, 160
daghestanicus	antibiotic 6613	Gram-positive	113
echinatus	echinomycin	Gram-positive, *Trichomonas*	114
floridae	viomycin	see p. 328	146, 147
fradiae	actinomycins	antitumor	115
fulvissimus	valinomycin	mycobacteria, *B. subtilis*, *Staphylococcus aureus*	116
graminofaciens	streptogramin	*S. aureus*, *B. subtilis*, *Streptococcus pyogenes*	117
griseolavendus	grasseriomycin	Gram-positive, Gram-negative, mycobacteria, fungi	118
griseoplanus	alazopeptin	antitumor	119
griseus	etamycin	see p. 333	170a
griseus	grisein	*E. coli*, *S. aureus*, Salmonellae, Shigellae	120
griseus var. *spiralis*	aspartocin	Gram-positive, streptococci, staphylococci	121
hachijoensis	leucopeptin	*B. subtilis*, mycobacteria, phytopathogens	122
hawaiiensis	bryamycin	Gram-positive	123
kitazawaensis	carcinocidin	Gram-positive	124
lactis	nisin	see p. 330	
lactis	diplococcin	Gram-positive, mycobacteria	125
lathumensis	lathumycin	Gram-positive	126
lavendulae	pleocidin	Gram-positive, Gram-negative, mycobacteria, fungi, yeasts	127
lavendulae	mycothricin	Gram-positive, Gram-negative, mycobacteria, fungi, yeasts	128
lavendulae	streptothricin	Gram-positive, Gram-negative, mycobacteria, fungi	129
loidensis	vernamycin	Gram-positive, mycobacteria	171
loidensis	doricin	Gram-positive	173
luteochromogenes	phthiomycin	mycobacteria	130
mariensis	marinomycin	antitumor	131
matensis	matomycin	Gram-positive	132
mauvecolor	enomycin	antitumor	202

Table 10 (*continued*)

Streptomyces sp	Antibiotic	Activity (in vitro)	Ref.
mauvecolor	peptimycin	antitumor	203
melanogenes	melanomycin	antitumor	133
mitakaensis	mikamycins	Gram-positive	172
olivaceus	antibiotic P. 114	Gram-positive	134
ostreogriseus	ostreogrycins	Gram-positive	135
parvullus	actinomycins	antitumor	136
phaeoverticillatus	iyomycin	antitumor	115a
pristinae spiralis	pristinamycins	see p. 333	168
puniceus	viomycin	see p. 328	146
pyridomyceticus	pyridomycin	mycobacteria	137
racemochromogenes	racemomycins	Gram-positive	138
roseochromogenes	roseothricins	Gram-positive, Gram-negative, mycobacteria	139
rubrireticula	A 216, S 280	Gram-positive	205
sioyaensis	siomycin	Gram-positive, mycobacteria	140
Streptomyces sp	etamycin	see p. 333	170
Streptomyces sp PAL 1162	amidomycin	fungi, yeasts	141
Streptomyces sp	thiostrepton	see p. 329	154
Streptomyces sp	rufamycins (or ilamycins)	mycobacteria	154a, 154b
Streptomyces sp	doricin	mycobacteria	173
Streptomyces sp	actinogen	antitumor	204
subtropicus	albomycin	Gram-positive, spirochaetes	142
vinaceus	viomycin	see p. 328	147
violaceus	aspartocin	Gram-positive	121
sp probably *Virginiae*	staphylomycin	Gram-positive	143
xanthophaeus	geomycin	Gram-positive, Gram-negative, *Entamoeba histolytica*	144
zaomyceticus	glumamycin	Gram-positive	145

Brucella bronchiseptica is used as the test organism in the plate assay of the sulfates. In assaying the sodium sulfomethyl derivatives, conversion to the parent antibiotics is a prerequisite of the test and this is effected by dissolving the standard and test substances in glycine buffer at pH 2.0.

Some Available Products

Aerosporin Otic Solution (Burroughs Wellcome & Co. (U.S.A.), Inc.): (In acidified propylene glycol, polymyxin B sulfate 0.1%.)

Coly-mycin Otic Drops (Warner-Chilcott Laboratories): (Colistin sulfate 3 mg, neomycin sulfate 3.3 mg, hydrocortisone acetate 10 mg, and thonzonium bromide 0.5 mg/ml.)

Cortisporin Otic Drops (Burroughs Wellcome & Co. (U.S.A.), Inc.): (Polymyxin B sulfate 10,000 units, neomycin sulfate 5 mg, and hydrocortisone 10 mg/ml.)

Lidosporin Otic Solution (Burroughs Wellcome & Co. (U.S.A.), Inc.): (Polymyxin B sulfate 10,000 units and lidocaine hydrochloride 50 mg/ml in propylene glycol.)

Terramycin with Polymyxin B (Chas. Pfizer & Co., Inc.): (Oxytetracycline hydrochloride 5 mg and polymyxin B sulfate 10,000 units/g.) Ointment for ophthalmic and otic use.

Neosporin (Burroughs Wellcome & Co. (U.S.A.), Inc.): (Polymyxin B sulfate 5000 units, neomycin sulfate 5 mg, and zinc bacitracin 400 units/g.) Ophthalmic ointment.

Mycitracin (The Upjohn Co.): (Bacitracin 500 units, neomycin base 3.5 mg, and polymyxin B sulfate 5000 units/g.) Ophthalmic ointment.

Aerosporin Brand Polymyxin Sulfate (Burroughs Wellcome & Co. (U.S.A.), Inc.).

Colimycin Pediatric Suspension (Warner-Chilcott Laboratories).

Thiosporin (Burroughs Wellcome & Co. (U.S.A.), Inc.): (Sodium sulfomethyl-polymyxin B.)

Coly-mycin Injectable (Warner-Chilcott Laboratories): (Sodium sulfomethyl-colistin.)

Dynamyxin (Chas. Pfizer & Co., Inc.): (Sodium sulfomethylpolymyxin B.)

Antibiotics Derived from *Streptomyces* spp

Table 10 gives some indication of the polypeptide antibiotics which have been isolated from different species of *Streptomyces*. The number is increasing rapidly as different species are screened. Many of the examples included here have been incompletely characterized or are complex mixtures still requiring fractionation. The possibility must be borne in mind that many of these antibiotics may prove to be identical or at least to contain common constituents. Only a limited number have proved valuable as therapeutic agents and these are discussed individually below. For the purpose of this discussion they have been divided into two main groups, miscellaneous polypeptides and peptide lactones.

MISCELLANEOUS POLYPEPTIDE ANTIBIOTICS FROM *Streptomyces* spp

Viomycin. Viomycin is a tuberculostatic antibiotic isolated from cultures of *Streptomyces puniceus* (146). It is identical with vinacetin A produced by *Streptomyces vinaceus* (147). The antibiotic is recovered from the filtrate of submerged cultures by adsorption on charcoal, by precipitation with various acidic dyestuffs, or by the use of cationic exchange resins (148). Viomycin is a strongly basic water-soluble polypeptide, readily forming highly colored crystalline salts such as the hydrochloride, sulfate, or naphthalene-2-sulfonate. It is stable in acid solution but less so under alkaline conditions.

The sulfate is isolated as water-soluble hydrated purple crystals, mp 280°C (decomp), $[\alpha]_D^{25} = -32°$ ($c = 1$ in water). Its solution, when adjusted to pH 5–6, is quite stable. Alkaline solutions of the antibiotic are unstable.

The unit (USP) of viomycin is defined as 1 mg of the pure base and the activity of viomycin preparations is expressed in terms of such units. Standardizations are conducted using either *Klebsiella pneumoniae* in turbidimetric assays or *Mycobacterium butyricum* or *Bacillus subtilis* in plate assays. The sensitivity of the tests may be increased by adding subinhibitory concentrations of sulfadiazine, which synergize the activity of the viomycin.

From acidic hydrolisates, CO_2, urea, L-serine, L-β-lysine, α,β-diaminopropionic acid, and a guanidine derivative, viomycidine (**11**) have been isolated (149). A number of structures have been proposed for the antibiotic (150), of which the most recent is that of (**12**) below (151).

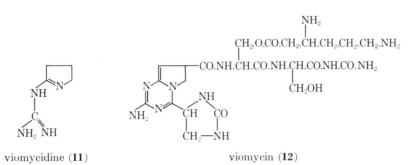

viomycidine (**11**)   viomycin (**12**)

Particular interest in viomycin lies in its tuberculostatic activity. Because of certain toxic manifestations the drug is not recommended when routine measures normally employed in tuberculotherapy prove sufficiently adequate (152). Medication, preferably accompanied by other tuberculostatic agents, is of importance in treating streptomycin-resistant infections (153). The pantothenate is considered to be better tolerated and less toxic than the sulfate.

Dosage. Customarily prescribed dosage levels are 2 g im twice a week or 30–75 mg/kg of body weight im daily, preferably accompanied by streptomycin and *p*-aminosalicylic acid.

Contraindications are preexisting renal damage. Toxic symptoms include allergic reactions, eosinophilia, damage to vestibular mechanisms, dizziness, and deafness.

Some Available Products

Vinactane (Ciba Pharmaceutical Co.): (Viomycin sulfate.)

Viocin (Chas. Pfizer & Co., Inc.): (Viomycin sulfate.)

Vionactane (Ciba Pharmaceutical Co.): (Mixture of viomycin sulfate and viomycin pantothenate.)

Thiostrepton, a crystalline sulfur-containing antibiotic, was isolated from cultures of *Streptomyces azureus* (154). Its constitution has not yet been elucidated, but on acid hydrolysis it releases L-threonine, L-alanine, D-cystine, L-isoleucine, and two thiazole-4-carboxylic acid derivatives, thiostreptoic acid (**13**) and thiostreptine (**14**) (155).

(**13**)   (**14**)

The antibiotic crystallizes readily from a mixture of methanol and chloroform, mp ca 250°C (decomp), $[\alpha]_D^{23} = -61°$ ($c = 1$ in dioxan), $[\alpha]_D^{23} = -98.5°$ ($c = 1$ in glacial acetic acid). It is insoluble in water and the lower alcohols but soluble in dioxan, pyridine, chloroform, and acetic acid. In the uv spectrum (methanol), three maxima are detected at 240, 280, and 305 mμ. It is standardized by plate assay, using *Staphylococcus aureus*. Although thiostrepton is highly active against Gram-positive bacteria and is useful in the treatment of bovine mastitis, particularly when penicillin is contraindicated, there has been little general interest in this antibiotic.

Albomycin, a member of the so-called sideromycin group of antibiotics (211), is a basic polypeptide containing iron and sulfur. It is produced by *Streptomyces* *subtropicus* (142,156) and is similar to, if not identical with, grisein, isolated from strains of *Streptomyces griseus* (120,157). It has one free amino group and gives, on hydrolysis—in addition to the amino acids N^δ-hydroxyornithine, serine, glutamic acid, alanine, proline, and glycine—a pyrimidine, present in the intact antibiotic as a 3-methylcytosine–sulfonyl serine moiety (158). The complete structure is as yet unknown. The chelated iron is removed with simultaneous biological inactivation by treatment with acetone and restored with ferric chloride. The sulfate, a red amorphous powder, is insoluble in water, slightly soluble in lower alcohols, but insoluble in most organic solvents.

Its toxicity is comparable to that of penicillin and the antibiotic is effective against penicillin-resistant strains of staphylococci and pneumococci. The standard unit is defined as the activity associated with 0.014 µg of albomycin sulfate. Dose levels are recommended as up to 3 million units subcutaneously, intramuscularly, and intravenously, and 100,000–200,000 units intrathecally.

Nisin is a mixture of cyclic polypeptides, of unknown constitution, produced by cultures of *Streptomyces lactis* (159) and *Streptomyces cremoris* (160). The major component, nisin A, was separated by countercurrent distribution (161). Methionine, alanine, aspartic acid, leucine, isoleucine, histidine, lysine, proline, lanthionine and β-methyllanthionine were liberated on hydrolysis. Nisin A therefore differs from subtilin (isolated from *B. subtilis*), in which tryptophan replaces methionine, and in which the additional amino acids phenylalanine, glutamic acid, and sarcosine are also found. Recent work by Gross (161a) has shown that dehydroalanine occurs in nisin and that the fragment dehydroalanyllysine occupies the carboxyl terminal position. This is the first time that the uncommon amino acid dehydroalanine has been found in a naturally occurring peptide antibiotic, and its presence presumably plays a predominant role in promoting antibiotic activity.

Nisin and subtilin, together with duramycin (from *Streptomyces cinnamoneus* var. *azacoluta*) (111) and cinnamycin (from *Streptomyces cinnamoneus*) (112), probably form a group of closely related antibiotics, characteristic in that the sulfur-containing amino acids lanthionine and β-methyllanthionine are present in each.

The principal use of the nisins has been to prevent contamination of cheeses and other milk products by *Clostridia* spp (162).

Rufamycin (ilamycin). Rufamycins A and B, isolated from a strain of *Streptomyces* (154a) are now known to be identical with ilamycins B1 and B2, respectively (154b). These antibiotics are cyclic heptapeptides specifically active against *Mycobacteria*, including strains resistant to isonicotinic acid hydrazide, streptomycin, and kanamycin, but rufamycin B is considerably less active than rufamycin A. The structures of these antibiotics have now been established and that of rufamycin A is particularly interesting in that it possesses the uncommon amino acids 3-nitrotyrosine, *N*-4-dimethylglutamic acid-γ-semialdehyde (γ-formyl-*N*-methylnorvaline), and 2-amino-4-hexenoic acid (dehydronorleucine), as well as a substituted tryptophan derivative.

PEPTIDE LACTONES DERIVED FROM *Streptomyces* spp

The Actinomycins. A complex group of yellowish-red, highly toxic polypeptides, the actinomycins are produced by various species of *Streptomyces*. The subject matter is very involved and the reader is referred to the reviews listed in reference 163 for the nomenclature and structures of the large number of actinomycins which have been described.

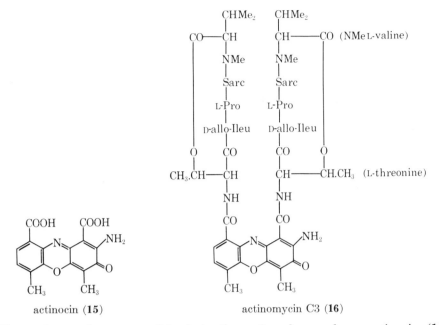

actinocin (**15**)   actinomycin C3 (**16**)

The actinomycins are peptide derivatives of a chromophore, actinocin (**15**), a phenoxazonedicarboxylic acid liberated under mild hydrolytic conditions. The acid is linked to two 16-membered peptide lactones via the amino group of threonine residues. The two peptide lactones may be either identical or different and a typical structure is seen in that of actinomycin C3 (**16**) above (164). In actinomycin D, D-valine residues replace those of D-alloisoleucine. The lactone bridge between the hydroxyl group of the threonine and the carboxyl group of the terminal N-methyl-L-valine is a common feature of these antibiotics.

The mode of action of the actinomycins in biological systems has been ascribed to the inhibition of DNA-dependent RNA synthesis, and special interest in these substances lies in their cytostatic action. Their value as antitumor agents and their activity against lymphogranulomatosis is being pursued vigorously. Encouraging results have been recorded with actinomycin C3 and actinomycin D incorporated in the treatment regimen of patients with Hodgkin's disease and nephroblastoma. The adverse and potentially severe reactions encountered during treatment with the actinomycins require careful supervision, and considerable effort is being directed toward the synthesis of active but less toxic analogs (165).

The Streptogramin or "Synergistic" Family of Antibiotics. In recent years a number of composite antibiotics have been isolated from various *Streptomyces* spp, streptogramin (117) being the first of this particular type. The components of these antibiotics can be classified into two groups, A and B, according to their structures (see Table 11). These antibiotics are unique in so far as, in their activity against Gram-positive organisms, the members of group A produce a synergism with the antibiotics of group B. The total complexes are therefore more active microbiologically than the individual components (166,167,196). Although the antibiotics of both groups inhibit protein synthesis, structurally they differ enormously; those of group A are macrolides

Table 11. The Streptogramin Family of *Streptomyces* Antibiotics

Antibiotic complex[a]	Group A (macrolides), antibiotic	Group B (polypeptides)	
		Antibiotic	Synonym
streptogramin	streptogramin A	streptogramin B	
staphylomycin	staphylomycin M1	staphylomycin S	
	staphylomycin M2		
ostreogrycin	ostreogrycin A	ostreogrycin B	streptogramin B
	ostreogrycin G		synergistin B-1
(antibiotic E129)	ostreogrycin C		mikamycin B
	ostreogrycin D		pristinamycin IA
	ostreogrycin Q		vernamycin Bα
		ostreogrycin B1	vernamycin Bγ
		ostreogrycin B2	vernamycin Bβ
			pristinamycin IB
		ostreogrycin B3	
mikamycin	mikamycin A	mikamycin B	
pristinamycin	pristinamycin IIA	pristinamycin IA	
(antibiotic 7293 RP)	pristinamycin IIB	pristinamycin IB	
vernamycin	vernamycin A	vernamycin Bα	
		vernamycin Bβ	
		vernamycin Bγ	
		vernamycin Bδ	
		doricin	
synergistin	synergistin A1	synergistin B-1	
(antibiotic PA114)		synergistin B-3	
		etamycin	viridogrisein

[a] See Table 10 for *Streptomyces* producing-strain.

(210) whilst those of group B are cyclic polypeptides having a lactone structure. The structures of the macrolide antibiotics have not been completely elucidated. Etamycin (viridogrisein) is the only member of this family of antibiotics which is homogeneous but is included in group B because of its structural relationship to the other members.

Thus, for example, as indicated in Figure 6, Vanderhaege and Parmentier (143) found that from the crude antibiotic staphylomycin, isolated from *Streptomyces* sp, probably *virginiae*, two homogeneous fractions, referred to as factor M1 and factor M2, could be obtained by chromatography on silica gel. Both these factors were active against micrococci. On further fractionating the residual material, after removal of these two antibiotics, a third homogeneous substance, staphylomycin S, was isolated. Staphylomycin S had little activity against micrococci but was considerably more active against *B. subtilis* than was factor M1. Moreover, the addition of staphylomycin S to factor M1 increased the activity of the latter to micrococci by as much as 2.5-fold.

Similarly, Ball et al. (192) observed that the crude ostreogrycin isolated from *Streptomyces ostreogriseus* could be separated by countercurrent distribution, partition chromatography, etc, into three fractions named ostreogrycins A, B, and G. Fractions A and G both were active against *Staphylococcus aureus* and *Streptococcus pyogenes* and their activities were substantially potentiated by addition of ostreogrycin B. Synergistic effects were subsequently found (see Table 11) in the groups of antibiotics associated with pristinamycin (168), mikamycin (172), vernamycin (171,193), and synergistin (134). Pristinamycin, for example, was resolved into four components, pristinamycins IIA and IIB (group A—macrolides) and pristinamycins IA and IB (group B—polypeptides).

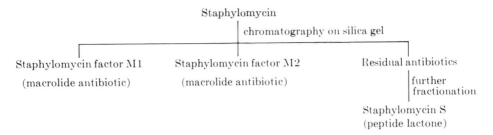

Staphylomycin

chromatography on silica gel

Staphylomycin factor M1   Staphylomycin factor M2   Residual antibiotics
(macrolide antibiotic)   (macrolide antibiotic)   further
                                                                          fractionation

                                                                 Staphylomycin S
                                                                 (peptide lactone)

Fig. 6. Fractionation of staphylomycin.

As with the actinomycins, the subject matter is rather complex. Several of these composite antibiotics have common constituents and moreover, as techniques of fractionation improved, products hitherto considered to be homogeneous were resolved further. Thus ostreogrycin B was separated into the four components B, B1, B2, and B3 (179,180) and vernamycin B into vernamycins Bα, Bβ, Bγ, and Bδ (193). Further investigations then revealed that the structures of many of the individual antibiotics were identical; for example, ostreogrycin B, pristinamycin IA, mikamycin B, and vernamycin Bα are now recognized as being one and the same antibiotic (172a). Other identities are to be seen under Synonyms in Table 11.

The synergizing factors, which, in addition to the ostreogrycins B (134,135,171), vernamycins B (171), mikamycin B (172), staphylomycin S (143,172) and pristinamycins I (168), also include etamycin (170), echinomycin (114) and doricin (173), have certain structural features in common. They possess either a 19- or a 22-membered lactone ring associated with the hydroxyl function of a threonine residue and a chromophore, a heterocyclic acid such as 3-hydroxypicolinic acid, which acylates the amino group of the threonine. The remaining portion of the lactone ring is invariably formed by a peptide chain consisting, in part, of uncommon amino acids. They are probably biogenetically related to the actinomycins in which 16-membered lactone rings are featured.

A typical structure is seen in that of etamycin (**17**).

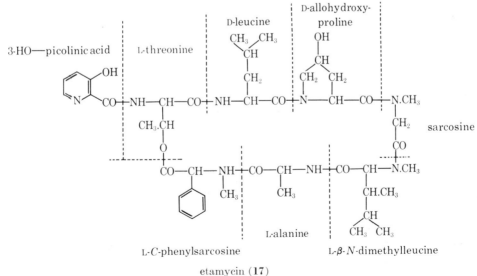

etamycin (**17**)
(22-membered lactone ring)

The close structural relationships between these various antibiotics can be seen from the general formula (18).

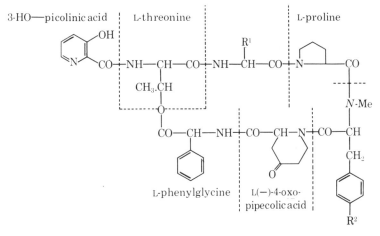

(19-membered lactone ring (18))

	R^1	R^2
staphylomycin S	$-CH_2.CH_3$	$-H$
ostreogrycin B (or vernamycin Bα)	$-CH_2.CH_3$	$-N(CH_3)_2$
ostreogrycin B1 (or vernamycin Bγ)	$-CH_3$	$-N(CH_3)_2$
ostreogrycin B2 (or vernamycin Bβ)	$-CH_2.CH_3$	$-NH.CH_3$
ostreogrycin B3	$-CH_2.CH_3$	$-N(CH_3)_2$
	(L(−)-4-oxopipecolic acid is absent)	
vernamycin Bδ	$-CH_3$	$-NH.CH_3$

Synergistic action is not restricted to the specific natural antibiotic complex; thus, mikamycin B, staphylomycin S, and etamycin potentiate the activity of mikamycin A (194); for details of biological investigations the reader is referred to the literature cited in reference 195.

These antibiotics have, as yet, had no wide application in medicine. Pristinamycin is administered orally and has been used clinically to treat cases of infections due to *Staphylococcus aureus*, particularly resistant to penicillin, *Streptococcus faecalis*, and *Hemophilus influenzae* (169). Other members of the group have been tried in experimental infections and clinical practice, eg, etamycin as a tuberculostatic agent and staphylomycin S in staphylococcal infections, but it is beyond the scope of this article to assess their ultimate value.

Peptide Lactones Possessing No "Hetero" Component. Telomycin, isolated from a *Streptomyces* sp (197), and antibiotics LL-AO 341 from *Streptomyces candidus* (198) are essentially different from the peptide lactones described above in that they possess no "hetero" component. The structure of telomycin has been deduced as that of a cyclic monopeptide lactone with the hydroxyl of threonine participating in the formation of the ring structure (199,212).

$$\beta \quad \text{(threonine)}$$
$$Asp \rightarrow Ser \rightarrow NH.CH.CO \rightarrow alloThr \rightarrow Ala \rightarrow Gly \rightarrow trans\text{-}3\text{-}HO\text{-}Pro$$
$$CH_3.CH$$
$$O \leftarrow cis\text{-}3\text{-}HO\text{-}Pro \leftarrow dehydroTry \leftarrow \beta\text{-}MeTry \leftarrow \beta\text{-}Ho\text{-}Leu$$

telomycin

Table 12. Antibiotic Depsipeptides (Peptolides)

Microorganism	Antibiotic	Hetero acids	Activity (in vitro)	Ref.
Fusaria lateritium	lateritiin I	D-α-HO-isovaleric	*Mycobacterium phlei, Staphylococcus aureus*	(174)
	lateritiin II	D-α-HO-isovaleric	*M. phlei, S. aureus*	(174)
Fusaria avenaceum	avenacein	D-α-HO-isovaleric	*M. phlei, S. aureus*	(174)
Fusaria sambucinium	sambucinin	D-α-HO-isovaleric	*M. phlei, S. aureus*	(174)
Fusaria fructogenum	fructogenin	D-α-HO-isovaleric	*M. phlei, S. aureus*	(174)
Fusaria orthoceras var. *enniatinium*	enniatin A	D-α-HO-isovaleric	*M. paratuberculosis, S. aureus*	(175)
Fusaria orthoceras var. *enniatinium*	enniatin B	D-α-HO-isovaleric	*M. paratuberculosis, S. aureus*	(175)
Fusaria orthoceras var. *enniatinium*	enniatin C	D-α-HO-isovaleric	*M. paratuberculosis, S. aureus*	(175)
Streptomyces fulvissimus	valinomycin	{ L-lactic, D-α-HO-isovaleric	*M. tuberculosis, Bacillus subtilis, S. aureus*	(116)
Streptomyces PRL 1642	amidomycin	D-α-HO-isovaleric	phytopathogens, *Candida albicans*	(141)
Pithomyces sp	angolide	L-α-HO-isovaleric		(162)
Pithomyces chartarum[a]	sporidesmolide I	L-α-HO-isovaleric		(176)
	sporidesmolide II	L-α-HO-isovaleric		(176a)
	sporidesmolide III	L-α-HO-isovaleric		(187)
Pithomyces maydicus	sporidesmolide IV	{ L-α-HO-isovaleric, L-α-HO-isocaproic		(188)
Isaria cretacea	isariin	D-β-HO-dodecanoic		(177)
Serratia marcescens	serratamolide	D-β-HO-decanoic		(178)

[a] *Pithomyces chartarum* (Berk. & Curt.) M. B. Ellis is synonymous with *Sporidesmium bakeri* Sydow (Commonwealth Mycological Institute Herbarium No. 74473).

Telomycin is active against Gram-positive organisms and has been administered intramuscularly for the treatment of infections originating from *S. aureus* and *Diplococcus pneumoniae.*

The Antibiotic Cyclic Depsipeptides

The final group of polypeptide antibiotics, the cyclic depsipeptides or peptolides, is of interest chemically but has contributed little to human and veterinary medicine. As agricultural fungicides, some small measure of success has been recorded. The main sources of these substances are the Fungi Imperfecti and *Streptomyces* spp. Reviews on their isolation, structure, synthesis, and biological activity can be found in reference 181.

Of the examples given in Table 12, lateritiins I and II, avenacein, sambucinin, and fructogenin are peptolides of unknown structure. The remainder can conveniently be classified into three groups:

1. The **enniatins, valinomycin, amidomycin,** and **angolide** are heteromeric cyclic peptides in which an alternating series of amide and ester bonds persist throughout their cyclic structures.

Of these, angolide presents the least complex structure, a cyclotetrapeptolide (**19**) (186).

$$\text{L-}\alpha\text{-HO-isovaleric acid}\rightarrow\text{L-isoleucine}$$
$$\uparrow\qquad\qquad\downarrow$$
$$\text{D-alloisoleucine}\leftarrow\text{L-}\alpha\text{-HO-isovaleric acid}$$

angolide (**19**)

Enniatins A and B, in which *N*-methylamino acids are encountered, were originally considered to be tetrapeptolides. The hexapeptolide structures, (**20**) and (**21**) respectively, have been confirmed by total synthesis (183). The structure of enniatin C is still in doubt.

$$\text{L-}N\text{-methylisoleucine}\rightarrow\text{D-}\alpha\text{-HO-isovaleric acid}\rightarrow\text{L-}N\text{-methylisoleucine}$$
$$\uparrow\qquad\qquad\qquad\qquad\downarrow$$
$$\text{D-}\alpha\text{-HO-isovaleric acid}\leftarrow\text{L-}N\text{-methylisoleucine}\leftarrow\text{D-}\alpha\text{-HO-isovaleric acid}$$

enniatin A (**20**)

$$\text{L-}N\text{-methylvaline}\rightarrow\text{D-}\alpha\text{-HO-isovaleric acid}\rightarrow\text{L-}N\text{-methylvaline}$$
$$\uparrow\qquad\qquad\qquad\qquad\downarrow$$
$$\text{D-}\alpha\text{-HO-isovaleric acid}\leftarrow\text{L-}N\text{-methylvaline}\leftarrow\text{D-}\alpha\text{-HO-isovaleric acid}$$

enniatin B (**21**)

In valinomycin, two hetero acids occur, L-lactic acid and D-α-hydroxyisovaleric acid. The structure was first postulated as a cyclooctapeptolide (184), but total synthesis has shown it to be that of a dodecapeptolide (**22**) (185).

$$\text{D-valine}\rightarrow\text{L-lact}\rightarrow\text{L-valine}\rightarrow\text{D-}\alpha\text{-HO-isoval}\rightarrow\text{D-valine}\rightarrow\text{L-lact}$$
$$\uparrow\qquad\qquad\qquad\qquad\qquad\qquad\downarrow$$
$$\text{D-}\alpha\text{-HO-isoval}\leftarrow\text{L-valine}\leftarrow\text{L-lact}\leftarrow\text{D-valine}\leftarrow\text{D-}\alpha\text{-HO-isoval}\leftarrow\text{L-valine}$$

valinomycin (**22**)

Although amidomycin is known to have an alternating sequence of D-valine and D-α-HO-isovaleric acid residues, etc, the complete structure has not yet been deduced.

2. The **sporidesmolides** I, II, III, and IV differ essentially from the peptolides of group 1 in not possessing an alternating series of amide and ester bonds.

D-valine→D-leucine→L-α-HO-isovaleric acid
↑   ↓
L-α-HO-isovaleric acid←L-*N*-methylleucine←L-valine

sporidesmolide I (**23**)

The structure of sporidesmolide III differs from that of sporidesmolide I (**23**) (189) only in the replacement of L-*N*-methylleucine by L-leucine (190). In sporidesmolide IV, L-α-HO-isocaproic acid replaces one of the L-α-HO-isovaleric acid residues (191). The structure of sporidesmolide II has not yet been proved.

3. **Serratamolide** and **isariin** are peptolides possessing β-hydroxyaliphatic acids, D-β-hydroxydodecanoic acid, and D-β-hydroxydecanoic acid, respectively.

D-β-HO-decanoic acid→L-serine
↑   ↓
L-serine←D-β-HO-decanoic acid

serratamolide (**24**)

Only the structure of serratamolide (**24**) has been positively elucidated.

Bibliography

1. E. P. Abraham and G. G. F. Newton, *Brit. Med. Bull.* **16,** 3 (1960).
2. R. Schwyzer, B. Iselin, H. Kappeler, B. Riniker, W. Rittel, and H. Zuber, *Helv. Chim. Acta* **46,** 1975 (1963); C. H. Li, J. Meienhofer, E. Schnabel, D. Chung, T. B. Lo, and J. Ramachandran, *J. Am. Chem. Soc.* **83,** 4449 (1961).
3. A. Osol and G. E. Farrar, eds., *The Dispensatory of the United States of America*, 26th ed., J. B. Lippincott Co., Philadelphia, Pa., 1967.
4. R. Braude, *Nutr. Abstr. Rev.* **23,** 473 (1953); R. Braude, H. O. Wallace, and T. J. Cunha, *Antibiot. Chemotherapy* **3,** 271 (1953); R. C. Klussendorf, *J. Am. Vet. Med. Assoc.* **125,** 155 (1954); *Proc. Am. Vet. Med. Assoc., 89th Meeting, 1952,* 356 (1953); U.S. Pat. 3,025,216 (1962), J. Ziffer and T. J. Cairney (to Pabst Brewing Co.).
5. J. Dekker, *Ann. Rev. Microbiol.* **17,** 243 (1963).
6. F. Kavanagh, ed., *Analytical Microbiology*, Academic Press, Inc., New York and London, 1963.
6a. J. Pinzelik, L. L. Nisonger, and F. J. Murray, *Appl. Microbiol.* **1,** 293 (1953); G. D. Darker, H. B. Brown, A. H. Free, B. Biro, and J. T. Gooley, *J. Am. Pharm. Assoc. (Sci. Ed.)* **37,** 156 (1948).
7. R. J. Dubos, *J. Exp. Med.* **70,** 1, 11, 249 (1939).
8. J. C. Lewis, K. P. Dimick, and I. C. Feustel, *Ind. Eng. Chem.* **37,** 996 (1945); U.S. Pat. 2,602,043 (1952), W. R. Mitchell (to Commercial Solvents Corp.).
9. R. D. Hotchkiss and R. J. Dubos, *J. Biol. Chem.* **140,** 791, 793, 803 (1940); *ibid.,* **141,** 155 (1941); U.S. Pat. 2,453,534 (1948), H. S. Olcott and H. L. Frankel-Conrat (to U.S. Secy. of Agriculture); R. D. Hotchkiss, *Adv. Enzymol.* **4,** 153 (1944).
9a. P. J. Weiss, M. L. Andrew, and W. W. Wright, *Antibiot. Chemotherapy* **7,** 374 (1957).
10. J. D. Gregory and L. C. Craig, *J. Biol. Chem.* **172,** 839 (1948).
11. L. C. Craig, J. D. Gregory, and G. T. Barry, *Cold Springs Harbor Symp. Quant. Biol.* **14,** 24 (1949).
12. L. K. Ramachandran, *Biochemistry* **2,** 1138 (1963).
13. E. Gross and B. Witkop, *Biochemistry* **4,** 2495 (1965).
14. S. Ishii and B. Witkop, *J. Am. Chem. Soc.* **85,** 1832 (1963).
15. R. Sarges and B. Witkop, *J. Am. Chem. Soc.* **87,** 2027 (1965).
16. R. Sarges and B. Witkop, *J. Am. Chem. Soc.* **87,** 2011 (1965).
17. R. Sarges and B. Witkop, *Biochemistry* **4,** 2491 (1965).
18. R. Sarges and B. Witkop, *J. Am. Chem. Soc.* **87,** 2020 (1965).
19. G. F. Gauze and M. G. Brazhnikova, *Ann. Rev. Soviet Med.* **2,** 134 (1944); *Lancet* **247,** 715 (1944).
20. R. Consden, A. H. Gordon, A. J. P. Martin, and R. L. M. Synge, *Biochem. J.* **39,** 362 (1945); A. R. Battersby and L. C. Craig, *J. Am. Chem. Soc.* **73,** 1887 (1951).

21. R. Schwyzer and P. Sieber, *Helv. Chim. Acta* **40**, 624 (1957); *Angew. Chem.* **68**, 518 (1958); Ger. Pat. 1,060,380 (1955), R. Schwyzer, B. Iselin, and M. Feurer (to Ciba A.G.).

22. S. Otani and Y. Saito, *Proc. Japan Acad.* **30**, 991 (1954); *Chem. Abstr.* **49**, 13362 (1955); S. Otani, H. Nagano, and Y. Saito, *Chem. Abstr.* **52**, 12403 (1958).

23. K. Kurahashi, *J. Biochem. (Tokyo)* **56**, 101 (1964); S. Otani and Y. Saito, *J. Biochem. (Tokyo)* **56**, 103 (1964).

24. P. Sergiev, *Lancet* **247**, 717 (1944).

25. R. Schwyzer and P. Sieber, *Helv. Chim. Acta* **41**, 1582 (1958); H. Aoyagi, T. Kato, M. Ohno, M. Konda, and N. Izumiya, *J. Am. Chem. Soc.* **36**, 5700 (1964); B. F. Erlanger and L. Goode, *Science* **131**, 669 (1960); E. Katchalski, A. Berger, L. Bichowsky-Solmnitzki, and J. Kurtz, *Nature* **176**, 118 (1955).

26. A. R. Battersby and L. C. Craig, *J. Am. Chem. Soc.* **74**, 4019, 4023 (1952).

27. A. Paladini and L. C. Craig, *J. Am. Chem. Soc.* **76**, 688 (1954); T. P. King and L. C. Craig, *J. Am. Chem. Soc.* **77**, 6624, 6627 (1955); M. A. Ruttenberg, T. P. King, and L. C. Craig, *Biochemistry* **4**, 11 (1965).

28. M. Ohno and N. Izumiya, *J. Am. Chem. Soc.* **88**, 376 (1966).

29. J. Kawamata and Y. Motomura, *J. Antibiotics (Tokyo), Ser. A.* **7**, 25 (1954); Y. Motomura, *J. Antibiotics (Tokyo), Ser. B.* **8**, 391 (1955).

30. Y. Motomura, *J. Antibiotics (Tokyo), Ser. A.* **10**, 179 (1957).

31. E. M. Barnes and G. G. F. Newton, *Antibiot. Chemotherapy* **3**, 866 (1953).

32. J. C. Lewis and K. Ijichi, *Appl. Microbiol.* **5**, 124 (1957); U.S. Pat. 2,850,427 (1958), G. Alderton and N. S. Snell (to U.S. Dept. of Agriculture).

33. G. G. F. Newton, *Brit. J. Exp. Pathol.* **30**, 306 (1949).

34. J. W. Foster and H. D. Woodruff, *J. Bacteriol.* **51**, 363 (1946).

35. M. Landy, S. B. Rosenman, and G. H. Warren, *J. Bacteriol.* **54**, 24 (1947); M. Landy, S. B. Rosenman, and G. H. Warren, *Proc. Soc. Exp. Biol. Med.* **67**, 539 (1948); I. Shibasika and G. Teuni, *J. Ferment. Technol. (Japan)* **31**, 339 (1953); *ibid.*, **32**, 115 (1954).

36. R. A. Turner, *Arch. Biochem. Biophys.* **60**, 364 (1956); H. Tint and W. Reiss, *J. Biol. Chem.* **190**, 133 (1951).

37. L. de Saint-Rat and H. R. Olivier, *Compt. Rend.* **222**, 297 (1946).

38. E. A. Johnson and K. L. Burdon, *J. Bacteriol.* **51**, 591 (1946).

39. F. Carvajal, *Antibiot. Chemotherapy* **3**, 765 (1953).

40. G. L. Hobby, P. P. Regna, N. Doughty, and W. E. Steig, *J. Clin. Invest.* **28**, 927 (1949); R. L. Peek and J. E. Lyons, *Ann. Rev. Biochem.* **20**, 367 (1951).

41. L. Quinn, *Antibiot. Chemotherapy* **2**, 221 (1952).

42. L. Delcombe, *Compt. Rend. Soc. Biol.* **146**, 789 (1952).

43. R. K. Callow and T. S. Work, *Biochem. J.* **51**, 558 (1952); R. K. Callow, R. E. Glover, P. D'Arcy-Hart, and G. M. Hills, *Brit. J. Exp. Pathol.* **28**, 418 (1947).

44. S. K. Majumdar and S. K. Bose, *Nature* **181**, 134 (1958); S. K. Majumdar and S. K. Bose, *Biochem. J.* **74**, 596 (1960); S. K. Majumdar and S. K. Bose, *Ann. Biochem. Exp. Med. (Calcutta)* **15**, 127 (1955).

45. R. B. Walton and H. B. Woodruff, *J. Clin. Invest.* **28**, 924 (1949); U.S. Pat. 2,602,767 (1952), R. B. Walton and H. B. Woodruff (to Merck & Co. Inc.).

46. M. Tsukamura, *J. Antibiotics (Tokyo), Ser. A.* **3**, 499 (1950).

47. A. L. Tiffin, *Nature* **181**, 907 (1958).

48. N. H. Hirschhorn, M. A. Bucca, and J. D. Thayer, *Proc. Exp. Biol. Med.* **67**, 429 (1948).

49. M. Vallée, *Compt. Rend. Soc. Biol.* **139**, 148 (1948).

50. G. J. Stessel, C. Leben, and G. W. Keitt, *Phytopathology* **42**, 20 (1953).

51. R. F. Wachter, N. Bohonos, and F. W. Quackenbush, *Antibiot. Chemotherapy* **1**, 399 (1951).

52. Y. Tanaka, *J. Antibiotics (Tokyo), Ser. B.* **9**, 1 (1956).

53. E. F. Jansen and D. J. Hirschmann, *Arch. Biochem. Biophys.* **4**, 297 (1944); J. C. Lewis et al., *Arch. Biochem. Biophys.* **14**, 415 (1947); K. P. Dimick, G. Alderton, J. C. Lewis, H. D. Lightbody, and H. L. Fevold, *Arch. Biochem. Biophys.* **14**, 1 (1947); A. J. Salle and G. J. Jann, *Proc. Soc. Exp. Biol. Med.* **60**, 60 (1945); W. Steenken and E. Wolinsky, *J. Bacteriol.* **57**, 453 (1949); J. J. Stubbs, R. E. Feeney, J. C. Lewis, I. C. Feustel, H. D. Lightbody, and J. A. Garibaldi, *Arch. Biochem. Biophys.* **14**, 427 (1947).

54. A. Stracher and L. C. Craig, *J. Am. Chem. Soc.* **81**, 696 (1959); G. Alderton and N. Snell, *J. Am. Chem. Soc.* **81**, 701 (1959); G. Alderton, *J. Am. Chem. Soc.* **75**, 2391 (1953).

55. A. A. Andersen, H. D. Michener, and H. S. Olcott, *Antibiot. Chemotherapy* **3**, 521 (1953).
56. S. K. Majumdar, *Indian J. Appl. Chem.* **22**, 228 (1959); S. K. Majumdar and S. K. Bose, *Biochem. J.* **74**, 596 (1960).
57. A. B. Banerjee and S. K. Bose, *Nature* **200**, 471 (1963).
58. F. L. Meleney, H. Anker, and B. A. Johnson, *Science* **102**, 376 (1945).
59. A. Arriagada, M. C. Savage, E. P. Abraham, N. G. Heatley, and A. E. Sharp, *Brit. J. Exp. Pathol.* **30**, 425 (1949).
60. G. G. F. Newton and E. P. Abraham, *Biochem. J.* **47**, 257 (1950).
61. D. Hendlin, *Arch. Biochem. Biophys.* **24**, 435 (1949); U.S. Pat. 2,828,246 (1958), T. E. Fresney and L. P. Allen (to Commercial Solvents Corp.); U.S. Pat. 2,627,494 (1953), W. L. Keko, R. E. Bennett, and F. C. Arzberger (to Commercial Solvents Corp.).
62. U.S. Pat. 2,609,324 (1952), M. Senkus and P. C. Markunas (to Commercial Solvents Corp.); U.S. Pat. 2,828,246 (1958), T. E. Fresney and L. P. Allen (to Commercial Solvents Corp.).
63. U.S. Pat. 2,776,240 (1957), A. W. Shortridge (to Commercial Solvents Corp.).
64. U.S. Pat. 2,556,375 (1951), P. P. Regna and I. A. Solomons (to Chas. Pfizer & Company, Inc.).
65. U.S. Pat. 2,774,712 (1956), A. L. Baron (to S. B. Penick & Co. Inc.); U.S. Pat. 2,803,584 (1957), E. B. Hodge and G. J. Lafferty (to Commercial Solvents Corp.); H. Anker, B. A. Johnson, J. Goldberg, and F. L. Meleney, *J. Bacteriol.* **55**, 249 (1948); H. M. Gross, W. A. Johnson, and G. J. Lafferty, *J. Am. Pharm. Assoc., Sci. Ed.* **45**, 447 (1956); H. M. Gross, *Drug Cosmetic Ind.* **75**, 612 (1954).
66. U.S. Pat. 2,834,711 (1958), E. Zinn and F. Chornock (to Commercial Solvents Corp.).
67. Ger. Pat. 1,079,278 (1959), A. R. Elliott and F. Chornock (to Commercial Solvents Corp.).
68. L. C. Craig, J. R. Weisiger, W. Hausmann, and E. J. Harfenist, *J. Biol. Chem.* **199**, 259 (1952); G. G. F. Newton and E. P. Abraham, *Biochem. J.* **53**, 597 (1953); J. R. Weisiger, W. Hausmann, and L. C. Craig, *J. Am. Chem. Soc.* **77**, 721, 3123 (1955).
69. L. C. Craig, J. R. Weisiger, and W. Hausmann, *J. Biol. Chem.* **200**, 765 (1953); G. G. F. Newton and E. P. Abraham, *Biochem. J.* **53**, 604 (1953).
70. I. M. Lockhart, E. P. Abraham, and G. G. F. Newton, *Biochem. J.* **61**, 534 (1955); I. M. Lockhart and E. P. Abraham, *Biochem. J.* **58**, 633 (1954); W. Hausmann, J. R. Weisiger, and L. C. Craig, *J. Am. Chem. Soc.* **77**, 721, 723 (1955); W. Hausmann, J. R. Weisiger, and L. C. Craig, *J. Biol. Chem.* **199**, 865 (1952); W. Konigsberg and L. C. Craig, *J. Org. Chem.* **27**, 934 (1962).
70a. W. Konigsberg and L. C. Craig, *J. Org. Chem.* **22**, 1345 (1957).
71. E. P. Abraham, *Biochemistry of Some Peptides and Steroidal Antibiotics*, John Wiley & Sons, Inc., New York, 1958, p. 1; L. C. Craig, *Amino Acids and Peptides with Antimetabolite Activity*, J. & A. Churchill Ltd., London, 1958, p. 226.
71a. G. G. F. Newton and E. P. Abraham, *Biochem. J.* **53**, 597 (1953).
72. W. Konigsberg and L. C. Craig, *J. Am. Chem. Soc.* **81**, 3452 (1959).
73. W. Konigsberg and L. C. Craig, *J. Org. Chem.* **22**, 1345 (1957).
74. D. L. Swallow and E. P. Abraham, *Biochem. J.* **72**, 326 (1959).
75. G. C. Ainsworth, A. M. Brown, and G. Brownlee, *Nature* **160**, 263 (1947).
76. R. G. Shepherd, P. G. Stansly, and H. J. White, *Bull. Johns Hopkins Hosp.* **87**, 43 (1947).
77. R. G. Benedict and A. F. Langlykke, *J. Bacteriol.* **54**, 24 (1947).
78. R. W. Milner, ed., *Antibiotics Derived from* Bacillus polymyxa (a Symposium), *Ann. N.Y. Acad. Sci.* **51**, 853–1000 (1949).
79. P. G. Stansly and G. Brownlee, *Nature* **162**, 611 (1949).
80. T. S. G. Jones, *Ann. N.Y. Acad. Sci.* **51**, 909 (1949).
81. Japan. Pat. 1546 (1952), Y. Koyama; *Chem. Abstr.* **47**, 6097 (1953); Y. Koyama A. Kurosava, A. Tuchiga, and K. Takahisada, *J. Antibiotics (Tokyo), Ser. B.* **3**, 457 (1950); T. Kurihara and K. Suzuki, *J. Pharm. Soc. Japan* **73**, 414 (1953).
82. G. F. Gauze, G. V. Kochetkova, T. P. Preobrazhenskaya, and N. S. Pevzner, *Chem. Abstr.* **54**, 25025 (1960).
83. S. A. Il'inskaya and V. S. Rossovskaya, *Antibiotiki* **3**, 10 (1958); A. S. Khokhlov and Ch'ih Ch'ang-ch'ing, *Biokhimiya* **26**, 296 (1961); *Chem. Abstr.* **55**, 16912 (1961); A. S. Khokhlov et al., *Antibiotiki* **5**, 3 (1960); *Chem. Abstr.* **55**, 5653 (1961); A. B. Silaev, V. M. Stepanov, E. P. Yulikova, and G. L. Murotova, *Zh. Obshch. Khim.* **31**, 1023 (1961); *Chem. Abstr.* **55**, 23367 (1961); *ibid.*, **32**, 818 (1962); *Chem. Abstr.* **56**, 13005 (1962); A. B. Silaev, E. P. Yulikova, and L. A. Baratova, *Zh. Obshch. Khim.* **31**, 2712 (1961); *Chem. Abstr.* **58**, 2363

(1963); N. V. Fedoseeva, A. B. Sílaev, and L. I. Andreeva, *Zh. Obshch. Khim.* **33**, 1019 (1963); *Chem. Abstr.* **59**, 8860 (1963); N. V. Fedoseeva, A. B. Silaev, and T. R. Telesnina, *Zh. Obshch. Khim.* **33**, 2760 (1963); *Chem. Abstr.* **60**, 656 (1964).

84. Brit. Pat. 645,750 (1950), S. Wilkinson (to The Wellcome Foundation, Ltd.); Brit. Pat. 646,258 (1950), S. R. M. Bushby (to The Wellcome Foundation, Ltd.).

85. Brit. Pat. 658,766 (1951), S. Wilkinson (to The Wellcome Foundation, Ltd.).

86. K. Vogler, R. O. Studer, W. Lergier, and P. Lanz, *Helv. Chim. Acta* **43**, 1751 (1960); *ibid.* **44**, 131 (1961); R. O. Studer and K. Vogler, *Helv. Chim. Acta* **45**, 819 (1962); R. O. Studer, W. Lergier, and K. Vogler, *Helv. Chim. Acta* **46**, 612 (1963); K. Vogler, R. O. Studer, P. Lanz, W. Lergier, E. Böhni, and B. Fust, *Helv. Chim. Acta* **46**, 2824 (1963).

87. M. Barnett, S. R. M. Bushby, and S. Wilkinson, *Brit. J. Pharmacol.* **23**, 552 (1964).

88. R. G. Petersdorf and J. J. Plorde, *J. Am. Med. Assoc.* **183**, 125 (1963).

89. W. Hausmann and L. C. Craig, *J. Am. Chem. Soc.* **76**, 4892 (1954).

90. M. Fujino, M. Inoue, J. Veyanagi, and M. Miyake, *Bull. Chem. Soc. Japan* **38**, 515 (1963); M. Fujino, *Bull. Chem. Soc. Japan* **38**, 517 (1963).

91. T. Ohno, S. Tajima, and K. Toki, *J. Agr. Chem. Soc. Japan* **27**, 665 (1953).

92. S. Wilkinson and L. A. Lowe, *Nature* **206**, 311 (1966); *Antimicrobial Agents Chemotherapy* **1966**, 651.

93. T. Suzuki, K. Hayashi, K. Fujikawa, and K. Tsukamoto, *J. Biochem.* (*Tokyo*) **54**, 555 (1963); *ibid.*, **56**, 335 (1964).

94. S. Wilkinson and L. A. Lowe, *Nature* **204**, 185 (1964).

95. T. Suzuki, K. Hayashi, Y. Suketa, and K. Tsukamoto, *Experientia* **22**, 354 (1966).

96. T. Suzuki, K. Hayashi, K. Fujikawa, and K. Tsukamoto, *J. Biochem.* (*Tokyo*) **57**, 226 (1965).

97. S. Wilkinson and L. A. Lowe, *Nature* **204**, 993 (1964).

98. K. Fujikawa, Y. Suketa, K. Hayashi, and T. Suzuki, *Experientia* **21**, 307 (1965).

99. F. J. Murray and P. A. Tetrault, *Proc. Soc. Am. Bacteriol.* **1**, 20 (1948); D. H. Peterson and L. M. Reinecke, *J. Biol. Chem.* **181**, 95 (1949); F. J. Murray, P. A. Tetrault, O. W. Kaufman, H. Koffler, D. H. Peterson, and D. R. Collingsworth, *J. Bacteriol.* **57**, 305 (1948); U.S. Pat. 2,676,133 (1954), P. A. Tetrault (to Purdue Research Foundation); J. H. Dowling, H. Koffler, H. C. Reitz, D. H. Peterson, and P. A. Tetrault, *Science* **116**, 147 (1952).

100. K. Vogler, R. G. Studer, P. Lanz, W. Lergier, and E. Böhni, *Helv. Chim. Acta* **48**, 1161 (1965); *ibid.* **48**, 1371 (1965); R. O. Studer, W. Lergier, and K. Vogler, *Helv. Chim. Acta* **49**, 974 (1966).

101. S. Wilkinson, unpublished work.

102. W. Hausmann and L. C. Craig, *J. Am. Chem. Soc.* **76**, 4892 (1954); W. Hausmann, *J. Am. Chem. Soc.* **78**, 3663 (1956); G. Biserte and M. Dautrevaux, *Bull. Soc. Chim. Biol.* **39**, 795 (1957).

103. Ger. Pat. 1,090,380 (1960), G. Ceriotti (to Farmaceutici Italia Soc. Anon.).

104. S. Nakamura, M. Arai, K. Karasawa, and H. Yonehara, *J. Antibiot.* (*Tokyo*), Ser. A. **10**, 248 (1957); *Chem. Abstr.* **53**, 22223 (1959).

105. J. M. Waisvisz, M. G. van der Hoeven, J. van Peppen, and W. C. M. Zwennis, *J. Am. Chem. Soc.* **79**, 4520 (1957).

106. B. Heinemann, M. A. Kaplan, R. D. Muir, and I. R. Hooper, *Antibiot. Chemotherapy* **3**, 1239 (1953).

107. Brit. Pat. 814,794 (1959) (to Bristol Laboratories); Belg. Pat. 607,157 (1961) (to Eli Lilly and Co.).

108. Brit. Pat. 920,563 (1963) (to Eli Lilly and Co.).

109. Japan. Pat. 6893 (1959), B. Hosotani and M. Soeda; *Chem. Abstr.* **54**, 831 (1960).

110. H. Brockmann, G. Pampus, and J. M. Manegold, *Chem. Ber.* **92**, 1294 (1959); H. Brockmann and H. Gröne, *Chem. Ber.* **87**, 1036 (1954); H. Brockmann and G. Pampus, *Angew. Chem.* **67**, 519 (1955); H. H. Martin and G. Pampus, *Arch. Mikrobiol.* **25**, 90 (1956).

111. O. Shotwell et al., *J. Am. Chem. Soc.* **80**, 3912 (1958).

112. Y. Hatsuta, *J. Antibiot.* (*Tokyo*), Ser. A. **2**, 276 (1949); R. Benedict et al., *Antibiot. Chemotherapy* **2**, 591 (1952); R. G. Benedict, *Botan. Rev.* **19**, 229 (1953).

113. M. G. Brazhnikova and E. B. Kruglyak, *Antibiotiki* **4**, 29 (1959); *Chem. Abstr.* **54**, 1653 (1960).

114. R. Corbaz et al., *Helv. Chim. Acta* **40**, 199 (1957); W. Keller-Schierlein, M. Lj. Mikhailovich,

and V. Prelog, *Helv. Chim. Acta* **42**, 305 (1959); B. Heinemann et al., *Antibiot. Ann.* **1954–1955**, 728.

115. R. Bossi, H. Hütter, W. Keller-Schierlein, L. Neipp, and H. Zahner, *Helv. Chim. Acta* **41**, 1645 (1958).

115a. Japan. Pat. 11,048 (1964), T. Hata, T. Sano, A. Matsumae, T. Hoshino, and S. Nomura.

116. H. Brockmann and G. Schmidt-Kastner, *Chem. Ber.* **88**, 57 (1958); H. Brockmann and H. Green, *Ann. Chem.* **603**, 213 (1957); R. Brown, J. Brenner, and C. Kelly, *Antibiot. Chemotherapy* **12**, 482 (1962).

117. J. Charney, W. P. Fisher, C. Curran, P. A. Machlowitz, and A. A. Tytell, *Antibiot. Ann.* **1955–1956**, 886.

118. K. Ueda, Y. Okimoto, H. Sakai, and K. Arima, *J. Antibiot. (Tokyo), Ser. A* **8**, 91 (1955); Japan. Pat. 6296 (1957), Y. Sumiki, K. Sakaguchi, and T. Asai.

119. S. E. de Voe et al., *Antibiot. Ann.* **1956–1957**, 730.

120. G. F. Gause, *Brit. Med. J.* **2**, 1177 (1955); M. G. Brazhnikova, N. N. Lomakina, and L. I. Murayeva, *Dokl. Akad. Nauk S.S.S.R.* **99**, 827 (1954); D. M. Reynolds, A. Schatz, and S. A. Waksman, *Proc. Soc. Exp. Biol. Med.* **64**, 50 (1947).

121. A. J. Shag et al., *Antibiot. Ann.* **1959–1960**, 194; J. H. Martin and W. K. Waksman, *J. Am. Chem. Soc.* **82**, 2079 (1960).

122. S. Kondo, M. Sezaki, M. Shimura, K. Sato, and T. Hara, *J. Antibiot. (Tokyo), Ser. A* **17**, 262 (1964); *Chem. Abstr.* **82**, 2079 (1960).

123. M. J. Cron, D. F. Whitehead, I. R. Harper, B. Heinemann, and J. Lein, *Antibiot. Chemotherapy* **6**, 63 (1960).

124. Japan. Pat. 6894 (1959), F. Okamoto, S. Kubo, T. Nara, and S. Tanaka; *Chem. Abstr.* **54**, 832 (1960).

125. A. E. Oxford, *Biochem. J.* **38**, 178 (1944); *ibid.*, **39**, XII (1945).

126. Neth. Pat. 106,644 (1963) (to N.V. Koninklijke Nederlandse Gist- en Spiritus Fabriek); *Chem. Abstr.* **62**, 11116 (1965).

127. J. Charney, W. S. Roberts, and W. P. Fisher, *Antibiot. Chemotherapy* **2**, 307 (1952).

128. C. P. Schaffner, J. H. Swartz, S. S. Chapman, and W. Huang, *Congr. Intern. Biochim., 3rd, Brussels, 1955*, p. 95; G. Rangaswami, C. P. Schaffner, and S. A. Waksman, *Antibiot. Chemotherapy* **6**, 675 (1956).

129. S. A. Waksman and H. B. Woodruff, *Proc. Soc. Exp. Biol. Med.* **49**, 207 (1942); P. C. Tussell, C. O. Fulton, and G. A. Grant, *J. Bacteriol.* **53**, 769 (1947).

130. K. Maeda, Y. Okami, R. Utahara, H. Kosaka, and H. Umezawa, *J. Antibiot. (Tokyo), Ser. A* **6**, 183 (1953); Y. Miyamoto and K. Maeda, *J. Antibiot. (Tokyo), Ser. A* **7**, 17 (1954).

131. M. Soeda, *J. Antibiot. (Tokyo), Ser. B* **12**, 300 (1959).

132. P. Margalith, G. Beretta, and M. J. Timbal, *Antibiot. Chemotherapy* **9**, 71 (1959).

133. R. Sugawara, A. Matsumae, and F. Hata, *J. Antibiot. (Tokyo), Ser. A* **10**, 133 (1957); Japan. Pat. 5899 (1959), F. Hata, R. Sugawara, A. Matsumae, and T. Sano.

134. D. C. Hobbs and W. D. Celmer, *Fed. Proc.* **18**, 246 (1959); D. C. Hobbs and W. D. Celmer, *Nature* **187**, 598 (1960); W. D. Celmer and B. A. Sobin, *Antibiotics Ann.* **1955–1956**, 437.

135. S. Ball and E. L. Smith, *Biochem. J.* **68**, 24P (1958); F. W. Eastwood, B. K. Snell, and A. Todd, *J. Chem. Soc.* **1960**, 2286.

136. H. Brockmann and H. Sieghard Petras, *Naturwiss.* **46**, 400 (1959).

137. K. Maeda, *J. Antibiot. (Tokyo), Ser. A* **10**, 94 (1957); K. Maeda, H. Kosaka, Y. Okami, and H. Umezawa, *J. Antibiot. (Tokyo), Ser. A* **6**, 140 (1953).

138. H. Tamyama and S. Takemura, *J. Pharm. Soc. Japan* **77**, 1210 (1957); *ibid.*, **78**, 742 (1958),

139. N. Ishida, *J. Antibiot. (Tokyo), Ser. A* **3**, 845 (1950); S. Hosoya, M. Soeda, H. Komatsu, and S. Imamura, *J. Antibiot. (Tokyo), Ser. A* **4**, 79 (1951); Y. Saburi, *J. Antibiot. (Tokyo), Ser. B* **6**, 402 (1953); T. Goto, Y. Hirata, S. Hogoya, and N. Komatsu, *Bull. Chem. Soc. Japan* **30**, 304, 729 (1957).

140. U.S. Pat. 3,082,153 (1963), H. Nishimura (to Shionogi and Company); *Chem. Abstr.* **59**, 2134 (1963).

141. L. C. Vining and W. A. Taylor, *Can. J. Chem.* **35**, 1109 (1957); *Bacteriol. Proc.* **1957**, 70.

142. B. Takahashi, *J. Antibiot. (Tokyo), Ser. A* **7**, 149 (1954); G. F. Gause, *Brit. Med. J.* **2**, 1177 (1955); M. G. Brazhnikova, N. N. Lomakina, and L. L. Murayeva, *Dokl. Akad. Nauk S.S.S.R.* **99**, 827 (1954).

143. P. de Somer and P. van Dijck, *Antibiot. Chemotherapy* **5**, 632 (1955); H. Vanderhaeghe, P. van Dijck, G. Parmentier, and P. de Somer, *Antibiot. Chemotherapy* **7**, 606 (1957); H. Vanderhaeghe and G. Parmentier, *Bull. Soc. Chim. Belge* **68**, 716 (1959); *J. Am. Chem. Soc.* **82**, 4414 (1960).

144. H. Brockmann and B. Franck, *Naturwiss.* **41**, 451 (1954); H. Brockmann and B. Musso, *Chem. Ber.* **87**, 1779 (1954); *ibid.*, **88**, 648 (1955).

145. M. Inoue et al., *Bull. Chem. Soc. Japan* **33**, 1014 (1960); *Chem. Abstr.* **55**, 691 (1961); Fr. Pat. 1,295,913 (1960) (to Takeda Pharmaceutical Ind., Ltd.); Y. Oka, M. Matsui, and T. Araki, *Takeda Kenkyusho Nempo* **20**, 207 (1961); *Chem. Abstr.* **61**, 15232 (1964); M. Inoue, *Bull. Chem. Soc. Japan* **34**, 885 (1961); *Chem. Abstr.* **56**, 3568 (1962); M. Fujino, M. Inoue, J. Veyanagi, and A. Miyake, *Bull. Chem. Soc. Japan* **34**, 740 (1961); *Chem. Abstr.* **56**, 12732 (1962).

146. A. C. Finlay et al., *Am. Rev. Tuberc.* **63**, 1 (1951); G. R. Bartz, J. Erlich, J. D. Mold, M. A. Penner, and R. M. Smith, *Am. Rev. Tuberc.* **63**, 4 (1951); J. Ehrlich, R. M. Smith, M. A. Penner, L. E. Anderson, and A. C. Bratton, Jr., *Am. Rev. Tuberc.* **63**, 7 (1951).

147. R. L. Mayer, C. Crane, R. De Boer, and E. A. Konopka, *Int. Congr. Pure Appl. Chem.*, *12th, New York, 1951;* U.S. Pat. 2,633,445 (1953), W. S. Marsh, R. L. Mayer, R. P. Mull, C. R. Scholz, and R. W. Towsley (to Ciba Pharmaceutical Products, Inc.); R. L. Mayer, P. C. Eisman, and E. A. Konopka, *Experientia* **10**, 335 (1954).

148. U.S. Pat. 2,633,445 (1953) (to Ciba Pharmaceutical Products, Inc.); U.S. Pat. 2,828,245 (1958), T. E. Freaney (to Commercial Solvents Corp.); Brit. Pat. 687,500 (1953) (to Chas. Pfizer & Company, Inc.).

149. J. R. Dyer, H. B. Hayer, E. G. Miller, and R. F. Nasser, *J. Am. Chem. Soc.* **86**, 5363 (1964); T. H. Haskell, S. A. Fusari, R. P. Frohardt, and G. R. Bartz, *J. Am. Chem. Soc.* **74**, 599 (1952).

150. J. H. Bowie, D. A. Cox, A. W. Johnson, and G. Thomas, *Tetrahedron Letters* **1964**, 45, 3305.

151. J. R. Dyer, C. K. Kellogg, R. F. Nasser, and W. E. Streetman, *Tetrahedron Letters* **1965**, 585.

152. K. Deuschle, *13th Conf. Chemotherapy of Tuberculosis, 1954,* p. 144; *Am. Rev. Tuberc.* **70**, 228 (1954).

153. "Current Practice," *Brit. Med. J.* **1963**, 1593.

154. J. F. Pagano, W. J. Weinstein, H. A. Stout, and R. Donovick, *Antibiot. Ann.* **1955–1956**, 554; J. Vandeputte and J. D. Dutcher, *Antibiot. Ann.* **1955–1956**, 560; B. A. Steinberg, W. P. Jambor, and L. O. Suydam, *Antibiot. Ann.* **1955–1956**, 562; U.S. Pat. 2,982,698 (1961), J. B. Platt (to Olin-Mathieson Chem. Corp.); U.S. Pat. 2,982,689 (1961), R. Donovick (to Olin-Mathieson Chem. Corp.).

154a. H. Iwasaki and B. Witkop, *J. Am. Chem. Soc.* **86**, 4698 (1964).

154b. T. Takita and H. Naganawa, *J. Antibiotics (Tokyo), Ser. A* **16**, 246 (1963); T. Takita, *J. Antibiotics (Tokyo), Ser. A* **16**, 211 (1963); T. Takita, H. Naganawa, K. Maeda, and H. Umezawa, *J. Antibiotics (Tokyo), Ser. A* **17**, 90 (1964); J. Veyanag, H. Iwasaki, M. Fujino, T. Kamiya, and S. Tatsuoka, *Symposium of the Chemical Structures of Natural Products, The University of Kyushu, Japan, 1963.*

155. M. Bodanzky, J. Alicino, A. J. Cohen, B. T. Keeler, J. Fried, J. T. Sheehan, N. J. Williams, and C. A. Birkhimer, *J. Am. Chem. Soc.* **86**, 2478 (1964); D. F. W. Cross, G. W. Kenner, R. C. Shepherd, and C. E. Stehr, *J. Chem. Soc.* **1963**, 2143; C. N. C. Drey, G. W. Kenner, H. D. Law, R. C. Shepherd, M. Bodanzky, J. Fried, N. J. Williams, and J. T. Sheehan, *J. Am. Chem. Soc.* **83**, 3906 (1961).

156. G. F. Gauze and M. G. Brazhnikova, *Novosti Med. Akad. Med. Nauk S.S.S.R.* **23**, 3 (1951); *Antibiotiki* **4**, 29 (1957); Yu. O. Sazykin, *Mikrobiologiya* **24**, 75 (1955).

157. D. M. Reynolds and S. A. Waksman, *J. Bacteriol.* **55**, 739 (1948); F. A. Kuehl, M. N. Bishop, L. Chaiet, and K. Folkers, *J. Am. Chem. Soc.* **73**, 1770 (1951).

158. J. Turkova, O. Mikes, and F. Sorm, *Collection Czech. Chem. Commun.* **30**, 118 (1965).

159. G. C. Cheeseman and H. J. Berridge, *Biochem. J.* **65**, 603 (1957); H. J. Berridge, G. G. F. Newton, and E. P. Abraham, *Biochem. J.* **52**, 529 (1952).

160. U.S. Pat. 2,935,503 (1960), H. B. Hawley and R. H. Hall (to Aplin & Barrett, Ltd.); H. Hirsch and A. T. R. Mattick, *Lancet* **11**, 5 (1947).

161. G. C. Cheeseman and N. J. Berridge, *Biochem. J.* **71**, 185 (1959).

161a. E. Gross and J. L. Morell, *J. Am. Chem. Soc.* **89**, 2791 (1967).

162. U.S. Pat. 2,785,108 (1957), H. B. Hawley (to National Research Development Corp.).

163. H. Brockmann, "The Actinomycins," in L. Zeichmeister, ed., *Fortschritte der Chemie organ-*

ischer Naturstoffe, XVIII, Springer-Verlag, Vienna, 1960; H. Brockmann, *Angew. Chem.* **72**, 939 (1960); *ibid.*, **66**, 1 (1954); *Fortschr. Chem. Org. Naturstoffe* **18**, 1 (1960); *Naturwiss.* **50**, 689 (1963); *Chemistry of Natural Products, Intern. Symp., Australia, 1960*, Butterworth & Co. Ltd., London, 1961, p. 405; S. A. Waksman, K. Katz and L. C. Vining, *Proc. Natl. Acad. Sci. (U.S.)* **44**, 602 (1958); A. W. Johnson, *Symposium on Antibiotics and Mould Metabolites*, The Chemical Society, London, 1956, p. 82.

164. H. Brockmann and B. Franck, *Angew. Chem.* **68**, 70 (1956).

165. A. B. Mauger and R. Wade, *J. Chem. Soc.* **1966**, 1406; H. Brockmann and H. Lackner, *Tetrahedron Letters* **1964**, 3523; G. Schmidt-Kastner, *Ann. N.Y. Acad. Sci.* **89**, 299 (1960–1961); E. Katz, *Ann. N.Y. Acad. Sci.* **89**, 304 (1960–1961); H. Brockmann, *Ann. N.Y. Acad. Sci.* **89**, 323 (1960–1961).

166. Lord Todd, *Int. Symp. Organic Chemistry of Natural Products, Brussels, 1962;* K. Okabe, *J. Antibiotics (Tokyo)*, Ser. A **12**, 86 (1959).

167. K. Watanabe, *J. Antibiotics (Tokyo)*, Ser. A **13**, 62 (1960).

168. Fr. Pat. 1,301,857 (1961) (to Rhône-Poulenc S.A.); J. Preud-Homme, A. Belloc, Y. Charpentie, and P. Tarridee, *Compt. Rend.* **260**, 1309 (1965); G. Jolles, B. Terlain, and J. P. Thomas, *Nature* **207**, 199 (1965).

169. M. Barber and P. Waterworth, *Brit. Med. J.* **1964**, 603; J. Monnier and R. Bourse, *Thérap. Semaine Hop.* **38**, 19 (1962).

170. J. C. Sheehan, G. Bohnsack, B. Franck, H. Gröne, H. Maxfeldt, and G. Suling, *Angew. Chem.* **68**, 70 (1956); R. B. Arnold, A. W. Johnson, and A. B. Mauger, *J. Chem. Soc.* **1958**, 4466; J. C. Sheehan, H. G. Zachau, and Q. R. Bartz, *J. Am. Chem. Soc.* **79**, 3933 (1957); B. Heinemann et al., *Antibiot. Ann.* **1954–1955**, 728.

170a. Q. R. Bartz et al., *Antibiot. Ann.* **1954–1955**, 777; T. H. Haskell, A. Maretzki and Q. R. Bartz, *Antibiot. Ann.* **1954–1955**, 784.

171. K. Watanabe, *J. Antibiotics (Tokyo)*, Ser. A. **14**, 14 (1961).

172. K. Okabe, *J. Antibiotics (Tokyo)*, Ser. A **12**, 86 (1959); K. Okabe, Y. Yonehara, and H. Umezawa, *J. Antibiotics (Tokyo)*, Ser. A **12**, 192 (1959); K. Watanabe, *J. Antibiotics (Tokyo)*, Ser. A **13**, 57 (1960); *ibid.*, **14**, 1 (1961); K. Watanabe, H. Yonehara, H. Umezawa, and Y. Sumiki, *J. Antibiotics (Tokyo)*, Ser. A **13**, 291 (1960); K. Watanabe, H. Yonehara, N. Tanaka, and H. Umezawa, *J. Antibiotics (Tokyo)*, Ser. A **12**, 112 (1959); S. Okoshi et al., *J. Antibiotics (Tokyo)*, Ser. A **13**, 137 (1960); M. Arai, K. Karasawa, S. Nakamura, H. Yonehara, and H. Umezawa, *J. Antibiotics (Tokyo)*, Ser. A **11**, 14 (1958).

172a. K. Watanabe, *J. Antibiotics (Tokyo)*, Ser. A **14**, 14 (1961).

173. I. Takahashi, *J. Antibiotics (Tokyo)*, Ser. A **6**, 117 (1953); M. Bodanzky and J. T. Sheehan, *Antimicrobial Agents Chemotherapy* **1963**, 38.

174. A. H. Cook, S. F. Fox, T. H. Farmer, and M. S. Lacey, *Nature* **160**, 31 (1947); *J. Chem. Soc.* **1949**, 1022.

175. Pl. A. Plattner and U. Nager, *Experientia* **3**, 325 (1947); *Helv. Chim. Acta* **31**, 665, 2192, 2203 (1948); Pl. A. Plattner, U. Nager, and A. Boller, *Helv. Chim. Acta* **31**, 594 (1948); E. Gäuman, St. Roth, L. Ettlinger, Pl. A. Plattner, and U. Nager, *Experientia* **3**, 302 (1947).

176. D. W. Russell, *Biochim. Biophys. Acta* **45**, 411 (1960); D. W. Russell and M. E. Brown, *Biochim. Biophys. Acta* **38**, 382 (1960).

176a. W. S. Bertraud, M. C. Probine, J. S. Shannon, and A. Taylor, *Tetrahedron* **21**, 677 (1965).

177. L. C. Vining and W. A. Taber, *Can. J. Chem.* **40**, 1579 (1962).

178. H. H. Wassermann, J. J. Keggi, and J. E. McKeon, *J. Am. Chem. Soc.* **83**, 4107 (1961); *ibid.*, **84**, 2978 (1962).

179. L. Todd, *Ind. Chim. Belge* **27**, 1423 (1962).

180. F. W. Eastwood, B. K. Snell, and A. Todd, *J. Chem. Soc.* **1960**, 2286.

181. M. M. Shemyakin, *Angew. Chem.* **72**, 342 (1960); E. Schröder and K. Lübke, *Experientia* **19**, 57 (1963); G. Losse and G. Bachmann, *Z. Chem.* **4**, 241 (1964).

182. C. G. Macdonald and J. S. Shannon, *Tetrahedron Letters* **1964**, 3133.

183. P. Quitt, R. O. Studer, and K. Vogler, *Helv. Chim. Acta* **46**, 1715 (1963); *ibid.*, **47**, 166 (1964); Pl. A. Plattner, K. Vogler, R. O. Studer, P. Quitt, and W. Keller-Schierlein, *Experientia* **19**, 71 (1963); *Helv. Chim. Acta* **46**, 927 (1963).

184. H. Brockmann and H. Green, *Ann. Chem.* **603**, 216 (1957).

185. M. M. Shemyakin, N. A. Aldanova, E. I. Vinogradova, and M. Y. Feigina, *Tetrahedron Letters* **1963**, 1921.

186. A. A. Kiryushkin, Y. A. Ovchinnikov, and M. M. Shemyakin, *Tetrahedron Letters* **1964**, 3313.

187. D. W. Russell, C. G. Macdonald, and J. S. Shannon, *Tetrahedron Letters* **1964**, 2759.

188. D. W. Russell and E. Bishop, *Biochem. J.* **92**, 19P (1964).

189. M. M. Shemyakin, Y. A. Ovchinnikov, V. T. Ivanov, and A. A. Kiryushkin, *Tetrahedron* **19**, 995 (1963).

190. Y. A. Ovchinnikov, A. A. Kiryushkin, and M. M. Shemyakin, *Tetrahedron Letters* **1965**, 1111.

191. Y. A. Ovchinnikov, A. A. Kiryushkin, and M. M. Shemyakin, *Tetrahedron Letters* **1965**, 143.

192. S. Ball, S. Boothroyd, K. A. Lees, A. A. Raper, and E. L. Smith, *Biochem. J.* **68**, 24P (1958).

193. M. Bodanszky and M. A. Ondetti, *Antimicrobial Agents Chemotherapy* **1963**, 360.

194. K. Watanabe, *J. Antibiotics (Tokyo)*, *Ser. A* **13**, 62 (1960).

195. N. Tanaka et al., *J. Antibiotics (Tokyo)*, *Ser. A* **12**, 290 (1959); *ibid.*, **11**, 127 (1958); *ibid.*, **15**, 28, 33 (1962); K. Watanabe, Y. Yonehara, N. Tanaka, and H. Umezawa, *J. Antibiotics (Tokyo)*, *Ser. A* **12**, 112 (1959).

196. Y. A. Chabbert and J. F. Acar, *Ann. Inst. Pasteur* **107**, 777 (1964).

197. M. Misiek, O. B. Fardig, A. Gourevitch, D. L. Johnson, I. R. Hooper, and J. Lein, *Antibiot. Ann.* **1957–1958**, 852.

198. H. A. Whaley et al., *Abstracts Sixth Interscience Conf. Antimicrobial Agents Chemotherapy, Philadelphia, Pa., 1966*, p. 23; H. A. Whaley, E. L. Patterson, M. Dann, P. Shu, M. E. Swift, J. N. Porter, and G. Redin, *Antimicrobial Agents Chemotherapy* **1966**, 587; H. A. Whaley, E. L. Patterson, M. P. Kunstmann, and N. Bohonos, *Antimicrobial Agents Chemotherapy* **1966**, 591.

199. J. C. Sheehan et al., *J. Am. Chem. Soc.* **85**, 2867 (1963).

200. N. Ishida, K. Miyazaki, K. Kumagai, and M. Rikamura, *J. Antibiotics (Tokyo)*, *Ser. A* **18**, 68 (1965).

201. "Official Assay Methods of Antibiotics Preparations" (in Japanese), (Dept. Public Welfare, F1, Japan, 1959), *J. Biochem. (Tokyo)* **54**, 25 (1963).

202. Y. Suhara, M. Ishizuka, H. Naganawa, M. Hori, M. Suzuki, Y. Okami, T. Takeuchi, and H. Umezawa, *J. Antibiotics (Tokyo)*, *Ser. A* **16**, 107 (1963).

203. H. Murase and H. Umezawa, *J. Antibiotics (Tokyo)*, *Ser. A* **14**, 113 (1961).

204. H. Schmitz, R. L. De Vault, and I. R. Hooper, *J. Med. Chem.* **6**, 613 (1963); H. Schmitz, W. T. Bradner, A. Gourevitch, B. Heinemann, K. E. Price, J. Lein, and I. R. Hooper, *Cancer Res.* **22**, 163 (1962).

205. S. Inouye, *J. Antibiotics (Tokyo)*, *Ser. A* **15**, 236 (1962); S. Inouye, *Agr. Biol. Chem. (Tokyo)* **26**, 563 (1962).

206. E. Borowski, H. Chmara, and E. Jereczek-Morowska, *Biochim. Biophys. Acta* **130**, 560 (1966); E. Borowski, H. Chmara, and E. Jereczek-Morowska, *Chemotherapia* **12**, 12 (1967); H. Chmara and E. Borowski, *Acta Microbiol. Polon.* **15**, 223 (1966); Z. Kurylo-Borowska, *Bull. Inst. Marine Med. Gdansk* **10**, 83, 151 (1959); G. Roncari, Z. Kurylo-Borowska, and L. C. Craig, *Biochemistry* **5**, 2153 (1966); Z. Kurylo-Borowska, *Biochim. Biophys. Acta* **95**, 590 (1965).

207. M. Sela and E. Katchalski, *Advan. Protein Chem.* **14**, 391 (1959); M. A. Stahman, ed., *Polyamino Acids, Polypeptides and Proteins*, Univ. of Wisconsin Press, Madison, Wis., 1962, p. 329; E. Katchalski, M. Sela, H. I. Silman, and A. Berger, "Polyamino Acids as Protein Models," in H. Neurath, ed., *The Proteins*, Vol. II, 2nd ed., Academic Press, Inc., New York and London, 1964, p. 405.

208. M. J. Fridecky and W. H. McGregor, *J. Med. Chem.* **9**, 255 (1966).

209. M. A. Pisano, B. A. Shidlovsky, H. Kovacs, and J. Kovacs, *Antimicrobial Agents Chemotherapy* **1966**, 457.

210. G. R. Delpierre, F. W. Eastwood, G. E. Gream, D. G. I. Kingston, P. S. Sarin, Lord Todd, and D. H. Williams, *Tetrahedron Letters* **4**, 369 (1966); G. E. Gream, *Structural Studies on Ostreogrycin A*, Ph.D. Thesis, Cambridge University, Cambridge, England, 1961; P. S. Sarin, *Structural Studies on Ostreogrycins A and G*, Ph.D. Thesis, Cambridge University, Cambridge, England, 1962.

211. H. Zähner, E. Bachmann, R. Hütter, and J. Nüesch, *Pathol. Microbiol.* **25**, 708 (1962).

212. J. C. Sheehan, D. Mania, S. Nakamura, J. A. Stock, and K. Maeda, *J. Am. Chem. Soc.* **90**, 462 (1967).

213. M. Iglöy and A. Mizsei, *J. Chromatog.* **28**, 456 (1967).

General References

M. W. Miller, *The Pfizer Handbook of Microbial Metabolites*, McGraw-Hill Book Co., Inc., New York, 1961.

P. Brian, "Antibiotics Produced by Fungi," *Botan. Rev.* **17**, 357 (1951).

E. B. Chain, "Chemistry and Biochemistry of Antibiotics," *Ann. Rev. Biochem.* **27**, 167 (1958).

W. Modell, ed., *Drugs in Current Use*, Springer Publishing Co., Inc., New York, 1966.

R. M. Evans, *The Chemistry of Antibiotics Used in Medicine*, Pergamon Press, London, 1965.

V. I. Bilai, *Antibiotic-Producing Microscopic Fungi*, Elsevier Publishing Co., Amsterdam, Netherlands, 1963.

E. Schröder and K. Lübke, *The Peptides*, Vol. II, *Occurrence and Action of Biologically Active Polypeptides*, Academic Press, New York, 1966.

K. Vogler and R. O. Studer, "The Chemistry of the Polymyxin Antibiotics," *Experientia* **22**, 345 (1966).

T. Wieland and H. Determann, "The Chemistry of Peptides and Proteins," *Ann. Rev. Biochem.* **35**, 651 (1966).

G. Hagemann, *Die Rohstoffe des Pflanzenreichs*, Vol. II, *Antibiotiques*, Verlag von J. Cramer, Weinheim, Germany, 1963.

M. Bodanszky and D. Perlmann, "Are Peptide Antibiotics Small Proteins?", *Nature* **204**, 840 (1964).

E. Schröder and K. Lübke, "Peptolide," *Experientia* **19**, 57 (1963).

W. Lhoest, "Industrial Preparations of Antibiotics," *J. Pharm. Belge* **19**, 335 (1964).

D. Gottlich and P. D. Shaw, eds., *Antibiotics*, Vol. I, *Mechanism of Action*, Springer-Verlag, Berlin, Germany, 1967.

S. Wilkinson
The Wellcome Research Laboratories
Beckenham, Kent, England

POLYPROPYLENE.   See Olefin polymers.

POLYSTYRENE.   See Styrene and styrene polymers.

POLYTHENE (POLYETHYLENE).   See Olefin polymers.

POLYVINYL COMPOUNDS.   See Vinyl compounds and polymers.

PORCELAIN.   See Ceramics; Dental materials, Vol. 6, p. 796.

POROMERIC MATERIALS

Synthetic leatherlike materials have been available for perhaps a hundred years as coated or rubberized fabrics and sheets. These materials have had very limited use in the field of shoe uppers, one of the largest and most physically demanding of markets for leather, because of basic deficiencies in moisture permeability, flex durability, ease of shoemaking, and visual and tactile esthetics. The unique microporous, highly interwoven, graded fibrous structure of leather is largely responsible for its value and success in this critical end use (Figs. 1 and 2). Repeated attempts have been made in the past fifty years or so to solve these difficulties and create a fibrous structure both resembling the natural product and having these key properties—a product that would be useful for shoe uppers, as well as innersoles, linings, and upholstery. These attempts can be classified into two general types according to the length of the fibers used in constructing the substrate:

1. Short-length fiber mats bonded with polymeric binder (eg, glue, latex, etc). This is essentially a papermaking approach.

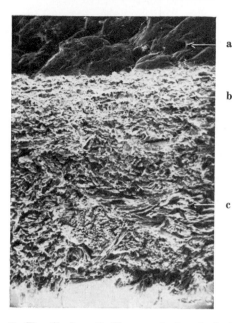

Fig. 1. Cross-sectional view of calf leather (160×): (**a**) finished surface; (**b**) grain side (fine fibers); (**c**) flesh side (coarse fibers).

2. Textile-length fiber mats bonded either with an external, polymer binder or by self-adhesion of selected kinds of fiber at the crossover points. This is a nonwoven-fabric approach.

Either of these substrate materials are then usually surface finished with permeable or nonpermeable coatings described in a later section.

In the early 1950s, E. I. du Pont de Nemours & Co. started a concerted effort to develop a product for the shoe-upper market, culminating in 1964 with the commercial introduction of Corfam, the first poromeric material. The term poromeric is derived from the concepts micro*porous* and poly*meric* and describes a microporous and permeable coriaceous sheet material based on urethan polymers and ester polymer fibers for generalized use in industrial arts.

Some related products are:

Short-Length Fiber Substrates. In this approach the fiber length is generally of the order of 1/8 in.; under special conditions fibers as long as 1/2 in. can be used.

Impregnated and coated papers have long been used as shoe components such as quarter linings, innersoles, and heel pads. Attempts to upgrade the tear and tensile strength of papers and retain or increase moisture permeability led in the 1920s and 1930s to kraft, rag, and similar strong-fibered papers saturated and bonded with natural rubber latex. The unsatisfactory resistance to perspiration, difficulty in curing, and unsatisfactory odor of the natural rubber, however, led in turn to its replacement by latexes of curable neoprene, acrylonitrile–butadiene interpolymer, or acrylic ester interpolymers (1). In manufacture, the latexes can be (*1*) added to the paper beater stock, or (*2*) applied to the dried porous paper or to the wet paper after sheet making. (Natural and synthetic fibers up to 1/2 in. long have also been added.) Papers thus made, after coagulation, drying, pressing, and curing of the binder, are coated and finished by techniques similar to those used for leather. A substantial body of patent literature exists for making such substrate materials (2). The finished product is now widely used in notebook and briefcase covers, as well as in shoe linings and innersoles where low cost is important and tensile strength and flex durability are less critical

(Fig. 3). No commercially significant shoe-upper material of this type however is yet known.

Closely paralleling this development, and perhaps older historically, has been the conversion of leather scrap into useful sheet materials both in the U.S.A. and in Europe. Selected scrap is disintegrated to fiber, excess dust removed, and the fiber slurried in

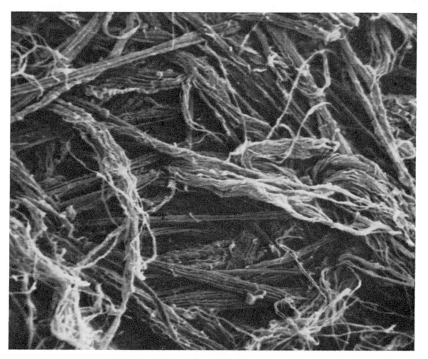

Fig. 2. Flesh side of calf leather (120×).

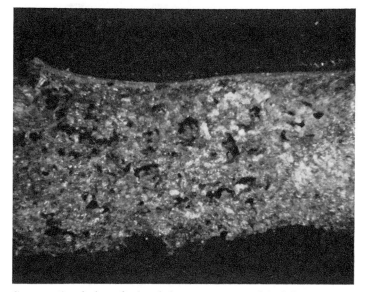

Fig. 3. Cross-sectional view of a bonded nonwoven material of the paper type (55×).

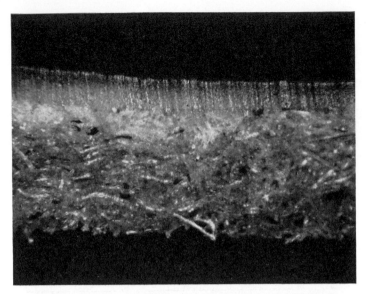

Fig. 4. Cross-sectional view of a poromeric material (28×).

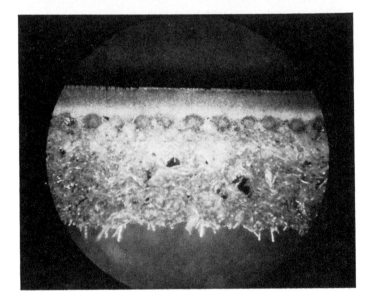

Fig. 5. Cross-sectional view of a poromeric material (28×).

water and converted into a sheet in combination with some kind of binder. Binders used include glues, soluble collagens, and natural or synthetic polymers in the form of latexes or solutions. Other fibers such as wood pulp, cellulose, cotton, rayon, and nylon may be blended with the leather fiber to improve the physical properties of the sheet. Drying, curing and finishing are handled as with the paper-type product. These reconstituted leather sheets are generally stiffer, less flex durable, have lower tensile strength and are less permeable to moisture vapor than the original hide product and are suited primarily for shoe innersoles, stiffeners, counters, linings, and sometimes outer soles (3). Practical shoe-upper materials have yet to be realized by this route.

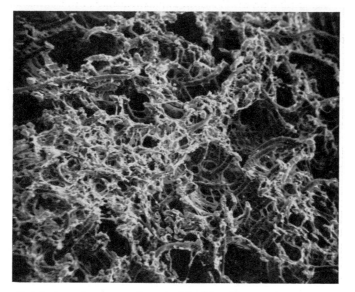

Fig. 6. Cross-sectional view of a poromeric material with a fibrous microporous structure (120×).

A somewhat different approach to making leatherlike sheets is based on reconstituted collagen. Chemical disintegration of untanned hide substance and leather waste to the fundamental collagen protofibril is carried out, and then, under carefully controlled conditions, these protofibrils in aqueous suspension reassemble to form a grosser-fibered pasty mass which can be formed into sheets or spread as coatings.

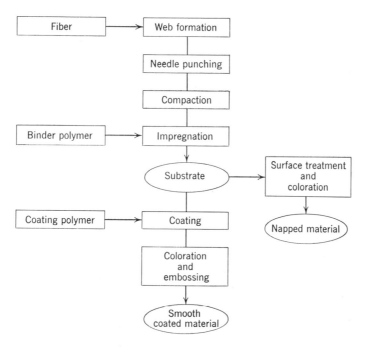

Fig. 7. Outline of the process for producing a poromeric material.

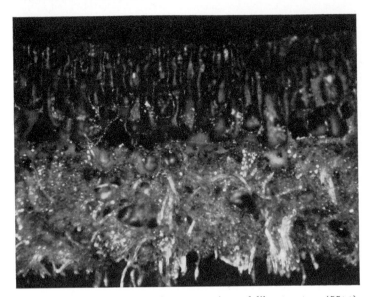

Fig. 8. Cross-sectional view of a poromeric suedelike structure (55×).

The resulting structure is of long-range technical interest; however, no practical commercial product has yet become available (4).

Textile-Length Bonded Fiber Mats (Nonwoven Substrates). Of the many approaches to a "true leatherlike" fibrous structure, those based on textile-length nonwoven fiber substrates, impregnated and finished with polymeric compositions, have been the most promising. Particularly challenging has been the refinement of this type of material to meet the demands of the shoe-upper market. Textile-length fibers (ranging from 1 to 3 in.) are used primarily to obtain the essential tear and tensile strength, flex durability, conformability, and permeability; properties not easily achieved with short-length fibers. The construction generally follows one of three types: (1) an impregnated nonwoven fabric, surface-coated with a plastic, (2) a nonwoven fabric bonded to a woven or knit fabric and then surface-coated, or (3) a woven or knit fabric, heavily napped on one or both sides to simulate a nonwoven fabric and then surface-coated. The surface coating may vary in composition and thickness and is preferably permeable to moisture vapor.

In recent years, many candidate materials for the shoe-upper market have been prepared and offered for test by a number of manufacturing companies both in the United States and in other countries. Development of these materials has been possible largely because of the many sophistications of polymer technology now available, for example, specialized fibers, binders, coatings, and finishes. The first microporous product to reach a significant commercial position was Corfam, a poromeric material trademarked by E. I. du Pont de Nemours & Co. Later products include Clarino, produced by Kurashiki Rayon, Ltd., Aztran, produced by B. F. Goodrich Co., and Ortix produced by ICI Fibers, Ltd. (5). Corfam, possessing a porous, densely fibrous structure, is neither an ordinary laminate nor a conventional coated fabric, but a precisely integrated structure in subtle gradations from a soft, fibrous texture on one side to a tough but microporous wear surface on the other. A network of microscopic pores (in the range of a million per square inch) traverse the sheet from back to front, affording a high level of useable moisture vapor permeability without visibly detracting from the appearance. It is based on a polyester fiber structure integrated with a microporous polyurethan binder/surface coating (Figs. 4–6). The process is complex, requiring rigid controls at every step. A generalized flow chart for a process used earlier in the development is shown in Figure 7. The construction of the fibrous phase and its relationship to the binder have been carefully chosen to produce the desired balance in the many critical physical properties. Surface finishes, to adjust color, gloss, surface slip, etc, use other polymers such as acrylic ester and vinyl interpolymers, and polyurethans. Variations in thickness, pliability and esthetic appearance have been developed to meet the broad range of needs of the shoe industry. Figure 8 shows a suedelike variation, a Corfam 400-type product (6).

Manufacture of Leatherlike Nonwoven Materials

Substrate Preparation. In general the bonded nonwoven substrate used in leatherlike materials, though related in part to the general class of nonwovens such as padding, clothing interliners, disposable fabrics, filters, etc, has necessitated its own special technology by virtue of the need for higher density, pleasant hand, and better fold resistance, shape retention, and moisture permeability. Most kinds of textile-length fibers have been used at one time or another, alone or in combination, in making nonwoven fabrics: cotton, wool, nylon, rayon, cellulose acetate, polyacrylonitrile, polyesters, poly(vinyl alcohol), poly(vinyl chloride), poly(vinylidene chloride), and polytetrafluoroethylene are the best examples. The properties of the fiber, ie tensile modulus, denier, degree of crimp, etc, are important factors controlling the character of the final products. Such fibers in the form of staple, $\frac{1}{2}$ to 3 in. long, are converted first into random nonwoven fiber batts by any one of the several commercial nonwoven fabric techniques.

Conversion of Staple to Nonwoven Batts. The conversion can be carried out by carding, garnetting or a similar mechanical combing process followed by multiple crosslapping of the web into a plied batt of relatively random fiber orientation in the plane of the batt. This batt is laced together by punching densely with barbed needles (ie, needle looming, needle punching, ligating, etc), providing some fiber orientation in the third dimension for laminar strength.

Air deposition can be used for the conversion. A fibrous batt suitably prepared and opened is combed by a high-speed toothed roll which pulls out individual fibers and flips them into the air stream. This stream is then sucked through a belt screen or perforated roll to deposit the fibers in a more nearly three-dimensional orientation (7). Punching with barbed needles may follow as mentioned before.

A third method is to slurry shorter length fibers ($\frac{1}{2}$–1 in. long) at very dilute concentration in water with the aid of suspending agents and then to form them into a web by conventional papermaking techniques.

Other techniques have also been devised for making nonwoven substrates; particularly noted are those in which the forming operation for the fiber is combined with the collecting operation for the web. Such fibers may be blown-spun from air-activated spray guns using polymer solutions or hot melts. Such nonwovens are characterized by essentially a semicontinuous filament construction rather than the staple fiber construction cited before (8).

Bonding. After forming the batt, a bonding operation is required. This may take the form of "mechanical" bonding in which the fibers are forcibly intertangled, for example by needle looming, by chemical treatment to coil and knit the fibers, or by the action of water during batt-making (9). Bonding can also be done by "chemical" adhesion of the fibers one to another. This may be done by impregnation with fluid adhesive materials which collect at the fiber crossover points, by dry thermoplastic powders or by use of combinations of different fibers which can be activated by heat, solvents, or certain hydrophilic chemicals to effect adhesion to each other (10). Many of these techniques lead to fairly open, sometimes fluffy, batts which require reimpregnation or pressing to consolidate them to a substrate useable as a leatherlike material. An alternate method comprises heavily impregnating the loose batts of fibers with essentially a nonadhesive plastic or elastomer so that the final sheet is a two-phase system having a porous binder structural phase full of "worm holes" and, lying wholly contained therein, a contiguous fibrous phase loosely occupying the "worm holes." The binder or impregnant can be selected from a broad range of elastomeric, thermoplastic or thermosetting polymers. Neoprenes, acrylic and vinyl ester copolymers, polyisobutylene, polyesters, polyether–urethans, polyester–urethans and phenol-formaldehyde resins have been used. These may be applied as solutions, dispersions, dry powders or even as preformed films, coagulated and dried where appropriate, and then hot-pressed to effect consolidation and bonding (11). Suitably compounded, the binder can be cured or insolubilized, for example during hot-pressing, to stabilize the overall structure. Pigments are often included. Many combinations and permutations of these basic themes for bonding have been devised.

Such heavily consolidated bonded nonwovens are generally stiff and nonpermeable due to binder–fiber adhesion and interaction. Many different aftertreatments to develop contiguous channels and restore pliability, permeability, and conformability have been investigated. These include the use of parting agents such as oils, detergents, waxes, and silicones to destroy matrix binder–fiber adhesion and serve as lubricants (12); controlled stretching of the sheet in one or more directions to rupture the matrix binder–fiber bonds and open up the structure (13); swelling of the fiber with a solvent to expand the matrix "worm holes" (for example, nylon fiber swollen in hot water), followed by setting or curing of the matrix and deswelling the fiber (14); and mechanical working of the sheet in a solvent composition to dissolve out a fibrous component or fiber coating (15).

Preparation of an Impregnated Batt. The following example illustrates one method of providing a substrate for leatherlike materials:

A quantity of 3 den, $1\frac{1}{2}$ in. long nylon staple fiber is blended with an equal quantity of a similar-sized rayon fiber, opened and carded on a textile card to form a uniform batt of approximately $1\frac{1}{2}$ oz/sq yd weight. This batt then is cut and the sections cross-layed to a total weight of 9 oz/sq yd to help randomize fiber orientation. The batt, suitably supported, is immersed in a wetting agent solution, dried and then soaked in a plasticized poly(vinyl chloride) latex. The excess latex is removed between wringer rolls and the latex coagulated in situ by immersion in a bath of an electrolyte solution such as alum, magnesium sulfate, or acetic acid in methanol. After coagulation, the impregnated web is washed, dried and pressed at about 400 psi and 150°C between platens. Shims may be used in the press to control thickness. A smooth, fibrous leatherlike substrate results. The density and pliability of the completed structure can be varied over a wide range by adjusting the solids content of the latex or the wringing pressure after impregnation, or the temperature, pressure or shim thickness used during the pressing step. The inherent degree of plasticization of the binder, ie its modulus of elasticity, also has a noticeable effect on the pliability of the final sheet.

Liquid binders, though perhaps the most versatile to use, require special care to obtain uniform impregnation of the fiber batt. Where latexes are used, coagulation of the latex in situ must occur before drying, otherwise the latex will migrate to the outer surfaces of the batt during drying leaving a starved center which easily delaminates. The composition may include latent coagulating agents, such as sodium fluorosilicate, which, when heated, alter the pH and coagulate the latex. The latex-impregnated batt can also be dried with dielectric heat, exposed to coagulating vapors, freeze-coagulated or, as in the example, dipped in a separate coagulating bath. Application of a coagulant to the fiber and drying before impregnation is also effective to avoid binder migration. Polymer solution impregnants can be similarly deposited without migration by means of (1) latent curing agents which insolubilize the polymer upon heating, or (2) by dipping the batts into baths of nonsolvent to precipitate the polymer (for example a polymer solution in acetone may be coagulated by dipping in a water bath), or (3) hot impregnation by a solution which gels on cooling (16). Plastisols of poly(vinyl chloride) are convenient impregnants since they are highly fluid, essentially 100% effective solids, and are readily immobilized in the impregnated batt by simple heating to 150°C or thereabouts. Such liquid impregnants offer wide latitude in formulation. Pigments and fillers as well as a wide range of plasticizing and stabilizing agents can be included in the impregnants; eg latexes can be whipped to a froth before application, leaving, upon coagulation, a porous bonded nonwoven material (17).

Surface Finishing. Permeability to moisture vapor is usually regarded as a key property for a leatherlike material. It is particularly desired for shoe uppers and is a factor in the comfort of shoes along with moisture absorption. (Air permeability on the other hand does not seem to be a significant comfort factor.)

Though it is not difficult to make soft pliable bonded nonwoven materials that are highly permeable and thus potentially useful as shoe uppers, these materials fuzz badly by scuff abrasion in use. A surface coating, sufficient to eliminate the fuzzing, is accordingly required and it must have a high level of inherent moisture permeability if it is to avoid sealing off the substrate. Further, a surface coating is needed to adjust gloss, color, and tactile esthetics.

Considerable ingenuity has been applied over the years to resolve these problems and create permeable sheet materials that at the same time have good surface appearance and acceptable mechanical and wear properties. A substantial body of patent literature has resulted covering a broad range of microporous products useful for shoe uppers, as well as for insoles, battery separators, filters, raincoats, upholstery, etc. Mechanical perforation of sheets provides some permeability but seriously detracts from the surface appearance and limits the products in which the material can be used. Embossed perforated leathers and coated fabrics for shoe uppers, insoles and upholstery are well-known examples of the compromise possible. To avoid the restrictions of visible perforations, fine needles have been used to prick holes at high concentration in both solid and blown surface coatings and films (18). These holes result in a haze or even a distinct pattern in the surface appearance and are prone to seal off due to regain of the polymer stressed around each hole as well as by plugging with dirt, wax, etc. Alternatively spark treatment of plastics has been used to make fine holes that will stay open (19). Laser beams can similarly be employed (20).

Other means of making permanent holes have been examined. Woven, knit or nonwoven fabrics when coated or impregnated with a fluid composition can be rendered porous by forcibly blowing or sucking a gas through the interstices in the fabrics while solidifying the composition (21). The composition also can be applied as a froth or, when incorporating a separate chemical blowing agent, can be post-blown to a porous structure (22). Reactive polyurethans which are self-blowing can be coated to produce a porous sheet (23). Inclusion of volatile liquids in the composition can also be used to blow a porous structure, eg water in poly(vinyl chloride) plastisols (24). Coating and impregnating compositions which contain soluble particles such as salt, ureas, sugar, and starches can be leached with chemicals designed to degrade or dissolve the particles, leaving behind the porous, permeable matrix (25). In a refinement of this technique, soluble fibers in the upper layers of the fabric structure are leached out by solvents producing a network of fiber-sized holes (26). This provides not only the desired permeability but also can be used to eliminate the surface fuzz problem described before. In another technique, swellable but insoluble hydrophilic particles are included in the surface which, upon solvent treatment and drying, leaves a network of channels (27). Another variation calls for the inclusion in the coating composition of a substantial volume of fine fragile hollow spheres. When the final structure is worked, crushing the spheres, a permeable network is left (28).

Inclusion of fillers such as calcium carbonate, clay, ground slate, and pumice in elastomeric coating compositions up to the critical level of pigment volume content makes possible permeable sheet structures. In this technique, a balance is achieved between having the volume of filler particles large enough to establish a network of microscopic passageways yet not so large as to impair the tensile strength, flexibility and abrasion resistance. Latex, solution, or calender-type stocks can be so formulated and have been made on a commercial scale (primarily for rainwear) (29).

A quite different approach is involved in causing polymer solutions to precipitate slowly in the presence of nonsolvent liquids or vapors, producing a microporous permeable structure. One of the earliest examples of this type was a microbiological filter made by coagulating cellulose nitrate or cellulose acetate from acetone–acetic acid solutions using water (30). Nylon similarly can be produced in a microporous form from calcium chloride–methanol solutions using water as the precipitant (31). A number of other polymers, eg poly(vinyl chloride) and polyacrylonitrile, have been used in this way to make leatherlike coatings, shoe innersoles, battery-plate separators, etc (32). In a variation, solutions of poly(vinyl alcohol) when gelled with formaldehyde yield a fine-pored sponge (33). Other micropore processes suited to hard polymers such as poly(vinyl chloride) depend upon precipitation of a latex in the presence of a solvent–nonsolvent blend or upon sintering dry powders or dispersions in selected solvents and plasticizers (34). The resulting structures can have a wide range of pore sizes but are usually rather stiff and low in flex durability and are suited to insoles, filters, etc. Softer, elastomeric polymers on the other hand tend to give impermeable though tougher structures on precipitation, but can be sprayed from volatile solvents to make microporous, moisture-permeable films (35).

All of the above techniques rely on the presence of actual open passageways, albeit microscopic, to carry moisture vapor, ie they are porous to air. Alternatively, coatings made from polymers that are inherently permeable to moisture have been prepared. Vinyl, acrylic, ether, ester or urethan type interpolymers having a substantial concentration of moisture-sensitive groups are examples. Pendant or intralinear polyethylene oxide groups are relatively inexpensive and adaptable to inclusion in a broad range of polymers. Various salt groups, eg carboxylate, sulfonate, quaternary ammonium and sulfonium groups, have also been reported as useful (36). Such coatings although permeable to moisture vapor, tend to be undesirably water-sensitive, that is, they become swollen, with a sticky surface, and lose tensile and abrasion strength, thus limiting their practical applications. As an alternative, dispersing such moisture-sensitive polymers in a matrix of hydrophobic polymer can provide a more workable balance of properties. These particles provide the channels for diffusion of moisture vapor without permitting passage of liquid water or air. For example, plasticized poly(vinyl chloride) coatings containing crosslinked sodium polyacrylate salt particles have been used. Similarly, crosslinked N,N-alkylacrylamide copolymers, starches, collagen fibrils, cellulose flocs, etc, can be dispersed in various elastomeric coatings on fabric. These may be coupled with the swell/deswell technique described above (37).

The general phenomenon of moisture-vapor permeability of porous materials, polymers, and other sheet materials has been extensively investigated and reported in the literature. Both gaseous diffusion and "activated" diffusion are involved (38–40).

Physical Properties

Table 1 lists typical physical properties of various types of leather and leatherlike materials. Attention is drawn to the wide differences in tensile and tear strength, pliability, and moisture-vapor permeability of the materials without necessarily associating these with values acceptable for any given end use.

Tensile and tear strengths are, as might be expected, generally a function of the inherent strength, concentration, and staple length of the fibrous components, and adhesion of the binder for the fiber (41).

Pliability and conformability are complex functions of the bending modulus of the fiber and binder used, of the concentration and resilience of the fiber network, and of the adhesion of the binder for the fiber as well as of the thickness of the structure. Further, machine-measured pliability may differ from the "psychological" pliability for similar structures as sensed by such subjective tests as hand, feel, break, drape, fold, etc. As might be expected, correlation of these properties with performance on shoemaking machinery is highly complex.

Flex durability, ie resistance to flex cracking, is an important property in some end uses, especially in shoe uppers where the vamp area is severely flexed (42). Formulating the coating compositions requires proper choice of the flexural modulus, the inherent adhesion, the degree of stress flow and the long-range stability to moisture, atmospheric oxygen, perspiration, shoe-care products, and sunlight. The nature of the substrate itself also affects the flex durability of the surface coatings. Fiber content and structure, void content, flexural modulus of the binder, and binder–fiber adhesion and thickness are among significant substrate factors to be adjusted.

Scuff and abrasion resistance of the finished material is important in many end uses, for example, shoes (children's shoes in particular) and luggage. A balance between the hardness and toughness of the coating compositions has to be taken into account. An improper balance leads either to ready flex cracking or to an unsightly fuzzing as the surface coatings are worn away, exposing the tougher fibrous structure underneath.

A physical characteristic often encountered, though undesirable, in leatherlike materials is roughening. This is the propensity of the sheet material, upon being

Table 1. Physical Properties of Leather and Leatherlike Materials

	Weight, oz/yd	Thickness, mil	Tensile strength, lb/in.	Density, g/cm³	5% Tensile modulus, lb/in.	Elongation to break, %	Tongue tear strength,[a] lb	Stitch tear strength,[b] lb	Permeability to water vapor, g/((100 m²)(hr))	Flex, mm
Corfam[c]										
213	15.2	35	70/50	0.58	25/5	30/43	6–10	13	3500	>10
214	18.0	45	84/60	0.54	25/7	30/40	6–12	16	3500	>10
216	20.0	60	92/60	0.49	25/8	34/40	6–12	16	3500	>10
404	12	45	50/30	0.34	5/2	80/120	4/6	13	8000	6
expanded vinyl A	18.5	55	60/60	0.49		12/12	12/12	35	0	2
expanded vinyl B	34.5	64	126/64	0.72	31/15	20/16	5.5/7.5	21/10	0	6
polyester–urethan C	29.4	70	98	0.56	28	20			4700	5
polyether–urethan D	21.7	66	81/45	0.44	20/3	8/46		20	1500	2
polyester–urethan E	25	63	82	0.52	13	75		25	0	1
latex-bonded paper	14	31	40	0.61		2	6/8	7	900	0.1
calf leather	24.5	50	90/160	0.68		30–40	6	20–45	5–10000	>10
side leather	32	70	100–200	0.62		20–50	7	20–45	1–4000	>10
cordovan	40	66	90	0.84		20–30	5	25	2–7000	>10

[a] ASTM D-39 and D-2261.
[b] American Leather Chemists' Association.
[c] Du Pont's registered trademark.

stretched, to develop an unsightly orange-peel-like surface appearance. This is particularly significant for smooth, fine-grain shoe-upper materials where such stretching can be encountered in heel and toe lasting of shoes. Roughening largely derives from structural differences and inhomogeneities within the substrate of such properties as density, elastic modulus of fiber and of binder, and fiber and void distribution. It appears primarily in finished bonded nonwovens but is also found in conventional coated fabrics where it shows under tension as a regular pattern simulating the cloth underneath, from whence is derived the trade term "pull clothy." The lower layers of leather also show it in increasing degrees, as in so-called corrected leathers. Various routes to eliminate the condition are evident in recent products including development of high degrees of uniformity in the substrate, the use of thick or less pliable surface coatings to bridge over the potential surface peaks and valleys, and the use of an "insulating" layer of woven cloth or of spongy material between the coating and the bonded nonwoven substrate. The use of low gloss or heavily embossed surfaces also effectively obscures roughening. In top grain leather it appears that the coarser-fibered underlayer, though potentially a source of roughness, is effectively insulated from the surface by the increasingly finer, denser, more uniform structure of the top grain layer. Plastic sheets essentially free of fibers and random voids and other inhomogeneities do not show this defect.

Economics

Man-made materials have slowly been invading the markets traditionally held by leather as well as broadening the market areas which, on a basis of cost or of performance, would not be otherwise available to leather. Of the traditional markets, shoe soles, handbags, luggage and upholstery have been most heavily invaded; about 75%, 85%, 93%, and 98% respectively of the total market is now held by nonleather materials. In contrast, the shoe-upper market is still dominated (80%) by leather of various classes largely because of its esthetic appearance and permeability combined with good wear durability, a combination not present in conventional plastic-coated fabric materials before the advent of poromerics. The market for upper materials in shoes and slippers is shown in Table 2.

Conversion of such pairage figures to square footage is complicated by the spectrum of differences in shoe sizes, styles, and cutting efficiencies of shoe patterns. However, assuming an average of 1.6 ft² per pair, the above pairage for 1965, excluding imports, is believed to have consumed in the U.S. approximately the amounts of upper materials shown in Table 3.

Vinyl-coated fabrics, including regular, expanded, suede, and patent type, on various fabrics (woven and nonwoven), cost in the range of $0.20–0.35 per ft² depending on type, thickness, fabric backing, finish, and sometimes color. The more complex leatherlike materials, eg the poromeric Corfam, are in the range of $0.85–1.35 per ft², depending on thickness, finish, and other end-use requirements. Typical prices for

Table 2. U.S. Market for Upper Materials in Shoes, 1965,[a] million pairs

U.S. production	630
imports	87
total	717

[a] SOURCE: National Footwear Manufacturers' Association.

Table 3. Approximate Consumption of Upper Materials, 1965, million ft²

leather	770
patent leather	40
vinyl-coated fabrics[a]	120
poromeric	10
all other[b]	70
total	1010

[a] Includes standard, expanded, and patent or shiny types.

[b] Includes nylon, velvets, plastic mesh, and novelty fabrics.

shoe-upper leathers are calf, $0.90–1.40 per ft²; patent, $0.60–0.90 per ft²; side and kip, $0.45–0.60 per ft²; and cordovan $0.70–1.10. A significant aspect of these figures is that leather prices fluctuate, sometimes quite strongly, because weather, meat prices, disease, and other natural factors cause variations in the hide supply (hide prices account for 45–50% of the total cost of the finished leather). Man-made materials on the other hand are little affected by such natural factors and hence have a much more stable and attractive price pattern. A further aspect is that leather, being a natural product containing flaws and varying in size, requires the time and care of hand-cutting for shoe parts. The man-made materials, on the other hand, being uniform, of constant width, and available as roll goods, are well adapted to high-speed machine-cutting with less waste and corresponding economies in shoe manufacturing.

Man-made insole materials used currently are primarily coated, impregnated papers and approx 500 million ft² are used in shoes each year. A microporous sintered poly(vinyl chloride)-type insole is also available commercially, though it is less extensively used than the papers above. Sock and quarter linings consume about 400 million ft² of conventional vinyl-coated fabrics and about 100 million ft² of leather (sheepskin and kidskin). More exhaustive treatments of the markets for shoe-upper and related materials are available through the U.S. Department of Commerce, National Footwear Manufacturers' Association and trade magazines such as *Boot and Shoe Recorder*.

Bibliography

1. U.S. Pat. 3,027,595 (1962), U. Takai and T. Ishiyama; U.S. Pat. 3,098,262, R. Wisotsky (to Am. Biltrite Rubber Co.); U.S. Pat. 3,221,068, L. J. Wells (to Owens Illinois Corp.).
2. U.S. Pat. 1,489,330, K. L. Moses; U.S. Pat. 1,713,846, R. A. Marr; U.S. Pat. 1,817,323, H. D. Rice; U.S. Pat. 1,843,349, W. B. Van Arsdel (to Brown Co.); U.S. Pat. 1,843,372, G. Richter and W. B. Van Arsdel (to Brown Co.); U.S. Pat. 1,891,027, G. Richter (to Brown Co.); U.S. Pat. 2,159,639, M. O. Schur (to Brown Co.); U.S. Pat. 2,125,947 and 2,246,531, I. Novak (to Raybestos Manhattan); U.S. Pat. 2,558,634, J. J. Uber (to E.I. du Pont de Nemours & Co., Inc.).
3. U.S. Pat. 1,719,803, R. Ferretti; U.S. Pat. 1,829,511, R. Fortman; U.S. Pat. 2,172,028, R. C. McQuiston and H. C. Hopewell; U.S. Pat. 2,948,692, D. K. Pattiloch and C. Polowczyk (to Michigan Research Lab); U.S. Pat. 3,116,200, E. J. Majka and H. H. Young (to Swift & Co.); U.S. Pat. 3,154,430, P. M. Goodloe and L. MacKinnon (to Brown Co.).
4. U.S. Pat. 2,631,942, J. H. Highberger (to United Shoe Machine Corp.); U.S. Pat. 2,838,363, A. Veis and J. Cohen (to Armour & Co.); U.S. Pats. 2,934,446, and 2,934,447, J. H. Highberger (to United Shoe Machine Corp.); U.S. Pat. 3,034,852, T. Nishihara (to Japan Leather Co.); U.S. Pat. 3,063,892, F. Merriam and R. Whitmore (to United Shoe Machine Corp.); U.S. Pat. 3,071,477, H. B. Klevens; U.S. Pats. 3,071,483; 3,073,714; 3,122,599; and 3,136,682, S. T. Tu (to United Shoe Machine Corp.); U.S. Pat. 3,126,433, J. Cohen (to Armour & Co.).
5. *Chem. Eng. News* **45,** 19 (Feb. 27, 1967).

6. W. D. Lawson, C. A. Lynch, and J. C. Richards, "Corfam—Research Brings Chemistry to Footwear," *Research Mangement VIII*, 5–26 (Jan. 1965); L. Lessing, "Synthetics Ride Hell Bent for Leather," *Fortune* (Nov. 1964); "The Story of Corfam—25 Year Journey from Dream to Reality," *Boot and Shoe Recorder* (Oct. 1, 1963).

7. U.S. Pats. 2,451,915; 2,700,188; 2,703,441; and 2,744,294, F. Buresch (to Curlator Corp.); U.S. Pat. 2,890,497, H. Langdon (to Curlator Corp.).

8. U.S. Pat. 2,689,199, M. Pesce; U.S. Pat. 2,810,426, D. Till and C. Smallman (to American Viscose Corp.); U.S. Pat. 2,903,387, W. Wade (to American Viscose Corp.); U.S. Pats. 2,950,752 and 2,988,469, P. C. Watson and H. O. McMahon (to American Viscose Corp.); U.S. Pat. 3,232,819, D. Satas (to Kendall Co.).

9. U.S. Pat. 2,326,038, C. J. Kaprina and P. T. Gates (to Drycor Felt Co.); U.S. Pat. 2,372,484, J. A. Gould; U.S. Pat. 2,373,033, K. J. Kopplin; U.S. Pat. 2,495,926, E. P. Foster; U.S. Pats. 2,774, 126 and 2,774,128, H. A. Secrist (to Kendall Co.); U.S. Pat. 2,840,881, A. W. Bateman (to E. I. du Pont de Nemours & Co., Inc.); U.S. Pat. 2,862,251, F. Kalwaites (to Johnson & Johnson); U.S. Pat. 2,882,585, B. Weikert (to E. I. du Pont de Nemours & Co., Inc.); U.S. Pat. 2,908,064, H. G. Lauterbach (to E. I. du Pont de Nemours & Co., Inc.); U.S. Pat. 2,970,365, D. Morgenstern; U.S. Pat. 3,081,515 (1963), H. W. Griswold and G. W. Pearce (to Johnson & Johnson); U.S Pat. 3,090,099, A. M. Smith (to Chatham Manufacturing); U.S. Pat. 3,214,-819, J. A. Guerin and H. Jeandron.

10. U.S. Pat. 2,011,914, G. Schwartz (to E.I. du Pont de Nemours & Co., Inc.); U.S. Pats. 2,181,043 and 2,441,390, H. Boedinghous (to American Felt Co.); U.S. Pat. 2,689,199, M. R. Pesce; U.S. Pat. 2,695,855, J. F. Stephens (to Gustin-Bacon Manufacturing); U.S. Pat. 2,719,795, C. Nottebohn (to Pellon Corp.); U.S. Pat. 2,730,478 (Jan. 19, 1956), W. A. Morgan (to E. I. du Pont de Nemours & Co., Inc.); U.S. Pat. 2,730,479 (Jan. 10, 1956), J. Gibson (to E. I. du Pont de Nemours & Co., Inc.); U.S. Pat. 2,913,365, M. F. Kilty, et al. (to C. H. Dexter Sons); U.S. Pat. 2,920,992, J. Hubbard (to E. I. du Pont de Nemours & Co., Inc.); U.S. Pat. 2,978,785, L. P. Wenzell, Jr. and L. Lovin (to Celanese Corp.); U.S. Pat. 3,067,482 (Dec. 11, 1962), J. L. Hollowell (to E. I. du Pont de Nemours & Co., Inc.); U.S. Pat. 3,117,055 (Jan. 7, 1964), E. Guandique and M. Katz (to E. I. du Pont de Nemours & Co., Inc.).

11. U.S. Pats. 2,715,588 (Aug. 16, 1955) and 2,715,591 (Aug. 16, 1955), B. Graham (to E. I. du Pont de Nemours & Co., Inc.); U.S. Pat. 2,917,405 (Dec. 15, 1959), N. Gaylord (to E. I. du Pont de Nemours & Co., Inc.); U.S. Pat. 2,994,617 (Aug. 1, 1961), J. Proctor (to E. I. du Pont de Nemours & Co., Inc.); U.S. Pat. 3,083,134, J. H. Fairclough (to Tootal Broadhurst Lee Co.).

12. U.S. Pat. 2,994,617 (Aug. 1, 1961), J. Proctor (to E. I. du Pont de Nemours & Co., Inc.); U.S. Pat. 2,994, 630 (Aug. 1, 1961), R. Osborn (to E. I. du Pont de Nemours & Co., Inc.).

13. U.S. Pat. 2,757,100 (July 31, 1956), V. Simril (to E. I. du Pont de Nemours & Co., Inc.).

14. U.S. Pat. 2,809,398, K. Stiehl and J. Valenteyn (to Deutsche Gold- und Silber-Scheideanstalt); U.S. Pat. 2,858,570 (Nov. 4, 1958), J. C. Richards (to E. I. du Pont de Nemours & Co., Inc.); Fr. Pat. 1,389,341, Kurashiki Rayon Co.

15. U.S. Pat. 2,773,286 (Dec. 11, 1956), B. Graham and J. Piccard (to E. I. du Pont de Nemours & Co., Inc.); Ger. Pat. 1,182,425, H. Boe (to Freudenberg Co.).

16. U.S. Pat. 2,723,935 (Nov. 15, 1955), E. A. Rodman (to E. I. du Pont de Nemours & Co., Inc.); U.S. Pat. 3,087,833, A. H. Drehlich (to Johnson & Johnson); Japan. Pat. 3,718(66), Toyo Rubber Co. Ltd.; Japan. Pat. 18,238(65), Toyo Cloth Co. Ltd.

17. U.S. Pat. 2,879,197, I. Muskat, et al. (to Fiber Bond Corp.); U.S. Pats. 2,719,806 and 3,035,943, C. Nottebohm (to Pellon Corp.).

18. U.S. Pat. 2,994,617 (Aug. 1, 1961), J. Proctor (to E. I. du Pont de Nemours & Co., Inc.); Fr. Pat. 1,394,229, W. Glander (to Pneumatiques Fabriqués).

19. U.S. Pats. 2,212,324; 2,388,069; and 2,550,366, J. W. Meeker; U.S. Pat. 2,683,208, A. M. Andrews; U.S. Pat. 2,763,759, S. Mito (to Shibata Rubber Ltd.); Brit. Pat. 730,221, H. Eberle and I. Saladin.

20. U.S. Pat. 3,226,527, W. H. Harding.

21. U.S. Pat. 2,721,811, W. Dacy, R. Gregg, and N. Hess (to U.S. Rubber Co.); U.S. Pat. 2,875,-088, K. Stiehl and F. Heinrich (to Deutsche Gold- und Silber-Scheideanstalt); Ger. Pat. 1,027,-632, J. H. Benecke.

22. U.S. Pat 2,832,997, K. Bristol (to Goodyear Tire & Rubber Co.); U.S. Pat. 3,214,290 (1965), W. Larner and C. Schollenberger (to B.F. Goodrich Co.); Fr. Pat. 1,394,229, W. Glander (to Pneumatiques Fabriqués); Japan. Pat. 5,316(65), R. Kawaguchi.

23. Ger. Pat. 883,959, R. Moroni; Ger. Pat. 897,399, W. Tischbein (to Farbenfabriken Bayer).

24. U.S. Pat. 2,777,824, H. Leeds (to Perma-Stamp Products Co.); U.S. Pat. 2,864,777, J. Greenhoe (to Monsanto Chemical Co.); U.S. Pat. 2,960,728, L. Beer (to Monsanto Chemical Co.).

25. U.S. Pat. 2,819,981, R. Schornstheimer (to B. F. Goodrich Co.); U.S. Pat. 2,835,607, C. Segner (to B. F. Goodrich Co.); U.S. Pat. 2,983,960, V. Jilge (to Goppinger); U.S. Pat. 3,054,691 (1962), H. Mever and H. Nelson (to U.S. Rubber Co.).

26. U.S. Pat. 2,832,713 (April 29, 1958), W. Ragan (to E. I. du Pont de Nemours & Co., Inc).; U.S. Pat. 2,773,286 (Dec. 11, 1956), B. Graham (to E. I. du Pont de Nemours & Co., Inc.).

27. U.S. Pat. 2,809,398, K. Stiehl and J. Valenteyn (to Deutsche Gold- und Silber-Scheideanstalt).

28. U.S. Pat. 3,143,436, L. Dosman (to U.S. Rubber Co.).

29. U.S. Pat. 2,626,941, B. Habeck (to Wingfoot Corp.).

30. U.S. Pat. 1,421,341, R. Zsigmondy.

31. U.S. Pat. 2,359,878, O. E. Schupp (to E. I. du Pont de Nemours & Co., Inc.); U.S. Pat. 2,783,894 (1957), S. Lovell and J. H. Bush (to Millipore Filter Corp.); Belg. Pat. 650,763, Courtaulds Ltd; Brit. Pat. 957,377, T. Aokii (to Toyo Cloth Co. Ltd.); Fr. Pat. 1,400,910, Kurashiki Rayon Co; Japan. Pat. 2,734(63), X. Nose (to Shibata Rubber Co); Japan. Pat. 15,792(62), S. Kokura.

32. U.S. Pats. 2,846,727 and 2,848,752, M. F. Bechtold (to E. I. du Pont de Nemours & Co., Inc.); U.S. Pat. 2,926,104, A. Goetz; U.S. Pat. 3,000,757 (Sept. 19, 1961), R. Johnston and E. K. Holden (to E. I. du Pont de Nemours & Co., Inc.); U.S. Pat. 3,100,721 (Aug. 13, 1963), E. K. Holden (to E. I. du Pont de Nemours & Co., Inc.); U.S. Pat. 3,190,765 (June 22, 1965), E. Yuan (to E. I. du Pont de Nemours & Co., Inc.).

33. U.S. Pat. 2,609,347, C. L. Wilson.

34. U.S. Pat. 2,371,868, H. Berg and M. Doriat (to Alien Prop. Cust.); U.S. Pat. 2,700,625, T. C. Morris and E. A. Chandler (to B & B Chemical Co.); U.S. Pat. 2,762,784 (1956), O. Foust and E. G. Seems (to United Shoe Machine Corp.); U.S. Pat. 3,067,469, W. Yarrison (to Rogers Corp.).

35. U.S. Pat. 3,109,750 (Nov. 5, 1963), I. D. Roche (to E. I. du Pont de Nemours & Co., Inc.); U.S. Pat. 3,232,819, D. Satas (to Kendall Co.).

36. U.S. Pats. 2,773,050 and 2,839,479, J. Caldwell and R. Gilky (to Eastman Kodak); U.S. Pat. 2,870,129, F. C. Merriam (to United Shoe Machine Corp.); U.S. Pat. 2,883,316, J. Leahy and F. C. Merriam (to United Shoe Machine Corp.); U.S. Pat. 2,976,182, J. Caldwell and C. Dannelly (to Eastman Kodak); Belg. Pat. 630,578, J. Peters and E. Müller (to Farbenfabriken Bayer).

37. U.S. Pat. 2,908,657, F. W. Boggs (to U.S. Rubber Co.); U.S. Pat. 2,794,010, J. L. Jackson (to E. I. du Pont de Nemours & Co., Inc.); U.S. Pat. 2,809,398, K. Stiehl and J. Valenteyn (to Deutsche Gold- und Silber-Scheideanstalt); U.S. Pat. 2,832,747, H. L. Jackson (to E. I. du Pont de Nemours & Co., Inc.); U.S. Pat. 2,884,387 (1959), H. Bieber and H. P. Gregor; U.S. Pat. 3,169,885, M. Golodner (to Interchemical Corp.); Belg. Pat. 626,803, P. Mueller (to Farbenfabriken Bayer).

38. P. Meares, *Polymers—Structure and Bulk Properties*, D. Van Nostrand Co., Inc., Princeton, N.J., 1965, Chap. 12.

39. C. A. Kumins, "Transport Phenomena in Polymeric Films," *J. Polymer Sci.* [C] **10** (1965).

40. H. G. Spencer, "Effects of Chemical Composition on Diffusion and Permeability of Water Vapor in Polymer Films," *J. Paint Tech. Eng.* **486**, 757–765 (July 1965).

41. J. W. Hearle and P. J. Stevenson, "Non-Woven Fabric Studies Part IV," *Textile Res. J.* **34** (3), 181 (March 1964); D. R. Petterson and S. Backer, "Mechanics of Non-Wovens Part VII," *Textile Res. J.* **33** (10), 809 (Oct. 1963).

42. *Satra Bulletin*, Shoe & Allied Trades Research Association, Kettering, England, March 1966.

J. L. HOLLOWELL

E. I. du Pont de Nemours & Co., Inc.

PORTLAND CEMENT. See Cement.

POTASSIUM

Elemental potassium was first produced by Sir Humphry Davy in 1807 by electrolysis of fused potassium hydroxide. It was the first alkali metal to be isolated and was followed soon by sodium.

For many years, both metals remained commercially unimportant. Later, sodium became the more important because of the cheaper process and raw materials from which it was made. The two elements act so similarly that sodium is used except in those cases where potassium has economic advantage despite its higher cost. In 1964 production of sodium was 1600 times as great as that of potassium.

Physical and Chemical Properties

Some of the properties of potassium are given in Table 1.

Among the alkali metals, the boiling points are lower for those of higher atomic weight. Thus, potassium is more volatile than sodium.

There are three naturally occurring isotopes:

mass	39	40	41
natural abundance, %	93.08	0.0119	6.91

The isotope ^{40}K is radioactive, with a half-life of 10^9 yr. This has been used in geological age calculations. In the decay of ^{40}K, 88% emits a β particle and leads to ^{40}Ca, but 12% goes by K-capture to ^{40}A; indeed, this is the reason why argon is so much more abundant, in the atmosphere, than the other group-VIII gases.

Potassium is a soft solid at room temperature, having a silvery-white metallic luster. Sodium and potassium are miscible in all proportions, giving a mobile silvery liquid. The eutectic 77.2% potassium has a freezing point of $-12.3°C$. The phase diagram for NaK (pronounced "nack") is shown in Figure 1 (1–5).

Table 1. Physical and Chemical Properties

Property	Value
atomic weight	39.096
atomic number	19
density at 20°C	0.86
at 100°C	0.819
melting point, °C	63.7
boiling point, °C	760
crystal structure	body-centered cubic
important spectral line, Å	7664.9
ionization potential of gaseous atoms, V	4.32
specific heat, cal/g, solid	$0.1728 + 0.000142t^a$
liquid	$0.1422 + 0.000668t^a$
heat of fusion, cal/g	14.6
heat of vaporization, cal/g	496.0
viscosity at 250°C, cP	0.258
heat capacity at 200°C, cal/g	0.189
thermal conductivity at 200°C, cal/(sec)(cm²)(°C/cm)	0.107
surface tension at 100°C, dyn/cm	86
electrical resistivity at 200°C, μohm-cm	21.85

[a] Where t is temperature in °C.

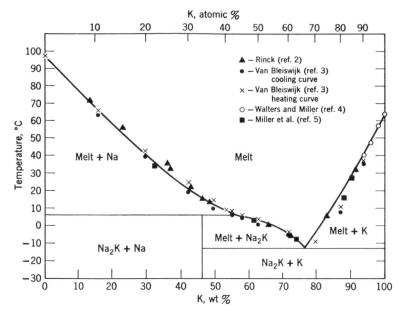

Fig. 1. NaK phase diagram (1–5).

In the system Na–K–Cs, the ternary eutectic (3% Na, 24% K, 73% Cs) melts at −76°C (6).

Potassium possesses chemical similarity to the other members of the alkali metal family, but an important difference from sodium is that it burns in air to the superoxide, KO_2, whereas sodium gives the monoxide, Na_2O, at low temperatures, but at higher temperatures (beginning at about 160°C) the peroxide, Na_2O_2.

Table 2. Inorganic Reactions of Potassium

Reactant	Reaction	Product
O_2	fairly rapid	K_2O or KO_2
N_2, A, He	no reaction	
H_2	rapid reaction above 300°C	KH
H_2O	very rapid	$KOH + H_2$
C (400°C)	dissolves to solid solution, no carbide formed	potassium–graphite up to 40% K
NH_3	reacts easily	KNH_2
CO	forms carbonyls (sometimes explosive)	
S	in molten state	H_2S
CO_2	reacts	K_2CO_3 + reduction products
F	reacts violently	KF
Cl	reacts violently	KCl
Br	detonates	KBr
I	reacts–ignites	KI
H_2SO_4	explosive reaction	K_2SO_4
metal oxides and salts	reduction	free metal, potassium salts or oxides

Liquid ammonia is the best solvent for potassium, and also for sodium. Potassium is also soluble in ethylenediamine, aniline, and mercury.

Inorganic Reactions. Some of the inorganic reactions of potassium are listed in Table 2. At relatively high temperatures, potassium reduces silicates, sulfates, nitrates, carbonates, phosphates, oxides, and hydroxides of the heavy metals, often with the separation of the metal (7).

Miscellaneous Reactions. Potassium (and also its alloy with sodium) forms mixtures with chlorinated hydrocarbons and these mixtures are explosive. The sensitivity to shock of $NaK + CCl_4$ mixtures has been reported to be 150–200 times greater than that of mercury fulminate (8).

Manufacture and Production

Although sodium is commercially prepared by the electrolysis of molten sodium chloride to which calcium chloride is added to lower the melting point, unfortunately, the analogous process cannot be used for potassium production, because potassium attacks the graphite electrodes and because of the possible danger of explosion due to the formation of potassium carbonyl which is sometimes formed by this process. Potassium can also be produced by electrolysis of the hydroxide but this technique has many setbacks and is rarely used. It was the first method employed in the preparation of elemental potassium. Some work was conducted on developing alternate electrodes of other materials; however, this was more or less tabled in favor of the thermochemical process, using the reduction of a potassium salt by sodium.

Rinck (9), from comprehensive investigations, described the equilibria between molten salts and metals in the alkali and alkaline earth groups. Potassium chloride was selected for the thermochemical reduction because of its ready availability and low cost. As found by Rinck, the equilibrium $Na + KCl \rightleftharpoons K + NaCl$ is established rapidly even though a salt and a metal layer are formed. This attainment of equilibrium is probably aided by the partial mutual solubility of the phases which is appreciable at the high temperatures employed.

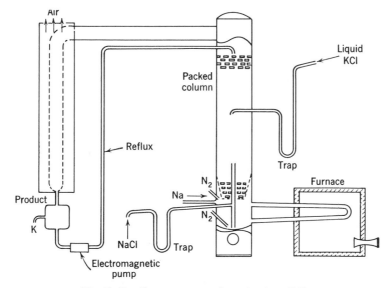

Fig. 2. Continuous process for potassium (11).

The initial process was a batch reaction of sodium with potassium chloride to produce NaK. This was then later fractionated by distillation to produce pure potassium. This two-step process produced considerable tonnages of metallic potassium at a price far below that for which it had formerly been sold. By combining the two operations into a continuous process the prices were lowered still further.

Continuous Process. Figure 2 depicts diagrammatically the equipment used in the continuous process (10). It consists of four basic components all constructed of type 316 stainless steel: a furnace and boiler tubes for vaporizing sodium; a column packed with stainless-steel Raschig rings (see Vol. 1, p. 65) in which the lower portion acts as a reaction and stripping section, and the upper portion acts as a fractionating section; a salt-feed and drainage system; and a condensing system.

The energy requirements of the process are supplied from a gas-fired furnace in which boiler tubes of 3-in. pipe containing sodium are heated both by convection and radiation. The boiler tubes are of an open hairpin type welded to the column at a sufficient angle (approx 3°) to permit natural circulation of the sodium. The column is 18 in. in diam and 21 ft in length, and is fabricated from 0.25-in. plates rolled and butt-welded with 720 in. of weld.

Molten potassium chloride is introduced into the column through a trap. The 6-ft fractionating section of the column is equipped with a 6-in. vapor takeoff line which serves as a condenser. Electromagnetic alternating current conduction pumps are used for reflux feed through the top of the column and continuous sodium feed to the bottom of the column.

During operation there is continuous introduction of the raw materials, molten sodium, and molten potassium chloride to the column. The sodium is vaporized in the boiler tubes and ascends the column, coming into contact with the descending liquid potassium chloride to establish the equilibrium $Na + KCl \rightleftharpoons K + NaCl$, resulting in both sodium and potassium vapors. Potassium is separated by fractionation in the upper section of the column, condensed, and collected. Sodium chloride is continuously removed and discarded. The column is operated slightly above atmospheric pressure through use of traps and by introducing nitrogen into the sodium liquid and vapor phases, and the molten sodium chloride phase in the bottom of the column. This arrangement serves as a liquid-level device when measuring the nitrogen pressures required to maintain a constant flow through these lines. If suitable contact of the liquid potassium chloride and gaseous sodium is maintained, all the potassium can be extracted from the potassium chloride. Proper reflux adjustment assists in maximum utilization of the potassium chloride and separation of potassium and sodium in the fractionating section. Reflux ratios are easily regulated by adjusting the electromagnetic pump which returns a portion of the product to the column. Potassium of 99.5 + % purity can routinely be produced at a rate of approx 200 lb/hr. Any desired mixture of sodium and potassium can be produced by controlling the column operation.

Production. There are few commercial producers of potassium in the world, although many companies produce pilot amounts for their own needs and for resale. The more prominent manufacturers of potassium are listed below.

Mine Safety Appliances Company (MSA)	U.S.A.
Degussa	Germany
Chori	Japan
Techsnabexport	U.S.S.R.

Technical-grade potassium contains 98% K, the balance being mainly Na. The price depends upon the quantity, approximately as follows:

Quantity, lb	Price, $/lb
10	4.50–5.00
500	2.00–2.25
25,000	1.50–1.75

Technical-grade potassium is packed under nitrogen; 1-lb bricks and 0.5-oz sticks are packed under oil, because they are cast in ordinary atmospheres without inert-gas protection.

Commercial potassium can readily be upgraded to 99.99% by zone refining or distillation.

High-purity grade (O_2, 10–50 ppm; C, 10–50 ppm; Na, 10–50 ppm) is available, packed under argon.

U.S. production of potassium in 1964 was less than 100 tons.

Shipping containers for potassium, NaK, and other alkali metals are standard containers except that valves and downpipes are usually added. Carbon or stainless steel is usually used, and the containers are crated to protect external piping. Details of container construction are governed by purity requirements. Quantities below 100 g are usually packaged in ampuls which may be metal, of the standard type of flat-bottom glass tubing, or of a special type. Pure metals are normally supplied under inert gas. Ampuls are sometimes under vacuum. Commercial potassium is also supplied in round ingots under oil in 0.5-oz or 1-lb sizes (12).

Dangerous Properties, Hazards, and Toxicity

Potassium and NaK are classified as flammable solids by the ICC regulations. Flammable solids require yellow shipping labels. The hazards associated with handling these materials are mostly those associated with their flammability and high reactivity. Neither metal can be considered toxic in the usual sense because they have no appreciable vapor pressure, and they are too reactive to be ingested as the metal. Both can cause skin burns on contact with the skin or by leaving a caustic residue on the skin after they are removed. NaK and potassium burn with a relatively hot surface flame (2000°F) and with copious quantities of dense white smoke which is caustic and which makes visibility difficult. Techniques for handling these materials from room temperature up to 2000°F are well developed. The latest review of handling and fire fighting in alkali metal fires appears in Chapter 9 of reference 12. Potassium fires are in some ways easier to extinguish than sodium fires. Fire fighting requires the protection of personnel from caustic smoke and spattering, flaming metal. Inorganic salts (anhydrous) are the most widely used alkali metal extinguishant. Permissible salts are resin-covered NaCl, or free-flowing Na_2CO_3, $CaCO_3$, or SiO_2. On no account should carbon tetrachloride (or, of course, water) be used.

Potassium differs in hazards from sodium in that it reacts with atmospheric oxygen to form the superoxide KO_2 preferentially. Because the superoxide easily supplies free oxygen, it presents a hazard. Explosions have been experienced when the superoxide is reacted with easily reduced materials in a manner that frees the highly concentrated but loosely held oxygen. There are many references to explosive reaction of the superoxide with potassium metal, but it has not been experienced in daily spraying of potassium in air to form the superoxide since 1949 or in small-scale deliberate tests. It is probable that many explosions reported are really reactions of superoxide with organic materials used to coat potassium. When potassium or reaction residues containing potassium have been exposed to air and superoxides are suspected, the system should be treated as potentially hazardous and should be destroyed with care. Even after reaction of metallic residues with alcohols, the resulting solutions should be destroyed as explosions have been reported which may have been caused by oxidation of the solutions by exposure to air leakage.

Uses

The greater part of the production of metallic potassium is used in the manufacture of potassium superoxide, KO_2 (13); see Vol. 14, p. 763.

The next most important use of potassium is in the form of the alloy with sodium, NaK. NaK (78% K) has been used as a heat-transfer fluid in some nuclear reactors, and in some other applications. With its boiling point of 1446°F, and its low vapor pressure of 0.46 psia at 950°F, it has outstanding properties for high-temperature uses.

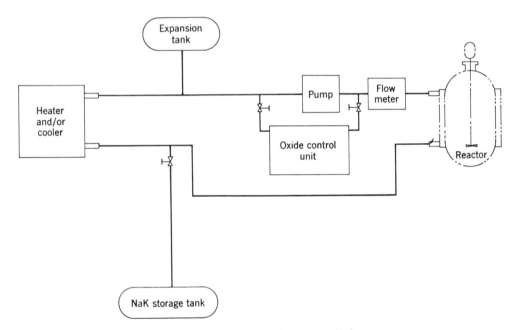

Fig. 3. NaK heat-transfer system (14).

At 1000°F and above, corrosion is less with NaK than with steam. At 950°F it has a density of 0.732 g/ml, specific heat of 0.21 cal/g, viscosity of 0.175 cP, and the remarkably high thermal conductivity of 15 Btu/(hr)(ft²)(°F/ft). It is possible to attain heat-transfer coefficients of 2000–10,000 Btu/(hr)(ft²)(°F), far higher than with organic chemical coolants (see Heat transfer media).

A typical NaK heat-transfer system is shown in Figure 3 (14). Small quantities of sodium and potassium oxides may build up in the system. They are more soluble in hot NaK than in cold. The "oxide control unit" shown in Figure 3 is basically a precipitate trap.

Such a system can be used to supply heat or to remove heat. Systems can be of any size. They are available commercially as components or as complete turnkey systems. A system employing 40,000 lb of NaK removing heat from a reactor at 850°F has been placed in commercial service in a chemical plant. The system is capable of 2,000,000 Btu/hr and NaK flow rates of 850 gal/min. Heat-transfer systems feature electromagnetic pumps and flowmeters, which have no moving parts, a definite advantage at high temperatures.

NaK is also used as a replacement for liquid water for heat transfer in consumable electrode furnaces for processing high-melting reactive metals, where its use is safer than the use of water, which can react explosively with the reactive metals in the event of a leak in the cooling system. In addition to the safety aspect, the use of NaK allows recovery of ingots that would normally be lost in the event of even a small-scale leak were the system using water as the coolant. The savings in recoverable ingots paid for one such system in a short time (15). Because NaK is less expensive than mercury, it is finding use in low-temperature applications as a replacement in heating controls, electrical contacts, and the electromagnetic control of valves.

NaK is used as liquid-metal brushes in homopolar generators as a source of very high current and low voltage. Four of these acyclic generators, each rated at 555,000 A and 45 V, are in service at the U.S. Air Force's Arnold Engineering Development Center, Tullahoma, Tennessee (16).

Another interesting use of NaK is as a scavenger for impurities in nonreactive gases and liquids. Inert gas purifiers employing NaK as a scavenger for impurities have been used for many years (17) and are now available commercially as recirculating models for glove-box applications (18). Inert gases can be purified to less than 1 ppm water content and less than 1 ppm oxygen content. Use of these systems can extend useful working time in glove boxes from short periods to essentially continuous usage by removing any contaminants that may diffuse through the gloves.

In some chemical applications either NaK or pure potassium can be used. Carload quantities of NaK were used from 1957 to 1964 as a transesterification catalyst (19).

The use of NaK permits the mixed glyceride esters of lard to be rearranged in a controlled manner to a more desirable mixture of fats than occurs naturally or than can be attained by random rearrangement. The greater activity of NaK at the crystallization temperature makes it more suitable than either sodium or sodium methoxide, which are used in randomization of the natural esters above the crystallization point. Directed interesterification with NaK results in lard that is better for baking because it is softer at low temperatures and firmer at high temperatures than either natural or randomized lard.

Reagents derived from potassium metal find many uses in organic syntheses involving condensations, dehalogenations, reductions, and polymerizations. Extensive literature exists on the reactions of potassium and its derivatives. Technical bulletins are available from producers (20).

Reference 21 gives directions for handling metallic potassium on a laboratory scale and for preparing useful derivatives such as the amide (22) and the t-butoxide (23). The most widely used derivative, the t-butoxide, is available commercially, and it has been employed in 1000-lb production runs. Literature on its potential uses has been compiled (24,25).

Potassium metal may find application as a seed material in magnetohydrodynamic

(MHD) (see Power generation) power plants for the conversion of heat directly to electricity or for use in topping conventional steam plants to increase efficiency of fuel use (26). Efficiency might be increased from a possible maximum of 45% attainable through extensive development of conventional steam plants to a suggested 65% maximum through use of ionized gas in magnetic fields to generate power preceding the conventional steam-turbine method of making power. Other power-generating MHD systems not associated with conventional power plants may employ potassium metal or metal-derived salts as a seed material.

Another MHD concept using potassium metal is reported under development at Atomics International, Division of North American Rockwell Corporation. Potassium is heated to 1600°F in furnaces and then introduced into a drift tube where it reaches speeds of up to 400 ft/sec. The conductive potassium liquid flowing in a magnetic field generates power. The company is planning a pilot plant with an MHD generator with an output of 1–2 kW electrical power.

Bibliography

"Potassium" treated in *ECT* 1st ed. under "Alkali Metals," Vol. 1, pp. 447–451, by Elizabeth H. Burkey, Jean A. Morrow, and Muriel S. Andrew, E. I. du Pont de Nemours & Co., Inc., Electrochemicals Dept.

1. C. B. Jackson, ed., *Liquid Metals Handbook, Sodium (NaK) Supplement*, 3rd ed., Atomic Energy Commission and Bureau of Ships, Department of the Navy, Washington, D.C., 1955, p. 33.
2. E. Rinck, *Compt. Rend.* **197,** 49 (1933).
3. G. L. C. M. Van Bleiswijk, *Z. Anorg. Chem.* **74,** 152 (1912).
4. S. L. Walters and R. R. Miller, *Ind. Eng. Chem. Anal. Ed.* **18,** 468 (1946).
5. R. R. Miller, C. T. Ewing, R. S. Hartman, and H. B. Atkinson, Jr., *NRL Rept. C-3105* (1947).
6. F. Tepper, J. King, and J. Greer, *Multicomponent Alkali Metal Alloys*, MSAR Rept. 66-131, MSA Research Corp., Evans City, Pa., 1966.
7. H. N. Gilbert, *Chem. Eng. News* **26,** 2604 (Sept. 6, 1948).
8. H. Staudinger, *Z. Elektrochem.* **31,** 549 (1925).
9. E. Rinck, *Ann. Chim.* **18,** 397 (1932).
10. U.S. Pat. 2,480,655 (Aug. 30, 1949), C. B. Jackson and R. C. Werner (to MSA Co.).
11. C. B. Jackson and R. C. Werner, "Handling and Uses of the Alkali Metals," *Advan. Chem. Ser.* *19*, p. 172 (1957).
12. J. W. Mausteller, F. Tepper, and S. J. Rodgers, *Alkali Metal Handling and Systems Operating Techniques*, Gordon and Breach, Science Publishers, Inc., New York, 1967.
13. C. B. Jackson and R. C. Werner, "Handling and Uses of the Alkali Metals," *Advan. Chem. Ser. 19*, pp. 169–177 (1957).
14. *Liquid Metal Heat Transfer Systems for Process Heat Control*, MSAR Rept. 59-57, 2nd rev. ed., MSA Research Corp., Evans City, Pa., 1959.
15. D. E. Cooper and E. D. Dilling, "Liquid Metal Cooling for Consutrode Melting," *J. Metals* **12,** 149–151 (Feb. 1960).
16. *Machine Design* 34 (Jan. 1962).
17. *Inert Gas Purification System*, MSAR Rept. 67-194, MSA Research Corp., Evans City, Pa., 1967.
18. *KSE Inert Gas Purification System*, Kewaunee Scientific Equipment, Adrian, Mich.
19. L. H. Going, *J. Am. Oil Chemists' Soc.* **44,** 414A (1967).
20. *NaK and Potassium Technical Bulletin*, MSAR Bulletin MD-65-1, MSA Research Corp., Evans City, Pa., 1965.
21. R. Adams et al., eds., *Organic Reactions*, Vol. 4 (1948), John Wiley & Sons, Inc., New York, p. 132; *ibid.*, Vol. 6 (1951), p. 42.
22. N. Rabjohn, ed., *Organic Syntheses*, Coll. Vol. IV, 2nd ed., John Wiley & Sons, Inc., New York, 1963, p. 963.

23. *Ibid.*, p. 149.
24. *Technical Bulletin*, MSAR Bulletin MD-65-2, MSA Research Corp., Evans City, Pa., 1965.
25. J. H. Harwood, *Industrial Applications of Organometallic Compounds*, Chapman & Hall, Ltd., London, 1963.
26. R. A. Coombe, *Magnetohydrodynamic Generation of Electrical Power*, Reinhold Publishing Corp., New York, 1964.

M. BLUM
Atomergic Chemetals Company
JOHN H. MADAUS
MSA Research Corporation

POTASSIUM COMPOUNDS

Potassium compounds were used in antiquity. Potassium carbonate was leached from ashes in Pompeii and "strengthened" with lime (converted to the hydroxide) for soapmaking. The increase in the use of alkali paralleled the growth of western civilization and so much wood was consumed in its production that the forests of Europe were being threatened when LeBlanc's invention led to the general substitution of sodium carbonate at the time of the French Revolution.

The Chinese, to make gunpowder centuries ago, obtained potassium nitrate by leaching soil where nitrogen from urine had combined with mineral potassium. Later Europeans did the same, and by the time of the Napoleonic wars, this potassium nitrate was a strategic material and was still obtained from the same source, primarily from India. Many of the nineteenth-century "fathers of chemistry" were involved in the manufacture of gunpowder.

The usefulness of potassium compounds as fertilizers had been shown in experiments, but their effects are not as striking as those of nitrogen compounds for instance, and essentially none were used as such before the recovery of potassium chloride from the "rubbish salt" in the Strassfurt salt mines was started in 1860. This cheap potash not only displaced most other sources of supply for existing uses, but its aggressive exploitation led directly to the creation of a worldwide potassium fertilizer market. Now, 90% of potash production is used in fertilizers.

The term "potash" of course originated when the product was leached from ashes. When the chloride became the prime potassium compound, it was also called potash, and now the term is frequently applied to other potassium compounds that are used in quantity.

The world's almost complete dependence on Germany for potash was dramatized by World War I and this resulted in the development of many marginal and new sources. Today Germany has less than 25% of the world's commercial capacity, and with the recent discovery of immense new reserves in Canada, the European deposits will diminish in importance.

Occurrence—Economics

Potassium is the seventh most abundant element in the earth's crust, about equal to sodium, and potassium compounds occur naturally in all parts of the world. However, since by far the largest use of potassium is as a fertilizer, its usage is strongly affected by its cost. Thus, commercial occurrence, where recovery is profitable, is

Table 1. Estimated World Reserves of Soluble Potassium Compounds, million short tons of K_2O

Location	Production capacity, 1965	Reserves
Canada	2.0[a]	17,500
U.S.S.R.	2.0	24,000[b]
U.S.A.	3.6	450
West Germany	2.2	9,500
East Germany	2.0	10,000
France	1.8	350
Spain	0.5	300
Dead Sea	0.3	2,000
total	14.4	

[a] Announced expansion of productive capacity will raise this figure to 8.2 million tons by 1970.

[b] Few reliable data have been published about the reserves in the U.S.S.R. and this figure is subject to question.

limited to a very small part of the earth's surface, although the deposits are still quite widespread as the figures in Table 1 indicate.

It is standard to give figures on production, potassium content of ores and fertilizer, etc, in terms of equivalent K_2O. However, freight has become a major part of the cost, and the application of fertilizer is becoming more exact. These factors have led to the majority of potash production being in the form of comparatively pure, simple compounds (eg KCl). For these, actual tonnage figures are frequently given.

At least 90% of commercial occurrences are natural deposits of sylvinite, a mixture of KCl and NaCl, or carnallite, $KCl.MgCl_2.6H_2O$, from which KCl is recovered by flotation or leaching, evaporation, and crystallization. However, occasionally, because of special economic conditions or as a by-product, potash has been recovered from many other sources. As an extreme example, Table 2 shows the variety of sources from which potash was obtained in the U.S.A. during the World War I shortage, in which prices rose to above $900 per ton of K_2O.

The economic restrictions on developing potash sources are not widely appreciated. There are continual investigations of marginal deposits because there are many that appear attractive. For instance, in Italy there is an extinct volcano which contains 10^9 tons of K_2O as an ore (leucite, $K_2O.Al_2O_3.4SiO_2$) with a reasonably high potash content. Despite extensive investigations, there has been essentially no commercial production. Many such "sources" are described in the literature (1). Freight may be about equal to the manufacturing cost of potash, so location is an important factor in determining occurrences of commercial value.

Table 2. U.S.A. Sources of Potash, 1918

Source	K_2O, 1,000 tons	Source	K_2O, 1,000 tons
brine and salt lakes	39.7	sugar mill residue	1.4
seaweed	4.8	wood ashes	0.7
distillery residue	3.4	blast furnace dust	0.2
alunite, $K_2Al_6(OH)_{12}(SO_4)_4$	2.6	others	0.4
cement dust	1.5	total	54.7

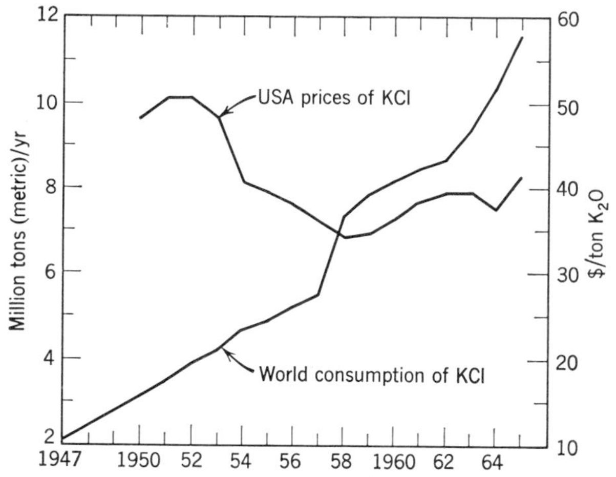

Fig. 1. Potash (KCl) market.

The relative stability of prices in the face of marked increase in demand (Fig. 1) implies that present sources are adequate. In fact, although consumption is expected to continue to increase rapidly, large increases in production capacity in Canada and possibly in the U.S.S.R. may result in lower prices for a few years. See also Table 5.

Potash Recovery from Natural Sources

MINING

Some commercial potash production comes from brines, but by far the largest amount comes from solid ores. These ores are usually layers in salt deposits which are presumably of marine origin. But the various salts are present in proportions markedly different from those in the sea, indicating that there must have been leaching, vaporizing, or chemical changes after the initial deposition. These effects are of geologic interest and the various deposits have been extensively studied from that point of view (2).

The ore is mined through shafts in a manner similar to that used for coal. The deposits are stratified, layers of satisfactory potash content (10–30% K_2O) being separated from each other by layers that are largely NaCl or solidified clay. It is desirable, of course, to mine only the richer layers, which, however, may be too thin for convenience, sloped steeply, or broken by geological upheavals. The result is that mining methods vary from pick and shovel work to a high degree of mechanization. The cost of labor and the customs of the country also affect the method chosen.

Of current interest are the large Canadian deposits in Saskatchewan. The ore zones are about 400 ft thick with one or multiple beds of commercial ore ranging from 5–10 ft in thickness. However, the ore is 3000 ft deep and is overlain by a stratum containing water at very high pressure. Because of this combination, the exploitation of these reserves involves considerably more risk and is more expensive than for normal potash deposits. In an attempt to reduce mining costs and the risk involved in sinking a shaft through the water formation, "solution mining" techniques are being developed. Solution mining methods have been used to produce NaCl for many years, but their application to notash is quite recent. Water, or NaCl brine, is pumped into the formation and a KCl–NaCl brine forced out. There is one commercial plant operating that uses solution mining, apparently successfully, but whether it can stay economically competitive with the larger and larger shaft mining operations in Canada remains to be seen.

Mining costs are a major part of total production costs. Table 3 gives approximate costs for modern U.S. and Canadian practice.

Table 3. Potash Mining Costs

Ore grade ($\%$ K_2O)	Cost per ton of KCl, $
10	13.00
20	5.50
30	3.50

SYLVINITE PROCESSING

Sylvinite is a mixture in varying proportions of KCl and NaCl crystals. It is the easiest ore to process. Indeed, some of the richest sylvinite ore is sold directly as "manure salts" at a low price. A simple treatment of sylvinite is to leach it with water to remove the NaCl. Some of the KCl is lost, but the process is suitable for small primitive operations.

Hot Leaching of Sylvinite. This process takes advantage of the different response to temperature in the solubility of KCl as compared to NaCl. Potassium chloride is very much more soluble in hot water than in cold; sodium chloride is only very slightly more soluble in water at 100°C than at 20°C, and in solutions saturated with respect to both KCl and NaCl it is actually less soluble at the higher temperatures. This is shown in Figure 2a, which plots against temperature the various triple points such as a and d in Figure 2b.

The ore is first crushed, so that the NaCl crystals are no longer attached to the KCl crystals. It is then mixed with recycle brine heated almost to boiling in sufficient quantity to dissolve the KCl. This brine is nearly saturated with NaCl, so little NaCl is dissolved. After saturation with KCl, the brine is cooled by vacuum evaporation, resulting in KCl crystallization.

As usual, there are complications in the commercial application of this theoretically simple process, whose flow diagram is illustrated in Figure 3. There are four general problems: (*1*) A major cost of the process is heating the cool mother liquor from the crystallizers before recycling it to the leach step. To minimize this cost, mother liquor is preheated in direct-contact condensers with vapor from the evaporator-cooler crystallizers (for increased heat efficiency, there are sometimes as many as twenty of the vacuum crystallizers in series). (*2*) There is usually enough clay, etc (frequently called "slime") in the ore to affect crystallization and the purity of the product. These slimes are removed in large settling tanks (thickeners). (*3*) Crystal size of the product is important from a sales standpoint. The factors affecting the crystallization of KCl have therefore been studied extensively (1). (*4*) Brine saturated with KCl accompanies the NaCl crystals and the clay when they are withdrawn from the main brine circuit, and competitive economics dictate that the KCl so lost be minimized. A centrifuging-washing step is sufficient for the granular NaCl tailings and the clay is usually washed by redispersing and rethickening. The amount of water that can be used for these recovery-washings is normally limited to the equiva-

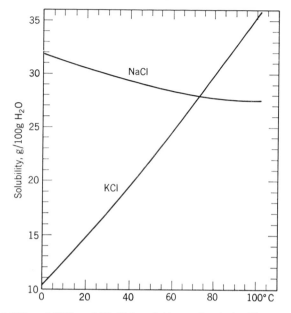

Fig. 2a. Solubilities of KCl and NaCl in solutions saturated with respect to both.

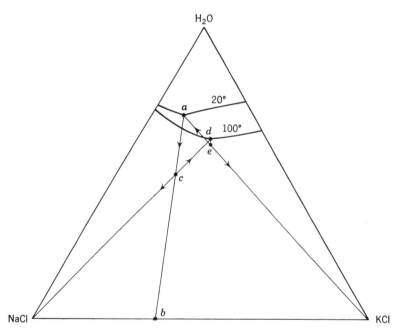

Fig. 2b. Solubilities in the system KCl–NaCl–H₂O. In the leach-crystallization processing of sylvinite, the mother liquor from the crystallizers (composition *a*) is used to leach sylvinite (composition, for example, *b*) in proportion to give an overall composition on the tie-line at *c*. At 100°C these will result in a liquor of "triple point" composition *d* and residual NaCl. When this leach liquor is cooled by evaporation in the vacuum crystallizers, sufficient water must be added to prevent the composition from moving no further than *e*. At 20°C, a mixture of composition *e* separates into solid KCl and the original mother liquor which is also a triple point.

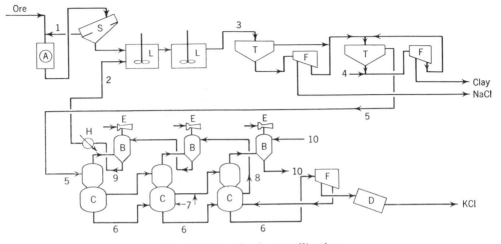

Fig. 3. Potash leach-crystallization.

A	crusher	1	oversize particles
B	barometric condensers	2	mother liquor, hot
C	vacuum cooler-crystallizers	3	slurry: saturated brine, NaCl, clay
D	dryer	4	flocculating agent and H_2O
E	steam ejectors	5	clear hot saturated brine
F	centrifuges	6	brine and KCl crystals
L	leach tanks	7	H_2O equal to evaporation
T	"thickener" settlers	8	mother liquor, cool
H	heater	9	mother liquor, preheated
S	screen	10	cooling water

lent of the bleed from the recycling brine circuit which is required to control impurities such as $MgCl_2$. For more effective use of the wash-water, it is frequently hot although this increases corrosion. A recent development is the use of flocculating agents which permit centrifuging of the slimes.

Flotation Processing of Sylvinite. Most of the potash of Canada and the U.S.A. is recovered from the ore by flotation (qv) methods which are widely used in the processing of other minerals. The essentials of this process are to treat the ore with a "collector," a hydrophobic material (eg, an aliphatic amine) which will selectively coat one of the constituents (the KCl) of the ore. Air is then bubbled through a slurry of the ore, and the air bubbles attach themselves to the coated particles and float them to the surface, while the uncoated particles sink. Some plants have been built in which the NaCl is floated away from the KCl, but generally the reverse is the more desirable process. On a large scale and particularly with high-analysis ores, the flotation process is much cheaper than one involving dissolution and crystallization. It has been the process of choice in the Carlsbad, New Mexico area and in Canada, and its use is spreading to other parts of the world. The design and operation of a flotation plant is highly dependent on subtle differences in the ore composition. It is difficult to achieve high purity in the product, and some ores prove intractable to the flotation technique.

Figure 4 outlines a typical KCl flotation process. Some of the important points are: (1) The flotation action is affected by the surface-weight ratio of the particles; therefore, the crushing operation (required to "unlock" the KCl crystals from the NaCl) should produce as uniform a particle size as possible, which normally requires

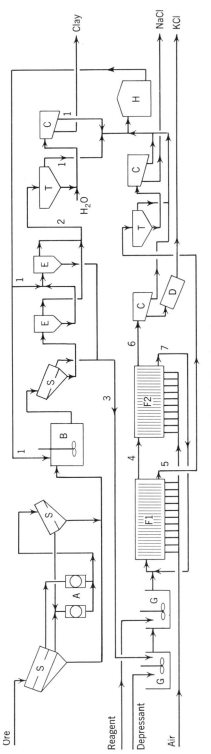

Fig. 4. Potash flotation plant.

A   crushers
B   "scrubber"
C   centrifuge
D   dryer
E   "classifier" settlers
F1   "rougher" flotation cells
F2   "cleaner" flotation cells
G   "conditioners"
H   brine tank
S   screen
T   "thickener" settlers

1   saturated clear brine
2   brine, clay, and KCl fines
3   KCl–NaCl slurry, clayfree
4   "rougher concentrate" (froth)
5   "rougher tails" (NaCl slurry)
6   "cleaner concentrate"
7   "cleaner tails"

several crushers and intermediate screening. Sometimes there are parallel trains of flotation cells for different particle sizes. (*2*) Clay (or "slime") present in the ore radically affects the flotation step and must be removed by violent washing and subsequent hydraulic classification using brine. There are KCl fines accompanying the slow-settling clay, and there is some clay left in the brine-ore slurry produced from the classifiers. This latter clay must be neutralized by a depressant (eg, starch) to minimize the usage of the expensive flotation agent. Sometimes roasting the ore will change the character of the clay so that it causes less difficulty. (*3*) The separation achieved in the flotation cells, depending as it does on particle size and cleanliness as well as chemical composition, is also imperfect. It is common to require a "cleaner" train of cells following a "rougher" train to achieve the required product purity. The coarse fraction of the product from the first flotation step often will meet product purity specifications. In this case, it is separated from the finer fraction by screening and only the finer fraction is run through a series of "cleaner" flotation cells. (*4*) In some ores, particularly European ores, the crystal "unlocking" size is small and it is necessary to crush the ore to such a small size that the grain size of the purified product is too small for the market. A "granulation" or "compaction" step is then necessary. (*5*) In flotation plants little water is evaporated, and although some water is bled from the system to control the concentration of soluble impurities, this is minimized because of the accompanying loss of KCl. Thus only a limited amount of water can be added to the system while recovering entrained brine from slimes and salt tailings. Centrifugation or filtration is used to minimize brine losses with NaCl tailings, while several stages of differential settling, countercurrent decantation systems, or centrifuging, utilizing flocculating agents, are used to minimize brine losses with the slimes.

Other Methods of Processing Sylvinite. Several other methods for separating KCl crystals from NaCl crystals have been used or proposed. None are presently of commercial importance.

Tabling is the treatment of an ore similar to the "panning" of gold. A slurry is run down a sloping, grooved table which shakes sideways. Heavier particles are preferentially jerked toward one side of the table and are collected while the lighter particles are washed toward the other side by a second liquid stream. The partially separated middlings are recycled. In potash applications, the KCl crystals are selectively coated with a material similar to the flotation "collectors" and oil to agglomerate them, thus magnifying the difference in density between KCl and NaCl (3). It is not practicable to obtain by this method a purity much above 80% (50% K_2O).

Heavy liquids, either organic liquids or inorganic suspensions with densities between those of the two materials to be separated, have been applied in some industries ("levigation"), but trials on sylvinite have not given commercially satisfactory results so far.

Electrostatic Separation. The sylvinite is crushed, screened and dried, and then passed through a vibratory trough. The KCl acquires a negative charge, the NaCl positive. On allowing the material to fall freely between charged plates separation is obtained, but the results have not been sufficiently promising to lead to commercialization (5).

Ammonia affects the solubility of NaCl and KCl in such a way that a leach-crystallization process might be improved (6). However, it appears doubtful that this would result in significant economies when compared to present practice.

Combination Method of Processing Sylvinite. Depending on ore quality, fuel costs, etc, many variations of the basic methods are employed, including combinations of methods. It is common to combine flotation with leaching. The major part of a plant's output may be produced as agricultural grade by flotation of a comparatively narrow particle-size range of the crushed ore. The screened-out fines, the unfloated "tails" from the flotation train, and the clay would be leached with hot brine to give, after crystallization, a high-purity product (7).

CARNALLITE PROCESSING

Most potash ores that are mined contain varying quantities of carnallite. Carnallite appears as a minor impurity in North American sylvinite ores, while it is a major potash-bearing ore in some European operations, and it is produced by crystallization in solar evaporation of some natural brines. Carnallite is a definite mineral, $KCl \cdot MgCl_2 \cdot 6H_2O$. The carnallite can be decomposed by using a regulated amount of water to dissolve the $MgCl_2$ without dissolving an impractical quantity of the KCl. NaCl is also left undissolved in most cases, so a sylvinite separation process must follow.

To handle fluctuations in ore quality, the $MgCl_2$ leach step is normally a multistage, countercurrent operation. To minimize KCl losses, a bleed stream from the

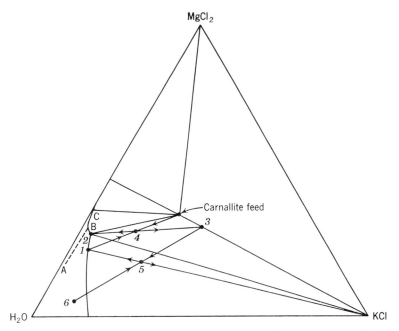

Fig. 5. Carnallite leach: phase diagram of $KCl–MgCl_2–H_2O$ saturated with NaCl. This is a system of four components, KCl, $MgCl_2$, NaCl, and H_2O. Any composition in this system can be represented in three dimensions by means of a regular tetrahedron, of which each vertex represents one of the components. The two-dimensional representation shown here can be regarded as a projection from the NaCl vertex onto the opposite face, which is the three-component system $KCl–MgCl_2–H_2O$. Mathematically, it is plotted by taking $KCl + MgCl_2 + H_2O = 100\%$ and neglecting NaCl. In the leaching operation, carnallite and an interstage liquid whose composition is represented by point *1* are mixed in the first stage in the proportions to give the overall composition *4;* this separates into a liquor of composition *2* (which is rejected) and a mixture of solids KCl and carnallite represented by point *3*. This solid mixture is mixed in the second stage with a crystallizer purge stream *6* to give an overall composition *5* which separates into KCl and the interstage liquor *1*.

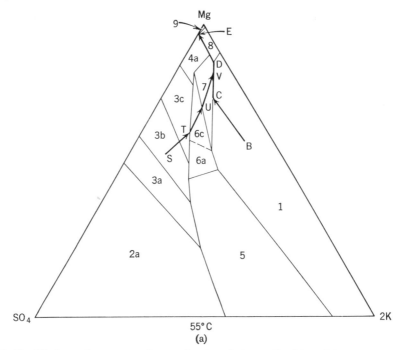

Fig. 6. Equilibrium when evaporating marine-type brines. In this multicomponent system with excess NaCl, a useful diagram results from plotting, as above, the remaining ion species on the basis of chemical equivalents with $SO_4 + Mg + 2 K = 100\%$. (Thus the left-hand corner represents sodium sulfate, and the other two corners are magnesium and potassium chlorides. Sodium chloride is

	Fig. 6a, 55°C	Fig. 6b, 0°C
KCl (sylvite)	1	1
Na_2SO_4 (thenardite)	2a	
$Na_2SO_4 \cdot 10H_2O$ (Glauber's salt)		2b
$3Na_2SO_4 \cdot MgSO_4$ (vanthoffite)	3a	
$Na_2SO_4 \cdot MgSO_4 \cdot 4H_2O$ (astracanite)	3b	
$Na_2SO_4 \cdot MgSO_4 \cdot 2.5H_2O$ (loweite)	3c	
$MgSO_4 \cdot H_2O$ (kieserite)	4a	
$MgSO_4 \cdot 7H_2O$ (epsomite)		4b

sylvinite separation process is used instead of fresh water for leaching. This operation is illustrated on the phase diagram, Figure 5.

The MgCl₂ leach helps with clay removal, but has two difficulties. One is that the resulting KCl and NaCl crystals are generally too small or too wide in size range to give a satisfactory flotation operation. The other is that the MgCl₂ waste stream may present a disposal problem. This is the case in many parts of Europe and has resulted in a decreasing value of carnallite ores.

POTASH RECOVERY FROM BRINES

The apparent availability of chemicals from natural brines has had wide appeal. But, as sources of potash, few are presently economic, and those few because of special circumstances.

Potash from the Dead Sea. Israel produces a few percent of the world's potash from the Dead Sea, and Jordan has plans to do the same. The brine is evaporated in large ponds, precipitating NaCl, until potash starts to precipitate; then it is transferred

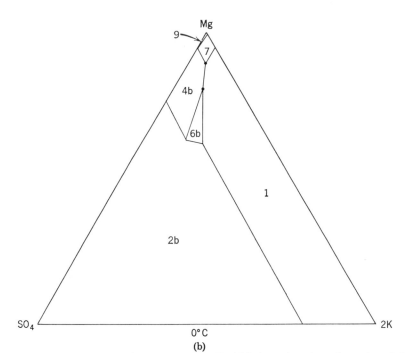

(b)

present in all parts of the diagram.)   The fields, as listed below, show how the ratios of these ionic concentrations determine what compound is the first, after NaCl, to precipitate as water is evaporated.   As a compound precipitates, the liquor concentration, in general, changes.   When the concentration is on the border between two fields, two compounds (in addition to NaCl) may precipitate together.

	Fig. 6a, 55°C	Fig. 6b, 0°C
K₃Na(SO₄)₂ (glaserite)	5	
K₂SO₄.MgSO₄.4H₂O (leonite)	6a	
K₂SO₄.MgSO₄.6H₂O (schoenite)		6b
K₂SO₄.2MgSO₄ (langbeinite)	6c	
KCl.MgSO₄.3H₂O (kainite)	7	
KCl.MgCl₂.6H₂O (carnallite)	8	7
MgCl₂.6H₂O (bischofite)	9	9

to other ponds.   In these, further evaporation precipitates the potash in the form of carnallite, $KCl.MgCl_2.6H_2O$, together with more NaCl.   The course of the two evaporations is shown on the phase diagram, Figure 5, first from the Dead Sea brine at A to the "carnallite point" at B, then in the second set of ponds from B to C.

The carnallite–NaCl mixture is dredged from the ponds and the $MgCl_2$ leached out as discussed above under Carnallite processing.   Then KCl is separated from the NaCl by hot leaching and cooling crystallization as described above under Hot leaching of sylvinite.

The Dead Sea brine contains only 1% KCl.   The enormous amount of water which must be evaporated would make the operation uneconomic if it were not for the practicality of solar evaporation in that area.   But this apparently free energy is not so in reality; the construction of the large leakproof ponds is very expensive.

Potash from Bonneville and Great Salt Lake Brines.   These two brines found in Utah illustrate the complexities usually encountered in natural brines.   Both result from the evaporation of the same prehistoric lake, but differ in composition.   Potash is being produced from the Bonneville brine. The Salt Lake brine has a composition such that potash production from it has been unprofitable. Recently, however, several companies have announced plans for large plants to recover a multitude of chemicals, including potash, from the Great Salt Lake.

At Bonneville, the brine (which is contained in the soil structure) is collected in drainage ditches or pumped from relatively porous strata, and solar-evaporated in three groups of ponds. In the first, NaCl is precipitated, in the second KCl and NaCl (sylvinite), and in the third, a mixture of NaCl, kainite, $KCl.MgSO_4.3H_2O$, and carnallite, $KCl.MgCl_2.6H_2O$. The third precipitate, after removal of the residual brine, is water-washed in place and the resulting solution, containing considerable KCl, is recycled to one of the first group of ponds. The KCl–NaCl mixture from the second step is harvested and the KCl separated by flotation (8).

The Bonneville brine has too many components for the phase relationship to be shown on a two-dimensional diagram, but the second and third evaporation steps are shown on the simplified diagram, Figure 6a. KCl is precipitated going from B to C; kainite and KCl, from C to D; and carnallite from D to E (all accompanied by NaCl). Figure 6 also illustrates the difficulty with Great Salt Lake brine. Point S on Figure 6 represents the composition of the Great Salt Lake brine and the course of its evaporation is STUVDE, precipitating the following compounds in sequence, along with NaCl.

astrakanite	$Na_2SO_4.MgSO_4.4H_2O$
loweite	$Na_2SO_4.MgSO_4.2.5H_2O$
langbeinite	$K_2SO_4.2MgSO_4$
kainite	$KCl.MgSO_4.3H_2O$
sylvite	KCl
carnallite	$KCl.MgCl_2.6H_2O$

The recovery of a single potash salt (such as, KCl or K_2SO_4) from one of these double salts is moderately complex; to recover it from a mixture of them is very complex, and this is complicated even further because the temperature in the ponds fluctuates from day to night and also seasonally, causing radical changes in the phase diagram; compare Figure 6 at 55°C with Figure 6b at 0°C. Another complexity is that supersaturation is a common phenomenon. It has been proposed that advantage be taken of this metastability to process Salt Lake brine (9). (Some of the compounds require 10^2–10^4 times as long to crystallize as others.)

At present, Great Salt Lake is being investigated intensively, and it is hoped that the recovery of a number of commodities (Mg, LiCl, Cl_2, Na_2SO_4, K_2SO_4, and MgO) will make a complex operation profitable.

The fundamental difficulty with Great Salt Lake brine, the high proportion of sulfate, is common to many brines which are directly derived from the ocean and have been considered as sources of potash (eg, residual brine from NaCl production or desalinization projects). Many treatments have been suggested, such as adding $CaCl_2$ (10); cooling to precipitate Na_2SO_4; ion exchange (11); or chelating (12); but it is doubtful that they can be economic for potash recovery alone (13).

Potash from Searles Lake Brine. This operation in California was the pioneering production of potash in the U.S.A., stimulated during World War I by the shutting off of German imports. The amazingly complex relationships of the salts in this brine presented a formidable puzzle to the original developers of this source of potash. The successful solution is often referred to as an outstanding demonstration of the practical usage of the phase rule.

The brine is withdrawn from a large crystal mass forming a "dry" lake in the California desert. KCl and K_2SO_4 are produced along with a number of other chemicals (compounds of boron, sodium, bromine, and lithium). The operation is described in Boron compounds, Vol. 3, pages 631–635. Although the brine, and therefore the process, are unique, the operation is of general interest as an outstanding example of thorough laboratory study, ingenious and practical application of theory, and good mechanical design, which were necessary and sufficient to change an unprofitable operation into a profitable one (14–16).

POTASH FROM LANGBEINITE

As explained below (under Potassium sulfate) there is a demand for potassium sulfate as a fertilizer. Potassium sulfate occurs in nature only as double salts, such as

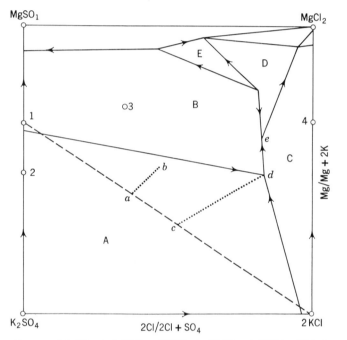

Fig. 7. Phase diagram, $MgSO_4 + 2 KCl \rightleftharpoons K_2SO_4 + MgCl_2$, at 55°C. This is a system of "salt pairs" which permits expressing the liquor concentrations of the four salts by only two numbers. In this case $X = 2 Cl/(2 Cl + SO_4)$ (using chemical equivalents) and $Y = Mg/(Mg + 2 K)$. The understanding is that the amount of water corresponds to a saturated solution. Lines of constant water proportion can be plotted on such a diagram, or the principal effect of water proportion can be shown by arrows on the borders between fields.

Point	1	langbeinite	$K_2SO_4.2MgSO_4$
	2	leonite	$K_2SO_4.MgSO_4.4H_2O$
	3	kainite	$KCl.MgSO_4.3H_2O$
	4	carnallite	$KCl.MgCl_2.6H_2O$
Area	A	liquor and solid K_2SO_4	
	B	liquor and solid leonite	
	C	liquor and solid KCl	
	D	liquor and solid kainite	
	E	liquor and solid langbeinite	

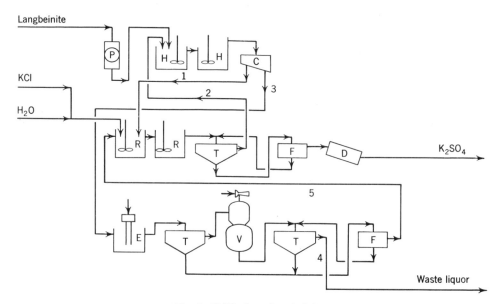

Fig. 8. K_2SO_4 from langbeinite.

C   centrifuge
D   dryer
E   evaporator, submerged combustion
F   filters
H   "hydrating" reactors
P   pulverizer
R   main reactors
T   "thickener" settlers
V   vacuum cooler-crystallizer

1   leonite
2   first mother liquor
3   second mother liquor
4   final mother liquor
5   recycle double salts

langbeinite, $K_2SO_4.2MgSO_4$, the use of which would, under some conditions, involve uneconomic transportation costs. A process for converting langbeinite to potassium sulfate is therefore required.

Langbeinite ores are generally mixtures of langbeinite with NaCl. The NaCl is removed by taking advantage of its much faster rate of solution. This requires careful particle-sizing, thorough agitation, and close control, but a 95% recovery of a 97% pure langbeinite can be achieved (17). A large proportion of the langbeinite is used as a fertilizer without further treatment, particularly in areas of magnesium deficiency.

Langbeinite is usually converted to K_2SO_4 by reaction with KCl:

$$K_2SO_4.2MgSO_4 + 4\,KCl \rightarrow 3\,K_2SO_4 + 2\,MgCl_2$$

Frequently, the operation is made attractive because the KCl is in the form of low-valued fines or wash water from a KCl refining operation.

The essentials of the process can be illustrated on the phase diagram Figure 7. If langbeinite and KCl are put into solution, the composition will lie on the dashed line, for instance point a, in the K_2SO_4 field. If water is evaporated K_2SO_4 will crystallize out and the composition of the remaining liquor will change, moving along the dotted line a–b. To crystallize only K_2SO_4, the evaporation must be stopped before point b reaches the leonite field B. In practice, instead of evaporating, the mixture is

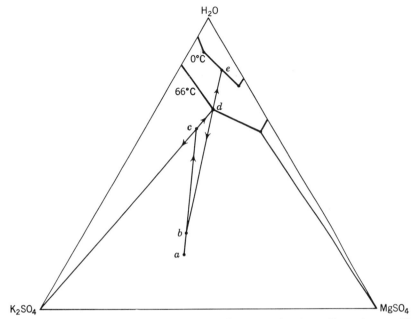

Fig. 9. Leaching operation in the production of K_2SO_4 from leonite. To a mixture of leonite (a) and recycle schoenite (b) water is added to give an overall composition at 66°C corresponding to point $c;$ this separates into K_2SO_4 and liquor of composition d. This liquor when cooled to 0°C separates into liquor of composition e, which may be rejected, and schoenite (b) which is recycled. By these steps about 80% of the potassium in the leonite can be recovered as K_2SO_4.

made up with an equivalent deficiency of water and mixed; to come to equilibrium then takes several hours even with finely ground feed. And for greater conversion, the operation is carried out along the line c–d (with recycle material forming part of the feed, the initial composition does not lie exactly on the dashed line). After equilibrium is reached and the product K_2SO_4 separated, the liquor may be evaporated at 55°C. Its composition then goes from d through e to f while KCl, leonite, and kainite are precipitated (and recycled). At about f, NaCl (a feed impurity) starts to precipitate and the remaining solution is discarded. In actual practice, evaporation is carried out at either higher temperatures, where mainly langbeinite and KCl are precipitated, or lower temperatures, resulting in the precipitation of KCl. The waste liquor (point f on Fig. 7), contains sufficient KCl for the NaCl content of the feed to have a serious effect on the efficiency of the process (18). A plant flow diagram is shown in Figure 8 (19). In this scheme, to improve efficiency, the langbeinite is first "hydrated" by mixing it with a mother liquor of composition d in Figure 7.

The K_2SO_4 produced in this manner is borderline in purity and particle size. Sometimes various agglomerating procedures are used or it is dissolved and then recrystallized.

In Europe, the supply-demand situation is such that K_2SO_4 is recovered from kainite, $KCl \cdot MgSO_4 \cdot 3H_2O$. The kainite is first converted to leonite, $K_2SO_4 \cdot MgSO_4 \cdot 4H_2O$, and brine according to the relationships shown in Figure 7. Then the separated leonite is converted to K_2SO_4 and a second brine by the relationships in Figure 9. The second brine is recycled to the first step, but the first brine is usually wasted, resulting in a low yield.

KCl, K_2SO_4, and KNO_3 supply 90% of the demand for potash fertilizers. But in special situations, a variety of semiprocessed ores and by-products are used. "Manure salts" may approximate one of the following:

langbeinite	$K_2SO_4 . 2MgSO_4$
schoenite	$K_2SO_4 . MgSO_4 . 6H_2O$
kainite	$KCl . MgSO_4 . 3H_2O$
sylvinite	KCl–NaCl

The first two may also be called "potassium magnesium sulfates." By-product sources are frequently the ashes of some waste materials with high potash content (eg, cotton-seed hulls, molasses distillation residue) or dusts from high-temperature operations (eg, cement kilns, blast furnaces) in which KOH or KCl volatilize.

Also, it is fairly common to treat purge streams from a process by neutralization or evaporation, and dispose of them as fertilizers. These find a ready market in mixed fertilizers.

For specialty fertilizer use where cost is not critical, there are of course a number of possible compounds. For instance, potassium ammonium phosphate has been investigated (20). See also Fertilizers.

Analysis

Accurate analysis of potassium is quite difficult. However, some reagents precipitate potassium ions with some degree of selectivity (1). The most common reagents are chloroplatinate, H_2PtCl_6, and tetraphenylborate, $NaB(C_6H_5)_4$. Numerous analytical procedures have been suggested for gravimetric, volumetric, and colorimetric determination of potassium. All the methods are limited with respect to selectivity, and require an elaborate pretreatment of the samples.

The gravimetric procedure is the most commonly used. In the chloroplatinate method, H_2PtCl_6 is added to a solution of mixed chlorides to form sodium and potassium chloroplatinates. The potassium chloroplatinate precipitates in aqueous ethyl alcohol solution with rubidium and cesium. The salts of potassium, rubidium, cesium, and ammonium of tetraphenylborate are highly insoluble and thus utilized as analytical tools. When only a small quantity of ammonium is present it is possible to complex it with formaldehyde before precipitation. Some volumetric procedures are available. Recently a method has been developed in which the potassium ion is precipitated by adding a measured, excess amount of standardized sodium tetraphenylborate solution, the precipitate filtered off, and the excess TPB in the filtrate determined by titrating with a standardized quaternary ammonium solution (eg, cetyltrimethylammonium bromide). The end point, where all the excess tetraphenylborate has been precipitated, is indicated by using bromophenol blue which forms a colored salt with any further addition of the quaternary ammonium salt (21,22).

Few reagents suitable for colorimetric analysis have been suggested. Cobaltinitrite dipicrylamine and chloroplatinate are among the others. The accuracy of this test is highly sensitive to interference by contaminants; recent investigations with dipicrylamine indicate that zinc as well as aluminum, iron, chromium, nickel, and copper affect the analytical results (23–26).

Two more analytical methods are extensively used, flame photometry and radio-activity.

Flame photometry (27–32) is relatively simple and less time-consuming. Results of the flame photometry test can be in close agreement with the gravitational methods. But the type of photometer, the preparation of the sample, and the technique used can affect the results considerably.

Potassium has a very slight radioactivity, and this can be used as an analytical tool. This method can be quite accurate (33–38), providing no radioactive contamination is present. The radioactivity phenomenon has been found useful for routine control purposes, prospecting, and geologic dating (39).

Many potassium compounds are used in medicine to such an extent that essentially all the U.S.A. production is manufactured to pass USP tests for purity.

Potassium Compared to Sodium

In many circumstances either a potassium compound or the corresponding sodium one can be used. The major area where this is not true is biology. KCl, of course, not NaCl, is used as a fertilizer (see Vol. 9, pp. 27, 31). In man, potassium and sodium have very different effects. Although they both readily diffuse through cell walls, Table 4 shows that in the body they are largely segregated.

Table 4. Ionic Concentrations of Potassium and Sodium in Body Fluids, meq/liter

Ion	Intracellular fluid	Extracellular fluid
K^+	160	4
Na^+	10	140

Table 5. Recent Comparative Prices of Potassium and Sodium Compounds, ¢/lb

Salt	Potassium	Sodium
acetate	31	26[a]
bicarbonate	9	3
bichromate	20	16[a]
borohydride	1,600	800
bromide	40	40
carbonate	8	4[a]
chlorate	12	10
chloride	19	11
chromate	50	16
citrate	45	37[a]
cyanide	43	18
ferricyanide	25	14
fluoride	36	15
hydroxide	10	5
iodide	145	213
nitrate	10	2
oxalate	42	22
silicate solution	6	2
sulfate	31	18

[a] Adjusted for hydrate water.

The metabolic mechanism that maintains this segregation is not understood; if metabolism is slowed, for instance in cold stored blood, K^+ diffuses out of the cells. A potassium deficiency causes neuromuscular troubles throughout the body; an excess affects the operation of the heart.

A considerable amount of potash (chiefly K_2CO_3) is used in the ceramic and high-quality glass industries because it has a different effect than soda on the melting points of the solid solutions involved. Potassium is fairly commonly specified as a component of gas reaction catalysts. Potassium has a slight natural radioactivity; sodium does not.

In everyday chemical technology, the choice between potassium and sodium compounds is based on cost or some physical property like solubility. Potassium salts

Table 6. Comparative Solubilities of Potassium and Sodium Compounds, g/100 g H_2O

Salt	Potassium		Sodium	
	0°C	100°C	0°C	100°C
acetate	217	412	119	170
bichromate	5	80	163	426
bromate	3	50	28	91
bromide	54	105	80	121
carbonate	107	154	7	46
chlorate	3	57	79	230
chloride	28	57	36	40
chromate	58	76	32	126
ferricyanide	31	78	19	67
fluoride	112	160	4	5
formate	300	770	44	160
hydroxide	97	178	42	347
iodide	128	208	159	302
nitrate	13	246	73	180
perchlorate	1	22	170	320
phosphate	80	190	2	108
hydrogen phosphate	84	282	2	102
dihydrogen phosphate	14	98	58	247
sulfate	7	24	5	43
sulfite	90	125	14	27
metabisulfite	28	133	50	82

are commonly thought of as more expensive and more soluble. Table 5 shows that potassium salts are, indeed, generally more expensive (these are published quotations; actual costs might be considerably less on long-term contracts, for instance), but Table 6 shows that the generalization on solubilities is invalid. Similarly, generalizations on purity, ease of crystallization, and formation of hydrates are not trustworthy. In many actual applications of a potassium salt, it is not easy to say why it has been chosen over the sodium salt.

Availability on commercial scale is a rough measure of reasonable cost and comparative usefulness. A review of a commercial chemical buyers' guide shows there are eighty-four cases in which both the sodium and the corresponding potassium compounds are offered, thirty-three cases of only the potassium, and 165 cases of only the sodium compound being similarly available.

Specific Potassium Compounds

Potassium Acetate. The acetate is usually made from the carbonate and acetic acid. It is very soluble and is used in the manufacture of glass, as a buffer, or dehydrating agent, and in medicine (diuretic). It is deliquescent and therefore a softening agent for papers and textiles.

Potassium Borohydride (Potassium Tetrahydroborate). See Vol. 11, pp. 210–217, also reference 40.

Potassium Bromide. Potassium bromide can be prepared by a variation of the process by which bromine from ocean water is absorbed (see Vol. 3, pp. 761–763), using potassium carbonate instead of sodium carbonate:

$$3 \ K_2CO_3 + 3 \ Br_2 \rightarrow 5 \ KBr + KBrO_3 + 3 \ CO_2$$

The potassium bromate is much less soluble than the bromide, and can largely be removed by filtration (41); the remaining bromate is reduced with iron. After filtering out the iron oxide, the KBr is crystallized.

An alternative method, which avoids the formation of bromate, is to treat iron turnings with a 35% aqueous solution of bromine. Ferrosoferricbromide, $Fe_3Br_8.$-$16H_2O$, is formed and may be crystallized out. The iron bromide is then boiled with a slight excess of 15% potassium carbonate solution.

$$Fe_3Br_8.16H_2O + 4 \ K_2CO_3 \rightarrow 8 \ KBr + 4 \ CO_2 + Fe_3O_4 + 16 \ H_2O$$

This particular bromide, $Fe_3Br_8.16H_2O$, is desirable in order to get in the second step a precipitate that is readily filtered. With care no final purification is necessary.

Potassium bromide is extensively used in photography and engraving. It is the usual source of bromine in organic synthesis, and in medicine it is the classical sedative.

Potassium Carbonate (potash, pearl ash). Potassium carbonate recovered from ashes was the prime potassium compound before 1870 ("pearl ash" was the recrystallized product) and marginal amounts are still produced similarly. Now the demand for Cl_2 has usually made it economic to produce KOH by electrolysis of KCl and therefrom K_2CO_3 by absorbing CO_2.

Before this development, two other processes were used. The two steps in the Engel-Precht process were:

$$2 \ KCl + 3MgCO_3.3H_2O + CO_2 \rightarrow 2MgCO_3.KHCO_3.4H_2O \ (insol) + MgCl_2$$
$$2 \ (MgCO_3.KHCO_3.4H_2O) + MgO \ (heated) \rightarrow 3 \ (MgCO_3.3H_2O) \ (insol) + K_2CO_3$$

Conditions in the second step must be controlled to ensure it is the trihydrate that is recycled to the first. The steps in the formate process are:

$$K_2SO_4 + Ca(OH)_2 + 2 \ CO \ (200°C, 30 \ atm) \rightarrow 2 \ KHCO_2 + CaSO_4 \ (insol)$$
$$2 \ KHCO_2 + O_2 \ (calcined) \rightarrow K_2CO_3 + CO_2 + H_2O$$

Conditions for the first step are chosen to avoid double salt precipitation and give an easily filterable $CaSO_4$.

Potassium carbonate cannot be made by the Solvay process used for Na_2CO_3.

The carbonate is usually purified only by washing after crystallization; however, it can be further purified by recrystallization. Occasionally, fractional crystallization is required to remove the impurities. It is sold as the sesquihydrate ($K_2CO_3.1.5H_2O$), anhydrous ("calcined"), and as a 47–50% liquor. Typical analyses of the technical grade are given in Table 7.

Table 7. Typical Analyses of K_2CO_3, % of total including water

	Calcined	47–50% Liquor
KOH	0.1	0.03
KCl	0.01	0.02
$KClO_3$		0.01
Na	0.02	
Si		0.0005
Fe	0.0002	
Ni	0.000003	

Table 8. Grades of Potassium Chloride

Grades	% KCl
"manure salts"	25–35
product from marginal operations	63–79
flotation grade	95–97
crystallized, agricultural	98–99
crystallized, industrial	99.5–99.9

Table 9. Typical Analysis of Flotation Grade of Potassium Chloride

Assay	%	Assay	%
Na	1.0	SO_4	0.3
Ca	0.05	water insoluble	0.5
Mg	0.1	HCl insoluble	0.3
Fe	0.05	H_2O	0.3
Al	0.03		

About 60% of the K_2CO_3 made is used in glass manufacture and about half the remainder to manufacture other potassium compounds. It is significantly more soluble than Na_2CO_3 (Fig. 10), so that it has been used as a noncorrosive antifreeze (42). An increasing amount is used as a regenerable absorbent for CO_2 and CO_2 + H_2S (43). About 60,000 tons will be manufactured in 1967.

Potassium Bicarbonate. The bicarbonate is made by absorbing CO_2 in a carbonate solution. KOH is carbonated to K_2CO_3 which is carbonated further to form $KHCO_3$. The changes in solubility during carbonation are shown in Figure 11. Usually the carbonate is crystallized, washed, and redissolved before the carbonation and crystallization of the bicarbonate. The solutions may also be filtered. Thus, the purest carbonate is made by calcining (heating) the bicarbonate. $KHCO_3$ is more stable than $NaHCO_3$ at normal temperatures, but decomposes at about 190°C.

The bicarbonate is used in foods and medicine. It has been found to be about twice as effective as $NaHCO_3$ in dry powder fire extinguishers, perhaps because the potassium affects the free-radical mechanism of flame propagation. However, it is not easy to give the material the proper handling characteristics. Solubilities are shown in Figures 10 and 11.

Potassium Chloride (potash, muriate of potash). Ninety percent of the potash is won from natural sources as potassium chloride, and it is this compound from which nearly all other potassium compounds are derived. Potassium chloride is the form used primarily in the fertilizer industry. In the U.S.A., in industry, potassium chloride is referred to as "muriate of potash" even though this expression is exceedingly out of date.

The recovery from ores and brines is described above. There are various grades of this prime product, as shown in Table 8. A typical analysis of flotation grade is given in Table 9. The purity can be improved somewhat by a more thorough washing step in the recovery operation, but the magnitude of the insolubles indicates the limitation of separation by flotation. Even in crystallized KCl there are insoluble

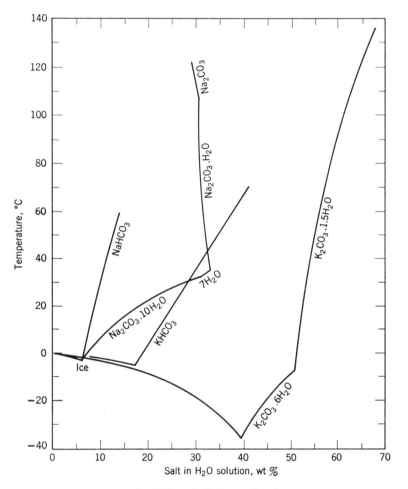

Fig. 10. Solubility of alkali metal carbonates.

fines which have not been removed by the settlers preceding the crystallizers, and inclusions of mother liquor in the crystals. KCl is normally further purified by recrystallization. KBr is an interesting minor impurity because it forms solid solutions with KCl (unlike NaBr and NaCl). Thus, KBr is not eliminated on crystallization. The proportion of KBr to KCl in the crystals is, however, only about a fifth in the solution so that recrystallization can be made quite effective.

Potassium Formate. The formate is made by the reaction (44):

$$CO + KOH \rightarrow HCOOK$$

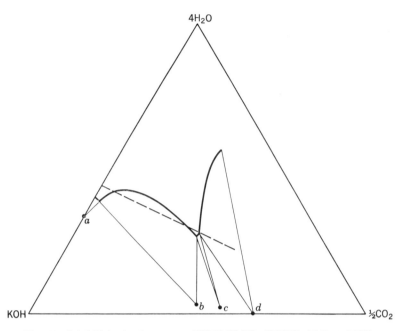

Fig. 11. Solubilities in the system KOH–K_2CO_3–$KHCO_3$–H_2O at 25°C.

Solid phases

a	KOH . $2H_2O$	c	K_2CO_3 . $2KHCO_3$. $1.5H_2O$
b	K_2CO_3 . $1.5H_2O$	d	$KHCO_3$

The proportions plotted above are chemical equivalents of KOH and CO_2, and units of four moles of water in order to make the diagram more legible. The dashed line shows the course of carbonating a 50 wt % solution of KOH.

Carbon monoxide (eg, by-product from phosphorus manufacture or extract from synthesis gas) is freed of acidic gases and absorbed in 50–80% KOH at 100–200°C with a partial pressure of CO greater than 100 psi. The reaction is fairly slow (see Formic acid).

Potassium formate melts at 167°C and decomposes almost entirely to the oxalate at about 360°; above and below this temperature different decomposition products are formed (see Oxalic acid). Most of the formate produced is thus converted.

Potassium Hydroxide (caustic potash, lye, potash lye). Formerly made by the reaction

$$K_2CO_3 + Ca(OH)_2 \rightarrow 2\,KOH + CaCO_3 \text{ (insol)}$$

nearly all potassium hydroxide is now made by the electrolysis of potassium chloride. This is done in cells similar to those used for NaOH–Cl_2 production, of which there are numerous designs (45) (see Alkali and chlorine). In diaphragm cells the product liquor contains 10–15% KOH and about 10% KCl; most of the KCl crystallizes out during the concentration by evaporation and subsequent cooling as shown in Figure 12, but the practical limit of purification leaves about 1% of KCl in the KOH. In mercury cells potassium metal is produced as amalgam and separated from the brine before being converted to KOH; the product KOH is much purer (<0.01% KCl) and concentrated enough (45%) to be sold directly. Largely for these reasons, most of

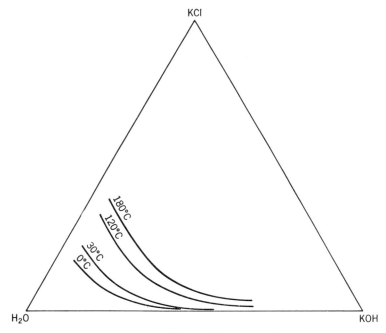

Fig. 12. Solubility of KCl in KOH solution (by wt).

European potassium hydroxide is made in mercury cells and the industry in the U.S.A. is moving in that direction (see Cell comparison under Alkali and chlorine, Vol. 1, p. 695). The purification effected by the amalgam step does not affect sodium; it must be minimized in the KCl feed. A drawback to producing KOH in mercury cells is that the KCl normally must be fed as a solid; this accentuates the difficulty of removing impurities which are usually higher in commercial KCl than in NaCl (Mg, V, Cr, Mo, Fe, and Al cause trouble in cell operation).

Large amounts are used as 45 or 50% solutions; small amounts are concentrated to about 61% (corresponding to the dihydrate) and cast into sticks or pellets; the rest is concentrated to 90–92% and sold as solid (in drums), flake, or lumps. These solid forms contain 6–8% of water. To reduce the water content would require melting in a vacuum. Up to 1.5% of K_2CO_3 (from the atmosphere) is common. Typical analyses are shown in Table 10.

Standard steel tanks are usually used to store KOH solutions, but strong solutions attack steel (more than NaOH) at temperatures approaching 200°F, so that when

Table 10. Typical Analyses of Technical KOH, wt %

Assay	Diaphragm		Mercury	
	Flake	Liquor	Flake	Liquor
KOH	91.4	50.1	92.0	45.6
KCl	1.2	0.6	<0.01	0.001
K_2CO_3	1.8	0.2	0.3	0.03
Fe	0.003	0.0006	0.001	0.00003
Ni	0.001		0.0005	
Na	0.06	0.01	0.04	0.01

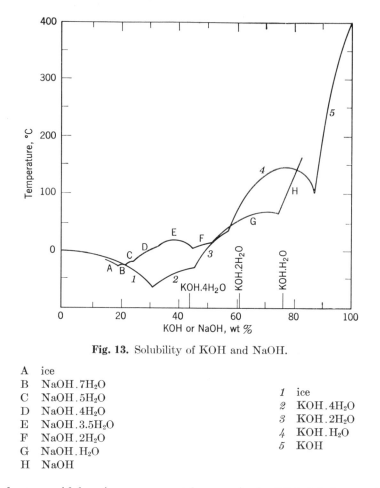

Fig. 13. Solubility of KOH and NaOH.

A   ice
B $NaOH.7H_2O$
C $NaOH.5H_2O$
D $NaOH.4H_2O$
E $NaOH.3.5H_2O$
F $NaOH.2H_2O$
G $NaOH.H_2O$
H   NaOH

1   ice
2 $KOH.4H_2O$
3 $KOH.2H_2O$
4 $KOH.H_2O$
5   KOH

heating tanks to avoid freezing, care must be exercised. Nickel is frequently used at the higher temperatures.

The solubility and viscosity of KOH solutions are significantly different from those of NaOH, particularly at low temperatures (see Fig. 13).

A large proportion of the KOH produced is used in the manufacture of "soft" soap; this is employed in liquid soaps, special applications, and as mixtures with the more common sodium soaps. Considerable KOH is consumed in textile operations, although here also much more NaOH is used. Other uses are in greases, catalysts, engraving and lithography, alkaline batteries, rubber fabrication, and the manufacture of other potassium compounds. About 175,000 tons were used in 1967.

Potassium Iodide. Some iodide is made by the iron and carbonate process described for the bromide. However, most of the U.S. production is by absorbing iodine in KOH (46):

$$3 I_2 + 6 KOH \rightarrow 5 KI + KIO_3 + 3 H_2O$$

About 80% of the iodate crystallizes from the reaction mixture and is separated for sale. Of the remainder 90% is removed by evaporation, fusion, and heating to about 600°C:

$$2 KIO_3 \rightarrow 2 KI + 3 O_2$$

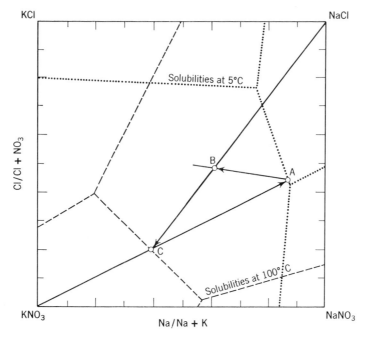

Fig. 14. Phase diagram, $KCl + NaNO_3 \rightleftharpoons KNO_3 + NaCl$, in H_2O.

Since the iodate is a poison, it is completely removed, frequently by a final reduction with carbon. After resolution in water, there are further purification steps before recrystallization; iron, barium, carbonate, and hydrogen sulfide may be used to precipitate sulfates and heavy metals.

About half the iodine consumed is used to make potassium iodide; production is almost a thousand tons a year. Its main uses are in animal and human food, pharmacy, and photography.

Potassium Nitrate. There was an increased demand for gunpowder in the mid-nineteenth century, and KNO_3 from natural deposits (including about 10% in Chile saltpeter) and production from excrement and ashes in "niter plantations" was not sufficient to meet the need ($NaNO_3$ being too deliquescent). About this time cheap KCl from Germany became available and, to supply this excess demand, some KNO_3 was made from KCl using nitric acid. However, the majority was made by the following reaction:

$$KCl + NaNO_3 \rightarrow KNO_3 + NaCl$$

The reaction is forced in the desired direction by the change of solubilities with temperature as shown in Figure 14. A mother liquor of composition A in Figure 14 is warmed and sufficient equimolar quantities of KCl and $NaNO_3$ are dissolved to move the composition to B. The temperature of the solution is raised to 100°C and water is evaporated; $NaCl$ crystallizes and the solution composition moves to C. The $NaCl$ is filtered out and the solution cooled to 5°C, which results in KNO_3 crystallization. Before cooling, it is necessary to add back the water evaporated to prevent the precipitation of $NaNO_3$ and $NaCl$. On a diagram such as Figure 14 it is not convenient to show the amounts of water at saturation, giving the absolute solubilities. The location of point A is chosen according to the absolute solubility in order to minimize the evaporation requirement.   See also Phase rule.

This process suffers from control difficulties and the buildup of impurities in the liquor.   It is usually necessary to recrystallize the KNO_3, and the bleed stream necessary to control the impurity level in the main process has a substantial effect on yield (47).

In Europe the availability of NH_4NO_3 and demand for NH_4Cl have resulted in the use of a similar process for the reaction

$$KCl + NH_4NO_3 \rightarrow KNO_3 + NH_4Cl$$

In recent years, large ammonia plants have so lowered the cost of nitric acid made from ammonia that it is presently the preferred source of the nitrate ion. KNO_3 has been made from K_2CO_3 and HNO_3, but the cost is high enough to limit this process to special situations.

Under certain conditions, the reaction

$$KCl + HNO_3 \rightarrow KNO_3 + HCl$$

would be economically attractive.   It is reported to proceed when the HCl is extracted by a solvent (eg, isoamyl alcohol) (48), but when an attempt is made to drive the reaction by boiling off the HCl, the reaction is:

$$3\ KCl + 4\ HNO_3 \rightarrow 3\ KNO_3 + Cl_2 + NOCl + 2\ H_2O$$

There has been considerable effort toward making this process economic by recovering the NOCl (nitrosyl chloride) as a usable product.   Recently this has been accomplished by a plant in which the NOCl is oxidized by a recycle HNO_3 stream to give more Cl_2 (which is much more valuable than HCl) and NO_2 which is reabsorbed in water to form a recycle HNO_3 stream (49).

These additional reactions are:

$$2\ NOCl + 4\ HNO_3 \rightarrow 6\ NO_2 + Cl_2 + 2\ H_2O$$
$$4\ NO_2 + O_2 + 2\ H_2O \rightarrow 4\ HNO_3$$

and the sum of the reactions, including the ammonia oxidation, is:

$$4\ KCl + 4\ NH_3 + 9\ O_2 \rightarrow 4\ KNO_3 + 2\ Cl_2 + 6\ H_2O$$

A simplified flow diagram of such a process is shown in Figure 15.   A novelty in this system is that KNO_3 is recycled to the water stripping column.   High KNO_3 contents shift the HNO_3 azeotrope from 70% HNO_3 to over 80% HNO_3, and make it possible to produce acid containing 80% HNO_3 or more by fractionation.   In a variation, the NOCl is oxidized by oxygen (50).   In a large plant of this type, the cost of the KNO_3 is low enough that its use as a fertilizer is attractive; as a result the U.S. production of KNO_3 has increased manifold.

Potassium nitrate is used for fertilizer (especially for foliage or seed application and to avoid caking problems in mixed fertilizers); in pyrotechnics; occasionally in explosives; in glass manufacture; as a food preservative; as a eutectic with $NaNO_3$ and $NaNO_2$ (mp 142°C) in the heat treating of steel; and in medicine.

Potassium Nitrite.   Potassium nitrite is made by absorbing oxides of nitrogen in carbonate solution:

$$NO + NO_2 + K_2CO_3 \rightarrow 2\ KNO_2 + CO_2$$

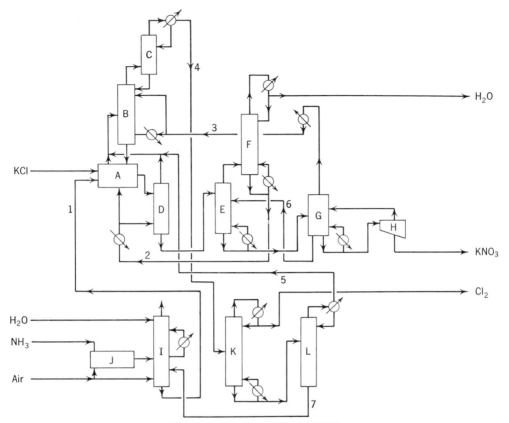

Fig. 15. KNO₃ from NH₃ and KCl.

A   KCl–HNO₃ reactor
B   NOCl oxidizer
C   acid eliminator   1   HNO₃
D   gas stripper   2   weak HNO₃
E   water stripper   3   strong HNO₃
F   water–HNO₃ fractionator   4   NO₂–Cl₂
G   evaporator-crystallizer   5   recycle NO₂–Cl₂–NOCl
H   centrifuge   6   KNO₃ slurry
I   NO–NO₂ absorber   7   NO₂
J   NH₃ burner
K   Cl₂ fractionator
L   NO₂ fractionator

An alkaline solution and a considerable excess of NO are necessary to minimize the formation of the nitrate which is more difficult to remove by fractional crystallization than is the case with the sodium compound.

The process can be carried out in a special absorber in the absorption train of an ammonia–nitric acid plant, similar to the manufacture of sodium nitrite (51–53). By proper staging of liquid streams and of oxygen (air) addition to the gas stream, the optimum NO/NO₂ ratio can be maintained in the nitrite absorber without an overall loss of nitrogen oxides.

For potassium peroxide, K₂O₂, potassium superoxide, KO₂, see Peroxides and peroxy compounds, inorganic.

Potassium Phosphates. The complex field of phosphates is described in the article Phosphoric acids and phosphates; here we briefly discuss only the few potassium phosphates of commercial interest.

Phosphoric acid is cheap enough (it is used in fertilizer manufacture) for practically all potassium phosphates to be made from it. The simple "ortho" phosphates: potassium dihydrogen phosphate, KH_2PO_4, dipotassium hydrogen phosphate, K_2HPO_4, and tripotassium phosphate, K_3PO_4, are made by adding KOH to H_3PO_4. If purity is a consideration, K_2CO_3 may be used, but some KOH is necessary to go all the way to K_3PO_4. If impure "wet process" H_3PO_4 is used, ferric oxide and aluminum, calcium, and magnesium phosphates are precipitated in that order as the pH is raised, and are usually filtered out (with some difficulty). If the di- or tribasic phosphate is desired, the neutralization is done continuously to avoid the low solubility of KH_2PO_4.

The potassium orthophosphates have buffering, chelating, and cleaning capabilities, but their cost compared to that of sodium compounds severely limits their use to special situations, usually where solubility is important, eg the removal of H_2S from gases in a process similar to the use of amines (54); in this use the high solubility minimizes the heat requirements.

If it is attempted to make the orthophosphates by adding KCl to H_3PO_4 and boiling off HCl, unless a considerable excess of H_3PO_4 is used, dehydration occurs to, for instance, the metaphosphate, KPO_3, which polymerizes to an insoluble, high-molecular-weight (10^4–10^6) compound. Processes have been developed to make this potassium polymetaphosphate from KCl economically as a fertilizer (55–57). (In spite of its comparative insolubility, the elements are available to plants.) The manufacturing costs are high so it cannot compete with the widely used sodium compounds in other fields, but it is such a concentrated fertilizer that freight savings could make it competitive.

When dipotassium phosphate is heated to 400°C it is dehydrated,

$$2\ K_2HPO_4 \rightarrow K_4P_2O_7 + H_2O$$

to tetrapotassium pyrophosphate. The pyrophosphates are complexing and surface-active agents to the extent that when mixed (as "builders") with soap or synthetic detergents they increase their effectiveness as well as lower the cost. (These mixtures are the "heavy duty" detergents.) Tetrapotassium pyrophosphate costs twice as much as the sodium compound, but far more of it is used in liquid detergents because it is twenty times as soluble and is slower to hydrolyze (revert back to the ineffective K_2HPO_4). About 25% of detergents are sold as liquids, so in nonfertilizer use of potassium compounds, potassium pyrophosphate ranks second only to KOH.

Potassium tripolyphosphate, $K_5P_3O_{10}$, is similar in manufacture and use to tetrapotassium pyrophosphate. The difference is that it is produced from equimolar amounts of mono- and dipotassium phosphates which must be thoroughly mixed during heating.

Potassium Sulfate (sulfate of potash). For some crops (tobacco and citrus) a fertilizer containing a significant amount of chloride is undesirable. This creates a considerable demand for potassium sulfate, but it means that commercial production must be at low cost. As described above, it is made from langbeinite ore, K_2SO_4.-$2MgSO_4$, and KCl which is contained in bleed-streams from a KCl plant. A similar (and complex) process has been worked out to use Canadian KCl and nearby deposits of sodium and magnesium sulfates to produce marketable K_2SO_4, Na_2SO_4, and $MgCl_2$ (58). In Italy a process was tried in which schoenite, $K_2SO_4 \cdot MgSO_4 \cdot 6H_2O$, crystallized from seawater bitterns, was reacted with $Ca(OH)_2$ to give K_2SO_4. The sulfate is also one of the many products recovered from Searles Lake brine, being essentially produced from KCl and burkeite, $Na_2CO_3 \cdot 2Na_2SO_4$ (59).

In unusual situations where HCl is valuable, K_2SO_4 can be made by the reaction:

$$2\,KCl + H_2SO_4 \rightarrow K_2SO_4 + 2\,HCl$$

driven to the right by vaporizing the HCl at high temperatures in the well-developed sodium sulfate manufacturing equipment (see Sodium compounds). A technically interesting proposal is to carry out the same reaction in water solution, driving the reaction by extracting the HCl with a solvent such as butanol (48). HCl is then removed from the solvent by water extraction or the addition of a less polar liquid. This process can use weak (inexpensive) H_2SO_4 at normal temperatures, but produces a weak (30%) HCl. Another variation is the application of the Hargreaves process for Na_2SO_4 (see Sodium compounds):

$$4\,KCl + 2\,SO_2 + O_2 + 2\,H_2O \rightarrow 2\,K_2SO_4 + 4\,HCl$$

Sulfur is burned with an excess of air, mixed with steam, and passed through a bed of porous KCl briquets. A countercurrent operation is economically necessary and is accomplished by proper switching of the gas stream through a number of stationary beds. Temperature control is a problem because the reaction is exothermic and the temperature necessary for a reasonable reaction rate (400°C) is fairly close, with this equipment, to the melting point of the KCl–K_2SO_4 eutectic (690°C). The product HCl is scrubbed from the exit gases, giving about a 30% solution. The Potash Company of America uses the Hargreaves process at Dumas, Texas. When high-purity potassium sulfate is required, the preferred route is recrystallization.

In addition to its use as a fertilizer, potassium sulfate is used in the production of alum, $KAl(SO_4)_2 \cdot 12H_2O$ (see Vol. 2, p. 64), and in the production of SBR latex rubber. It is incorporated in resinoid grinding wheels as a filler in the bonding material. It is incorporated into the carbon rods of commercial motion picture projectors. In smokeless powder mixtures potassium sulfate acts as a flash reducer, and it has been suggested in propellants. For special gypsum products the addition of potassium sulfate helps control setting time; the compound can be used as a filler in a thermosetting resin for potting applications. U.S. production of potassium sulfate is about 500,000 tons/yr.

Potassium bisulfate (potassium acid sulfate). If K_2SO_4 is made by the reaction

$$2\,KCl + H_2SO_4 \rightarrow K_2SO_4 + 2\,HCl$$

it is convenient to manufacture $KHSO_4$ similarly; in fact it is considerably easier to go to $KHSO_4$ than to K_2SO_4. However, the bisulfate is usually manufactured by mixing K_2SO_4 with strong H_2SO_4 and fusing. (To crystallize $KHSO_4$ from a water solution, a considerable excess of H_2SO_4 is required.)

Potassium bisulfate can be thought of as a conveniently solid strong acid. In solution, it behaves as though K_2SO_4 and H_2SO_4 were present separately. The acid characteristics are used in organic syntheses, eg esterification. The low melting point (210°C) and the acidity of $KHSO_4$ make it useful as a flux.

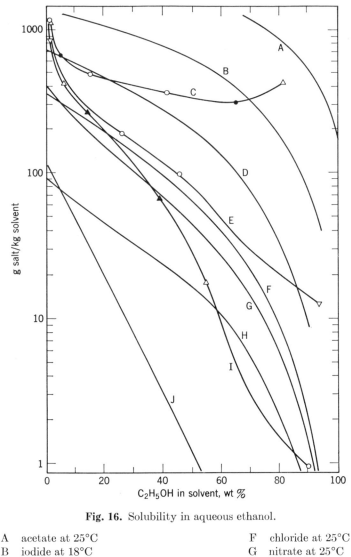

Fig. 16. Solubility in aqueous ethanol.

A	acetate at 25°C	F	chloride at 25°C
B	iodide at 18°C	G	nitrate at 25°C
C	hydroxide at 17°C	H	chlorate at 30°C
D	bromide at 30°C	I	carbonate at 25°C
E	fluoride at 25°C	J	sulfate at 25°C

Composition indicated by a symbol is in equilibrium with another phase indicated by same symbol on same curve.

Potassium Sulfites. The sulfites are of most interest as carriers of SO_2 with its mild reduction and oxidation capabilities. The metabisulfite, which crystallizes instead of the bisulfite,

$$2\ KHSO_3 \rightarrow K_2S_2O_5 + H_2O$$

is favored because, in addition to carrying more SO_2, it is more stable than the sulfite.

The sulfites are normally made by absorbing SO_2 in K_2CO_3 (or KOH if impurities are no problem). If the SO_2 comes from burning sulfur, little excess air is permissible since the sulfite solutions are very readily oxidized. A suspension of K_2CO_3 may be used, minimizing the handling of water. Metallic tin is sometimes used to remove traces of iron or inhibit oxidation by air (60).

The sulfites are used in textile printing and dyeing, as a disinfectant and food preservative, and in photography.

General Properties

Figure 16 gives solubilities of various potassium compounds in aqueous ethanol, solubility in alcoholic solutions sometimes being the basis for using the potassium rather than the sodium compound. See, however, the remarks above under Potassium compared to sodium, p. 385.

Bibliography

"Potassium Compounds" in *ECT* 1st ed., Vol. 11, pp. 12–29, by W. A. Cunningham, University of Texas.

1. *Mellor's Comprehensive Treatise on Inorganic and Theoretical Chemistry*, Vol. 2, Suppl. 3, John Wiley & Sons, Inc., New York, 1963.
2. *N.Y. State Museum Bull.* No. 275 (1928).
3. J. H. Perry, *Chemical Engineers' Handbook*, 3rd ed., McGraw-Hill Book Company Inc., New York, 1963.
4. *Phosphorus Potassium* **13**, 36 (1964).
5. U.S. Pat. 2,927,010 (March, 1960), Ira M. Le Baron (to International Mineral & Chemical Corp.); U.S. Pat. 3,052,349 (Sept. 4, 1962), R. E. Snow.
6. R. A. Gaska, R. D. Goodenough, and G. A. Stuarts, *Chem. Eng. Progr.* **61** (1), 139–144 (1965).
7. J. D. Buehler and N. G. Watson, *Phosphorus Potassium* **23**, (June–July, 1966).
8. Pablo Hadzeriga, *Trans. Soc. Mining Engrs.* (June, 1964), pp. 169–174.
9. D. E. Garrett, *Chem. Eng. Progr.* **59** (10), 59–60 (1963).
10. G. T. Gadre, A. V. Rao, and H. M. Bhavnagary, *J. Sci. Ind. Res. India* **17A**, 141 (1958).
11. Anon, *Eng. Mining J.* **167** (7), 90–91 (1966).
12. J. B. Butt, J. A. Talmadge, and H. R. Savage, *Chem. Eng. Progr.* **60** (11), 50–55 (1964).
13. J. A. Talmadge, J. B. Butt, and H. J. Solomon, *Ind. Eng. Chem.* **56** (7), 45–65 (1964).
14. S. D. Kirkpatrick, *Chem. Met. Eng.* **45** (9), 488–492 (1938).
15. G. R. Robertson, *Ind. Eng. Chem.* **34** (2), 133–137 (1942).
16. J. V. Hightower, *Chem. Eng.* **58** (8), 104 (1951).
17. G. T. Harley and G. E. Atwood, *Ind. Eng. Chem.* **39** (1), 43–47 (1947).
18. N. C. White and C. A. Arend, *Chem. Eng. Progr.* **46** (10), 523–530 (1950).
19. Anon., *Chem. Eng.* **57** (1), 168–172 (1950).
20. A. Zuorykin and V. Ketkovich, *Zhurnal Prikladnoi Khimii* **16** (11–12), 394–396 (1943).
21. E. D. Schall, *Anal. Chem.* **29** (7), 1044–1046 (1957).
22. B. Bullock and P. L. Kirk, *Ind. Eng. Chem. Anal.* **7** (3), 178–180 (1935).
23. C. P. Sideris, *Ind. Eng. Chem. Anal.* **14** (10), 821–822 (1942).
24. I. W. Wander, *Ind. Eng. Chem. Anal.* **14** (6), 471–472 (1942).
25. M. F. Adams and J. L. St. John, *Ind. Eng. Chem. Anal.* **17** (7), 435–436 (1945).
26. R. Faber and T. P. Dirkse, *Anal. Chem.* **25** (5), 808–810 (1953).
27. C. L. Fox, *Anal. Chem.* **23** (1), 137–142 (1951); W. R. Inman, R. A. Rogers, and J. A. Fournier, *Anal. Chem.* **23** (3), 482–483 (1951); E. J. Broderick and P. G. Zack, *Anal. Chem.* **23** (10), 1455–1458 (1951); S. B. Knight, W. C. Mathis, and J. R. Graham, *Anal. Chem.* **23** (11), 1704–1706 (1951).
28. A. J. Cavell, *Analyst* **77**, 537–539 (1952).
29. R. D. Caton Jr. and R. W. Bremner, *Anal. Chem.* **26** (5), 805–813 (1954); C. L. Ford, *Anal. Chem.* **26** (10), 1578–1581 (1954).
30. J. W. Berry, D. G. Chappell, and R. B. Barnes, *Ind. Eng. Chem. Anal.* **18** (1), 19–24 (1946).

31. *ASTM Symp. Spec. Tech. Publ.* No. 116, 1951, p. 13.
32. M. G. Reed and A. D. Scott, *Anal. Chem.* **33** (6), 773–775 (1961).
33. W. G. Harris, W. V. Kessler, J. E. Christian, and E. D. Schall, *Agr. Food Chem.* **12** (2), 144–146 (1964).
34. R. B. Barnes and D. J. Salley, *Ind. Eng. Chem. Anal.* **15** (1), 4–7 (1943).
35. A. M. Gavdin and J. H. Pannell, *Anal. Chem.* **20** (12), 1154–1156 (1948).
36. H. N. Wilson, D. S. Lees, and W. Broomfield, *Analyst* **76,** 355–361 (1951).
37. H. Friedman, *Eng. Mining J.* **152** (10), 90–91 (1951).
38. J. E. Christian, L. W. Combs, and W. V. Kessler, *Science* **140,** 489–490 (1963).
39. G. W. Wetherill, *Science* **126,** 545 (1957).
40. W. S. Fedor, M. D. Banus, and D. P. Ingalls, *Ind. Eng. Chem.* **49** (10), 1664–1672 (1957); *Metal Hydride Inc. Tech. Bull.* 1958.
41. U.S. Pat. 1,392,905 (Oct. 11, 1921), E. Barstow and C. Jones (to Dow Chemical).
42. Anon., *Chem. Eng. News* (March 27, 1967), p. 21.
43. *Solvay Tech. Ser. Bull. 661.*
44. U.S. Pat. 1,930,146 (Oct. 10, 1933), D. F. Othmer (to Eastman Kodak Co.).
45. H. A. Sommers, *Chem. Eng. Progr.* **53** (9), 409–417 (1957).
46. Anon., *Chem. Week* (Dec. 5, 1953), p. 80.
47. S. A. Chodkiewicz, *J. Appl. Chem. London* **2,** 639–641 (Nov. 1952).
48. U.S. Pat. 2,902,341 (May 1, 1956), A. Baniel (to Makhtsavei Israel).
49. M. L. Spealman, *Chem. Eng.* **72** (23), 198–200 (1965).
50. J. S. Sconce, *Chlorine: Its Manufacture, Properties and Uses,* Reinhold Publishing Corp., New York, 1962.
51. U.S. Pat. 991,356 (April 9, 1910), H. Pauling (to Salpetersäure Industrie).
52. U.S. Pat. 1,978,431 (June 13, 1929), W. F. Kirst (to E. I. du Pont de Nemours & Co., Inc.).
53. U.S. Pat. 2,032,699 (July 23, 1932), J. W. Hayes (to Solvay Process Co.).
54. H. W. Wainwright, G. C. Egleson, C. M. Brock, J. Fisher, and A. E. Sands, *Ind. Eng. Chem.* **45** (6), 1378–1384 (1953).
55. Anon., *Chem. Eng. News* (Sept. 23, 1963), p. 66.
56. Anon., *Chem. Eng.* **70** (9), 62–64 (1963).
57. R. L. Copson, G. R. Pole, and W. H. Baskervill, *Ind. Eng. Chem.* **34** (1), 26–32 (1942).
58. B. Gunn, *Can. J. Chem. Eng.* **43,** 193 (1965).
59. *Ind. Eng. Chem.* **34** (2), 133 (1942).
60. *Ullmann's Enzyklopädie der technischen Chemie,* Vols. 1–18, Urban & Schwarzenberg, Munich, 1951–1967.

Joseph J. Jacobs
Jacobs Engineering Co.

POTENTIOMETRY.   See Electroanalytical methods.

POTTERY.   See Ceramics.

POTTING, POTTING COMPOUNDS.   See Embedding.

POWDER METALLURGY

Powder metallurgy is defined as, "The art of producing metal powders and objects shaped from individual, mixed, or alloyed metal powders, with or without the inclusion of nonmetallic constituents, by pressing or molding objects which may be simultaneously heated to produce a coherent mass, either without fusion, or with the fusion of a low melting constituent only." This definition was given by the Powder Metallurgy Committee of the American Society for Metals in 1946 and it has not been significantly changed since that time. Powder metallurgy, then, encompasses the technology and application of metals in powder form, from the manufacture of the powders to the manufacture of a finished item.

In general practice metal powders or mixtures of various powders are fashioned into some form by first flowing them into a die cavity and applying pressure to form a compact, and then, in a separate operation, heating the compact to form a coherent mass. Or, the uncompacted powder may be heated without first applying pressure. The shape and size of the cavity may be exactly as required by the finished part or it may be some intermediate configuration. The pressing operation is usually carried out at room temperature; however, warm or even hot pressing is sometimes used. The purpose of the pressing operation is to consolidate the powder into a mass which can be handled and which has a certain dimensional configuration. During pressing a coherent mass is formed through the processes of interparticle binding and interlocking. The application of heat during pressing, or as a separate step, is such as not to cause melting of the powder. The temperature to which the pressed compact is then heated is below, but usually very close to, the melting point of the metal if it is elemental, or liquidus temperature of any alloy which may form. During heating, called "sintering," the bonding which was initiated in pressing is carried further by the solid-state movement of atoms.

Apart from the technique of sintering below the melting point is a special technique which combines powder and fusion metallurgy. In this procedure part of the structure is liquid for a part or for all of the sintering time. In some instances the sintering temperature is high enough to melt one constituent which may or may not solidify during the heating time. In some instances a metal skeleton is infiltrated with another metal which melts at a lower temperature.

Supplementary operations may be required after sintering. A sintered ingot may be worked by any number of metalworking procedures, such as swaging, rolling, or drawing. Shaped items, such as machine parts and structural components, may require some machining, plating, or other finishing operations.

Products. The techniques of powder metallurgy are used to produce a wide range of products. Among these are high-melting metals, composite metals, metal–nonmetal combinations, porous metals, laminated products, alloys of unusual composition, metals of high purity, machine parts, and coatings. Besides the special effects possible through the use of powder, sintered metal is often as strong and ductile as its cast counterpart and can be worked with equal success.

There are two general reasons for using the powder-metallurgy approach for the manufacture of metal items (see also Table 1):

1. To fabricate products which cannot be manufactured by other methods.
2. To fabricate products more advantageously—products of superior, special, or desirable properties; or products made more economically.

Table 1. The Use of Metal Powders to Manufacture a Variety of Items (1)[a]

Products	Materials used
Products which cannot be manufactured by methods other than powder metallurgy	
metals with high melting points	
incandescent lamp filaments, nonconsumable welding	
electrodes, resistance wire for high-temperature furnaces	W, Mo
electronic tube components	W, Mo, Ta, Nb
heavy alloys for high mass and radiation shielding	W–Ni–Cu
chemical-resistant containers	Ta
materials in which certain components of a composite must	
retain properties which would be lost if melted	
hard-metal alloys such as cemented carbides	carbides of W, Cr, Mo, Va, Nb, Ta, Ti, Zr; nitrides, borides, silicides
products with properties impossible to obtain by conventional	
methods	
catalysts	Pt, Ni, Fe, Cu
porous electrodes for alkaline batteries	Ni, Fe, Co
porous bearings, machine components, filters, and	
diaphragms	Cu, Fe, Sn, stainless steel
friction materials	Cu–Sn, Fe, Pb, Sn, Al; oxides, silicides
cermets (combinations of metal and ceramic materials)	Al; oxides, borides, carbides, silicides with Fe, Ni, Ca, W, Mo, etc
magnetic cores of insulated particles	Fe
structures in which certain components do not alloy	
electrical contacts	W–Ag, Mo–Ag, Mo–Cu, W–Cu, W + Mo with oxides
materials in which ablation is provided by the volatilization	
of one component	W–Ag
Products which may be manufactured more advantageously by powder metallurgy	
materials for which mass production is cheaper by	
powder metallurgy	
machine and structural parts such as cams, gears,	
spacers, lock hardware, etc	Fe, Cu, Pb, Sn, Al
materials in which high purity, exact composition, or a	
high degree of structural homogeneity is essential	
permanent magnets	Fe–Ni–Co–Al
electronic metals with high permeability	Fe, Ni
semiconductor heat sinks	W, Mo, W–Ag
coins, medals, and jewelry	Ag, Au, Pt
dental alloys	Au, Pt
glass sealing alloys	Fe–Ni–Co
nuclear and space applications	Be, Th, U, Zr

[a] After Bell (1), with modifications.

History. The history of powder metallurgy probably began with the use of silver, copper, and bronze powders for decorative purposes. At about 3000 BC record was made by the Egyptians of the use of a spongy iron for the fashioning of implements. The iron was made by reducing iron oxide with charcoal, and hammering the soft spongy mass into shape.   Throughout recorded time there have been numerous instances of powder-metal technology mainly associated with precious metals.

Between 1750 and 1825 considerable attention was given to the manufacture of platinum powder, and modern powder metallurgy can be said to have stemmed from these developments.   Sobolevski is generally given credit for laying down the foundation of modern powder metallurgy.   Sobolevski manufactured platinum shapes by compacting the powder into a cylindrical mass, heating the compact to bond the particles, and hot-forging the resulting metal.

The first commercial application of powder metallurgy occurred when first carbon, and then later osmium, was used for incandescent filaments.   These materials were mixed with a binder, extended into wire, and sintered.   Between 1903 and 1911 tantalum and zirconium were also used for this application.   The Coolidge process for pressing, sintering, and working tungsten was developed starting in 1900 and tungsten has been used for incandescent filaments since that time.

The tungsten carbide industry was a direct outgrowth of the tungsten filament industry when it was found necessary to have a harder material than steel for use as wire drawing dies.   It was noted that tungsten carbide, a hard material, could be consolidated by the use of cobalt and the resulting metal could be fashioned into a hard wear-resistant wire drawing die.   Cutting tools containing similar compositions were a direct growth of this die requirement.

Infiltration techniques, porous materials, iron-powder cores for radio tuning devices, magnets, and tungsten–copper–nickel compositions were developed during the period 1900–1930.

Only during the period after 1930 did iron-powder technology advance to a commercial extent.   The most spectacular development of iron parts made through powder metallurgy was during World War II in Central Europe, where paraffin-impregnated sintered iron driving bands for projectiles were extensively used.   Production reached a peak of 3500 tons/month for this application.

Without a doubt the advent of mass production in the U.S. automotive industry made possible usage of iron and copper powders in large tonnage.   This utilization has been the backbone for much of the industrial development even in fields unrelated to the automotive industry.

Since the end of World War II, and especially with the advent of space and nuclear technology, developments have been widespread with regard to the powder metallurgy of refractory metals such as tungsten, molybdenum, niobium, chromium and titanium, and to the nuclear metals such as beryllium, uranium, zirconium, thorium, and tantalum.

A number of literary works are worthy of mention.   *Principles of Powder Metallurgy*, by W. D. Jones was published in 1937 in England.   This book has since been brought up to date and in 1960 was published as *Fundamental Principles of Powder Metallurgy*.   P. Schwarzkopf gave an extensive description of the field in 1947.   Also in 1947, the first Russian publication by Balshin appeared.   The first U.S. publication was by Hausner and appeared in 1948.   A year later, the first of four volumes of *Treatise on Powder Metallurgy*, a major work by Goetzel, was published in the U.S.

In 1946, an organization called the Metal Powder Association was founded by a group of metal-powder producers in the U.S.   This Association was reorganized in 1958 as the Metal Powder Industries Federation.   Under this organization, the various segments of the industry are organized into separate divisions.   The divisions and their functions are outlined below.

Powder Metallurgy Parts Manufacturers Association: Manufacturers of powder-metallurgy parts for sale on the open market.

Metal Powder Producers Association: Manufacturers of metal powder, granular and flake, and additives used in powder-metallurgy processing.

In-Plant Powder Metallurgy Association: Manufacturers of powder-metallurgy products for in-plant use, plus fabrication of other products using powder-metallurgy techniques.

Table 2. U.S. Consumption of Iron Powder,[a] 1000 tons

Year	Iron powder-metallurgy parts	Total consumption	Year	Iron powder-metallurgy parts	Total consumption
1956	7	32	1962	30	51
1957	12	31	1963	38	58
1958	10	22	1964	45	73
1959	19	34	1965	58	86
1960	17	33	1966	63	100
1961	20	35			

[a] Capacity is approximately double consumption.

Magnetic Powder Core Association: Fabricators of magnetic cores from iron or ferrite powders, makers of permanent magnets, suppliers of raw material used in core manufacture, and fabricators of molybdenum permalloy cores.

Powder Metallurgy Equipment Association: Manufacturers of primary equipment used in the powder-metallurgy process.

American Powder Metallurgy Institute: Organized in 1959 as a technical division to accommodate individuals interested in powder metallurgy.

The purposes of the Federation are to improve and promote metal powders and products of powder metallurgy through investigation, research, and interchange of ideas. It is concerned with education in the science, practice, and application of metal powders and powder metallurgy, and related arts through meetings, technical exhibits,

Table 3. Shipments of Copper and Copper-Alloy Powders, 1000 tons

Year	Shipments	Year	Shipments
1960	19	1964	28
1961	20	1965	31
1962	24	1966	33
1963	25		

and publications. It collects and disseminates information pertaining to technical facts, standards, and other data fundamental to metal-powder and powder-metallurgy applications.

Typical of the information available from the Metal Powder Industries Federation are the data given in Tables 2 and 3, which give the total U.S. consumption of iron and copper powders and indicate in a very representative way the growth of the powder-metallurgy industry.

Manufacture of Powders

There are nine basically different methods for the manufacture of metal powders.

1. Machining—usually produces a relatively coarse particle size.

2. Milling—in ball mills, impact mills, gyratory crushers, eddy mills, and others, results in fine powders of brittle materials.

3. Atomization—breaking up a stream of molten material in gases or liquids.

4. Condensation of metal vapor—deposition on cooler surfaces.

5. Reduction of metal oxides (sometimes other compounds)—in solid or gaseous media.

6. Decomposition of metal hydrides—vacuum treatment of hydrides which results in powder of fine particle size.

7. Decomposition of metal carbonyls—liquid or gaseous metal carbonyls are decomposed and form a fine powder.

8. Electrolytic deposition from salts or solutions—seldom forms powder directly, but an adherent mass of the material which has to be mechanically comminuted.

9. Precipitation of a metal from molten magnesium on halide—Kroll process for titanium and zirconium.

Metal-Powder Characteristics (3)

A perfect and complete characterization of a metal powder presents difficulties due to the large number of variables involved, the complexity of the properties, and the sometimes close correlation between two or more of the variables. Nevertheless, only three basically different types of variables are involved in the characterization of a powder: those that are closely connected with an individual powder particle; those that refer to the mass of particles which form the powder; and those that refer to the voids. It must be remembered that, in a mass of loosely heaped powder, 60–70 % or more of the volume consists of voids.

CHARACTERISTICS OF INDIVIDUAL PARTICLES

Particle Size. The precise determination of the particle size—usually referred to as the particle diameter—can actually be made only for spherical particles. For any other particle shape a precise determination is practically impossible; it represents an approximation only, based on an agreement with respect to the testing methods.

In practical powder metallurgy, one distinguishes between particles which are larger than 44 μ and "fines," which are smaller than 44 μ. The dividing size, 44 μ, is the aperture of the finest sieve used, 325 mesh (U.S. Standard). The term "powder of −325-mesh size" is therefore not too meaningful. The fact that in practical powder metallurgy most of the powders used for parts production are usually larger than 5 μ justifies the characterization of a powder as −325-mesh size, to a certain extent.

For more precise measurements of particle size, and especially of "subsieve-size particles" (fines), one has to apply other methods for size determination. These methods are described in detail in several books (4,5). See also Size measurement of particles.

Particle Shape. Metal-powder particles are produced in a great variety of shapes, as shown in Figure 1. The shape usually depends to a large extent on the method of fabrication of the powder. It is most difficult to describe the frequently very complex shape of a powder particle. Several methods have been proposed for the characteriza-

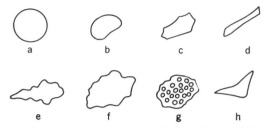

Fig. 1. Various shapes of metal powder. LEGEND: a, spherical; b, rounded; c, angular; d, acicular; e, dendritic; f, irregular; g, porous; and h, fragmented.

tion of the particle shape; it can be expressed as a deviation from a sphere of identical volume; or as the ratio between length, width, and thickness of a particle, as well as in terms of some shape factors. Several other methods have been proposed to characterize the particle shape; however, they all have their shortcomings.

Particle Density. The density of a metal-powder particle is not necessarily identical with the theoretical density of the material from which it is produced. This is due to the fact that many methods for fabrication of powders result in porous particles. The porosity of powder particles sometimes makes it difficult to determine their actual size and surface area.

Particle Surface. Any reaction between two powder particles starts on the surface. The amount of surface area compared to the volume of the particle is, therefore, an important factor in powder technology. The particle surface configuration—whether it is smooth or contains sharp angles—is another important factor. Table 4 shows in a very general way that the particle surface area depends strongly on the process of powder production, which usually determines the particle shape.

Table 4. Approximate Surface Area of Powder Particles Fabricated by Various Methods (2)

Process of powder production	Particle shape	Approximate surface area[a]
carbonyl process	uniform spherical	πD^2
atomization	round irregular spheroids	1.5–$2D^2$
reduction of oxides	irregular spongy	7–$12D^2$
electrolytic process	dendritic	7–$12D^2$
mechanical comminution		
crushing	angular	3–$4D^2$
ball-milling	flakes or leaves	varies over wide range

[a] D represents diameter.

Microstructure. A powder particle usually consists of many crystal grains of various sizes. The microstructure, ie, the crystal grain size and grain orientation, also depends on the method of powder fabrication. However, in many cases a correlation exists between particle size and grain size. In metal powders made by atomization, ie, from the molten phase, the smaller atomized particles solidify faster than the larger ones, and therefore in small-size atomized powder particles there is usually less grain growth, producing the smaller grains rather than coarse ones.

Because it affects the activity of the powder particle, and to a certain extent also determines the amount of material transported by grain boundary diffusion, the grain structure of the particle is of importance.

Surface Oxide Layer. Whether surface oxide layers can be reduced in a reducing gas atmosphere (Cu, Fe, Ni, W, Mo, etc), or no reduction occurs (Al, Be, etc) depends on the type of metal to be treated.

The problems of nonreducible surface oxide layers are of importance in the production of metals which are strengthened by dispersion, where the thin oxide layer causes the strengthening (SAP (sintered aluminum powder with 10–14% aluminum oxide) materials). For a given thickness of the oxide layer, the amount of oxide in a powder changes with the particle size. The thickness of the oxide layer of an individual particle depends on the conditions under which the oxidation occurs (Tables 5 and 6).

Table 5. Thickness of Oxide Film on 99.6% Pure Aluminum on Exposure to Atmosphere, at Room Temperature (2)

Time of exposure, days	Thickness of oxide film, μ	Time of exposure, days	Thickness of oxide film, μ
0	0	4	0.0065
1	0.0025	8	0.008
2	0.005	16	0.0088

Table 6. Oxide Content of Aluminum Flake Powder in Relation to Particle Thickness

Particle thickness, μ	Oxide content, vol %	Particle thickness, μ	Oxide content, vol %
0.1	30	100	0.03
1.0	3	1000	0.003
10	0.3		

For metals whose oxide layers can be reduced during sintering in reducing atmosphere, the type and amount of oxide crystals which are converted to metal crystals greatly affect the activity of the particle surface due to the increased mobility of atoms during the conversion of the crystal lattice from the oxide to the metallic state. There is, in many cases, an optimum amount of oxide which determines the sinterability of the respective powders, and their physical properties after sintering.

Activity. The term "activity" refers to the property of a powder particle to react with its environment; the activity determines the type and rate of the reaction.

The total activity of a powder particle consists of the activity of the bulk and that of the surface. Both activities depend on the type and number of defects in the crystal lattice, and it must be borne in mind that these defects usually exist in large numbers on the surface. Surface activity increases with increasing ratio of surface area to volume. Small particles, therefore, are usually of greater activity than larger ones. The shape and surface configuration of the particle also influence the activity. Particles with sharp-angled corners are more active than particles with rounded smooth surfaces.

Due to the fact that grain boundaries also contribute to the activity of a particle, one frequently observes that particles with small crystal grains are more active than particles consisting of larger grains. With respect to diffusion, the activity of particles consisting of single grains is much less than that of multicrystal particles.

The activity of a powder particle determines the rate of material transport by bulk and surface diffusion, the rate of adsorption and absorption, and similar reactions with the environment.

CHARACTERISTICS OF A MASS OF POWDER

A mass of powder consists of a large quantity of particles; the characteristics of some iron powders are shown in Table 7.

Table 7. Characteristics of Three Types of Iron Powders (2)

Type of powder	Average particle size, μ	Particle size distribution, mesh				Specific surface area, m²/g	Apparent density, g/cm³
		+150	−150 +200	−200 +325	−325		
electrolytic	78	29.26	16.39	54.16		265	3.32
	63	21.98	16.00	50.10	10.0	452	2.56
	53	2.38	21.0	74.0	3.0	1150	2.05
reduced	68	28.5	15.5	54.5	1.0	516	3.03
	51		6.5	81.5	12.0	945	2.19
	6	3.5	2.0	13.5	78.5	5160	0.97
carbonyl	7	2.5	0.1	1.0	95.5	3460	3.40

Average Particle Size. This term refers to a statistical diameter, the value of which depends to a certain extent on the method of determination. The average particle size can be calculated either from the particle size distribution or by measuring the powder permeability, or by gas adsorption methods.

The Fisher subsieve sizer is a widely used instrument for measuring the average particle size; it actually determines the flow rate of a gas through the powder bed under a controlled pressure differential. For porous or very irregularly shaped particles, the data obtained with the Fisher subsieve sizer are sometimes questionable. This, however, is also true for gas adsorption methods.

Particle Size Distribution. For many powder-metallurgy processes, the average particle size is not necessarily a decisive factor, but the distribution of the particles of various sizes in the powder mass is decisive. The distribution curve can be irregular or can show a rather regular distribution with one maximum but can also have more than just one maximum or can be perfectly uniform. How much the particle size distribution affects other powder characteristics will be shown and discussed below.

Specific Surface. The total surface area of 1 g of powder is called its specific surface. It is usually expressed in cm²/g or m²/g. Inasmuch as any reaction between powder particles starts on their surface, the specific surface area is an excellent indicator for the conditions under which the reaction will start and also for the rate of the reaction.

The specific surface area depends on size, shape, and surface conditions of the particles. Table 7 shows some characteristic data for electrolytic, reduced, and carbonyl iron powders, which differ not only in shape, but also in size and size distribution. The data given show the average particle size, particle size distribution, specific surface area, and apparent density. The specific surface area correlates in general with the average particle size. The great difference in surface area between the 6-μ reduced powder and the 7-μ carbonyl powder, however, cannot be explained in terms of particle size, but mainly by the difference between the very irregular-shaped reduced and the spherical carbonyl iron powders.

Determination of the specific surface area can be made by a variety of adsorption measurements or by air permeability determinations.

Apparent Density. This terms refers to the weight of a unit volume of loose powder, usually expressed in g/cm³. It is a main characteristic of powders, and depends on the material density as well as particle shape, size, size distribution, and the method of measurement (6).

The apparent density of a powder actually depends on the friction conditions between the powder particles, which is a function of the relative surface area of the particles and the surface conditions; it depends, furthermore, on the packing arrangement of the particles, which again depends on particle size, but mainly on particle size distribution and the shape of the particles. The characteristics of a powder which determine its apparent density are rather complex; some general statements with respect to the powder variables and their effect on the density of the loose powder, however, can be made.

1. The smaller the particles, the greater is the specific surface of the powder, which increases the friction between particles, and the lower is the apparent density. This is shown in Table 7 for irregular-shaped electrolytic iron powder. This statement, however, is not true for powder particles with very low friction because of their spherical shape, as also shown in this table for atomized (spherical) stainless-steel powder.

2. Powders with very irregular-shaped particles are usually characterized by a lower apparent density than the more regular or spherical ones. This is shown in Table 8 for three different types of copper powders, the particle size distribution of which was made identical, but which differed in particle shape. Data in this table indicate that the particle shape is one of the most decisive factors which determine apparent density.

Table 8. Effect of Particle Shape of Three Types of Copper Powders of Identical Particle Size Distribution on Apparent and Tap Density (2)

Particle shape	Apparent density, g/cm³	Tap density, g/cm³	Increase, %
spherical	4.5	5.3	18
irregular	2.3	3.14	35
flake	0.4	0.7	75

3. In any mixture of coarse and fine powder particles, there is usually an optimum mixture which results in maximum apparent density. This optimum mixture is reached when the fine particles fill the voids between the coarse particles.

Tap Density. Tapping a mass of loose powder—or more specifically, the application of vibrations to the powder mass—separates the powder particles for a moment, and in this way overcomes the friction between them. This short-time lowering of the friction results in an improved powder packing between the particles and in a higher apparent density of the powder mass. The tap density is always higher than the apparent density. The amount of increase from apparent to tap density depends mainly on particle size and shape.

Flow of the Powder. Whether or not a powder flows freely through an orifice, depends on the characteristic of the orifice (which is standardized for tests) (7). The flow, therefore, does not depend only on the friction between powder particles, as it does for the apparent density, but also on the friction between the particles and the wall of the orifice. The flow is usually expressed by the time (in seconds) necessary for a specific amount of powder (usually 50 g) to flow through the orifice.

Inasmuch as friction conditions determine the flow characteristics of a powder, one can assume that coarser powder particles of spherical shape flow fastest and powder particles of identical diameter but more irregular shape flow more slowly. Finer particles may start to flow but stop after a short time and need tapping in order to start again. Very fine powders of less than approx 20 μ do not flow at all. Addition of some fine powder particles to coarser ones which may increase the apparent density usually decreases the flow quality.

Metal powders with a thin oxide film which flow well may flow poorly when the oxide film is removed and the friction between the particles therefore increases.

The free flow of a powder is a necessity for automatic-fill compacting dies for production purposes. Powders which flow badly need vibratory filling in order to overcome friction, and powders which do not flow at all can be used only for manual filling of the die cavity.

This brief discussion of the characteristics of powders and particles indicates clearly that a perfect characterization is rather difficult, and that considerably more work in this field has to be done in order to correlate the powder behavior during compacting and sintering with the characteristics of the powder, and to predict the powder behavior from its characteristics.

CHARACTERISTICS RELATING TO THE VOIDS (2)

Characteristics of porosity in a mass of loose powders include total pore volume, P; pore volume between powder particles, P_1; pore volume within powder particles, $P_2 = P - P_1$; number of pores between powder particles, n; average pore size, P_1/n; pore size distribution; and pore shape.

Consolidation

Metal powders are consolidated by using pressure followed by heating, by heating alone, or by heating during the application of pressure (8). The purpose of consolidation is to achieve a coherent mass of definitive size and shape for further working or heating.

It is generally agreed that during pressure application three overlapping phenomena occur: first, rearrangement or packing of the powder particles; second, elastic and plastic deformation; and third, cold working of the particles. Many attempts have been made to develop mathematical relationships between compacting pressure and such factors as density and strength of the compact and strength of the sintering (9–12). Any such relationship may hold for a few powders within a narrow range of pressures and has not been found to be of great practical significance. The reasons generally given for the bonding of particles and formation under pressure of a coherent mass are (a) liquid surface cementation; (b) interatomic forces such as surface adhesion, cold welding, and surface tension; and (c) mechanical interlocking of particles (13).

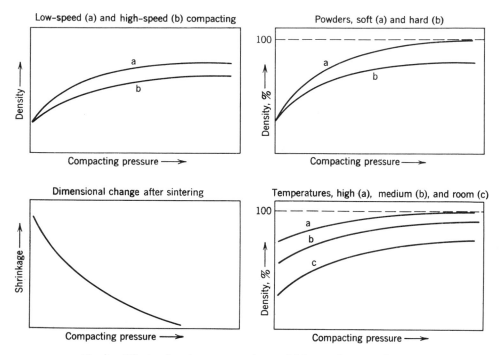

Fig. 2. Effects of various compaction variables on the pressed compact.

The idea of *cementation* supposes that the heat generated in a compact is sufficient to cause the surface layer of atoms to melt and run together during pressure application causing sufficient bonding. Although there is a measurable temperature rise within the bulk of the compact, and probably a much greater temperature rise on the atomic level, this idea is not widely held.

Plasticity of the metal crystals plays a dominant role in *interatomic bonding*. This is basic with the metal, but is affected to a large extent by the condition of the individual powder particles. Metals having a face-centered cubic atomic arrangement are more ductile than those whose atom arrangement is body-centered cubic, and close-packed hexagonal metals are the least plastic. Gold, silver, lead, and iron are extremely plastic metals, while chromium and tungsten deform with great difficulty. Plasticity also depends upon such factors as the nature and history of the powder, impurities present (especially on the surface), and friction conditions between the particles. Powders which exhibit a high degree of plastic deformation form many areas of metal contact and therefore many atomic bonds, while powders composed of harder particles form relatively few atomic bonds.

Probably the most important powder property governing the formation of atomic bonds is the surface condition of the particles, especially with respect to the presence of oxide films. If heavy oxide layers are present they must be penetrated by projections on the particles. This results in only local rather than widespread bonding. A ductile metal such as iron with a heavy oxide layer may not form as strong or as many bonds as a less ductile metal which is relatively free of oxide.

Mechanical Interlocking. The fact that irregular-shaped powder particles form denser and stronger compacts under pressure than regular-shaped powder particles leads very quickly to a theory of interlocking particles. Interlocking is probably the major strengthening mechanism and also is probably responsible for providing increased surface contact for cold welding. The mechanism of interlocking plays a major role in the strengthening of compacts made from metals such as tungsten and chromium, which normally are not plastic at room temperature.

A great number of factors influence the characteristics of a pressed compact. Among these are characteristics of the powder; rate of pressure application; maximum pressure applied; shape of die cavity; temperature during compaction; additions such as lubricants and alloy agents; die material and surface condition; and manner of pressure application. A number of generalizations with regard to the effect of various compaction variables on the pressed compact are shown in Figure 2.

CONSOLIDATION TECHNIQUES

Unidirectional Compacting. Pressing of metal powders in a die of specific dimensions and configuration is the most frequently used technique for the consolidation of powders in the manufacture of machine parts and for ingots. Powder is flowed into a die cavity, generally by an automatic arrangement, the bottom punch or punches acting as the bottom of the cavity, and application of pressure is in one direction parallel to the direction of powder flow into the cavity. Pressing may be single-action, where either the bottom or top punch is held rigid and the corresponding punch moves to press the powder, or double-action, where both punches move. Double-acting punches are used to produce a more uniformly dense compact. After pressure application, the top punch is removed and the compact is ejected from the cavity by the bottom punch. The cavity is then reformed and is ready for another charge of powder. This cycle is repeated automatically at a rate which varies with the part size, complexity, and flowability of the powder. Production of parts may vary from 5/min to 25/min. Pressing equipment producing relatively small simple parts operates at up to 200 parts/min. Table 9 gives the ranges of pressures that are used for various materials during die compaction.

Table 9. Tonnage Requirements and Compression Ratios[a] for Various Powder Products (13a)

Type of compact	Tons/in.^{2}	Compression ratio
brass parts	30–50	2.4–2.6:1
bronze bearings	15–20	2.5–2.7:1
carbon products	10–12	3.0:1
copper graphite brushes	25–30	2.0–3.0:1
carbides	10–30	2.0–3.0:1
alumina	8–10	2.5:1
steatites	3–5	2.8:1
ferrites	8–12	3.0:1
iron bearings	15–25	2.2:1
iron parts, low density	25–35	2.0–2.4:1
medium density	35–40	2.1–2.5:1
high density	35–60	2.4–2.8:1
iron-powder cores	10–50	1.5–3.5:1
tungsten	5–10	2.5:1
tantalum	5–10	2.5:1

[a] Compression ratio is the dimensional relationship between the loose powder and compacted powder at a given compacting pressure.

Isostatic Pressing.   In equipment employing the isostatic process, pressure is transmitted through a liquid medium, either oil or water, to a flexible container holding the powder. The liquid transmits the pressure uniformly throughout the chamber, applying the same unit pressure on all areas of the flexible container. Density distribution within the pressed compact, therefore, is very uniform.

Isostatic compaction is used mainly for the formation of large compacts where the number of parts is limited. These parts, which may vary from a few inches to 6 ft in length, are then sintered, and used as extrusion, swaging, or drawing billets, or are machined into more intricate shapes. The isostatic process is also used where a limited number of items with complicated shapes are desired, or where an extreme degree of density uniformity is necessary.

In general, the close tolerances possible in the rigid die compaction method are not possible by isostatic methods, mainly due to the fact that the mold changes dimension during pressure application. The limitation on size of parts made by this method appears to be controlled more by the boiler codes of the various states rather than by the size of equipment which can actually be constructed. Isostatic pressing looms as one of the more important processes in the future powder metallurgy industry. Attempts are being made to mechanize the process for the manufacture of small precision parts.

Powder Rolling (14).   Powder conveyed either horizontally or vertically through a set of steel rolls is compacted in the roll gap and emerges as a porous sheet. This sheet is then sintered, rerolled (warm or cold, depending upon the material), annealed, and finish-rolled to obtain desirable properties. The rolling mills and furnaces are arranged for continuous production. Green strength of the sheet as it emerges from the roll gap is the limiting factor for both the thickness and width of the sheet. Roll size, roll gap, roll speed, and rate of powder feed are the major factors to be controlled. Powder properties, of course, are always of major importance. In powder rolling, compaction occurs essentially in only one direction since very little pressure is transmitted sideways.

Powder rolling eliminates much of the equipment needed for melting, casting, and rolling to produce thin sheet. Sheet can be rolled close to finished size with a minimum loss of material. Most scrap generated by this process can be reclaimed as powder. This technique also permits the production of clad materials by using a metal strip as the carrier for the powder through the roll gap. Powder rolling is used in Canada to produce strip from which blanks are made for the Canadian five-cent piece. In the U.S., considerable quantities of nickel and nickel–iron–cobalt powders are rolled into strip for various electronic applications.

Continuous Compacting.   A method for producing ingots of unlimited length and relatively large cross-sectional area was developed by Emley and Deibel at Westinghouse Electric Corporation (15). In this process, loose powder is placed in a three-sided trough and compressed by a plunger consisting of a flat pressing surface, part of which is parallel to the powder surface and part of which is inclined to the powder surface. The powder moves as a unit and pressure strokes operating over the length of the sloping portion of the punch cause the powder to be compacted. Although not in general practice, this process has been used to compact electrodes for consumable arc melting.

High-Energy-Rate Compacting.   The rapid compaction of metal powders in rigid dies can also be accomplished by the application of high unit pressures at high speed

(16). Special presses have been built which employ a **pressure-upsetting** system for rapid movement of the compacting tools.   Explosives are also used. Single- and double-acting presses have been developed which are capable of generating millions of psi pressure in short periods of time. The rams in presses employing explosives move at the rate of several thousand feet per second, causing compaction to occur in microseconds. Shock fronts from explosives with pressures close to 2 million psi are generated.

High-energy-rate forming techniques have been used mainly for laboratory studies or to produce compacts having special properties. To date, this is not a generally used procedure, although it holds much promise.

Slip Casting. The slip casting of metal powders into useful items has received considerable attention since the 1950s (17,18). In the laboratory the process is interesting; however, industrially it has found only limited application. The process is used to produce some very complicated and large parts from refractory metals.

Slip casting of metal powders closely follows ceramic-slip casting techniques. Slip, which is a viscous liquid containing finely divided metal particles in a stable suspension, is poured into a plaster of Paris mold of the shape desired. As the liquid is absorbed by the mold, the metal particles are carried to the mold wall and deposited there. This occurs equally in all directions and equally for metal particles of all sizes so that a uniformly thick layer of powder is deposited at the mold wall. Thickness of the deposit is a function of time, absorbency of the mold, and viscosity of the slip.

Drying of the part is very critical and must be done uniformly to avoid cracking. If the particle size distribution of the powder is correct, the small particles will fill the voids between the larger ones, forming a dense structure. Grain structure after sintering is close to isotropic due to the uniform deposit of particles on the mold wall.

Vibratory Consolidation (18). Powders are vibrated in a mold or other container in which they will be sintered, or in a metal container which will be used for extrusion or other metalworking process. Vibratory consolidation has been shown to produce packings of UO_2 particles up to 95% of theoretical density.

Hot Pressing. Hot pressing may be used either to consolidate a powder which has poor compactability at room temperature, or to combine compaction and sintering into one operation. The technique is essentially the same as described for unidirectional die compacting. Heating of the powder is accomplished by either heating the entire die ensemble in a furnace or by induction heating. In most instances a protective atmosphere must be supplied.

Hot pressing produces compacts which have superior properties, mainly because of higher density and finer grain size. Closer dimensional tolerances than can be obtained with pressing at room temperature are also possible. Hot pressing is used only where the higher inherent cost can be justified and has recently been useful in producing reactive materials. Its major use, however, is in the laboratory rather than as a production technique.

Extrusion, Swaging, or Rolling. Metalworking techniques are often used to consolidate metal powders. Metal powders first formed into ingots by isostatic pressing or slip casting, or metal powders encased in a suitable container may be subjected to any number of operations such as extrusion, swaging, or rolling. Where a container is not used, it is essential that a protective atmosphere be employed. This type of consolidation is usually done at elevated temperature. For contained powder, the case becomes a sheath during working which is subsequently removed by either machining or chemical methods.

COMPACTING LUBRICANTS (19,20)

The surface area of most moldable metal powders is in the range of 500–700 cm²/g; finer powders can be as high as 1500 cm²/g of material. A very large number of individual particles are involved. For example, 1 cm³ uniformly filled with 2-μ spherical particles having a surface area of 1200 cm²/g contains approx 1.2 billion particles. Because of this large surface area, a considerable amount of friction has to be overcome during powder consolidation. To one degree or another, friction is present in all of the consolidation methods. Slip casting probably is the one method in which friction plays a minor role.

Dry lubricants are usually added to the powder in order to decrease the effects of friction. A few of the more common lubricants are zinc stearate, lithium stearate, calcium stearate, stearic acid, paraffin, graphite, and tungsten disulfide. Lubricants are generally added to the powder in a dry state in amounts of 0.25–1.0% of the weight of the metal powder. Some lubricants are added by making a slurry of the powder and lubricant, drying, and screening. In some instances, lubricants in liquid form are applied to the die wall.

Lubricants used for powder consolidation purposes must protect die and punch surfaces from wear, burn out of the compact during sintering without leaving objectionable residues or effects, have small particle size, overcome the major share of the friction which is generated between the tool surfaces and powder particles, be easily mixed with the powder, and must not impede powder flow.

Sintering (21–24)

Sintering, the heat treatment of metal-powder compacts, can be defined as, "bonding of particles in a mass of powder by molecular (or atomic) attraction in the solid state, through the application of heat, causing strengthening of the powder mass and normally resulting in densification and recrystallization due to material transport" (24a).

During the sintering treatment, which usually occurs below the melting point of the metal powder (exception: liquid-phase sintering of some powder mixtures), a material movement takes place in the solid state which results in some changes of the properties of the compacted powder, as shown in Figure 3. With increasing sintering temperature or time, the strength of the powder mass increases, electrical resistivity

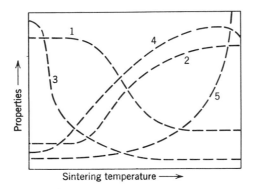

Fig. 3. Effect of sintering on various properties. LEGEND: 1, porosity; 2, density; 3, electrical resistivity; 4, strength; and 5, grain size.

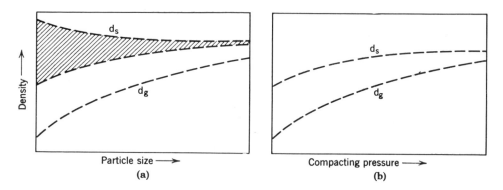

Fig. 4. Effect on density of (**a**) particle size and (**b**) compacting pressure. LEGEND: d_g, density as compacted; and d_s, density as sintered.

decreases, porosity decreases, and density, therefore, increases. The grain structure also undergoes some changes, and recrystallization and grain growth occur. The sintering treatment occurs either in a neutral or in a reducing atmosphere in order to avoid oxidation of the metal-powder mass during the high-temperature sintering treatment.

The movement or transport of material during sintering is rather complex, and can be caused by several mechanisms, such as, surface diffusion; volume or lattice diffusion; grain boundary diffusion; evaporation and condensation; and plastic or viscous flow (24,25). Probably several of these mechanisms act simultaneously, and the respective dominant mechanism depends on the type of powder material, the particle size and shape, and especially on the temperature of sintering. A precise distinction of the actual amount of material moved by each of these simultaneously acting mechanisms has not yet been possible.

Assuming this division as one of the main mechanisms for material transport during sintering, one may assume that it is based mainly on the diffusion of vacancies either in the lattices of the surface of the powder particle or in the lattices of the bulk material. Grain boundaries may act as sinks for these vacancies. It is this vacancy movement which causes the porosity of the powder compact to decrease during sintering.

Pressed powder compacts are characterized by a porosity, or total pore volume, of approx 60–75%. The number and size of the pores can be correlated with the size and shape of the powder particles from which the compact has been prepared, and the pressure applied during compacting. During sintering, the porosity undergoes a number of changes which can be described briefly as follows:
1. With increasing sintering temperature or time, the total porosity decreases.
2. The pores which originally are irregular or angular in shape become spherical.
3. The average pore size becomes larger.
4. The total number of pores decreases.
5. The smaller pores disappear first.
6. The number of larger pores increases slightly.

The decrease of porosity during sintering results in a dimensional shrinkage and, accordingly, in the densification of the powder compact. Density and rate of densification during sintering are strongly affected by the powder particle size, the pressure applied during compacting (Fig. 4), and the sintering temperature and time. They

Table 10. Sintering Temperature and Time[a] (23)

Material	Temp, °F	Time, min
bronze	1400–1600	10–20
copper	1550–1650	12–45
brass	1550–1650	10–45
iron, iron–graphite, etc	1850–2100	8–45
nickel	1850–2100	30–45
stainless steel	2000–2350	30–60
alnico magnets	2200–2375	121–150
ferrites	2200–2700	10–600
90% tungsten–6% nickel–4% copper	2450–2900	10–120
tungsten carbide	2600–2700	20–30
molybdenum	3730	120[b]
tungsten	4250	480[b]
tantalum	4350[b]	480[b]

[a] In high-heat chamber.   [b] Approximate.

depend further on the type of metal from which the powder has been prepared. The average sintering temperatures for various types of metals depend on their melting points and are shown in Table 10.

Sintering with a liquid state refers to the sintering of a powder mixture of two or more components, of which at least one component has a relatively low melting temperature compared to the other components. The sintering temperature is then to be selected so that the low-melting component forms a liquid phase in which the solid powder particles of the other components rearrange. In this way, a high density of the powder compact can be achieved. For liquid-phase sintering, the amount of low-melting component has to be smaller than that of the high-melting components.

The properties of the sintered material depend to a large extent on the atmosphere in which sintering occurs. One distinguishes between reducing (hydrogen, dissociated ammonia, carbon monoxide, or hydrocarbons) and neutral (vacuum, argon, helium, nitrogen, or carbon dioxide) gas atmospheres. Many types of metal powders are susceptible to surface oxidation and must be sintered in a reducing atmosphere in order to get rid of their oxide films. The selection of the atmosphere depends on the type of material to be sintered, whether a reaction between the metal and the atmosphere is

Table 11. Various Methods of Heating for Sintering Purposes

Method	Temp, °C
gas	1100
resistance wire heading	
nichrome	1150
kanthal A	1300
molybdenum	1800
tungsten	2500
silicon carbide	1350
carbon short-circuit tube[a]	2750
direct resistance of the compact	3200
induction heating	3000

[a] Current goes directly through the furnace tube and no other heating elements are necessary.

desired or not, and the kind of reaction desired. Cost consideration is also a factor for the selection of the gas.

Several types of furnaces, either batch or continuous, may be used for sintering, as listed in Table 11. The maximum temperature to be reached in a sintering furnace depends on the furnace type and the methods of heating (23). See Furnaces.

Postsintering Treatments

The sintering process concludes what is generally regarded as the powder-metal-lurgy process, ie, the production, consolidation, and sintering of metal powders. However, machine parts may require a number of operations including heat treatments, and ingots generally require further processing to useful items.

In most instances the nature of the postsintering treatment depends to the largest extent upon the fact that the treatment is being performed on a sintered structure of a density which is lower than its theoretical density. In many instances, the sintered item can be handled identically as a machined or cast item; however, there are sufficient occasions when the properties of the sintering must be given special consideration with regard to further treatments, so that these treatments can logically be considered an extension of the powder-metallurgy process.

Postsintering treatments can be put into three main categories:

1. Working treatments consisting of restricted plastic deformation, such as re-pressing; or unrestricted plastic deformation, such as forging, swaging, drawing, extru-sion, or rolling.

2. Heating treatments, including resintering for stress relieving, densification, or annealing; age precipitation; quench or surface hardening, including carburizing, cyaniding, and nitriding.

3. Finishing treatments, including shaping operations such as machining, broach-ing, sizing, burnishing, straightening, deburring, and abrading; also surface treatments, such as plating, coloring, impregnating, dipping, or spraying.

Restricted plastic deformation is that which takes place entirely within the confines of a closed die cavity. A sintered part may be placed back into the die cavity and pres-sure applied to the part. This pressure generally is of the same magnitude as the orig-inal compaction pressure. This second application of pressure for the purpose of restricted plastic deformation can be broken down into three categories:

1. Sizing—a final pressing of a sintered compact to secure desired size. The compact may have expanded, shrunk, or changed dimensions slightly during sintering. The sizing operation is to correct the dimensions of the part.

2. Repressing—the application of pressure to a previously pressed and sintered compact, usually for the purpose of improving some physical property. Tensile strength, hardness, and density are increased in this manner.

3. Coining—the pressing of a sintered compact to obtain a definite surface con-figuration. This differs from sizing and repressing in the fact that it is done to change the shape of the item. For example, slight dimensional changes as would occur with a trademark would be coined into the part in preference to incorporating the mark on the face of the original compaction punch. Or more drastic dimensional changes may be made. In some instances the sintered piece is used as a blank and the major share of the configuration is made during coining.

In general practice, sizing, repressing, and coining are done at room temperature.

Elevated temperatures may be used by heating the die and the part. A protective atmosphere generally must be provided in this latter case.

Unrestricted plastic deformation includes all of the metalworking procedures generally applied to cast ingots. Powder-metallurgy ingots made by die pressing and sintering, or isostatic pressed and sintered ingots may be forged, swaged, drawn, rolled, or extruded. These processes may also be applied to a mass of loose or loosely sintered powder. In most instances it is necessary to recognize that the powder-metallurgy ingot being worked has lower density and sometimes lower workability than cast ingots. Working is generally done at elevated temperatures, although not above the recrystallization point of the metal, and in many cases neutral atmospheres must be provided. These atmospheres may be provided by enclosing the operation in a protective gas or by enclosing the work in a sheath and providing the proper atmosphere within the sheath.

A number of *heating operations* are used to change the properties of the sintering. In general, it can be said that when the inherent porosity is taken into consideration, heat treatments performed on powder-metallurgy sinterings do not differ from the same treatments performed on cast or wrought metal, and the results are similar.

The most common heating operation is *resintering*. For machine parts this is usually done under conditions similar to those of the original sintering operation, except that the first sintering is generally done at a lower temperature. Its purpose is to stress relieve or anneal cold work imparted to the part during coining or repressing. When resintering is to take place, worked ingots are annealed in the usual manner for further workability.

Resintering is also undertaken for further densification. Cold working, as in repressing or coining, not only reduces the porosity in both number and size, but also ruptures oxide films within the compact, creating new metal contact area. A resumption of sintering will enable diffusion to proceed with fewer obstructions at a lower temperature and will be more effective. Resintering generally causes an increase in ductility and density with some loss in strength; however, the combination of hardness, tensile strength, and ductility is usually much improved over the sintered product.

Sintered metals may be softened or hardened by a number of procedures which are common practice in treating cast or wrought metals. Pure copper or silver may be annealed by *quenching* from above the recrystallization temperature. Certain copper-base alloys which are *precipitation-hardened*, such as copper–beryllium, copper–nickel–beryllium, copper–iron, and copper–aluminum–iron, are made ductile by forming a maximum solid-solution phase through quenching. Precipitation hardening can be achieved in copper alloys and *age hardening* in aluminum alloys, such as those that contain up to 5% copper and 1.5% silicon, or 0.5% magnesium and 0.5% manganese. An 85% Fe–15% Cu alloy is a standard material which can be precipitation-hardened.

Sintered steel prepared from powders can also be heat treated in the same manner as cast or wrought steels. Because of the greater amount of exposed surface area in the form of porosity, care must occasionally be taken to provide a protective atmosphere.

Sintered steels may be austenitized, quenched, and tempered. *Surface hardening* includes pack or gas carburization, cyaniding, or nitriding. Cyaniding involves heating the sintering in contact with molten cyanide. Nitriding involves heating in a nitrogen-containing atmosphere. See Metal surface treatment.

It is not always possible to achieve either the desired shape or surface finish directly by the press-and-sinter method. *Machining* may be required to change the shape somewhat or to form reentrant angles, etc. Burnishing, abrading, buffing, plating, coloring, deburring, and tumbling may also be required.

Applications

Structural Parts. A considerable portion of the activity in powder metallurgy centers around the manufacture of structural and machine parts from iron- and copper-base powders. Approximately 142 million lb of iron and iron-base alloy powders, and 66 million lb of copper and copper-base alloy powders were used in 1966 to produce a wide variety of metal-powder structural parts, and this consumption figure is expected to double by 1970. The major utilization of copper powder is in the manufacture of self-lubricating bearings and the major usage of iron powder is in the manufacture of structural parts. Data from the Metal Powder Industries Federation show that in 1966, 62% of all the iron powder shipped (which was 200 million lb) was utilized for the

Fig. 5. Typical powder-metallurgy structural parts.

manufacture of powder-metallurgy parts, the remainder being used for molding electrodes, flame cutting, and electronic, magnetic, and miscellaneous applications. These parts may range in weight from 8-lb gears and cams to miniatures weighing only a fraction of an ounce which can be held thousands to the handful. They may be made in an imposing array of materials including iron, iron alloys, steel, alloy steel, stainless steel, brass, bronze, nickel, nickel–silver, copper, copper–graphite, and special alloys. Properties of the parts can be made to far exceed the required properties for most applications. There are limitations, of course, and these will be discussed later, but when the powder-metallurgy approach to the manufacture of parts applies, the economics are very favorable and a considerable cost saving results.

Figure 5 shows a typical array of parts made from metal powders and Table 12 gives typical properties of some powder metals (26). A more complete listing of properties can be found in the reference.

The overriding motivation for the manufacture of these parts by the powder-metallurgy method is economic. The basis for this is (a) almost full utilization of raw material (essentially 100% of the powder is compacted); (b) the compact is made to be at or very close to the finished dimensions of the part (elimination of machining operations is a large factor in the economics); and (c) high-volume production, as already discussed, is essential to the process.

Powder metallurgy as a process for the manufacture of structural parts is in competition with sand casting, die casting, stamping, screw-machine production, general machining other than screw machining, forging, and plaster mold casting. Most metals in powdered form cost more per pound than corresponding metals available in finished mill forms. This price difference in raw material is effectively offset by the drastically reduced manufacturing cost for the finished part. In this respect, where the powder-metallurgy process can be applied, it generally competes poorly with screw machining, favorably with most casting methods, and extremely well with general machining practices.

There are some deterring factors. One of the major ones is the limitations with respect to size and especially to shape. Each individual part must be studied to determine whether it can be produced economically by powder metallurgy. Besides the high cost of the powder, with relation to cast or wrought metal, compacting tools are expensive. Minimum production is generally considered to be 50,000 parts; however, some parts are produced in quantities as low as 5000.

Processing. Powders are blended or mixed with each other and with a lubricating agent. They are then fed into automatic molding presses where they are shaped into a "green" or molded part called a compact. The compact is then heated at a specific temperature under a protective gas atmosphere, generally 2050°F for iron and steel, 2300°F for stainless steel, and 1800°F for copper and copper alloys. In some instances a separate presintering treatment may be performed at some lower temperature in order to volatilize the pressing lubricant and/or to sinter the compact to a specific degree for subsequent repressing. In many instances the part is completed after a single sintering. In other cases repressing, coining, or various heat treatments are necessary.

The most important properties of a good molding-grade powder are flow rate, particle size and size distribution, apparent density, green strength, compressibility, and dimensional stability during sintering. A powder must flow well in order to fill all parts of the die cavity evenly and move through the automatic equipment. The

Table 12. Typical Properties of Some Powder Metals

Material	PMPA[a] designation	Density, g/cm³	Condition[b]	Ultimate tensile strength, 1000 psi	Yield strength, 1000 psi	Elongation, %	Transverse fiber strength, 1000 psi	Shear strength, 1000 psi	Impact strength, ft-lb	Hardness, Rockwell	Compressive yield strength, 1000 psi
iron											
99% Fe, min[c]											
	F-0000-N	5.7–6.1	AS	19	15	5	39		4	20 RH	
	F-0000-S	7.0	AS	35	25	11	65		5	10 RB	
99% Fe, min[d]											
	F-0000-T	7.3	AS	40	26	12	70	35		20 RB	
	F-0000-U	7.5	AS	41	27.5	30	71			22 RB	
steel											
99% Fe–1% C											
	F-0010-S	7.0	AS	60		3.0	120		2		
	F-0010-S	7.0	HT	65		0.5	120		5.0	100 RB	
	F-0010-T	7.3	AS	68		3.0	140		3.0		
	F-0010-T	7.3	HT	127		2.5	235	100	6.0	105 RB	
97.4% Fe–1.5% Ni–0.5% Mo–0.6% C											
	FN-0206-T	7.2	AS	90	72	2.5	180	47	9.2	95 RB	
	FN-0206-T	7.2	HT	140	120	0.5	207		4.3	35 RC	
90% Fe–10% Cu											
	FC-1000-N	5.8–6.2	HT	54		1.0	103		3.5	30 RC	
92% Fe–7% Cu–1% C											
	FC-0710-S	6.8	HT	110		1.5	209.5		7.0	40 RC	
90% Fe–7% Ni–2% Cu–1% C											
	FN-0710-S	6.8	HT	135		1.5	262		6.5	42 RC	
	FN-0710-T	7.2	HT	157		2.0	285		8.6	44 RC	
80% Fe–20% Cu											
	FX-2000-T	7.1 min	HT	128		0.5	209.5	65	11.0	35 RC	

Material	Designation[a]	Density	Condition[b]							
stainless steel										
302		6.2–6.5		35–50		2.5			40–60-RB	20–40
303L	SS-303L-P	6.0	AS	35	32	2.0		20		50
316		6.2–6.6		55		2.0				
316L	SS-3166-R	6.65	AS	58	51	8.1	135	4.5	65 RB	80
410	SS-410-R	6.4	HT	110					29 RC	
410L		6.8	HT	100		0.8			30 RC	
aluminum alloy										
90.5% Al–5% Sn–4% Cu		2.2–2.3		18		1.5				20
copper										
100% Cu		8.5	AS	30	15	29			70 RF	
		8.6	repressed	35		18			70 RF	
brass										
90% Cu–10% Zn		7.6		23		7				
90% Cu–10% Zn–0.5% Pb		7.9	AS	33.7		29			69 RH	
70% Cu–30% Zn		7.5	AS	27.5		8			81 RH	
bronze										
90% Cu–10% Sn	BT-0010-S	6.8–7.2	AS	20	20	2–3	42		43 RF	
copper–nickel alloys										
90% Cu–10% Ni	BN-0010-W	8.0	AS	46	16	11	100		80 RF	
64% Cu–18% Ni–18% Zn		8.3	AS	45	30	30	94		32 RB	
nickel and alloy										
100% Ni	N-0000-W	8.6	AS	73		34	110		45 RB	
67% Ni–30% Cu–3% Fe	BN-0330-W	8.0	AS	52	22	19.5	119		50 RB	

[a] Powder Metallurgy Parts Association.
[b] AS designates As Sintered and HT designates Heat Treated.
[c] Sponge iron.
[d] Electrolytic iron.

particle size and size distribution must maximize the compact density. There is a close relationship between particle size distribution and such factors as powder flow, apparent density, and compressibility. Since the amount of powder portioned out for each compact is charged to a cavity of constant volume, the apparent density becomes extremely important. Although changes in depth of die cavity can be made with relative ease, it is most desirable that the powder has uniform apparent density batch-to-batch and hour-to-hour.

A high compressibility is always desired. Compressibility is the density to which a powder may be pressed at any given pressure. As the compressibility of a powder increases, the pressure needed to obtain any given density decreases. Lower pressures are always desirable since they result in lower tool and machine wear. High compressibility is generally associated with high green strength of the compact. The compact must have enough strength to be transported either mechanically or by hand. Green strength of a pressed compact, like density, is generally considered a property of the powder.

The greatest problems in manufacturing structural parts by powder metallurgy are the changes in configuration which occur during sintering. Dimensional changes are generally a function of the powder, while shape changes are a function of density inequalities in the compact. Configuration changes must be controlled by either a combination of powder properties or postsintering treatments such as sizing.

Compacting Tools. Much could be said about tooling, for it is in this area combined with the choice of powders, that the myth of the "black magic," as it has often been called, of powder metallurgy has arisen. Compacting tools must be properly designed, constructed, and fitted to the press. Compacting tools are generally designed on the

Fig. 6. Porous bearing materials (top) and structural parts (center), which are made by pressing metal powders followed by sintering and oil impregnation; and filters (bottom) made by loose-powder sintering. Courtesy Amplex Division, Chrysler Corporation.

basis of the performance of a given type of powder from a given manufacturer. They may be made of either heat-treated steel or carbide. This is determined by economics. The carbide tools are more expensive; however, many more parts may be produced with them than can be produced with the steel tools.

Porous Materials (27,28). Porous materials are powder-metallurgy parts in which the void space, which determines the porosity, is controlled as to amount, type, and degree of interconnection. Porous parts include self-lubricating bearings, bushings, machine parts, and metallic filters. Their manufacture represents a significant portion of the powder-metallurgy industry.

Porous bodies are made by both the press-and-sinter technique, as in the production of porous machine parts; and by loose-powder sinter techniques, as in the production of filters. Figure 6 shows a representative array of these parts (27).

Self-lubricating Parts. Self-lubrication depends upon the presence of oil within the pores of the bearing or bushing. This built-in oil reservoir provides a protective oil film which acts to separate the bearing from the shaft, in a motor for example, preventing metal-to-metal contact. During operation, the rotating shaft draws the oil in the bearing to the surface through the combined action of friction and pressure. When not under load, most of the oil is drawn back into the bearing, due to capillary action, leaving a layer of oil between the two metal parts.

Most bearing materials are made from bronze powders. Composition may vary from 5 to 12% tin and from 0 to 6% graphite. Standard compositions are 90.5% Cu–7% Sn–2.5% graphite; 89% Cu–7% Sn–4% graphite; 93% Cu–7% Sn; 96% Cu–4% graphite; and 100% Cu. Compositions containing copper with up to 8% Pb or up to 40% Zn are also used.

Porous bearings are also made from iron to a certain extent. Iron–lead alloys containing 2–6% Pb and 2–4% graphite, as well as iron–copper compositions, are used. The major advantages of iron-base materials are their higher hardness and strength, and the fact that their coefficient of thermal expansion is close to that of the steel shaft. However, iron-base materials are generally not rated as high as copper-base materials as self-lubricating bearing materials.

Aluminum bearing compositions have been known for some time; however, they were not manufactured as commercial products until the 1960s. Aluminum bearings have excellent corrosion resistance against oxidized oils and are light in weight. Compositions generally include tin or lead.

Production of these parts is on an automatic, rapid, high-volume basis since their shape is generally not complicated. Powder mixtures contain organic lubricants in amounts of a few percent. Molding is accomplished unidirectionally in a closed die cavity at pressures from 20–40 tons/in.^{2}. During sintering the lubricant volatilizes, facilitating some control over its interconnection of the voids. It is also common practice to add certain substances (known as pore-forming agents) to the powder which volatilize during sintering. Some of these are ammonium carbonate, ammonium bicarbonate, camphor, and sodium bicarbonate. The sintering of bronze bearings is interesting since it is an example of liquid-phase sintering in which the liquid is present during only part of the sintering time. Alloying of the liquid causes it to solidify.

Bronze bearings are sometimes first presintered at 700–900°F in a lower-temperature part of the furnace in order to enable more accurate control of the degassing lubricants. During this treatment, the bronze alloy is formed by the diffusion of liquid tin into the copper. This structure is solidified in the furnace. Upon higher-temperature treatment the tin-rich phase liquefies and is absorbed by the copper-rich matrix.

A sizing operation is then carried out in order to gain accurate dimensions and produce a smooth surface. Sizing is done on the same type of equipment that is used for molding and involves forcing the part back into a cavity of the dimensions desired and applying pressure. Oil is impregnated into the part either before or after sizing. The resulting part is an oil-impregnated bearing containing approx 20% oil by vol.

A broad range of ferrous and nonferrous compositions are used to form self-lubricating finished machine parts. Among these materials are iron, brass, low-carbon and low-nickel steel, copper, nickel–silver, and stainless steel. Processing is essentially the same as for conventional bearings. In many instances the self-lubricating machine part differs from the conventional bearing only in shape and the fact that these parts must have the capability to withstand shear and compressive stresses which are considerably greater than for bearings.

An important application of self-lubricating machine parts is the oil-pump gear used in automotive engines. This part is made from a eutectic steel composition (0.83% carbon) and contains graphite inclusions. The gear teeth are wear-resistant and also resistant to plastic deformation, while oil can flow through the interconnected porosity, furnishing lubrication for the gear and also corrosion resistance.

Filters. Porous metal objects are also manufactured by a sintering treatment only, without the application of pressure. The technique of loose-powder sintering, combined with close control of pore size and total pore volume, is used to produce porous filters and related objects.

Corrosion-resistant metals such as bronze, nickel, stainless steel, and copper are used. The bronze compositions generally contain 5–12% tin. Powder mixtures and, in many instances, tin-plated copper powders are used. The powder particles are generally spheres and are carefully controlled as to size and size distribution. These powders are considerably coarser than those used for self-lubricating bearings and machine parts and the resulting interconnected porosity is much greater.

The powders are loaded into molds made of graphite, ceramic, or steel. The loaded molds are placed in a furnace and sintering takes place at close to the melting point of the metal. In the case of the tin-plated copper powder, the sintering temperature is above the melting point of the tin, which melts and diffuses into the copper, thereby contributing to void formation.

In addition to filtering gases and liquids, porous items made by the loose-powder sinter technique are used for the diffusion of air for aeration of liquids, the physical separation of immiscible liquids, pressure-gage equalizers in instrumentation, flow control, flame arresters, and sound deadeners.

Friction Materials (qv) (29,30). Friction materials are in the classification of metal–nonmetal combinations, and their manufacture represents one of the applications which can be accomplished best through the powder-metallurgy process. Clutch plates, brake bands, brake drums, and packing compositions are examples of friction materials.

A friction material is composed of a metal matrix, generally consisting of copper for its major proportion, to which a number of other metals such as tin, zinc, lead, and iron are added. Friction-producing components such as silica, emery, or asbestos, and also graphite for lubricity are important constituents.

Copper, because it inherently has high heat conductivity, is resistant to frictional heat during service, and is readily moldable, is generally used as a base metal, composing 60–75% of the weight. Tin or zinc powders are used in amounts of 5–10%. These metals are soluble in the copper and strengthen the matrix through the formation of a solid solution during sintering.

Iron or other higher-melting metals which are insoluble in copper are added in amounts of 5–10%. Harder particles, such as iron imbedded in the soft copper base, increase the coefficient of friction and also exert a scouring action on the surface. Lead, which is also insoluble in copper, is added in amounts of 5–15%. Lead disperses in the matrix, acting as a lubricant during molding and as a lubricating film during operation of the friction material if the surface temperature is such that the lead becomes liquid. Lead also enhances the smooth engagement of sliding surfaces, preventing erratic brake or clutch action. Graphite, added in amounts of 5–10% by wt, has effects similar to lead. Silica, emery, or other similar friction-producing materials, are added in amounts from 2–7%. Slight variations in this material have profound effects on the coefficient of friction. A typical composition is 62% copper, 7% tin, 12% lead, 8% iron, 7% graphite, and 4% silica.

Of major importance in friction materials is the ability of the surface to be worn away in a uniform manner in order to provide new friction-producing ingredients at the surface.

Manufacture of these items consists of unidirectional cold pressing a mixture of the ingredients at relatively low pressures of 10–20 tons/in.^{2} in steel dies. Large parts are sintered in bell-type furnaces, and small parts are sintered in conventional furnaces, always under a reducing atmosphere. Bonding of the pressed compact to a backing plate is usually accomplished during sintering. A number of compact-steel plate assemblies are stacked on top of each other and a pressure is applied to the stacked assemblies during sintering. Postsintering treatments such as bending to shape, drilling holes, or machining to dimensions are usually necessary.

Electrical and Electronic. Powder metallurgy is the only means of achieving some properties which are demanded of many materials used in the electrical and electronic industries.

Electric Contact Materials (31–33). The following methods, which utilize the powder-metallurgy technique, are used to produce electric contact materials:

1. Slicing of rod previously made from powder.
2. Infiltration of a porous refractory skeleton.
3. Compaction and sintering of powders.

Tungsten contacts, cut from rod, are resistant to deformation under a large number of cycles at relatively high forces, have high hardness and strength, have the ability to switch high currents without detrimental arcing or welding, and have minimum vaporization in an arc (if one should form). These contacts meet the requirements of many automotive, aviation, and appliance applications; however, they are limited in their use because of an insulating oxide film which forms during switching.

Copper and silver combined with refractory metals, such as tungsten, tungsten carbide, and molydenum, form a major class of electrical contacts. Fabrication may be by pressing a mixture of the powders and sintering, or by infiltrating a previously pressed and sintered refractory skeleton with molten copper or silver in a separate heating operation. The composition in the case of infiltration is controlled by the porosity of the refractory skeleton. Copper–tungsten contact materials are used primarily in power circuit breakers and transformer tap charges. They are normally confined to an oil bath because of the rapid oxidation of copper in air. Copper–tungsten carbide compositions are used where greater mechanical wear is necessary.

Tungsten–silver contacts made in a similar manner as tungsten–copper can be operated in air due to the greater nobility of silver. Three standard compositions of this class include tungsten–silver, tungsten carbide–silver, and molybdenum–silver.

A third group of electrical contacts include silver–nickel, silver–cadmium oxide, and silver–graphite combinations. These materials are characterized by having low contact resistance, some resistance to arc erosion, and excellent nonsticking characteristics. These materials can be considered midway in overall properties between silver alloys on the one hand and silver or copper-refractory compositions on the other hand. Silver–cadmium oxide compositions are the most popular of this class. They find wide application in aircraft relays, motor controllers, and line starters and controls.

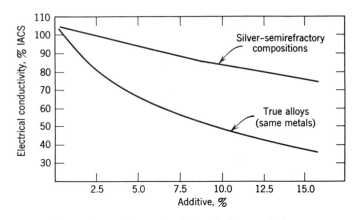

Fig. 7. The graph shows the superior conductivity of silver-semirefractory compositions for electrical contacts when made by powder-metallurgy methods compared with solid-solution alloys of the same base metal. SOURCE: Doty (31).

Figure 7 shows the superior conductivity of silver–nickel or silver–cadmium oxide contacts when compared with contacts made by standard melting techniques and formed from solid-solution alloys.

A group of contact materials called sliding contacts are used in transferring current in motors and generators. Sliding contacts are often called "brushes." (See also Vol. 4, p. 222.) High electrical conductivity, wear resistance, lubricating qualities, and some arc erosion resistance are of prime importance for high-current applications. Compositions are usually of copper and graphite, with the graphite ranging from 5 to 70%, silver and graphite, or bronze and graphite.

Magnets (31) (see also Magnetic materials). Permanent-type magnets known as Alnico 2, 4, and 5 are made by pressing and sintering powder mixtures. These materials are basically alloys of aluminum, nickel, and iron with additives such as cobalt, copper, and titanium. Advantages of sintered Alnico over cast Alnico are greater mechanical strength and closer tolerances without costly finishing operations.

Soft magnetic parts include iron pole pieces for small dc motors or generators, armatures for generators, and sintered and rolled iron–nickel alloys for radio transformers, measuring instruments, etc.

Iron-powder cores, more commonly known as "dust cores," are manufactured for ac self-inductance coils for high-frequency applications in telephone, radio, and television systems. Radio and television cores are produced by compressing a suitable iron powder without subsequent sintering. The major advantage of a core is its ability to afford a large change of inductance by a simple movement in one direction in or out of the coil. Fine iron powders of the electrolytic or carbonyl types are used as core material. These cores exhibit minimum eddy-current and hysteresis losses and the magnetic permeability returns to its original value after application of large magnetizing forces.

Electrolytic Capacitors (31). Tantalum, because of its high melting point of 2850°C, is produced as a metal powder. Tantalum powder, molded, sintered, and worked to wire and foil, is the basic material used to build some types of tantalum capacitors. Other capacitors are made by compacting and sintering the tantalum powder.

Batteries (qv). Nickel powder is used to form a porous sheet around a woven wire grid. The sheet, with up to 90% porosity, is used as a reservoir for nickel and cadmium compounds and as an electron take-off in sintered nickel–cadmium rechargeable storage batteries. The advantage of the porous plate lies in the large surface area per unit weight or volume. The porous sheet may be made either by sifting nickel powder into a ceramic mold of the correct size and containing the woven screen, or by applying a slurry to a perforated thin nickel-plated iron sheet. The composite is then sintered at a temperature which will effect strengthening but not densification.

Mercury dry-battery anodes are pressed compacts of zinc–mercury amalgam. Mercury batteries were first developed and produced during World War II for the Signal Corps for use in walkie-talkie communication systems. Today, practically all hearing aids utilize this type of battery.

Incandescent Lamps, Electronic Tubes, and Resistance Elements (see Electron tube materials). Items fashioned in any form from molybdenum and tungsten usually fall within the bounds of powder metallurgy since these metals are normally first produced as a powder. The powders are compacted into an ingot, the ingot is sintered by electrical resistance or standard furnacing methods, and the resulting bar is swaged, drawn, or rolled to various mill shapes. Also, both molybdenum and tungsten are used as targets in x-ray tubes, for structural shapes such as lead and grid wires in electron tubes, and as resistance elements in furnaces.

Iron–nickel and iron–nickel–cobalt alloys are prepared in wire and sheet form by either rolling an isostatic-pressed ingot or direct rolling and sintering of metal powders. These materials have numerous applications in the electronic field as glass-sealing alloys since their coefficient of thermal expansion is close to that of certain glasses.

Refractory Materials (34). Those metals having extremely high melting temperatures and those which are more resistant to deformation when hot are considered refractory metals. This generally refers to metals having melting points above the range of iron (2797°F), cobalt (2723°F), and nickel (2647°F). Tungsten, rhenium, tantalum, molybdenum, and niobium, with melting points of 6170, 5755, 5425, 4730, and 4474°F, respectively, are considered refractory. Other high-temperature-melting metals often considered refractory are osmium (4900°F), boron (3690°F), titanium (3035°F), thorium (3182°F), zirconium (3366°F), and vanadium (3450°F). The refractory metals group also includes alloys of these metals as well as hard-metal combinations and certain cermets. See also High-temperature alloys.

Refractory metals are associated with powder metallurgy mainly due to the fact that at these high melting temperatures their ores are not easily melted and the methods used in their extraction produce a powder or sponge. Tungsten and molydenum are reduced from oxides, tantalum and niobium are produced either by reduction or by fusion electrolysis. These powders are then subjected to the standard powder-metallurgy procedures.

Present-day manufacture of refractory metals has grown mainly from the technology of producing filament wire for incandescent lamps. A quick review of the process for the manufacture of tungsten products from powder will demonstrate the powder-metallurgy process wherein an ingot is manufactured to be subsequently worked into other forms (as opposed to those processes wherein the ultimate shape and size of the product are produced during initial consolidation).

Tungsten powder of approx 5-μ average particle size, derived from the hydrogen reduction of tungsten oxides, is compacted into ingots measuring 0.5–0.75 in. high and wide, and 18–24 in. long. This bar is extremely weak and must be heated in hydrogen in a standard muffle furnace in order to strengthen it before the standard sintering treatment. Sintering is done in bell-shaped furnaces under a hydrogen atmosphere. Heating is by resistance, and treatment is carried on until a certain density is reached. In this instance, the bar undergoes considerable linear shrinkage amounting to 12–16%. The sintered bar is dense enough to be heated and worked in air. The bar is then worked at temperatures of 900–1200°C) (metallurgically, cold working since recrystallization does not take place) by swaging and drawing, with intermediate annealings, to incandescent filament sizes. During working, the sintered bar increases in tensile strength and ductility, and becomes 100% dense.

Unrestricted working, such as swaging, drawing, rolling, etc, may be performed on slabs or ingots of the other metals prepared by any of the consolidation and sintering techniques previously described.

Refractory Metal Alloys. Alloys with refractory or nonrefractory metals are made by direct mixing of the metal powders or by the incorporation of compounds of the solute in the processing for subsequent reduction to the metal. In most instances, alloying is by solid-state diffusion during sintering. Tungsten and molybdenum form a continuous series of solid solutions and represent an important group of alloys. The chief advantage of these alloys is the considerably greater reduction in diameter possible during working in comparison with pure molybdenum and the better workability in comparison with pure tungsten.

Tungsten with addition of up to 5% thoria is used for thermionic-emission cathode wires and as filaments for vibration-resistant incandescent lamps. Tungsten–rhenium alloys are used as heating elements and thermocouples. Tantalum and niobium form continuous solid solutions with tungsten. Iron and nickel are used as alloy agents for specialized applications. One of the more commercially interesting alloys of tungsten is the tungsten–nickel–copper alloy nominally containing 93% W–5% Ni–2% Cu (35). This alloy is the "heavy met" composition, so called because its sintered density may exceed 17 g/cm^3, and it has sufficient ductility to be worked. The alloy is utilized where it is necessary to secure a high mass having good impact strength, ductility, and tensile strength. (Pure tungsten, for example, would have more mass but would be brittle.) This alloy is also widely used to form containers for radioactive materials.

Cemented Carbides (see Vol. 4, p. 92). Cemented carbides are metal–nonmetal combinations containing tungsten carbide as the major constituent, along with other hard-metal components in minor amounts, embedded in a matrix of cobalt. The manufacture of cemented carbides, which are generally used as carbide cutting tools, began at the beginning of the twentieth century with attempts to replace cast tungsten carbide dies for the drawing of fine tungsten filament wire with products made from tungsten carbide (WC) powder. Originally, this powder was compacted and sintered at high temperatures. The resulting structure was uniform in structure, but brittle. The addition of iron or cobalt as a binder with a low melting point occurred between 1915 and 1925.

Cemented carbides have their major application as cutting tools for the entire metalworking industry. They are also used in armor-piercing projectile cores and tips, and for carbide shot. Wear parts requiring corrosion resistance are also produced of cemented carbides. Included are such parts as burnishing tools and dies, pump valves, sandblast nozzles, gages, inserts in snow tires, and rock drills and guides of many types. Carbide compositions containing only tungsten carbide and cobalt were recognized early as being unsuitable for machining the tougher materials. The turning point in the history of cemented carbides came when Schwarzkopf and co-workers in Austria replaced plain tungsten carbide with solid solutions of tungsten, molybdenum, and titanium carbides. Since that time, many carbides have been utilized as additions to the base tungsten carbide for special-purpose cutting tools. Among these are carbides of tantalum, niobium, hafnium, zirconium, and vanadium. Tungstenfree compositions have also been developed as well as compositions containing diamonds.

The favorable properties of cemented carbides are their extreme hardness and toughness which are retained at the elevated temperatures that may occur between tool and work during cutting.

Production of cemented carbides begins with the manufacture of the hard-metal carbide. Tungsten carbide is made by heating a mixture of lampblack with tungsten powder so that WC, with a combined carbon of 6.25%, is produced. The percentage of free and combined carbon is of extreme importance. Tantalum and titanium carbides are made by heating a mixture of carbon with metal oxide. Multicarbide powders, such as Mo_2C–WC, TaC–NbC, and TiC–TaC–WC, are made by a variety of methods, the most important of which is carburization of powder mixtures.

These carbides are mixed with cobalt in a wet ball-milling operation. Water, benzene, or other organic materials may be used. Milling produces an intimate mixture of cobalt attached to the carbide particles. This is followed by mixing with a lubricant or other binder, such as paraffin, camphor, or stearic acid, in a separate operation. Screened, the mass results in a lubricated flowable powder. The powder is then cold molded in conventional presses and tooling. A low-temperature, presinter treatment is carried out in order to strengthen the part through sintering of the binder metal, and to evaporate the pressing lubricant. The presintered part is then formed by machining into the desired shape and dimensions. This is followed by high-temperature sintering between 1350 and 1550°C for 1–2 hr. This sintering treatment is characterized by fusion of the binder metal, solution of the carbides into the liquid phase, and precipitation at low-energy areas. The result is to form recrystallized grains of carbide embedded in a matrix of a solution of carbides and matrix metal. Linear dimensional shrinkage of from 21 to 25% occurs.

Cermets. High-temperature applications brought about by advances in both space and nuclear technology during the past fifteen years has necessitated a hunt for materials to fill the gap between cobalt- and nickel-base superalloys, and the refractory metals such as tungsten and molybdenum. It was found that pure ceramics were strong at elevated temperatures but lacked sufficient ductility to be worked at room temperature, while metal alloys, although ductile at room temperature, were not strong enough at the higher temperatures.   Mixtures of ceramics and metals were investigated as a method of achieving a material having both the high-temperature strength of ceramics, plus sufficient ductility and thermal conductivity contributed by the metal to provide resistance from thermal shock at high temperatures and workability at room temperature.   Because these compositions represented a new class of materials for structural application at high temperature, the words "ceramals" and "cermets," which combine parts of the words "ceramic" and "metal," are used. Actually, the cemented carbides can be considered cermets although they are generally not thought of in that way.

The cermet class of materials contains a large number of compositions which can be generalized as follows:

1. Titanium carbides—mixtures of a hard and a soft phase containing TiC or TiN and Ni–Cr, Co–Cr, Ni–Cr–Co, Ni–Al, or Ni–Mo.   See Carbides.

2. Borides—generally borides of zirconium, titanium, and chromium with metals. See Vol. 3, p. 673.

3. Dispersions—flake aluminum powders with surface oxide up to 14% Al_2O_3 have been pressed, sintered, and worked to a material known as SAP (sintered aluminum powder).   The main characteristic of this product is its high strength at elevated temperatures.   Nickel with small additions of thoria, known as TD-nickel, is also considered as one of the most promising high-temperature cermets.

Space Materials (36,37).   The major driving forces behind the growth of powder metallurgy in space technology have been the difficulty of handling many materials with conventional fusion-metallurgy techniques, the need for controlled porosity, and the overwhelming requirement of special and unique properties.   The space program to date has utilized all of the available techniques and materials in the solution of very specialized problems and has had to develop new ones.   The general areas of interest for the application of powder metallurgy in space technology are low-density components with emphasis on porous tungsten for W–Ag structures; beryllium metallurgy; discrete-particle hardening systems; and chromium–magnesium oxide alloy systems for high-temperature strength and room-temperature ductility.

Special beryllium powders have been produced to have greatly different particle size and shape, and purity than normal beryllium powders.   Properties such as strength and sheet fabricability are affected accordingly.

Plates of beryllium metal were used as heat shield shingles on the cylindrical section of the body of the Mercury spacecraft used in some of the first unmanned suborbital flights.   A fairing for the Agena B space vehicle interstage structure used beryllium machined from a pressed compact 72 in. in diam and 28 in. high.   This metal has also been used as the nose cap of the ascent shroud in several of the Ranger-Mariner space-probe series.

Beryllium has a favorable stiffness-to-density ratio and good thermal properties which make it acceptable as a shielding material against micrometeorites.   However, beryllium, as currently produced, is inherently brittle and has limited use.   Also, the tendency toward crack propagation during manufacture is a problem that must be solved before the potential of this metal can be fully realized.

Special tungsten powders have been developed for space applications.   Spherical tungsten particles are used to form porous tungsten bodies for use as an ionizing surface in ion-propulsion engines. Granular tungsten particles made from the direct reduction of tungsten hexafluoride have a special substructure which leads to a more ductile end product than regular oxide-reduced tungsten. Silver-infiltrated tungsten parts are made to have a density before infiltration of 70–80% of theoretical, 90% of the porosity ultimately being infiltrated with silver. These parts are used where the ablative cooling provided by the silver during solid-vapor change of state and transpiration cooling through the resulting porosity are desirable, as in reentrant vehicles. See also Ablation.

Space technology has always demanded materials which can operate at temperatures between those of superalloys and refractory metals and which have high-temperature strength during operation and room-temperature ductility for fabrication. Part of the problem has been answered by the development of dispersion-strengthened and oxide alloy systems. Thoria-dispersed nickel products of E. I. du Pont de Nemours & Co., Inc. are produced by a precipitation of basic nickel compounds, whereby thoria particles of about 1000-Å size are coated with layers of nickel to the extent that a 2% thoria dispersion is obtained in the end product. Chromium–magnesium oxide systems are also important for this purpose.

Space technology also utilizes many standard products. Among these are sintered magnetic materials such as Alnico 2 and 6, sintered bronze bushings, electrical contacts, and tantalum capacitors.

High vacuum is one of the main characteristics of space. Bearings with liquid lubricants would lose the lubricant through evaporation. Bearings produced by powder-metallurgy techniques having imbedded MoS_2 have been found to be favorable under space conditions.

Nuclear Applications (38). The use of powder metallurgy in the fabrication of bodies for fuel elements, control, shielding, moderator, and other components of a nuclear-power reactor is an extremely interesting and important application. Fuel elements and other reactor components are more easily fashioned in the solid state since their components may be highly reactive as liquids. The materials which compose many of the fuel, moderator, and control parts of a reactor would be thermodynamically unstable if heated to temperatures approaching those required for melting. These same materials are stable under powder-metallurgy process conditions. It is possible, for example, to incorporate uranium or ceramic compounds in a metallic matrix, or to produce parts which are very near to the size and shape desired without effecting drastic changes in either the structure or surface conditions of the parts, since only a minimum, if any, postsintering treatment will be necessary.

The metals to which the powder-metallurgy process is applied in nuclear technology are beryllium, zirconium, uranium, and thorium. Uranium and thorium are used as fuel materials, beryllium for moderating purposes, and zirconium as a material of construction. The fuel material most widely used is UO_2 particles imbedded in a matrix of aluminum or stainless steel. Reactor technology makes use of these materials in their pure form and also as alloys and metal-ceramic combinations.

These metal powders must be handled in ways which are somewhat different from those for ordinary metal powders. Beryllium powder is extremely toxic, zirconium is highly pyrophoric, uranium and thorium powders are both toxic and pyrophoric. The vapors resulting from the burning of uranium are also extremely toxic. These powders are generally handled in closed containers, called dry boxes, which are large enough to permit working with them from the outside with rubber gloves. The dry boxes are usually filled with a protective atmosphere such as argon or helium.

Beryllium powders have extremely poor compactability at room temperature, and when sintered in argon show very little densification. Sintering in vacuum results in considerably more densification; however, most beryllium presently used is made by hot pressing.

Both zirconium hydride and zirconium metal powders compact to fairly high densities at conventional pressures. During sintering the zirconium hydride decomposes, and at the temperature of decomposition, zirconium particles start to bond. Sintered zirconium is ductile and can be worked without difficulty. Pure zirconium is seldom applied in reactor engineering, but the powder is used in conjunction with uranium powder to form uranium–zirconium alloys by solid-state diffusion. These alloys are important in reactor design since they change less under irradiation and are more resistant to corrosion.

Uranium powder may be formed into a coherent mass by cold compacting, sintering, repressing, and annealing; however, the resulting density and strength is low even when pressures as high as 175 tons/in.^{2} are used for repressing. Uranium can be consolidated into a workable structure by hot pressing.

Thorium powders may also be cold compressed and sintered to workable structures. The sintered properties of thorium are more sensitive to processing than most other metals.

Bibliography

"Powder Metallurgy" in *ECT* 1st ed., Vol. 11, pp. 43–64, by Werner Leszynski, American Electro Metal Corporation.

1. G. R. Bell, "Pressing and Sintering Metal Powders," *J. Chem. Met. Mining Soc. S. Africa* **56** (6), 260 (Jan. 1956).
2. H. H. Hausner, "Basic Characteristics of Metal Powders," in A. R. Poster, *Handbook of Metal Powders*, Reinhold Publishing Corp., New York, 1966. (This is an excellent review of particle characteristics.)
3. A. R. Poster, *Handbook of Metal Powders*, Reinhold Publishing Corp., New York, 1966. (List of commercially available (U.S.) metal powders, characteristics and testing of metal powders.)
4. R. R. Irani and C. F. Callis, *Particle Size: Measurement, Interpretation and Application*, John Wiley & Sons, Inc., New York, 1963.
5. H. E. Rose, *The Measurement of Particle Size in Very Fine Powders*, Chemical Publishing Co., Inc., New York, 1954.
6. ASTM Standard B 212-48 (standard method of test for apparent density of metal powders), ASTM Standard B 329-61 (standard method of test for apparent density of refractory metals and compounds by the Scott volumeter), American Society for Testing and Materials, Philadelphia, Pa.
7. MPIF Standard 3-45 (method for determination of flow rate of metal powders), Metal Powder Industries Federation, New York.
8. H. H. Hausner, "Discussion of the Term 'Compacting' in Powder Metallurgy," *Planseeber. Pulvermet.* **12** (3), 172–180 (Dec. 1964).
9. D. Train and C. J. Lewis, "Agglomeration of Solids by Compaction," *Trans. Inst. Chem. Engrs. (London)* **40**, 235–240 (1962). (Excellent for bibliography.)
10. M. J. Donachie, Jr. and M. F. Burr, "Effects of Pressing on Metal Powders," *J. Metals* **15**, 849–854 (Nov. 1963). (Excellent for theoretical considerations and bibliography.)
11. R. W. Heckel, *Trans. AIME* **221**, 671 (1961).
12. R. W. Heckel, *Trans. AIME* **222**, 1073 (1962).
13. C. G. Goetzel, *Treatise on Powder Metallurgy*, Vol. I, Interscience Publishers, Inc., New York, 1949, pp. 259–312. (This is excellent for both theoretical and practical readers. Vols. II (1950), III (1952), and IV (1963) should also be noted.)
13a. "Compacting Presses and Tooling," *Powder Metallurgy Equipment Manual*, Part II, Metal Powder Industries Federation, New York, 1965, p. 15.

14. S. Storchheim, "Metal Powder Rolling—A New Fabrication Technique," *Metal Progr.* **69,** 120–126 (Sept. 1956).

15. F. Emley and C. Deibel, "A New Method for Compacting Metal or Ceramic Powders into Continuous Sections," *Proceedings of the General Session on Powder Metallurgy of the Fifteenth Annual Meeting of the Metal Powder Industries Federation,* pp. 5–13.

16. P. D. Peckner, "High Energy Rate Forming Processes—Their Present and Future," *Mater. Design Eng.,* **51,** 89 (July 1960).

17. H. H. Hausner and A. R. Poster, "Slip Casting of Metal Powders and Metal-Ceramic Combinations," in W. Leszynski, ed., *Powder Metallurgy,* Interscience Publishers, Inc., New York, 1961, p. 461.

18. H. H. Hausner, "Compacting and Sintering of Metal Powders Without the Application of Pressure," *Intern. Symp. Agglomeration, April 12–14, 1961.* (Excellent review and bibliography on pressureless consolidation methods.)

19. I. Ljengberg and P. G. Arbstedt, "Influence of Lubrication and Die Surface on the Pressing Characteristics of Metal Powders," *Proc. Ann. Meeting Metal Powder Assoc.* **12,** 78–92 (1956).

20. H. H. Hausner and I. Sheinhartz, "Friction and Lubrication in Powder Metallurgy," *Proc. Ann. Meeting Metal Powder Assoc.* **10,** 6–27 (1954).

21. H. H. Hausner, ed., *Modern Developments in Powder Metallurgy: Proceedings International Powder Metallurgy Conference, 1966,* Plenum Press, New York, 1966.

21a. E. V. Lenel and G. S. Ansell, "Creep Mechanisms and Their Role in the Sintering of Metal Powders," in reference 21, Vol. 1, pp. 281–296. This is a theoretical discussion.

22. M. H. Tikkanen and S. Yläsaari, "On the Mechanism of Sintering," in reference 21, Vol. 1, pp. 297–309. (This is a theoretical discussion.)

23. "Sintering Furnaces and Atmospheres," *Powder Metallurgy Equipment Manual,* Part I, Metal Powder Industries Federation, New York, 1963.

24. F. Thümmler and W. Thomma, "The Sintering Process," *Met. Rev.* (115). (This is the most complete and recent review of sintering theory.)

24a. *Definitions of Terms Used in Powder Metallurgy,* MPIF Standard 9–62, Metal Powder Industries Federation, New York.

25. H. H. Hausner, "Grain Growth During Sintering," in Special Report No. 58 of the Iron and Steel Institute, London, 1954, pp. 102–112.

26. "P/M Parts," *Materials and Processes Manual No. 242, Materials Engineering,* 85–100 (July 1967).

27. Reference 13, pp. 503–542.

28. *Products of Powder Metallurgy,* Engineering Manual E-64, Amplex Division, Chrysler Corp.

29. Reference 13, pp. 543–558.

30. B. J. Collins and C. P. Schneider, "Sintered-Metal Friction Materials," in reference 21, Vol. 3, pp. 160–165.

31. A. S. Doty, "Powder Metallurgy in the Electrical and Electronic Industries," *Proc. Ann. Meeting Metal Powder Assoc.* **12,** 46–55 (1956). (Best for general review of field.)

32. G. A. Meyer, "The Role of Powder Metallurgy in Manufacture of Electrical Contacts," *Metal Progr.* **86,** 95–99 (June 1965).

33. G. A. Meyer, "How to Select Electrical Contacts," *Metal Progr.* **87,** 92–95 (July 1965).

34. Reference 13, pp. 3–73.

35. J. F. Kuzmick, "Development of Ductile Tungsten Base Heavy Metal Alloys," in reference 21, pp. 166–172.

36. C. G. Goetzel and J. B. Rittenhouse, "Powder Metallurgy Applications in Space Vehicle Systems," *J. Metals* **17,** 876–879 (Aug. 1965).

37. H. H. Hausner, "Powder Metallurgy in the Space Age," *J. Metals* **16,** 894–900 (Nov. 1964).

38. H. H. Hausner, "Application of Powder Metallurgy in Nuclear Engineering," *Proc. Ann. Meeting Metal Powder Assoc.* **12,** 27–45 (1956).

ARNOLD R. POSTER
Metals Sintering Corp.
HENRY H. HAUSNER
Consulting Engineer

POWER GENERATION

The term power generation in the engineering sense implies the production of mechanical or electrical power from some other source of energy such as thermal, hydroelectric, or electrochemical energy. Power-generation devices of widespread engineering application utilize either air, steam, or water as the working medium. Those devices which utilize air are internal-combustion engines and gas turbines. Those which employ steam are reciprocating steam engines and steam turbines. Hydraulic turbines are used for the generation of power from water stored at elevation.

In recent years a great deal of research has been focused on several other means of power generation which may prove important in the future. These are magneto-hydrodynamic and electrogasdynamic generators, fuel cells, and thermonuclear fusion. Other forms having special-purpose applications are thermoelectric and thermionic generators. The present article will deal principally with the more conventional methods of power generation with only a brief treatment of the others.

The various prime movers for conventional power production may be classified as follows:
1. Internal-combustion engines
    a. Otto cycle engines
    b. Diesel cycle engines
2. Gas turbines
    a. Simple open-cycle gas turbines
    b. Open-cycle gas turbines with regeneration
    c. Closed-cycle gas turbines
3. Steam engines
4. Steam turbines
    a. Straight-through turbines
    b. Bleeder turbines
    c. Automatic extraction turbines
5. Hydraulic turbines

In the following sections each type of prime mover will be discussed, after which steam, hydroelectric, and nuclear power plants will be considered. A short discussion of other more recent forms of power generation and a look at present and future prospects will conclude the article.

Internal-Combustion Engines

Internal-combustion engines are used principally in automobiles, aircraft, trucks, locomotives, ships, excavating machinery, and all types of apparatus where relatively small amounts of power are required. They are also used for the production of electrical energy in small stationary power plants.

The principal fuels for this type of engine are gasoline, fuel oil, and natural gas. The method of producing power is by the expansion of the working substance against a piston which reciprocates back and forth inside a cylinder. The reciprocating motion of the piston is converted into rotary motion by means of a connecting rod, crankshaft, and flywheel, the latter serving as a device for smoothing out variable forces exerted against the crankshaft.

Internal-combustion engines can be built with one cylinder or many, depending upon the application. For small tools, only one cylinder may be necessary, while for

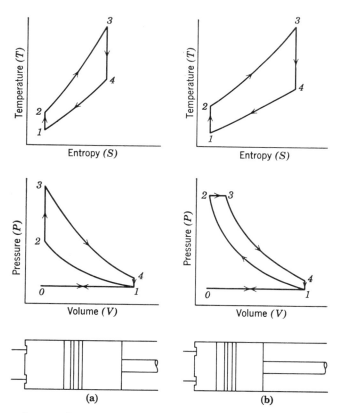

Fig. 1. Pressure–volume and temperature–entropy diagrams for ideal internal-combustion engine cycles. (**a**) Four-stroke Otto cycle; (**b**) four-stroke diesel cycle.

large diesel power plants, automobiles, or aircraft engines, many cylinders may be required. Cylinders may be arranged in a variety of ways, but the most popular are the in-line and V arrangements used in automobiles and stationary diesel-engine power plants. Other arrangements are the opposed piston type and the radial type. The former is used principally in diesel engines and the latter in aircraft engines.

Internal-combustion engines are built in sizes ranging from small model airplane engines to large units capable of delivering several thousand horsepower. Rotating speeds vary from about 50 to 5000 rpm, depending upon the size and design employed. Thermal efficiencies are usually high in well-designed units, ranging from about 20% for automotive and aircraft engines to as high as 40% for diesel locomotive and large stationary diesel power-plant engines. These efficiencies are for the engines alone and do not include such losses as those of the electric generator and auxiliaries in a power plant or the losses between engine crankshaft and wheels in an automobile or diesel locomotive. For a diesel power plant, auxiliary losses will bring the average overall efficiency down to about 30–35%. In an automobile or locomotive, losses between crankshaft and wheels are so great that actual overall thermal efficiencies from fuel to traction output are about half that of the engines themselves.

Internal-Combustion Engine Cycles. The two most important cycles employed for internal-combustion engines are represented in Figure 1 on pressure–volume and temperature–entropy diagrams. The cycles shown are ideal cycles, in which all processes are assumed to take place in a thermodynamically reversible manner. In the case of the Otto cycle engine, intake begins at point O in Figure 1a. The piston moves toward the crank end under the impetus of the flywheel and intake air accompanied by a charge of gasoline vapor or gaseous fuel is drawn into the cylinder along the line 0–1. At point 1 the intake valve closes and the piston returns to the head end, compressing the mixture of air and fuel isentropically to point 2. Here a spark ignites the fuel and the entrapped gases are heated at constant volume to the high temperature represented by point 3. From this point the hot gases expand rapidly, forcing the piston to the right and delivering a powerful turning moment to the crankshaft and flywheel. At point 4 the exhaust valve opens and the pressure drops at constant volume to point 1. From here the piston returns to point 0, discharging the hot gases to the exhaust.

In the case of the diesel cycle, exactly the same processes are followed except that fuel is injected into the cylinder in atomized form at point 2 (Fig. 1b), and combustion takes place at constant pressure from points 2 to 3. From points 3 to 4, the expansion continues, but without additional energy supply from the fuel. At point 4 the exhaust valve opens and the hot combustion gases fall in pressure at constant volume to point 1. They are then forced out of the cylinder at constant pressure to complete the cycle.

The cycles described above are called four-stroke cycles because four strokes of the piston (intake, compression, expansion, and exhaust) are required to complete the cycle. By arranging exhaust and intake ports around the cylinder near the end of the expansion stroke of the piston, it is possible to displace the exhaust gases with a new charge of fresh air before the piston returns again on its compression stroke. With such an arrangement the piston itself uncovers the exhaust ports near the end of the power stroke. Shortly thereafter the intake ports are also uncovered by the piston and a fresh supply of air, under a slight pressure generated in the crank case by the moving piston, is swept into the cylinder, driving the exhaust gases out. This procedure eliminates the necessity of a separate intake and exhaust stroke and permits the cycle to be completed with only two strokes, compression and expansion. Engines which operate in this manner are called two-stroke cycle engines. They may operate on either the Otto or the diesel cycle, depending upon the manner in which the fuel is admitted and burned.

In all actual engines the processes depart rather widely from those just described because of frictional effects, the necessity of cooling the cylinder to prevent overheating, the imperfect control of the fuel injection rate, leakage of air and gases past the piston, imperfect combustion, variation of the properties of air and combustion gases with temperature and pressure, and many other less evident factors. Because of this, thermal efficiencies computed from the ideal cycles must be multiplied by a correction factor in order to obtain actual thermal efficiencies.

Internal-Combustion Engine Cycle Efficiencies. There are many ways in which the efficiency of internal-combustion engines may be expressed. Since the primary purpose of an engine is to secure work output at the expense of thermal input, the overall thermal efficiency is perhaps the most important. Because the thermal efficiency of the ideal cycle can easily be computed, and also because it is the ultimate yardstick of accomplishment, this efficiency is often evaluated first and the other efficiencies are found from it. The ideal cycle efficiency, η_T, for the Otto cycle may readily be computed from the pressure–volume or temperature–entropy diagram. It is

$$\eta_T = 1 - \frac{1}{r_c^{k-1}} \tag{1}$$

where r_c = ratio of compression, V_1/V_2 (Fig. 1a), and k = isentropic exponent for air, C_p/C_v.

If it is assumed that throughout the cycle air has a value of k equal to 1.4, corresponding to cold air, the ideal cycle is said to be computed on the cold-air standard. If the value of k is taken to be 1.3, corresponding to hot air, it is said to be computed on the hot-air standard. Efficiencies computed on the hot-air standard are less than those computed by the cold-air standard but are somewhat closer to those actually encountered in practice because of the high average temperature of combustion gases in actual engines.

For the ideal diesel-cycle engine the thermal efficiency is given by

$$\eta_T = 1 - \frac{1}{r_c^{k-1}} \left[\frac{r_f^k - 1}{k(r_f - 1)} \right] \tag{2}$$

where r_c = ratio of compression, V_1/V_2 (Fig. 1b), r_f = fuel cutoff ratio, V_3/V_2 (Fig. 1b), and k = isentropic exponent for air, C_p/C_v.

Actual thermal efficiencies are somewhat lower than those computed by equations 1 and 2. The factor by which the ideal-cycle efficiency must be multiplied in order to give the brake thermal efficiency is called the brake engine efficiency. For well-designed engines at rated load this factor is usually in the neighborhood of 50–60%.

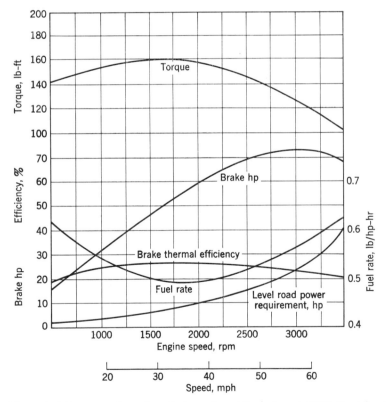

Fig. 2. Characteristic curves for a six-cylinder automobile engine at 100% throttle opening.

Applications and Performance Characteristics.   Internal-combustion engines operating on the Otto cycle are well adapted to applications where speed and power requirements vary over a wide range. This is particularly true of automobile and aircraft engines, which must be capable of adjusting rapidly to sudden variations in load and speed. With modern methods of carburetion, the correct fuel–air ratio is automatically supplied at all speeds, making it possible to operate at near peak efficiency regardless of operating conditions.

Diesel engines are widely used for stationary and marine power plants, and for railroad locomotives. For stationary power-plant application it is essential that the frequency of the electrical current generated remain constant. This permits a constant-speed design yielding optimum efficiency throughout the normal load range. In locomotive applications diesel engines usually drive electric generators, which in turn furnish electrical power to traction motors. With this arrangement the speed of the diesel engine can be held at values conducive to highest efficiency while variations in train speed and load can be handled electrically.

Diesel engines are also widely used for trucks and heavy-duty excavating and road-building equipment. For these applications the engines must be designed to maintain reasonably high efficiencies throughout wide ranges of speed and load.

Typical performance curves for a modern six-cylinder automobile engine are illustrated in Figure 2. Curves of brake horsepower, torque, fuel consumption, and brake thermal efficiency are plotted versus engine speed in revolutions per minute and corresponding speed in miles per hour for 100% throttle opening. The curves illustrate the small variation of fuel consumption in pounds per horsepower-hour with engine speed. A curve of road horsepower required to achieve these speeds in the particular automobile for which the engine is designed is also plotted. The difference between the brake horsepower and the road horsepower represents the amount of excess power available for acceleration or to overcome steep grades and other retarding factors. Curves plotted for reduced throttle openings would have similar characteristics.

Gas Turbines

Simple Open-Cycle Gas Turbine Without Regeneration.   An important recent advance in the field of power generation has been the development of the gas turbine. Besides providing a novel method of power generation, it has also furnished the basic power plant for modern jet-propulsion aircraft.

The most simple gas-turbine cycle is essentially the Brayton cycle illustrated in Figure 3. The compressor, which may be of either axial or centrifugal type, draws air into the inlet at point 1 and compresses it isentropically to point 2. From there the air flows to a combustion chamber, where either a liquid or gaseous fuel is supplied. In the combustion chamber the air is heated and expanded to point 3. It then flows through the turbine, where it performs work by surrendering energy before exhausting again to the atmosphere at point 4. The work performed by the air in passing through the turbine is sufficient to drive the turbine and compressor and in addition supply a substantial portion to the generator.

The efficiency of the ideal open-cycle gas turbine shown in Figure 3 is easily computed from the temperature–entropy diagram, provided the assumption is made that air follows the perfect gas laws, that the specific heat of air at constant pressure is a

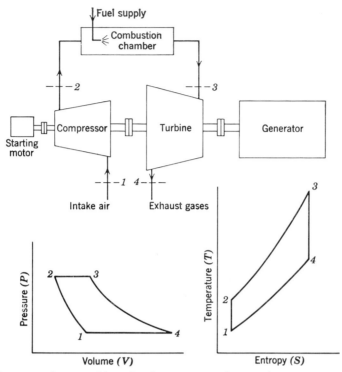

Fig. 3. Simple open-cycle gas turbine, showing pressure–volume and temperature–entropy diagrams for ideal cycle.

constant, and that the weight of fuel supplied contributes a negligible additional weight to the heated air flowing through the turbine. The thermal efficiency of the ideal cycle is

$$\eta_T = 1 - \frac{1}{r_p^{(k-1)/k}} \tag{3}$$

where η_T = thermal efficiency of ideal cycle, r_p = pressure ratio, P_2/P_1, and k = isentropic exponent for air, C_p/C_v.

In an actual gas turbine, the compressor and turbine both have internal efficiencies of less than 100%, so that the net energy delivered to the generator or shaft of the turbine will be substantially less than values computed by equation 3.

Open-Cycle Gas Turbine with Regeneration. The efficiency of the simple open-cycle gas turbine can be improved considerably by employing a regenerator in which the exhaust gases are passed countercurrent to the air leaving the compressor. In this manner air is heated by the exhaust gases before entering the combustion chamber, thereby reducing the amount of heat which must be supplied by the fuel.

If a source of cooling water is available, the compression process can be divided into two stages with intercooling between them. In this manner the work of compression can be reduced and the efficiency of the entire cycle improved. Another improvement in overall efficiency can be realized in larger units if the expansion process is divided into two parts with reheat to the initial temperature employed before the second expansion. This is usually accomplished by the use of a high- and a low-pressure turbine with a second combustion chamber placed between them.

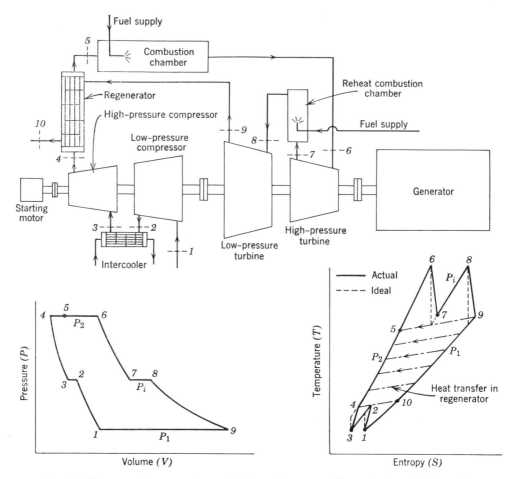

Fig. 4. Diagram of open-cycle gas turbine with regeneration, reheat, and intercooling.

A cycle employing regeneration, intercooling, and reheat is illustrated schematically in Figure 4 along with corresponding pressure–volume and temperature–entropy diagrams.

Pressurized Closed-Cycle Gas Turbines. One disadvantage of the open-cycle gas turbine is the large size of the unit as compared, for example, to a steam turbine of corresponding capacity. The reason is that air under low pressure has a rather high specific volume and therefore demands a large-size compressor and turbine to furnish even moderate amounts of power. For this reason exceedingly large units would have to be employed to produce a power output comparable to that of a modern central station steam turbine.

To overcome this difficulty, pressurized closed-cycle units have been proposed. In the closed cycle, air exhausting from the turbine is not discharged to the atmosphere but is cooled and returned to the compressor inlet to be used again. With this arrangement, air under several atmospheres' pressure can be employed in the cycle, thereby reducing the volume of air required for a given power generation. Gases other than air, which might be more suitable from a thermodynamic standpoint, may also be used if desired.

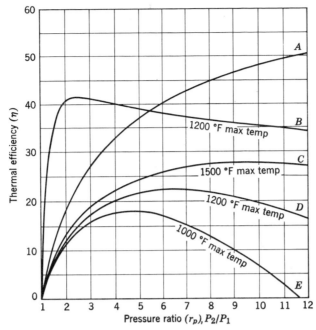

Fig. 5. Curves of thermal efficiency of various gas-turbine cycles.

The closed-cycle gas turbine has the advantage of smaller-size compressor and turbine but the disadvantage of requiring an abundant source of cooling water for reducing the turbine exhaust air temperature to compressor inlet temperature. Also, in place of a combustion chamber it requires a separate furnace in which heat liberated by the fuel is transferred through metal walls to the air. Due to the low heat-transfer coefficient of air the rate of heat transferred through the tube wall per square foot of surface must be very low in order to avoid excessive metal temperatures. This results in very large and costly heaters as compared to equivalent-capacity steam boilers. To alleviate this problem working gases having a higher heat-transfer coefficient, such as helium, have been considered.

These factors have tended to offset other advantages which are inherent in the pressurized closed cycle. For this reason, closed-cycle units have not as yet been built in the U.S. They have, however, received considerable attention in Europe and are of interest as indicating a possible line of future development.

Gas-Turbine Characteristics. Figure 5 is a series of curves representing the efficiency of various gas-turbine cycles as a function of pressure ratio. Curve A is for the ideal cycle as computed for air, using $k = 1.4$. With this cycle, the efficiency depends only on the pressure ratio and increases with increasing pressure ratio. Curves C, D, and E represent cycle efficiencies computed for an open-cycle gas turbine without regeneration, but with internal efficiencies of the compressor and turbine less than 100% and with three maximum air temperatures 1500, 1200, and 1000°F. For these curves the internal efficiency of the compressor was taken as 85% while that of the turbine was taken as 87%. The intake air temperature was assumed to be 80°F, with a value of k equal to 1.4. The curves indicate that for a given turbine and compressor efficiency the cycle efficiency reaches a maximum value at a definite pressure ratio which depends upon the maximum temperature T_3. For a maximum tem-

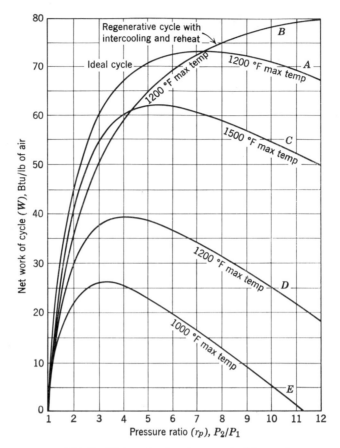

Fig. 6. Net work of various gas-turbine cycles.

perature of 1000°F a peak cycle efficiency of only about 18% can be expected, whereas with 1200 and 1500°F, peak cycle efficiencies of 22 and 28%, respectively, can be reached. Because of mechanical and generator losses, actual efficiencies would be about 90–95% of those indicated by the curves.

Improvement which can be realized by the use of regeneration together with intercooling and reheat is illustrated by curve B. For this curve a maximum cycle temperature of 1200°F was assumed and the specific heat for air at constant pressure was taken as 0.24 for the compressor and 0.26 for the turbine in order to simulate actual conditions more closely. Values of k computed from these specific heats were also used. The efficiency of each portion of the compression process was assumed to be 85%, while that for each portion of the expansion process was assumed 87%. The regenerator was assumed to heat the air to within 50°F of the temperature of the exhaust gases leaving the turbine. The division between high- and low-pressure processes in both the compressor and turbine was chosen so that maximum efficiency would be obtained. This occurs when the intermediate pressure P_i is equal to $\sqrt{P_1P_2}$. Curve B shows that for this particular cycle maximum efficiency occurs at a very low pressure ratio but that the efficiency is always much higher than for the corresponding open cycle without regeneration, reheat, or intercooling (curve D). With conditions similar to those indicated for this more complicated cycle, actual thermal efficiencies greater than 30% should be realized for all loads carried except the very lightest. Figure 6 is a series of curves depicting net work output versus pressure ratio for the several cycles. These indicate a maximum output at some particular pressure ratio, depending on the maximum temperature assumed and the efficiency of turbine and compressor. Comparison of these curves with those of Figure 5 indicates that for the same conditions of operation, maximum work output does not necessarily occur at the same pressure ratio as maximum efficiency.

Gas-Turbine Applications. Gas turbines are used for numerous purposes, but the most important application is for jet-propulsion aircraft. For this application air flows into the compressor at the front end of the engine and is compressed to several atmospheres before entering a ring of small combustion chambers located between the compressor outlet and turbine inlet. In these chambers a special grade of kerosine fuel is burned, heating the air to between 1200 and 1500°F. From the combustion chambers the hot gases expand through a turbine, thereby furnishing the motive power for driving the compressor which is attached to the turbine shaft. The hot gases continue their expansion through the exhaust nozzle of the engine, creating a high-velocity jet which drives the plane forward by the force of reaction. Jet-propulsion engines are most efficient at very high speeds and at high altitudes where the ambient air temperature is low.

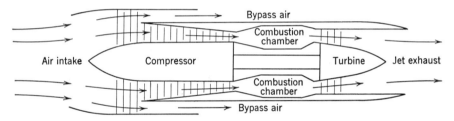

Fig. 7. Diagram illustrating principle of operation of the bypass or fan-jet engine.

A modification of the conventional jet engine is the bypass or fan-jet engine illustrated in Figure 7. In this version, the blading of the first few stages of the compressor is lengthened and a portion of the air flowing into the compressor is discharged without passing through the combustion chamber or turbine.

In effect, this is equivalent to combining the advantages of a propeller-driven craft with those of a jet, since the bypassed air is accelerated in the lengthened portion of the compressor blading and performs the same function as the air moving through an ordinary propeller. The remainder of the air travels through the jet engine in the conventional manner. Use of the fan-jet increases the thrust, particularly at takeoff, thus reducing the length of runway required. It also reduces fuel consumption significantly during flight, thereby increasing range and economy of operation.

Gas turbines are also used for locomotive and marine applications, but only to a limited extent due in part to the low efficiency of the simple open-cycle gas turbine compared to the diesel engine. Much effort has gone into the development of an automotive gas turbine but with only moderate success. A few gas-turbine-powered trucks and automobiles have been built and tested, but many problems remain to be solved before they can be marketed on a commercially profitable basis.

An important application for stationary units is in the oil and gas industry, where gaseous or liquid fuel is cheap. Here gas turbines can be economically employed to drive axial or centrifugal compressors for numerous purposes such as transporting gas from the field to metropolitan areas through large high-pressure pipe lines.

Another application in the oil industry is the Houdry process for refining gasoline (see Petroleum (refinery processes)). In this process, air leaving the compressor passes over a hot catalyst, where it supplies oxygen for burning off carbon which has collected. The resulting hot combustion gases are passed through a turbine, and enough work is obtained to drive the compressor and still supply a small amount of by-product power. A similar application exists in the steel industry, where blast-furnace gas is used as fuel in a gas turbine which compresses the air required for operation of the blast furnaces.

In the electric utility industry, gas turbines may be employed for peak-load generation or for standby service. Another possible application is to supply power for fully automatic booster stations at the end of long transmission lines. They are also used to a limited extent in combined gas turbine–steam turbine cycles which offer some improvement in station heat rate over conventional cycles. These will be discussed in the section devoted to steam power plants.

Steam Engines

The reciprocating steam engine operates on the principle of the expansion of steam against a piston which moves back and forth inside a cylinder. For many years this type of engine carried the burden of power generation, but the advent of internal-combustion engines and steam turbines has now reduced its application to a minimum. The principal reason for this is that the steam engine is definitely limited in size, speed, and capacity, and, except in the smallest sizes, cannot possibly compete with the steam turbine on an economic or fuel economy basis. Moreover, even in the smaller sizes mentioned, cheaper power-generating devices which require no steam generator are available. Also, attractive electrical rates have played a significant role in the replacement of steam engines with electric motors.

Nevertheless, there are sometimes cases where the installation of a steam engine is the proper choice. Such cases are those in which steam generation equipment is needed or already available and where the exhaust steam from the engine can be used for heating or process work. Whenever such conditions exist, only a careful overall study of costs of alternative methods of supplying power can reveal the proper selection of prime mover.

In Figure 8 the solid lines represent an ideal indicator diagram for a typical steam engine cylinder. The diagram represents graphically the pressure inside the cylinder versus position of the piston. Steam produced in a separate steam generator is admitted under high pressure, forcing the piston toward the crank end to the point of cutoff 1. At this point the intake valve closes and steam is allowed to continue its expansion until the piston reaches the end of its power stroke at point 2. The exhaust valve then opens and the pressure drops at constant volume to exhaust pressure, following which steam is forced out as the piston moves toward the head end under the impetus of the flywheel.

In an actual engine, the exhaust valve is closed near the end of the piston's forward movement, thus trapping a small amount of steam in the head end of the cylinder. This steam is compressed as the piston moves further forward and serves as a cushion against impact when new steam is admitted at the beginning of the power stroke. An actual indicator card for a typical steam engine is similar in shape to the one shown dotted in Figure 8. This card contains considerably less area than does the ideal card, and points where the intake and exhaust valves open and close are much less sharply defined. This characteristic is common to all steam engines but in some designs is less pronounced than in others.

Early steam engines nearly all used a D-slide valve design (Fig. 8) or its equivalent. This was a slow-acting valve which resulted in considerable pressure drop as the steam passed in and out of the cylinder through the valve openings. Later, designs were developed which largely eliminated this effect by producing a more rapid valve action. The most important of these was the Corliss valve, which became popular around the turn of the twentieth century.

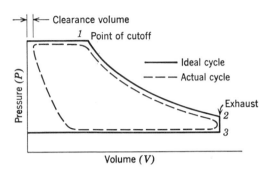

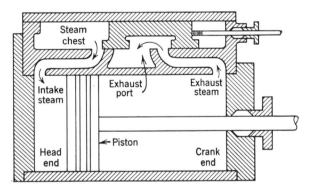

Fig. 8. Schematic diagram of D-slide valve steam engine cylinder together with ideal and actual indicator diagrams for head end.

One of the most widely used steam engines is the uniflow engine. In this engine steam is admitted at either end of the cylinder and exhausts near the center, where the piston itself uncovers the exhaust ports. With this type of engine the problem of initial condensation of steam is reduced to a minimum, since the hottest portions of the cylinder, where intake occurs, are not cooled by exhaust steam as in other types of engines.

The approximate horsepower obtainable from a steam engine is easily estimated by first determining from the ideal indicator diagram the mean effective pressure acting on the piston. This in turn is multiplied by the piston area, length of stroke, number of power strokes per minute, mechanical efficiency, and a diagram factor to correct for failure to achieve ideal conditions. The result when divided by 33,000 (33,000 ft-lb/min = 1 hp) gives the brake horsepower. For the ideal diagram of Figure 8 the mean effective pressure, P_m, in lb/ft² is given by

$$P_m = (P_1 V_1 / V_2) \ (1 + \log_e V_2 / V_1) - P_3 \tag{4}$$

where P_1 = pressure of steam admitted to the engine cylinder, in lb/ft²; V_1 = volume occupied by steam at point of cutoff, in ft³; V_2 = volume occupied by steam at end of stroke, in ft³; and P_3 = exhaust pressure of steam, in lb/ft².

For a double-acting steam engine in which expansion occurs on both sides of the piston, the brake horsepower, *bhp*, developed per cylinder is given by

$$bhp = \left[\left(\frac{P_m L A N}{33,000} \right)_{\text{head end}} + \left(\frac{P_m L A N}{33,000} \right)_{\text{crank end}} \right] \eta_M F_D \tag{5}$$

where P_m = mean effective pressure, in lb/ft²; L = length of stroke, in ft; A = area of piston against which steam acts, in ft²; N = revolutions per minute; η_M = mechanical efficiency of engine; and F_D = diagram factor for the engine.

For D-slide valve and uniflow engines the value of F_D at rated load is about 0.75, while for Corliss valve engines it is about 0.80. The mechanical efficiency is in the neighborhood of 95%. The expansion ratio V_2/V_1 usually varies between 4 and 6. Because of limitations imposed by the valves, steam temperatures should not exceed 600°F, and steam pressures should not be above about 250 psig.

Steam Turbines

The steam turbine is the basic prime mover for the production of large quantities of power. All steam turbines operate on the same principle, the expansion of steam through a series of nozzles and blade elements designed to convert the energy of expansion directly into rotational motion. The usual design consists of a large rotor

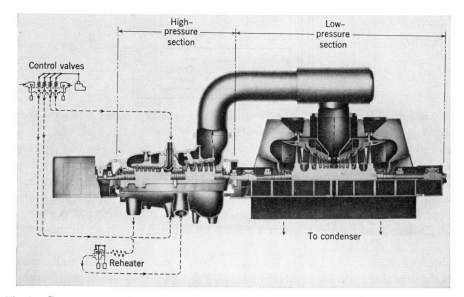

Fig. 9. Cutaway view of 3600-rpm, tandem-compound, double-flow, reheat steam turbine with separate control valves, double-shell high-pressure section with nozzle boxes. Courtesy General Electric Company.

suspended in a casing or cylinder. Attached to the rotor are rows of blading extending radially outward between which steam flows on its way to the turbine exhaust. Suspended radially inward from the casing are also rows of blading forming nozzle passages which fit between the rows of blading attached to the rotor. The velocity of steam expanding through the turbine is increased in the stationary nozzle passages, and the jet thus created is directed against the blades on the rotor causing it to spin at high speed.

A moderate-size steam turbine typical of those utilized for central station service in the late 1960s is illustrated in Figure 9. It is a 3600 rpm, tandem compound, double-flow, condensing, reheat turbine obtainable in ratings up to 300,000 kW for steam conditions of 2400 psi, 1050°F initial temperature with reheat to 1000°F. Superimposed on the diagram is a schematic representation of the steam flow path through the turbine. Steam enters the turbine through the control valves which automatically regulate the rate of flow in accordance with the load to be carried. After flowing leftward through the first seven stages of the high-pressure section it leaves the turbine and is returned to the steam generator for reheat to 1050°F before being reintroduced to the turbine through another valve, as indicated. After passing through five more stages of blading it leaves the high-pressure section of the turbine and is directed into the low-pressure section. Here it is divided into two paths, each flowing in opposite directions through six more stages of blading before being exhausted into the condenser located beneath the low-pressure section. At various points along the path of flow, openings are provided from which steam may be extracted for the purpose of heating boiler feedwater.

Classification of Steam Turbines. Turbines may be divided into two basic classifications, condensing and noncondensing. Condensing turbines are those in which steam after expanding through the blading is exhausted into a condenser which operates under low pressure, usually between 1 and 1½ in. of mercury absolute. In the condenser, latent heat contained in the exhaust steam is removed by the circulation of large quantities of cooling water through bundles of tubes surrounded by the steam. The condensate collected at the condenser outlet is pumped through a series of feedwater heaters back to the boiler.

Noncondensing turbines are those in which steam is exhausted either to the atmosphere or to some other apparatus at atmospheric pressure or above. They are often used in plants where power is generated as a by-product and where exhaust steam is to be used for process work or for heating .

Because of the relatively large loss in thermal efficiency resulting from high exhaust pressure, all central station steam power plants employ condensing turbines. These are attached to large electric generators, which generate power at high voltage. This power is distributed to the customer through complex electrical networks which include substations and transformers for reducing the voltage to values appropriate to the various industrial, commercial, and household applications.

Turbines, whether condensing or noncondensing, may be divided into three additional classifications: (1) straight-through turbines; (2) bleeder turbines; and (3) automatic extraction turbines.

Straight-through turbines are those in which steam flows through the turbine from inlet to exhaust without any portion being added or abstracted. This type of turbine is employed principally for driving pumps, fans, or other high-speed equipment, or for generating relatively small amounts of power.

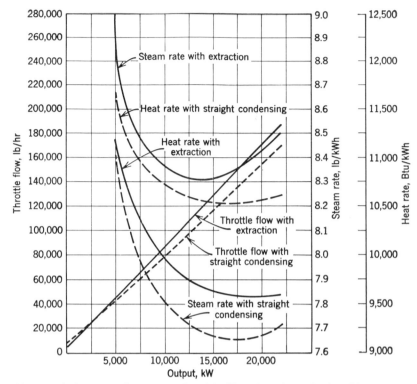

Fig. 10. Characteristic curves for a 20,000-kW ASME-preferred standard turbine generator. Steam conditions: 850 psig, 900°F, 1 in. Hg absolute. Solid lines are for four-heater performance.

Bleeder turbines are those from which steam is extracted at various points along the path of flow for the purpose of heating condensate feedwater on its way to the boiler. With this type of turbine no attempt is made to maintain the pressure of the extracted steam constant. As a result, it varies almost directly in proportion to the load being carried. This type of turbine is the only kind widely used in modern central station power generation. The reason is that with bleeding of steam for heating feedwater a much higher thermal efficiency can be achieved. In actual installations the total quantity of steam bled from the turbine is about 30% of that supplied to the throttle. The percentage increase in overall thermal efficiency realized by the use of a bleeder turbine over a straight-through turbine for the same steam conditions is about 10%.

Automatic extraction turbines are those designed to permit the extraction of steam at constant pressure at one or more points along the path of flow. Steam thus extracted may be used for process work or for heating. Since with this type of machine it is desired to hold both the speed and extraction pressure constant regardless of load carried, special valve arrangements are necessary. Automatic extraction turbines are ideal for industrial plants in which it is desired to generate electric power and at the same time supply steam for other processes at some desired intermediate pressure. The design can be arranged to exhaust to a condenser at low pressure or to some other apparatus such as a heating system at moderate pressure.

Characteristic Curves for Steam Turbines. Figure 10 shows a set of characteristic curves for a typical 20,000-kW, 3600-rpm, ASME-preferred standard turbine

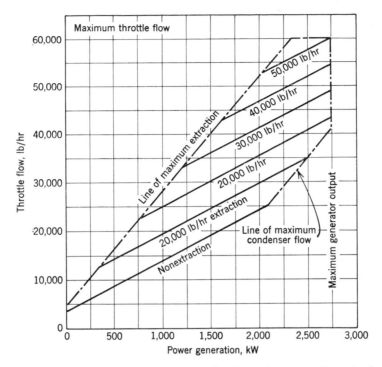

Fig. 11. Curves of throttle flow versus power generation for various extraction rates for a 2000-kW automatic extraction turbine.

operating at 850 psig and 900°F with four extraction openings for feedwater heating. Curves are shown for both extraction and nonextraction operation. It will be noted that for either case the throttle flow varies almost linearly with load. This is typical of all steam turbines, whether large or small. It will also be noted that for extraction operation the heat rate is a minimum in the neighborhood of rated load where maximum economy is usually desired.

Figure 11 is another set of curves showing throttle flow versus load for a typical 3600-rpm single automatic extraction turbine. Throttle pressure and temperature are 400 psig and 600°F, respectively. Exhaust pressure is 2 in. of mercury absolute and extraction pressure 35 psig. The curves indicate that for any constant load an increase in extraction flow of 10,000 lb/hr requires an increase in throttle flow of about 5600 lb/hr. The line of maximum extraction on the left represents the limiting amount of steam which can safely be extracted at any given load without reducing exhaust flow to a value too small to carry away the frictional heat generated in the turbine stages beyond the point of extraction. The line on the lower right represents the limiting load that can be carried without overloading the condenser. Maximum generator capacity is seen to be 2750 kW while maximum throttle flow is 60,000 lb/hr.

Steam Turbines for Central Station Power Plants. Central station power plant turbines of only a few thousand kW can be found today but by far the major portion now being built are for capacities exceeding 100,000 kW. In fact, at the end of the year 1966, more than half of the new generating capacity on order was for units exceeding 500,000 kW. At that time one unit of 1,000,000-kW capacity was already in service and five more exceeding this size, one as large as 1,150,000 kW, were scheduled to be put into service between 1969 and 1971. Because of rapid progress and improvement, most of these turbines are individually designed to meet the particular conditions of a given plant. However, by making use of the same components in different combinations, considerable cost reduction can be achieved.

Turbines for fossil-fueled power plants use highly superheated steam with one or more reheats. Typical steam conditions at inlet for the newer units of 500,000 kW and above are pressures of around 3500 psia and temperatures of about 1000°F. Most of the units employ one reheat to somewhere between 1000 and 1050°F but some employ two reheats, each to roughly the same 1000–1050°F temperature level.

Because of economical and technical limitations presently imposed by water-cooled nuclear reactors, turbines designed for pressurized-water and boiling-water nuclear plants are limited to a maximum inlet pressure of about 950 psia. Also, since a successful nuclear superheater has not yet been developed, steam is supplied to these turbines in the dry saturated state at a temperature of about 540°F. Because of these disadvantages, turbines employed in nuclear power plants are considerably larger and less efficient than those in fossil-fueled plants. In addition, they require complicated devices for extracting moisture which is released from the steam as it expands through the turbine. These factors make the turbine more difficult to design and maintain. However, the lower efficiency achieved is not as important for a nuclear plant as for a fossil-fuel plant because of the relatively low cost of nuclear fuel.

Steam Power Plants

Rankine Cycle Steam Power Plant. The Rankine cycle is the basic cycle from which all modern steam power plant cycles have evolved. It is named after the famous British engineer and scientist James Rankine (1820–1872). Figure 12 is a sketch of the equipment required to perform the cycle together with the corresponding temperature–entropy and enthalpy–entropy diagrams. Steam generated in the boiler enters the steam turbine at point 1. After expanding isentropically through the turbine, it enters the condenser at point 2. Here heat is removed at constant pressure until the steam is condensed to saturated liquid at point 3. It is then collected in a hot well and pumped back into the boiler at point 4, where sufficient heat is added at constant pressure to vaporize and superheat it to the original condition represented by point 1.

The work of the cycle is the difference between the work of the turbine and the work of the feedpump. From the steady flow energy equation this may be shown to be $(h_1 - h_2) - (h_4 - h_3)$. The heat added is $(h_1 - h_4)$. The thermal efficiency of the cycle is therefore given by

$$\eta_T = \frac{(h_1 - h_2) - (h_4 - h_3)}{(h_1 - h_4)} = \frac{(h_1 - h_2) - PW}{(h_1 - h_3) - PW} \tag{6}$$

where h = enthalpy of working substance, in Btu/lb of working substance; and PW = feed-pump work $(h_4 - h_3)$, in Btu/lb of working substance.

The pump work PW is negligibly small compared to other quantities except for pressures above about 400 psig. Graphically the work of the ideal cycle is represented by the enclosed area W on the temperature–entropy chart, and the heat rejected is represented by the area Q_R. The heat added is represented by the sum of these two areas. In the actual cycle, expansion through the turbine occurs inefficiently, causing

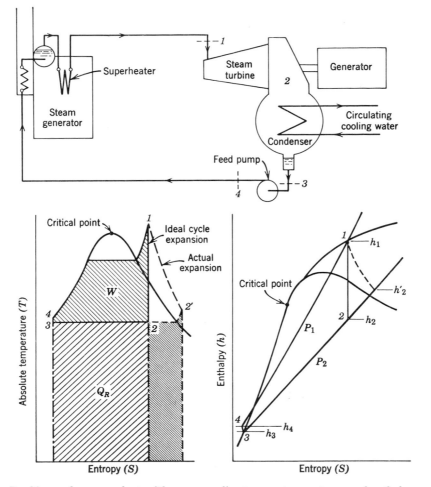

Fig. 12. Rankine-cycle power plant with corresponding temperature–entropy and enthalpy–entropy diagrams.

the steam to leave the turbine at point 2′ instead of 2. This means that a greater heat rejection takes place in the condenser. This additional heat is represented by the dash-dotted area on the temperature–entropy chart or by the enthalpy difference $(h_2' - h_2)$ on the Mollier chart.

Because of the greater heat rejection, the cycle efficiency is reduced. The ratio of the actual energy released by the steam during its expansion $(h_1 - h_2')$ compared to the ideal release $(h_1 - h_2)$ is called the turbine internal efficiency. In modern central station steam turbines this is on the order of 85%. The actual output of the generator is less than the energy release $(h_1 - h_2')$ by the exhaust loss, mechanical losses, and generator losses. In modern units, these losses constitute about 5% of the generator output, making the overall output on the turbogenerator equal to about 80% of that represented by the ideal isentropic expansion $(h_1 - h_2)$. This percentage is called the overall engine efficiency of the turbogenerator unit.

From the area represented on the temperature–entropy chart it is obvious that, other things being equal, the higher the initial pressure and temperature the higher will be the cycle efficiency. For this reason there has been a gradual trend toward higher pressures and temperatures in power plant design.

The Regenerative Cycle. The regenerative cycle is similar to the Rankine cycle except that certain modifications are employed to increase the overall thermal efficiency. In the basic regenerative cycle steam is bled from the turbine at several points for the purpose of heating the condensate feedwater before returning it to the boiler. The reheat regenerative cycle is the same as the regenerative cycle except that steam, after partially expanding through the turbine, is withdrawn and reheated at constant pressure to a higher temperature (usually equal or close to the initial steam temperature) before being returned to the turbine for completion of expansion. One thermodynamic advantage of reheat is the increase in thermal efficiency resulting from the addition of heat to the cycle at a higher average temperature than for the straight regenerative cycle. Another advantage is that steam is exhausted with less moisture content. This reduces frictional losses and water erosion in the last stages of the turbine, thereby increasing the efficiency still more.

A typical modern central station reheat-regenerative power plant cycle designed for a turbine such as that illustrated in Figure 9 is shown schematically in Figure 13. Temperature-entropy and enthalpy-entropy diagrams are also shown for the cycle. Steam, after being generated in the boiler, is superheated and enters the turbine at point *1*. It expands with some increase in entropy to point *A*, where it is withdrawn from the turbine and, after a portion is extracted for feedwater heating, is returned to the boiler for reheat at constant pressure before being reintroduced into the turbine at point *2*. The steam then resumes its expansion through the turbine, and as it passes the various extraction points, *B*, *C*, *D*, and *E*, a portion is withdrawn from each for feedwater heating. The remaining steam continues its expansion to the turbine exhaust and enters the condenser at point *3*. In the condenser its latent heat is removed by circulating water. The condensate is collected and pumped through two closed feedwater heaters and into the deaerating heater, where it is further heated and where any dissolved permanent gases are driven out. After leaving the deaerating heater, the feedwater enters the feedpumps and is pumped through the next two feedwater heaters and economizer into the boiler. Drains from the two feedwater heaters are cascaded back to the deaerating heater through traps as indicated in the diagram. A distilled-water tank is provided for addition of purified makeup water to the cycle.

The temperature–entropy and enthalpy–entropy diagrams show the weight of working substance involved in each portion of the cycle. From the diagrams it is clear that none of the extracted steam flows to the condenser and consequently less heat is rejected than in the case of the corresponding Rankine cycle. This means that a larger portion of the heat added is converted into work and that the efficiency of the cycle is better.

The dash-dotted lines in the diagram represent the path the steam would follow had an ideal cycle been assumed. The solid lines are those representing the approximate actual path of the steam. The entropy increase during expansion through the turbine results from internal friction which is converted into heat. This raises the enthalpy of the expanded steam by the amount indicated on the enthalpy–entropy diagram.

An interesting modification of the regenerative cycle is to employ a gas turbine in conjunction with it. In one such arrangement a gas turbine is added to the stand-

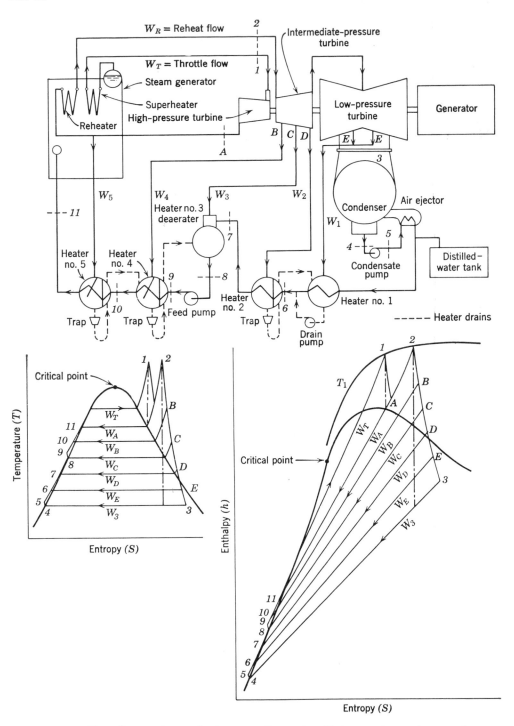

Fig. 13. Flow diagram for a reheat-regenerative cycle with temperature–entropy and enthalpy–entropy diagrams.

ard steam cycle in such a manner that the exhaust gases from the gas turbine are used to supply oxygen for combustion of fuel in the steam generator. This is feasible because only about 25% of the oxygen in the compressed air is chemically used in the combustion chamber of the gas turbine. The remaining 75% remains available in the exhaust gases and can be used to burn fuel in the boiler furnace. Indications are (1) that such an arrangement will permit a gain of 4 or 5% in station heat rate. Another possibility is to employ a steam generator with a pressurized boiler furnace in which air from the gas-turbine compressor supplies oxygen for burning the fuel in the furnace under several atmospheres pressure. With this arrangement the boiler furnace serves as the combustion chamber for the gas turbine as well as the heat source for the generation of steam. After passing through the boiler furnace, the hot gases are returned to the gas turbine for the production of power, and then exhausted through feedwater heaters of the steam portion of the cycle before being directed to the stack. The gain in heat rate with this system is expected to average 5 or 6%. Many other combinations utilizing the exhaust heat from gas turbines for steam-cycle improvement also appear attractive. Several combined schemes such as described above began to be employed in power-generation plants in the early 1960s.

Industrial Steam Power Plants. The term power plant is often used loosely to designate any plant in which steam is generated regardless of whether or not power is produced. In the more exact sense, an industrial steam power plant is one in which power is generated from steam, either for use by the company in its own plant or for sale as by-product power to a neighboring utility. In the oil, steel, and chemical industries large quantities of steam are often required. Whenever this is the case, a careful economic analysis will reveal whether or not it is an advantage to generate power and, if so, how much.

Since it costs little more to build a high-pressure steam generator than a low-pressure steam generator, it may prove to be a decided economic advantage to build the former and install an automatic extraction turbogenerator to furnish the necessary power requirements for the plant. At the same time, steam will be provided at the desired pressure levels for process work or for heating the building. This might prove especially attractive in cases where steam could be extracted at two pressure levels, a high pressure for process work and a low pressure for heating during the winter months. During the summer months, the low-pressure extraction could be curtailed and additional power generated could be employed for the operation of an air-conditioning system. During seasons of the year when excess power is generated, arrangements can usually be made to sell this power to a utility at a mutually satisfactory rate.

Because of the wide variety of needs, there is no single industrial power plant cycle. However, any cycle which is adopted will be essentially either the Rankine or the regenerative cycle with modifications for extracting steam at various pressure levels and in various amounts for process work. Great care must be exercised in planning an industrial plant if optimum economic advantage is to be obtained.

Hydroelectric Power Generation

The subject of hydroelectric power generation is exceedingly complex because of the many complicating factors which have to be considered. These include not only technical problems but often also problems related to the economic well-being of whole populations which might be affected by the type of hydroelectric development undertaken. For this reason only a brief discussion of this method of power generation will be included.

Types of Hydroelectric Power Plants. Hydroelectric power plants may be classified roughly as high-head, medium-head, and low-head plants, depending upon the height of the water level in the reservoir above the plant. Although no definite line of demarcation exists between them, high-head plants are usually considered to be those operating on heads of about 500 ft or more, while low-head plants are those operating on heads of less than approximately 50 ft. High-head plants require much less flow than do low-head plants of the same capacity. For this reason turbines and generators may be designed for higher speeds, permitting smaller units and housing. This is an advantage but is somewhat offset by the fact that long conduits or penstocks are necessary between dams and power plant.

Because of the great volumes of water which have to be handled, turbine generators for low-head plants are necessarily large low-speed machines. They are usually of the reaction type and may be designed for axial or radial flow. Medium-head plants partake of the characteristics of either low- or high-head plants in accordance with the degree of similarity with one or the other.

Dams vary greatly in design, depending on the type of service for which they are to be used. In arid regions of the West, dams are usually built for the primary purpose of storing water during the fall, winter, and spring for irrigation during the summer. These dams may also have facilities for hydroelectric power generation, but unless a given flow is assured throughout the entire year such facilities are usually built for limited service only.

Another type of dam is the flood-control dam. The purpose of this dam is to provide a storage reservoir capable of holding large volumes of water when flood conditions arise. Such dams may or may not be compatible with the demands of electric-power generation. If, for example, the reservoir is maintained at a high level for power generation there will be little reserve capacity to absorb flood water and its primary purpose will be defeated. On the other hand, if the reservoir is allowed to fall to a low level in order to provide storage space for flood conditions, power generation may at times have to be curtailed altogether should the anticipated flood conditions fail to occur.

Hydroelectric plants are often built on streams with an assured annual water flow. In these cases it is usually economically sound to provide generating equipment that can utilize whatever power is available in the river, additional power being supplied by steam plants.

A recent development in the hydroelectric field is the pumped-storage plant. This is a facility which can be operated in conjunction with either a steam system or a conventional hydroelectric system. The purpose of the plant is to help level out the peaks and valleys in the load curve, thereby increasing the capacity and efficiency of the overall system. The pumped-storage plant consists of two reservoirs, one at high elevation and one at a lower elevation, connected to each other through a reversible pump-turbine unit. During times when the demand for electrical energy is light, additional power can be generated in the steam or hydro plants of the system for pumping water from the lower to the higher reservoir. Conversely, when demand for electrical energy is high and cannot be carried by the other plants alone, the water in the upper reservoir can be used to generate the additional power by returning it to the lower reservoir through the pump-turbine unit. A number of pumped-storage systems were already in operation in the United States in the mid-1960s.

Plant Sizes. Hydro plants have been built for heads varying all the way from about 5 ft to as much as 5000 ft. The largest hydroelectric development in the United

States is in the Pacific Northwest where in the mid-1960s there was a total capacity of about 15 million kW of which about 7 million was Federal and 8 million non-Federal. By 1975 the total was expected to rise to over 25 million kW. The largest single installation in the United States is the Grand Coulee Dam on the Columbia River which employs eighteen units of 108,000 kW each, giving a total capacity of 1,944,000 kW. This is smaller than the 5,000,000 kW installation at Krasnoyarsk, Russia, which will contain ten 500,000-kW units. However, it is ultimately planned to add twelve 600,000-kW units to Grand Coulee, giving it a total capacity of over 9,000,000 kW.

It has been estimated that, if fully utilized, there is a potential hydroelectric capacity of 154 million kW in the United States if Alaska is included (2). Among the major rivers where the potential is the largest are the Columbia and Snake Rivers in the Northwest, the Colorado River in the Southwest, the Sacramento–San Joaquin River in California, and the Yukon River in Alaska.

Nuclear Power Plants

The first commercial nuclear power station in the United States was the Shippingport plant of the Duquesne Light Company which began operation in December 1957. The success of this reactor, and others which followed, provided the necessary impetus for the rapid growth of this new form of power generation.

Basically, the difference between a nuclear power plant and a conventional power plant lies in the source of heat supply. In a conventional plant, heat is obtained from the combustion of fossil fuel in a boiler furnace, combustion chamber, or internal-combustion engine cylinder, as the case may be. In a nuclear power plant, heat is usually obtained from the release of energy associated with the fissioning or splitting of uranium-235 (^{235}U) into lighter elements. During the fissioning process, a small amount of the mass of the original ^{235}U disappears and is converted into heat, leaving product elements having a slightly lower mass.

Uranium found in nature consists of about 99.3% ^{238}U and 0.7% ^{235}U. Unfortunately, ^{238}U, which is so much more plentiful, is not easily fissioned, so only 0.7% of the present supply of natural uranium is directly available for producing heat. Since each pound of ^{235}U will yield 35 billion Btu if completely fissioned, it follows that there are 35 billion $\times$ 0.007 = 245 million Btu of energy available in each pound of natural uranium. Comparing this to a good grade of coal, which during combustion releases about 13,000 Btu/lb, one can readily see that more than 200,000 times as much energy can be obtained from one pound of natural uranium than can be obtained from one pound of coal. Actually, not all of the ^{235}U present in the natural uranium can be fissioned in a nuclear reactor so that the ratio of heat actually obtainable from natural uranium as compared to coal is somewhat less than 200,000 to one. Nevertheless, the ratio is still so large as to make the weight of nuclear fuel required, compared to fossil fuel, almost insignificant.

By the middle of the 1960s it became apparent that nuclear power plants of 500,000 kW and larger could compete successfully on an economic basis with fossil-fuel-fired plants of the same size. Moreover, calculations showed that as the size of the plant increased, the competitive advantage over fossil fuel also increased. This fact, coupled with the additional incentive to reduce air pollution, resulted in a sharp increase in the number of orders for nuclear power plants in the mid-1960s. By the end of 1966, almost 25% of all new units of 500,000 kW and above, under construction or on order in the United States, were for nuclear plants.

A careful study of the economics of the Browns Ferry plant of the Tennessee Valley Authority (3) showed that fuel costs for its two huge 1,100,000-kW units would come to only 1.25 mill/kWh for nuclear fuel as compared to 1.69 mill for coal. Furthermore, it was demonstrated that over a projected 25-year period the overall savings, in terms of present worth for a nuclear plant, in comparison to a comparable coal plant, would amount to about $71 per kW of capacity or a total of $156 million for the plant.

It should be emphasized that such huge savings can only be achieved with very large units. However, with the present trend toward high-voltage interconnections between one large power system and another, plants of this size can easily be accommodated. It therefore appears certain that there will be a trend toward nuclear power and that by the year 2000 this will be the predominant means of power generation.

Principle of Operation. When the nucleus of a ^{235}U atom absorbs or captures a neutron the atom fissions into two lighter elements and simultaneously ejects two or three neutrons. Should one or more of these neutrons be slowed down to the proper speed for capture by another ^{235}U nucleus, it too will fission and release two or three more neutrons. By making the conditions such that the first nucleus fissioned produces at least one neutron which fissions a second nucleus, and the second nucleus produces at least one neutron which fissions a third, etc, it is clear that the process can be made to perpetuate itself. Since each fission results in the conversion of a small amount of mass into energy a great deal of heat is released. This heat can be used for the generation of power.

The sustained reaction described above is accomplished in a device called a nuclear reactor. In a nuclear power plant the reactor performs the same function of heat generator as does the boiler furnace in a steam power plant. The design of the reactor is too complex to discuss in detail in this article, but essentially it consists of a large vessel in which an array of fuel rods are distributed in a suitable geometric pattern in a region of the vessel called the core. The fuel rods consist of long cylindrical metal containers in which the nuclear fuel is encased. The preferred fuel for most reactors is uranium dioxide made up in the form of pellets which fit into the metal casing. In most reactors for central station power generation, the fuel is enriched by increasing the percentage of ^{235}U from the 0.7% found in natural uranium to anywhere between 1.5 and 5% of ^{235}U. The purpose of the metal containers is to protect the fuel from the water or other coolant flowing through the core.

Inserted between the fuel rods are a number of control rods whose purpose is to capture excess neutrons and thereby limit the number which are allowed to be absorbed by the nuclear fuel. When the control rods are fully inserted, sufficient neutrons are captured by the control rods to prevent any possibility of a self-sustained nuclear reaction. As the control rods are gradually withdrawn from the core, more neutrons become available for capture by the fuel and eventually a point is reached where the reaction becomes self-sustaining. By properly positioning the control rods, the number of fissions occurring and the consequent rate of heat release can be accurately controlled.

Most neutrons released during fission have velocities in the neighborhood of 10,000 miles per second, corresponding to energies on the order of 1 MeV (million electron volts). Neutrons with this velocity are called fast neutrons. For easy

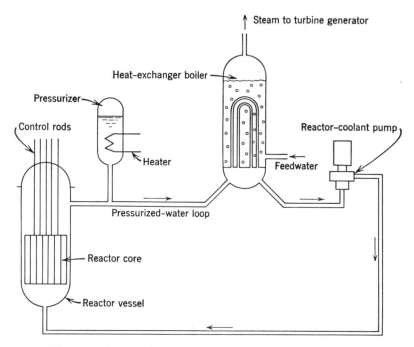

Fig. 14. Diagram showing concept of pressurized-water reactor.

capture by ^{235}U, the neutrons must be reduced in speed to a few miles per second corresponding to energies of about 0.025 eV. This can be accomplished by surrounding the fuel rods with a moderator which is a material capable of slowing down the neutrons as they collide with the molecules of the moderator.

The most commonly used moderators are water, heavy water, graphite, and certain organic liquids. In many reactors the moderator also serves as the coolant and, as in the case of water, may even serve as the working medium for the power-producing thermodynamic cycle.

An abundance of different types of reactors have been proposed but only a few have actually been employed for the commercial production of power. Reactors may be classified in a number of ways, but perhaps the most common and meaningful is according to the type of moderator employed, the coolant used, and the method of utilizing the coolant. Classified in this manner the most important for the production of power are pressurized-water reactor; boiling-water reactor; high-temperature gas-cooled reactor; liquid-metal-cooled reactor; gas-cooled, graphite-moderated, natural uranium reactor; heavy-water reactor; organic-cooled reactor.

By far the most widely used reactors in the United States are the pressurized-water reactor (PWR) and the boiling-water reactor (BWR). In the *pressurized-water reactor*, illustrated in Figure 14, ordinary water serves as both coolant and moderator. The reactor coolant pump circulates this water through a loop containing the reactor vessel and the tubes of a heat-exchanger boiler. The water in this loop is maintained at a sufficiently high pressure to prevent boiling and transfers the heat gained from the reactor core to feedwater entering the heat-exchanger boiler. Steam generated from the feedwater is then directed into the turbine generator for the production of electric power.

The *boiling-water reactor* (BWR) is similar to the pressurized-water reactor except that steam is generated inside the reactor vessel itself, rather than in a separate boiler, and is used directly for the production of power, as shown in Figure 15. The boiling water also serves as coolant and moderator.

The *high-temperature gas reactor* (HTGR) operates in a manner similar to the pressurized-water reactor except that the coolant which circulates through the reactor and boiler is gaseous helium rather than pressurized water. Also, the reactor core employs graphite as the moderator.

In the *liquid-metal-cooled reactor* the coolant is liquid sodium and the moderator is graphite. This reactor employs two loops of circulating liquid sodium. In the first loop the sodium picks up heat in the reactor vessel and in a heat exchanger transfers this heat to liquid sodium flowing in the second loop. In the second loop the heat is transferred to water for the generation of steam in a special boiler designed for the purpose. This double loop is required because of the danger inherent in the sodium–water reaction which could occur in the steam generator. This could have a serious effect on reactor operation and cooling. The double loop reduces the chance of a reactor disturbance should a leak or tube rupture in the steam generator cause a sodium–water reaction.

The *gas-cooled, graphite-moderated, natural uranium reactor* was developed and used in England for the double purpose of generating power and producing plutonium-239. In contrast to the other reactors, it employs natural uranium as fuel and uses CO_2 as the coolant. *Heavy-water reactors* employ heavy water (D_2O) as both moderator and coolant and operate in much the same manner as does the pressurized-water reactor. *Organic-cooled reactors* also operate in a similar manner but use organic liquids as the moderator and coolant.

Nuclear Plant Design. While nuclear steam power plants vary in design and construction according to the type of reactor employed, they nevertheless all have certain fundamental characteristics which can be illustrated by considering a particular plant. Figure 15 shows a greatly simplified version of the principal components of the Browns Ferry plant (4) of the Tennessee Valley Authority, the largest plant on order at the end of 1966. The boiling-water reactor vessel with its core and control rods is illustrated on the left and the steam turbine, electric generator, condenser, feedwater heaters, and boiler feedpumps are shown on the right. A more detailed cross-sectional view of the plant is shown in Figure 16. Here the heavy concrete containment sphere which completely surrounds the nuclear reactor is clearly in evidence. The sphere is necessary for two reasons. First, to shield the remainder of the plant from the radiation which emanates from the reactor and which must be brought to a sufficiently low level to be completely harmless to all personnel and equipment. Second, it has to serve as a containment vessel for any steam or water which might be released should the reactor vessel rupture, or should any other mishap occur which could release radioactive material.

In addition to the heavy concrete containment vessel, an added precaution is provided by the suppression chamber. As can be seen in the illustration, large pipes lead from the containment vessel into a huge toroidal-shaped chamber containing water. Should a nuclear excursion occur in which great quantities of steam were released into the containment vessel, the steam would immediately be dumped into the water of the suppression chamber where it would be condensed. This would automatically relieve any excessive pressure rise that might otherwise occur and

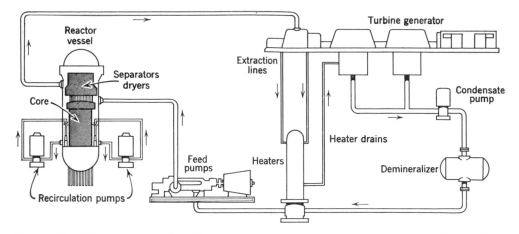

Fig. 15. Simplified diagram of the boiling-water reactor and principal components of the Browns Ferry
nuclear plant of the Tennessee Valley Authority.   Courtesy Tennessee Valley Authority.

would eliminate the possibility of rupture of the containment vessel.   Another method
is to use an ice bed rather than water for condensing the steam.   The ice can be kept
frozen by continuous mechanical refrigeration.

In addition to the features described above, there are innumerable others which
distinguish a nuclear plant from a conventional plant.   Among the most important
are the provisions which must be made for the safety of personnel and the handling
and replacing of fuel.   These involve very elaborate mechanical devices for manipulat-
ing radioactive materials, including special storage facilities, provision for shipment of
spent fuel elements, etc.

Many improvements are still necessary before the nuclear plant can reach
its ultimate potential.   One is to develop a satisfactory nuclear superheater for
pressurized- and boiling-water reactors so that steam can be supplied to the turbine in
a superheated state as it is in a fossil-fueled plant.   Another, and more important one,
is to develop a breeder reactor which can generate power and at the same time produce
more fissionable fuel from either ^{238}U or thorium-232 than is consumed by the reactor.   Both ^{238}U and thorium-232 are fertile materials which are plentiful and
which can be converted into fissionable plutonium-239 or uranium-233 by bombardment with fast neutrons.   Unless this objective is achieved, there will be insufficient
nuclear fuel to meet future demands.   Steady progress is being made in this direction,
and there seems little doubt that success will be attained.

Other Methods of Power Generation

Many other devices for the production of power are under development but for
technical or economic reasons will probably play only a minor role in the foreseeable future.   Among these are the magnetohydrodynamic (MHD) generator, the
electrogasdynamic generator, thermonuclear fusion devices, fuel cells, and thermoelectric and thermionic generators.   Since all are still in the research and development
stage, only a brief discussion of each will be undertaken here.   For further information
the reader is referred to references in the bibliography.

Magnetohydrodynamic Generator.   With this device an electric current is produced by expanding a highly ionized gas at high velocity and high temperature

through a channel across which is imposed a strong magnetic field. If the magnetic poles are placed on opposite sides of the channel, and electrodes along the other two sides, an electric current will be generated in the gas that will flow across the channel from one electrode to the other. By connecting the electrodes to an external load, a continuous current of electrical energy will result. In effect, the moving ionized gas serves the same purpose as does the armature winding on a conventional electric generator.

To achieve the desired high efficiency and to aid in ionization, gas temperatures in the neighborhood of 5000°F are needed. These may be obtained by burning hydrocarbons or by other methods such as in a nuclear reactor. To achieve the required degree of ionization, it is necessary to add a suitable seed material to the gas, usually a compound of one of the alkali metals such as cesium, potassium, or sodium.

As presently visualized, a magnetohydrodynamic (MHD) generator could be used in conjunction with a conventional power plant by passing the high-temperature ionized gas through the MHD generator and using the still hot exhaust gas for generating steam in a boiler.

Advantages of MHD are the lack of moving parts and the fact that power is generated directly from high-temperature gases. Studies carried out for a group of electric utility companies (5) indicate that a 500,000-kW plant in which 70% of the power is generated by MHD and the balance by conventional means, would have an efficiency of about 53%. This compares to about 40% for the best existing steam power plants.

One disadvantage of the MHD generator is that it generates direct current which would have to be converted to AC for suitable transmission and distribution. Also, there are many formidable problems, mostly due to the high temperature required, that have to be solved before this type of power generation can become a practical reality.

Electrogasdynamics (EGD). Like magnetohydrodynamics, this is a method of directly converting the enthalpy of a working fluid to electrical energy.

The generator consists of a duct which has an electric potential imposed on it in the direction of the flow. The working fluid is seeded with unipolar ions as it enters the duct. The energy in the working medium is used to transport the ions against the potential imposed. The ions are then collected at the duct outlet at high potential. When the inlet ion source and outlet collector are connected with an external load, a flow of electrical energy will result.

The great advantage of this process is that it does not require the extremely high temperatures of MHD; it can be made into a power-generation scheme without the need for combining it with a steam plant of overall efficiencies comparable to that achievable with MHD.

The disadvantage of the process resides in the fact that very-low-current, high-voltage electrical power is produced. Due to electrostatic field effects the maximum channel size is severely limited so that many thousands of channels in parallel and series are required to result in power levels of commercial interest.

Very intensive work on the EGD power generation system was started in this country in 1966.

Fusion Power. A great deal of interest has been centered in recent years on the possibility of generating power by thermonuclear fusion. It has long been known that the heat generated in the sun comes from the fusion of four hydrogen nuclei into a helium nucleus. If this could be duplicated on earth in a controlled manner, there would be an inexhaustable supply of fuel in the rivers, lakes, and oceans of our planet. Thermonuclear fusion has already been achieved with the H-bomb but this occurs in an uncontrolled burst which cannot be harnessed for continuous power generation.

An alternative to the fusion of hydrogen nuclei is the fusion of deuterium (heavy hydrogen) nuclei, called deuterons, into helium-3 and helium-4. In a series of fusion processes, five deuterons can react to form one helium-3 nucleus and one helium-4 nucleus with two neutrons and one proton left over (6). The energy released as a result of the decrease in mass during the process is 24.8 MeV (1 MeV = 3.8×10^{-14} cal = 1.51×10^{-16} Btu). Deuterium occurs in ordinary water in the ratio of about one pound in every 30,000 and each pound of deuterium would be capable of yielding approx 10^{11} Btu if all nuclei could be fused. On this basis the amount of energy obtainable by fusion of the deuterium in one pound of ordinary water would be $1/30,000 \times 10^{11} = 3.33 \times 10^6$ Btu. This is over 250 times as much energy as can be obtained by burning one pound of coal having a heating value of 13,000 Btu/lb.

It has been estimated that there is approx 10^{17} lb of deuterium in the ocean so that the total energy available would be $10^{11} \times 10^{17} = 10^{28}$ Btu. Consumption of electrical energy in the world in 1965 was about three trillion kWh per year. Since it requires roughly 10,000 Btu to produce 1 kWh, the rate of energy consumption for power production in 1965 was about 3×10^{16} Btu per year. At this rate there would be enough deuterium available in the ocean to last over 300 billion years. Should the world power consumption eventually level off at 300 times present requirements, there would still be enough deuterium to last a billion years.

To achieve a sustained fusion reaction with deuterium, the nuclei must be given sufficient energy to overcome the forces of repulsion between them. The only practical method of accomplishing this appears to be that of subjecting a low-density deuterium gas to temperatures on the order of 400 million degrees Kelvin or more. At such high temperatures all electrons have been stripped from their atoms, and the gas, now completely ionized, is called a plasma.

At first it might appear that such a plasma would be impossible to confine because the walls of any containing vessel would melt. This is not the case, however, since the density of the gas is so low that not enough atoms would be striking the walls of the container to cause damage. The real problem is that the energy in the atoms striking the walls would be lost and the plasma could not be kept at the desired temperature level. The solution to this problem is to confine the plasma inside a magnetic field, shaped in an appropriate manner to contain the plasma by the action of the magnetic field on the ionized particles of the plasma. Such a magnetic field is sometimes termed a magnetic bottle.

The temperature level required to initiate the fusion process would be accomplished in two steps. The first would be to heat the plasma by ohmic resistance to a high level by inducing an electric current to flow through it. This would be followed by a sudden compression of the gas, utilizing the magnetic field to squeeze the plasma into a much smaller volume.

Estimates are that the plasma in a controlled fusion reactor will probably have a density of about 10^{15} particles per cm³. This compares with 3×10^{19} particles for an ordinary gas at standard pressure and temperature. At the temperature level required for fusion, the plasma would be under a pressure of about 1500 psia. A magnetic field strong enough to contain this would be required.

To date it has been impossible to achieve a magnetic field of the proper geometry to hold the plasma for a sufficient length of time to sustain fusion. The problem is the instability generated by the interaction of plasma and magnetic field permitting escape of the plasma through the confining magnetic walls.

At least half a dozen countries are presently working on the enormously difficult problems which must be solved before fusion power can become a reality. No prediction can be made as to when success will be achieved, but the problem will eventually have to be solved if there is to be enough energy to supply the world's ultimate need for power.

Fuel Cell. The fuel cell is a device for producing electricity directly from a chemical energy source by the process of galvanic oxidation. This occurs in much the same manner as in a conventional storage battery except that the fuel cell does not store electrical energy and the electrodes and electrolytes are not consumed. Instead, the fuel and its oxidant are continuously fed into separate chambers on opposite sides of the cell and the oxidation process involves a transfer of electrons from the fuel molecules to the oxidizer molecules through an external circuit which contains the electrical load.

The fuel cell has the advantage of containing no moving parts and of producing electric power directly without the intervention of a heat-engine cycle. The latter feature is particularly important since the fuel cell operates at essentially constant temperature and does not depend on a large temperature differential to obtain high efficiency.

A simplified diagram of a hydrogen–oxygen fuel cell is shown in Figure 17. It consists of a fuel electrode called the anode and an oxidant electrode called the cathode. These are separated by an ion-conducting electrolyte. The fuel, which in this case is hydrogen, but which could just as well be natural gas, a hydrocarbon, or any other suitable substance capable of chemical oxidation, is fed continuously into the fuel chamber where it is exposed to the anode. There the hydrogen dissociates into hydrogen ions and electrons. The electrons flow through the external electrical circuit to the cathode while the hydrogen ions migrate through the electrolyte. Both the electrons and the hydrogen ions join at the cathode to combine with the oxygen to form water which is continuously removed.

Theoretical efficiency of the hydrogen–oxygen fuel cell varies with the temperature at which the reaction takes place. At room temperature it is approx 94% and decreases gradually to about 54% at 3140°F. The maximum practical efficiency of fuel cells is much lower than this, and is not expected to exceed 70% under the most optimistic conditions.

Efforts are being made by the gas industry to develop fuel-cell packages capable of generating electric power for individual homes, schools, shopping centers, and apartment buildings, using natural gas as the fuel and air as the oxidant. Such package units would offer the prospect of an alternate source of power which would hopefully be competitive with that furnished by the electric utility industry. At present this goal appears to be rather far in the future.

Thermoelectric Generators. Thermoelectric generators utilize the Seebeck effect which operates on the same principle as does a thermocouple. If two wires of dissimilar metal are joined together at the ends to form a loop, an electric current will circulate through the wires if one of the junctions is held at a higher temperature than the other. The current obtainable with metal junctions is very small but if junctions

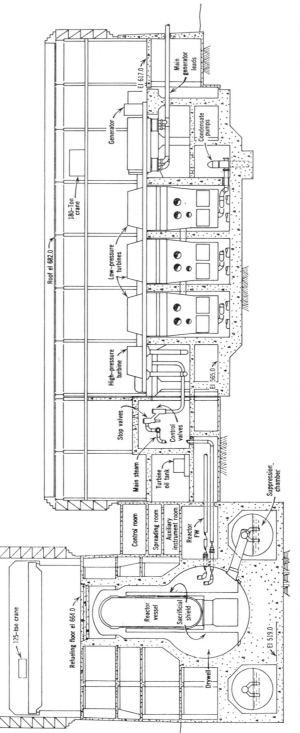

Fig. 16. Cross-sectional view of Browns Ferry plant showing containment vessel with water suppression chamber.   LEGEND: El = elevation; FW = feedwater.   Courtesy Tennessee Valley Authority.

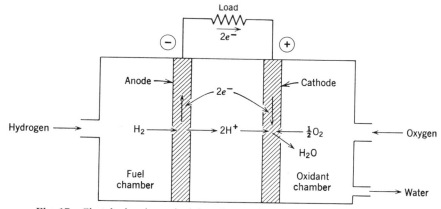

Fig. 17. Sketch showing principles of operation of hydrogen–oxygen fuel cell.

of p- and n-type semiconductors are used, it becomes much larger. By using several hot and cold junctions connected in series by semiconducting materials, the voltage causing the current to flow can be increased in proportion to the number of junctions. Many different thermoelectric generators have been built, or are being developed for use in outer space and other remote location applications (5). The capacity of these units varies from about 2.5 to 5000 W and the efficiency ranges from a low of 0.7 to a high of 6%. Fuels for keeping the hot junctions warm range from various hydrocarbons to radioisotopes such as strontium 90. Solar radiation supplied directly or through parabolic collectors may also be used for heating the junctions.

Because of their low efficiency and low power output, thermoelectric generators are not expected to have a significant effect on present methods of large-scale power generation.

Thermionic Generators. If a metal is heated to a sufficiently high temperature, electrons will be emitted from its surface. This principle may be used to generate electric power in a device called a thermionic generator. If two parallel metal plates are separated by an ionized gas, and if one plate is heated and the other kept cool, electrons will flow through the ionized gas from the hot plate to the cold plate. By connecting the two plates through an external circuit, a path will be provided for the return of the electrons to the hot plate and a continuous electric current will flow.

In common with the thermoelectric generator, the thermoionic generator has the advantage of no moving parts but the disadvantage of being subject to the same Carnot-cycle efficiency limitations as are other heat engines. Tests on a large number of laboratory models reported in reference 5 show efficiencies ranging from 5 to 16% with power densities varying between 1 and 22 W/cm^2. Emitter temperatures in these tests ranged from 1200 to 1800°C.

Applications for the thermoionic generator appear to be mostly in vehicles for outer space where compactness, low weight, and a high sink temperature are needed. They are not expected to achieve significance for commercial power production.

Present Power Generation and Future Trends

The total power produced in the United States from all sources is difficult to estimate because of lack of exact information on how much is actually developed by the various kinds of transportation vehicles. Nevertheless, since reasonably accurate statistics are available for the rate of energy consumption by the transportation sector of our economy as compared to that for the generation of electrical power, a fairly reliable estimate can be made.   In reference 5 (page 8), the amount of energy consumed by the transportation sector of the United States was reported as 9.19×10^{15} Btu in 1960.   For that same year the total energy consumed for the generation of electric power was 9.28×10^{15} Btu.   This indicates that the total energy consumed by all transportation vehicles is roughly equal to that consumed in the generation of electric power.

Figures published in reference 7 yield the following breakdown for electric power consumption in the United States during 1965, expressed in billions of kWh:

Type of Consumption

Residential	*Industrial*	*Commercial*	*All Other*	*Total*
279.8	533.7	201.4	36.8	1051.7

Of the total of over 1 trillion kWh, 101.5 billion kWh was generated in industrial plants and the remainder in electric utility plants.   Approx 81% of all electric power generated in the United States comes from thermal plants and the remainder from hydroelectric plants.   Future projections, however, indicate a gradual reduction in the percentage of new hydroelectric plants.

During the past few decades power production in the United States has been doubling about every ten years.   This tremendous growth is expected to continue for the foreseeable future.   Projections (7) indicate an expected total electric power generation of slightly over 2 trillion kWh by 1975 and 2.75 trillion by 1980.   Other estimates (2) are on the same order of magnitude.   To meet this rapidly rising demand, much added new capacity will be required.   Forecasts indicate a rise from slightly over 200 million kW of generating capacity in 1965 to almost 600 million by 1980.   Among the future load builders that will assure this growth are accelerated industrial activity, widespread adoption of electric home heating and air conditioning, the ever-expanding use of electrical appliances, and perhaps eventually, the development of a successful electric automobile.

Along with increased power output will come more efficient operation, transmission, and distribution of electric power with better load factors and lower fuel cost per kilowatt-hour.   The latter will be brought about by better engineering and optimum use of nuclear fuel.   Contributing to better load factors will be the interconnection of large electric utility systems into network pools capable of taking advantage of the diversity of load from one geographical region to another.   These factors all combine to make the outlook for future power generation exceedingly bright.

Bibliography

"Power Generation" in *ECT* 1st ed., Vol. 11, pp. 65–87, by R. A. Budenholzer, Illinois Institute of Technology.

1. R. C. Sheldon and T. D. McKone, "Performance Characteristics of Combined Steam-Gas Turbine Cycles," *Proc. Am. Power Conf.* **24**, 350–370 (1962).
2. *National Power Survey—A Report by the Federal Power Commission*, U.S. Govt. Printing Office, Washington, D.C., 1964.

3. *Comparison of Coal-Fired and Nuclear Power Plants for the TVA System*, Office of Power, Tennessee Valley Authority, Chattanooga, Tennessee, June, 1966; also summarized in *Elec. World* **166**, (4), 50–52 (July 25, 1966).

4. J. R. Parrish, G. M. Roy, and F. G. Bailey, "Nuclear Power Plant of TVA at Browns Ferry—Background and Description," *Proc. Am. Power Conf.* **29** (1967).

5. A. B. Cambel et al., *Energy R&D and National Progress*, U.S. Govt. Printing Office, Washington, D.C., 1964.

6. S. Glasstone, *Controlled Nuclear Fusion*, U.S. Atomic Energy Commission, Division of Technical Information, Washington, D.C.

7. A. J. Stegeman, "17th Annual Electrical Industry Forecast," *Elec. World* **166** (14), 113–128 (Oct. 3, 1966).

General References

S. W. Angrist, *Direct Energy Conversion*, Allyn and Bacon, Inc., Boston, 1965.

R. L. Bartlett, *Steam Turbine Performance and Economics*, McGraw-Hill Book Co., Inc., New York, 1958.

S. S. L. Chang, *Energy Conversion*, Prentice-Hall, Inc., Englewood Cliffs, N.J., 1963.

E. F. Church, Jr., *Steam Turbines*, 3rd ed., McGraw-Hill Book Co., Inc., New York, 1950.

R. L. Daugherty, *Hydraulic Turbines*, 3rd ed., McGraw-Hill Book Co., Inc., New York, 1920.

M. M. El-Wakil, *Nuclear Power Engineering*, McGraw-Hill Book Co., Inc., New York, 1962.

S. Glasstone and A. Sesonske, *Nuclear Reactor Engineering*, D. Van Nostrand Co., Inc., Princeton, N.J., 1963.

S. Glasstone and R. C. Lovberg, *Controlled Thermonuclear Reactions*, D. Van Nostrand Co., Inc., Princeton, N.J., 1960.

C. D. G. King, *Nuclear Power Systems*, The Macmillan Co., New York, 1964.

L. C. Lichty, *Internal-Combustion Engines*, 6th ed., McGraw-Hill Book Co., Inc., New York, 1951.

R. L. Loftness, *Nuclear Power Plants*, D. Van Nostrand Co., Inc., Princeton, N.J., 1964.

L. E. Newman, A. Keller, J. M. Lyons, and L. Wales, *Modern Turbines*, John Wiley & Sons, Inc., New York, 1944.

E. F. Obert, *Internal Combustion Engines*, 2nd ed., International Textbook Co., Scranton, Pa., 1950.

R. F. Post, "Fusion Power," *Sci. Am.* **197**, 73–84 (1957).

P. J. Potter, *Power Plant Theory and Design*, 2nd ed., Ronald Press Co., New York, 1959.

J. K. Salisbury, *Steam Turbines and Their Cycles*, John Wiley & Sons, Inc., New York, 1950.

B. G. A. Skrotzki and W. A. Vopat, *Power Station Engineering and Economy*, McGraw-Hill Book Co., Inc., New York, 1960.

B. G. A. Skrotzki and W. A. Vopat, *Steam and Gas Turbines*, McGraw-Hill Book Co., Inc., New York, 1950.

C. W. Smith, *Aircraft Gas Turbines*, John Wiley & Sons, Inc., New York, 1956.

W. Staniar, *Prime Movers*, McGraw-Hill Book Co., Inc., New York, 1966.

A. Stodola, *Steam and Gas Turbines* (trans. by L. C. Lowenstein), McGraw-Hill Book Co., Inc., New York, 1927.

C. F. Taylor and E. S. Taylor, *The Internal Combustion Engine*, 2nd ed., International Textbook Co., Scranton, Pa., 1966.

E. T. Vincent, *The Theory and Design of Gas Turbines and Jet Engines*, McGraw-Hill Book Co., Inc., New York, 1950.

M. J. Zucrow, *Aircraft and Missile Propulsion*, John Wiley & Sons, Inc., New York, 1958.

R. A. BUDENHOLZER
American Power Conference
Illinois Institute of Technology

PRASEODYMIUM, Pr. See Rare earth elements.

PRECIPITATION HARDENING. See Metal treatments.

PRESSURE MEASUREMENT

Knowledge of the pressure existing in a pipeline, tank, process tower, boiler, molding press, airplane cabin, space cabin, and many other units is an absolute necessity in most phases of industry, and in research and development.   Knowledge of the pressure data enables the engineer to operate within safe design limits, and the researcher to establish the optimum conditions for product yield and product quality.

Pressure Terms

Pressure is defined as force per unit of area.   It can be expressed in a wide range of units; Table 1 gives interconversion factors among lb/in.^{2} (psi), kg/cm^2, mm Hg (Torr), in. Hg, ft of water, and cm of water.

Table 1. Conversion Table of Pressure Units Based on Water at 60°F (62.367 lb/ft^3) and Hg at 60°F (846.32 lb/ft^3)[a]

Known pressure unit	lb/in.^{2} (psi)	kg/cm^2	mm head Hg (Torr)	in. head Hg	ft head of water	cm head of water
cm head of water	0.014209	0.00099902	0.73691	0.029012	0.032808	
ft head of water	0.43310	0.030451	22.461	0.88430		30.480
in. head Hg	0.48977	0.034434	25.400		1.1308	34.468
mm head Hg (Torr)	0.019282	0.0013557		0.039370	0.044521	1.3570
kg/cm^2	14.223		737.63	29.041	32.840	1001.0
lb/in.^{2} (psi)		0.070309	51.862	2.0418	2.3089	70.376

[a] Multiply known pressure units by factors given to obtain the required pressure units.

Atmospheric pressure (barometric pressure) is the pressure exerted by the column of air on the earth's surface, at a specified place and time.   It varies with elevation above and below sea level and with weather conditions.   To eliminate the normal ex-

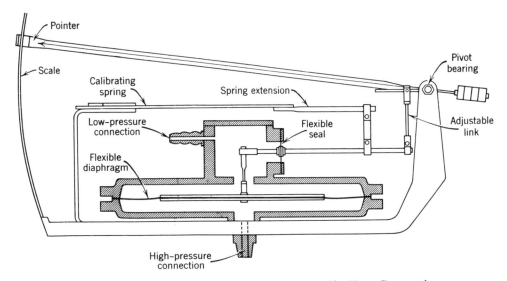

Fig. 1.   Slack-diaphragm pressure gage.   Courtesy The Hays Corporation.

isting variables, a *standard* or *normal atmosphere* having a pressure of 1,013,250 dyn/cm² has been established. This is equal to the pressure exerted by a column of mercury 760 mm high, at a temperature of 0°C, or 29.921 in. Hg, or 14.696 psi.

Absolute pressure is the pressure measured from zero pressure. But pressure gages frequently read in *gage pressure*, or *vacuum pressure* (see Vacuum technique). Gage pressure is equal to the absolute pressure minus the atmospheric pressure; this is convenient when a vessel is under a moderate pressure in excess of the ambient atmospheric pressure. It is often reported in lb/in.² *gage*, psig. The expression psia is often used when it is desired to emphasize that the measurement is absolute. A gage reading vacuum pressure reports the amount by which the pressure on it is less than atmospheric. A compound gage can register either gage or vacuum pressure.

Torr. This International Standard unit is now used for reporting less-than-atmospheric pressures on an absolute basis. It is equal to $1/760$ of a standard atmosphere, or 1 mm Hg.

Expressions such as "low," "medium," or "high," applied to pressure or vacuum, have come to designate ranges approximately as follows:

Pressure	*Gage pressure, psig*	*Vacuum*	*Vacuum pressure, Torr*
very high	over 5,000 (can be up to 100,000 or even higher)	low	25–760
		medium	10^{-3}–25
		high	10^{-6}–10^{-3}
high	500–5,000	very high	10^{-9}–10^{-6}
medium	50–500	ultra high	0–10^{-9}
low	0–50		

Elements for Pressure Measurement

Pressures and/or vacuums are generally measured by means of mechanical direct actuated elements. When measurement of very high pressures or vacuums between absolute zero and 25 Torr (25 mm Hg) are required, specialized elements are necessary. Most of the elements in use are described and many of them are illustrated in the subsequent sections.

The mechanical direct actuated pressure elements are the diaphragm, inverted bell, diaphragm capsule, bourdon tube including spirals and helixes, spring and bellows, and absolute pressure gage. The specialized units are the strain gage, electromagnetic, piezoelectric, thermoelectric, and ionization sensors.

Diaphragm Pressure Elements. A diaphragm is a pressure element which moves in a direction perpendicular to its flexible surface. Diaphragms may be fabricated from natural materials or from various synthetic materials including metals. They may be substantially flat or have one or many convolutions in their surfaces. The thinner the diaphragm material and the larger its effective area (pressure area) the lower the pressure range it can measure. In the design of this type of element, and in fact of all pressure elements, it is essential that the movement of the element always be less than the movement which would exceed the elastic limit of the diaphragm material. Exceeding the elastic limit would result in a permanent set or stretch of the diaphragm with resulting shift and error in the pressure measurement.

Figure 1 illustrates a typical arrangement for a direct-deflection type of diaphragm-actuated pressure gage. The process pressure produces a force which moves the diaphragm and its linkage into the cantilever spring to which is attached the pointer or pen arm to indicate or record the pressure.   The pressure range can be changed by increasing or decreasing the gradient of the cantilever spring.   This type of element is supplied for pressure ranges from 0–0.2 to 0–120 in. of water.   To protect against overload pressures, the clearance between the diaphragm and its housing is small enough to prevent any excessive movement of the diaphragm.

Inverted-Bell-Type Pressure Element.   Figure 2 shows a cross-sectional view of an inverted-bell-type pressure indicator.   This unit is made up of two inverted bells, partly immersed in oil which acts as a liquid seal, supported at their upper ends on a balanced pivoted beam.   The process pressure is introduced under the bell on the

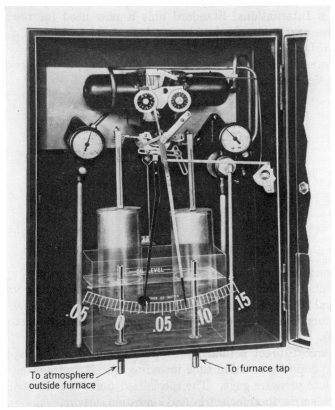

Fig. 2. Balanced-beam bell-type pressure gage.

right-hand side and atmospheric pressure is under the bell on the left-hand side.   An increase in process pressure forces the right-hand bell to rise and, through a suitable linkage, connects to a pointer or pen arm to indicate or record the pressure.   The two-bell arrangement permits lower pressure ranges and compensation for ambient pressure changes.   The available ranges are from about 0–0.2 to 0–10 in. of water.   A single-bell version can be supplied for ranges from about 0–0.6 to 0–10 in. of water. Both types of gage can be used on gage pressure, gage vacuum, or compound ranges. When subjected to overload pressures, these gages will lose their oil if a fast, large overload is applied, or if the overload is applied slowly, the bell will lift out of the oil seal and vent the process pressure.

Fig. 3. Diaphragm capsule pressure element.

Diaphragm Capsule Pressure Element. This pressure element is made up of two or more circular formed metal diaphragms which are welded together at both their inner and outer edges around their complete periphery. Figure 3 shows a typical assembly. The fabricated unit becomes a flexible sac or container, sealed off at one end and open to a connecting tube at the other end for the process pressure connection. The diameter and number of diaphragms used to make up the complete unit depend on the material of the diaphragm and the pressure range desired. The process pressure is applied to the inside of the capsule through the connecting tube; it expands the capsule with a resulting movement at the closed end. The actuating linkage for the pointer or pen arm is attached to this closed end. Diaphragm capsules are used for pressure ranges from 0–10 in. of water to 0–100 psi. The materials may be phosphor bronze, stainless steel, or alloys of any type.

Bourdon Tube Pressure Elements. A bourdon tube is made from a flattened or elliptical tube, with one end sealed shut and the other end opened to the process pressure through a connecting tubing. The final shape of the tube along with the amount of flatness determines the trade name of the element and identifies the overall shape and form. There are spiral-, helix-, and "C"-type bourdon tubes.

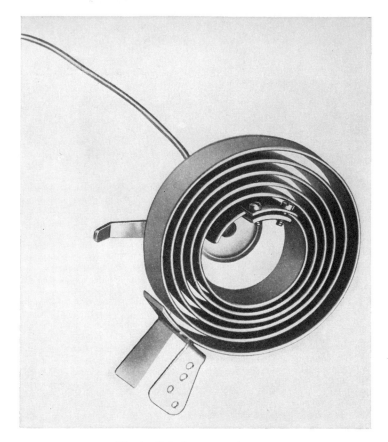

Fig. 4. Spiral pressure element.

Figure 4 shows a spiral and Figure 5 shows a helix. These elements are made from a thin-wall tube which is flattened to produce a long, narrow elliptical cross section. It is then formed into a spiral or helix as illustrated. When the process pressure is applied through the connecting tube, the resulting force tends to uncoil or straighten out the tubing. The rotating motion of the spiral or helix through a suitable linkage arrangement can be used to actuate a pointer or pen arm. The spiral is normally used for pressure ranges from 0–20 to 0–4000 psi, and the helix from 0–100 to 0–100,000 psi. The material used may be bronze, steel, stainless steel, or special alloys.

Figure 6 shows a "C"-type bourdon tube. This also is made from a thin-wall tube which may be flattened a small amount or a large amount, depending on the material and the pressure range. The tubing is formed into a "C" shape, with one end closed and free to move, and the other end fixed and opened to a connecting tube for the process pressure. The force from the applied pressure tends to straighten out the tube, thus producing tip travel. A suitable linkage will transfer this tip travel to a pointer or pen arm. These elements are used for pressures from 0–15 to 0–10,000 psi. The material used is bronze, steel, stainless steel, or special alloys.

Spring-and-Bellows Pressure Elements. Figure 7 shows a cross section of a spring-and-bellows pressure element. The bellows is formed from a length of thin-wall tubing by hydraulic extrusion in a die. This bellows is enclosed in a metal shell which

Fig. 5. Helix pressure element.

is connected by tubing to the process pressure. A compression-type spring is mounted inside the bellows resting against its bottom and restrained at the top by a form-fitted nut. A rod resting on the bottom of the bellows transmits any vertical motion of the bellows through a suitable linkage arrangement into a pointer or pen readout. As the process pressure inside the metal shell is increased, the bellows moves vertically upward and compresses the spring. The bellows-spring gradient is small compared to the spring gradient so that the pressure range is a function of the spring gradient only. A spring-and-bellows pressure element can be used on pressure ranges from about 0–5 in. of water to 0–50 psig. The lower pressures require bellows of a larger diameter than the higher pressures. The bellows is usually made of phosphor bronze or stainless steel but can also be supplied in many special metals.

Absolute Pressure Gage Element. When industrial process "low-vacuum" measurements are required, between 0–100 mm Hg and 0–30 in. Hg abs, it is frequently necessary to compensate for the normal variations in atmospheric or barometric pressure. Figure 8 shows a spring-and-bellows element which automatically compensates for the barometric pressure changes. The element includes a double bellows arrangement with both bellows fixed at the top and bottom and the adjacent end of each bellows attached to a movable plate, which transmits the bellows movement through a suitable linkage to a pointer or pen. The upper bellows is evacuated to a near perfect vacuum (absolute zero) and is then sealed off. The process vacuum is applied to the lower bellows, which then tends to collapse (close) the lower bellows, moving the center plate down. If the barometric or atmospheric pressure changes, the upper bellows will expand or contract, depending on any decrease or increase in the barometer. The bellows may be made of phosphor bronze or stainless steel.

Differential Pressure Gage Element (Meter Body). The formed bellows, diaphragm capsule, and single diaphragm are all used in the differential-pressure type of meter bodies. These units can be used to measure differences in pressure between two pipes, two stills, etc, from 0–1 in. of water up to 0–700 psi and with operating pressures as great as 10,000 psig. Figure 9 illustrates a formed-bellows-actuated meter body. The high-pressure and low-pressure bellows are joined together by means of the center stem assembly. The entire volume inside the bellows is filled with liquid and sealed off. When the process pressure at the high-pressure tap is greater than the process pressure at the low-pressure tap, the high-pressure bellows moves to the right and, through the center stem and liquid fill, moves the low-pressure bellows to the

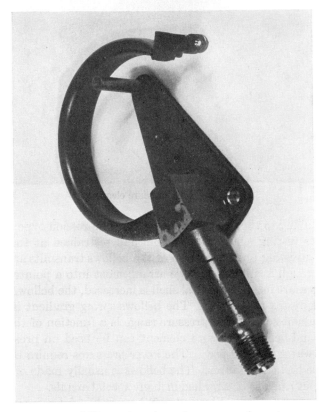

Fig. 6. "C"-type bourdon tube pressure element.

right. Motion stops when the force on the range spring equals the force of the differential pressure (difference between the high-pressure and low-pressure process pressure). The cable and motion take-off arm translate the center stem movement to the torque tube and this connects to a linkage mechanism for positioning the pointer or pen arm.

Installation and Maintenance of Pressure Gages. The industrial pressure gages must be protected from excessive overload pressures, high process temperatures, and corrosive or solid entrained fluids which would deteriorate or clog up the pressure element. The instruction data supplied with the gage will outline exactly what precautions must be taken on the specific unit used.

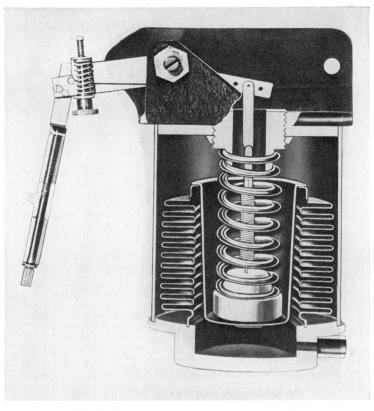

Fig. 7. Spring-and-bellows pressure element.

In checking the accuracy of a pressure gage, a primary standard or a certified secondary standard pressure unit must be employed. A primary standard would be a dead-weight tester for pressures of 20 psig and higher, and a "U"-tube manometer would be required for pressures of 1 in. of water to 20 psig. A secondary standard would be a high-precision bourdon tube pressure gage with certified accuracy of calibration and pressure ranges of 20 psig and higher, and a certified accuracy precision well-type manometer for pressures of 1 in. of water to 20 psig.

Specialized Types of Pressure Elements. All of the previously described pressure elements can be combined with various pneumatic and electrical devices to provide pressure transducers. The pneumatic transducers operate from a 20-psi pressure, clean air supply into a fixed nozzle, and a movable flapper system. The process pressure element, through a mechanism, sets the flapper in relation to the nozzle such that at minimum process pressure the space between the nozzle and flapper is maximum and the output pressure is minimum (3 psig). With maximum process pressure the space is minimum and the output is maximum (15 psig). A normal full-scale travel of the flapper is about 0.003 in.

In the electric transducers, some of the sensors used are strain gage, thermoelectric, and ionization. There are numerous other types which are somewhat specialized and will only be mentioned here. They are ultrasonic, electromagnetic, piezoelectric, capacitance, variable reluctance, variable permeability, vibrating wire, and photo-electric.

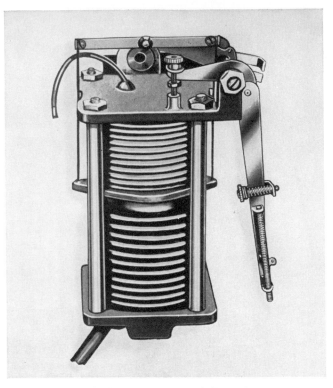

Fig. 8. Absolute pressure gage bellows element.

The *strain gage* consists of a small wire grid bonded to a plastic impregnated paper or cloth which is then cemented to the surface of the process pressure sensing device (usually a diaphragm). When the process pressure is applied, the resulting force moves the diaphragm, which produces a change in the length and diameter of the wire, changing its electrical resistance. This change in resistance is a measure of the force or pressure applied. A precision dc or ac resistance-bridge type of instrument must be used to measure this resistance change in equivalent pressure units. These sensors are used on pressures of 1 psi and greater.

The thermoelectric and ionization sensors are used primarily for the measurement of ultra high, very high, and high vacuums. The *thermoelectric* sensor operates on the principle that the heat loss from a hot wire varies as the pressure of the gas or vapor surrounding the hot wire varies. This variation in heat loss with pressure is relatively large in the high vacuum ranges for which it is used.

Figure 10 illustrates a resistance-bridge type of thermoelectric sensor where the heat lost by the coil of resistance wire in the measuring cell is indicated directly by resistance change in a leg of the bridge circuit. The compensating cell contains a second coil of resistance wire and this is sealed off at a pressure well below 1 Torr abs. This coil is designed so that changes in its resistance with temperature change will balance those changes in the measuring cell resistance and thus automatically compensates for temperature variations.

Figure 11 shows the diagram of a thermocouple type of thermoelectric sensor. The filaments are continuously and uniformly heated by means of the constant voltage

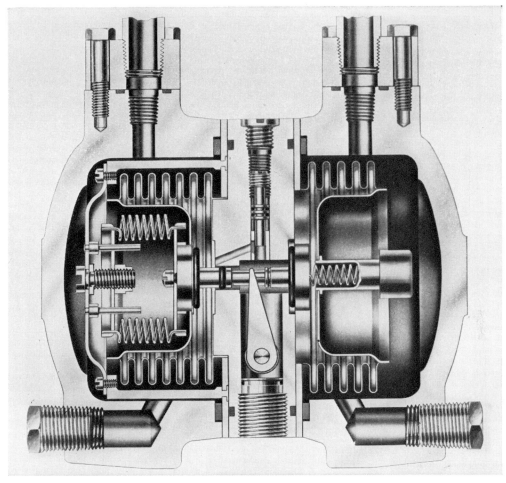

Fig. 9.   Differential pressure gage element—bellows type.

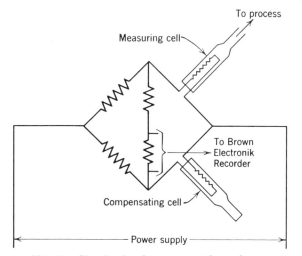

Fig. 10.   Circuit of resistance-type thermal gage.

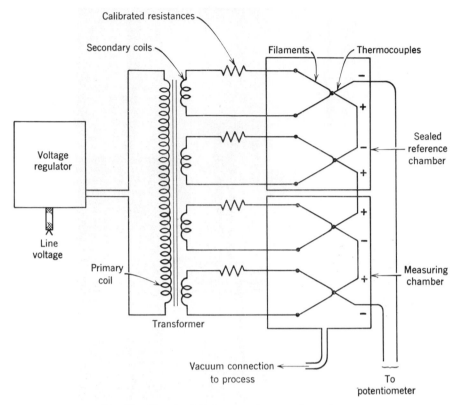

Fig. 11. Circuit of thermocouple-type thermal gage.

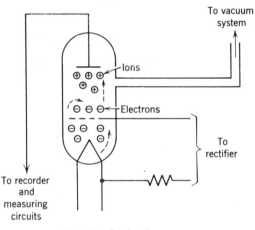

Fig. 12. Ionization gage.

regulator and transformer. There are two sections, a sealed one under high vacuum and a second one connected to the process pressure. A small sensitive thermocouple is located on each of the filaments and each pair of couples are connected in series to increase the generated emf. The two thermocouples in the reference chamber are connected in opposition to the two in the measuring chamber. Thus, their generated emf's oppose each other. This difference in emf is a measure of the difference in pressure between the reference chamber and the measuring chamber. This type of sensor is used in the high and medium vacuum ranges.

The *ionization* sensor is illustrated in Figure 12. The operation is based on the ability of electrons emitted from a hot filament to bombard the molecules of the residual gas in an evacuated system, forming an electric current flow from the resulting ions. The magnitude of the current flow is directly proportional to the number of ions formed. This is an indication of the amount of gas present, which is a measure of the vacuum pressure. The sensor is essentially a triode tube and the electron emission from the cathode is held constant by a precision bridge circuit. The electrons are attracted to the grid, which is at a high positive potential with respect to the cathode, and the momentum of the electrons carries them past the grid to the plate. The plate is held at a negative potential with respect to the grid and repels the electrons, driving them among the molecules of the gas. This bombardment of the gas causes ions to form and, with an existing potential difference, the ions are attracted to the plate, and the current flow is proportional to the number of ions formed. The current flow is proportional to the amount of gas present, actually the number of molecules present, and the magnitude of the current flow is a measure of the vacuum. Ionization sensors are used in ultra high and very high vacuums and must be protected against too high pressures, which would burn out their filaments.

Bibliography

American Society of Mechanical Engineers, *High Pressure Measurement Symposium, New York, 1962*, Butterworth Inc., Washington D.C., 1963.

T. G. Beckwith, and L. N. Buck, *Mechanical Measurements*, Addison-Wesley Publishing Co., Inc., Reading, Mass., 1961.

G. C. Carroll, *Industrial Process Measuring Instruments*, McGraw-Hill Book Co., Inc., New York, 1962.

D. M. Considine, *Process Instruments and Controls Handbook*, McGraw-Hill Book Co., Inc., New York, 1957.

"Diaphragms Sense Pressure in Four New Techniques," *Prod. Eng.* **38**, 40–42 (March 13, 1967).

A. E. Fribance, *Industrial Instrumentation Fundamentals*, McGraw-Hill Book Co., Inc., New York, 1962.

Instrument Society of America, *ISA Transducer Compendium*, Plenum Press, Inc., New York, 1963.

"Pressure Sensing Takes on New Dimensions of Accuracy," *Prod. Eng.* **38**, 44–46 (Jan. 30, 1967).

NOTE: In addition, all of the major instrument manufacturers have available descriptive and instructive data on their pressure gages and transducers.

CHARLES F. CUSICK
Honeywell Inc.

PRESSURE VESSELS

In chemical processing industries two factors among others are outstanding, namely, the yield of the product and the speed at which the desired yield is attained. Among the conditions which will influence these factors, the most important are temperature and pressure. While the temperature range in which the desired yield may be obtained at reasonable speed is comparatively moderate, approx -100 to $4500°C$, the pressure range is enormously wider in industrial applications. For example, in the synthesis of acetylene from light hydrocarbon vapors, a pressure of less than 1 atm is preferred, while in the manufacture of synthetic diamonds a pressure of about 100,000 atm is required. Between these two extremes, the chemical processing industries have been using various pressures such as those given in Table 1.

Table 1. Pressures Used in Industrial Applications

Application	Pressure,[a] atm	Application	Pressure,[a] atm
nitric acid	1–10	methanol synthesis	50–350
synthetic ethanol	65–70	hydrogenation of coal	350–600
hydrogenation of vegetable oil	20–350	acetic acid synthesis	650–700
hydrogenation of petroleum distillates	200–350	ammonia synthesis	200–1,000
urea synthesis	200–400	polyethylene	50–2,000
oxo process	250–300	synthetic diamond	100,000–110,000

[a] Note that 1 atm = 14.7 psia.

There is no agreed-on dividing line between high and low pressures, but some authorities in the chemical processing industry consider any pressure above 50 atm (about 750 psia) is in the high-pressure field.

High-pressure technology concerns mainly (a) the production and maintenance of the pressure (see Pumps and compressors), (b) the design of vessels and other components of the system, and (c) provision for resistance to corrosion in a manner that is more precise than the practice used in dealing with ordinary pressures.

See also Pressure measurement.

Design and Fabrication of Pressure Vessels

With the advent of large capacity chemical plants, operating at high pressure levels, the size of individual vessels and accessories also increased in size to previously unknown regions, and the question of safety became extremely important. Even with normal-size vessels, safety should always be a mandatory consideration in designing, fabricating, testing, and operating a high-pressure vessel.

In designing a high-pressure vessel, the procedure may run as follows: The first step is to decide the size and shape of the vessel as required by functions which the vessel is to perform. Then comes the choice of materials of construction which will resist the attack by substances with which the vessel will come in contact. Next, provisions for heat transfer and temperature control should be worked out based on thermodynamics. The safe thicknesses of the vessel wall and other parts and attachments should then be calculated based on stresses in the vessel wall and the strength of the materials selected. The method of fabrication may be chosen according to the costs involved, but equally important considerations are those concerning transportation, including loading at the fabricator's shop and unloading at the plant site. Finally, the types of closures used may be selected. Detailed dimensions of the chosen closures should be worked out and checked for stresses at all vital points for safety.

Materials of Construction. High-strength weldable steels should be used in the construction of pressure vessels. Generally, smaller vessels are fabricated from low-carbon steels of intermediate strength that do not require special heat treatment. Larger and thicker vessels use steels that require quenching and tempering to increase the strength in the steel plates and in the finished vessel. It is very difficult to achieve a uniform heat treatment throughout the steel in a large pressure vessel. For this reason, various types of multilayer vessels use steels that do not require heat treatment to increase the mechanical strength. High-pressure vessels often require alloy protection on the inside surfaces to prevent corrosion. It is very difficult and expensive to provide alloy protection in solid forged or rolled-plate high-pressure vessels. In such cases, alloy weld overlay or clad plate must be used. Multilayer vessels can be fabricated readily with only the inner shell made of the high-cost corrosion-resisting material. The outer layers, built up by methods described below, may then be made of low-cost steel. The use of multilayer vessels for corrosive service is, therefore, preferred over solid-wall vessels.

Design Requirements and Criteria. Elaborate codes for pressure vessels have been approved and adopted by various authoritative bodies or regulatory agencies, such as the ASME Code, the British Standards, DIN (Germany), Service des Mines (France), and local codes issued by municipalities, states, etc. There are also proprietary design formulas as well as proprietary materials of construction which may be at variance with the established codes. If these are to be used, it is necessary to obtain permission from the regulatory agencies operating in the area. If there are no regulations at all in the area, then good commercial practice would be to design the vessel using a safety factor of 3.0–3.5 based on ultimate strength, or a safety factor of 2.0 based on yield strength of the material, and using the recommendations contained in a suitable code selected for the project as far as possible.

According to the recommendations in the ASME Code (1), the minimum wall thickness of a pressure vessel may be calculated by the following formulas:

$$t = \frac{PR}{SE - 0.6\,P} \tag{1}$$

(for cylindrical vessels when P does not exceed $0.385\,SE$);

$$t = \frac{PR}{2\,SE - 0.2\,P} \tag{2}$$

(for spherical vessels when P does not exceed $0.665\,SE$);

$$t = R\left[\left(\frac{SE + P}{SE - P}\right)^{1/2} - 1\right] \tag{3}$$

(for cylindrical vessels when P exceeds $0.385\,SE$);

$$t = R\left[\left(\frac{2\,SE + 2\,P}{2\,SE - P}\right)^{1/2} - 1\right] \tag{4}$$

(for spherical vessels when P exceeds $0.665\,SE$).

In these formulas, t = thickness, in.; P = internal pressure, psia; R = inside radius of the vessel, in.; S = maximum allowable stress in the vessel wall, psi; and E = welding efficiency (see Welding). (The maximum value of E permitted by the code is nominally 0.8, but the technology of fabricating pressure vessels has advanced so much during recent years that the welding efficiency is actually close to 1.00 and an E value of 0.95 is now considered conservative.)

With the limitations as imposed by the factors $0.385\,SE$ and $0.665\,SE$, respectively, formulas 1 and 2, according to the ASME Code, would be applicable to pressures of up to 5000 psia for cylindrical vessels and up to 8680 psia for spherical vessels (assuming carbon steel SA-30, SA-201, or SA-285 is used without prestressing, a maximum allowable stress of 13,750, and a welding efficiency of 0.95). But if stronger steels are used, the S value will be larger, and the restrictions for the use of these formulas will be shifted to cover correspondingly higher pressures.

However, in spite of these provisions, designers of pressure vessels prefer other formulas for all vessels operating above 3000 psia. These formulas, mostly proprietary, have been carefully developed, tested, and proved to be reliable as well as economical.

In developing these formulas, to check them by rupture tests with semiplant-size vessels or laboratory models, such as described by Blair, Crossland, and others (2–4), is not satisfactory, because high-pressure vessels are never intended to be stressed anywhere near the rupture point. The behavior of a high-pressure vessel in the vicinity of the operating pressure is entirely different from that of the same vessel at rupture pressure. At or near the rupture pressure the metal in the wall is plastic, but at the normal operating pressure, the metal is elastic. The pressure should always be operated within the plastic limit of the metal, especially when the vessel wall is prestressed, as most modern pressure vessels are.

Furthermore, it is the stresses in the wall at and near the inside surface that are most important. The inside portion at the vessel wall, when it is not prestressed, often has unit stresses numerically much higher than the operating pressure, and the unit stress in the outer portion of the vessel wall is much smaller. The criterion of design is, therefore, to ascertain by calculation the unit stresses at all key points in the vessel wall, especially in the regions next to the inside surface and at the interface of the adjacent layers of a multilayer vessel, where there is prestress, and to see that at these points the unit stress not only does not exceed the yield strength of the material, but is well below it, preferably only one-half of it. The reason for this is given below.

In the ASME Code it is specified that a high-pressure vessel should be put to a hydrostatic test of at least 1.5 times the maximum operating pressure. If, in the design of the vessel, the maximum unit stress is set below the yield strength, but very close to it (say, 90% of it), the hydrostatic test would certainly exceed it as $0.90 \times 1.5 = 1.35$, that is, 35% above the yield strength. Under such a condition, the vessel will not fail, but most of the prestress in the inner layers of the vessel will be lost. This loss of prestress means that the safety factor of the vessel is reduced; and it cannot be restored throughout the life of the vessel.

The stresses at the inside surface of a high-pressure vessel are not simple stresses. They are the combinations of tangential stress (tensile), radial stress (compressive), longitudinal stress, and prestresses. To include these stresses in the calculation of the wall thickness for safe operation is mandatory but it is rather involved, especially in the case of the prestressed multilayer construction. Different authors have proposed different methods. One of the simpler methods is described by Timoshenko. Examples of calculations are given in his book (5).

FABRICATION OF PRESSURE VESSELS

There are six basic types of construction used for high-pressure vessels:

1. Solid-wall, forged.
2. Solid-wall, rolled-plate.
3. Multiwall, rolled-plate.
4. Multilayer.
5. Coil-layer.
6. Wrapped, interlocking bands.

Solid-Wall, Forged (see Fig. 1). When high-pressure processes were initially developed, the vessels were relatively small, design and fabrication were simple, and the vessels were forged. As the size of plants increased, the size of the vessels increased also until the practical forging limit (about 100 tons in weight) was reached. To meet the demand for still larger vessels, sections of the vessels were forged as rings which were then welded together to complete the fabrication. Economic factors, however, generally limit the use of forged vessels for high-pressure applications to small diameters and to weights of less than 150 tons.

Solid-Wall, Rolled-Plate (see Fig. 2). Solid-wall pressure vessels fabricated from thick plates bent into ring sections and welded longitudinally are used quite extensively for larger diameters and pressure applications generally below 4000 psi. To some degree they are limited by the strength of the plate and adequacy of welding, but the principal limitations are the availability of thick plates (approx 6 in., max) and the fabricator's capacity for bending these plates. The strength of the steel plates can be increased either by increasing the alloy content of the steel or by quenching and tempering. Fabrication difficulties increase with alloy content, and welding becomes more difficult. Preheating and postheating temperatures are greatly increased and the possibility of cracks in the welds and heat-affected zones is also increased. Quenching and tempering of a steel vessel can increase its strength, but achieving uniform physical properties in a large fabricated vessel becomes very difficult. These fabrication problems must be taken into consideration in selecting the materials of construction and the type of heat treatment for the equipment. High-pressure vessels of solid-wall, rolled-plate construction are used extensively for vessels weighing 50–500 tons.

Multiwall, Rolled-Plate (see Fig. 3). To avoid the problems inherent in the fabrication of thick solid-wall, rolled-plate vessels, multiwall vessels fabricated from rolled-plate cylinders are often used. There are essentially two methods of fabricating these vessels. One method consists of heating the sections of the outer cylindrical shell and shrinking them onto the sections of the inner cylindrical shell to produce prestressing. Multiwall shell sections and the end sections are then welded together to make the vessel. The second method consists of fabricating a complete pressure vessel by welding the various inner-shell sections to each other and to the vessel end sections and then hydraulically expanding the inner cylinder into the outer cylinder. In either method, an interfacial fit or interfacial pressure is achieved between inner and outer cylindrical sections. The thickness of each rolled-plate cylinder is in the range of 2–3 in., and generally the maximum number of cylinders that are shrunk together is four. The main disadvantage of this construction is that outer cylinders cannot be fabricated until after the inner cylinders are completed so that the proper interfacial fit can be achieved in shrinking or expanding operation. The size of the fabricator's heating furnace limits the size of the vessel in the shrunk-type construc-

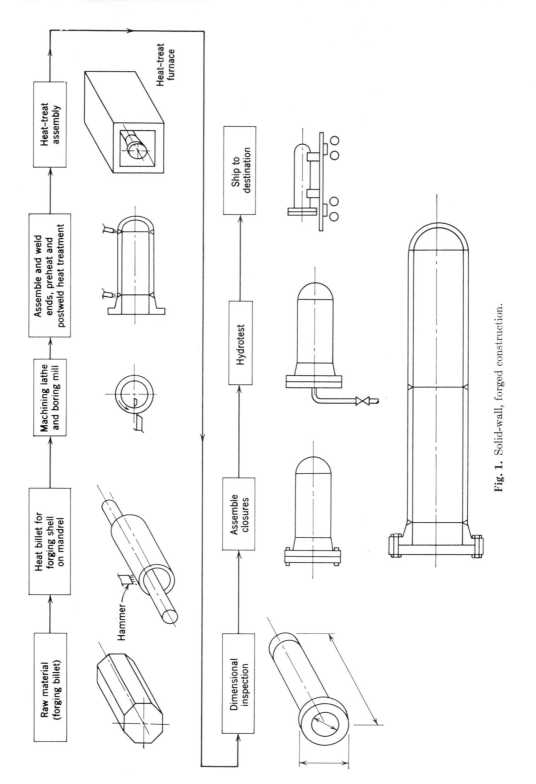

Fig. 1. Solid-wall, forged construction.

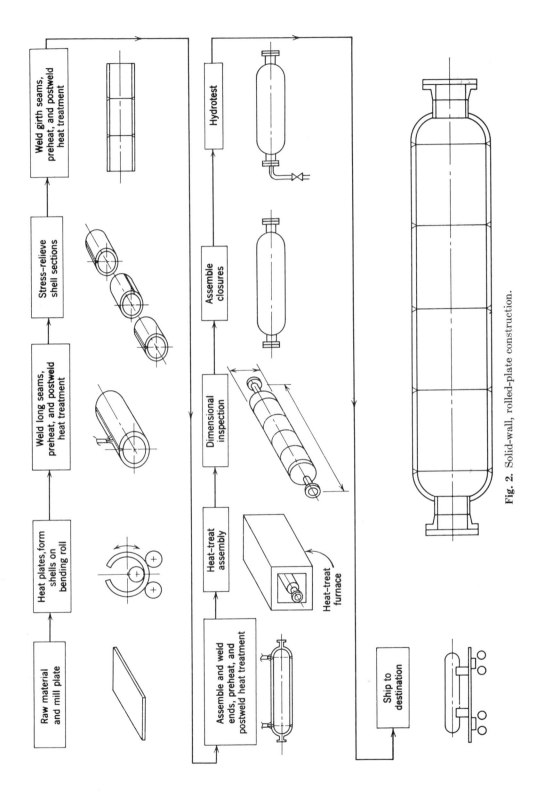

Fig. 2. Solid-wall, rolled-plate construction.

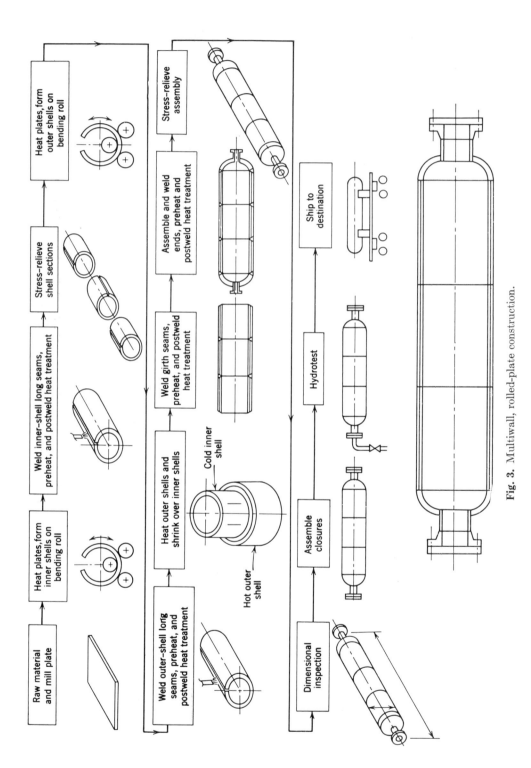

Fig. 3. Multiwall, rolled-plate construction.

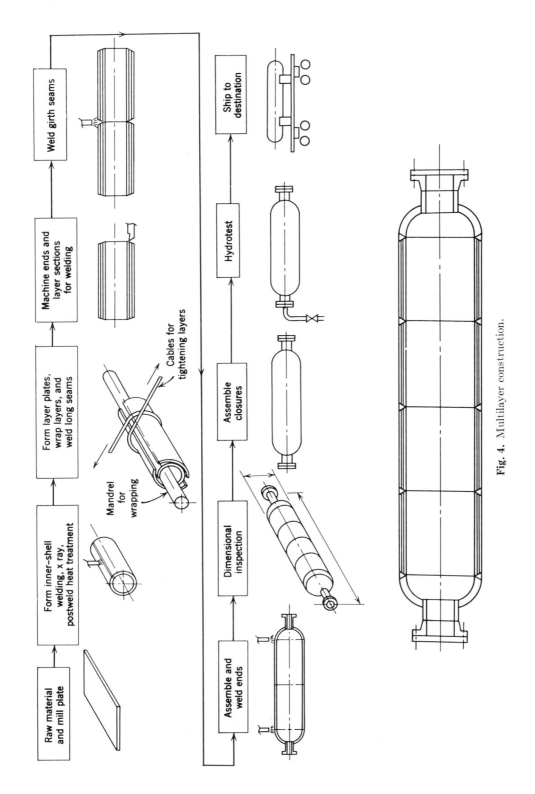

Fig. 4. Multilayer construction.

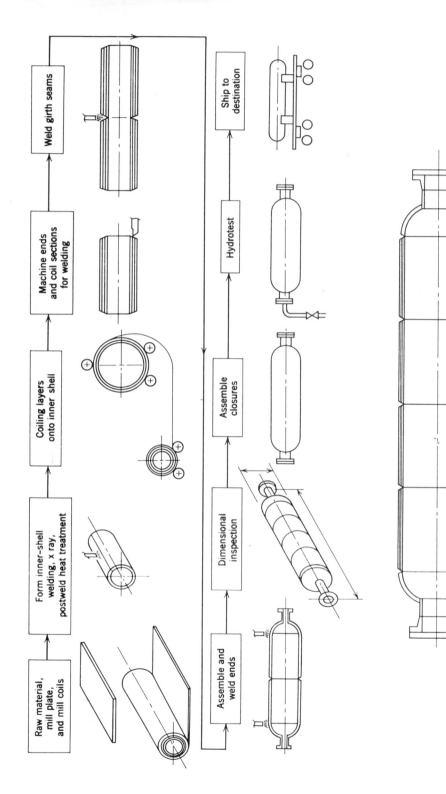

Fig. 5. Coil-layer construction.

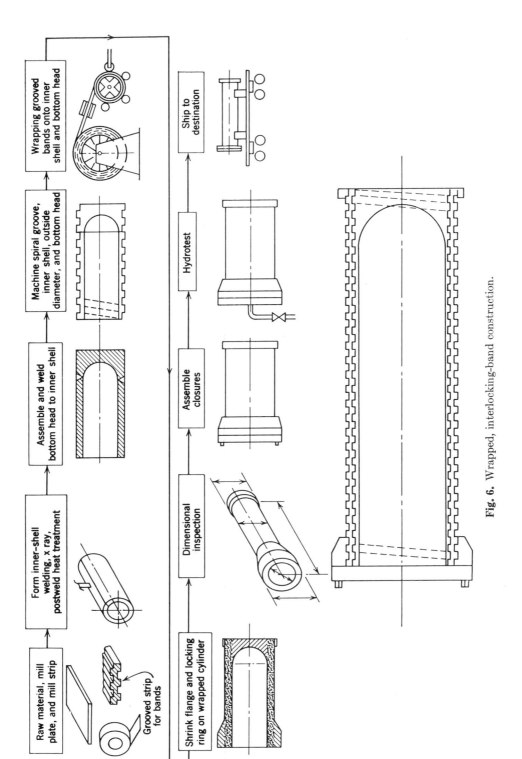

Fig. 6. Wrapped, interlocking-band construction.

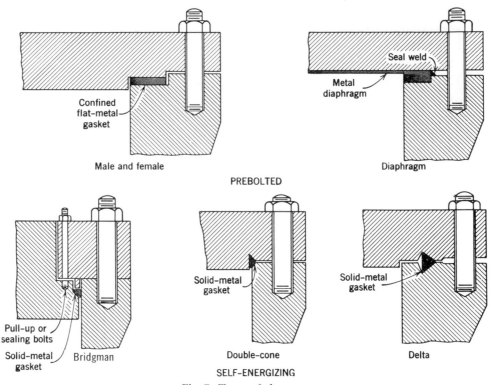

Fig. 7. Types of closures.

tion. In the hydraulic expansion process, pressures in the range of 10,000–20,000 psi must be used to expand the inner vessel hydraulically into the outer cylinders. Many vessels of the multiwall construction have been fabricated in sizes weighing 100–400 tons.

Multilayer (see Fig. 4). Multilayer vessels were developed in the 1930s when it became evident that the forging capacity of the steel industry could not meet demands of the chemical industry for high-pressure vessels and multiwall vessels were too expensive to fabricate. Multilayer construction consists of fabricating cylindrical shell sections that are built up of concentric 0.25–0.50-in. thick welded rings, each wrapped tightly around the core rings (the liner) and the successive rings until the desired thickness is obtained. This type of construction has several advantages. There is practically no limitation to the size of the vessel. Stress-relieving heat-treatment is not required and this permits field assembly and even field modifications.

Multilayer cylindrical shell sections are made by first fabricating an inner shell section approx 0.50 in. thick which can be made of any weldable material, ferrous or nonferrous. After the inner shell is fabricated, layer plates approx 0.25 in. thick are bent to conform to the outside radius of the inner shell and applied to it in one to three sections. These sections are then tightened to the inner shell by wrapping a steel cable or band completely around it and pulling the cable tight against the inner shell by hydraulic force applied to the ends of the cable. With the layer plates pulled tightly by the cable, longitudinal seams in the plates are welded. A combination of weld shrinkage in the longitudinal seams and the pressure exerted by the wrapping cable or band produces a precompression in all the layers except the last layer, on the outside, which is in tension. This method of fabrication produces a very uniform stress throughout the whole thickness of the wall of the vessel. Such multilayer vessels are used extensively in high-pressure service in sizes weighing from 50 to 600 tons and heavier.

Coil-Layer (see Fig. 5). Coil-layer vessel construction is a modification of multilayer design. It is now being successfully used in high-pressure processes. Coil-layer construction consists of fabricating cylindrical shell sections by tightly winding a sheet of continuous steel onto an inner shell until the desired wall thickness is achieved. Advantages of this construction are essentially the same as for the multilayer construction. Sheet steel used for this purpose is in long sheets, about $\frac{1}{8}$ in. thick and 5 ft wide. When the desired thickness is attained, rolling is continued so that further tightening of the layers and a precompression in the layers are obtained. The result is equivalent to that attained in multilayer construction. Coil-layer vessels are used in sizes weighing from 50 to 600 tons.

Wrapped Interlocking Bands (see Fig. 6). Another modification to the multilayer construction was the development of the wrapped, interlocking-bands vessels (6,7). This method was developed in Germany just before World War II and was used fairly extensively throughout Europe. This construction consists of fabricating an inner shell and attaching it to the bottom section of the vessel. This subassembly is then placed in a lathe and three parallel spiral grooves are machined on the outside of the inner-shell and bottom-section assembly. A continuous strip with grooves on both sides is then heated and wound around the shell. In the winding operation, the strip is pressed into the grooves by special contoured pressure rollers and then quenched. The procedure is continued until the desired thickness is attained. Upon completion of the winding, a flange is shrunk over the upper end of the cylinder and a forged locking ring is shrunk over the other end at the wrapped bottom section. Wrapped, interlocking-bands vessels are built to a maximum length of about 60 ft and an outside diameter of about 6 ft with operation pressure up to 10,300 psia (700 atm).

Closures (see Fig. 7). For the closures of the high-pressure vessels, welded end closures and bolted closures may be used. Welded end closures consist of formed ellipsoidal or hemispherical heads of forged or formed plate construction. These heads are welded to the cylindrical shell section of the vessel in a fabricator's shop. Welded end closures are used when it is not necessary to remove or replace internals. Bolted closures are generally made of one of the following designs that have proved successful in operation at high pressures: (a) simple bolted closure that requires the bolt to be stressed so that when the internal pressure is acting on the closure, sufficient gasket load remains to prevent leaking; or (b) self-sealing closure that requires prebolting to seal the gasket at low pressure and seals itself as the internal pressure increases. Generally the self-sealing type of closure requires much more precise machining to produce the narrower tolerances that are desired.

Shipment and Erection. The simplest way to furnish a high-pressure vessel is as a shop-fabricated unit shipped in one piece. Most fabricators can shop-fabricate vessels up to 400 tons. Shipping of one-piece shop-fabricated vessels is limited by the outside diameter and for most locations this is approx 12 ft. Erection of one-piece vessels on the foundation is relatively simple when appropriate and adequate hoisting equipment is available. If the fabrication, shipping, or lifting limitations are exceeded, the vessel must be fabricated in sections and shipped in pieces for field assembly. The problems involved in the field assembly of a high-pressure vessel are quite extensive. Welding of the thick shell seams requires preheating and the seam cannot be positioned for ideal welding conditions. After the completion of welding, the assembled vessel must be stress-relieved, x-rayed, and hydrostatically tested.   Use of multilayer vessels for field fabrication greatly reduces these problems.

Bibliography

"Pressure Technique" in *ECT* 1st ed., Vol. 11, pp. 100–114, by Roger Williams, Jr., Roger Williams Technical & Economic Services, Inc.

1. *Am. Soc. Mech. Engrs. Boiler and Pressure Vessel Code*, Sect. VIII, 1965, pp. 9–10, 41, 170–171.
2. J. S. Blair, *Engineering* **170,** 218 (1950).
3. B. Crossland and S. A. Bones, *Engineering* **179,** 80–83, 114–117 (1955).
4. B. Crossland, S. M. Jorgensen, and S. A. Bones, *Am. Soc. Mech. Engrs., Trans.* **81,** 95–114 (May 1959).
5. S. Timoshenko, *Strength of Materials*, Part II, 3rd ed., D. Van Nostrand Co., Inc., Princeton, N.J., 1956, pp. 205–214.
6. U.S. Pat. 2,326,176 (Aug. 10, 1943), J. Schierenbeck.
7. J. F. Ellis, *U.S. Bur. Mines, Inf. Circ. 7375* (1946).

SAMUEL STRELZOFF AND B. C. WALTON
Chemical Construction Corporation

PRIMING COMPOSITIONS. See under Explosives, Vol. 8, p. 652.

PRINTING INK. See Inks.

PRINTING PROCESSES

Johannes Gutenberg is generally credited with being the inventor of printing in the Western world, about 1450 AD. Actually, movable type was used to print from plates on a press many years earlier by the Chinese, Japanese, and Koreans. What Gutenberg contributed to printing was the realization of its cultural and commercial possibilities and bringing to western civilization the integrated concept of using movable type to print on paper with ink on a press. This raised the level of publishing books from the slow laborious practice of handwriting to a practical production process. It is considered to be one of the main factors that advanced civilization from the Dark and Middle Ages, when knowledge was restricted to the privileged few, to modern times when education is available to all. From hand-set type we have advanced to machine composition and even computer-set type.

The graphic arts are now a big industry. As a whole it has a growth rate similar to that of the gross national product, or about 4% a year. However, the growth rate for book printing, packaging, lithography, and color printing is about double this. In many of the large cities and states of the U.S., such as New York, Illinois, and California, printing ranks among the leading industries. Among all U.S. industries in 1966 it ranked third in the number of industrial establishments, sixth in payroll paid, and seventh in value added by manufacture, which is a value exclusive of the cost of materials used. According to official statistics of the Printing and Publishing section of the U.S. Department of Commerce, the printing and publishing industry in 1966 produced products valued at over $20.2 billion (1). Packaging, which also uses the printing processes extensively, produced another $17 billion of shipments. Newspapers had shipments valued at over $5.5 billion; magazines and other periodicals over $2.7 billion; books $2.7 billion; and the value of shipments for commercial and advertising printing was about $6.2 billion. The remaining $3.1 billion represented printing for business forms, checks, greeting cards, maps, art reproduction, and other specialties. These amounts do not include the printing done as office duplicating (see Reprography).

Printing Processes. There are four major printing processes, *(1) relief* or *letterpress*, *(2) intaglio* or *gravure*, *(3) planographic* or *lithography*, and *(4) stencil* or *porous* printing. These are illustrated in Figure 1.

Letterpress traditionally excelled in the reproduction of text matter, and the meaning of the word "printing" was formerly confined to this process. Recent improvements in the other processes have made it possible for them to produce text matter equivalent in quality to letterpress, and the term "printing" has now come to embrace reproduction by all four of these processes.

In *relief* printing the image or printing area is raised above the nonprinting area. Ink is applied to the raised surface which is brought into direct contact with the paper or other surface to be printed on. Relief printing or letterpress is the process by which

Fig. 1. The four major printing processes: relief (letterpress), intaglio (gravure), planographic (lithography), and porous (screen process) (30). Courtesy The Printing Industries of America.

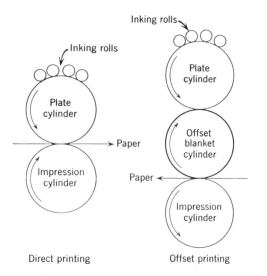

Fig. 2. Printing cycle for direct and offset printing.

this book is printed. This process is also used for magazines, newspapers, advertising brochures, etc. Hand-set or machine-set cast-metal type can be used for direct printing, but for long runs it is usual to prepare, by means to be discussed later, *printing plates* or engravings from the type. Plates are made of all illustrative material to be printed. The printing plates can be zinc, magnesium, or copper, and may be plated with nickel or chromium. They may also be of plastic. When rubber plates and water-base or solvent-type inks are used, the process is called *flexography*. *Letterset* is the name used when relatively thin relief plates are used for printing by the offset principle (described below). See also Type metal.

In the *intaglio* process the nonprinting area is at a common surface level and the printing area is recessed and consists of wells etched or engraved to different depths. The most common method of intaglio printing is gravure. Solvent-type inks with the consistency of light cream are transferred to the whole surface and a metal "doctor" blade, or a special wiping paper, is used to remove the excess ink from the nonprinting surface. Gravure is used to print longrun magazines, catalogs, newspaper supplements, preprints for newspapers, and plastic laminates. Paper currency, stock and bond certificates, stamps, some greeting cards, letterheads, business cards, and other specialties are printed by the intaglio process, which is also called steel die and copper-plate engraving. In these methods a special wiping paper is used to clean the plate instead of a doctor blade.

In the *planographic* or lithographic process the image and nonimage areas are on the same plane, but the image area is grease-receptive and water-repellent, the non-image area water-receptive and grease-repellent. The ink therefore adheres only to the image areas, from which it is transferred to the surface to be printed, usually by the offset method (see below). This process is used for printing general commercial literature, books, catalogs, greeting cards, letterheads, business forms, checks, art reproductions, labels, packages, etc.

In the *stencil* or *screen* process a stencil representing the nonprinting areas is applied to a silk or stainless steel fine-mesh screen to which ink with the consistency of paint is applied and transferred to the surface to be printed by scraping with a rubber squeegee. This process is used for printing displays, posters, signs, instrument dials, etc.

Printing Methods. When the image is transferred directly from the image carrier to the paper it is known as *direct printing*. Most letterpress and gravure and all screen process printing is done in this way. In *indirect* or *offset* printing the image is transferred from the image carrier to an intermediate rubber-covered cylinder from which it is transferred to the paper (see Fig. 2). Most lithography is printed this way so that lithography is often referred to as "offset printing." Letterpress and gravure can also be printed by the offset method. The development of the offset principle, and a discussion of its advantages, is given below under History of lithography (p. 528).

By far the greatest number of plates and image carriers for the printing process are made by *photomechanical* means. These are systems that involve photographic images and light-sensitive coatings which, with chemical etching or other treatment, lead to a printing surface.

The Original

The first step in all printing processes is to prepare the original, or copy, to be reproduced. This can be in many and varied forms, consisting of type matter and/or pictures.

In some cases the original can be produced directly on the plate surface as in stone lithography, linoleum blocks, steel die and copperplate engraving, and screen process printing. In all other printing the original is converted to some other form by mechanical or photomechanical means.

A vast amount of printing begins with the operation known as type setting, which can be done by hand (much as Johannes Gutenberg did it) or by machine. The second major milestone in the printing industry was reached when Ottmar Mergenthaler invented the *Linotype* machine in 1886. This is known as a line-casting machine because it casts a slug or line of type at a time. The Intertype (Harris Industries, Inc.), invented in 1911, is a similar machine. The *Monotype* machine, invented by Tolbert Lanston in 1887, casts single characters at a time from tape punched on a special keyboard by machine. Line-casting machines can also be operated by punched tape. The tape can be punched on special machines or on a computer. All these processes, referred to as *hot-metal* processes, result in raised cast-metal type consisting of an alloy of lead, tin, and antimony known as *type metal* (qv).

As distinguished from hot-metal type there is another form of type composition commonly called *cold type*. This term embraces all forms of type composition not represented by cast metal. It includes composition for reproduction produced on ordinary typewriters, using special carbon paper ribbons, or special typewriters like the Varityper (Varityper Corp.) or Justowriter (Friden Co., Inc.); phototypesetting machines like the Harris-Intertype Fotosetter or Photon Zip, and even the high-speed computer typesetters using Charactron (General Dynamic Electronics) tubes and capable of setting type at speeds of over 1000 characters per second, like the Mergenthaler-CBS Linotron and RCA Videocomp (1a).

The hot-metal type as set can be locked up in a special device called a chase and used on a flat bed or platen press for direct printing by letterpress. For using other methods of printing, an inked proof is pulled from the locked-up type form, using a proof press. This becomes the photographic copy that is needed to make the photomechanical printing plates. Cold type necessarily is handled in this way.

Pictorial Originals. Pictures or illustrations can be pen and ink sketches; line drawings; black-and-white photographs; color photographs; color films or transparencies; paintings made with oils, water colors, pastel crayons, or egg tempera; etc (2). All these originals must be photographed to convert them into the proper positive or negative films for the photomechanical plate processes by which they will be reproduced. Mechanically or photographically produced conversions of already existing printing, type, or printing plates can also be used as copy to produce plates for printing by another printing process. For example, advertisements or articles printed in a magazine by letterpress are often reprinted by lithography for special use or distribution. Offset duplicating of letters, magazine articles, etc, is another example.

Copy Assembly. To produce a satisfactory printed result the copy must be clean, sharp, in focus, square, in the right position, and at the correct size. If the printed job consists of combinations of type and pictorial matter, it can be pasted up before photography, provided everything is in the correct size proportion. On complicated jobs, such as color advertising, magazines, books, etc, in which the copy can come from a number of sources, the separate pieces of copy are photographed at the correct size and assembled in the film form. This completed form is called a *flat* and the operation of film assembly is known as *stripping*.

Process Photography

Process photography is the name given to the photographic techniques used in the graphic arts processes. All the printing processes using photomechanical methods for making printing plates require photography for the production of the negatives or positives used. Some platemaking methods require negatives and others require positives. In addition, the photographic materials used can be continuous tone, line, or halftone. Many of the materials and techniques used in process photography are similar to those described in the article on Photography, to which the reader is referred for discussion of the theory and principles of photography. The highly specialized photographic methods, techniques, and materials used in the graphic arts are described

Fig. 3. A halftone reproduction and its appearance viewed with a strong magnifying glass (30).
Courtesy The Printing Industries of America.

here. The photographic requirements of the various printing processes are both diverse and exacting. The successful prosecution of any printing process using photo-mechanical methods for making the printing members depends to a great extent on the quality of its photographic components.

Letterpress, lithography, and screen process printing are monotone processes, ie, at one time or in one impression on the press, they can only print a solid of the color on the press in the image areas and no color in the nonimage areas. They cannot print intermediate tones. Most pictures or scenes to be reproduced have many intermediate tones between the shadows and the highlights. In order to reproduce such a picture, these processes must use a "halftone." This is an optical illusion in which the tones are represented by solid dots which all have equal spacing but vary in area (see Figs. 3 and 4). The techniques for producing halftones are described later. Because of this need for halftone, letterpress, lithography, and screen process printing require the use of both line and halftone photography.

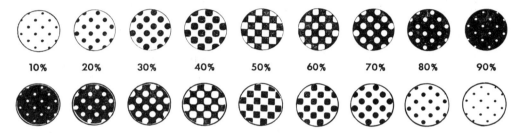

Fig. 4. Diagram of halftone dots. The dots in the upper row are positive, those in the lower row are negative. Courtesy Graphic Arts Technical Foundation.

Gravure, on the other hand, is capable of printing varying thicknesses of ink to produce pictures with a wide range of tones. In this process an overall screen or half-tone pattern is used only to maintain a constant height for the doctor blade to scrape over. The individual image wells are all the same size and shape but vary in depth. Continuous-tone positives for the pictures and line positives for the line and text copy are used as the photographic materials in this process. This is known as conventional gravure. There are now other methods of printing gravure in which special halftone positives are used. Plates or cylinders made from these have image wells in which both the area and the depth can be varied.

Collotype, or photogelatin, is a continuous-tone printing process. In this process plates are coated with bichromated gelatin and are exposed through continuous-tone negatives. The gelatin is hardened in proportion to the amount of exposure received and, after processing, prints ink density in proportion to the exposure.

Recently, techniques have been developed for making lithographic plates from continuous-tone negatives or positives. This process is known as "screenless lithography."

In the *direct* printing processes the image must be reverse reading on the plate, ie, from right to left, in order to read correctly or from left to right on the printed surface. For these processes the negatives or positives used to make the plates must be straight reading (from left to right) on the emulsion side. For the printing processes using the *offset* principle the reverse is true. The plate must be straight reading, so the negative or positives used to make them must be reverse reading on the emulsion side.

EQUIPMENT

Cameras. The most common piece of equipment used in process photography is the process camera. It is like an oversized enlarger except that most cameras are horizontal. These cameras have either a shock- or vibration-resistant bed or overhead suspension. Some vertical cameras and enlargers are also used (Fig. 5). Cameras usually vary in size (that is, the size of the film used to photograph on) from 16 × 20 in. to 40 × 40 in. Larger and smaller cameras have been built for special purposes.

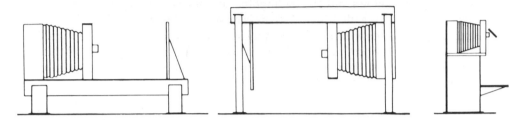

Fig. 5. Diagram of horizontal (bed and overhead types) and vertical cameras (30). Courtesy The Printing Industries of America.

Lenses. Special process lenses are used on process cameras. They should be color corrected (apochromatic) and relatively free of other aberrations, especially distortion. For this reason most process lenses are symmetrical in design and their maximum apertures are between F/8 and F/11. Focal lengths vary from 8 in. for wide-angle lenses used on enlargers and compact horizontal and vertical cameras to 48 in. for lenses used on some of the larger cameras. Since the regular photographic process produces negatives which are reverse reading (right to left) on the emulsion side, prisms are sometimes used on cameras to produce negatives that are straight reading (left to right) on the emulsion side.

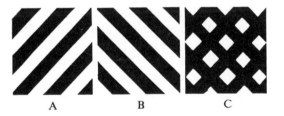

Fig. 6. Construction of the crossline halftone screen. A and B show the opaque rules on each of two glass plates. C shows the crossline pattern formed after the two plates are cemented (30). Courtesy The Printing Industries of America.

Halftone Screens. To produce the halftone images needed by most of the printing processes special halftone screens are used. There are both glass and contact screens. Glass screens are usually crossline screens with a grid of rulings. They consist of two pieces of glass, each with inked rulings, cemented together at right angles to each other (Fig. 6). The rulings are approximately the same width as the clear spaces between them and they vary in spacing from 60 to 300 lines per inch. Screens of 60–85 lines are used for letterpress newspapers; 120–133 line screens for letterpress magazines; 133–150 line screens for lithography. Contact screens are on film and are usually made from glass screens. Most contact screens consist of variable-density vignetted dots in a

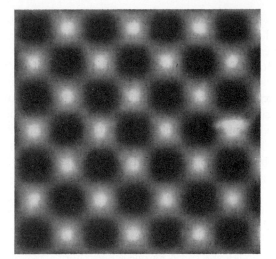

Fig. 7. Part of a vignetted dot contact screen, greatly enlarged.   Courtesy Eastman Kodak Company.

pattern corresponding to the screen ruling of the original screen from which they are made (Fig. 7).

Glass screens are used with a fixed separation distance from the film so they are mounted on special precision holders in the camera.   The screens can be either square or circular.   If circular, the holder is arranged so that it can be rotated to provide the different screen angles needed for color reproduction (see under Color reproduction).

The contact screens are used in contact with the film on which exposure is to be made so their use requires vacuum backs on process cameras or enlargers when these are used.   Contact-screen halftones can also be made in a vacuum printing frame.

Equipment for Processing.   Developing and fixing (processing) is usually done in trays in temperature-controlled sinks.   Since automatic processors were introduced about 1960, much of the industry is converting to their use.   Not only have they increased production and introduced economies in time and cost, but the product is more consistent in quality.   They are used for contact and camera line, halftone, and continuous-tone negatives and positives.

Lights and Exposure Controls.   To assure better consistency of product, arc lights for exposure are being replaced by pulsed xenon and quartz iodine lamps, and light-integrating devices are being used to control exposures on cameras, enlargers, and printing frames.   These are especially important when automatic processors are used.

MATERIALS

Photographic Emulsions.   Three types of photographic emulsions are used in photomechanical processes.   For line and halftone reproductions high-contrast orthochromatic or panchromatic emulsions of the *lith* type are needed.   These emulsions are thin, have a high silver content and fine grain, and their characteristic curves show little or no toe, very high gamma (on the order of 6–10), and maximum density of over 4.0.   For single-color gravure and other continuous-tone photography, a low-contrast orthochromatic *commercial* type of emulsion is used.   These emulsions have a long scale with a long straight-line portion and a maximum density of about 2.0. For color-separation photography low-contrast panchromatic emulsions with characteristics similar to those of the commercial film are used.

Film Support. Glass is seldom used now as a support for photographic emulsions. Cellulose nitrate and cellulose acetate, which were the first film bases used, are likewise seldom used, and this is also true for the mixed ester bases which consisted of cellulose acetate and butyrate. Of the cellulose esters the one most commonly used now is cellulose triacetate (see Cellulose esters). It has good mechanical strength and fair resistance to hygroexpansion (stretch or shrinkage due to the absorption or desorption of moisture). The copolymer of vinyl acetate and vinyl chloride has been used as a film base but its use is almost completely discontinued because it has a low softening temperature (about 140°F). Polycarbonate and polystyrene bases are used to some extent but by far the most popular film base is *polyester* (qv). This has the best mechanical properties coupled with a low temperature coefficient and with low hygroexpansion.

Processing. Regular continuous-tone developers such as are described in the article on Photography are used for the commercial and color separation films. Fixing of all films with regular hypo (sodium thiosulfate) and high-speed x-ray type (ammonium thiosulfate) is also the same as described there. Development of the high-contrast lith-type films, however, is different. To increase the contrast of these emulsions a special type of developer is used (3). A typical formula for such a developer follows:

Kodak D-85 developer

water (not over 90°F), ml	750
sodium sulfite (anhydrous), g	30
paraformaldehyde, g	7.5
potassium metabisulfite, g	2.6
boric acid crystals, g	7.5
hydroquinone, g	22.5
water	to make 1 liter

Note that this developer does not contain an alkali which is required for development. The alkali is formed by reaction of the paraformaldehyde, which is converted to formaldehyde in solution, with the sodium sulfite, forming sodium hydroxide and a formosufite addition product, according to the following equation:

$$HCHO + Na_2SO_3 + HOH \rightarrow NaOH + HCHO.NaHSO_3$$

Paraformaldehyde–hydroquinone-type developers owe their extreme contrast and density properties to the "infectious" nature of the development (4).   In this type of process, density and contrast continue to build up in exposed areas because alkali is being formed while sodium sulfite is removed from the reaction site. This happens at the expense of fine detail. Fine lines and letters tend to fill in. In order to preserve this detail and increase resolution, agitation can be stopped during development so that the developer becomes exhausted at the development sites. This is known as still development.

Dot Etching. There are a number of chemical reducers that can be used to dissolve and remove silver from negatives or positives. These are often used to remove stains or "fog." By far their greatest use is in *dot etching* which is used in color reproduction to reduce the size of dots on halftone positives without reducing their density, thereby reducing the amount of color in the area dot-etched, that will be printed by plates made from these positives (5). This is a most important means of manual color correction which is necessary when color changes in the original are required. A typical reducer is Farmer's reducer. Its formula is as follows:

stock solution A	water, liter	1
	potassium ferricyanide, g	80
stock solution B	water, liter	1
	hypo (sodium thiosulfate), g	255

For use take 1 part of A, 4 pts of B, and 32 pts of water. The chemical reactions involved in the use of this reducer on a photographic emulsion are as follows:

$$4 \text{ Ag} + 4 \text{ K}_3\text{Fe(CN)}_6 \rightarrow \text{Ag}_4\text{Fe(CN)}_6 + 3 \text{ K}_4\text{Fe(CN)}_6$$

$$3 \text{ Ag}_4\text{Fe(CN)}_6 + 16 \text{ Na}_2\text{S}_2\text{O}_3 \rightarrow 4 \text{ Na}_5\text{Ag}_3(\text{S}_2\text{O}_3)_4 + 3 \text{ Na}_4\text{Fe(CN)}_6$$

LINE PHOTOGRAPHY

Line copy is that which consists entirely of solids, lines, figures, or text matter. In photography the copy is usually placed on the copyboard of the camera; illuminated by high-intensity lights, such as carbon arc, pulsed xenon, or quartz iodine; and focussed to the correct size on a ground glass in the film plane. The film is placed on the vacuum back of the camera which is put in the image plane in place of the ground glass, and the exposure is made through a shutter operated by an automatic timer or a light integrating meter. In all photography but especially in line photography it is important that (1) the image is at the correct size and in sharp focus, and (2) the exposure is correct. If the focus is not sharp and/or the exposure not right, fine lines or serifs on type will blur or disappear, or the type will be too broad or too fine. After exposure and processing, the negative should be clear and transparent in the areas corresponding to the image on the copy and opaque in the areas corresponding to the white paper on the copy.

Contact Negatives and Positives. A camera is not needed to make contact positives from negatives. These are made by placing an unexposed film and the negative in a vacuum frame in which contact is maintained between the two films by exhausting the air between a plate covered with a corrugated rubber blanket and a sheet of flawless plate glass. When the films are placed emulsion to emulsion, the image on the positive will be straight reading. If it is desired to have the positive reverse reading as is needed in the "deep etch" and some of the "bimetal" platemaking methods of lithography, the negative is placed so that its emulsion side is away from the emulsion side of the unexposed film. If a good point source of light is used and the exposure is timed accurately, the positive image will not show much sign of light spread which would result in image sharpening. Controls like the GATF sensitivity guide, Star Target (6), and Dot Gain Scale (7) should be used to control the exposure and the processing.

In situations where multiple negatives or positives are needed, these can be made by going back and forth from negative to positive. Exposure and development are extremely critical to prevent image sharpening or spread. Also, new *duplicating films* are available which allow one to make a duplicate negative from a negative or a duplicate positive from a positive. Sometimes, as in color reproduction, considerable handwork, such as dot etching, is done on positives to produce the correct tone values. After this is done it is safer to make duplicate positives than to risk the chance of a tone change in going to an intermediate negative and then to the positive. The duplicating films require a special light source for exposure as well as a special developer for processing.

HALFTONE PHOTOGRAPHY

Tone Reproduction. The need for halftones and the screens used for halftone photography have already been described. Tone reproduction and contrast of reproduction are the conditions that halftone photography attempts to satisfy. If a stepped gray scale is considered (as in Fig. 3), good *tone reproduction* in halftone photography is defined as the result achieved when the darkest area of the subject prints as a solid tone and the lightest areas as a white with no evidence of a screen in either tone. The intermediate tones have varying sizes of dots in a regular progression from about 5% dot area in the highlight end to about 90% dot area in the shadow end of the scale.

High contrast is defined as the condition which exists when two or three steps of the gray scale in the shadow end print solid and/or several steps in the highlight end print white, with a corresponding increase in density increment between the other steps of the gray scale.

Low contrast is defined as the condition when the solid contains 80–90% dot area and/or the white end of the scale has dots of 10–20% dot area with a corresponding decrease in density increment between gray scale steps in the rest of the scale.

The contrast can be increased or decreased at either end of the scale without affecting the rest of the scale appreciably. When the contrast of the light end of the scale is increased the effect is called *highlighting* or *drop-out*. In order to get better separation between tones in the shadow end of the gray scale, especially in dark subjects, the contrast of the shadow end of the scale is increased by a technique known as *flashing*. This is an overall exposure of the film to light with the halftone screen in place. This exposure effectively overcomes the inertia of the film so that the rest of the exposure is off the toe and on the straight-line portion of the sensitimetric curve, thereby evening out the increment between gray-scale steps in the dark or shadow end of the scale without affecting the other tones appreciably.

Glass Screens. In photography through a glass screen the screen is accurately positioned in the camera so that it is at a fixed distance from the emulsion of the film to be exposed. During exposure each of the square openings in the screen grid acts as

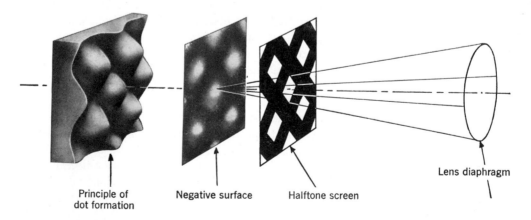

Principle of   Negative surface   Halftone screen   Lens diaphragm
dot formation

Fig. 8. Principle of halftone dot formation.   Courtesy Graphic Arts Technical Foundation.

a pinhole which produces an image or dot element proportional in size to the amount of light reflected from the corresponding area of the copy (Fig. 8). If the part of the copy being photographed is dark there will be little exposure and the dot will be small. If the part is light so that it reflects a lot of light, the dot area will be large. In a middle-tone area the dot pattern will appear like a checkerboard. The distance between the dot elements is the same and corresponds to the spacing between the line rulings in the screen. Only the areas change according to the tone values they represent. The tone reproduction, or the range of tones that can be reproduced, and the resolution of the image depend on the lens aperture and the screen distance or the separation between the screen and the film emulsion. The contrast can be lowered by reducing the lens aperture and by flashing with white light. The larger the aperture and the shorter the screen distance the higher the contrast and the sharper the reproduction. There are a number of formulas and aperture systems for making halftone negatives or positives with glass screens.

Contact Screens. Photography with contact screens is different. As the name implies, the photography is done with the screen in contact with the emulsion of the film to be exposed. The contact screen consists of a grid of vignetted dot elements. In making the contact screen from a glass screen the screen distance, the lens aperture, processing, and other conditions are adjusted so that each dot element on the contact screen has a predetermined density distribution which varies, depending on whether the screens are designed for making positives or negatives. Some screens have silver images and are gray. In others the silver is converted to a magenta dye image. Because of the fixed-density distribution in the dots, contact screens have relatively fixed tone-reproduction characteristics with limited variability.

Contrast of reproduction can be varied in several ways. It can be lowered by flashing the film to yellow light with the screen in place. The overall exposure lowers contrast by making the dots larger in the dark tones and the shadows and decreasing the difference in dot sizes between gray-scale steps. Contrast can be increased by turning the screen so that its emulsion side is away from the emulsion of the film to be exposed. The separation of the thickness of the film base of the screen increases the contrast of reproduction by increasing the difference in dot sizes between gray-scale steps but it reduces the resolution or sharpness slightly. The contrast of the highlights can be increased by removing the screen and continuing the exposure without the screen for a short time. This drops the dots out of the white portions of the copy and increases the difference in dot sizes in the light end of the gray scale.

With dyed screens contrast can be varied additionally with the use of filters. A yellow filter reduces contrast; a magenta filter increases it. Most dyed screens are magenta in color. With a yellow filter over the lens during photography, the contrast or density distribution across the individual dots in the screen is increased. With such high contrast in the dots in the screen a large difference in intensity of the light reflected from different areas of the original produces a small difference in dot sizes in the reproduction so the contrast, or density difference between neighboring steps on the gray scale, is reduced. When a magenta filter is used, the contrast of the individual dot elements in the screen is reduced. With low contrast in the screen dots, a small difference in light intensity from different areas of the original produces a large difference in dot sizes of the reproduction so the contrast is increased.

Dot Fringe. Since maximum contrast is desired in the individual dot elements the same type of lith film and paraformaldehyde–hydroquinone developers is used as for line and contact photography. In camera halftones made through a glass screen the dots have a variable density gradient, especially at the edges, which is called "dot fringe." The amount of this fringe differs depending on the exposure conditions, film, and processing. It can be detected by dark-field illumination. Because of this fringe glass-screen halftones may be dot-etched considerably; ie, a 60% tone may be reduced chemically to a 10% tone (see Fig. 3). Contact-screen halftones do not have as much fringe and therefore cannot be dot-etched as much before losing density all over. While the fringe is desirable for dot-etching, it is very undesirable for platemaking as the dot size on the plates can vary depending on the amount of exposure given the plates. To eliminate this disadvantage on critical work, contact or duplicate negatives or positives are usually made from halftones. On these the density distribution across the dots is more uniform and the amount of fringe is reduced appreciably.

Gravure. The type of screen used in conventional gravure is different from the screens described. Its only purpose is to maintain a grid of constant height that the doctor blade can scrape over. The conventional gravure screen consists of clear lines and black squares with the lines having about one-third the width of the black squares. Screen rulings of 150–300 lines per inch are used. These are still used for printing text matter by gravure. Halftones for the variable-area gravure processes can be made with special contact screens or by using specially shaped apertures in the lens when using the glass screen.

COLOR REPRODUCTION

Until after the middle of the nineteenth century all color printing was done like painting. A separate plate or printing was used for each different color in the original to be produced. For example, if there were a red, an orange, and a yellow, each of these three would be printed separately. A. du Hauron was the first to depend on color mixture in printing to produce intermediate colors. In 1869 he produced the first three-color print on paper, using yellow, red, and blue as the three colors. Today, practically all color reproduction is done by the method known as *four-color process printing* (8). In this method the color original is separated into four different images, each of which is printed from a separate printing plate, member, or image carrier, with a different ink to recreate a visual impression of the color original. The four colors generally used are yellow, magenta (blue-red), cyan (blue-green), and black. The different colors in the reproduction are produced by combinations of the yellow, magenta, and cyan inks. The black is used mainly to make the shadows neutral in color. If the color inks are properly transparent, combinations of them will produce almost every color in the spectrum. Variations of the four-color process method are the *three-color process* printing in which yellow, magenta, and cyan are the printing colors; the *two-color process* printing in which orange and cyan are used as the printing colors; and the *fake color process* printing in which the regular four color inks are used but the color separations for each of the colors is made manually and not from a color original. This discussion will be concerned only with three- and four-color process printing, which are the most extensively used and are based on the same general principles.

Color Theory. Like color photography (qv), process color printing is based on the Young-Helmholtz theory of three-color vision. In this theory white light, which is a combination of all the wavelengths of light, is considered to consist of three primary colors, blue, green, and red. These are broad bands of color as distinguished from the physical concept of color in which each wavelength of light varies in color from every other wavelength.

There are three different types of receptors in the cones on the retina of the eye, each sensitive to one of the primary colors of light. When the eye views a natural scene or a color picture, painting, or transparency, each of its different receptors records, or separates, the colors in the scene to which it is sensitive, and sends impulses to the brain. The brain takes the impulses from the cones and recreates the scene. The fidelity of the scene recreated by the brain depends on the experience of the viewer and the condition of the cones. If the sensitivity of one or more of the different receptors is impaired or lost, color blindness results and the visual impression of color is distorted.

In 1861 Clerk Maxwell demonstrated with spinning discs that white light could be produced from broad bands of blue, green, and red light, and that any other color could be produced by appropriate mixtures of these colors (9) (see the article on Color photography for illustrations in color of this principle). Illuminating an area or spinning a disc with approximately equal areas of blue, green, and red light or sectors produces white light. Covering the red area with a black sector and spinning produces a blue-green color which is called *cyan*. Cyan reflects blue and green light and absorbs red light. Covering the green area with the black sector produces a blue-red color which is called *magenta*. Magenta reflects blue and red light and absorbs green light. Covering the blue area produces a *yellow* color. Yellow reflects red and green light and absorbs blue. These are recognized as the colors of the printing inks used in three- and four-color process reproduction. These are sometimes called *complementary* colors but are usually referred to as *subtractive primaries*. Each is a combination of two colors left when one primary color is subtracted from white light. Blue, green, and red light are usually called additive primaries as these colors of light add together to form white light. When two subtractive primaries are printed over each other they form an additive primary. When yellow and cyan are overprinted green is produced; yellow and magenta form red; magenta and cyan form blue.

When all three subtractive primaries are overprinted they should form black. Actually a brown is produced. This is because the colors as in color photography are not ideal. An ideal magenta should reflect all the red and blue light and absorb all the green. Actual magentas are good in red reflectance and green absorption but are poor in blue reflectance. They behave as though they have yellow in them. An ideal cyan should reflect all the blue and green light and absorb red light. Actual cyans are poor in blue and green reflectance and fair in red absorption. They are dirty and behave as though they have red in them. Yellows are quite good. Most yellows reflect green and red light well and absorb blue. Color pigments are poorer in their spectral characteristics than the dyes used in color photography. A typical good set of process color inks consists of dispersions of benzidine yellow, rhodamine Y (magenta), and phthalocyanine blue (cyan) pigments in the proper vehicles. For greater permanence or resistance to fading rubine is often substituted for or mixed with the rhodamine. Rubine is a poorer pigment in blue reflectance than rhodamine so its use further affects color balance. See also Color measurement.

Color Separation. In color reproduction we use the three-color theory of vision and try to duplicate the operations the eye and brain perform when a color scene is viewed. It would be possible to photograph the natural scene directly for color reproduction. In most instances, however, the scene is photographed on color film (as described in the article on Color photography) and the transparency, or a color print made from it, is used as the original for reproduction. The copy can also consist of paintings, drawings, or other colored originals. These are mounted on the copy holder of the camera or enlarger and illuminated properly. Color filters corresponding in color transmission to the additive primary colors of light, blue, green, and red are used on the lights or in the lens during exposure to divide the original into three separate color records or separations, each representing one of the primary colors (10). A negative is produced in the camera. This is usually a continuous-tone negative but it can also be a halftone negative as is done in the method of *direct screening* (11).

The negative made through the blue filter is a recording of all the blue light reflected from or transmitted (in the case of transparencies) through the copy. When a positive is made from this negative it becomes a recording of the red and green colors in the original. In effect the negative has served to subtract the blue from the original. The color that reflects red and green light is yellow. In color reproduction the positive made from the blue filter or blue separation negative is printed with yellow ink. The negative made through the green filter is a recording of the green light reflected or transmitted and the positive made from this negative is printed in magenta ink. Likewise the negative made through the red filter records the red light from the original and the positive made from it is printed in cyan ink. Thus, in photography, the negatives separate the color original into three members, each representing a primary color of light. In printing, each negative is converted into a positive member which is printed in the subtractive primary colored ink complementary to the color of the filter used to make the negative.

Color Correction. In theory, color reproduction is as simple as this. In practice, however, it is much more complicated. Again, because the printing ink colors are not ideal a reproduction made according to these simple principles lacks crispness, cleanness, and color saturation (12). Most colors except yellows and reds are dirty and muddied. There is too much yellow in the reds and greens and too much red in the blues and purples. As mentioned earlier, even the best magenta ink does not reflect enough blue light and acts as though it has yellow in it. Wherever magenta ink is printed there will be an excess of yellow. The reds are orange and the blues dirty and purplish. Because the reflectances of blue and green light are weak in cyan inks they act as though they have yellow and magenta in them. Wherever cyan ink is printed there will be an excess of yellow and magenta, making the greens yellowish and dirty and further contributing to the blues being dirty and purplish.

To eliminate these faults color correction must be done on the negatives, positives, or printing plates to remove the excess color resulting from the improper spectral reflectances of the printing inks used. The amount of correction needed depends on the inks used and their departure from ideality. Because of the excess yellow in the magenta and cyan inks, the amount of yellow in the yellow printer (positive made from the blue separation negative) must be reduced in the areas where magenta and cyan print with yellow. Because of the excess magenta in the cyan inks, the amount of magenta in the magenta printer (positive made from the green separation negative) must be reduced in proportion to the amount of cyan printing with magenta. This color correction can be accomplished in many ways: by hand, photographic masking, or electronic scanning. See also Color measurement.

Hand correction can be done by retouching the continuous-tone separation negatives or continuous-tone positives made from them as used in conventional gravure. In lithography, in the newer powderless etching photoengraving processes, and in the variable-area gravure processes it is usually done on halftone positives by chemical reduction of the silver in the dots, thereby reducing their size (5). This is called *dot etching*. In conventional photoengraving and gravure the final corrections are made directly on the engraved plates or cylinders by hand tooling or local chemical etching and it is called *reetching* or *fine etching*.

Hand correction is an art that requires considerable skill and is very time-consuming and costly. It is rapidly being replaced by photographic masking and electronic scanning. It is needed, however, in instances where the colors in the original are not right and must be changed, or where the client is not completely satisfied with the original and wants to make changes. In such instances hand correction must be used to supplement the correction done by masking or scanning. Even the most sophisticated color-correction system must resort to hand retouching when the original is not correct and changes must be made in the colors in it.

Photographic masking is done by making supplementary images on film that are used (*1*) in contact with the original when it is a color transparency; (*2*) in a special holder in the back of the camera; or (*3*) in contact with the separation negative. The photographic masks in (*1*) and (*2*) are used while the color-separation negatives are being made; those in (*3*) are used while the halftone positives are being made from the separation negatives. The film masks in (*1*) are either silver or colored such as Kodak Trimask or Gevaert Multimask. The masks in (*2*) can be silver, dyed magenta, or colored. The masks in (*3*) are always silver. While (*1*) and (*2*) are used to some extent, by far the most versatile system of masking is (*3*). Following is a description of such a system (10).

The color-separation negatives are made, using the appropriate filters. The blue separation negative is made, using a Wratten No. 47 blue filter. The green separation negative is made with a Wratten No. 58 green filter. The red separation negative is made with a Wratten No. 25 red filter. A fourth separation negative for the black printer is made, using a Wratten No. 8 yellow filter (see Filters, optical). With the exception of the black printer, the color-correction masks are made from the color-separation negatives. To correct the color errors in one separation negative a positive is made from another separation negative to a predetermined density range depending on the set of inks to be used for printing. With a well-balanced set of process color inks consisting of benzidine yellow, rhodamine Y, and phthalocyanine blue pigments a positive is made from the green separation negative with a density range corresponding to about 40% of the full range of the negative. This low-range positive mask is placed in register with the image on the blue separation negative. A halftone positive representing a color-corrected yellow printer is made from this combination. The positive mask serves to subtract yellow from the magenta and cyan printing areas where these colors print with yellow.

The 40% figure comes from the *color matrix* for a good set of inks. This is a diagram showing the *optical reflection densities* of the three printing inks measured through the three color-separation filters. Such a matrix for a well-balanced set of process color inks would look like this:

	Filters		
Printed inks	*Red 25*	*Green 58*	*Blue 47*
yellow	0.01	0.06	1.00
magenta	0.10	1.20	0.48
cyan	1.25	0.40	0.16

An ideal set of inks would have a matrix like this (13):

Printed inks	Filters		
	Red 25	*Green 58*	*Blue 47*
yellow	0.00	0.00	1.50
magenta	0.00	1.50	0.00
cyan	1.50	0.00	0.00

Optical density is a measure of light absorption. The figures that appear in the spaces in the first matrix where there is 0.00 in the second matrix are measures of the color errors in the colors. Note that in the first matrix the ratios of blue to green densities for the magenta and cyan inks are the same. In both cases they are 0.40 (0.48:1.20 = 0.16:0.40 = 0.40). This indicates a set of *balanced inks* (as regards the magenta and cyan) and means that a single 40% mask made from the green separation negative placed on the blue separation negative will correct the errors in blue reflectances of both the magenta and cyan inks. If the ratios were different, then two separate masks would be needed or the masking would need to be supplemented by hand correction since the yellow in one color would be either over- or undercorrected.

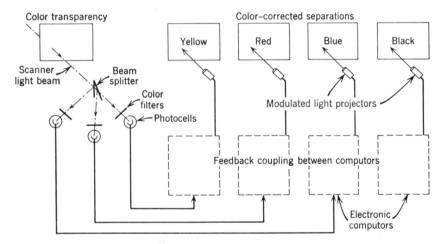

Fig. 9. Diagram of a typical electronic scanner for color separation and correction. Courtesy Graphic Arts Technical Foundation.

To correct the magenta error in the cyan ink a positive is made from the red separation negative in a percentage equivalent to the ratio of the green to red densities, or 32%. This positive is placed in register with the image on the green separation negative from which a color-corrected halftone magenta printer is made.

The red-filter negative or cyan printer does not require any color correction but it is usually masked to increase the color saturation of cyan printing in solids. The mask is usually made from the yellow separation negative (black printer). Its strength depends on the strength of the four color inks and their gray balance in four-color process printing.

To keep black from printing in all the colors and thereby dirtying them, a special mask is made for the black printer (yellow-filter negative). The mask is made from the riginal using a combination of filters that transmits a narrow band of spectral yellow light. The use of this mask ensures a minimum of black printing in the colors and just enough to make the shadows and deep tones neutral in color.

Electronic scanning can be used to produce the equivalent of color correction by photographic masking. Depending on the system employed, a light beam is used to scan a color transparency, a color print, a set of separation negatives, a painting, or a piece of original colored art (Fig. 9). A photocell evaluates each minute area electronically in terms of the proportions of each of the three printing colors that will be used. It translates these color values into electrical currents which are fed into four separate computers, one for each color and one for the black printer, which is computed from the

Fig. 10. A typical moiré pattern formed by two overlapping screen images. Courtesy J. A. C. Yule.

other three signals. The computers modify the currents, depending on the inks, paper, tonal range, and other conditions to be met in the color reproduction. The modified currents are then fed into an exposing light. This light varies ini ntensity in proportion to the corrected values of each element in the area scanned as it exposes the corrected color separation on film.

Most of the scanners in use produce continuous-tone negative or positive color separations which must be converted to halftones by conventional photographic means. As in photographic masking, scanners cannot introduce local color changes such as changing the color of a background or dress from red to blue, etc. Such changes must be made by hand retouching on the separations or by dot-etching on the halftone positives.

Screen Angles. In the printing processes where halftones are needed they can be made in the usual way using either glass screens or contact screens as described in the section on halftone photography. The angles of the halftones for each individual color, however, must be changed in order to avoid objectionable patterns known as moiré (Fig. 10). When two screen patterns of the same ruling are placed over each other an interference or beat pattern is formed which varies in spacing, depending on the angle between the screens. The pattern is minimized when the angle is 30°. With conventional crossline screens in which the patterns repeat every 90° there are only three possible positions at which 30° angles can be maintained between colors. This is ideal for three-color printing. In four-color printing, however, either two colors must be printed at the same angle or one color is printed at an intermediate angle. Because the most objectionable patterns are generally caused when there are slight errors (within ½°) between colors, the practice has been adopted of printing the yellow, which is a

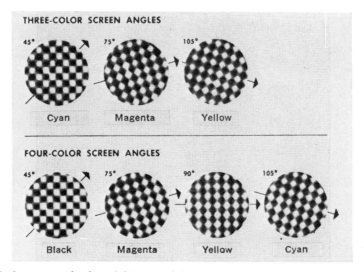

Fig. 11. Typical screen angles for minimum moiré patterns in three- and four-color process printing. Courtesy Graphic Arts Technical Foundation.

light and less noticeable color, at 15° between two other colors, usually the magenta and cyan (Fig. 11). The closer the colors are, the more severe is the pattern. For this reason screen angles are often changed, depending on which are the predominating or critical colors in a reproduction. If red is the critical color, the yellow is usually left at 90 or 0°, the cyan at 15 or 105°, and the magenta is placed at 45°. If green is the important color, the cyan is placed at 45°.

There will always be some pattern. This is aggravated in printing by slight misregister between printing colors on the press and by improper transfer of ink known as poor trapping. Proper trapping is the condition in printing when the same amount of ink transfers to a previously inked area as to unprinted blank paper. Poor trapping is the condition when less ink transfers to an inked area than to blank paper. This is a serious defect in printing on high-speed multicolor presses on which ink must transfer to wet ink films. If the ink is not formulated to trap properly, poor trapping will result which shows up as weak overprint colors and accentuated moiré patterns.

Photomechanical Methods of Platemaking

Printing-image carriers can be produced in any or a combination of six different ways:

1. Manually, using hand tools, engravers, knives, etc, for the relief, intaglio, and stencil processes; greasy crayon or tusche for lithographic plates.

2. Mechanically, using engraving and geometric lathes, ruling machines, pantographs, etc, for the relief and intaglio processes; hand transferring and benday machines for lithographic plates.

3. Electrochemically, using electrodeposited metals to produce longer-wearing images.

4. Electronically, in which relief and intaglio image carriers are produced by electronic engravers.

5. Electrostatically, in which relief and lithographic plates are produced using xerographic and/or electrofax principles.

6. Photomechanically, in which the printing images are produced from photographic images.

The photomechanical method is by far the most important as it is a vital part of all the other methods except 1 and 2. This method has been responsible not only for speeding up the reproduction of pictorial and text matter, but for improving their quality.

Each of the different types of printing has platemaking or image-forming methods that are characteristic of the type of printing. Letterpress plates are quite thick (up to 0.918 in.) and are usually made for individual subjects or pages. They are composed into larger forms for printing by locking up or arranging the individual plates and cast-metal type, if it is used, into the correct position, called an "imposition," in a frame, or chase, for printing on a flat-bed or platen press. Cast-metal type cannot be used for printing on a rotary press. It must be converted to plates. Plates for printing on a rotary press must be thinner and curved for mounting on the press cylinder (see below under Presses). In lithography and letterset printing, the images are composed into the proper position on a single plate (from 0.012 to 0.030 in. in thickness) which is mounted on the plate cylinder of the press as a unit. These are called "wraparound" plates. This type of plate can also be used in gravure but, most often, gravure is printed from copperplated cylinders which have been etched and chromium plated after the images have been transferred to them.

In addition to printing from cast-metal type, letterpress can be printed from *original, duplicate,* or *wraparound* plates. Original letterpress plates are made on zinc, magnesium, or copper by the method known as *photoengraving.* Duplicate plates for printing are plastic, rubber, stereotypes (see p. 526), or electrotypes (see p. 526), depending on the type of mold from which they are made. Wraparound plates can be either plastic or metal. Lithographic plates are usually made on aluminum and can be *surface, deep etch,* or *bimetal.* They can be plant-coated, precoated, or presensitized. As stated, some sheet-fed gravure is printed from copper plates, but the majority of gravure printing is done from copperplated cylinders. The printing image is produced on these using carbon tissue, photographic transfer film, or direct coatings. Screen-process stencils are made on a silk or stainless-steel screen and can be made using carbon tissue, other transfer film, or coating directly on the screen for the printing image. All these processes of platemaking use photomechanical methods.

CHEMISTRY OF THE PHOTOMECHANICAL PRINCIPLE

Photomechanical methods use photographic images exposed on light-sensitive coatings that are either directly on the printing member or can be transferred to it. The distinguishing feature of the light-sensitive coatings used is that on exposure to light they undergo changes in physical characteristics, usually solubility in water or other chemicals, so that they can be developed to produce images that either serve as the printing images or as resists for producing the printing images. In most instances the light-exposed or *hardened* coatings must remain soluble in other chemicals so that they can be removed after the images have been produced.

In carrying out the photomechanical principle, means must be provided for applying the light-sensitive coating to the printing member in the processes where the printing plates are coated directly. A *whirler* is used for this purpose. It consists of a rotating table on which the plate is placed for coating. It is in a housing that can be heated and made light-tight. The table can be either horizontal, vertical, or at 15° from the vertical. During coating the sensitizer solution is poured near the center of the plate as it rotates. The rotation of the plate causes the solution to spread out to the edges of the plate by centrifugal force on a horizontal whirler and by a combination of centrifugal force and gravity on the vertical type. A fairly even coating is produced, the thickness of which depends on the speed of rotation, density and viscosity of the solution, amount of moisture on the plate at the time of coating, roughness of the surface of the plate, relative humidity, and temperature. Wipe-on plates do not need a whirler. They can be coated by hand or on a simple roller coating machine.

For exposure of the coated plate to the negative or positive a *vacuum frame* such as is used for making contact exposures in photography can be used. Since most photomechanical coatings are of the print-out type they need a lot of light. *Arc lights* or *pulsed xenon lights* are used for exposure. *Light-integrating meters* can be used for controlling exposures. For exposing large plates in lithography and wraparound letterpress where multiple exposures of the same subjects are often required, a special apparatus known as a *photocomposing* or *step-and-repeat* machine is used. Other equipment needed in photomechanical platemaking are developing sinks, tables, pads, wipes, squeegees, etc. Special apparatus is needed in gravure and screen-process printing for coating directly on, or transferring carbon tissue or transfer film to, the cylinders or screens.

Until recently the majority of the coatings used in photomechanical processes were bichromated colloids. A number of these have been replaced by diazo compounds, photopolymers, silver halide photographic emulsions, and even electrostatics.

Bichromated Colloids (14). Bichromated colloid coatings are used for all four major printing processes. Bichromated shellac, albumin, glue, and polyvinyl alcohol are used in photoengraving. Bichromated albumin, casein, gum arabic, and polyvinyl alcohol are used in lithography. Bichromated gelatin is used in collotype or photogelatin, and it is the active ingredient in carbon tissue used in gravure and screen-process printing. Ammonium bichromate is usually used as the sensitizer. Potassium bichromate is sometimes used in collotype coatings for special long-scale or low-contrast effects.

Our knowledge of the photochemistry of bichromated colloid coatings leaves much to be desired. The coating solutions are fairly stable, but when dried, light makes them insoluble by a process similar to leather tanning. Part of the Cr^{6+} is reduced to Cr^{3+}, and a colloidal complex, $(Cr_2O_3)_x \cdot (CrO_3)_y$, is formed. At the same time, the coating undergoes a sol–gel transformation. As the light exposure proceeds, the gel becomes stronger and less capable of hydration. The isoelectric point also changes. For example, the isoelectric point of egg albumin is approx 4.9, whereas that of a suitably exposed bichromated albumin coating is between 3.8 and 4.0. The resulting protein gel is oleophilic and capable of retaining greasy ink even under conditions of maximum hydration at or near its isoelectric point.

The light sensitivity of bichromated colloid coatings is governed by a number of factors, of which the following are the most important:

1. The *bichromate colloid ratio.* Sensitivity increases with the bichromate concentration up to the point where crystallization of the bichromate takes place.

2. The *coating thickness.* Sensitivity decreases with increased coating thickness. Only wavelengths of light below 4500 Å are very effective for exposure and the yellow coating itself acts as a light filter.

3. The *pH value.* Sensitivity of the dried coating increases as its pH value decreases.

4. The *moisture content.* Sensitivity increases with hygroscopic moisture content.

5. The *temperature.* Sensitivity increases with temperature.

The dried bichromated colloid coating gradually becomes insoluble in the absence of light. This is called "dark reaction." This deterioration is more rapid, the higher the temperature and relative humidity are. For this reason, plates must be exposed and developed within a time limit established by experience. For example, an albumin-coated plate may be usable for three or four days at 75°F and 30% relative humidity. But at 90°F and 75% rh, it cannot be developed any more after about 2 hr.

Since insolubilization of the coating is a chemical reaction its rate is the product of all the factors. If any one factor is low the result is low. This accounts for the fact that bichromated coatings can be stored in a refrigerator even though the relative humidity is very high because the temperature is low.

Consistent success in platemaking requires control of the bichromate–colloid ratio, coating thickness, pH, temperature, relative humidity, and light exposure. With an exposing light of constant intensity, exposure can be timed. With a fluctuating light source an integrating light meter is necessary. Controls such as the GATF (Graphic Arts Technical Foundation) sensitivity guide are available to indicate variations in sensitivity and help control it. The GATF sensitivity guide is a continuous-tone gray scale with an increment of about 0.15 density units between numbered steps. The number of steps that print solid on the plate are a function of the light sensitivity of the coating and the light intensity of the light used for exposure. If the light intensity is constant, the number of solid steps on the sensitivity guide can be used as a measure of coating sensitivity and a means of controlling or compensating for it when it changes. A difference of two steps in the sensitivity guide is equivalent to either doubling or halving the sensitivity, depending on whether it is increased or reduced.

Diazo Coatings. Diazo resins are used primarily as coatings for lithographic presensitized and wipe-on plates (15). It is possible to use them for these purposes as they are not affected as much by temperature and relative humidity as the bichromated colloids. The diazo resin most commonly used for negative plates (plates made from negatives) is the condensation product of 4-diazodiphenylamine with formaldehyde (**1**), which is usually furnished as the zinc chloride salt. Diazo oxides such as pyrido[1,2-*a*]benzimidazol-8-yl 3(4*H*)-diazo-4(3*H*)-oxo-1-naphthalenesulfonate (**2**) are used for both negative and positive plates.

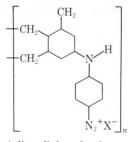

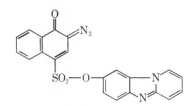

4-diazodiphenylamine–
formaldehyde condensate (**1**)

pyrido[1,2-*a*]benzimidazol-8-yl 3(4*H*)-diazo-4(3*H*)-oxo-
1-naphthalenesulfonate (**2**)

The mechanisms of the photochemical reactions of diazo and diazo oxide compounds are not known exactly. They are suspected to be like the photochemical reactions of similar but less complex diazo materials. The following equations show the photochemical decomposition of diazonium salt (comparable to that of diazo resin (**1**)) and 2-diazo-1(2*H*)-naphthalenone (comparable to that of diazo oxide (**2**)):

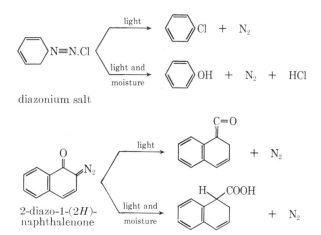

diazonium salt

2-diazo-1-(2*H*)-
naphthalenone

The solubility of the complex diazo polymer (**1**) is due to the presence of ionic diazo groups. The destruction of these groups by light renders the decomposed polymer insoluble in water. On exposure to a negative the exposed and photochemically decomposed image becomes the insoluble ink-receptive printing image. The diazo oxide (**2**) can be used for either negative or positive plates, depending on the solubility differential of the photochemically decomposed product in acid and alkaline solutions. The light-exposed material is less soluble in acid than in alkaline solutions. If acid solutions are used, the exposed material remains as the printing image so it is a negative plate system. If alkaline solutions are used the unexposed material remains as the printing image so it is a positive plate system. While theoretically the same plate could be used for both systems, in actual practice the particular resin is selected that works best for one or the other system.

As already stated, diazo compounds are not affected as much by temperature and relative humidity as bichromated colloids. Extended exposure to temperatures above 125°F can cause decomposition of the diazo compound, resulting in scum (unwanted ink-receptive material in the nonprinting areas) on presensitized plates. Also solutions of diazo resin (**1**) deteriorate on standing (16). This is not much of a problem on presensitized plates where the manufacturer coats the plates but it is particularly troublesome on wipe-on plates. If solutions of diazo resin (**1**) are allowed to stand too long before the plates are coated, the plates may not develop properly and may take ink or "scum" on press. In any case, the age of the coating is a serious source of variability. The best practice is to mix only an amount that will be needed for a twenty-four-hour period. Not much deterioration takes place during this short period.

In addition, the diazo resin (**1**) is very reactive, so metals must be specially pretreated prior to coating. This is especially true for presensitized plates. Otherwise short storage life results. (Usual storage life for diazo presensitized plates is one year.) Most wipe-on and presensitized plates use aluminum as the base metal. The surface treatments (17) used to protect the metal from reaction with the diazo resin include silicates, anodizing, potassium zirconium fluoride (potassium fluorozirconate, $KZrF_5$, see Vol. 9, p. 685) (18), organic phosphates (19), phosphates (20), acrylic monomers (21), titanium tetrachloride (22), tetraisopropyl titanate (see Vol. 1, p. 848) (23), böhmite ($Al_2O_3 \cdot H_2O$, see Vol. 2, p. 42) (24), phosphomolybdates (25), and a cycloaliphatic polyphosphoric acid such as phytic acid (26). Plates coated with diazo oxides do not require these special treatments. The plate surface must be clean and usually some form of mechanical roughening or *graining* is used to increase the surface area of the plate and improve its wettability for coating.

Photopolymer Coatings. Photopolymer coatings are insolubilized by polymerization or crosslinking during exposure. These coatings are very inert and have excellent abrasion resistance. Photopolymer coatings are used for making letterpress and lithographic plates from negatives. They are also used for making printed circuits. Two types of photopolymer coatings are used, (*1*) those that are developed in organic solvents, and (*2*) those developable in water or alcohol solutions. Coatings of the first type are mainly cinnamic ester resins and are used extensively for lithographic plates and printed circuits. Coatings of the second type are made with polymethacrylate and polyamide and are used mainly for relief or letterpress plates. There is some information about the first type but little is known about the second, except what appears in the patent literature. The main feature of these coatings is that they are affected very little by temperature and relative humidity and therefore have a very long shelf life as precoated materials.

Cinnamic Ester Resins. Cinnamic resins of polyvinyl alcohol, cellulose, and starch are known, but the preferred lithographic coating materials are based on epoxy resins. The structural formula for the cinnamic ester of an epoxy resin of epichlorhydrin and 4,4'-isopropylidenediphenol (bisphenol A, see Vol. 1, p. 912) is given below.

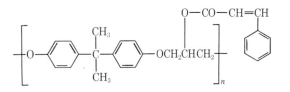

In the exposure of cinnamic ester resins, the photochemical reaction most probably involves a crosslinking mechanism between cinnamic ester units in the polymer chains, producing a rigid, insoluble structure. The principle of the crosslinking mechanism for the classical dimerization reaction of cinnamic acid to form *trans,trans*-2,4-diphenyl-1,3-cyclobutanedicarboxylic (truxillic) acid is shown as follows:

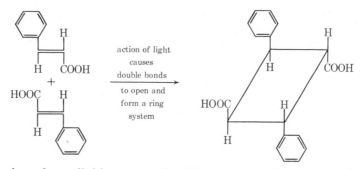

The number of crosslinkings per unit of light or time of exposure is increased by a number of compounds, including hydrocarbons, amines, nitro compounds, ketones, quinones, etc. Commercial coatings based on cinnamic resins usually include an organic sensitizer selected from these compounds.

The cinnamic resins are water insoluble and the solubility differential is established by developing the coating in a suitable solvent system. In practice this is done either in a vapor degreaser or by using an emulsion of the solvent dispersed in an aqueous phase of gum and phosphoric acid. The photochemical reaction renders the exposed areas insoluble and these form the printing image.

In addition to being little affected by temperature and relative humidity, these coatings have excellent water, acid, and abrasion resistance. On a lithographic press they are capable of long runs. Some plates have run satisfactorily for editions in excess of 1,000,000 impressions.

The acid resistance of these coatings has made them useful for the production of printed circuits in which the exposed coating becomes the acid resist for the metal etching bath. With the stress on miniaturization created by the space program, printed circuits have become an important factor in this program as well as in commercial electronics.

Polymethacrylate Coatings. Polymethacrylate (and also polyamide) coatings are two types of photopolymerizable coatings used to produce relief plates for letterpress and/or letterset printing. The polymethacrylate plate consists of a base metal sheet coated with an antihalation layer to keep light from reflecting back into the coating, and a coating containing monomeric and polymeric methyl methacrylates, polyethylene glycol dimethacrylate, ethyl acrylates, polyvinyl acetate, polystyrene, etc, and a photoinitiator or addition polymerization catalyst like benzoin, benzoin methyl ether, α-methylbenzoin, α-allylbenzoin, diacetyl, or 1,1′-azodicyclohexane–carbonitrile (28). The coating can also contain polymerization inhibitors (antioxidants like hydroquinone, *tert*-butyl catechol, etc) to prevent spontaneous polymerization before it is desired. Plates are conditioned in a carbon dioxide atmosphere for this reason. Light exposure activates the photoinitiator which causes polymerization and crosslinking of the various monomers and polymers in the coating. Maximum differentiation in solubility between exposed and unexposed areas is produced when an appreciable proportion of the monomers and polymers consists of crosslinking materials. In coatings with a high proportion of monomers and a low proportion of polymers the unexposed coating is soluble in an alkaline solution. With a higher proportion of polymers, organic solutions would be required for development.

Polyamide (nylon) coatings are not photosensitive in themselves. To produce light-sensitive coatings the polyamides are mixed with photosensitive polymerizable unsaturated compounds which are capable of crosslinking with the polyamides on exposure to light (29). Materials useful for this purpose are N,N'-methylenebisacryl-amide, N,N'-hexamethylenebismethacrylamide, and related compounds. As with polymethacrylate coatings, a polymerization inhibitor and photoinitiator are needed to complete the coating composition. Polymerization inhibitors are antioxidant materials like pyrogallol, quinone, hydroquinone, methylene blue, etc. The photoinitiators used are benzophenone, benzoin, benzaldehyde, acetophenone, and similar compounds. It is believed that during exposure crosslinkings are formed between the polyamide resins and the photosensitive polymerizable unsaturated compounds. The photoinitiator serves to speed up the reaction so that the exposure time is reduced. Since these coatings consist mainly of polymers and only a small percentage of monomers they must be developed in alcohol solutions.

As far as is known polyamide coating-technology has not been applied to making lithographic plates. Some work has been done to adapt polymethacrylate coatings to lithography with some degree of success. A lithographic plate is being marketed that is based essentially on this technology. It is made from negatives and is capable of runs in excess of 200,000 impressions.

Silver Halide Photographic Systems. Silver halide photographic systems in one form or another are used in all four major printing processes. In these systems the colloid in the photographic emulsion, usually gelatin, is hardened or tanned corresponding to the exposed and developed silver image. In the system used for letterpress, gravure, and screen process printing, the unhardened gelatin in the nonprinting areas is removed by soaking in hot water. In these processes the hardened gelatin serves as a resist or stencil for etching in the case of letterpress and gravure, and for printing in the case of screen process. In the system used for lithography, the photographic material becomes the printing plate; the tanned gelatin is ink receptive while the unexposed and unhardened gelatin remains water receptive.

Letterpress System. The silver halide photographic system used to produce letterpress relief plates consists of four layers. From top to bottom, they are (1) a silver halide photographic emulsion; (2) a white pigmented layer; (3) a relatively thick layer of modified cellulose acetate; and (4) a sheet of lacquered steel (30). The plates are used for wraparound printing, mainly letterset, and they are made in three thicknesses, 0.017, 0.025, and 0.030 in. The plate can be handled in yellow light; multiple exposures can be made on it as on lithographic plates; and arc or pulsed xenon lights are used for exposure.

After exposure the image is visible, due to the contrast of the white pigmented layer, so that corrections can be made prior to development. Development is done in a tanning developer (see Photography) during which the gelatin is tanned as the silver is developed in the image areas. The plate is washed in hot water to remove the unexposed, unhardened gelatin after which it is thoroughly dried in a warm-air cabinet. Development and drying takes about 5 min. At this stage unwanted printing areas can be easily removed. For processing the plate is held magnetically to the drum of a special processor. Cellulose acetate is dissolved from the nonprinting areas of the plate during the processing operation, while the photographic image serves as a resist to protect the printing areas from being etched away. The processing cycle consists of stations for scrubbing, heating, and cooling the plate. The actual removal of the cellulose acetate is accomplished by an oscillating endless belt. About 20 min of processing time is required for full depth in the plate. The 0.017 in. plate is etched to a depth of 0.007 in.; the 0.025 in. plate is etched to a depth of 0.011 in.; and the 0.030 in. plate has a depth of 0.016 in.

Gravure and Screen Process Systems.   In gravure and screen process printing a transfer image is applied to the printing member. In gravure the image, transferred to a plate or cylinder, serves as a resist for etching. In the screen process it serves to form the nonprinting areas of the screen which prevent the passage of ink through it. "Carbon tissue" has been used extensively for these purposes. Carbon tissue consists of a coating of pigmented gelatin on paper which is sensitized with bichromate and dried before use. Besides the handling, its use requires carefully controlled conditions and expert skill. Since about 1950 a photographic transfer film has been available that is simpler to use and more reliable in results than carbon tissue (31).

Positives are used to make the exposures on the film. The exposed film is developed in a tanning developer which hardens the gelatin in the exposed areas in proportion to the amount of silver developed or the amount of exposure received. The film can either be stored for future use or it can be laid down on the plate, cylinder, or screen. After laydown, the backing is stripped from the film and it is washed in hot water. This dissolves and removes the gelatin from the unexposed, unhardened areas which correspond to the image areas. The tanned gelatin becomes the resist for etching of the copper in gravure and serves to block the holes of the screen in the nonprinting areas for screen-process printing.

Lithographic System.   Many attempts have been made to convert photographic emulsions to lithographic printing surfaces. Many of these have been based on the "bromoil" principle. In this process a photographic print is developed in a nontanning developer and fixed in a nonhardening fixing bath. The developed image is then bleached in a copper–bichromate bleach and fixed. The bleach dissolves the silver and the fixer removes it, leaving differentially tanned gelatin corresponding to the silver image. After proper soaking the tanned gelatin in the image can be inked with an oil-base ink, producing a print with an unusual depth or three-dimensional effect. The inked image can also be transferred to another surface using a press so that the original print serves as a printing plate. While the process is reasonably simple in principle it is very difficult to carry out, requiring considerable skill and experience.

Many modifications of this process have been tried for printing but none has been completely successful (32). A modification which has been reasonably successful in making color prints is the "dye transfer" process. In this process the images are made on film, the untanned gelatin is dissolved or washed off in hot water, and the differentially tanned gelatin image is used to transfer dye solutions to paper or other support. This is the basis of the Technicolor process for making movie release prints that are used in theaters (see Vol. 5, p. 835). Actually the gravure transfer film is also a modification of this process.

Recently a process has been introduced for making lithographic plates from photographic emulsions which has met with considerable success in copying or reprography (33). It is a process in which a positive is printed from a positive. A camera is used so the image can be enlarged or reduced. The intermediate negative is eliminated as the photographic material becomes the printing plate. The photographic material consists of three gelatin emulsion layers on a paper base. From top to bottom they are (*1*) a silver halide prefogged emulsion; (*2*) a silver halide sensitized emulsion; and (*3*) an emulsion containing a photographic developer. During exposure light is reflected from the white or nonprinting areas of the subject to be reproduced. This light penetrates the prefogged emulsion and enters the sensitized emulsion. The areas on the original which are black or the image areas absorb light and do not reflect any back to the photographic material.

After exposure the plate is placed in a special processor which contains two solutions, an activator and a stop bath. The activator penetrates the three emulsions and dissolves the developer. The developer migrates into the sensitized emulsion layer and develops the silver halide that was exposed by the light reflected from the nonprinting areas of the original. All the developer is exhausted in these areas and none migrates to the outer fogged emulsion so the silver halide in this layer does not develop in these areas. In the areas that were not exposed (corresponding to the image areas on the original) the developer penetrates the sensitized layer and develops the fogged silver halide in the emulsion on the top layer. After development, which takes about 20 sec, the plate is placed in an acid stop bath which stops the developer action and fixes the image.

Since the developer is of the tanning type the gelatin in the top layer corresponding to the developed silver image is hardened and becomes ink receptive. The gelatin in the undeveloped nonimage areas remains unhardened and is water receptive. The difference between the ink and water receptivity of these two areas is not very great so these plates are rather critical to make and run. Exposures must be within close tolerances; line work and halftones require different exposure levels so it is difficult to reproduce subjects that contain both types of images. Special inks are desirable for printing; and ink-water balance on the press is critical. Despite these limitations it is estimated that more duplicating or reprographic printing is done by this system than by any other.

Electrostatics. Electrostatically produced images can also be used for photomechanical platemaking. Two electrophotographic processes are in common use for producing images. These are xerography and electrofax. In these processes a photoconductive surface accepts and holds a uniform electrostatic charge in the absence of light, but loses the charge when exposed to light. When such a surface is exposed to a light image the charge is retained only in the unexposed (image) areas. The charged image can be developed by attracting finely divided oppositely charged pigmented particles. These are positive-positive processes.

In xerography or xerox (34) the photoconductor consists of selenium in a suitable binder coated permanently on a drum or plate. The powder image is electrostatically transferred to paper for final "fixing," which can then be used as a copy or can be used as a plate for an offset duplicating press from which a number of copies can be printed. It can also be transferred to a metal plate, which after proper fixing of the image and treatment of the nonprinting areas becomes a lithographic plate for appreciable runs.

In the electrofax process (35) the photoconductor is zinc oxide in a suitable binder coated directly on the paper or other support. This process can be used to make lithographic plates, and plates for duplicating or reprography, but is not used to make plates for larger presses. It has also been tried for making relief plates. In this process the metal comes coated with zinc oxide in a binder. Prior to use, the coating is charged with a corona discharge. A positive is exposed on the coated plate and the printing image is developed with an acid-resistant toner which is fused after development. The plate is then etched in a powderless etching machine that eliminates undercutting by side etching of the image elements (see below under Photoengraving).

A number of platemaking methods have been described in this section on the

Chemistry of the photomechanical principle. The discussion has been necessarily disjointed because of the subdivision by photomechanical systems rather than printing processes. How the methods fit into the various platemaking systems and how they are used in the different printing processes is described in the following sections.

Photoengraving

Photoengraving is defined as the photomechanical production of relief plates for letterpress and letterset printing in line, halftone, and color.

History. The origin of photoengraving is uncertain, and development of the process has been the result of the efforts of many workers. Probably the first crude attempt at photographic etching was made by Niepce in about 1815, but the first etched line blocks were made by Gillot in Paris in 1859. Gillot transferred line impressions from lithographic stone to zinc plates and etched away the bare metal, leaving the inked lines in relief. To reproduce pictorial subjects, Fox Talbot in England suggested the breaking up of tones into printing dots by means of a screen, but it was not until 1882 that Meissenbach produced the first practical halftone blocks using a single-line screen, which he turned 90° during the exposure. F. E. Ives first produced halftones with the sealed crossline screen about 1886, and this type of screen was perfected and offered to the trade by Levy in 1891. Once the halftone process became practical, the color-reproduction theories of Clerk Maxwell and Du Hauron were applied. Three-color process plates were produced by Kurtz and Ives in 1892. Black was added later, resulting in the four-color process in use today.

Types of Engravings. There are two general types of engravings, line and halftone. These are divided into five groups: (*1*) line engravings in one color; (*2*) halftone engravings in one color; (*3*) combination line and halftone engravings in one color; (*4*) sets of engravings for multicolor printing either in line or halftone, or in line and halftone combinations; and (*5*) four-color process engravings for full color printing.

Photoengraving Metals. Zinc, magnesium, and copper with small amounts of other alloying metals are the three commonly used metals for photoengraving original plates. Zinc and magnesium are used almost exclusively in the U.S. for line engravings while copper is used for halftones and for line engravings where fine lines and many molds are involved. In Europe zinc and magnesium are used for halftones as well as line engravings. In the U.S. copper is seldom used as a printing plate. It is used as the original to make the mold from which electrotype duplicate plates are made. The actual printing is done from the electrotypes, thereby preserving the original in case of damage to the printing element.

Etching. In photoengraving the metal in the nonprinting areas is removed by chemical etching or mechanical routing. Nitric acid is used as the etchant for zinc and magnesium. Ferric chloride is used for copper. There is a very wide range in the depth of etching. On a 133-line halftone engraving it varies from 0.0014 in. in the shadows to 0.0020 in. in the middletones and 0.0029 in. in the highlights. It can vary from about 0.020 in. on line engravings for printing on high-finish papers to over 0.040 in. (36) for flexographic printing on rough papers like the liner for corrugated board.

The main problem in etching is to maintain the correct dot or line area at the proper etch depth. Classically this has been done by either of two ways, (*1*) *scale compression*, and (*2*) *successive four-way powdering*. *Scale compression* is done in photographing the negative. Much larger white dots are left in the highlights to compensate for the lateral etching that reduces the area of the highlight dots. It is difficult to control middletone and shadow dot size by this method. By *four-way powdering* is meant the protection of the sides of etched image elements with acid-resistant materials to prevent attack on the sides of the images as the proper depth is achieved. The acid-resistant materials consist of fusible natural resins like dragon's blood, asphaltum, colophony, shellac, mastic, damar, copal, and synthetic resins of the phenol–formaldehyde type. Four-way powdering is a manual operation that is time consuming and requires considerable skill and judgment.

Powderless Etching. About 1953 a breakthrough was made in efforts to speed up the etching process and improve its consistency. This was the powderless etching system developed by Swayze and Easley of Dow Chemical Co. (37). A special etching machine is required and the etching bath consists of an emulsion that continuously applies an acid-resistant coating on the sides of the image elements to control sidewise etching and depth of etch. The etch bath consists essentially of nitric acid, dioctyl sodium sulfosuccinate, diethylbenzene (mixed isomers), gelatin, and a wetting agent. The mechanism of the reaction is not known for sure but it is suspected that the diethylbenzene and succinate ester form an acid-resisting film on the etched areas which protects the sides of the image elements while the bottom continues to etch. Swayze and Easley claim that the resist-coated areas are heat sinks in which the temperature is cool enough for the film to remain on the slopes. In the bottom, active etching gives locally high temperatures and the oil-surfactant layer is soluble or nonadherent. This system is usable on both magnesium and zinc.

A mechanically similar system has been developed for etching copper (38). In this system ferric chloride is the etchant and one of the film-forming additives used is formamidine disulfide, $NH:C(NH_2)SSC(NH_2):NH$. Mechanically this mixture works in a manner similar to that of the powderless etching system used on magnesium and zinc. Chemically it is quite different. The protective banking agent that prevents side etching is the reaction product of the organic compound and copper dissolved from the plate. This forms a gelatinous deposit on the sides of image elements being etched.

While these powderless etching systems are being used almost exclusively in present-day photoengraving, some engravings are still being made by the old methods. In this discussion both systems will be described briefly.

Line Engravings. Line engravings are made from photographic line negatives of text matter, type, line drawings, graphs, block diagrams, etc. A typical process for making these plates in the conventional way without powderless etching includes the following steps:

1. Clean the zinc surface by scrubbing it with powdered pumice and water, followed by a weak acid wash.

2. Coat the plate in a whirler with bichromated albumin solution, and dry. (Bichromated shellac can also be used.)

3. Expose the coated plate to light in contact with a line negative.

4. For albumin coatings, coat the exposed plate with etching ink; develop it under running water by light rubbing with cotton to remove the unexposed albumin coating; and dry. Shellac coatings are developed in alcohol and water.

5. Powder the ink image with powdered resin and heat to sinter the resin.

6. Paint out the margins of the plate with an acid-resistant paint or lacquer. The backs of the plates are factory-coated.

7. Etch the bare metal with nitric acid to leave the protected lines and solids in relief. To prevent undercutting the image, this is done in several stages. After each etch or bite, the plate is reinked and powdered, the resin being brushed in four directions to protect the sides of the lines, then reheated to sinter the resin.

8. When the plate has been etched to the desired depth, the resist (acid-resistant paint or lacquer) is removed with a solvent, large nonimage areas are routed out to a depth of 0.020 in. or more, and the edges are trimmed and beveled.

When powderless etching is used steps 1 and 3 are the same. In step 2 a bichromated PVA (polyvinyl alcohol) sensitizer is used because other sensitizers are attacked by the acid-organic solvent mixture used in the etching machine.

4. Develop the exposed plate in water.

5. Bake the PVA coating at a temperature of 325°F to complete the polymerization and convert it to an acid-resistant enamel.

6. Apply a descumming agent to remove any bichromate still remaining in the coating.

7. Wash plate thoroughly to remove all traces of descumming agent.

8. Mount plate in etching machine; turn on machine and let etch for 5–12 min.

Halftone Engravings. Halftone engravings in the U.S. are usually made on copper and they require halftone negatives. A typical process for making these plates in the conventional manner without powderless etching involves the following steps:

1. Clean the copper plate with a detergent to remove grease and sand with FFF pumice.

2. Coat the plate with a solution of bichromated fish glue in a whirler and dry it.

3. Expose the coated plate to light in contact with a halftone negative.

4. Place the exposed plate in a solution of Methyl Violet dye to color the coating; then develop it under water to remove unexposed coating; and dry.

5. Heat the plate (burn in) to convert the coating on the image areas to an acid-resistant enamel.

6. Paint the margins with asphalt paint or lacquer. The backs are factory-coated.

7. Etch away the bare metal to leave the halftone image in relief. The metal is etched with 42°Bé ferric chloride solution in several stages. After each bite the plate is dusted four ways with powdered dragon's blood to prevent undercutting of the dots. Since the depth of etching varies with the tone of the subject, the shadow areas are painted (staged out) with acid-proof varnish after the first or second bite and etching is continued. Staging is repeated for each successively lighter tone. The final etch determines the depth in the highlights.

8. The etched plate is cleaned and proved with ink to determine if the tone values are correct. If not, it is reetched locally to reduce the dots to the desired size.

9. When the proof is satisfactory, the plate is trimmed and beveled, and any large blank areas are routed to increase their depth.

The etching can be done in a tray, but is usually carried out in an etching machine. There are three types of etching machines: one splashes the etch against the plate; another type sprays the etch; still another type etches electrolytically, using a sodium chloride bath (see Electrolytic machining methods). Uniform, controlled etching requires controlled renewal of the etching bath to maintain a nearly constant composition and concentration.

The procedure for the powderless etching of halftone engravings on copper is the same as for powderless etching of zinc or magnesium line engravings. Either bichromated glue or PVA can be used as the sensitized coating. The chemicals used are different but the operations are similar. In the etching machine a gelatinous film deposit forms on the areas etched. The etchant spray breaks up the film so that etching takes place in the bottoms or open areas and flushes the material sideways to accumulate as a protective bank along the sides of the relief image elements. Because the etchant strikes the "banking agent" on the sidewalls at a large angle it does not have enough force to dislodge the protective material and sidewall etching is inhibited.

Photopolymer Plates. Original photoengravings can also be made on the photopolymer materials mentioned in the previous section. There are four steps in making the polymethacrylate plate: (*1*) Conditioning of the plates in a carbon dioxide atmosphere to remove oxygen from the coating which retards the action of the photoinitiator; (*2*) exposure to negatives; (*3*) washout in an alkaline solution which dissolves the unexposed areas; and (*4*) drying. In the making of sensitized polyamide or nylon plates the plates are (*a*) exposed, (*b*) developed, and (*c*) dried. Development is carried out in an alcohol solution.

Wraparound plates are relief plates on thin metal shells that vary in thickness from 0.017 to 0.030 in. The plates are the full size of the plate cylinder and they are flexible enough to be mounted on the plate cylinder for printing. These plates are used on special wraparound presses on which the plates print directly on the paper. They are used even more extensively for printing letterset on offset presses.

There are a number of wraparound plates in use. Polymethacrylate plates are used extensively. They are made in the same way as the photoengraving plates. Another prominent plate for this use is the silver halide photographic relief plate which is described in the previous section. Many wraparound plates are made using full-size zinc, magnesium, or copper plates made with powderless etching techniques. A variation of these plates is one which consists of an 0.018-in. zinc sheet molecularly bonded to a 0.012-in. aluminum sheet (39). The relief image is produced on the zinc using conventional powderless etching techniques.

Electromechanical Engraving. Engravings can also be produced electromechanically on special equipment which scans an original photoelectrically and simultaneously etches a plastic printing plate with a heated stylus. One has been used successfully to produce engravings for small newspapers, printers, and engravers ever since it was introduced in 1947 (40). This unit has been improved with the introduction of a variable-tone reproduction unit and another unit which is capable of enlarging or reducing the image.

A more advanced electromechanical engraver makes photoengravings on plastic sheets directly from colored copy (41). It makes four-color corrected plates, either enlarged or reduced, directly from the color original which can be a transparency or flat art. It is the only one of the small scanners that can enlarge or reduce the image and produce screened separations from the original. Its main disadvantage is the time required—4–6 hours for a set of separations at an enlargement ratio of $6 \times$ to $8 \times$. Also repairs and local corrections cannot be made on the plates, and molds for electrotypes are difficult to make.

Duplicate Plates. Line and halftone photoengravings can be used directly in letterpress printing. Generally, however, the original engravings are used to make molds from which duplicate plates are made for the actual printing. There are four types of duplicate plates, stereotypes, electrotypes, plastic plates, and rubber plates.

Stereotypes are used almost exclusively in letterpress newspaper printing (42). They are also used to some extent in the printing of books and short-run trade magazines. In the making of stereotypes a matrix or mat, as it is called, is molded from the original engraving or type with heat and pressure in a matrix material consisting of a sheet of cellulose fibers with a smooth coated malleable surface. Plastics can also be used for molds. After proper treatment and mounting of the mat, a stereotype is made by pouring molten metal in the mat. After casting and cooling, the stereotype is trimmed and curved into individual plate units for mounting on the press for printing. For long runs the plates can be nickel or chromium plated (42).

Electrotypes are duplicates used for high-quality commercial, book, and magazine letterpress printing (43). There are many kinds of electrotypes. They are all made in essentially the same way by taking an impression of the original engraving in hot vinyl plastic which is sprayed with silver to conduct current after which a thin shell of copper or nickel is deposited by an electrolytic process. The shell is then backed with molten metal. As with stereotypes, electrotypes are plated with nickel or chromium for long runs.

Plastic and Rubber Plates. These duplicate plates have the advantages of light weight in comparison with metals, and simplicity of curving for mounting on printing cylinders (44). They are quite durable but they are relatively poor for the rendition of fine halftone images. The matrix material for these plates is a rigid board impregnated with a thermosetting resin of the phenolic type. Plastic plates are molded from thermoplastic vinyl resins. Rubber plates are molded from either natural or synthetic rubber or combinations of them, depending on the solvents used in the inks for printing. The rubber is vulcanized during the molding process to increase its hardness and resistance to solvents. The hardness is varied, depending on the materials to be printed. In flexographic printing, for which rubber plates are used exclusively, the hardness of the plates varies from 45 to 55 on the Durometer A scale (see Vol. 10, p. 818).

Gravure Platemaking and Cylindermaking

History. The resin-grain photogravure process was invented in about 1881 by Karl Klietsch. A clean copper plate was dusted with resin powder which was then sintered to produce a reticulated acid resist. A sheet of carbon tissue (paper coated on one side with a pigmented gelatin layer), previously sensitized with a bichromate and exposed to light in contact with a continuous-tone positive, was then moistened and squeegeed into contact with the prepared copper surface. After being dried, the plate was soaked in warm water to remove the paper and soluble parts of the gelatin, leaving a "gelatin relief" resist. Etching was done with ferric chloride solution which penetrated the thinner parts of the gelatin resist first and produced gradations in depth, the shadow areas of the picture being etched deepest and the highlights little or not at all. Areas protected by the resin remained unetched. Printing was done by covering the plate with ink and removing the excess with a scraper or "doctor." The resin screen provided "lands" to support the doctor blade. The remaining ink was then transferred to paper by pressure.

While this process had high artistic value, it never became commercially important because of difficulties in controlling the resin screen, and because it was limited to flat plates. It remained for Karl Klietsch in 1895 to adapt the crossline screen to photogravure and initiate the modern commercial process. Modifications for multicolor printing have been made (45,46).

Printing Surfaces. Modern gravure printing is done principally from images etched in cylinders on web presses, and is generally referred to as *rotogravure*. On sheet-fed presses the printing element is a thin copper plate wrapped around the cylinder. Preparation of the printing surface is essentially the same for both cylinders and plates.

For monochrome printing by conventional gravure, bichromate-sensitized carbon tissue or transfer film is first contact printed through a continuous-tone positive, and then given a second exposure in contact with a screen consisting of transparent lines and opaque square dots, 150 or 175 to the inch. The ratio of line to dot width is usually 1:3. The exposed carbon tissue or transfer film is then moistened and squeegeed into contact with the clean copper surface. Warm water is applied and the paper of the carbon tissue or backing of the film is peeled off. The gelatin thus transferred to the copper surface is further developed with warm water to produce a gelatin relief resist. Etching is done with 37–45°Bé (35–43%) ferric chloride solution. This solution etches the copper to different depths, depending on the thickness of the gelatin resist in the different tone areas. The areas corresponding to the screen lines remain unetched and provide "lands" to support the doctor blade in printing. For long runs, the etched cylinder or plate is chromium-plated to resist wear.

For multicolor printing, the principal process consists in making both a special halftone positive with a lateral dot formation which is similar to conventional gravure in the shadows but with varying dot sizes, and a continuous-tone positive for each color. These are contact-printed successively, in register, onto a sheet of carbon tissue, and the gelatin is transferred to the copper cylinder (45). Development and etching are essentially the same as for monochrome printing cylinders. The printing surface thus consists of disconnected ink cells of varying size and depth corresponding to the tone values desired. In the direct transfer process (46) only the special halftone positive is made. This is contact-printed directly onto the copper cylinder previously sensitized with a photopolymer of the cinnamic ester type. After being etched, the printing surface consists of disconnected ink cells of varying size but approximately the same depth. A number of modifications of these two processes are in commercial use in present-day rotogravure. For long runs the cylinders are chromium-plated.

Gravure plates can be used only for one image, which can be rerun. The image cannot be removed and the plate reused. On gravure cylinders, however, the electroplated copper containing the old image is stripped off and the cylinder is replated for reuse (47).

The photochemistry of bichromated gelatin is presumably similar to that of other bichromated colloids. Light sensitivity is governed by the same factors, namely, the bichromate–protein ratio, thickness of layer, pH value, moisture content, and temperature. Thickness of layer, however, has an added importance, since the purpose of exposure of the so-called carbon tissue is to insolubilize the gelatin layer to different depths, depending on the intensity of light transmitted by different tones of the positives. The bichromate is yellow and absorbs actinic light, but its effect does not produce sufficient differentiation in depth of hardening within the layer. To accomplish this, the gelatin layer is pigmented with a reddish-brown, semitransparent pigment.

After the gelatin layer has been transferred face down to the copper surface, treatment with warm water dissolves away the unhardened parts, leaving a gelatin relief resist. The thinnest areas are penetrated first by the ferric chloride solution, are etched deepest, and print the shadow tones of the picture. The areas where the resist is thickest are penetrated last by the etch, are etched the least, and print the lightest tones.

Lithographic Platemaking

History. Lithography was invented by Alois Senefelder, a Bavarian, around 1800. He discovered that if he drew characters on smooth Solnhofen limestone with a greasy crayon and then dampened the surface with gum water, he could repeatedly ink the greasy design and pull impressions on paper. He called the process chemical printing, or lithography (stone writing) and developed it into a successful printing process. For about 100 years, practically all lithographic printing was done from flat stones. It was entirely a manual operation until 1865, when the first flat-bed power press was introduced. Around 1900, the first direct rotary press appeared. The rotary principle was revolutionary, since it necessitated a change in the printing medium from stone to thin metal plates.

In 1906 another revolutionary change, the offset principle, was introduced. Until then, all lithographic printing on paper involved a direct transfer of ink from the stone or plate to the paper. The rotary offset press embodied an additional cylinder covered with a rubber blanket between the plate and impression cylinders. Thus, the ink was transferred first from the plate to the rubber blanket, then from the blanket to the paper. The offset principle was not new, having been used in metal decorating as early as 1875, when a rubber blanket cylinder was added to the flat-bed stone press. Until 1906, when A. S. Harris and Ira Rubel simultaneously invented the rotary offset press, no one made use of the offset principle in printing on paper.

The offset press possesses the following important advantages:

1. The rubber printing surface conforms to irregularities in the paper surface. Less printing pressure is needed, and print quality is improved. Halftones of high quality can be printed on rough papers.

2. Paper does not come into contact with the metal printing plate. The plate is therefore less subject to abrasive wear and can run much longer editions.

3. Speed of printing is increased. The effect of press improvements on printing speeds is shown by the following statistics for sheet-fed presses:

Press	*Printing speed, impressions/hr*
litho hand press	10–20
litho power press	1200
direct rotary press	2000
rotary offset press	4000–10,000

4. The image on an offset printing plate reads "right" instead of "in reverse." This facilitates both hand and photographic preparation.

5. Less ink is required for equal coverage. This decreases the tendency of the printed sheets to smudge and set off (produce a mirror image on the back) in the delivery pile, and speeds up drying.

The first offset presses were single-color, but it was not long before two-, three-, and four-color presses were developed. The proportion of multicolor offset presses has constantly increased. These include two-, three-, four-, five-, and six-color presses. Web or roll-fed offset presses were also developed and their number has steadily increased.

Commercial sheet-fed offset presses range in size from 17×22 in. to 55×78 in. Web presses range in web width from $7\frac{1}{2}$ to 76 in. In addition, there are a large number of so-called offset duplicating presses in sizes of 10×14 to 14×20 in. These are mostly used in offices and plants for noncommercial printing.

These mechanical developments have been made possible only through improvements in the quality of printing plates and in the efficiency of platemaking methods. Science, particularly chemistry, has made a great contribution to these improvements. At first, the printing image on stone was original art work. Then the hand-transfer process that enabled multiple printing images to be made from the original art was developed. Shortly after the advent of the offset press in 1906, methods were developed for making printing plates photographically, and the term *photolithography* was coined. At the present time, practically all printing plates are of this type. Original stone plates are still in use by artists.

The first photolithographic printing plates were sensitized to light with bichromated egg albumin. Other light-sensitive materials are now used in the same way, and the term "surface plate" applies to this group. Deep-etch plates made their appearance about 1930. Bimetal plates, although developed during the late 1930s, did not come into general use until after World War II. This period also saw the development of paper and plastic plates, primarily for the small duplicating presses. About 1950 the presensitized plates on metal were developed. These, along with wipe-on plates developed about 1957, are now replacing albumin for surface plates. The latest development is the photopolymer plate.

Plate Materials. While stone is still used to a limited extent by artists as a printing surface for lithography, by far the majority of lithographic printing is done from aluminum plates. These plates are manufactured in thicknesses from 0.009 to 0.025 in., depending on the size and type of press, with thickness tolerances of ± 0.0005 in. for the smaller sizes and ± 0.001 in. for the larger sizes. Also they must be flat with no buckles. Other metals such as zinc, mild steel, and stainless steel are used as bases for bimetal plates and they must be made to the same tolerances as those for aluminum plates.

The plates are grained or roughened prior to coating or processing. This is generally done in a flat, circularly oscillating tub by means of steel "marbles," abrasive grit, and water, but it can also be done by dry grit blasting, or brush graining using nylon or steel brushes and abrasive. Grain depth usually varies from 3 to 8 μ. The plate grain provides anchorage for the coating and the ink and recesses that help the surface carry moisture. Surface treatments (see under Photomechanical methods of platemaking), however, have made possible the use of finer grains, and even many grainless plates are being employed. Paper, plastic, and foil-laminated plates are also used for the smaller sizes of presensitized, direct-image, projection, and electrostatic plates.

Chemistry of Photolithography. Before describing the platemaking processes, something should be said about the chemistry of the photolithographic principle. As previously stated, the image areas on a lithographic plate must be ink-receptive and refuse to be wet by water, and the nonimage areas must be water-receptive and refuse to be wet by ink. The wider the difference in ink and water receptivities of these two areas the better the plate is and the easier it will be to print. The chemistry of the production of the images was discussed under Chemistry of the photomechanical principle. What needs to be discussed here is the chemistry of the nonimage areas and how they are rendered water-receptive or desensitized.

Roughening of the plate surface by graining is one way to improve wettability. Another has been the use of surface treatments, especially on the diazo-sensitized plates. A most important way is by the use of hydrophilic materials like gum arabic, or arabogalactan. Gum arabic is the most widely used desensitizer in lithography. See Resins, water-soluble; Resins, natural. It is a natural gum harvested from acacia trees. A mixture of calcium and magnesium salts of arabic acid, it has enough free carboxyl groups in the molecule to give good adhesion to metal surfaces. It is usually used in combination with phosphoric acid and salts like ammonium bichromate, diammonium monohydrogen phosphate, and zinc or magnesium nitrate as a mixture to produce a hydrophilic layer on a lithographic plate. This is called a desensitizing etch or simply an "etch." The gum arabic provides the water-receptive surface. The acid and salts serve as buffers and conditioners to passivate the metal surface and promote better adhesion of the gum to it. The gum arabic is used as a dilute solution (about 8° Bé or 15%) and dried on the plate as a protective layer to keep dirt, dust, fingerprints, and other grease smudges from printing.

The chemistry of plate desensitization is not well understood. The fact that desensitizing etches deposit an insoluble but hydrophilic gum film on the nonprinting areas has been established by dye absorption, contact angle measurements, and radioactive tracer techniques. A suitable gum in the etch is essential. Without it, the only desensitizing effect is due to the subsequent gumming up, the final step in plate preparation. Only gums that contain free carboxyl groups seem to have appreciable desensitizing action.

The effect of negative ions on the desensitizing film seems to be important but not much is known about it. All that is known at present is that dichromate, phosphate, nitrate, tannate, and gallate ions increase desensitization, whereas chloride and sulfate ions generally decrease it. Any particular desensitizing etch has its own optimum pH value; most have pH values between 2.0 and 2.5.

Platemaking Processes

The many different processes by which lithographic printing plates are made can be distinguished by the way the image is produced. *Surface* plates are those in which the light-sensitive coating eventually becomes the image carrier that accepts ink during the printing cycle on the press. *Deep-etch* plates are those in which the coating has been removed from the image areas which are then chemically coppered and/or lacquered and inked so they become the image carrier on the press. *Bimetal* plates are similar to deep-etch plates in that the coating is removed from the image areas but these areas consist of brass or copper either as the base metal or electroplated on another base metal. Other types of plates used mostly in duplicating or in printing on small presses are *direct-image* plates on which the image is drawn or typed directly on the plate; *projection* plates on which the image consists of a specially hardened photographic emulsion which is ink-receptive on the press; and *electrostatic* plates on which the images are produced by fused ink-receptive toners (48).

SURFACE PLATES

Until the advent of presensitized and wipe-on plates, the most popular surface plates were those made with bichromated albumin or casein. The most recent addition to this group of plates is the photopolymer plate.

Albumin plates are almost obsolete now but a description of them is useful, if for no other than historical reasons. These steps are involved in making an albumin plate: (1) counteretch the metal plate with a weak acid solution (0.75% HCl) to make sure it is chemically clean; (2) coat with bichromated albumin or casein emulsion; (3) expose to a negative; (4) apply a developing ink (dilute solution of a pigmented greasy mixture); (5) develop in water or a very dilute ammonia solution (1 oz NH_4OH to 1 gal of soln); (6) apply a surface treatment to remove residual protein from the nonprinting areas; (7) desensitize the plate with an "etch"; and (8) gum with a dilute solution of gum arabic (about 8°Bé). Unless a surface treatment is used to remove residual coating from the nonprinting areas, these plates give trouble in printing on the press. The nonprinting areas are sensitive and pick up ink spottily or scum.

Presensitized and wipe-on plates of the diazo type (see under Photomechanical methods of platemaking) are much simpler to make and generally print cleaner than albumin plates, because the surface treatments used on them prior to coating are very water-receptive and inhibit any tendency to scum. Presensitized plates are already coated. Wipe-on plates are coated with a solution of the diazo resin by wiping the coating on with a sponge and drying it down with a cloth or by applying the coating on a simple roller coater. After exposure to a negative, the presensitized and wipe-on plates can be handled in the same manner. An emulsion lacquer consisting of a pigmented lacquer, acidified gum arabic solution, and a suitable emulsifier is applied over the whole plate. The acidified gum dissolves the coating from the unexposed nonimage areas and the lacquer deposits on the exposed image areas, rendering them visible and ink-receptive. After washing, the plate is gummed and it is ready for use. Wipe-on coatings, once mixed, should be used within twenty-four hours as they deteriorate on standing. The diazo resins themselves should be kept in a refrigerator as they decompose on standing at ambient temperatures.

There are some presensitized plates that can be made from positives. These systems use diazo oxides and the developing solutions after exposure are alkaline (see under Chemistry of the photomechanical principle), which remove the exposed areas and leave the unexposed ones as the printing areas. These are inked to protect them and the plate is gummed. Several positive wipe-on systems have been developed. They are not used extensively because of the difficulty in achieving proper tone values consistently. One system has been used to some extent for screenless printing in which continuous-tone positives are used in place of halftones (49).

Photopolymer plates of the cinnamic ester type have been used for some time (see under Chemistry of the photomechanical principle). These are available as wipe-on or presensitized plates. All are exposed to negatives. Since the coatings are water-insoluble, they must be developed in organic solvents. This can be done by (1) wiping the solvents over the plate, (2) using a vapor degreasing machine, or (3) using an emulsion of the solvent with the desensitizing agent for rendering the non-image areas water-receptive. The plates are desensitized with an etch and gummed.

The most recent of the photopolymer plates uses a system similar to that for the polymethacrylate plates (see under Chemistry of the photomechanical principle). This is a presensitized plate which is first exposed to a negative, then developed in an aqueous solution, desensitized, gummed, and reexposed to light to harden the image areas for long runs (50).

Printing Characteristics of Surface Plates. As with all bichromated coatings, albumin and casein plates are affected by temperature and relative humidity. Also, if not made properly or if a surface treatment is not used after development, they have a tendency to scum on the press. Presensitized and wipe-on plates are not affected much by relative humidity but can deteriorate if exposed for any length of time to temperatures exceeding 125°F. They are not very resistant to abrasion on the press so they are not practical for runs over 75,000 impressions. (There is a prelacquered presensitized plate that is capable of longer runs than this.) Photopolymer plates have good resistance to temperature and relative humidity and to abrasion on the press. They are capable of runs in excess of 250,000.

DEEP ETCH

There are several presensitized deep-etch plates but by far the majority of deep-etch plates are made using grained aluminum plates and bichromated gum arabic coating. Most plates in England and on the European continent are made using anodized aluminum. The most popular plate in the U.S. is what is known as the "copperized" aluminum plate, in which copper is deposited chemically on the image areas. In making this plate the following steps are taken:

1. Counteretch the grained aluminum plate with a solution containing about 4 oz of 85% phosphoric acid and water to make 1 gal of solution.

2. Coat with bichromated gum arabic solution. A typical coating formula is as follows: gum arabic solution (14°Bé), 3 quarts (96 oz); ammonium bichromate, $6\frac{3}{4}$ oz; ammonium hydroxide (28% NH_3), $4\frac{3}{4}$ oz; water to make 1 gal; pH of final solution 8.5–9.5; and density about 14°Bé. Average thickness of coating is 12–13 μ.

3. Expose through positives.

4. Stage out (or paint out) all areas which did not expose but are not to print (such as dust specks, film edges, crop marks, etc) with a pigmented cellulose nitrate (nitrocellulose) lacquer (alcohol soluble).

5. Develop in a nearly saturated salt solution. Water cannot be used for development because the exposed coating is too soluble in water. The solubility differential between exposed and unexposed bichromated gum arabic is maximized in almost saturated salt solutions containing an organic acid. A typical formula for such a developer is 39% calcium chloride solution (40°Bé), 122 oz; lactic acid (85%), $6\frac{1}{2}$ oz. The solution is worked over the plate with a plush pad until metal is reached in the printing areas or until step 9 is reached on the GATF sensitivity guide. The developer is squeegeed off and two more fresh applications of developer are made for the same length of time or until step 6 is reached on the GATF sensitivity guide.

6. Deep etching is also done with a nearly saturated salt solution with a formula such as a 39% soln of calcium chloride (40°Bé), 89 oz; zinc chloride, 35 oz; 48% ferric chloride soln (50°Bé), $25\frac{1}{4}$ oz; hydrochloric acid (37%), $1\frac{1}{4}$ oz. This solution is worked over the plate with a plush pad for 1–$1\frac{1}{2}$ min and squeegeed off.

7. Alcohol wash. This is done to remove the residue from deep etching. About four washes of anhydrous denatured ethyl alcohol or anhydrous isopropyl alcohol are used. The first wash removes the staging lacquer. Vigorous rubbing with embossed paper wipes is recommended to remove iron deposited in the image areas during the

deep-etching step. Some platemaking procedures recommend an application of developer for 2–3 min at this stage to remove the iron.

8. Copper deposition. While the plate is still wet with the last alcohol wash, the copperizing solution is poured on the plate. The formula for such a solution follows: isopropyl alcohol (99%), 1 quart; cuprous chloride, 1 oz; hydrochloric acid (37%), 1 oz. Copper deposition will be complete in about 5–7 min after which the plate is washed with two more applications of anhydrous alcohol.

9. Application of lacquer and developing ink. When the plate is thoroughly dry it is coated with a thin layer of ink-receptive vinyl-type lacquer, which has excellent "nonblinding" characteristics, ie, it does not wet with acid and gum. After the lacquer is thoroughly dry, developing ink is applied, rubbed down well, and dried.

10. Removal of light-hardened stencil. The lacquered and inked plate is soaked for about 10 min in warm water (about 100°F) to soften the gum stencil, after which it is scrubbed under running water to remove all visible traces of the stencil together with its coating of lacquer and ink.

11. Desensitization. An "etch" is applied to the plate and rubbed over it for about 1½ min.

12. Gum. The etch is rinsed off. The plate is squeegeed to remove most of the water and placed on a flat table. A solution of 8°Bé gum arabic is applied over the whole plate and rubbed down smooth until it is dry. Continue drying with a fan.

Deep-etch plates are very dependable and durable and are used for the majority of medium- to long-run quality lithographic jobs. They are used extensively for color printing, for web offset, and for packaging printing. Their major disadvantage is the time required for staging or painting out unwanted work on the plates. If any spots are missed in the platemaking operation it means holding up a press while the spots are polished off the plates.

BIMETAL PLATES

On bimetal plates the ink-receptive image and the water-receptive nonimage areas consist of different metals (51). The image metal is usually copper but can be brass; the nonimage metal can be chromium, aluminum, or stainless steel. The feature of these metals is that copper is ink-receptive in the presence of ions like phosphate and nitrate which render chromium, aluminum, and stainless steel water-receptive.

There are two types of bimetal plates in use: Type I which has the image metal (copper) plated on the nonimage metal (aluminum or stainless steel); Type II which has the nonimage metal (chromium) plated on the image metal (copper or brass).

Type I Bimetal Plates. These plates consist of 2–2.5 μ of copper electroplated on aluminum or stainless steel. They are usually made from negatives. The regular platemaking procedure for these plates is as follows:

1. Clean with pumice and 2% sulfuric acid.
2. Coat with a deep-etch type of light-sensitive coating.
3. Expose to light through a negative.
4. Develop with a deep-etch developer as in deep-etch platemaking.
5. Wash with alcohol and dry as in deep-etch platemaking.
6. Etch away the bared copper in the nonimage areas. A 40% ferric chloride soln (42°Bé) is used when the base metal is stainless steel. Ferric nitrate solution is used when the base metal is aluminum.

7. Remove the stencil from the image areas with pumice and 2% sulfuric acid.

8. Ink the copper image with a rub-up ink which is like a developing ink but with a higher consistency.

9. Etch and gum the plate as in deep-etch platemaking.

There are some presensitized plates of this type that can be made from positives. These have diazo oxide coatings. After exposure through a positive and development in an alkaline developer which dissolves the exposed coating, the unexposed image areas are protected with a fixing solution which prevents the acid in the copper etch from attacking the image.

Type II Bimetal Plates. These plates consist of 1–2 μ of chromium electroplated on 3–8 μ of copper which is plated on a base metal which can be zinc, aluminum, mild steel, or stainless steel. Some of these plates which are used on web presses have also been made by plating the chromium directly on sheets of copper or brass. These plates are always made from positives. The platemaking procedure for these plates follows:

1. Remove the gum. After plating, gum arabic is applied to the chromium to protect it and keep it water-receptive. This gum is washed off with water. Sometimes the plates are counteretched with dilute sulfuric acid or phosphoric acid.

2. Coat with a deep-etch coating.

3. Expose to light through a positive. Positives should have slightly smaller dots than for deep-etch plates because there is some lateral etching as the chromium is removed, which enlarges the printing image elements slightly.

4. Stage as in deep-etch platemaking.

5. Develop as in deep-etch platemaking.

6. Etch through the chromium layer in the image areas. A suitable chromium etch formula (52) is as follows: 34% aluminum chloride solution (32°Bé), 3 quarts; zinc chloride (technical granular), 5¼ lb; phosphoric acid (85%), 5 fl oz.

7. Alcohol-wash as in deep-etch platemaking.

8. Sensitize copper to ink. The image areas are covered with a thin solution of asphaltum or a mixture of asphaltum and oleic acid. This protects the copper from corrosion and renders it ink-receptive.

9. Remove the gum stencil as in deep-etch platemaking.

10. Etch and gum as in deep-etch platemaking.

Bimetal plates are the most rugged plates used in lithography, being capable of runs exceeding a million impressions. They are used under the most difficult conditions of printing such as on poorer grades of board and paper. They have very good abrasion resistance. They require a minimum of water to keep the nonprinting areas clean and, because they are relatively smooth, the images are solid, clear, and sharp. They are the easiest plates to handle on the press because a single treatment is all that is needed to restore them to printing condition when something happens on the press. A treatment with dilute nitric or phosphoric acid renders the copper ink-receptive while the chromium, aluminum, or stainless steel remain water-receptive. With other types of plates this type of treatment can damage the image areas while helping the nonimage areas and much more careful treatment is needed on the press. The main disadvantage of bimetal plates is their cost.

OTHER LITHOGRAPHIC PLATEMAKING PROCESSES

The subjects considered in this section are collotype, screenless-printing, letterset, direct-image, projection, and electrostatic plates.

Collotype is often called *photogelatin* (53). While this is strictly not lithography, it is similar in principle. Collotype is printed both from glass plates on flat-bed presses and metal plates on direct rotary presses on which the image is transferred directly from the plate to the paper. The plates are made using a coating of bichromated gelatin. Potassium bichromate is generally used as the sensitizer as it has a longer scale of reproduction than ammonium bichromate (it will reproduce more steps on a gray scale). A continuous-tone negative with a density range of about 1.2 and a gamma close to 1.0 produces reproductions of good quality. The gelatin is differentially hardened inversely to the density of silver in the negative. The plate is developed by washing in water after exposure. The temperature at which the coating is dried and the temperature of the washwater control the degree of reticulation of the gelatin. The reproductions are not truly continuous tone but show the irregular pattern of the reticulation. Before printing on the press the plates are soaked in a glycerine or ethylene glycol bath. The gelatin swells in inverse proportion to the amount of light that is received during exposure.

Screenless printing is a process for printing from continuous-tone positives on diazo-sensitized plates using regular lithographic presses and techniques. A positive presensitized and a positive wipe-on process have been found to print a fairly long tone scale. The length of the scale is a function of the coating thickness and the grain of the plate (54). A continuous-tone positive is made to the same tone scale as the plate. The plate is processed carefully as printing by this method is equivalent to printing with controlled "scum."

Direct-image, projection, and electrostatic plates are used mainly for duplicating printing on small presses. These plates usually have a paper, resin-impregnated, or plastic base. They do not have quality capabilities suitable for commercial advertising printing but there are numerous other applications for this type of printing.

Direct-image plates are like the original lithographic plates drawn on stone. They are called "masters" and the image can be drawn, lettered, painted, ruled, traced, typed, or written on them using pencil, crayon, ink, carbon paper, fabric or carbon paper ribbon, rubber stamp, numbering machine, brush, or air brush. Preprinted masters can be made by printing the image by letterpress or offset with oil-base inks. Guide lines and instruction can be printed with water-color inks as these will not print. These plates are ideal for systems printing and are used extensively in personalized check printing for "magnetic ink character recognition" (MICR).

Making direct-image plates is very simple. Only two steps are involved, as follows:

1. Apply the image to the plate by any of the methods or materials mentioned. Be careful to protect the plate from grease spots, such as fingerprints, grease or oil from the machine, etc, as these will print.

2. Mount the plate on the press, go over it with the etch designed for the plate, start the press running, drop the ink and dampening rollers on the plate, and start printing.

With paper-base plates the fountain solution used on the press must be the one designed for this type of plate. Most of these fountain solutions contain glycols or glycerine. The inks should be designed to work with these polyalcohols as some inks tend to emulsify with these materials.

Projection plates are made by the process described under Chemistry of the photomechanical principle (see p. 517), and are printed like the direct-image plates.

Electrostatic plates are also described in this section (p. 521).

Image Carriers for the Stencil Processes

There are two stencil processes in general use, stencil duplicating and screen process printing. *Stencil duplicating* is described in the article on Reprography.

Screen process image carriers can be produced manually or by photomechanical means (55). The screens can consist of silk bolting cloth with "taffeta weave" with mesh counts from 100 to 200 openings per lineal inch. Nylon screens are used for textile printing and metal screens of phosphor bronze and stainless steel are used for fine detail printing in meshes as fine as 300. The screen material is attached to a rigid frame and stretched tightly so that it is level and smooth. The stencil is applied to the bottom side of the screen (the side in contact with the surface to be printed on), ink with a consistency similar to thick paint is used in the screen and the ink is transferred by rubbing it over the screen surface with a rubber squeegee. Screen life approaches 100,000 impressions.

Manual stencils are made by knife-cutting special film stencil materials. These consist of two plastic layers. The image to be printed is cut through one layer. This part of the stencil is placed in contact with the underside of the screen. A solvent is applied that is insoluble in the ink but attaches the cut stencil to the screen, after which the backing layer is removed. Manual stencils can also be produced by artists drawing directly on the screens with special materials. When screen process is used for art reproduction it is called *serigraphy*.

Photomechanical stencils are of two types, direct coatings and transfer films. Direct coatings are either bichromated gelatin or bichromated PVA. The coated screens are exposed through a positive, washed out, and inspected. These screens are used for printing electronic components. They are not very practical for short-run commercial work because of the difficulty of reclaiming the screen after use.

There are four transfer film methods of making screens, (1) carbon tissue as used in gravure; (2) unsensitized film; (3) presensitized film; and (4) photographic transfer film. The carbon-tissue method is almost the same as gravure except that the tissue is transferred to a temporary vinyl support for development before application to the screen. The unsensitized and presensitized films are similar in their use in that they eliminate the double transfer necessary with carbon tissue. These materials are mounted on plastic films. The unsensitized film has to be sensitized before use with an alcoholic solution of ammonium bichromate. The photographic transfer film has been described under Photomechanical methods of platemaking.

Printing

This section on printing contains brief descriptions of the equipment used for printing by each process and how the printing is performed. In general, printing is done with the paper fed into the press in sheets—sheet fed—or from rolls—web fed. Newspapers and magazines are printed on presses which are web-fed. Many presses are multicolor. They can print a number of colors in succession. Usually each color requires a separate complete unit—inking, plate, and impression mechanism—on the press. A two-color press would have two such units, a four-color one would have four. *Perfecting* presses print both sides of the sheet in one pass through the press. They can be either *blanket to blanket* as in most web offset presses and some sheet-fed offset presses for printing books, or the units can be in line and the sheets are turned over between printings.

LETTERPRESS PRINTING

Letterpress presses are of three types, platen, flat-bed cylinder, and rotary. These are illustrated in Figure 12. Platen presses have two flat surfaces, the bed and the platen. Type and plates can be mounted on the bed. These are inked by inking rollers and the impression is made or "pulled" on sheets fed manually or automatically on the platen. Maximum size of platen presses is 18 × 24 in. They are used for many different purposes, such as printing of paper and paperboard, envelopes, embossing, steel-rule die-cutting, and gold-leaf stamping.

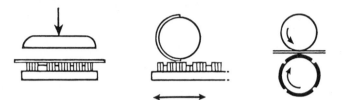

Fig. 12. Diagram of platen, flat-bed, and rotary presses for letterpress printing (30). Courtesy The Printing Industries of America.

Flat-bed cylinder presses are available with horizontal and vertical beds. They too can print type and plates. The horizontals print larger sheets (up to 42 × 56 in.) than the platen presses and were designed in three types, single color, two color, and perfecting. Their manufacture was discontinued in the U.S. in 1962. Some are still being built in Europe. The vertical presses are popular job presses with a maximum sheet size of 14 × 20 in. and a rated speed of 5000 impressions per hour (iph).

By far the greatest amount of letterpress is printed on rotary presses. This is the type on which much long-run commercial work, packaging, newspapers, and magazines are run. The sheet-fed presses are made in sizes up to $54\frac{1}{2}$ × 77 in. with rated speeds as high as 6000 iph. Plates must be curved for mounting on these presses. Stereos, electros, photopolymer, and wraparound plates can be used on these presses. One type of wraparound press is built like a sheet-fed offset press with three cylinders. The plate is mounted on what would be the blanket cylinder and what would normally be the plate cylinder is used as a large ink drum to get even ink distribution.

Web-fed rotary letterpress presses are of many sizes and styles. In magazine printing there are presses of the unit type, which have a separate complete unit for each color printed, and the common impression cylinder type, often called "satellite" type, on which the printing units are situated around one large cylinder which serves as the impression cylinder for all the printing units. Newspaper presses are built in couples with each unit printing both sides of the paper in succession, usually 16 pages— 8 pages on each side—at a time. Flexographic presses are of three types: (*1*) stack type; (*2*) central impression cylinder (similar to common impression cylinder magazine press); and (*3*) in-line (similar to unit type press). See Figure 13.

Because pressure is needed for ink wetting and transfer and because of the variable size of the image elements in letterpress the same amount of printing pressure or "squeeze" exerts more pressure on highlight dots than on shadow dots. This necessitates considerable "makeready," to even out the impression so that the highlights print correctly and do not puncture the paper. Precision electros, wraparound plates, and premakeready systems have helped reduce makeready time but it is still

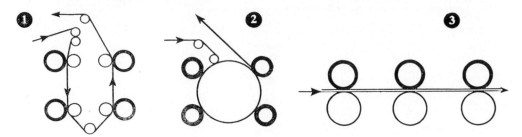

Fig. 13. Diagram of stack-type, central impression cylinder-type, and in-line type of flexographic presses (30). Courtesy The Printing Industries of America.

appreciable for quality printing and is a reason letterpress is being replaced by other processes for some types of work.

GRAVURE

Not much gravure is printed from sheet-fed presses which use plates. By far the greatest amount of gravure is printed from cylinders on rolls of paper or film. The cylinders are removable and can change in diameter so that different print lengths can be accommodated from job to job if necessary. This is desirable in packaging but unnecessary in magazine printing. The gravure printing unit consists of a printing cylinder, an impression cylinder, and an inking system, as indicated in Figure 14. Ink is applied to the printing cylinder by an ink roll or spray and the excess is removed by the doctor blade and returned to the ink fountain. The impression cylinder is covered with a resilient rubber composition that presses the paper into contact with the ink in the tiny cells of the printing surface.

Gravure ink consists of pigment, a resin binder, and a volatile solvent. It is quite fluid and dries entirely by evaporation. For high-speed printing, the solvents are quite volatile, and the inking system must be enclosed. In multicolor printing, where two or more gravure units operate in tandem, each color must be dried before the next is printed. The web, therefore, is passed through a heated dryer after each impression; in some cases the dryers are connected to a solvent-recovery system.

Single-color rotogravure yields excellent pictorial reproduction on a wide range of papers. Its reproduction of type matter and line drawings leaves something to be desired, however, because the screen reduces sharpness somewhat. Color reproduction is mostly done in three and four colors on multicolor presses. Gravure is widely used for newspaper magazine supplements, magazines, mail-order catalogs, cartons, and

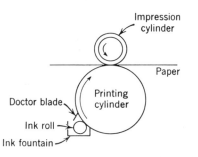

Fig. 14. Diagram of a gravure printing unit.

labels, and in the printing of cellophane, plastic films, foils, and plastic laminates. It is the most practical process for the printing of "gold" bronze, aluminum, and opaque whites.

A serious problem in gravure printing has been the necessity for very smooth papers. Otherwise there are "skips" in the printing. The introduction of trailing-blade-coated papers about 1957 was a big boon to gravure but it did not help in printing on newsprint or rough boards. The development of the "electrostatic assist" by the Gravure Research Institute (56) has helped to solve this problem and raise the general level of quality of gravure printing on all paper stocks.

LITHOGRAPHY

The function of the lithographic press, based on the principle that grease and water do not mix, is to produce prints of acceptable quality. Construction of a sheet-fed offset printing unit is shown in Figure 15. Multicolor presses consist of 2–6 of the units shown in Figure 15 in tandem but with a single feeder and delivery. There are some presses that use a common impression cylinder for printing two colors. For web presses, paper is fed from a roll, and delivery is in the form of cut sheets or folded signatures. Most web offset presses are of the blanket-to-blanket design in which two units print simultaneously on both sides of the sheet and one blanket acts as the impression cylinder for the other blanket and vice versa.

Lithographic ink is basically a concentrated dispersion of pigment in a viscous oil vehicle, with various additives to give it suitable working properties. One type contains a drier to accelerate hardening of the vehicle after printing. In another type, the oil vehicle consists of a resin dissolved in a volatile solvent. This type dries by evaporation of the solvent and penetration of the solvent into the paper. Various combinations of drying oil, resin, and solvent are also used. (See Inks.) For lithographic ink, careful selection of ingredients is essential. Since the ink comes into intimate and continuous contact with water during printing, it must be free from any tendency to bleed or to form an ink-in-water emulsion. The formation of water-in-ink emulsion is unavoidable, but this does no harm unless the working consistency of the ink is damaged. During normal printing, the ink takes up from 5 to 30% of water as a

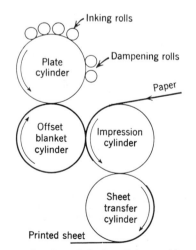

Fig. 15. Diagram of a sheet-fed offset lithographic printing unit.

water-in-ink emulsion.   The surface chemistry of this ink-water relationship is little known.

In the printing cycle, water or "fountain solution" is fed to the plate just before it contacts the inking or form rollers.   This is done by means of rollers covered with cotton flannel, called molleton, or with parchment paper, to which the water is metered from its fountain.   Also rubber composition and plastic rollers are used to transfer the fountain solution to the plate.   Very little moisture is required.   The moisture film produced on the plate is continuous on the nonimage areas of the plate and acts as a barrier preventing adhesion of ink.   Any moisture on the greasy image areas is discontinuous and does not prevent transfer of ink to them.   To keep the nonprinting areas clean during long runs, the dampening water must contain some acid and a desensitizing gum.   It is assumed that their function is to maintain the desensitizing film produced when the plate was made, but little is known of the surface chemistry involved.   With well-desensitized plates, the pH value of the fountain solution or dampening water may be as high as 5–6. With poorly desensitized plates it may have to be as low as 3–4.   New dampening systems use isopropyl alcohol as a dampening solution ingredient in concentrations as high as 30%.   This does not seem to have any deleterious effect on the paper, ink, or plate.

The standard offset blanket has a three-ply fabric base, on one surface of which is a skim coat of a rubber compound, 0.012–0.015 in. thick.   The total thickness is approx 0.064 in.   This blanket is wrapped around the blanket cylinder and held under a tension of about 50 lb/in. of width.   The rubber surface receives ink from the image areas of the plate and transfers it to the surface being printed.   The life of the blanket is limited since it is susceptible to mechanical damage, to swelling resulting from absorption of ink vehicle, and to development of tackiness and glazing, which are caused by oxidation stimulated by absorbed ink driers, principally cobalt and manganese soaps. Great improvements in resistance to ink vehicles and driers have been made through the development of synthetic rubber compositions and suitable antioxidants.   Also, new compressible blankets have been developed which improve sharpness of printing.

While lithographic printing can be done on practically all types of paper, certain special requirements are necessary for best results in long runs.   These include the following:

   1.   Freedom from loose surface fibers and unbound mineral filler.
   2.   Sufficient bond or "pick" strength to resist the pull of tacky lithographic inks.
   3.   Minimum tendency to curl.
   4.   Freedom from chemicals that could sensitize the plate or cause the formation of an ink-in-water emulsion
   5.   In coated papers, resistance of the coating adhesive to water.

Offset lithography produces quality printing on both rough and smooth papers, but the trend in recent years has been toward coated papers because they require less ink and give more brilliance to colors.   See Paper.

COLLOTYPE PRINTING

In collotype or photogelatin printing no dampening is used during printing as on a lithographic press.   The presses are direct printing and the plates are mounted on them after they have been soaked in the glycerine or ethylene glycol bath.   The gelatin takes ink in proportion to the amount of exposure it has received.   The shadow areas with a lot of exposure take the most ink; the highlight areas, with only a small amount of exposure, take very little ink. The hygroscopic polyalcohols absorb moisture from the air to maintain proper moisture content in the gelatin which, in turn, controls the tone reproduction. The relative humidity of the pressroom is gradually increased to compensate for the loss of moisture from the gelatin at each impression. As the moisture content of the gelatin decreases, its tone reproduction flattens so more moisture is needed to increase contrast. Eventually a point is reached, where the flattening can no longer be compensated by raising the relative humidity in the air and the plate has to be resoaked. The relative humidity must be lowered and the cycle between moisture content of the gelatin and relative humidity starts again. Between 500 and 1000 good prints are obtained between soakings. While collotype is capable of beautiful printing, no two prints are exactly alike as the contrast of the printing varies with the moisture content of the gelatin and this is continually changing. It is a short-run process, slow and expensive.

REVERSE LITHOGRAPHY

The conventional lithographic process depends upon having a plate on which the image is preferentially wet by an oil-type ink and the nonimage area is preferentially wet by water. The ink is thus formulated from water-immiscible oils or hydrocarbon solvents and the fountain solution is substantially water. Printing inks made from water-miscible glycols, glycerin, or water obviously do not fulfill these requirements and thus cannot be used in lithography in the conventional process. However, by designing a plate on which the image area is preferentially wet by the water-miscible ink while in the presence of a volatile hydrocarbon solvent which preferentially wets the nonimage area, a reversal of the process has been achieved. This permits lithographic printing of water-miscible, hydrocarbon-immiscible, inks, and is known as reverse lithography, a process developed by Interchemical Corporation.

Although it is not being used commercially, the characteristics of reverse lithography which suggest its use in certain areas are the attainment of lithographic quality with inks which cannot be printed by conventional lithography and yet have certain inherent characteristics desired in the finished print. These applications could include low-odor food packaging, food insert printing, safety inks for printing overall designs on bank checks, waxed wrappers, and other applications where rapid drying by steam is desirable. Complete elimination of the aqueous fountain solution may suggest other applications.

Plates for this process can be made by developing an image stencil and subsequently applying a silicone composition which, when hardened by heat or otherwise, forms the nonimage area. During processing, the image stencil is removed to provide the image area.

The inks can be made in a variety of formulations depending upon the particular requirements. One important class of inks for this process is the so-called moisture-set type of ink based upon glycol and containing resins which are water-insoluble and which thus can be set by moisture either from the atmosphere, by steaming, or by interaction with the stock. This type of ink also has the characteristic of being very low in odor.

The fountain or dampening solution is essentially a volatile aliphatic hydrocarbon solvent instead of the aqueous solution used in conventional lithography.

Except for modification of the dampening unit, standard lithographic presses may be used. Only one dampening form roller is used and this is a precision-set, specially coated, elastomeric roller which should be positively driven rather than friction driven to prevent slippage and thus provide true rolling precision application of the hydro-carbon solvent.

SCREEN PROCESS PRINTING

Screen printing equipment can be very simple, consisting only of a table, screen frame, and squeegee. However, power screen presses with mechanical feed and delivery are in common use, producing 450–3500 prints per hour, depending on the sheet size. Special presses are designed to print objects of irregular shape such as milk and soft-drink bottles, using ceramic colors, plastic and metal containers, etc.

Screen process inks are usually of the drying-oil type and have the consistency of thick paints. The amount of ink applied in screen printing is far greater than in letterpress printing or lithography, and the prints must be racked separately until dry, or passed through a heated tunnel, before they can be piled.

Screen printing is in common use for the production of art prints, posters, decalcomania transfers, greeting cards, menus, and program covers. It is particularly adapted to the printing of fabrics, felt, leather, metals, glass, ceramic materials, and plastics, both flat and in finished form. By printing an adhesive size and then dusting with cotton, silk, or rayon flock, the finished design can be made to appear like felt or suede leather.

Screen printing has distinct advantages for short runs because of the simplicity of the equipment needed. For longer runs, the advantage is soon lost since other printing methods are so much faster. For many of the applications listed, however, screen printing is the only practical process.

ELECTROSTATIC PRINTING PROCESSES

There are two electrostatic printing processes that are of interest and show potential for growth. These are electrostatic screen printing and electrostatic powder gravure.

Electrostatic screen printing is an interesting application of screen process printing (59). It is a pressureless process for printing on objects of irregular shapes, such as aspirin tablets, fried eggs, corrugated board, plywood, textiles with deep patterned weaves, etc. It is used regularly for printing on apples. The equipment consists of a charged stainless-steel screen which carries a stencil image. Dry toner, placed on the screen, becomes charged too. The screen is positioned over the object to be printed, which rests on a plate which has a charge opposite to the one on the screen. This sets up an electrostatic field which causes the toner particles to flow toward the object to be printed, leaving an image on it corresponding to the stencil on the screen. The toner image can be fixed in a number of ways, by heat, solvent spray, vapor, etc. Web-fed equipment has been designed, using the image on an endless screen belt which is claimed to be capable of printing speeds of 3000 ft/min.

Electrostatic powder gravure printing, as the name implies, is a combination of electrostatic transfer and a gravure cylinder in which the cells are filled with powdered ink which is then doctored, charged, and transferred electrostatically to the substrate (60,61). The resulting image is then fixed to the substrate by heat or solvent fusion. This process was developed by Interchemical Corporation.

As in conventional gravure, the cells on the cylinder provide the image. It is also practical to print type and lines without screening.

The powdered inks for this process are composed of combinations of resinous materials with colorants dispersed therein.

While electrostatic powder gravure is still in the experimental stages, web printing has been accomplished by the use of a rotary press utilizing a corona wire or metal roller as the counter electrode. The charge on the paper caused by emission from the corona wire keeps the web in contact with the gravure cylinder. When using a metal roller as the counter electrode the web is in contact with it, thus permitting printing through a gap or with light impression pressure.

Electrostatic powder gravure printing can also be done on round plastic or glass containers by suitably charging the round container to effect transfer of the powdered ink.

Finishing

After printing, the printed material is subjected to a number of finishing operations. Most printing is done on large sheets with a number of the same or different subjects on the sheet. Labels are varnished and cut to size after printing. Calendars are cut to size and stapled. In check printing, some are cut to size and stapled; some are perforated, cut, stapled, or drilled for insertion into a binder. Some greeting cards are embossed, dusted with gold bronze, and folded. Some printing is folded into pamphlets for mailing. Some is folded into "signatures" (of usually 16 or 32 pages) which later are bound together in various ways to make books. Some printing, like letterheads, is just cut and packaged into reams. Most package printing is scored and die-cut for shaping into packages later. Printed metal is formed into cans, boxes, trays, and even into odd shapes like toys and globes. There are other finishing operations such as pasting, mounting, laminating, and collating, depending on the end use of the product. These operations are mostly mechanical and, with the exception of those using glue, none are affected or influenced by advance in chemical technology.

Comparison of the Three Major Printing Processes

Letterpress is a simple printing process, dealing with the direct transfer of ink to paper. Color proofs made on a four-color proof press are reliable guides for printing. Water-base, moisture-set, as well as oil-base inks can be used. Once printing conditions have been established, letterpress prints consistently at high speeds on reasonably priced paper. Color variation is at a minimum. Ease of making duplicate plates and flexibility of changing plates are big advantages, especially in magazine production where many regional editions are printed.

The disadvantages of letterpress are (*1*) cost of engravings; (*2*) slow make-ready on the press; (*3*) poor reproduction of vignettes (pictures that shade off gradually at the edges); (*4*) poor trapping of inks on multicolor presses, requiring extensive undercolor removal; and (*5*) necessity to print on smooth papers for good halftone and color rendition.

Gravure is an even simpler printing process than letterpress. It is capable of very high quality in single color and multicolor and can print brighter colors with cheaper pigments than other processes. It prints at very high speeds. In multicolor printing there is no problem with trapping as colors are dried between each printing. Color is easy to control with an automatic viscometer.

The disadvantages of gravure more than outweigh its advantages. They are (1) prohibitive cost of cylinders except for very long runs (500,000 or more); (2) absence of a reliable proofing system—full-size presses are needed for proofing critical work; (3) inflexibility of cylinders, for regional editions of magazines, for instance; and (4) "skips" in printing due to the need for smooth papers—being alleviated by the "electrostatic assist." Electronic and even laser engraving of cylinders may improve reliability and reproducibility and relieve some of the other disadvantages such as cost and proofing.

Lithography is a complicated printing process, yet it is the cheapest of the processes to carry out. It is capable of high quality of reproduction. It is especially superior in the rendition of vignettes and blending of tones as required in the reproduction of skin tones. Plates are easy to make and are less expensive than photoengravings and gravure cylinders. Press speeds are reasonably high so that running costs are in line with the other processes. It can print on rough, textured surfaces. In web printing it is the only one of the processes that can use the blanket-to-blanket principle which allows perfecting printing at a reasonable investment for equipment.

The main disadvantages of lithography are (1) need for an ink-water balance which results in higher waste; (2) need for tacky inks which calls for stronger, more expensive papers; and (3) overall contact of paper with the blanket in the impression nip, necessitating flat paper in good moisture balance with the pressroom atmosphere; otherwise wrinkles or misregister will result. These disadvantages are being studied in research and solutions are being found. New dampening systems are minimizing the problems with ink-water balance. With better dampening, ink systems can be improved and simplified and lower-tack inks may be possible. New presses with higher speeds taking smaller sheets ease the requirement for flat paper.

Reviewing these advantages and disadvantages it may be concluded that lithography is an ideal process for text and pictorial reproduction for short and medium runs, sheet-fed or web; letterpress is good for text matter, flexibility, broad lettering, solid backgrounds and expanses of color on packaging; gravure is best for long-run pictorial reproduction such as packaging and mail-order catalogs. Research going on in each of the processes could result in improvements that could change this picture overnight. Also other printing processes, like electrostatics, could be contenders for markets now enjoyed by lithography, letterpress, or gravure.

ACKNOWLEDGMENT: The author would like to express his appreciation to Mr. Paul W. Greubel of Interchemical Corporation, New York, for the sections on Reverse lithography and Electrostatic powder gravure.

Bibliography

"Printing and Reproducing Processes" in *ECT* 1st ed., Vol. 11, pp. 126–149, by R. F. Reed and M. H. Bruno, Lithographic Technical Foundation.

1. *U.S. Bureau of the Census Annual Survey of Manufacturers—1966.* General statistics for industry groups and industries, M66(AS)-1. U.S. Government Printing Office, Washington, D.C. 1967.
1a. M. H. Bruno, "What's Ahead for Printing," *Inland Printer/Am. Lithographer* (Jan. 1968).
2. W. J. Stevens and J. A. McKinven, *How to Prepare Art and Copy for Offset Lithography*, Duval Publishing Co., N.J., 1948.
3. C. B. Neblette, *Photography: Its Materials and Processes*, 6th ed., D. Van Nostrand Co., Inc., Princeton, N.J., 1962.
4. C. E. K. Mees and T. N. James, *Theory of the Photographic Process*, 3rd ed., The Macmillan Co., New York, 1966.

5. B. R. Halpern, "Tone and Color Correcting," *GATF (Graphic Arts Technical Foundation) Bull. No. 510-511* (1956).
6. G. W. Jorgensen, "GATF Star Target," *GATF Res. Progr. No. 52* (1961).
7. Z. Elijin, "GATF Dot Gain Scale," *GATF Res. Progr. No. 69* (1965).
8. C. Shapiro, ed., *Lithographers Manual*, Graphic Arts Technical Foundation, Pittsburgh, Pa., 1966, p. 7:1.
9. R. M. Evans, *An Introduction to Color*, John Wiley & Sons, Inc., New York, 1948.
10. E. Jaffe, E. Brody, F. Preveil, and J. W. White, "Color Separation Photography for Offset Lithography," *GATF Bull. No. 509* (1959).
11. F. R. Clapper, "Improved Color Separation of Transparencies by Direct Screening," *J. Photogr. Sci.* **12**, 28 (1964).
12. J. A. C. Yule, *Principles of Color Reproduction*, John Wiley & Sons, Inc., New York, 1967, Chap. 4.
13. Reference 8, p. 7:13.
14. G. W. Jorgensen and M. H. Bruno, "The Sensitivity of Bichromated Coatings," *GATF Publ. No. 218* (1954).
15. A. H. Smith, "The Use and Application of Synthetic Coatings in Photolithography," *Printing Technol.* **11** (1), 19 (April 1967).
16. A. R. Materazzi, "Some Studies on Wipe-On Lithographic Plate Coatings," *TAGA (Technical Assoc. of the Graphic Arts) Proc. 1967*, p. 229.
17. J. Kosar, *Light-Sensitive Systems: Chemistry and Application of Nonsilver Halide Photographic Processes*, John Wiley & Sons, Inc., New York, 1965, Chap. 7.
18. U.S. Pat. 3,160,506 (1964), G. F. O'Connor and S. L. Chin.
19. U.S. Pat. 3,220,832 (1965), F. Uhlig.
20. G. W. Jorgensen, in *TAGA Proc. 1952*.
21. U.S. Pat. 3,064,562 (1962), E. Deal.
22. U.S. Pat. 3,196,785 (1965), R. L. Eissler.
23. U.S. Pat. 3,211,376 (1965), J. L. Sorkin and D. C. Thomas.
24. U.S. Pat. 3,210,184 (1965), F. Uhlig.
25. U.S. Pat. 3,247,791 (1966), R. F. Leonard.
26. U.S. Pat. 3,307,951 (1967), D. N. Adams and D. C. Thomas.
27. Reference 15, p. 25.
28. U.S. Pat. 2,760,863 (1956), L. Plambeck.
29. U.S. Pat. 3,081,168 (1963), R. M. Leckley and R. L. Sorenson.
30. V. Strauss, *The Printing Industry*, Printing Industries of America, Washington, D.C., 1967, p. 221.
31. W. N. Vinton, "New Developments in Rotofilm," *Gravure Magazine*, p. 20 (Dec. 1951).
32. U.S. Pat. 2,273,740 (1942), B. F. Terry.
33. "The Photo Direct Process—How It Works," *Multigraph Sales Training Bull.* Vol. XII, No. 23, Addressograph Multigraph Co., Cleveland, Ohio.
34. R. M. Schaffert, *Electrophotography*, Pitman Publishing Corp., New York and London, 1965.
35. M. L. Sugarman, "Electrofax—A New Tool for the Graphic Arts," *TAGA Proc. 1955*, p. 59.
36. J. S. Merth and G. L. Monsen, *Photomechanics and Printing*, Merth Publishing Co., Chicago, 1957.
37. J. A. Easley, "The Dow Method of Etching Magnesium," *Penrose Annual* **49**, 87 (1955).
38. P. Booth and M. C. Rogers, "Powderless Etching of Copper," *TAGA Proc. 1961*, p. 1; U.S. Pats. 3,033,725 and 3,033,793 (1962).
39. E. R. Buckley, in *Proc. 17th Ann. Conf. Res. Eng. Council Graphic Arts Industry, 1967*, p. 53.
40. S. Whinne, R. N. Hotchkiss, and F. P. Willcox, "Fairchild Variable Response Unit," *TAGA Proc. 1955*, p. 48.
41. O. Eisenschmid, "Electronic Masking and Engraving Equipment," *Photoengravers Bull.* p. 195 (Nov. 1960).
42. Reference 36, p. 205.
43. Reference 36, p. 206.
44. Reference 36, p. 207.
45. U.S. Pat. 2,040,247 (1937), A. Dultgen.
46. U.S. Pat. 2,182,559 (1939), C. L. Henderson.
47. U.S. Pat. 1,831,645 (1931), E. S. Ballard.

48. R. F. Reed, *Offset Lithographic Platemaking*, Graphic Arts Technical Foundation, Pittsburgh, Pa., 1967.
49. U.S. Pat. 3,282,208 (1966), M. Ruderman.
50. P. J. Hartsuch, "Progress in Litho Plates," *Graphic Arts Monthly* **39**, 90 (Nov. 1967).
51. U.S. Pat. 2,291,854 (1942), P. Whyzmuzis.
52. U.S. Pat. 2,599,914 (1952), P. J. Hartsuch and C. Wachtl.
53. G. B. Mayer, "Collotype," *Inland Printer* (Dec. 1932–May 1933).
54. I. Pobboravsky and M. Pearson, "Study of Screenless Lithography," *TAGA Proc. 1967*, p. 229.
55. Reference 30, p. 270.
56. D. Smith, "Electrostatic Printing," *Penrose Annual* **59**, 143–150 (1966).
57. U.S. Pat. 3,167,005 (1965), P. Gruebel.
58. P. Gruebel, "Reverse Lithography," *TAGA Proc. 1963*, p. 361.
59. C. Childress, "A True Electrostatic Printing Process," *Penrose Annual* **59**, 151 (1966); S. B. McFarlane, "Electrostatic Printing's Year of Progress," *Penrose Annual* **60**, 180 (1967).
60. U.S. Pat. 3,296,965 (1966), B. Reif et al.
61. D. Smith, "Electrostatic Gravure Powder Printing," *Gravure Magazine* (Oct. 1965).

MICHAEL H. BRUNO
International Paper Company

PRODUCER GAS. See Gas, manufactured.

PROLINE (2-PYRROLIDINECARBOXYLIC ACID), $C_5H_9NO_2$. See Amino acids.

PROPANE

The more important properties of propane, $CH_3CH_2CH_3$, are summarized in Table 1.

Propane forms a solid hydrate with water at low temperatures. This solid material can cause plugging of transmission lines when propane and propane-containing

Table 1. Physical Properties of Propane

Property		Property			
boiling point, at		heat of fusion, cal/g	19.10		
760 mm Hg, °C	−42.07	heat of vaporization,			
freezing point, °C	−187.69	at 760 mm, cal/g	101.76		
density, d_4^{25}	0.4928	heat of combustion of gas,			
refractive index, n_D^{20}	1.2898	kcal/mole[a]	488.53		
critical temperature, °C	96.8	heat of formation, kcal/mole[b]	−28.643		
critical pressure, mm Hg	31928	specific heat of vapor,			
critical volume, ml/g	4.358	cal/(g)(°C)[c]	0.4005		
surface tension, at		constants for the Antoine			
−50°C, dyn/cm	16.49	equation,[d] tempera-			
viscosity, cSt		ture range,	A	B	C
at −130°C	1.126	−130 to + 5°C	6.82973	813.200	248.00
at −90°C	0.590	+5 to +96.8°C	7.33829	1090.0	287.8
at −40°C	0.355				

[a] At 25°C and constant pressure.
[b] For liquid at 25°C.
[c] At 27°C and constant pressure.
[d] Log $P = A - B/(t + C)$, where P = mm Hg; t = °C.

gases are inadequately dried (1). The compositions and structures of the propane and butane hydrates (see Butanes) have been widely studied. Earlier work (2) had indicated a theoretical formula of $C_3H_8.17H_2O$ for the completely filled clathrate structure. More recent work (3), involving direct analysis of carefully prepared hydrate phases, gives the formula $C_3H_8.19.8H_2O$. Use of propane hydrate formation as a basic technique in water desalination has received attention recently both in the U.S. (4) and abroad (5). A small pilot plant has been in operation in the U.S. since 1965. The operation of the hydrate crystallizer and melter are apparently satisfactory, but some difficulties have been encountered in separating hydrate crystals from saline water (6). See also Water.

Production and Uses. Propane enters, to different degrees, into the composition of several grades of LPG (liquefied petroleum gas), and its production and consumption are largely discussed under Liquefied petroleum gas.

Propane is produced in both petroleum refining and natural gas processing. In both cases, it must be removed, generally along with the butanes, from large amounts of lower-boiling hydrocarbons, and in the case of refinery operations, from permanent gases, such as hydrogen (1–6).

Propane is widely used as a fuel. See Liquefied petroleum gas. Propane is a major source, by cracking, of ethylene (qv) and propylene (qv). It is also used in hydrocarbon oxidation (see Vol. 11, p. 228). Much smaller amounts of propane are chlorinated to a variety of derivatives. Vapor-phase nitration has been used to make mixed nitro derivatives (1- and 2-nitropropanes); see Nitroparaffins (7). Both the chlorination (8,9) and the nitration (10,11) reactions have been studied using modern gas-chromatographic methods to identify both major and minor products, and to characterize more definitely the reaction mechanisms involved.

The special physical properties and relatively low cost of propane have spurred interest in its use in a number of special areas. It is widely used as a refrigerant in chemical, petroleum refining, and gas processing operations. As a selective solvent, it is widely employed for removing asphaltic components from the higher-boiling fractions of crude oils (12). It has received some attention as a solvent for extracting oils from agricultural products (13). Use of propane injection for increasing production of crude oil from subterranean formations has been tried in large-scale tests in recent years, apparently with considerable success in raising overall crude oil recoveries (14).

Bibliography

1. J. P. LaCroix, *Rev. Inst. Franç. Pétrole Ann. Combust. Liquides* **7**, 34–49, 62–79 (1952).
2. J. H. Van der Waals and J. C. Platteeuw, *Advan. Chem. Phys.* **2**, 2 (1959).
3. P. J. Ceccotti, *Ind. Eng. Chem., Fundamentals* **5** (1), 106–109 (1966).
4. W. G. Knox, M. Hess, G. E. Jones, Jr., and H. B. Smith, Jr., *Chem. Eng. Progr.* **57** (2), 66–71 (1961).
5. I. N. Medvedev, *Chem. Abstr.* **63**, 11169h (1965).
6. A. J. Barduhn, *Chem. Eng. Progr.* **63** (1), 98–103 (1967).
7. H. B. Hass, E. B. Hodge, and B. M. Vanderbilt, *Ind. Eng. Chem.* **28**, 339–344 (1936).
8. G. Lanchec, *Chimie et Industrie* (*Paris*) **94** (1), 46–60 (1966).
9. B. Blouris, G. Lanchec, and P. Rumpf, *Compt. Rend.* **257** (23), 3609–3611 (1963).
10. A. P. Ballod, N. L. Galanina, I. V. Patsevich, A. V. Topchiev, and A. M. Yanyukova, *Neftekhimiya* **2**, 924–927 (1962).
11. T. Asahara, T. Kondo, and I. Hamada, *Kogyo Kagaku Zasshi* **62**, 1659–1661 (1959); *Chem. Abstr.* **57**, 9640b (1962).
12. S. Marple, Jr., K. E. Train, and F. D. Fosler, *Chem. Eng. Progr.* **57**, 44–48 (1961).

13. R. Rigamonti, G. Saracco, and A. Gianetto, *J. Appl. Chem.* (*London*) **15** (12), 600 (1965).
14. R. E. Sessions, *J. Petrol. Technol.* **15** (1), 31–36 (1963).

C. E. Morrell
Enjay Chemical Intermediates Laboratory

PROPANOLAMINES. See Alkanolamines.

PROPANOLS. See Propyl alcohols.

PROPARGYL ALCOHOL, $HC \equiv CCH_2OH$. See Vol. 1, p. 598.

PROPELLANTS. See Explosives, Vol. 8, p. 659.

PROPENE. See Propylene.

PROPIONALDEHYDE

Propionaldehyde (propanal (IUPAC)), CH_3CH_2CHO, is a low-boiling, colorless, flammable liquid, having a pungent aldehyde odor. It finds application as a chemical intermediate.

Propionaldehyde occurs in onions and other vegetables, in flower parts, and in cheese and other dairy products. None of these serve as a source of the aldehyde.

Physical and Chemical Properties

Constants. The principal constants of propionaldehyde are shown in Table 1. Vapor pressure data may be determined by the following equation (P = mm Hg, t = °C) (1):

$$\log P = 7.07980 - \frac{1166.99}{t + 230}$$

Propionaldehyde is completely miscible with alcohol, ether, and many other organic solvents. Its behavior with water is unusual, in that there is a temperature below which there is complete miscibility, as shown in Figure 1.

Table 1. Physical and Chemical Constants of Propionaldehyde

freezing point, °C	−81
boiling point, °C, at 760 mm Hg	47.9
at 10 mm Hg	−38
vapor pressure at 20°C, mm Hg	258
specific gravity, 20/4°C	0.7970
20/20°C	0.7982
refractive index, n_D^{20}	1.3619
viscosity, cP, at 0°C	0.430
at 25°C	0.320
specific heat at 20°C, cal/g	0.522
heat of vaporization at 1 atm, Btu/lb	214
heat of combustion, cal/g	7400
flash point, °F, Tag open cup	15–19
Tag closed cup	−30

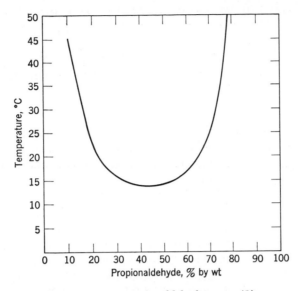

Fig. 1. System propionaldehyde–water (3).

Propionaldehyde does not form minimum boiling mixtures with alcohols, ethers, chlorinated hydrocarbons, and many other materials (2). Table 2 shows the binary azeotropes that have been reported for the aldehyde with water (3) as well as other agents (2).

Table 2. Properties of Binary Azeotropes of Propionaldehyde

Other component	Propionaldehyde, wt %	Bp, °C	Pressure at bp, mm Hg
water	99.8	25	300
	98	47.5	760
	95.7	80	2000
carbon disulfide	40	40	760
n-propyl nitrite	82 (approx)	47.3	760

Reactions. Propionaldehyde undergoes the general reactions of aldehydes and resembles acetaldehyde (qv). Upon exposure to ultraviolet radiation, iodine, or heat, propionaldehyde decomposes to give mainly carbon monoxide and ethane (4). Among the products resulting from shortwave ultraviolet radiation, 3,4-hexanedione has been identified (5). Pyrolysis proceeds by free radical mechanisms to butane, ethane, ethylene, carbon monoxide, and hydrogen (6).

Propionaldehyde is stable when dry and stored in nitrogen atmosphere (1). However, it can be made to form homopolymers as well as copolymers with other aldehydes. Self-condensation in the presence of cation-exchange resins leads to linear polymers of polyoxymethylene with pendent ethyl groups (**1**) (7). With trifluorochloroethylene and butyl lithium the trimeric polymer (**2**) is favored (8). The formation of crystallized polypropionaldehyde is catalyzed by organometallics (9–11), and by complex metal sulfates (12). Copolymers with acetaldehyde have been reported (13,14). Propionaldehyde forms interchain linkages with gelatin (15).

Propionaldehyde can be oxidized to propionic acid using air (16), hypochlorite (17), bromine (18), and many other common agents. It can be converted directly to propionic anhydride in the presence of air and cobalt and copper acetates (19). Hydrogenation in the presence of suitable catalyst gives n-propyl alcohol (20,21). The Tishchenko reaction is favored by catalysis with aluminum ethoxide and propionaldehyde thus can be converted to n-propyl propionate (22). Under alkaline conditions excess formaldehyde reacts with propionaldehyde to form 2-hydroxymethyl-2-methyl-1,3-propanediol ("trimethylolethane," see Vol. 1, p. 594) (23,24). However, when catalyzed by boron trifluoride (25), or secondary amine salts (26), methacrolein, CH_2=$C(CH_3)CHO$, results. Methyl ethyl ketone and propionaldehyde react under basic conditions to form 4-hydroxy-3-methyl-2-hexanone (27).

At 200°C and over alumina catalyst, ammonia and propionaldehyde react to form pyridine bases including 3,5-dimethylpyridine and 2,3,5-trimethylpyridine (28). At 300–500°C and with copper–zinc catalyst, propionitrile is formed (29). At 500–700°C over chromic oxide on alumina, acrylonitrile results (30). The oxime can be prepared in the usual way by reaction with hydroxylamine (31). Under acid conditions, the aldehyde reacts with urea or thiourea to form white condensation products (32).

Acetals of propionaldehyde are made in the usual way by refluxing the desired alcohol with the aldehyde in the presence of an acid catalyst. These can be cleaved to the unsaturated ether. For example, the dibutyl acetal of propionaldehyde yields butyl propenyl ether (33).

$$CH_3CH_2CH(OC_4H_9)_2 \rightarrow CH_3CH{=}CHOC_4H_9 + C_4H_9OH$$

The diphenyl acetal also has been prepared (34). Acetic anhydride converts the aldehyde to propylidene diacetate, $CH_3CH_2CH(OOCCH_3)_2$ (35). With ketene and aluminum chloride catalyst, the resulting compound is β-valerolactone (36), but when sulfonic acid catalyst is employed, the product is propenyl acetate (37). With ion-exchange catalysis, acetoacetic ester and propionaldehyde undergo the Knoevenagel condensation reaction to give three distinct products: ethyl propylidene acetoacetate; 1-methyl-2-carbethoxy-3-ethylcyclohex-6-en-5-one; and 1-methyl-2,4-dicarbethoxy-cyclohex-6-en-5-one (38). Under similar conditions, but with diethyl malonate, the aldehyde forms diethyl propylidene malonate, and tetraethyl propylidene dimalonate (39). Propionaldehyde reacts, via the Grignard mechanism, with ethyl magnesium bromide to form three products: the addition compound 3-pentanol, $(C_2H_5)_2CHOH$; the reduction product n-propyl alcohol, $C_2H_5CH_2OH$; and the tertiary alcohol, 3-ethyl-3-pentanol, $(C_2H_5)_3COH$ (40).

Manufacture

Three commercial processes for the manufacture of propionaldehyde are in use. The dehydrogenation of n-propyl alcohol (41) employing copper compounds or iron oxide (42) seems to have no commercial value in the U.S. because the alcohol is more valuable than the aldehyde. It is the simplest of the three routes, however, and is preferred when relatively small amounts of the aldehyde are required. The Fischer–Tropsch process, using ethylene, carbon monoxide, and hydrogen, has received considerable attention (43,44). Yields as high as 95% have been claimed (45), but the process seems to have commercial value only in Europe. The oxo synthesis is the most popular route, especially in the U.S. (see Oxo process). It involves the reaction of ethylene, carbon monoxide, and hydrogen, and thus is similar to the Fischer–Tropsch method, but ratios and conditions differ (46,47).

Propionaldehyde can be prepared in a variety of other ways, all of which could have commercial significance under special situations. These include pyrolysis of acetals (48); partial oxidation of hydrocarbons (49); isomerization of propylene oxide (50); dehydration of 1,2-propanediol vapor over silica (51); and rearrangement of allyl alcohol in the presence of iron pentacarbonyl (52).

Commercial propionaldehyde usually contains about 2% water. It can be dried by passage through commercial drying agents, following which it should be distilled. For commercial purposes, drying usually is not necessary.

Capacity is far in excess of actual production because oxo units are multipurpose and can be directed as needed. In practice, these units are almost totally used to manufacture butyraldehyde and higher aldehydes so that propionaldehyde is a very minor product. Propionaldehyde is so similar to its companion compounds, acetaldehyde and butyraldehyde, that it offers little novelty to compete with these high-volume materials. Therefore its uses are limited to those products that demand the three-carbon configuration. The aldehyde is not listed as an article of commerce in the usual trade publications and most of it is used captively. However, it can probably be obtained from companies that use oxo technology for other aldehydes. Pricing history is not readily available, but is governed by the economics of derivatives and general availability.

The Bureau of Explosives classifies propionaldehyde as a flammable liquid, and requires shipping under a red label. It is usually stored in aluminum or stainless steel, but phenolic-resin-lined carbon steel also may be used. Reaction equipment usually is stainless steel, but aluminum also is satisfactory.

Propionaldehyde should be handled with adequate ventilation, and its contact with skin, eyes, and clothing should be avoided. The following toxicological properties have been reported (3): single oral LD_{50}, rats, 1.41 g/kg body weight; single skin penetration LD_{50}, rabbits, 5.04 ml/kg body weight; single inhalation of concentrated vapor, rats, 5 min killed 2 of 6; eye injury, rabbits, moderate.

Analysis

Propionaldehyde can be determined by spectrophotometric methods, as, for instance, in tobacco smoke (53), but gas-liquid chromatographic methods are almost always employed. Thus the aldehyde has been measured in water (54), cigar smoke (55), combustion products of hydrocarbon fuels (56), and in the mixed products of cool flame combustion (57).

Uses

"Trimethylolethane" (see Vol. 1, p. 594) is prepared by methylolation of propionaldehyde with formaldehyde (58); this intermediate finds use in alkyd resin systems and about 5 million lb was produced in the U.S. in 1966.   Hydrogenation of propionaldehyde to *n*-propyl alcohol (see Propyl alcohols) is an important source of this alcohol and about 5 million lb was made by this route in 1966.   Propionic acid (qv) can be made by oxidation of propionaldehyde.   In 1966 in the U.S., about 20 million lb of the acid was made from the aldehyde.   Minor uses, especially in the area of medicinal and agricultural specialties are difficult to estimate.   Propionaldehyde for these uses may be purchased in drum quantities through distributors, or may be generated in situ from *n*-propyl alcohol.

Bibliography

"Propionaldehyde" in *ECT* 1st ed., Vol. 11, pp. 169–173, by M. J. Curry, Celanese Corporation of America.

1. T. E. Smith and R. F. Bonner, *Ind. Eng. Chem.* **43**, 1169–1173 (1951).
2. L. H. Horsley, *Azeotropic Data* (Advances in Chemistry Ser., No. 6), American Chemical Society, Washington, D.C., 1952.
3. *Aldehydes*, Union Carbide Corp., 1960.
4. W. J. Blaedel and F. E. Blacet, *J. Am. Chem. Soc.* **67**, 1283–1285 (1945).
5. G. Leuschner and K. Pfordte, *Ann. Chem.* **622**, 6–9 (1959); *Chem. Abstr.* **53**, 17891 (1959).
6. K. J. Laidler and M. Eusuf, *Can. J. Chem.* **43** (1), 268–277 (1965).
7. M. J. Astle and M. L. Pinns, *J. Org. Chem.* **24**, 56–60 (1959).
8. R. Meier and F. Boehler, *Chem. Ber.* **90**, 2344–2349 (1957); *Chem. Abstr.* **52**, 10022 (1958).
9. G. Natta et al., *Atti Accad. Nazl. Lincei, Rend., Classe Sci. Fis., Mat. Nati.* **28**, 18–26 (1960); *Chem. Abstr.* **55**, 19768 (1961).
10. T. Saigusa and H. Fujii, *Makromol. Chem.* (in English) **44–46**, 398–407 (1961); *Chem. Abstr.* **55**, 22104 (1961).
11. J. Furukawa et al., *Makromol. Chem.* (in English) **37**, 149–152 (1960); *Chem. Abstr.* **54**, 16902 (1960).
12. Japan. Pat. 22,606 (Oct. 12, 1964), K. Noro and H. Takida (to Nikon Chemical Industry Co., Ltd.).
13. Japan. Pat. 10,436 (May 26, 1965), H. Daimon (to Japan Carbide Industries Co., Inc.).
14. Brit. Pat. 981,289 (Jan. 20, 1965) (to Farbwerke Hoechst, A.G.).
15. R. A. Milch, *Gerontologia* (in English) **10** (2–3), 117–136 (1964–1965).
16. W. K. Langdon and E. J. Schwoegler, *Ind. Eng. Chem.* **43**, 1011–1012 (1951).
17. I. F. Suknevich and A. A. Chilingaryan, *Chem. Ber.* **68B**, 1210–1216 (1935).
18. B. G. Cox and P. T. McTigue, *Australian J. Chem.* **17** (11), 1210–1216 (1964).
19. U.S. Pat. 2,491,572 (Dec. 20, 1949), S. B. McFarlane (to Celanese Corp. of America).
20. C. C. Oldenburg and H. Rase, *A. I. Ch. E. J.* **3**, 462–466 (1957).
21. Ger. Pat. 1,076,109 (Feb. 25, 1960), O. Probst, K. Rehn, and G. Theilig (to Farbwerke Hoechst, A.G.).
22. W. C. Child and H. Adkins, *J. Am. Chem. Soc.* **45**, 3013 (1923).
23. U.S. Pat. 2,292,926 (Aug. 11, 1942), M. M. Brubaker and R. A. Jacobsen (to E. I. du Pont de Nemours & Co., Inc.).
24. G. J. Laemmle, J. G. Milligan, and W. J. Peppel, *Ind. Eng. Chem.* **52**, 33–36 (1960).
25. U.S. Pat. 2,549,457 (April 17, 1951), W. F. Gresham (to E. I. du Pont de Nemours & Co., Inc.).
26. U.S. Pat. 2,848,499 (May 12, 1958), A. F. MacLean and B. G. Frenz (to Celanese Corp. of America).
27. S. G. Powell, H. C. Murray, and M. M. Baldwin, *J. Am. Chem. Soc.* **55**, 1153–1154 (1933).
28. M. P. Oparina, *J. Russ. Phys.-Chem. Soc.* **61**, 2001–2010 (1929).
29. U.S. Pat. 2,452,187 (Oct. 26, 1948), W. F. Gresham (to E. I. du Pont de Nemours & Co., Inc.).
30. U.S. Pat. 2,412,437 (Dec. 10, 1946), C. R. Wagner (to Phillips Petroleum Co.).
31. Belg. Pat. 636,819 (March 2, 1964), H. Doerfel and P. Raff (to Badische Anilin- & Soda-Fabrik, A.G.).
32. Neth. Pat. Appl. 6,404,923 (Nov. 5, 1964), and Ger. Pat. Appl. (May 4, 1963), (by Ruhrchemie, A.G.).

33. Brit. Pat. 776,056 (June 5, 1957) (to Ruhrchemie, A.G.).

34. V. Isagulyants et al., *Zh. Prikl. Khim.* (in Russian) **38** (8), 1878–1890 (1965); *Chem. Abstr.* **63,** 13493 (1965).

35. E. H. Man, J. J. Sanderson, and C. Hauser, *J. Am. Chem. Soc.* **72,** 847–848 (1950).

36. U.S. Pat. 2,469,110 (May 3, 1949), H. J. Hagemeyer, Jr. (to Eastman Kodak Co.).

37. U.S. Pat. 2,422,679 (June 24, 1947), D. C. Hull and A. H. Agett (to Eastman Kodak Co.).

38. P. Mastagli and N. Andric, *Bull. Soc. Chim. France* **1957,** 792–793; *Chem. Abstr.* **51,** 16303 (1957). (Discusses kinetics using ion-exchange resins.)

39. A. Sakurai, *Sci. Papers Inst. Phys. Chem. Res.* (*Tokyo*) **53,** 250–255 (1959); *Chem. Abstr.* **54,** 19478 (1960).

40. R. Hamelin, *Bull. Soc. Chim. France* **1961,** 926–930; *Chem. Abstr.* **55,** 27027 (1961). (Suggests mechanisms for formation of products.)

41. U.S. Pat. 2,173,111 (Sept. 19, 1939), R. L. Hasche (to Eastman Kodak Co.).

42. V. A. Komarov and P. V. Maslov, *Zh. Prikl. Khim.* (in Russian) **38** (2), 394–398 (1965); *Chem. Abstr.* **62,** 16041 (1965).

43. U.S. Pat. 2,542,747 (Feb. 20, 1951), P. L. Barrick (to E. I. du Pont de Nemours & Co., Inc.).

44. W. Hall, R. Kokes, and P. Emmett, *J. Am. Chem. Soc.* **82,** 1027–1037 (1960).

45. Neth. Pat. Appl. 6,412,249 (April 26, 1965), and Swiss Pat. Appl. (Oct. 24, 1963) (by Lonza, Ltd.).

46. U.S. Pat. 2,763,693 (Sept. 18, 1956), J. C. Vander Woude and P. M. Morris (to Eastman Kodak Co.).

47. E. Bosshard, *Promotionsarb.* (*Zürich*) No. 3351 (1963); from *J. Appl. Chem.* (*London*) **15** (3), *i*–259 (1965). (A review with 52 references.)

48. U.S. Pat. 2,759,979 (Aug. 21, 1956), H. Hagemeyer and M. A. Perry (to Eastman Kodak Co.).

49. U.S. Pat. 2,776,317 (Jan. 1, 1957), W. H. Reeder (to Dresser Operations Inc.).

50. U.S. Pat. 2,855,370 (Oct. 7, 1958), L. G. Lundsted (to Wyandotte Chemicals Corp.).

51. U.S. Pat. 2,501,042 (March 21, 1950), J. L. Gear (to Celanese Corp. of America).

52. U.S. Pat. 2,548,171 (April 10, 1951), R. T. Olsen (to General Aniline & Film Corp.).

53. J. Mold and M. McRae, *Tobacco Sci.* **1,** 40–46; published in *Tobacco* **144** (10), 24–30 (1957).

54. U. Schwenk et al., *Brennstoff-Chem.* **42,** 192–199 (1960); *Chem. Abstr.* **55,** 22935 (1961).

55. A. Schepartz and P. McDowell, *U.S. Dept. Agr. ARS 73–74* (1961).

56. K. J. Hughes, R. W. Hurn, and F. G. Edwards, *Gas Chromatog. Intern. Symp., 2nd, East Lansing, Mich., 1959,* 171–182 (1961).

57. G. Kyryacos, H. Menapace, and C. Boord, *Anal. Chem.* **31,** 222–225 (1959).

58. J. G. Milligan and W. J. Peppel, *Ind. Eng. Chem.* **52,** 33–36 (1960).

Joseph J. Wocasek
Celanese Chemical Co.

PROPIONIC ACID

Propionic acid (propanoic acid (IUPAC)), CH_3CH_2COOH, is a water-white liquid with a sharp irritating odor resembling strong vinegar. It is freely soluble in water, alcohol, ether, chloroform, and other acids.

Propionic acid is found in dairy products such as milk, butter, and cheese, especially after fermentation or spoilage. It occurs in the vapors resulting from the carbonization of wood and coal, and at one time the distillates from charcoal production were the prime source of the acid. It also is found in the black liquor acids from sulfite pulp production.

Propionic acid finds use in the production of esters, salts, polymer products, and specialty chemicals.

Physical and Chemical Properties

Constants. The principal constants for propionic acid are shown in Table 1. Table 2 lists some binary azeotropes of propionic acid (1–5).

Table 1. Physical and Chemical Constants of Propionic Acid

melting point, °C	−22
boiling point, °C	141.1
vapor pressure, mm Hg, at 28.0°C	5
at 52.0°C	20
at 85.8°C	100
at 122.0°C	400
specific gravity, 20/4°C	0.992
20/20°C	0.9952
refractive index, n_D^{20}	1.3874
viscosity at 25°C, cP	1.035
surface tension in air at 20°C, dyn/cm	26.70
coefficient of cubical expansion	
at 0–133°C/°C	1.102×10^{-3}
critical temperature, °C	337.6
critical pressure, atm	53.0
specific heat at 20–137°C, cal/g	0.726
heat of fusion at melting point, cal/g	23.4
heat of vaporization at 139.3°C, cal/g	98.9
heat of combustion of liquid, cal/g	4931.5
flash point, Cleveland open cup, °F	150
weight at 20°C, lb/gal	8.28

Table 2. Properties of Binary Azeotropes of Propionic Acid at 760 mm Hg

Other component	Propionic acid, wt %	Bp, °C
water	4.5	99.2
pyridine	67.2	148.6
N,N-dimethylpropionamide	23.6	179.3
heptane	2	97.8
octane	24	120.9
nonane	54	134.3
decane	80.5	139.8

The system acetic acid–propionic acid also has been studied (6), as has that of acetic anhydride–propionic acid (7). In addition, propionic acid forms a ternary azeotrope with pyridine and undecane, boiling at 147.1°C, and containing 55.4% propionic acid and 26.4% pyridine (1).

Reactions. Propionic acid reactions are typical of those for a lower monocarboxylic acid such as acetic acid. Salts, amides, esters, the acid chloride, and the acid anhydride are formed in the usual way. Chlorination under ultraviolet radiation provides a mixture of chlorinated propionic acids (8). Refluxing the acid with aluminum alkyls, R_3Al, gives aluminum tripropionate, $Al(OOC_3H_5)_3$, as well as the partial intermediates $R_2Al(OOC_3H_5)$ and $RAl(OOC_3H_5)_2$ (9). Methyl propionate results from the reaction, at 270°C, with dimethyl ether, using activated carbon and phosphoric acid as catalysts (10). Shortwave ultraviolet irradiation causes the formation of dimers at the alpha methylene group (11). Gas-phase reaction with acetylene produces vinyl propionate (12,13) in a manner analogous to making vinyl acetate (see Vinyl compounds).

Manufacture

Formerly, the principal source of propionic acid was the liquid condensate secured from the manufacture of charcoal. This is a very minor source today. The oxo process (qv) is the major method of manufacture in the U.S. Ethylene and carbon monoxide are reacted under reductive conditions to produce propionaldehyde (qv), after which further oxidation converts the aldehyde to the acid (14–17). Large quantities of acid also are obtained from liquid-phase oxidation of propane (18), butane (19), mixed paraffins (20), and paraffin wax (21) (see Hydrocarbon oxidation). The oxo and hydrocarbon-oxidation routes are important both in the U.S. and in Europe. A further process is the direct oxidation of 1-propanol with nitric acid (22).

In the U.S. there are five commercial producers of propionic acid. In 1966, production was about 30 million lb, and this was about equally distributed between captive use and merchant sales. There were also several million pounds of imports. Producers and estimated capacities are listed in Table 3 (23), but oxo capacity is flexible and could be directed toward more propionaldehyde as required.

Table 3. Propionic Acid Producers, Capacities, and Processes

Producer	Capacity, million lb	Process
Celanese Chemical Company	10	hydrocarbon oxidation
Cliffs Dow Chemical Company	0.5	wood carbonization
Commercial Solvents Corporation	0.2	nitroparaffin by-product
Tennessee Eastman Company	10	oxo
Union Carbide Corporation	10	oxo

The price of propionic acid has declined through the last two decades as the newer processes, oxo and hydrocarbon-oxidation, have made more material available and new or expanded uses have developed. In 1955 propionic acid listed at 20.75¢/lb at the works; in 1967 the list price was 14.75¢/lb delivered. Expansions may cause a further lowering of costs and the savings can be passed on to the consumer. In addition, more acid is available from European sources and, with lower import duties, pressure on U.S. pricing may be greater than in the past.

Propionic acid is not classed as a flammable liquid by ICC regulations; however, it requires the normal handling precautions which would be accorded any organic compound of comparable flash point and vapor pressure. The acid usually is shipped in aluminum or stainless steel, or in steel drums with a polyethylene liner. Uncoated steel is not recommended.

Because of the widespread use of propionate salts in food products and animal feeds, the metabolism and toxicity of the acid and its salts have been studied intensively (24–26). The acid and its salts are considered to have low toxicity.

Analysis

The assay of a propionic acid sample may be determined by titration with standard base in the usual manner. The acid has been detected in weak solutions by paper chromatography (27), but usually it is measured by gas chromatography. Thus, it has been determined in mixed acids (28), in sewage (29), and in foods (30).

Uses

Propionic acid has relatively few commercial uses, and these require the propionate configuration to fit specific applications. In general, propionic acid outlets are limited by competition from acetic acid, which is available in vastly greater quantity and is cheaper. The acid has been used as a catalyst in the manufacture of polyester resins (31), and epoxy resins have been modified by esterification with the acid (32). The acid or its anhydride find a major use in the production of cellulose tripropionate and cellulose acetate propionate for plastics and fibers. Tung oil tripropionate is reported to impart antifungal properties to paint (33). An important outlet is the production of propionate salts by reaction with the corresponding carbonate or hydroxide (34). Both calcium and sodium propionates find extensive use as additives to inhibit mold and "rope" in baked goods; and as components of cattle and poultry feeds to prevent ketosis (35), as a fungistat (36), and to improve feed utilization (37,38). Ammonium propionate reportedly reduces viscosity and serves as a wetting agent in silver halide–gelatin emulsion systems in photography (39). Calcium propionate has been suggested as a scorch retarder for butyl rubber (40), and the zinc and cadmium salts serve as catalysts in making terephthalate polyesters (41). Vinyl propionate has received considerable study in the U.S. (42–44) and Europe (45–47) in copolymer systems for a variety of end uses.

A number of commercial weed-killing agents are derivatives of propionic acid, eg, 2-(2,4,5-trichlorophenoxy)ethyl 2,2-dichloropropionate, sodium 2,2-dichloropropionate, and 2-(2,4,5-trichlorophenoxy)propionic acid. (See Weed killers.) Various esters are useful in the flavor and perfume industries and in lacquers as special solvents. Methyl 2-cyclohexanyl propionate is used as a solvent in production of hydrogen peroxide from anthraquinhydrone (48); the benzyl ester is a perfuming agent for resinous products (49); *tert*-butyl propionate is claimed as an antidetonation improver in leaded gasoline (50); the vapors of the ethyl and butyl esters are antibacterial agents (51); and 2-chloroallyl propionate is an agent for washfast textile finishes (52). The octadecylamine salt is reported to be a molding assisting agent for silicate powder (53).

A probable use pattern of propionic acid, in 1967 in the U.S., is given in Table 4 (54).

Table 4. U.S. Uses for Propionic Acid, 1967

End use	Propionic acid, million lb
propionate salts	14.5
cellulose esters	12.5
herbicides	6.5
all others	1.5
total	35.0

Bibliography

"Propionic Acid" in *ECT* 1st ed., Vol. 11, pp. 173–177, by A. W. Goos, Cliffs Dow Chemical Company.

1. L. H. Horsley and W. S. Tamplin, *Azeotropic Data II* (Advances in Chemistry Ser., No. 35), American Chemical Society, Washington, D.C., 1962.
2. W. Trabczynski, *Bull. Acad. Polon. Sci., Classe III* (in English) **4,** 623–625 (1956); *Chem. Abstr.* **51,** 6253 (1957). (Binary azeotropes of propionic acid and *n*-alkanes.)
3. M. Raja Rao and C. Venkata Rao, *J. Appl. Chem.* (*London*) **6,** 269–276 (1956). (Binary azeotropes of propionic acid and alicyclic and aromatic hydrocarbons; also ternaries of these with water.)
4. M. Biancini and D. DeFilippo, *Gazz. Chim. Ital.* **88,** 1202–1214 (1958); *Chem. Abstr.* **53,** 21109 (1959).
5. P. Dakshinamurtz et al., *J. Appl. Chem.* (*London*) **11,** 226–228 (1961).
6. V. Sumarokov and Z. Volodutskaya, *J. Appl. Chem. U.S.S.R.* (*English Transl.*) **29,** 799–800 (1956); *Chem. Abstr.* **51,** 6304 (1957).
7. I. Golubev and V. Olevskii, *Tr. Gos. Nauchn. Issled. i Proektn. Inst. Azotn. Prom.* (8), 58–62 (1957); *Chem. Abstr.* **53,** 21107 (1959).
8. P. Traynard and P. Verrier, *Compt. Rend.* **250,** 2570–2572 (1960); *Chem. Abstr.* **55,** 22116 (1961). (Kinetic studies.)
9. K. Pande and R. Mehrotra, *Z. Anorg. Allgem. Chem.* (in English) **286,** 291–295 (1956); *Chem. Abstr.* **51,** 3348 (1957).
10. R. Flid et al., *Zh. Obshch. Khim.* **27,** 1460–1465 (1957); *Chem. Abstr.* **52,** 3676 (1958).
11. K. Pfordte and G. Leuschner, *Ann. Chem.* **622,** 1–6 (1959); *Chem. Abstr.* **53,** 17891 (1959).
12. K. Mizutani et al., *J. Chem. Soc. Japan, Ind. Chem. Sect.* **59,** 101–103 (1956); *Chem. Abstr.* **51,** 1030 (1957).
13. Ger. Pat. 933,689 (Sept. 29, 1955), O. Horn and R. Kraemer (to Farbwerke Hoechst A.G.).
14. Ger. Pat. 765,969 (June 1, 1953), W. Reppe and H. Kroeper (to I. G. Farbenindustrie A.G.).
15. Ger. Pat. 951,924 (Nov. 8, 1956), W. Kolsch and H. Pistor (to Badische Anilin- & Soda-Fabrik, A.G.).
16. U.S. Pat. 3,151,155 (Sept. 29, 1964), J. W. McKoy and N. Swanson (to Dow Chemical Co.).
17. Brit. Pat. 824,116 (Nov. 25, 1959), E. Crisp and G. Whitfield (to Imperial Chemical Industries, Ltd.).
18. Brit. Pat. 771,991 (April 10, 1957), A. Elce, I. Robson, and D. Young (to Distillers Co., Ltd.).
19. U.S. Pat. 2,770,637 (Nov. 13, 1956), R. L. Mitchell and O. V. Luke (to Celanese Corp. of America).
20. Brit. Pat. 805,110 (Nov. 26, 1958), G. Lawson-Hall and A. Millidge (to Distillers Co., Ltd.).
21. Ger. Pat. 847,145 (Aug. 21, 1952), Ludwig Mannes (to Henkel & Cie. GmbH).
22. Brit. Pat. 771,583 (April 10, 1957), (to Celanese Corp. of America).
23. *Directory of Chemical Producers*, Stanford Research Institute, Menlo Park, Calif., 1966.
24. K. Bassler, *Z. Lebensm.-Untersuch.-Forsch.* **110,** 28–42 (1959); *Chem. Abstr.* **53,** 17290 (1959). (A review with 99 references.)
25. J. W. Young, *Dissertation Abstr.* **25** (4), 2135 (1964).
26. B. F. Dowden and H. J. Bennett, *J. Water Pollution Control Federation* **37** (9), 1308–1316 (1965).
27. H. Cats and H. Onrust, *Chem. Weekblad* **54,** 456–459 (1958); *Chem. Abstr.* **53,** 4595 (1959).
28. A. James, *Fette, Seifen, Anstrichmittel* **59,** 73–77 (1957); *Chem. Abstr.* **52,** 6816 (1958).
29. H. Painter and M. Viney, *J. Biochem. Microbiol. Technol. Eng.* **1,** 143–162 (1959).

30. W. Diemair and E. Schams, *Z. Lebensm.-Untersuch.-Forsch.* **112,** 457–463 (1960).

31. U.S. Pat. 3,197,439 (July 27, 1965), H. E. Frey (to Standard Oil Co. (Indiana)).

32. Fr. Pat. 1,376,814 (Oct. 30, 1964), N. H. Reinking and A. E. Barnabeo (to Union Carbide Corp.); (U.S. Pat. Appl. Oct. 12, 1962).

33. L. Goldblatt, L. Hopper, and R. Mayne, *Paint Varnish Prod.* **49** (8), 44–46, 85 (1959).

34. U.S. 2,895,990 (July 21, 1959), M. Larrison and J. Henry.

35. L. Schultz, *Proc. Cornell Nutr. Conf. Feed Manuf., Ithaca , N.Y., 1954,* 76–81.

36. C. Trolle-Lassen, *Arch. Pharm. Chemi* **65,** 679–685 (1958); *Chem. Abstr.* **52,** 20398 (1958).

37. J. M. Elliot et al., *J. Nutr.* **87** (2), 233–238 (1965).

38. Fr. Pat. 1,383,733 (Jan. 1, 1965), P. Bogdonoff, G. W. Thrasher, and J. N. Henson (to Commercial Solvents Corp.).

39. Ger. Pat. 1,057,870 (May 21, 1959), A. Zuendel and E. Krietsch (to VEB Filmfabrik Agfa Wolfen).

40. U.S. 2,985,608 (May 23, 1961), J. Higgins and W. Smith (to Esso Research & Engineering Co.).

41. Brit. Pat. 753,880 (Aug. 1, 1956) (to Chemstrand Corp.).

42. U.S. Pat. 2,983,696 (May 9, 1961), S. Tocker (to E. I. du Pont de Nemours & Co., Inc.).

43. U.S. Pat. 3,189,663 (June 15, 1965), K. Nozaki (to Shell Oil Co.).

44. U.S. 3,184,440 (May 18, 1965), R. N. Chadha, D. E. Jefferson, and F. X. Werber (to W. R. Grace & Co.).

45. D. Mangaraj et al., *Makromol. Chem.* (in English) **84,** 225–229 (1965); *Chem. Abstr.* **63,** 8505 (1966).

46. Fr. Pat. 1,392,122 (March 12, 1965), H. Wilhelm et al. (to Badische Anilin- & Soda-Fabrik, A.G.).

47. Neth. Pat. Appl. 6,413,427 (May 21, 1965) (by Badische Anilin- & Soda-Fabrik, A.G.).

48. Ger. Pat. 963,150 (May 2, 1957), C. Lefeuvre (to Laporte Chemicals, Ltd.).

49. Japan. Pat. 8547 (Nov. 24, 1955), Seikichi Oshima.

50. R. S. Aries, *Rev. Inst. Franç. Petrolé Ann. Combust. Liquides* **15,** 1881–1885 (1960); *Chem. Abstr.* **55,** 9848 (1961).

51. J. Maruzzella, M. Garofalo, and J. Chiaromonte, *Am. Perfumer* **76** (2), 35–37 (1961).

52. Ger. Pat. 965,966 (July 4, 1957), W. Kunze (to Cassella Farbwerke Mainkur, A.G.).

53. G. Izumi and M. Kita, *Kogyo Kagaku Zasshi* (in Japanese) **68** (6), 1087–1089 (1965); *Chem. Abstr.* **63,** 15116 (1966).

54. Industry estimates.

JOSEPH J. WOCASEK
Celanese Chemical Co.

n-**PROPYL ACETATE,** $CH_3COOCH_2CH_2CH_3$.   See Esters, organic.

PROPYLAMINES. See Amines.

PROPYL ALCOHOLS

n-PROPYL ALCOHOL

n-Propyl alcohol (1-propanol (IUPAC)), $CH_3CH_2CH_2OH$, is a clear, colorless liquid, readily soluble in water, ether, alcohols, and acids. It is used as a solvent and as a chemical intermediate. It occurs in brandies, malt liquors, and in the fermentation and spoilage products of a wide variety of vegetable substances.

Physical and Chemical Properties

Constants. The principal constants of n-propyl alcohol are given in Table 1 (1,2). n-Propyl alcohol forms a number of binary azeotropes (3) as shown in Table 2. Several important ternary azeotropes in which water is one component (3) are listed in Table 3.

Reactions. n-Propyl alcohol undergoes the reactions common to all primary low-molecular-weight alcohols (see Alcohols). Oxidation provides propionaldehyde, propionic acid, and other products, depending on the catalyst and the severity of the oxidizing conditions. Oxidation in the presence of lead acetate favors the aldehyde (4). Air oxidation over ferric oxide provides the aldehyde, but also diethyl ketone and

Table 1. Physical and Chemical Constants of n-Propyl Alcohol

freezing point, °C	-127.0
boiling point at 760 mm Hg, °C	97.15
vapor pressure, mm Hg, at 20°C	14.5
at 60°C	153
at 80.56°C	393
vapor density (air = 1)	2.07
specific gravity, 20/4°C	0.8032
20/20°C	0.8046
refractive index, n_D^{20}	1.3854
viscosity at 20°C, cP	2.256
surface tension at 20°C, dyn/cm	23.8
coefficient of cubical expansion, 0–94°C	0.956×10^{-3}
Reid vapor pressure at 100°F, psi	0.1
critical temperature, °C	263.7
critical pressure, atm	49.9
evaporation rate (butyl acetate = 1)	1.3
specific heat, cal/g, at 0°C	0.526
at 25°C	0.586
heat of vaporization, cal/g, at 60°C	178.9
at 80.56°C	171.6
at 97.15°C	162.6
heat of combustion, cal/g	8020
flash point, Tag open cup, °F	96
autoignition temperature, °C	540
lower explosive limit, % by vol in air	2.6
upper explosive limit, % by vol in air	13.5
electrical conductivity at 25°C, mho/cm	2×10^{-8}

Table 2. Properties of Binary Azeotropes Containing n-Propyl Alcohol

Other component	n-Propyl alcohol, wt %	Bp,[a] °C
water	68.2	indefinite (47 mm Hg)
	70.4	56.68 (200 mm Hg)
	71.0	71.92 (400 mm Hg)
	71.5	81.68 (600 mm Hg)
	71.69	87.72
nitromethane	51.6	89.09
nitroethane	68.2	94.49
1-nitropropane	91.2	96.95
2-nitropropane	75.1	95.97
1-propanethiol	8.65	66.4
3-pentanone (diethyl ketone)	57	94.9
propyl acetate	31.4	59.96 (200 mm Hg)
	39.2	77.06 (400 mm Hg)
	49	94.7
carbon tetrachloride	11.5	72.8
chlorobenzene	80	96.5
benzene	17.1	77.1
cyclohexane	18.5	74.69
toluene	50	92.6
styrene	84	38.5 (50 mm Hg)
p-xylene	92	
n-hexane	4	73.1

[a] At 760 mm Hg except where otherwise indicated.

Table 3. Ternary Azeotropes Containing n-Propyl Alcohol and Water at 760 mm Hg

Third component	Alcohol, wt %	Water, wt %	Third component, wt %	Bp of mixture, °C
carbon tetrachloride	11	5	84	65.4
trichloroethylene	8.1	7.1	84.8	
3-pentanone	20	20	60	81.2
2-hexanone				
(methyl n-butyl ketone)	63	27	10	87
propyl acetate	10	17	73	82.45
1,1-di-n-propoxyethane	51.6	27.4	21.0	87.6
1,1-di-n-propoxymethane	44.8	8	47.2	86.4
2-methylpentanal	58	28	14	86
benzene	9	8.6	82.4	68.5
cyclohexane	10	8.5	81.5	66.6

propyl propionate (5). The action of nitric acid, however, results mostly in propionic acid and some acetic acid (6). Liquid-phase oxidation by air, in water, with suspended zinc oxide and ultraviolet radiation gives peroxides and propionaldehyde (7), but with platinum as a catalyst, propionic acid in 90% yield is the result (8). Vapor-phase air oxidation gives initially propionaldehyde and hydrogen peroxide, and then methanol, formaldehyde, and carbon monoxide (9).

n-Propyl alcohol is decomposed by ultraviolet radiation to simple degenerative products (10). Deoxygenation of the alcohol goes through the propyl carbonium ion to cyclopropane and propylene (11). Rate constants have been calculated for the dehydration of propyl alcohol to propene in the presence of various amounts of hydrogen chloride (12). When the alcohol vapor is passed over titanium dioxide, dehydrogenation to aldehyde occurs, but more severe conditions result in dehydration (13). However, if acetic acid is present, excellent yields of n-propyl acetate result (14).

n-Propyl esters can be prepared in the usual way using acidic catalysts. Dipropyl ether can be made by autoclaving the alcohol in the presence of boron trifluoride; the by-product is a mixture of alkyl benzenes (15). Under high pressure and heavy metal salts catalysis, carbon monoxide reacts with n-propyl alcohol to form equal quantities of butyric and isobutyric acids (16). When heated in the presence of strong bases, 2-methyl-1-pentanol and 2,4-dimethyl-1-heptanol result (17). Ammonia and n-propyl alcohol vapor react over nickel catalyst on alumina to form propionitrile in high yield (18). However, high-pressure ammonolysis of the alcohol over alumina gives a mixture of propyl amine and propane (19). Alkylene epoxides add on to propyl alcohol to form glycol ethers (20). Epichlorohydrin adds on in a similar manner to give chloropropyl propyl ether and polyethers (21,22).

Manufacture

n-Propyl alcohol is made commercially in two ways: from ethylene via oxo technology, and by oxidation of propane. In the oxo synthesis of aldehydes by the action of carbon monoxide on olefins, the residue after distillation of the principal products can be further fractionated, or can be hydrogenated and distilled to yield several alcohols, among them propyl alcohol (23–25). More frequently, the alcohol is made directly by an oxo process in which reasonably pure ethylene is used, forming propionaldehyde (qv) which then is hydrogenated to n-propyl alcohol (26,27). In the U.S. more n-propyl alcohol is made by oxidation of propane than by the oxo route (28). An interesting new route to the alcohol is the hydration of propylene (29). Ordinarily one would expect isopropyl alcohol to be the result, but the choice of catalyst and other variables direct the addition. Thus, mixed zinc and tungsten oxides (30), and lithium aluminum hydride (31) have been shown to be effective for securing n-propyl alcohol.

Fusel oil, a by-product of the distillation of fermented products, contains a percentage of n-propyl alcohol (see Vol. 2, p. 378) but is not a commercial source.

In the U.S. n-propyl alcohol is made by the oxo process by Union Carbide Corporation, and by the oxidation of propane by Celanese Chemical Company. True capacities cannot be stated. Oxo units are flexible and thus propionaldehyde is only one of several directed products. In the case of propane oxidation, n-propyl alcohol is a coproduct along with other oxygenated materials and hence its volume is governed by the total product profile. The 1966 output of propyl alcohol by both methods is estimated to have been about 25 million lb, most of which was sold to the merchant market. n-Propyl alcohol is considered to be a product in limited supply; for this reason its price has remained fairly constant over the years, and in fact has increased somewhat. In 1952 the delivered price was 10.0¢/lb; its 1967 listing was 12.5¢/lb.

n-Propyl alcohol is not classified as a flammable liquid by ICC regulations; however it should be handled in much the same manner as any organic material of similar flash point and vapor pressure. The alcohol is available commercially in tank car, tank truck, and drum quantities.

n-Propyl alcohol is a material of low toxicity, and no ill effects have been reported from its industrial use. Its narcotic and toxic effects are very similar to those of isopropyl alcohol, being somewhat greater than those of ethyl alcohol but less than those

of butyl alcohol. Action on skin or mucous membrane is comparable to that of other industrial alcohols. No cumulative effects have been noted from repeated exposure either by inhalation or skin contact (1). In acute toxicity studies, the mean lethal respiratory dosage for dogs was 2.42 g/kg of body weight (32).

Analysis

n-Propyl alcohol can be absorbed on silica gel (33), and molecular sieves have been used to separate it from other alcohols such as methanol and ethanol (34). Similar separation can be accomplished by elution chromatography (35). Gas chromatography is the principal mode of separation and analysis. Thus, n-propyl alcohol has been determined in alcoholic mixtures (36), brandies (37), perfumes, cosmetics and drugs (38), fusel oil (39), and exhaust gases of automotive engines (40).

Uses

n-Propyl alcohol is used principally as a solvent and as a chemical intermediate. The largest volume is employed as a solvent in printing inks (see Inks) (41) and it is especially valuable in polyamide inks for printing plastic film and sheeting. Other solvent applications include nail polish (42) and other lacquers in place of ethanol–butanol mixtures (43); the medium for the polymerization (44) and spinning (45) of acrylonitrile, and for high-pressure production of polybutyraldehyde (46); and the dyeing of wool (47). It is a solvent for the carboxymethylation of cellulose (48), and a cosolvent in polyvinyl chloride adhesives (49); it is both a gelatilizing and plasticizing agent for cellulose acetate foil and film (50). Improved copper plating is said to result when n-propyl alcohol is added to the bath (51). It is used as a degreaser for metals, as a coupling and dispersing agent in cleaning preparations and floor waxes, and as a component of medium-duty brake fluids. Though its toxicity is very low it has value as an antimicrobial agent in jet fuels for the control of gel formation (which sometimes takes place by bacterial action) (52), and is an effective sporicide for peach rot fungi (53).

As a chemical intermediate, n-propyl alcohol finds its major use in the preparation of propyl acetate. (See Solvents.) Other outlets include the propylated ureas, propyl amine for pesticide production, and numerous esters having small but specific application. The polyethers resulting from reaction of the alcohol with ethylene oxide or propylene oxide are useful surface-active agents (54).

Bibliography

"n-Propyl Alcohol" in *ECT* 1st ed., Vol. 11, pp. 178–182, by M. J. Curry, Celanese Corporation of America.

1. *Normal Propyl Alcohol*, Celanese Chemical Co., New York, April 1967.
2. K. Williamson and R. Harrison, *J. Chem. Phys.* **26**, 1409–1411 (1957).
3. L. H. Horsley and W. S. Tamplin, *Azeotropic Data II* (Advances in Chemistry Ser., No. 35), American Chemical Society, Washington, D.C., 1962.
4. R. E. Partch, *J. Org. Chem.* **30** (8), 2498–2502 (1965).
5. V. A. Komarov and P. V. Maslov, *Zh. Prikl. Khim.* (in Russian) **38** (2), 394–398 (1965); *Chem. Abstr.* **62**, 16041 (1965).
6. Brit. Pat. 771,583 (April 3, 1957) (to Celanese Corp. of America).
7. M. Markham et al., *J. Am. Chem. Soc.* **80**, 5394–5397 (1958).
8. K. Heynes and L. Blazejewicz, *Tetrahedron* **9**, 67–75 (1960).

9. C. F. Cullis and E. J. Newitt, *Proc. Roy. Soc. (London) Ser. A* **257**, 402–412 (1960).
10. A. J. Harrison and J. S. Lake, *J. Phys. Chem.* **63**, 1489–1492 (1959).
11. P. S. Skell and I. Starer, *J. Am. Chem. Soc.* **82**, 2971 (1960).
12. V. Tsvetkova et al., *Dokl. Akad. Nauk SSSR* **124**, 139–141 (1959); *Chem. Abstr.* **53**, 16954 (1959).
13. A. Tolstopyatova, *Dokl. Akad. Nauk SSSR* **133**, 130–133 (1960); *Chem. Abstr.* **54**, 24451 (1960).
14. J. F. Spangenburg, *Ind. Quim. (Buenos Aires)* **7**, 393–401 (1945); *Chem. Abstr.* **41**, 4028 (1947).
15. I. Romadane and J. Pelchers, *Izv. Vysshykh Uchebn. Zavedenii Khim. i Khim. Tekhnol.* **2** (3), 381–383 (1959); *Chem. Abstr.* **54**, 4358 (1960).
16. Brit. Pat. 775,689 (May 29, 1957) (to Badische Anilin- & Soda-Fabrik A.G.).
17. C. Weizmann, E. Bergmann, and L. Haskelberg, *Chem. Ind. (London)* **1937**, 587.
18. M. Popov and N. Shuikin, *Izv. Akad. Nauk SSSR Otd. Khim. Nauk* **1959**, 1992–1998; *Chem. Abstr.* **54**, 9745 (1960).
19. V. A. Krishnamurthy and M. R. A. Rao, *J. Indian Inst. Sci.* **39**, 138–160 (1957).
20. G. Gee et al., *J. Chem. Soc.* **1959**, 1338–1344.
21. Ger. Pat. 1,033,411 (July 3, 1958), C. Borchard and H. Dannenbaum (to Bisterfeld & Stolting).
22. S. Sekiguchi et al., *Kogyo Kagaku Zasshi* (in Japanese) **68** (2), 286–289 (1965); *Chem. Abstr.* **63**, 14667 (1966).
23. Ger. Pat. 891,245 (Sept. 28, 1953), H. Nieuburg (to Badische Anilin- & Soda-Fabrik A.G.).
24. Ger. Pat. 914,375 (Aug. 2, 1945), H. Nieuburg (to Chemische Verwertungsgesellschaft Oberhausen mbH).
25. Ger. Pat. 1,080,535 (April 28, 1960), O. Probst et al. (to Farbwerke Hoechst A.G.).
26. Ger. Pat. 921,931 and 921,932 (Jan. 7, 1955), W. Reppe et al. (to Badische Anilin- & Soda-Fabrik A.G.).
27. Ger. Pat. 1,076,109 (Feb. 25, 1960), O. Probst et al. (to Farbwerke Hoechst A.G.).
28. "Chemicals at Corpus Christi," *Chem. Ind.* **62**, 738–740 (1948).
29. U.S. Pat. 2,830,091 (April 8, 1958), B. Friedman and F. Morritz (to Sinclair Refining Co.).
30. Ger. Pat. 1,041,938 (Oct. 30, 1958), O. Bankowski and G. Hoffmann (to VEB Leuna-Werke "Walter Ulbricht").
31. U.S. Pat. 2,873,290 (Feb. 10, 1959), D. Esmay and C. Johnson (to Standard Oil Co. (Indiana)).
32. D. C. MacGregor, E. Schonbaum, and W. G. Bigelow, *Can. J. Physiol. Pharmacol.* **42** (6), 689–696 (1964).
33. A. Bonetskaya and K. Krasil'nikov, *Proc. Acad. Sci. USSR Phys. Chem. Sect. (English Transl.)* **114**, 421–424 (1957); *Chem. Abstr.* **52**, 16833 (1958).
34. F. Oehme, *Chemiker Ztg.* **83**, 330–333 (1959); *Chem. Abstr.* **54**, 2853 (1960).
35. R. Sargent and W. Rieman, *J. Org. Chem.* **21**, 594–595 (1956).
36. S. Dalnogare and C. E. Bennet, *Anal. Chem.* **30**, 1157–1158 (1958).
37. L. Fleischmann, *Ric. Sci.* **29**, 1194–1198 (1959); *Chem. Abstr.* **53**, 22724 (1959).
38. T. Storto and A. DiPrima, *Riv. Ital. Essenze-Profumi, Piante Offic.-Oli. Vegetali-Saponi* **42**, 537–547 (1960); *Chem. Abstr.* **55**, 8771 (1961).
39. A. Webb and R. E. Kepner, *Am. J. Enol. Viticult.* **12**, 51–59 (1961).
40. K. J. Hughes, R. W. Hurn, and F. G. Edwards, *Gas Chromatog. Intern. Symp., 2nd, East Lansing, Mich., 1959*, 171–182 (1961).
41. W. D. Schaeffer, *Am. Ink Maker* **43** (5), 54–56, 58, 61, 128, 130 (1965).
42. Fr. Pat. 994,011 (Nov. 9, 1951), A. Bianchi.
43. E. Gambardella, *Lakokrasochnye Materialy i ikh Primenenie* **1960** (6), 27–31; *Chem. Abstr.* **55**, 12879 (1961).
44. M. Katayama and Z. Saito, *Chem. High Polymers (Tokyo)* **13**, 11–17 (1956); *Chem. Abstr.* **51**, 5429 (1957).
45. V. Groebe and K. Meyer, *Faserforsch. Textiltech.* **10**, 214–224 (1959); *Chem. Abstr.* **53**, 23061 (1959).
46. M. Gonikberg and V. Zhulin, *Vysokomolekul. Soedin.* **3**, 262–267 (1961); *Chem. Abstr.* **55**, 26506 (1961).
47. E. Atlung, *Tidsskr. Textiltek.* **16**, 17–18 (1958); *Chem. Abstr.* **52**, 9605 (1958).
48. Brit. Pat. 807,576 (Jan. 21, 1959) (to Wyandotte Chemicals Corp.).
49. Brit. Pat. 1,002,039 (Aug. 18, 1965), G. Schmidt and L. van Vlerken.
50. Ital. Pat. 572,339 (Jan. 24, 1958) (to Ferrania Societá per Azioni).
51. Ger. Pat. 1,087,424 (Aug. 18, 1960), H. Horstmann et al. (to Schering A.G.).

52. U.S. Pat. 2,975,042 (March 14, 1961), C. R. Summers (to Gulf Oil Corp.).
53. J. M. Ogawa and S. Lyda, *Phytopathology* **50,** 790–792 (1960).
54. U.S. Pat. 3,203,955 (Aug. 31, 1965), D. R. Jackson and L. G. Lundsted (to Wyandotte Chemicals Corp.).

JOSEPH J. WOCASEK
Celanese Chemical Co.

ISOPROPYL ALCOHOL

Isopropyl alcohol (2-propanol (IUPAC)), $CH_3CHOHCH_3$, is the simplest of the secondary alcohols (see Alcohols). The name "isopropanol," although widely used in industry, is incorrect because it combines the -ol of the Geneva system with the name for a branched-chain instead of a straight-chain hydrocarbon (see Vol. 1, p. 533).

Isopropyl alcohol is a mobile, colorless, low-boiling, flammable, water-miscible liquid with a characteristic alcoholic odor. It is similar to ethyl alcohol in physical properties but differs somewhat in chemical properties. There are many and varied applications for isopropyl alcohol. By far the most important use is as a feedstock for acetone production. Other uses range from isopropyl alcohol rubbing compound to deicer and fuel, to a wide variety of solvent and chemical intermediate uses, including glycerol, amines, acetate ester, etc.

Isopropyl alcohol was first reported by Berthelot in 1855 (1). His synthesis was based on the reaction between propylene and sulfuric acid to form isopropyl hydrogen sulfate which was then hydrolyzed to form the alcohol. Berthelot failed, however, to recognize the true nature of the compound. In 1862, Friedel prepared isopropyl alcohol by reduction of acetone with sodium amalgam (2), but he also failed to recog-

Table 1. Physical Properties of Pure Isopropyl Alcohol

freezing point, °C	−89.5 (7)
boiling point at 760 mm Hg, °C	82.4 (7)
	82.26 (8,9)
density, g/ml, at 20°C	0.7864 (10)
	0.7887 (11)
at 25°C	0.7809 (9)
refractive index, n_D^{20}	1.37757 (11)
	1.37711 (10)
viscosity at 20°C, cP	2.431 (11)
surface tension at 20°C, dyn/cm	21.7 (12)
coefficient of expansion	$V_t = V_o(1 + 0.0010743t + 0.000000328t^2)$ (8)
critical temperature, °C	234.9 (11)
critical pressure, atm	53 (11)
specific heat at 20°C, cal/(g)(°C)	0.608 (13)
heat of fusion, cal/g	21.08 (13)
heat of vaporization at 82.4°C, cal/g	160 (14)
heat of combustion, cal/g	7970 (11)
	7942 (15)
flash point, Tag open cup, °F	59 (16)
autoignition temperature, °C	460 (16)
lower flammability limit, % by vol in air	2.02 (17)
upper flammability limit, % by vol in air	7.99 (17)

Table 2. Vapor Pressure of Isopropyl Alcohol (14,16)

Temperature, °C	Pressure, mm Hg	Temperature, °C	Pressure, mm Hg
−26.1	1	40	105.6
−7.0	5	50	176.8
0	8.9	60	288.5
10	17.0	70	454.8
20	32.4	80	691.8
30	59.1	90	1020.7

Table 3. Constant Boiling Mixture (Isopropyl Alcohol–Water) (11)

boiling point at 760 mm Hg, °C	80.4
composition, vol % alcohol	91.3
wt % alcohol	87.7
refractive index, n_D^{20}	1.37685
specific gravity, 20/20°C	0.8180
25/25°C	0.8149
viscosity at 25°C, cP	2.106

Table 4. Specific Gravity of Isopropyl Alcohol–Water Mixtures (18)

Specific gravity, 20/20°C	Alcohol, vol %	Alcohol, wt %
0.9900	8.1	6.5
0.9800	16.6	13.3
0.9600	32.1	26.2
0.9400	43.2	36.1
0.9200	52.5	45.0
0.9000	61.1	53.5
0.8800	69.2	61.9
0.8600	76.6	70.3
0.8400	83.84	78.68
0.8200	90.67	86.88
0.8000	96.50	94.80
0.7900	99.08	98.60
0.7863	100.00	100.00

Table 5. Other Physical Properties of Isopropyl Alcohol–Water Mixtures (18)

Alcohol, wt %	d_4^{25}	n_D^{25}	Viscosity at 25°C, cP
0	0.9971	1.3325	0.891
10	0.9810	1.3413	1.397
20	0.9666	1.3503	2.059
30	0.9478	1.3574	2.587
40	0.9256	1.3626	2.917
50	0.9022	1.3669	3.059
60	0.8786	1.3700	3.033
70	0.8549	1.3729	2.848
80	0.8310	1.3747	2.545
90	0.8067	1.3756	2.204
100	0.7808	1.3751	2.061

nize its true identity. It remained for Kolbe, in the same year, to identify and name isopropyl alcohol (3).

Isopropyl alcohol is generally considered to be the first petrochemical. A pilot plant for its production was built in 1919 (4) by Melco Chemical Company. Shortly after, the Standard Oil Company of New Jersey secured rights to the process and was producing isopropyl alcohol from propylene at its Bayway (Linden, N.J.) refinery by December 1920. Total U.S. production of isopropyl alcohol in 1965 was 1.5 billion lb (5), and, in 1966, was estimated at 1.65 billion lb (6).

Physical Properties

Selected physical properties of pure isopropyl alcohol and mixtures of isopropyl alcohol with water and with other substances are shown in Tables 1–7.

Table 6. Selected Binary Azeotropes of Isopropyl Alcohol at 760 mm Hg (11)

Other component	Isopropyl alcohol, wt %	Bp of mixture, °C
carbon disulfide	8.0	44.6
chloroform	4.2	60.8
n-hexane	22	61
carbon tetrachloride	18	67.0
cyclohexane	33	68.6
benzene	33.3	71.92
trichloroethylene	28	74
ethyl acetate	23	74.8
methyl ethyl ketone	30	77.3
isopropyl acetate	52.3	80.1
toluene	69	80.6
tetrachloroethylene	80.6	81.7

Table 7. Ternary Azeotropes Containing Isopropyl Alcohol and Water at 760 mm Hg (11)

Third component	Isopropyl alcohol, wt %	Water, wt %	Third component, wt %	Bp of mixture, °C
isopropyl ether	12.2	6.1	81.7	61.0
cyclohexane	18.5	7.5	74.0	64.3
benzene	18.7	7.5	73.8	66.5
methyl ethyl ketone	9.7	11.9	78.4	73.9
isopropyl acetate[a]	10.9	11.1	78.6	76.0

[a] Obtained from plant operation.

Chemical Properties

The chemistry of isopropyl alcohol mainly involves that of the hydroxyl group. Isopropyl alcohol is a secondary alcohol. Hence its chemistry differs in several important respects from that of ethyl alcohol or other primary alcohols, such as n-propyl alcohol, in ease of conversion to ethers and esters, products obtained by oxidation and from catalytic reactions, etc. On the other hand, isopropyl alcohol undergoes many of the reactions typical of lower-molecular-weight primary alcohols.

Active metals, such as sodium and potassium, react readily with isopropyl alcohol to form metal isopropoxides (19) with evolution of hydrogen.

$$2\ CH_3CHOHCH_3 + 2\ M \rightarrow 2\ CH_3CHOMCH_3 + H_2$$

Aluminum isopropoxide may be prepared by refluxing isopropyl alcohol (99%) with aluminum turnings and catalytic amounts of mercuric chloride (20). Substantially complete reaction is reported by Brown with a nonanhydrous isopropyl alcohol–aluminum system (21).

Isopropyl halides (22) are readily formed by reaction of isopropyl alcohol with the corresponding halogen acid. The order of reactivity of the halogen acids is HI > HBr > HCl.

$$CH_3CHOHCH_3 + HX \rightarrow CH_3CHXCH_3 + H_2O$$

Alternately, isopropyl halides may be prepared by the reaction between phosphorus trihalides and isopropyl alcohol.

$$3\ CH_3CHOHCH_3 + PX_3 \rightarrow 3\ CH_3CHXCH_3 + H_3PO_3$$

Under different conditions (lower temperature in presence of, eg, pyridine) the phosphite is predominantly formed when phosphorus trichloride is reacted with isopropyl alcohol.

$$3\ CH_3CHOHCH_3 + PCl_3 \rightarrow ((CH_3)_2CHO)_3P + 3\ HCl$$

A process for the preparation of isopropyl nitrate (23) involves feeding separate streams of the alcohol and 40% nitric acid into a still from which the nitrate is continuously removed by distillation while maintaining a stream of inert gas. A urea concentration effective to destroy nitrous acid is also maintained.

Carboxylic acid esters of isopropyl alcohol are prepared by reaction of isopropyl alcohol with the acid in the presence of an acidic catalyst (see Esterification, Vol. 8, pp. 326–335) and often an entrainer (see Azeotropy, Vol. 2, p. 847). Isopropyl acetate, for example, may be prepared by reaction of isopropyl alcohol with acetic acid using sulfuric acid catalyst and toluene as the entrainer. The reaction is reversible. As is the case with most esters of water-soluble alcohols and acids, the selection of the proper conditions to minimize the reverse reaction is essential to high yields.

$$CH_3CHOHCH_3 + CH_3COOH \underset{}{\overset{H_2SO_4}{\rightleftharpoons}} CH_3CH(OOCCH_3)CH_3 + H_2O$$

A common laboratory method for the preparation of isopropyl esters is the reaction between the alcohol and an acid chloride.

$$CH_3CHOHCH_3 + RCOCl \rightarrow RCOOCH(CH_3)_2 + HCl$$

Acid anhydrides, likewise, can be employed in the laboratory to yield esters of isopropyl alcohol.

$$CH_3CHOHCH_3 + (RCO)_2O \rightarrow RCOOCH(CH_3)_2 + RCOOH$$

Ether–alcohols of isopropyl alcohol may be prepared by reaction of isopropyl alcohol with ethylene oxide or propylene oxide. The reaction is catalyzed by a base such as sodium hydroxide. Higher adducts are also formed in the reaction since the oxide is free to react with the product ether–alcohol hydroxyl group also.

$$CH_3CHOHCH_3 + \overline{OCH_2CH_2} \overset{base}{\longrightarrow} CH_3CH(OC_2H_4OH)CH_3$$

2-isopropoxyethanol

Isopropyl alcohol may be dehydrated to yield diisopropyl ether or propylene. The predominant reaction is determined by the type of catalyst that is used and the reaction conditions (24).

$$2 \text{ CH}_3\text{CHOHCH}_3 \rightarrow (\text{CH}_3)_2\text{CHOCH(CH}_3)_2 + \text{H}_2\text{O}$$

$$\text{CH}_3\text{CHOHCH}_3 \rightarrow \text{CH}_3\text{CH}{=}\text{CH}_2 + \text{H}_2\text{O}$$

Isopropyl alcohol is dehydrogenated to acetone over a wide variety of catalysts including metals, oxides, and mixtures of metals and oxides. The reaction is endothermic (15,900 cal/g-mole at 327°C). This reaction is of basic commercial importance since this represents the largest single use of isopropyl alcohol.

$$\text{CH}_3\text{CHOHCH}_3 \rightarrow \text{CH}_3\text{COCH}_3 + \text{H}_2$$

Isopropyl alcohol may also be partially oxidized to acetone by the same types of catalysts used in the dehydrogenation. The oxidation reaction has certain disadvantages including difficulty of temperature control and somewhat lower yield (25).

$$\text{CH}_3\text{CHOHCH}_3 + \tfrac{1}{2}\text{O}_2 \rightarrow \text{CH}_3\text{COCH}_3 + \text{H}_2\text{O}$$

Manufacture

Two methods of manufacture are of commercial importance—both involve the hydration of propylene. U.S. manufacturers (Enjay Chemical Co., Shell Chemical Co., and Union Carbide Corp.) use the so-called indirect hydration or esterification–hydrolysis method. A newer method, direct catalytic hydration, is used by at least two European manufacturers—Imperial Chemical Industries, Ltd. (26) and Hibernia-Chemie GmbH (27).

Indirect Hydration. Basic reactions in the production of isopropyl alcohol by this method are the formation of isopropyl hydrogen sulfate and the subsequent hydrolysis to isopropyl alcohol and sulfuric acid. This is the same basic method first reported by Berthelot (1).

$$\text{CH}_3\text{CH}{=}\text{CH}_2 + \text{H}_2\text{SO}_4 \rightarrow (\text{CH}_3)_2\text{CHOSO}_3\text{H}$$

$$(\text{CH}_3)_2\text{CHOSO}_3\text{H} + \text{H}_2\text{O} \rightarrow \text{CH}_3\text{CHOHCH}_3 + \text{H}_2\text{SO}_4$$

In the production of isopropyl alcohol, some diisopropyl sulfate is also formed by the reaction of propylene with some of the isopropyl hydrogen sulfate produced in the initial reaction.

$$\text{CH}_3\text{CH}{=}\text{CH}_2 + (\text{CH}_3)_2\text{CHOSO}_3\text{H} \rightarrow ((\text{CH}_3)_2\text{CH})_2\text{SO}_4$$

The diisopropyl sulfate may, in turn, hydrolyze to form isopropyl hydrogen sulfate and isopropyl alcohol.

$$((\text{CH}_3)_2\text{CH})_2\text{SO}_4 + \text{H}_2\text{O} \rightarrow (\text{CH}_3)_2\text{CHOSO}_3\text{H} + \text{CH}_3\text{CHOHCH}_3$$

The diisopropyl sulfate may also react with isopropyl alcohol to form isopropyl hydrogen sulfate and diisopropyl ether.

$$((\text{CH}_3)_2\text{CH})_2\text{SO}_4 + \text{CH}_3\text{CHOHCH}_3 \rightarrow (\text{CH}_3)_2\text{CHOSO}_3\text{H} + (\text{CH}_3)_2\text{CHOCH(CH}_3)_2$$

In addition to the reactions shown, polymer formation and other reactions due to impurities in the feed are of concern—eg, *sec*-butyl alcohol from butenes, and acetone from methylacetylene. The total of organic impurities in commercial isopropyl alcohol is well under 0.1%. The principal organic impurity is acetone. There are traces of other organic compounds including acids, higher alcohols and ketones, and hydro-

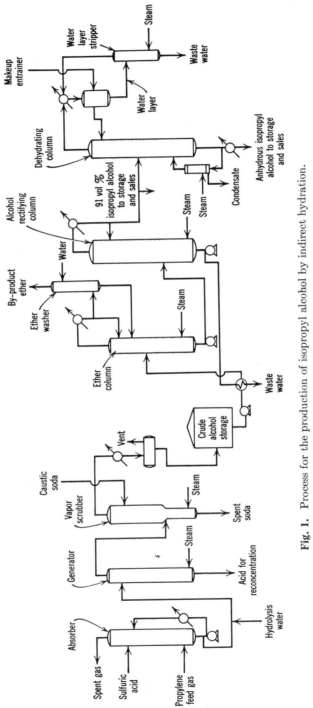

Fig. 1. Process for the production of isopropyl alcohol by indirect hydration.

carbons. Figure 1 is a generalized flow plan for the production of isopropyl alcohol and by-product isopropyl ether.

Crude propylene produced by the thermal and/or catalytic pyrolysis of petroleum hydrocarbons, is scrubbed to remove hydrogen sulfide and thiols. Higher-molecular-weight hydrocarbons are removed by distillation, and acetylenic compounds are removed by hydrogenation. The concentrated propylene (50 mole % or more) is then absorbed under suitable conditions of pressure (100–400 psig) and temperature (60–90°C) in sulfuric acid (70–80 wt %) to produce mixed isopropyl sulfates. The mole ratio of propylene absorbed per mole of sulfuric acid runs from 1.0 to 1.5. The major part of the propylene is removed in the absorption process. The spent gas, containing largely propane after caustic soda scrubbing, is used for fuel or liquefied petroleum gas (qv) (28). The heat of reaction in the absorber is removed by recycling, through a heat exchanger, a sufficient quantity of the extract (mono- and diisopropyl sulfates) to maintain the desired temperature.

The extract is withdrawn from the absorber at a uniform rate and is diluted with water to hydrolyze the sulfate esters. The diluted solution flows to the generator where the alcohol and ether are stripped from the weak acid solution by means of live steam at atmospheric pressure. The weak acid passes from the bottom of the generator and is concentrated to the proper strength for recycle to the absorber. The alcohol vapors pass through a scrubbing tower, where acidic compounds and entrained acid are removed by caustic soda. The neutralized vapors are then condensed and pumped to crude storage.

The crude alcohol, containing 45–55 vol % isopropyl alcohol, some isopropyl ether, water, and a small percentage of hydrocarbons and other impurities, is pumped to a finishing system consisting of three or more fractionating columns and auxiliary facilities. In the first column, the ether is separated from the alcohol. The ether is passed through a water washer to remove any remaining alcohol. The alcohol–water mixture passes from the ether column to the rectifying column, where the binary azeotrope (91.3 vol % alcohol) is distilled off, the bottoms consisting of water.

The 91% alcohol is sold as such or sent to a dehydrating column where, with the aid of an entrainer (azeotropic agent), the remaining water is removed from the alcohol. Entrainers in common use are benzene and isopropyl ether (ethyl ether, which forms a binary azeotrope with water, is sometimes used, but at pressures substantially above atmospheric). Upon condensation, the ternary azeotrope flows to a decanter, where two layers form. The upper layer, which is mainly entrainer and alcohol, is returned to the top of the column as reflux. If desired, the lower layer, containing mostly water, may be stripped to recover the small amount of dissolved alcohol and entrainer. Finished anhydrous isopropyl alcohol is removed from the base of the column through a heat exchanger to storage.

Because of the corrosive conditions that exist in the crude alcohol section of the plant, it is important that the materials of construction be resistant to sulfuric acid at the various concentrations and temperatures required by the process. After the alcohol leaves the vapor scrubber in the crude section, it is neutral. Thus, steel is a satisfactory material for tanks, lines, and columns in the finishing section. However, where product purity and freedom from contamination are critical, stainless-steel equipment is frequently used (29).

Direct Catalytic Hydration. The indirect hydration process has certain inherent disadvantages. Expensive equipment is required to handle and reconcentrate the acid.

Further, the heat required for the acid reconcentration step is usually quite substantial. Considerable work has therefore been done on the development of propylene hydration schemes which do not use sulfuric acid. The processes which have been studied generally involve contacting the olefin and water in the presence of a suitable catalyst at elevated temperature and pressure in order to produce the desired isopropyl alcohol directly.

$$CH_3CH{=}CH_2 + H_2O \rightleftharpoons CH_3CHOHCH_3$$

High pressures, relatively low temperatures and high steam-to-propylene ratios favor conversion to the alcohol.

Both vapor-phase and mixed-phase (trickle) systems have been studied. When the hydration catalyst is active at low temperatures, the reaction is usually conducted in the presence of a large excess of (liquid) water. Using sulfonated styrene–divinylbenzene ion-exchange resins, Kaiser and co-workers (30) studied the effects of temperature, pressure, space velocity, and feed composition on conversion and selectivity. Once-through propylene conversions up to 50% were obtained at 149°C, 1000 psig. When the catalyst used is not active at low temperatures, vapor-phase operation is used to avoid extreme pressures. The thermodynamic equilibria prevailing at higher temperatures limit the propylene conversion to quite low levels. The conversion reported (31) for vapor-phase operation over phosphoric acid impregnated on Celite brand of diatomaceous earth at 225–250°C, 550 psig is only 3.8%.

The flowsheet for isopropyl alcohol production by direct hydration is quite analogous to that used for ethyl alcohol (see Vol. 8, p. 435). Olefin and water are passed over a fixed bed of catalyst. The reactor effluent is cooled to recover an aqueous alcohol stream. Recycle olefin is scrubbed to remove additional alcohol. The crude alcohol is then purified in a manner similar to that described earlier for the indirect hydration route.

The first plant to manufacture isopropyl alcohol by the direct catalytic hydration method was in England (Imperial Chemical Industries, Ltd., at Billingham in 1951). ICI uses a tungsten oxide catalyst system (26), high pressure, 200–250 atm, and temperatures of 200–300°C. Polymer formation is extremely small and after separation of unconverted propylene, the dilute solution of isopropyl alcohol is distilled to produce the binary azeotrope. Both propylene and water are recycled to the reactor. Hibernia-Chemie GmbH started commercial operation of the direct catalytic hydration process in 1966 at Wanne-Eickel, West Germany (27). Hibernia employs a vapor-phase system in which the catalyst is phosphoric acid impregnated on a clay base (32).

Economic Aspects

Isopropyl alcohol has been the largest single chemical use for propylene for many years (33). It is one of the few oxygenated organic chemicals to surpass the billion-pound-per-year level. Table 8 shows production figures for the period 1955–1966. The published price of anhydrous isopropyl alcohol (Table 8) remained constant from 1959 to mid 1966. The current published price (34) has increased to 48¢/gal (91 and 95% isopropyl alcohol are 4 and 2¢/gal less, respectively).

Slightly over half the isopropyl alcohol consumed is used in the production of acetone (6). Hence, isopropyl alcohol production has been closely related to the demand for acetone. Acetone is also produced as a by-product in the manufacture of phenol via the cumene process, from natural gas oxidation, and as a by-product from

Table 8. Isopropyl Alcohol Production[a] and Price History

Year	Production, billion lb (5)	Published price,[b] ¢/gal
1955	0.925	39
1960	1.180	46
1961	1.189	46
1962	1.326	46
1963	1.466	46
1964	1.504	46
1965	1.537	46
1966	1.650 (est) (6)	48

[a] Converted to 100% isopropyl alcohol basis.
[b] Tank car delivered price for anhydrous isopropyl alcohol.

glycerol manufacture. An earlier route—fermentation—appears pretty much out of the picture due to high carbohydrate cost (6). The cumene process accounted for an estimated 20% of U.S. acetone production in 1964 (ten years after introduction of the cumene process). Estimates are that cumene will play an increasingly important part in the production of acetone (35). Future growth of cumene acetone will, of course, depend on the demand for phenol.

Specifications and Test Methods, Analysis, Storage, and Handling

Specifications and Test Methods. Three basic grades of isopropyl alcohol, differing mainly in water content, are marketed in the U.S.: 91 vol %, 95 vol %, and anhydrous. Typical sales specifications and test methods for these grades are shown in Table 9. Other grades marketed include a cosmetic-grade isopropyl alcohol (91 vol % and anhydrous) containing a masking agent (perfume), and an electronic-grade having low conductivity. Other, generally more restrictive qualifying specifications

Table 9. Typical Sales Specifications for Isopropyl Alcohol

Property	91%	95%	Anhydrous	ASTM test method
purity, % by vol, min	91.0	95.0	99.85	
specific gravity, 20/20°C, min	0.8175	0.8035		D 268
max	0.8185	0.8055	0.7866	
acidity, % by wt as acetic acid, max	0.002	0.002	0.002	D 1613
nonvolatile matter, mg/100 ml, max	1	2	1	D 1353
water solubility test[a]	........clear at infinite dilution........			
distillation, °C				D 1078
initial, min	79.7	80.0	81.3	
dry point, max	80.7	83.0	83.3	
range, max			1.0	
color, Pt–Co, max	10	10	10	D 1209
appearance	....clear and free of suspended matter....			
odor	..............no foreign..............			
residual odor	none	none	none	D 1296
water content, wt %, max			0.1	D 1364

[a] Designed to detect presence of water-insoluble contaminants such as hydrocarbons.

Table 10. Qualifying Specifications for Isopropyl Alcohol

Property	ACS reagent 1960	USP XVII reagent	NF XII	ASTM D-770-64	Fed TT-I-735a grade A
acidity, % by wt as acetic acid, max	0.0008	0.002	0.002	0.002	0.002
alkalinity, % by wt as NaOH, max	0.0005	0.0005			
appearance					CFSM[a]
color, Pt–Co, max		colorless	colorless	10	10
corrosion on copper					no pitting or black stain
distillation, initial bp, min–dry point, max, °C			81–83		81.3–83.0
range, °C, max	1.0	1.0		1.5 (incl 82.3)	
nonvolatile matter, g/100 ml, max	0.0007	0.0007	0.005	0.005	0.002
odor			characteristic	characteristic	characteristic
residual				none	none
purity, % by wt, min			99		
refractive index, n_D^{20}			1.3763–1.3780		
specific gravity, 20/20°C	0.7883	0.7883	0.7869	0.790	0.787
ultraviolet spectrum	smooth curve[b]	smooth curve			
max absorbance/cm					
at 210 mμ		1.00			
at 220	1.00	0.40			
at 230		0.20			
at 240	0.20				
at 245		0.10			
at 250	0.10				
at 260		0.05			
at 275	0.10				
at 300	0.05	0.02			
at 330		0.01			
water content, wt %, max	0.5	0.5		0.2	0.10
water solubility	clear	clear	miscible	no turbidity	no turbidity

[a] Clear and free of suspended matter.   [b] For spectrometric grade only.

for special purposes are imposed by various organizations and governmental agencies, as shown in Table 10. Test methods are generally detailed in the specifications.

Analysis. Determination of isopropyl alcohol in simple mixtures with water is most accurately and conveniently carried out by the use of specific gravity tables (18). The presence of isopropyl alcohol can be determined by means of some characteristic, such as the melting point of a readily purified derivative, eg, the 3,5-dinitrobenzoate (36), the xanthate (37), or the α-naphthylurethan (38). Other techniques include color reactions which may be standardized to serve as quantitative methods for detecting minute quantities of isopropyl alcohol. Many of the more reliable colorimetric methods depend on oxidation of isopropyl alcohol to acetone which yields highly colored reaction products in dilute solution. These color reactions were reviewed by Simmons (39). Microgram quantities of isopropyl alcohol can be determined photometrically in the presence of large amounts of acetone and acetic acid (40). A conductometric method has been developed for isopropyl alcohol–water mixtures (41). Gas chromatography has been employed in the detection of isopropyl alcohol in beer brewing (42). Gas chromatography is ideally suited to the determination of isopropyl alcohol in blends with other organic solvents, such as in lacquer thinners.

Storage and Handling. Plain steel tanks, piping, and equipment are generally used for the storage and handling of anhydrous isopropyl alcohol. Provisions to exclude atmospheric moisture are recommended to avoid rust problems. Aqueous solutions (91% and others) of isopropyl alcohol cause rusting of plain steel. Baked-phenolic-lined steel and stainless steel are used to avoid this and to maintain high quality. Aluminum can be used for aqueous solutions but is not recommended for anhydrous isopropyl alcohol due to its tendency to form aluminum isopropoxide.

Tanks for storage of isopropyl alcohol may be located either above or below ground. Above-ground tanks generally should be located 50 ft or more from buildings and should be surrounded by a dike. Underground tanks generally should be located at least 5 ft away from building foundations and should be coated with a corrosion-resistant material. All tanks should be suitably vented and each vent pipe should be protected with a flame arrester.

Pumps for handling isopropyl alcohol preferably should be of the centrifugal, self-priming type, with spark-proof electric motor drives. Standard valves, gaskets, and valve packings may be used. All equipment, pipelines, and tanks should be grounded as a protection against static electricity.

Isopropyl alcohol (Bureau of Explosives and freight descriptions "isopropanol") is shipped in tank cars, tank trucks, 55-gal iron drums, and a variety of smaller containers. Isopropyl alcohol is classed as a flammable liquid (Tag open cup flash point below 80°F). Hence, ICC regulations require a red caution label on all shipping containers. Containers also must comply with other applicable ICC regulations.

Health and Safety Factors

Ingestion of isopropyl alcohol does not produce a state of exhilaration, nor is its taste palatable except in very dilute solution. In these respects it differs sharply from ethyl alcohol. In human volunteers, a dose of 22.5 ml in water caused immediate signs and symptoms of a toxic reaction. The fatal dose for man has been estimated at about 166 ml, but its emetic and depressant properties limit the possibility of ingesting a fatal dose (43). The LD_{50} value for rats has been determined as 5.84 g/kg (44).

The undiluted liquid is severely irritating to the eyes and may cause eye injury if not removed promptly (45). Isopropyl alcohol is not a skin irritant. It is used as a local disinfectant; it is widely used as a rubbing compound in the home and in hospitals (mainly in the form of a 70 vol % solution in water).

Human subjects have described 200 ppm isopropyl alcohol vapor as the minimum odor threshold. Mild irritation of the eyes, nose, and throat was noticed at 400 ppm; at 800 ppm the effects were still not severe, but this concentration was uncomfortable and considered unsuitable for long periods of exposure. Only one case of intoxication from industrial exposure to isopropyl alcohol has been reported, and it is probable that other solvents associated with the alcohol in a mixture contributed to the toxic effect. However, several cases are on record of severe effects and even death from inhalation of high vapor concentrations resulting from the use of the alcohol as a sponging agent to reduce high fever (46–48).

The use of isopropyl alcohol in industrial applications does not constitute a health hazard. In very high vapor concentration it acts as an anesthetic, but exposures of this magnitude are unlikely in industrial areas. There is no evidence to suggest that prolonged or repeated exposures to low concentrations of vapor have any chronic toxic effect on man. A threshold limit of 400 ppm by vol of vapor in air has been established for daily 8-hr exposures. This level is low enough to prevent symptoms of anesthesia, but some mild irritation may be experienced (46). Workers should be warned that isopropyl alcohol is not a beverage substitute for ethyl alcohol. Eye protection should be worn wherever splashing may occur. First aid if overcome by vapor: Remove from contaminated environment and call a physician. Administer artificial respiration if breathing is irregular or has stopped. If the liquid has splashed into the eyes, immediately flush the eyes with water for at least 15 min and get prompt medical attention.

Uses

Since isopropyl alcohol has been available commercially at a relatively low price for many years it is not surprising that numerous uses have evolved. These uses can be classified as (a) chemical, and (b) solvent and other. Table 11 lists a breakdown of estimated 1965 consumption (6).

Table 11. Estimated 1965 Consumption Pattern for Isopropyl Alcohol[a] (6)

Uses	Million lb
chemical	
acetone	860
glycerol	40
isopropyl acetate	30
amines	30
hydrogen peroxide	10
other esters and miscellaneous	120
subtotal chemical	1090
solvent and other	
coatings	120
rubbing alcohol	50
drug and cosmetic	25
government use	10
general deicing	40
export	50
all other	195
subtotal solvent and other	490
grand total	1580

Courtesy *Oil, Paint, and Drug Reporter.*
[a] Basis: 100% isopropyl alcohol.

Chemical Uses. *Acetone* (qv). The single largest use for isopropyl alcohol is as a feedstock in the production of acetone by catalytic dehydrogenation. Future growth of this use will, of course, be influenced by alternate routes to acetone, particularly via the cumene process.

Isopropyl Acetate (see Esters; Solvents). This important ester is a widely used, fast-evaporating, active solvent component of nitrocellulose lacquers and flexographic inks. It is also used in lacquer thinners as an active solvent.

Amines (see Amines, lower aliphatic). Isopropylamine and diisopropylamine are commercially available. One method of manufacture is by amination of isopropyl alcohol with ammonia in the presence of dehydrating catalysts. The herbicide 2,4-dichlorophenoxyacetic acid (2,4-D) (see Plant growth substances) is used in one form as the isopropylamine salt. Diisopropylamine is used in the manufacture of diisopropylammonium nitrite—a vapor-phase inhibitor against corrosion of iron and steel.

Glycerol (qv). One route to glycerol starts with the oxidation of propylene to acrolein, which is then reacted with isopropyl alcohol to form allyl alcohol and acetone. In a subsequent step the allyl alcohol is reacted with hydrogen peroxide in order to make glycerol.

Hydrogen Peroxide. One commercial process for the manufacture of hydrogen peroxide (qv) involves the oxidation of isopropyl alcohol. Acetone is also produced in this process.

Other Chemicals Derived from Isopropyl Alcohol. Isopropyl xanthate is used as a collector in the ore flotation process (see Flotation). Isopropyl myristate and isopropyl palmitate are widely used components of cosmetic formulations (eg, lipsticks, bath oils, creams, lotions, etc). Isopropyl oleate is used in lubricating-oil compositions. Aluminum isopropoxide (see Alkoxides, metal) is used as a chemical reducing agent. Isopropyl ether is used as an inert reaction medium and as a solvent in extractions. It has also found use in increasing the octane value of gasoline.

Solvent and Other Uses (see Solvents). Isopropyl alcohol is free of the government regulations and/or taxes that apply to ethyl alcohol. In addition it is somewhat lower in cost. These factors often dictate the use of isopropyl alcohol over ethyl alcohol. Isopropyl alcohol is, in turn, somewhat higher in cost than methyl alcohol. However, the greater toxicity of methyl alcohol, together with its increased flammability hazard, tend to favor the use of isopropyl alcohol in many cases. There are, of course, uses where the specific performance of these lower alcohols is more important than price or other factors and is the determining factor. For example, the odor of ethyl alcohol is the main reason it is the solvent of choice over isopropyl alcohol in cosmetics.

Coatings (qv). Isopropyl alcohol is used as a latent solvent in nitrocellulose lacquers. Nitrocellulose is often shipped wetted with isopropyl alcohol. The purpose of the alcohol is to reduce the flammability hazard in storage and transportation. Flexographic printing inks of the polyamide and nitrocellulose types frequently contain isopropyl alcohol as a solvent component. Phenolic varnishes used in paper coating, laminating, and impregnating often contain isopropyl alcohol.

Rubbing-Compound, Medicinal, and Sanitizing Uses. The majority of rubbing preparations used in the home and hospitals are based on isopropyl alcohol. The excellent germicidal properties of isopropyl alcohol have also led to its widespread use in sanitizers and disinfectants.

Solvent Extraction. Natural products of all sorts—from kelp to pectin to drugs, vitamins, resins, oils, gums, waxes, etc—are extracted and/or purified using isopropyl alcohol as the solvent. Impurities in white oils are extracted with isopropyl alcohol.

Aerosols (qv). House and garden-type insecticides, medicated sprays for treatment of minor cuts, glass cleaners, and a wide variety of other household specialties contain substantial amounts of isopropyl alcohol. However, the use of isopropyl alcohol in room sprays has declined in favor of hydrocarbon propellant–water systems.

Automotive. Windshield-wiper concentrates, aerosol windshield deicers, proprietary antistalling and gasline antifreeze compositions, etc generally are based on isopropyl alcohol. The use of isopropyl alcohol as a refinery-added antistalling component has declined sharply in recent years.

Cosmetics. The stronger, less pleasant odor of isopropyl alcohol (vs ethyl alcohol) has limited the use of isopropyl alcohol in cosmetics to highly scented and generally inexpensive products. Thus, there has been little penetration of the hair-spray market, for example, with isopropyl alcohol.

Other Uses. Isopropyl alcohol is an important denaturant component of special industrial solvents (see Ethyl alcohol). It is blended with methyl alcohol and used as a fuel for refrigerator-car heaters (used to maintain a safe temperature in the shipment of fruits and vegetables in the winter). It serves as a coolant in beer manufacture, cleaning and drying agent in the manufacture of electronic tubes, and deicer for aircraft propellers.

There are many other uses for isopropyl alcohol, some declining—eg, in gasoline antistalling—others just beginning to show promise, such as in the manufacture of fish protein concentrate (49) where isopropyl alcohol is used as an extractant. This new source of foodstuff may have substantial impact on the protein-starved populations of the world. It suffices to say that any product with the versatility demonstrated by isopropyl alcohol will be around for a long time.

Bibliography

"Isopropyl Alcohol" in *ECT* 1st ed., Vol. 11, pp. 182–190, by J. G. Park and C. M. Beamer, Enjay Company, Inc.

1. M. Berthelot, *Ann. Chim. Phys.* **43** (3), 399 (1855).
2. A. Friedel, *Ann. Chem.* **124,** 137 (1862).
3. *Richter's Organic Chemistry*, Vol. 1, P. Blakiston's Son & Co., Philadelphia, 1913.
4. C. Ellis, *The Chemistry of Petroleum Derivatives*, Reinhold Publishing Corp., New York, 1937.
5. U.S. Tariff Commission, *Synthetic Organic Chemicals, U.S. Production and Sales* (by year).
6. *Oil, Paint, Drug Reptr.* **190** (19), 42 (1966).
7. J. Timmermans and Y. Delcourt, *J. Chim. Phys.* **31,** 85 (1934).
8. R. F. Brunel, J. L. Crenshaw, and E. Tobin, *J. Am. Chem. Soc.* **43,** 561 (1921).
9. A. Wilson and E. L. Simons, *Ind. Eng. Chem.* **44,** 2214 (1952).
10. A. I. Vogel, *J. Chem. Soc.* **1948,** 1814.
11. International Critical Tables, III (1928), V (1929), VII (1930), McGraw-Hill Book Co., Inc., New York.
12. W. Ramsey and J. Shields, *J. Am. Chem. Soc.* **63,** 1089 (1941).
13. G. S. Parks and K. K. Kelly, *J. Am. Chem. Soc.* **47,** 2089 (1925).
14. G. S. Parks and B. Barton, *J. Am. Chem. Soc.* **50,** 24 (1928).
15. G. S. Parks and G. E. Moore, *J. Chem. Phys.* **7,** 1066 (1939).
16. C. Marsden, *Chem. Prod.* **18,** 102 (1955).
17. Louis and Entezam, *Ann. Combustible Liquides* **14,** 21 (1939).
18. *Isopropyl Alcohol*, Enjay Chemical Company, New York, 1966. (Contains over 1200 references on process, quality, uses, properties, etc.)
19. J. G. F. Druce, *J. Chem. Soc.* **1937,** 1407.
20. U.S. Pat. 2,394,848 (Feb. 12, 1946), T. F. Doumani (to Union Oil Co.).
21. C. F. Brown, *Paper, 116th Meeting, American Chemical Society, Atlantic City, Sept. 1949.*
22. J. F. Norris, W. S. Johnson, H. D. Hirsch, and C. R. McCullough, *Rec. Trav. Chim.* **48,** 885 (1929).
23. U.S. Pat. 2,647,914 (Aug. 4, 1953), W. G. Allan and T. J. Tobin (to Imperial Chemical Industries, Ltd.).

24. M. Katuno, *J. Soc. Chem. Ind., Japan* **42,** 422B (1939); **43,** 65B (1940).

25. P. W. Sherwood, *Petrol. Refiner* **33** (12), 144–155 (1954).

26. *Petroleum (London)* **16,** 19–21 (1953).

27. *Chem. Age* **95,** 132 (1966).

28. *Oil Gas J.* **52** (18), 111–118 (1953).

29. E. C. Fetter, *Chem. Eng.* **55,** 235 (Oct. 1948).

30. J. R. Kaiser et al., *Ind. Eng. Chem., Prod. Res. Develop.* **1** (4), 296–302 (1962).

31. U.S. Pat. 2,579,601 (Dec. 25, 1951), C. R. Nelson et al. (to Shell Development Co.).

32. Belg. Pat. 683,923 (Dec. 16, 1966) (to Hibernia-Chemie GmbH).

33. N. E. Ockerbloom, *Paper, 153rd National Meeting, American Chemical Society, Miami Beach, April 1967.*

34. *Oil, Paint, Drug Reptr.* **193** (2), 20 (1968).

35. *Chem. Eng. News* **42,** 26 (Dec. 7, 1964).

36. M. Orchin, *J. Assoc. Offic. Agr. Chemists* **25,** 839 (1942).

37. I. S. Shupe, *J. Assoc. Offic. Agr. Chemists* **25,** 495 (1942).

38. C. Neuburg and E. Kansky, *Biochem. Z.* **20,** 445 (1909).

39. W. H. Simmons, *Perfumery Ess. Oil Record* **18,** 168 (1927).

40. M. Mantel and M. Anbar, *Anal. Chem.* **36** (4), 936–937 (1964).

41. A. M. Arjuna, *Anales Real Soc. Espan. Fis. Quim. (Madrid), Ser. B* **61** (3), 591–594 (1965).

42. V. S. Bavisotto et al., *Am. Soc. Brewing Chemists Proc.* **1961,** 16–23.

43. D. H. Grant, "The Pharmacology of Isopropyl Alcohol," *J. Lab. Clin. Med.* **8,** 382 (1923).

44. H. W. Gerarde and R. E. Eckardt, *Intern. Congr. Occupational Health, 14th, Madrid, 1963* (in English) (2), 723–727 (1964).

45. C.P. Carpenter and H. F. Smyth, Jr., *Am. J. Ophthalmol.* **29,** 1363–1372 (1946).

46. F. A. Patty, *Industrial Hygiene and Toxicology*, Vol. II, Interscience Publishers, Inc., New York, 1949, pp. 853–857.

47. L. Adelson, *Am. J. Clin. Pathol.* **38,** 144–151 (Aug. 1962).

48. R. F. Garrison, *J. Am. Med. Assoc.* **152,** 317–318 (May 23, 1953).

49. D. G. Snyder, E. R. Pariser, W. M. Chapman, and G. M. Knobl, Jr., *Food Technol.* **21** (7), 70–72 (1967); (8), 56–59 (1967). (These are the first in a series of articles on fish protein concentrate to appear in *Food Technol.* The articles are clear, concise, and contain numerous references.)

ACKNOWLEDGMENT: The author gratefully acknowledges the technical contributions of R. C. Miller and R. A. Scala, Esso Research and Engineering Company.

E. J. WICKSON
Enjay Chemical Laboratory

PROPYLENE

Propylene (propene), $CH_3CH=CH_2$, at atmospheric conditions, is an invisible gas, heavier than air. It has a slightly sweet aroma, and it will burn readily in air at certain concentrations (see Table 1). Propylene is perhaps the oldest, and certainly it is one of the most important building blocks in the petrochemical industry; and it has been a major source of octane improvement in the gasoline market for many years. Enormous quantities are produced and consumed. Significant increases in demand are widely predicted by chemical and fuel consumers throughout the world.

Chemical Properties

Propylene, as shown here, is an isomer of cyclopropane, a homolog of ethylene in the olefin series, and an analog of propane, propadiene, and methylacetylene (see Table 2).

Because of the closeness of its boiling point to that of propylene, propane, which is relatively inert, is the most common impurity present when propylene is used in

Table 1. Physical Properties of Propylene (1)

Property	Value
melting point, °C	−185
boiling point, °C	−47.7
triple point, °C	−185.25
density, d_4^{-47}	0.6095
d_4^{20}	0.5139
d_4^{25}	0.5053
vapor density (air = 1.0)	1.49
viscosity, cP, at −185°C	15
at −110°C	0.44
critical temperature, °C	91.9
critical pressure, atm	45.4
critical density, g/ml	0.233
heat of fusion, kcal/mole	0.7176
heat of vaporization at −47.7°C, cal/g	104.62
heat of formation at 25°C, cal/mole	4,879
free energy of formation at 25°C, cal/mole	14,990
heat of combustion of gas, cal/mole	460,428
heat capacity (C_p) at 25°C, cal/(mole)(°C)	15.27
flammability limits in air, vol %, upper	11.1
lower	2.0
heating value (saturated with water vapor) at 60°F and 30 in. Hg, Btu/scf	2,297
flame temperature in air at 18°C, °C	
assuming complete combustion	2,200
actual	1,935
Van der Waals constants $((p + a/v^2)(v − b) = RT)$, in atm, liter, mole units	
a	8.379
b	0.08272
solubility, ml gas/100 ml solvent, at 20°C and atmospheric pressure	
in water	44.6
in ethyl alcohol	1,250
in acetic acid	524.5

Table 2. Propylene and Related Compounds

Name	Formula		Boiling point, °C
	Empirical	Structure	
ethylene	C_2H_4	$CH_2{=}CH_2$	−103.9
propylene	C_3H_6	$CH_3CH{=}CH_2$	−47.7
cyclopropane	C_3H_6	$CH_2{-}CH_2{-}CH_2$ (ring)	−32.9
propane	C_3H_8	$CH_3CH_2CH_3$	−44.5
propadiene	C_3H_4	$CH_2{=}C{=}CH_2$	−34.5
methylacetylene	C_3H_4	$CH_3C{\equiv}CH$	−23.2

laboratory or commercial processes. The other compounds containing three carbons are more readily separated from propylene by distillation and therefore their reactivities, while differing from those of propylene, are of interest only in special cases.

Propylene undergoes many of the olefinic reactions of ethylene but differs considerably from it in reactivity. This difference can be attributed to the nonsymmetry of its double bond relative to ethylene's, and to the presence of the methyl group.

In ethylene, the C=C bond is a symmetrical sp^2—sp^2 linkage, and all the C—H bonds are sp^2—$1s$ and are equivalent. In propylene, one of these C—H bonds is replaced by an sp^2—sp^3 C—C bond, which, because of its increased s character, produces a slight distortion in the neighboring C=C bond. The C—C bond itself is shortened to 1.51 Å (ref. 2, p. 50) relative to 1.54 Å for ethane (3). Coulson (4) and Mulliken (5) attribute the shortening not only to changes in hybridization but also to hyperconjugation (resonance) effects. Dewar (ref. 2, pp. 62–64) questions the resonance effects.

The stabilization energy of propylene, 2.46 kcal/mole, according to Dewar, is due not to resonance in the old sense but to a shortening of the C—C bond due to hybridization effects. In fact, the concept of stabilization due to resonance is based on the outdated assumption that C—C, and C=C bonds have fixed length and energy.

The concept of hyperconjugation, however, may be of value in explaining the reactions of propylene. In the valence bond method, three resonance structures can be visualized as contributing to the stabilization of propylene (3).

$$CH_3{-}CH{=}CH_2 \qquad \overset{H^{\oplus}}{\underset{}{CH_2{=}CH{-}\overset{\ominus}{\ddot{C}}H_2}} \qquad \overset{H\text{--------}}{\underset{}{CH_2{=}CH{-}CH_2}}$$

The center structure would be consistent with the existence of propylene's dipole of 0.34 D and has been commonly portrayed as arising from a shift of electrons.

$$H{-}\underset{\underset{H}{|}}{\overset{\overset{H}{|}}{C}}{-}CH{=}CH_2$$

The net result of these effects is shown in an increased reactivity of the methyl hydrogens and of the double bond relative to propane and ethylene, respectively. For example, the reactions with peroxyacetic acid, bromine, and sulfuric acid are roughly twenty-five times faster than those of ethylene.

The reactions of propylene which have been most intensively studied are generally those which are or have been of commercial importance.

Dimerization. In the polymerization of propylene by supported phosphoric acid, BF_3, or sulfuric acid, a mixture of products is formed by the carbonium ion route.

$$CH_3CH{=}CH_2 + H^{\oplus} \rightarrow CH_3{-}\overset{\oplus}{C}H{-}CH_3$$

$$(CH_3)_2\overset{\oplus}{C} + CH_3CH{=}CH_2 \rightarrow CH_3\overset{\oplus}{C}H{-}CH_2{-}C{-}(CH_3)_2 \xrightarrow{-H^{\oplus}} CH_3CH{=}CH{-}C(CH_3)_2$$

$$\overset{|}{H} \qquad\qquad\qquad \overset{|}{H} \qquad\qquad\qquad \overset{|}{H}$$

Depending on the reaction time, temperature, and catalyst strength, this typical initial product can react to form higher polymers, isomerize its double bond to the more stable tertiary position, or decompose by methyl shift or C—C bond scission. Terres (6) reported 76% 4-methyl-1-pentene and 24% 4-methyl-2-pentene under mild conditions over a phosphoric acid catalyst, while Wachter (7) reported the presence of both 3-methyl-2-pentene and 2-methyl-2-pentene at more severe conditions. The latter compound may comprise one third of the hexylenes from a typical Universal Oil Products Company (UOP) process.

Dimerization with newer types of supported alkali metal catalysts at mild conditions appears to proceed via an allyl anion to give selectively 4-methyl-1-pentene (8,9) unless unnecessarily long residence time allows isomerization to 2-methyl-2-pentene.

π-Complexed palladium(II) catalysts are reported to give linear hexylenes (hexenes), but rhodium(II) complexes give mixtures of singly or doubly branched hexylenes (10). A phosphine-modified π allyl nickel (O) system can be directed to form predominantly any of the three 2-methylpentenes or the two 2,3-dimethylbutenes, depending on the phosphine used (11).

Oligomerization and Co-oligomerization. Oligomers from the acid-catalyzed polymerization of pure propylene are predominantly nonylenes and dodecylenes, while the co-oligomer from propylene and mixtures of butylenes contains major amounts of heptylenes. Values estimated from Jones' data (12) are given in Table 3. Under the most severe conditions, an approach to dynamic equilibrium may be reached, as shown by the appearance of C_7, C_8, C_{10}, and C_{11} olefins from a propylene feed.

Table 3. Oligomers from the Acid-Catalyzed Polymerization of Propylene[a]

Feed	Polymer, mole %						
	C_6	C_7	C_8	C_9	$C_{10/11}$	C_{12}	Heavier
propylene (49% propylene, 51% saturates)	16	5	5	53	6	20	
propylene–butylene mix (19% propylene, 30% C_4 olefins, 51% saturates)	4	33	17	9	20	12	4

[a] Using solid phosphoric acid at 500–1000 psig and 200°C.

A study of the isomer distribution of typical heptylenes, nonylenes, and dodecylenes, as determined by infrared, showed a high concentration of branched structures, ie, types III, IV, and V (ref. 13, p. 10) (see Table 4).

Further insight to the structures of the heptylenes is obtained from analysis of branched octyl alcohol derived from the hydroformylation (oxo process) of reactive

Table 4. Isomer Distribution of Heptylenes, Nonylenes, and Dodecylenes

Infrared type	Olefin structure	Vol %		
		C_7	C_9	C_{12}
I	$RCH=CH_2$	1	1	2
II	$RCH=CHR^1$	12	14	10
III	$RR^1C=CH_2$	11	8	7
IV	$RR^1C=CHR^2$	54	35	26
V	$RR^1C=CR^2R^3$	22	42	55

heptylenes (ref. 13, p. 33). It can be seen from Table 5 that the average branching is close to two methyl side chains per molecule.

Table 5. Backbone Structure of Reactive Heptylenes Deduced from "Isooctyl Alcohol," RCH_2OH

Heptyl (R)	Mole %	Heptyl (R)	Mole %
C | C—C—C—C—C	15	C C | | C—C—C—C—C	50
C | C—C—C—C—C	15	C C | | C—C—C—C—C	30

No neo structure, ie,

$$-C-\overset{\displaystyle C}{\underset{\displaystyle C}{\overset{\displaystyle |}{\underset{\displaystyle |}{C}}}}-C$$

has been reported in any of the oligomers.

It is known that under severe acid-polymerization conditions an olefin containing this structure is unstable.

Higher Propylene Polymers. The conversion of propylene alone or with other olefins to high and stereoregular polymers is carried out with yet another class of catalysts such as dialkyl aluminum chloride/titanium trichloride. See Olefin polymers.

Disproportionation. The disproportionation of propylene to ethylene and butenes takes place selectively over molybdenum or tungsten catalysts on alumina at about 430°C and 450 psig. A true thermodynamic equilibrium appears to exist and the products at the 45% conversion level have been reported (14,15) to be those given below.

Product	Wt %	Product	Wt %
ethylene	35.3	*trans*-2-butene	25.6
1-butene	20.9	*cis*-2-butene	18.2

It is interesting to note that propylene dimer can be disproportionated to ethylene and butenes (16). This suggests that dimer might be an intermediate.

Hydrogenation. In its heat of hydrogenation, propylene agrees with other olefins having one and only one other carbon bond attached to the double bond, $RCH=CH_2$. This differentiates it from $CH_2=CH_2$ or $-RCH=CHR^1$ (ref. 17, p. 174).

Olefin	Structure	Heat of hydrogenation, kcal/mole, 82°C/ atm
ethylene	$CH_2=CH_2$	32.8
propylene	$CH_3CH=CH_2$	30.1
1-butene	$CH_3CH_2CH=CH_2$	30.3
1-pentene	$CH_3CH_2CH_2CH=CH_2$	30.1
cis-2-butene	$CH_3CH=CHCH_3$	28.6
cis-2-pentene	$CH_3CH_2CH=CHCH_3$	28.6

Burwell reported (18) that the mechanism of heterogeneous hydrogenation of propylene and other olefins was more complicated in detail than that of acetylenes and dienes due to hydrogen exchange and isomerization reactions preceding and accompanying hydrogenation.

Hydration. Hydration of propylene to isopropyl alcohol proceeds in the presence of a liquid or solid acid catalyst. Use of sulfuric acid proceeds in two steps (19,20).

$$CH_3CH=CH_2 \xrightarrow[\text{300 psi, 25°C}]{\text{85\% H}_2\text{SO}_4} \text{mono and diisopropyl sulfates} \xrightarrow[\text{H}_2\text{O}]{\text{20\% H}_2\text{SO}_4} (CH_3)_2CHOH \quad \text{95\% yield}$$

The mechanism of hydration is thought to involve formation of an isopropyl carbonium ion which exists in an equilibrium with the sulfate ester and isopropyl alcohol.

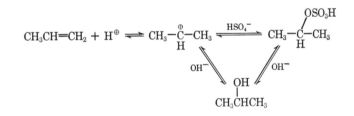

The kinetics of hydration over an ion-exchange resin have been discussed by Kaiser (21).

Alkylation (see Vol. 1, p. 882). Propylene is reacted with isoparaffins in the presence of H_2SO_4 or HF to give motor or aviation gasoline. A similar reaction with benzene gives cumene (isopropylbenzene).

Hydroformylation. As described in the Shell Oil Company patents, propylene reacts with CO and H_2 at 500 psig and 165°C in the presence of a tris(n-butyl)phosphine complex of cobalt octoate to give a 93% conversion of propylene and a 76% selectivity to 1-butanol (22). In the presence of KOH, but under similar conditions, a 94% propylene conversion and a selectivity of 87% to 2-ethylhexanol (23) is obtained.

The mechanism of hydroformylation is complex but it can be thought of as involving the reaction of an active form of the cobalt catalyst, $HCo(CO)_3$, with propylene to form an intermediate complex which undergoes an intramolecular rearrangement and then is decomposed to give a free aldehyde (24). The aldehyde can be further hydrogenated or can first undergo an aldol condensation to form a higher alcohol.

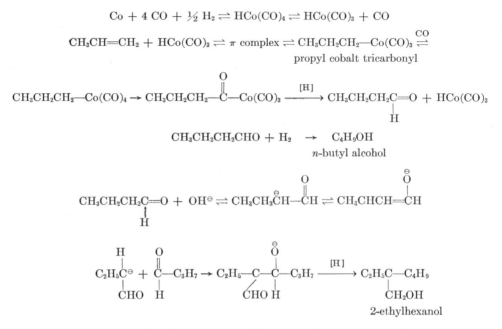

$$Co + 4\,CO + \tfrac{1}{2}\,H_2 \rightleftharpoons HCo(CO)_4 \rightleftharpoons HCo(CO)_3 + CO$$

$$CH_3CH{=}CH_2 + HCo(CO)_3 \rightleftharpoons \pi\ complex \rightleftharpoons CH_3CH_2CH_2{-}Co(CO)_3 \overset{CO}{\rightleftharpoons}$$

propyl cobalt tricarbonyl

$$CH_3CH_2CH_2{-}Co(CO)_4 \rightarrow CH_3CH_2CH_2{-}\overset{O}{\overset{\|}{C}}{-}Co(CO)_3 \xrightarrow{[H]} CH_3CH_2CH_2\overset{H}{\underset{}{C}}{=}O + HCo(CO)_3$$

$$CH_3CH_2CH_2CHO + H_2 \rightarrow C_4H_9OH$$

n-butyl alcohol

$$CH_3CH_2CH_2\overset{}{C}{=}O + OH^{\ominus} \rightleftharpoons CH_3CH_2\overset{\ominus}{CH}{-}\overset{O}{\overset{\|}{C}}H \rightleftharpoons CH_3CHCH{=}\overset{\overset{\ominus}{O}}{C}H$$

$$C_2H_5\overset{H}{\underset{CHO}{C^{\ominus}}} + \overset{O}{\overset{\|}{C}}{-}C_3H_7 \rightarrow C_2H_5{-}\overset{\overset{\ominus}{O}}{\underset{CHO}{C}}{-}\overset{}{\underset{H}{C}}{-}C_3H_7 \xrightarrow{[H]} C_2H_5\overset{}{\underset{CH_2OH}{C}}{-}C_4H_9$$

2-ethylhexanol

The reaction under Shell's conditions differs from that under the older conventional conditions (see Oxo process) in that the "anti-Markovnikoff" addition of the catalyst to form $-\overset{O}{\overset{\|}{C}}{-}C{-}Co$ intermediates is more favored, due apparently to the steric or electronic effects of the phosphine ligands. Tucci emphasizes the hydridic nature of this catalyst addition (25) at the π-complex stage.

Table 6. Comparison of Methods of Hydroformylation

	Conventional method (26)	Shell method (22)
catalyst	$CO_2(CO)_8$	$(Co(CO)_3(PBu_3))_2$
number of stages	2	1
stage conditions		
solvent	none	*n*-butanol
H_2/CO ratio	1.2:1	2:1
temperature, °C	110 (27)	165
pressure, psig	3,700	500
v/v per hr	0.3	0.66
product	alcohols	aldehydes and alcohols
final product[a]		
butyl alcohol on propylene, yield, mole %	80 (27)	84 (approx)
normal/iso ratio	3:2	10:1

[a] After hydrogenation step of conventional process.

A comparison of the effects of catalyst structure on the hydroformylation of propylene as indicated in Table 6 shows the lower pressure, better product distribution, and simpler operation using the phosphine-modified catalyst.

The use of alkali with Shell's catalyst in the 2-ethylhexanol process (23) is made feasible because of the high selectivity to the linear aldehyde structure in the initial hydroformylation stage. The result is the selective conversion of propylene to 2-ethylhexanol in one reactor.

Carbonylation. Propylene reacts at up to 400°C and 1000 psig with carbon monoxide and water in the presence of sulfuric acid or other strong acidic catalyst to give isobutyric acid (28). Work of Pawlenko (28) using 65% HBF₄ in *n*-hexane at 2000 psi and 40°C gave an 85.7 mole % conversion of propylene to a mixed product comprising isopropyl isobutyrate (69.7 mole %), isobutyric acid (7.8 mole %), and isopropyl heptanoate (22.5 mole %).

Epoxidation. Propylene has not been successfully oxidized to the oxide over the catalysts used for the conversion of ethylene to ethylene oxide (29). See Propylene oxide.

In the presence of propane, benzene, or acetaldehyde, etc, yields of up to 40% of propylene oxide were obtained (30–32), probably involving the "conjugate oxidation" (33) by an acyl peroxy radical mechanism (34), or other mechanism involving intermediate conversion of the added component to a peroxide.

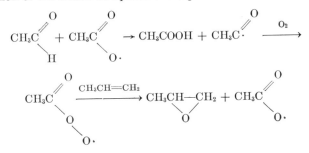

Propylene can be more selectively epoxidized by two other routes.
1. By use of a peroxyacid (35).

$$CH_3CH{=}CH_2 + CH_3COOOH \rightarrow CH_3CH{-}CH_2 + CH_3COOH$$
peroxyacetic acid

In a Union Carbide Corporation process (36) a 10:1 propylene/peroxyacetic acid mixture gave an 86% yield of propylene oxide.
2. By use of *t*-hydroperoxides (37).

$$PhC(CH_3)_2OOH + CH_3CH{=}CH_2 \xrightarrow[\text{100°C, 1000 psig}]{\text{Mo napthenate}} CH_3CH{-}CH_2 + PhC(CH_3)_2OH$$

The oxide is obtained in 95+% yield on propylene and 80–90% yield on the hydroperoxide in about 1 hr. *t*-Butyl and ethylbenzene hydroperoxides can also be used in this Halcon process.

Noncatalytic Oxidation. In the noncatalytic direct oxidation of propylene, a large number of oxygenated products are formed. In a Monsanto Company process (32) a 2:1 or 1:1 propylene/oxygen feed is oxidized in a stirred liquid solvent of esterified polyacyl esters of polyols such as propylene glycol diacetate at 850 psig, 170°C, and 8-min residence time. Propylene conversion of 40% is obtained with 20 mole % selectivity to propylene oxide, 25% to acetic acid, and minor amounts of other oxygenated products.

Catalytic Oxidation. Propylene, 5% in a steam/air mixture, can be selectively oxidized to acrolein over a cobalt molybdate/tellurium dioxide catalyst at 383°C and 4-sec contact time. At 89% propylene conversion, a 62% selectivity to acrolein is reported (38). See also Vol. 1, pp. 266–268. Using similar conditions, but in the absence of the tellurium, acrolein has been oxidized to acrylic acid at 76% selectivity and 80% acrolein conversion (39). The oxidation of propylene to acrolein in these cases undoubtedly proceeds by an allylic chemisorbed species at carbon atoms 1 and 3. This mechanism has been the subject of a review by Cullis (40).

Oxidation of propylene to allyl acetate can be accomplished at 8% propylene conversion and 86% selectivity by passing a 50% propylene, 25% oxygen, 25% acetic acid feed over a palladium–alumina catalyst at 400 v/v per hr and 140°C (41,42).

A two-step oxidation of propylene with palladium chloride to give a 92% yield of acetone involves the formation and hydrolysis of the complex,

$$\begin{matrix} CH_3CH \\ \| \\ CH_2 \end{matrix} \!\!-\!\! Pd \begin{matrix} Cl \\ \diagup \\ \diagdown \\ Cl \end{matrix} + H_2O \rightarrow CH_3COCH_3 + Pd + 2\ HCl$$

at 150 psig and 100°C (43). As in the Wacker process, the palladium is reduced. It is reoxidized in a separate step using a cupric chloride–air system.

$$Pd + 2\ CuCl_2 \rightarrow Cu_2Cl_2 + PdCl_2$$
$$\uparrow\!\!\downarrow HCl + O_2 \downarrow$$

Reaction with Oxygen and Ammonia. Propylene, ammonia, and oxygen in a 1:1:2 mole ratio react in a fluid bed of bismuthphosphomolybdate catalyst at about 450°C, 1-sec contact time, and 2-atm pressure to give the following yields on propylene (44): acrylonitrile, 73 wt %; acetonitrile, 11 wt %; and hydrogen cyanide, 13 wt %. See Vol. 1, p. 346.

Reaction with Nitric Oxide. Propylene reacts with NO at 700°C over a supported silver catalyst to give acrylonitrile (45). See Vol. 1, p. 346.

$$4\ CH_3CH\!\!=\!\!CH_2 + 6\ NO \rightarrow 4\ CH_2\!\!=\!\!CHCN + N_2 + 6\ H_2O$$

Reaction with Halogens. Propylene reacts with chlorine and bromine under a variety of conditions.

1. At room temperature in an inorganic solvent or in the vapor phase in the absence of light or catalysts.

$$X_2 + CH_3CH\!\!=\!\!CH_2 \rightarrow CH_3CHXCH_2X$$
$$\text{1,2-dihalopropane}$$

An ionic mechanism is commonly accepted.

$$\begin{matrix} H \\ CH_3C\!\!=\!\!CH_2 \end{matrix} + \overset{\delta\oplus\ \ \delta\ominus}{X\!\!-\!\!X} \rightarrow \left[\begin{matrix} H \\ CH_3C\!\!-\!\!CH_2 \\ \diagdown\ \diagup \\ X\!\oplus \end{matrix} \right] + X\ominus$$

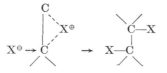

There is evidence from studies with higher olefins that the C—C bond does not rotate during such additions. This would preclude the existence of a single-bonded carbonium ion intermediate.

Iodine is not reactive under these conditions, while fluorine reacts violently and nonselectively. The halogenoid, tetrafluorohydrazine, F_2NNF_2, adds to propylene under these conditions by a free-radical mechanism to give 1,2-bis(difluoroaminopropane (46).

$$\begin{array}{c} CH_3CH\!-\!CH_2 \\ \mid \qquad \mid \\ NF_2 \quad NF_2 \end{array}$$

2. In water at 40°C (where $X_2 = Br_2$ or Cl_2).

$$X_2 + H_2O + CH_3CH{=}CH_2 \rightarrow \underset{\underset{OH}{|}}{CH_3CHCH_2X} + HX$$

propylene halohydrin

Here again an intermediate is postulated which is attacked by water to give predominantly an α chloro derivative and only 10% of the β chloro derivative. See Propylene oxide.

$$90\%\ \underset{\underset{OH}{|}}{CH_3CH\!-\!CH_2Cl} + 10\%\ \underset{\underset{Cl}{|}}{CH_3CH\!-\!CH_2OH}$$

3. At elevated temperatures (over 300°C). Chlorination of a fourfold excess of propylene (47) at 500°C and 1.8 sec gives a liquid product composed 85% of allyl chloride. The process probably is an abnormal free-radical process, $sn^{2\prime}$, where a chlorine radical adds to the double bond, forming an intermediate which is stabilized by hydrogen expulsion. By-products are 2-chloropropene, 1,2-dichloropropane, and di- and trichloropropenes.

$$CH_3CH{=}CH_2 + Cl\cdot \rightarrow CH_3\dot{C}HCH_2Cl \xrightarrow{-H\cdot} CH_2{=}CHCH_2Cl$$

Reaction with HBr and Other Unsymmetrical Reagents. HX compounds such as HCl, HBr, HI, H_2SO_4, ROH, RSH, and RCO_2H (48), in the absence of peroxides, add to the double bond of propylene in an ionic manner via the carbonium intermediate $CH_3\overset{\oplus}{C}HCH_3$ to give $CH_3C(X)HCH_3$. The reaction is usually acid catalyzed.

In the presence of peroxides the addition of HBr proceeds by a different mechanism to give 1-bromopropane, "disobeying" Markovnikoff's rule.

$$ROOR \rightarrow 2\ RO\cdot$$

$$RO\cdot + HBr \begin{array}{c} \overset{A}{\nearrow} ROH + Br\cdot \quad \Delta H = -23\ kcal \\ \underset{B}{\searrow} ROBr + H\cdot \quad \Delta H = +39\ kcal \end{array}$$

The exothermic reaction A is favored, and the bromide radical begins the following chain reaction:

$$CH_3CH{=}CH_2 + Br\cdot \rightarrow CH_3\dot{C}HCH_2Br \qquad \Delta H = -5\ kcal$$

$$CH_3\dot{C}HCH_2Br + HBr \rightarrow CH_3CH_2CH_2Br + Br\cdot \qquad \Delta H = -11\ kcal$$

It is seen that the overall reaction is to produce 1-bromopropane and to release 16 kcal/mole.

Many other reagents add to propylene.

$$B_2H_6 + 6\ CH_3CH{=}CH_2 \xrightarrow{0°C} 2\ (CH_3CH_2CH_2)_3B$$

$$O_3 + CH_3CH{=}CH_2 \xrightarrow{H_2O} CH_3CHO + H_2CO + H_2O_2$$

$$NaHSO_3 + CH_3CH{=}CH_2 \xrightarrow[H_2O,\ 25°C]{O_2} CH_3CH_2CH_2SO_3Na \qquad (ref.\ 17,\ p.\ 762)$$

$$H_2S + CH_3CH{=}CH_2 \xrightarrow[250°C]{NiS} CH_3CH_2CH_2SH + CH_3CHSHCH_3$$
$$normal/iso = 2{:}1\ (49)$$

Manufacture

Since no significant quantities of propylene occur naturally in oil and gas deposits, the availability of propylene stems from manufacturing operations intended primarily for the production of other hydrocarbon compounds. There are many sources based on several different techniques of splitting, cracking, and reforming hydrocarbon mixtures; but in all commercially important sources, the primary objective is the manufacture of either gasoline or ethylene. In the U.S. about 85% of all propylene is obtained from gasoline operations. Ethylene plants contribute about 15%, and this share will probably increase because of changes in technology in both refinery and petrochemical processes. Today, the potential availability of propylene in oil refineries can be estimated by a study of the refiners' capacity for thermal cracking, thermal reforming, and catalytic cracking; factors for estimating propylene are: about 3% of the design throughput of thermal crackers and reformers, and about 4.5% of the design throughput of catalytic crackers. This available propylene appears in the off-gas of the unit and can be recovered by techniques of distillation that are as complex as is necessary to give the desired degree of propylene purity.

First, the C_3 fraction must be isolated by two-step distillation in series, each with 30–40 trays and moderate reflux ratios, resulting in a C_3 mixture containing less than 2% C_2 and C_4 components. Any remaining C_2's will stay with the propylene product; so this is the controlling consideration in the design of the isolation equipment. At this point, removal of water, sulfur, carbon dioxide, or acetylene can be accomplished by special treatment, if required. The C_3 fraction containing propane and propylene is split by two distillation steps in series. Approximate values of relative volatility at various pressures and feed compositions are given in Table 7.

Table 7.   Relative Volatilities of the C_3 Fraction

Pressure, psia	C_3H_6 content, mole %	Relative volatility, propylene/propane
50	20	1.30
	80	1.20
100	10	1.25
	60	1.20
300	10	1.14
	90	1.11

The condensation of reflux with ordinary cooling water requires operating pressures of 250–300 psia, thereby suggesting the use of refrigeration to shift the pressure down in the range of better volatility ratios. Some measure of the need for additional trays at higher pressures is shown in the following comparison:

Operating pressure, psia	Theoretical trays (feed contains 40% C_3H_6)
30	62
50	66
100	75
200	97
300	125

Tray efficiencies are extremely high for C_3 separation, so that most actual performance data indicate that tray requirements are equal to the theoretical calculations, based on sound vapor–liquid equilibrium data, and good tray design.

The use of solvent distillation employing an extractive agent has not proved feasible for C_3 separation. It is true that solvents are known that will reverse the volatility ratio and improve the spread to 1.7 (for 50/50 acrylonitrile/acetonitrile); but the cost of handling the solvent is not economically justified (50).

The importance of polyolefin plastics and fibers has pointed up the need for high-purity propylene as a monomer essentially free of contaminants which have an effect on the polymerization catalyst. Reactive compounds of oxygen and sulfur are critical, as well as other olefinic and diolefinic hydrocarbons. Tolerable levels are usually below 10 ppm. Removal is accomplished by treating methods such as caustic wash to remove CO_2 and H_2S. Carbonyl sulfide is removed by contact with monoethanolamine. Traces of these compounds can be removed by a solid chemical adsorbent (51). Small amounts of water can be removed by molecular sieves. Mild hydrogenation can be employed to reduce undesirable unsaturated hydrocarbons, but in practice this has not been found necessary.

Economic Aspects

Refinery-based raw propylene usually occurs at about 50% concentration. Ethylene-based C_3's contain more than 90% propylene. The economics of recovery of the richer feed stream are about 1¢/gal better than the refinery-based scheme. Sherred and Fair (50) have reported the economic comparison given in Table 8 for a Gulf Coast plant producing 50 million lb/yr of 99+% propylene. These costs are for conversion only and do not include the value of the propylene in the raw stream, which

Table 8. Comparison of Expenditures for Recovery of Propylene (50)

Reason for expenditure	50% feed mix	90% feed mix
operating pressure, psia	300	300
actual trays	120	70
tray spacing, in.	18	18
column diameter, ft	6.5	5.5
steam, 1000 lb/hr	13.4	11.4
electricity, kW	35	20
conversion cost, ¢/gal	2.52	1.53
direct	1.73	1.07
indirect[a]	0.79	0.46
capital cost,[b] $1000	520	288

[a] Includes depreciation at 15% per year.   [b] Battery limits only (see Plant layout).

could be used to make polygasoline at a contained propylene value of about 8¢/gal. Thus, the cost of high-purity propylene is 9.5–10.5¢/gal, plus the cost of off-site capital, general overhead, and other special items peculiar to a given situation.

Specifications

As with most hydrocarbon products, the acceptable limits of quality vary with and use, and different suppliers offer a variety of grades to attempt to cover the important characteristics of the most profitable markets. Polymerization with metal–alkyl catalyst requires the most stringent limits in order to produce stereoregular polypropylene. In this market, typical specifications and an example of a typical analysis can be expected to be those given in Table 9.

Table 9. Propylene—Polymerization Grade

Compound	Specification limits, ppm, max[a]	Typical analysis, ppm[a]
propylene	99.5[b]	99.7[c]
saturated hydrocarbons	5,000	
other hydrocarbons		nil
propane		0.3[c]
propadiene	10	
methylacetylene	20	
ethylene	50	
ethane		50
butylene	1,000	
butadiene	20	
carbon oxides	10	1
carbonyl sulfide		1
hydrogen	2	
oxygen	5	4
water	10	10
sulfur	5	2

[a] Unless otherwise indicated.   [b] Wt %, min.   [c] Wt %.

Analytical Methods

Gas chromatography (see Vol. 5, p. 429) has displaced all other methods for determination of propylene content of mixtures containing other olefinic hydrocarbons.

The standard method for analysis of propylene is carried as ASTM designation D2163 in the 1966 revision of *ASTM Standards on Petroleum Products*. It is applicable to propylene in concentration ranges of 0.1% and above. Using a column designed as specified in the appendix of ASTM D2163, the components in the sample of propylene mixture are physically separated and stratified. As they pass the detector, usually a thermal conductivity sensor, a graphic plot of the composition profile is recorded on chart paper. Translation of this data plot is done by comparison with data obtained from calibration with known reference standards.

Continuous chromatographic analysis of the propane content in a propylene concentrate has been developed to optimize process control in large-scale plant operations (52). These analyzers cost about $12,000 each, and yet the data they produce save as much as $100,000/yr in increased productivity through closer process control, as compared with the conventional method of sampling once or twice per shift and waiting several hours for results from a central control laboratory.

The growing need for high-purity (99.5+%) propylene has come about by development of stereoregular polymers used in heavy volume to produce fibers and molded plastic items. The catalysts used are sensitive to the presence of trace quantities of propadiene, and the resulting polymer structure can be affected by the presence of propadiene; all of which can have a pronounced effect upon the economics of the polymerization process and the physical characteristics of the polymer produced. Propadiene in trace quantities can be analyzed by use of a column designed by Bua et al. (53). This method enables the determination of propadiene traces up to about 5 ppm. With the enrichment technique, it is possible to detect less than 1 ppm of propadiene.

Health and Safety

Propylene is a dangerous gas representing a serious fire and explosive hazard, but it is not particularly toxic. It will burn readily in air, and the flammability limits run between 2 and 11% by vol in air. Propylene is an inhalation anesthetic, but only in concentrations of 60% by vol or more. As such, it is a simple asphyxiant requiring ventilation to dissipate the physiological effects. If breathing has stopped, artificial respiration should be applied. Liquid propylene will cause skin burns from refrigeration effects of rapid evaporation.

The autoignition temperature of propylene is 927°F. In contact with oxidizing agents, it will react violently. Under extremely unusual conditions, it has been known to explode (995 atm, 327°C).

Uses

The consumption of propylene in the manufacture of gasoline is the major outlet in terms of volume, representing about 55% of the total. Chemical derivatives account for about 25%; and the remainder is not recovered as such, but is used as refinery fuel or is sold as liquefied petroleum gas (qv) in mixtures with propane and butane. U.S. supply is approx 20 billion lb, including both refinery and ethylene by-product sources. Propylene is expected to continue to play an important role in gasoline manufacture, because it represents a means of achieving an octane balance in maximizing the value of the refined products from a barrel of crude oil. Propylene is utilized by the refiner in two ways: alkylation with isobutane, and bulk acid polymerization. These techniques are applied to all available olefins including ethylene, propylene, butylenes, and pentylenes generated from the basic cracking and reforming operations carried out by the refiner. The quality of the resulting gasoline blending stock depends on the olefin composition, along with other process conditions. Economic factors must be weighed along with quality levels, so that a given octane rating can be achieved at the lowest possible capital outlay and with the lowest possible cost of utilities and catalyst per barrel of product.

In recent years the refiner has favored *alkylation with isobutane* as a method of octane improvement over the production of polymer gasoline as shown by the increase of alkylate gasoline capacity from about 250,000 to 550,000 bbl/stream day in the past ten years; while during the same period, polymer gasoline capacity decreased slightly. See Alkylation. Alkylate quality is about 95 octane (clear, F-1), depending on the olefin composition.

Another alkylation process employs *hydrofluoric acid* as the catalyst. If widely changing olefin composition is expected, this technique has the advantage of constant acid consumption; and there is no acid disposal problem (54). The process was developed by Universal Oil Products Company.

Polymer Gasoline. Propylene can be subjected to phosphoric acid polymerization to yield dimer, trimer, and tetramer mixtures having gasoline value (12). The fixed-bed catalyst consists of a solid support material coated or impregnated with phosphoric acid. A more recent process uses liquid bulk phosphoric acid instead, with advantages in temperature control, conversion level, and product recovery. Also the on-stream factor is higher because the catalyst can be replaced without a plant shutdown. Octane performance number is about 96 (clear, F-1). See also Vol. 10, p. 475.

Chemical Derivatives

Starting in 1920 with isopropyl alcohol, the markets for the chemical derivatives of propylene have grown so that worldwide requirements (not including Communist countries) in 1965 were about 9 billion lb of propylene a year (see Table 10). It is believed that there will be continued growth, mainly in propylene oxide, acrylonitrile, and polypropylene requirements.

Table 10. Estimated Non-Communist Chemical Markets for Propylene (1965), million lb

Product	U.S. (55)	Canada and Europe (56)	Asia (56)	Total[a]
isopropyl alcohol	1,450	830	32	>2,400
C_7–C_{12} oligomers	770	560	32	>1,380
propylene oxide	570 (57)	410	160	>1,240
acrylonitrile	550 (57)	250	290	>1,050
oxo products (excepting heptylenes)	410	465	95	980
polypropylene	390	330	181	940
cumene	300	500	52	850
glycerin	120	29		184
isoprene	110			110
epichlorohydrin	80			84
copolymers	10	1		11
miscellaneous	20			20
total	4,800	3,400	850	9,000

[a] Based on reference 56, but adjusted for differences in U.S. values.

Each of the products is made from propylene by use of technology which is constantly improving; however, at present the state of the art results in yield efficiencies that require the unit consumption levels given in Table 11. [See Acrylonitrile; Chlorohydrins; Cumene; Glycerol; Olefin polymers; Oxo process; Propyl alcohols; Propylene oxide.

Table 11.   Unit Consumption of Propylene (57)

Product	Consumption, lb propylene/lb product	Product	Consumption, lb propylene/lb product
isopropyl alcohol	0.90	"isooctyl" alcohol	0.58
propylene tetramer	1.27	polypropylene	1.05
propylene dimer	1.21	cumene	0.41
propylene oxide	0.94	glycerin	0.62
acrylonitrile	1.20	epichlorohydrin	0.70

Bibliography

"Propylene" in *ECT* 1st ed., Vol. 11, pp. 193–197, by John Happel and W. H. Kapfer, New York University.

1. "Selected Values of Physical and Thermodynamic Properties of Hydrocarbons and Related Compounds," *American Petroleum Institute Research Project 44, Natl. Bur. Std. (U.S.) Circ. 461,* 332 (1953).
2. M. J. S. Dewar, *Hyperconjugation,* The Ronald Press Co., New York, 1962, pp. 50, 62–64.
3. H. L. Heys, *An Introduction to Electronic Theory of Organic Compounds,* George Harrap & Co., Ltd., London, 1960, pp. 90–95.
4. C. A. Coulson, *Proc. Roy. Soc. (London), Ser. A,* **207,** 91 (1951).
5. R. S. Mulliken, *Tetrahedron* **5,** 253 (1959); **6,** 68 (1959).
6. E. Terres, *Brennstoff-Chem.* **34,** 355 (1953).
7. A. Wachter, *Ind. Eng. Chem.* **30,** 822 (1938).
8. J. B. Wilkes, *Paper PD22(1), World Petrol. Congr., 7th, Mexico City, April 2–8, 1967.*
9. U.S. Pat. 3,340,323 (Sept. 5, 1967), H. Maegerlein, E. Siggel, and G. Meyer (to Vereinigte Glanzstoff-Fabriken A.G.).
10. A. D. Ketley, *Gordon Research Conference on Organic Reactions and Processes, 1967.*
11. B. Bogdanovic and G. Wilke, *Paper 22(7), World Petrol. Congr., 7th, Mexico City, April 2–8, 1967.*
12. E. K. Jones, *Advances in Catalysis,* Vol. VIII, Academic Press, Inc., New York, 1956, pp. 221–231.
13. *Higher Oxo Alcohols,* Enjay Company Inc., New York, 1956, pp. 10, 33.
14. L. F. Heckelsberg, R. L. Banks, and G. C. Gailey, *Preprints, Am. Chem. Soc., Div. Petrol. Chem., ACS Natl. Meeting, April 2–5, 1968, General Papers,* p. 91.
15. P. H. Johnson, *Paper 21(4), World Petrol. Congr., 7th, Mexico City, April 2–8, 1967.*
16. *Chem. Week* **100,** 51 (April 15, 1967).
17. J. D. Roberts and M. C. Caserio, *Basic Principles of Organic Chemistry,* W. A. Benjamin Inc., New York, 1965, pp. 174, 762.
18. R. L. Burwell, *Chem. Eng. News* **44,** 56–57 (Aug. 22, 1966).
19. P. W. Sherwood, *Ind. Eng. Chem.* **54,** 37 (1962).
20. L. F. Hatch, *Isopropyl Alcohol,* McGraw-Hill Book Co., Inc., New York, 1961, p. 9.
21. J. R. Kaiser, *Ind. Eng. Chem. Prod. Res. Develop.* **1** (4), 296 (1962).
22. U.S. Pat. 3,369,050 (Feb. 13, 1968), C. R. Greene (to Shell Oil Co.).
23. U.S. Pat. 3,278,612 (Oct. 11, 1966), C. R. Greene (to Shell Oil Co.).
24. R. F. Heck and D. S. Breslow, *J. Am. Chem. Soc.* **83,** 4923 (1961).
25. E. R. Tucci, *Ind. Eng. Chem., Prod. Res. Develop.* **7** (1), 32–38 (1968).
26. *Hydrocarbon Process. Petrol. Refiner* **44,** 250 (Nov. 1965).
27. Brit. Pat. 1,002,105 (Aug. 25, 1965) (to Imperial Chemical Industries, Ltd.).

28. U.S. Pat. 1,924,766 (Aug. 29, 1933), G. B. Carpenter (to Du Pont); Ger. Pat. 1,226,557 (Oct. 13, 1966), S. Pawlenko (to Schering A.G.).
29. T. Suzuki, *Kogyo Kagaku Zasshi* **69,** 440 (1966).
30. L. M. Kaliberdo, A. S. Vaabel, et al., *Kinetika i Kataliz* **8** (2), 463–465 (March–April 1967).
31. Brit. Pat. 917,926 (Feb. 13, 1963) (to Escambia Chemical Co.).
32. U.S. Pats. 3,350,421 and 3,350,445 (Oct. 31, 1967), R. C. Binning, L. E. Bowe, and H. R. Null (to Monsanto Co.).
33. P. I. Valov, E. A. Blyumberg, and N. M. Emanuel, *Izv. Akad. Nauk SSSR, Ser. Khim.* **8,** 1334–1339 (1966).
34. N. M. Emanuel, *Paper 18(1)*, *World Petrol. Congr., 7th, Mexico City, April 2–8, 1967*, p. 11.
35. J. Imamura, N. Nagato, et al., *Kogyo Kagaku Zasshi* **69** (9), 1863–1868, A103–A104 (Sept. 1966).
36. U.S. Pat. 2,977,374 (March 28, 1961), B. Phillips and P. S. Starcher (to Union Carbide Corp.).
37. R. Landau, D. Brown, J. L. Russell, and J. Kollar, *Paper 18(8)*, *World Petrol. Congr., Mexico City, April 2–8, 1967; Chem. Eng. News* **45,** 17 (April 10, 1967).
38. U.S. Pat. 3,098,102 (July 16, 1963), J. R. Bethell and D. J. Hadley (to The Distillers Co. Ltd.).
39. U.S. Pat. 3,322,693 (Feb. 17, 1959), J. R. Bethell and D. J. Hadley (to The Distillers Co. Ltd.).
40. C. F. Cullis, *Ind. Eng. Chem.* **59,** 19–27 (1967).
41. Belg. Pat. 659,697 (open Aug. 12, 1965) (to Imperial Chemical Industries, Ltd.).
42. Can. Pat. 759,066 (May 16, 1967), W. Kronig and B. Frenz (to Farbenfabriken Bayer A.G.).
43. *Chem. Eng. News* **41,** 50–51 (July 8, 1963).
44. *Hydrocarbon Process. Petrol. Refiner* **41,** 187 (Nov. 1962); U.S Pat. 2,904,580 (Sept. 15, 1959), J. D. Idol, Jr. (to Standard Oil Co. of Ohio).
45. U.S. Pat. 2,736,739 (Feb. 28, 1956), D. C. England and G. V. Mock (to Du Pont); U.S. Pat. 3,338,953 (Aug. 29, 1967), S. C. Malhotra (to Du Pont).
46. R. C. Petry and J. P. Freeman, *Abstr. 152nd Natl. Meeting ACS, New York, Sept. 1966*, p. 546.
47. A. W. Fairbairn, H. A. Cheney, and A. J. Cherniavsky, *Chem. Eng. Progr.* **43,** 280 (1947).
48. U.S. Pat. 2,740,800 (April 3, 1956), M. Mention and P. Codet (to Usines de Melle).
49. F. T. Barr and D. B. Keyes, *Ind. Eng. Chem.* **26,** 1111 (1934).
50. J. A. Sherred and J. R. Fair, *Ind. Eng. Chem.* **51** (3), 249 (1959).
51. J. A. Anderson, *Speech, ACS Meeting, St. Louis, March 22, 1961.*
52. B. F. Dudenbostel, Jr., and W. Priestley, Jr., *Ind. Eng. Chem.* **48** (9), 55A (1959).
53. E. Bua, P. Manaresi, and L. Motta, *Anal. Chem.* **31** (11), 1910 (1959).
54. "Petrochemical and Petroleum Refining," *Chem. Eng. Progr. Symp. Ser.* **57** (34), 39–41 (1961).
55. Based on *Chem. Eng. News* **44,** 34–36 (June 13, 1966).
56. Based on *European Chem. News, Propylene Suppl.* **9** (241) (Feb. 25, 1966).
57. Based on R. B. Stobaugh, *Hydrocarbon Proc.* **16,** 143–154 (Jan. 1967).

William H. Davis
Texas National Bank of Commerce
Leland K. Beach
Enjay Chemical Laboratory

PROPYLENE CHLOROHYDRINS.   See Vol. 5, p. 309.

1,2-PROPYLENE GLYCOL, $CH_3CHOHCH_2OH$.   See Vol. 10, p. 649.

PROPYLENE OXIDE

Propylene oxide (1,2-propylene oxide, 1,2-epoxypropane),

$$CH_3\overset{\displaystyle O}{\overset{\displaystyle \diagup \diagdown}{CH-CH_2}}$$

is a low-boiling flammable liquid. A major industrial chemical since about 1950, it was first prepared in Wurtz's laboratory by Oser (1) in 1860 using the classical chlorohydrin synthesis. A century later this synthesis is still the major source, altered only by use of chlorine and propylene in place of propylene glycol and HCl as the source of the propylene chlorohydrin. In the intervening years a very considerable research effort has been made to develop a direct oxidation process for production of propylene oxide. Although published reports and patents indicate promise of ultimate success (2–9), no direct oxidation process has reached commercialization. The closest approach has been the production of propylene oxide as a minor by-product in the vapor phase oxidation of propane–butane by Celanese Corporation of America (10,11) and a peroxidation process by Halcon International, Inc., for which commercial plants are reported to be under construction (see below under Manufacture) (12).

Physical Properties

Table 1 summarizes the physical properties of propylene oxide. Although propylene oxide can exist as two optical isomers, except where specifically noted, this report will be concerned with the racemic mixture which is the usual commercial product.

Table 1. Physical Properties of Propylene Oxide

Property	Value	Ref.
boiling point, °C at 760 mm	34.23	13,14
vapor pressure, mm Hg at 25°C	569	13
freezing point, °C	−112.13	14
specific gravity, 25/25°C	0.826	13
density, g/ml at 25°C	0.823	13
refractive index, n_D^{25}	1.36322	15
viscosity at 25°C, cP	0.28	13
autoignition in air at 760 mm, °F	869	13
explosive limits in air, vol %	3.1–27.5	13
	2.91–30.5	16
flashpoint, open cup, °F	<−20	13
firepoint, open cup, °F	<−20	13
specific heat at 0°C, cal/(g)(°C)	0.47	13
heat of vaporization at 25°C, cal/g-mole	6667	17
heat of combustion at 25°C, kcal/g-mole	45.70	17
heat of formation, liq at 25°C, kcal/g-mole	28.84	17
critical temperature, °C	209.1	15
critical pressure, atm	48.6	15
critical density, g/ml	0.312	15
critical compressibility factor	0.2284	15
molar susceptibility $\times 10^6$	42.5	18
coefficient of expansion at 20°C per °C	0.00151	21
dipole moment, esu	1.88×10^{-18}	19
molar refraction, MR_D	15.67	20
molar polarization, P_∞ (25°C)	95.5	20

Table 2. Density and Vapor Pressure of Propylene Oxide (13)

Temperature, °C	Vapor pressure, mm Hg	Density, g/ml
−20	78	0.878
0	210	0.854
20	490	0.830
40	1000	0.805
60	1850	
80	3200	

More detailed data on vapor pressure and density as a function of temperature are given in Table 2.

The vapor–liquid equilibria of water and propylene oxide have been determined by Wickert et al. (22). They also reported the mutual solubility of water and propylene oxide as a function of temperature (Table 3). A hydrate, $C_3H_6O \cdot 16H_2O$, fp − 3°C, has been reported by Fyvie (8). Propylene oxide forms azeotropes with water, methylene chloride, ether, and several C_5 and C_6 hydrocarbons (23).

Table 3. Mutual Solubility of Water and Propylene Oxide (22)

Temperature, °C	Propylene oxide, wt %	
	Upper layer	Lower layer
3	90.5	41.8
10	89.6	40.8
24.5	86.6	39.9
35	84.6	39.2

Abderhalden et al. (24) reported the specific rotation of the two optical isomers as $\alpha]_D^{18} + 12.72°$ and $-8.26°$. Price and Osgan (25) report a value for (R)-propylene oxide in a 40% ether solution $\alpha]_D^{21} + 15°$. Franzus et al. (26) report a value of $\alpha]_D^{25} -8.39°$ in chloroform solution for (S)-propylene oxide.

Green (27) has calculated thermodynamic properties from spectroscopic data (Table 4).

Table 4. Thermodynamic Properties of Propylene Oxide per Mole in Gas Phase at 1 atm (27)

T, °K	$-(G° - H_0°)/T$, cal/°K	$H° - H_0°$, kcal	$S°$, cal/°K	$C_p°$, cal/°K	$-\Delta H_f°$, kcal	$\Delta C_f°$, kcal	$\text{Log}_{10} K_f$
0	0	0	0	0	17.59	−17.59	∞
273.16	56.03	3.014	67.05	16.17	21.69	−7.32	5.85
298.16	57.01	3.434	68.53	17.36	22.02	−6.01	4.40
400	60.68	5.455	74.32	22.28	23.23	−0.35	0.19
600	67.08	10.748	83.94	30.21	24.97	11.50	−4.19
800	73.72	17.38	94.44	35.63	26.00	23.83	−6.51
1000	77.92	24.97	102.89	39.92	26.49	36.37	−7.95

The molecular ionization potential and mass spectrum of propylene oxide are given by Gallegos and Kiser (28). Infrared and Raman spectra have been obtained by Kirchner (29), Field et al. (30), and by Shreeve et al. (31).

Reactions

Because of the highly strained oxirane ring, propylene oxide reacts readily with a wide variety of reagents. Reactions with mineral acids and ammonia occur spontaneously at room temperature in the absence of catalyst. Most other reactions require a catalyst such as alkali metal hydroxides or Lewis acids.

Base-catalyzed reactions occur through an S_N2 mechanism involving nucleophilic attack by the base on the carbon of the oxirane ring. The attack occurs preferentially on the primary carbon and the main product is the secondary alcohol:

$$\overset{O}{\overset{\triangle}{CH_3CHCH_2}} \rightarrow \overset{O^-}{\underset{|}{CH_3CHCH_2OR}} \overset{H^+}{\rightarrow} \overset{OH}{\underset{|}{CH_3CHCH_2OR}}$$
$$+ \ OR^- + H^+$$

Acid catalysis involves electrophilic attack by an acid on the oxygen followed by ring opening in either direction to give a mixture of two isomeric products (32,33):

$$\overset{O}{\overset{\triangle}{CH_3CHCH_2}} \overset{H^+}{\rightarrow} \left[\overset{\overset{H^+}{\diagup}}{\overset{O}{\overset{\triangle}{CH_3CHCH_2}}}\right] \overset{ROH}{\longrightarrow} CH_3CHOHCH_2OR + H^+$$
$$+ \ CH_3CHCH_2OH$$
$$\underset{|}{OR}$$

Usually alkaline catalysis is preferred because it yields a single isomer and avoids isomerization of the oxide, a side reaction which may occur with acid catalysis.

Reaction with Water. Propylene oxide reacts with water to form mono-, di-, tri-, and polypropylene glycols.

$$HOH + \overset{O}{\overset{\triangle}{CH_3CHCH_2}} \rightarrow CH_3CHOHCH_2OH$$

$$CH_2CHOHCH_2OH + \overset{O}{\overset{\triangle}{CH_3CHCH_2}} \rightarrow CH_3CHOHCH_2OCH_2CHOHCH_3, \text{ plus isomers}$$

The reaction is catalyzed by acids or bases but in commercial practice for the production of propylene glycol it is usually carried out at elevated temperatures (160–200°C) without a catalyst, to simplify recovery of products. The di- and higher propylene glycols are produced as isomeric mixtures (three dipropylene glycols, four tripropylene glycols, ten tetrapropylene glycols, etc). The three dipropylene glycol isomers have been isolated and identified (35). See Vol. 10, p. 651.

Table 5. Reaction of Propylene Oxide With Water

Moles H$_2$O per mole oxide	Composition of product, wt %		
	Propylene glycol	Dipropylene glycol	Tripropylene glycol
5	63.5	24.0	12.5
9	76.0	19.0	5.0
12	81.0	16.5	2.5
20	88.5	10.5	1.0
25	91.0	8.0	1.0

The ratio of mono- to polyglycols obtained is controlled by the ratio of water to propylene oxide reacted, as shown in Table 5 (36).

For the preparation of polypropylene glycols, propylene glycol is reacted with propylene oxide using an alkaline catalyst such as NaOH or KOH. The molecular weight of the polypropylene glycol is controlled by the ratio of propylene glycol to propylene oxide used.

Reaction with Alcohols and Phenols. With alcohols or phenols propylene oxide yields glycol ethers which can react further to form di-, tri- and polypropylene glycol ethers. When the reaction is base-catalyzed the secondary alcohol is formed almost exclusively. If acid catalysts are used the two isomers are formed in approximately equal amounts (34,38,39).

$$\overset{O}{\overset{\triangle}{ROH + CH_3CHCH_2}} \rightarrow ROCH_2CHOHCH_3 + ROCH(CH_3)CH_2OH$$

Reaction with Amines. Propylene oxide will add to ammonia readily even without catalyst to form mono-, di-, and triisopropanolamines, RNH_2, R_2NH, and R_3N, where R is principally the secondary alcohol $CH_2CHOHCH_2$—, with minor amounts where R is $CH_2OHCH(CH_3)$—; see Alkanolamines. A trace of moisture promotes the reaction. The ratio of mono- to di- and triisopropanolamines obtained depends upon the ratio of reactants. Primary amines will add either one or two moles of propylene oxide to form the corresponding secondary and tertiary amines. In all of the above reactions with ammonia and amines small amounts of polyglycol derivatives are also formed.

Reaction with Organic Acids. Propylene oxide will add to organic acids to form glycol monoesters. Both hydroxyl groups can be esterified, giving $RCOOCH_2CHOHCH_3$ and $RCOOCH(CH_3)CH_2OH$. The reaction is catalyzed by a trace of an alkali metal salt of the acid.

This reaction is complicated by two side reactions, especially if sufficient oxide is used to give complete conversion of the acid: formation of esters of dipropylene glycol (or higher glycols); and ester-exchange reaction resulting in formation of equilibrium mixtures of propylene glycol with its mono and diesters (40).

Reaction with Thio Compounds. Propylene oxide will react with hydrogen sulfide and with thiols (mercaptans) and thiophenols, even in absence of catalysts, to form the corresponding mercaptopropanols and glycol thioethers (41,42):

$$\overset{O}{\overset{\triangle}{CH_3CHCH_2}}\begin{cases} + H_2S & \rightarrow CH_3CHOHCH_2SH + CH_2OHCH(CH_3)SH \\ + RSH & \rightarrow CH_3CHOHCH_2SR + CH_2OHCH(CH_3)SR \\ + C_6H_5SH & \rightarrow CH_3CHOHCH_2SC_6H_5 + CH_2OHCH(CH_3)SC_6H_5 \end{cases}$$

With thiourea or potassium thiocyanate, propylene oxide is converted to propylene sulfide (43). Reaction of propylene oxide and carbon disulfide gives propylene trithiocarbonate (44):

$$\overset{O}{\overset{\triangle}{CH_3CHCH_2}} + CS_2 \rightarrow \begin{matrix} CH_3CH{-}S \\ | \quad\quad\;\; \\ CH_2{-}S \end{matrix}{>}CS$$

Reaction with Natural Products. Propylene oxide will react with hydroxyl groups in sugars, starch, cellulose, glycerol, etc, in the presence of alkaline catalyst to form hydroxypropyl ethers and polyglycol derivatives, some of which are of commercial importance (45,46).

Reaction with Inorganic Reagents. Propylene oxide is attacked by a variety of inorganic reagents. These reactions generally do not require a catalyst. They may be illustrated as follows (47,48):

$$HX + CH_3\overset{O}{\overset{\frown}{CHCH_2}} \rightarrow CH_3CHOHCH_2X \qquad (X = Cl, Br, I)$$

$$AsCl_3 + CH_3\overset{O}{\overset{\frown}{CHCH_2}} \rightarrow Cl_2AsOCH_2CHClCH_3 + ClAs(OCH_2CHClCH_3)_2 + As(OCH_2CHClCH_3)_3$$

Similar reactions occur with PCl_3, $POCl_3$, $TiCl_4$, $SbCl_3$, $SiCl_4$, etc.

Aqueous sodium bisulfite will react almost quantitatively with propylene oxide at 30–50°C to form the 2-hydroxypropanesulfonate (49):

$$NaHSO_3 + CH_3\overset{O}{\overset{\frown}{CHCH_2}} \rightarrow CH_3CHOHCH_2SO_3Na$$

Addition of HCN produces propylene cyanohydrin (50):

$$HCN + CH_3\overset{O}{\overset{\frown}{CHCH_2}} \overset{base}{\longrightarrow} CH_3CHOHCH_2CN$$

Dehydration of this product readily yields methacrylonitrile, $CH_3CH{=}CHCN$.

Miscellaneous Reactions. In a similar manner propylene oxide will react with amides, hydrazines, active methylene groups (such as occur in acetoacetic ester), heterocyclics containing reactive hydrogens such as phenothiazine, piperazine, etc.

Catalytic hydrogenation of propylene oxide yields propyl alcohol and acetone (51). Friedel-Craft addition of propylene oxide to aromatics yields 1-aryl-2-propanols (52).

$$ArH + CH_3\overset{O}{\overset{\frown}{CHCH_2}} \overset{AlCl_3}{\longrightarrow} CH_3CHOHCH_2Ar$$

Reaction of propylene oxide and CO_2 produces propylene carbonate (53):

$$CO_2 + CH_3\overset{O}{\overset{\frown}{CHCH_2}} \rightarrow \begin{matrix} CH_3CH{-}O \\ | \qquad\quad\ CO \\ CH_2{-}O \end{matrix}$$

This product is useful as a solvent and also can be used in place of propylene oxide in reaction with nucleophiles:

$$\begin{matrix} CH_3{-}CH{-}O \\ | \qquad\qquad CO + ROH \rightarrow ROCH_2CHOHCH_3 + CO_2 \\ CH_2{-}O \end{matrix}$$

Reaction of propylene oxide with aldehydes and ketones yields cyclic acetals or ketals (54):

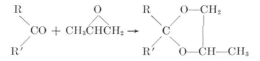

Isomerization of propylene oxide over Al_2O_3 or with acids yields largely propionaldehyde with some acetone (55). With Li_3PO_4 catalyst the oxide is isomerized almost quantitatively to allyl alcohol (56):

$$CH_3\overset{\displaystyle O}{\overset{\diagup\diagdown}{CHCH_2}} \xrightarrow{\text{acid}} CH_3CH_2CHO + CH_3COCH_3$$

$$CH_3\overset{\displaystyle O}{\overset{\diagup\diagdown}{CHCH_2}} \xrightarrow{\text{Li}_3\text{PO}_4} CH_2{=}CHCH_2OH$$

The latter reaction is reported to be the basis for a commercial process for glycerol (57).

Reaction of propylene oxide with Grignard reagents is a preparative method for synthesizing higher alcohols (58):

$$RMgBr + CH_3\overset{\displaystyle O}{\overset{\diagup\diagdown}{CHCH_2}} \to \underset{\underset{CH_3}{|}}{RCH_2CH}{-}OMgBr \xrightarrow{H^+} \underset{\underset{CH_3}{|}}{RCH_2CHOH}$$

Finally, the existence of two optical isomers of propylene oxide provides a source of some unique polymers.

Ferric chloride will react with two moles of propylene oxide to give a stable complex (59):

$$FeCl_3 + 2\ CH_3\overset{\displaystyle O}{\overset{\diagup\diagdown}{CHCH_2}} \to ClFe(OCH_2CHClCH_3)_2$$

This complex is an active catalyst for conversion of propylene oxide to high-molecular-weight, crystalline polymers. Price and co-workers (25,60) have postulated that polymerization occurs at stereoselective reaction centers of the solid phase of the catalyst. Such a stereoselective site will add either (R)-propylene oxide or (S)-propylene oxide but not both, resulting in a racemic mixture of two optically active polymers. They also observed that polymerization of (R)-propylene oxide with KOH catalyst produced optically active polymer. Another development in this field was the observation of Tsurata and his co-workers (61) that an optically active complex catalyst of (+)-borneol and diethylzinc preferentially polymerized (S)-propylene oxide from a racemic mixture, leaving residual unpolymerized propylene oxide which was slightly optically active.

Manufacture of Propylene Oxide

Propylene oxide is produced almost exclusively by the chlorohydrin process. This situation prevails because direct-oxidation processes for propylene oxide have not been developed to the efficiency of direct-oxidation ethylene oxide plants. As a result additional propylene oxide capacity can be obtained by converting existing chlorohydrin plants for ethylene oxide to the production of propylene oxide and building new direct-oxidation plants for ethylene oxide. Other sources of propylene oxide are becoming available and will be discussed briefly.

Chlorohydrin Process. The chlorohydrin process for propylene oxide production is the same as for ethylene oxide with a few exceptions to be noted. This is indicated by the patent literature which usually covers both ethylene and propylene chlorohydrin;

by the fact that in some commercial processes both chlorohydrins are produced simultaneously from a mixed ethylene–propylene feed; and finally, by the fact that ethylene chlorohydrin plants are readily converted to propylene chlorohydrin production.

Basically, two processes have been used commercially for producing chlorohydrins: (*1*) Olefins and an acid such as CO_2 are added simultaneously to aqueous calcium or sodium hypochlorite. The acid liberates hypochlorous acid which adds to the olefin to produce chlorohydrin. This was probably the first commercial process for producing chlorohydrins, used in Germany in World War I (62). (*2*) Present commercial practice involves passing chlorine, propylene, and water into a reactor tower and withdrawing dilute aqueous solution of the chlorohydrin. Many modifications of the reactor system have been proposed, including multiple towers, recycle of reactor liquor, etc (8,36,63–66).

The reaction mechanism for this process is thought to involve the formation of an intermediate propylene chloronium ion which can then react in several ways (8):

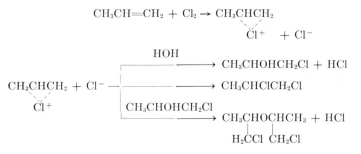

The addition of water to the chloronium ion can occur in two ways to produce the two isomeric chlorohydrins:

Of the above two carbonium-ion intermediates the secondary carbonium is much more stable and as a result the two chlorohydrin isomers are formed in an approximate ratio of secondary alcohol to primary alcohol of 9:1 (65).

For successful commercial operations the two by-product reactions must be suppressed. The addition of chlorohydrin to the chloronium ion to form bis(chloroisopropyl) ether is dependent on chlorohydrin concentration. In fact it can be the major product by suitable choice of operating conditions. To suppress this reaction the process must be operated to maintain a low chlorohydrin concentration. The formation of by-product propylene chloride is enhanced by conditions that will bring chlorine and propylene together. Again it is necessary to operate in dilute solution to avoid appearance of a separate propylene chloride oil phase which would preferentially dissolve chlorine and propylene and increase conversion to this undesirable by-product. The chlorohydrin process usually is operated to produce a chlorohydrin concentration of 3–4% (as compared to 5–7% for ethylene chlorohydrin plants). The effect of chlorohydrin concentration on yield has been reported by Ferrero et al. (36). The vent gases from the chlorohydrin tower are passed through a partial condenser to remove propylene dichloride and bis(chloroisopropyl) ether. The residual gas is scrubbed to remove HCl and, in some cases, recycled to the tower to recover any residual propylene. The propylene dichloride by-product is sold, largely as a solvent.

The dilute propylene chlorohydrin solution is mixed with a 10% slurry of lime and pumped to a steam-heated flash hydrolyzer. The propylene chlorohydrin is converted to propylene oxide. The oxide is flashed out of the reaction zone as quickly as possible to prevent its further hydrolysis to propylene glycol. The lime slurry is used in excess and this excess may be recovered for recycle in thickeners which provide for the removal of the spent $CaCl_2$ brine by decantation. This effluent consists of ~5% aqueous $CaCl_2$ containing traces of lime and propylene glycol. The lime used should contain less than 1% MgO because MgO promotes isomerization of the propylene oxide to aldehydes. In the production of chlorine for the chlorohydrin process an equivalent amount of caustic soda is obtained. This may be used in place of lime in the hydrolyzers if the economics warrant it.

The overhead from the hydrolyzer is largely propylene oxide and water. It is contaminated with propylene chloride, chloropropenes from dehydrohalogenation of the propylene chloride, and propionaldehyde from isomerization of propylene oxide. The propylene oxide is purified by fractionation in multiple distillation columns to produce specification-grade product. The most troublesome impurities are aldehydes and unsaturated chlorohydrocarbons. Many processes have been proposed for reducing these impurities to acceptable limits (67–70).

Table 6 shows the ratio of reactants to products in a typical propylene chlorohydrin plant.

Table 6. Ratio of Reactants to Products in Propylene Chlorohydrin Plant

	lb	moles
Reactants		
propylene (100% basis)	94	2.24
chlorine	159	2.24
lime (as CaO)	109	1.95
Products		
propylene oxide	100	1.72
propylene chloride	9	0.0796
dichloropropyl ethers	2	0.0117
CaCl₂ brine (100% basis)	215	1.95

The yield of propylene oxide based on propylene consumed can be increased by careful recovery of propylene in the vent gas, by operating the chlorohydrin towers at lower rates, and by operating to produce a more dilute chlorohydrin solution, resulting in less by-product propylene chloride. Such operation would be at the expense of lower production rate and higher utility cost. Thus the figures in the above table may vary considerably depending upon the objectives to be met by a particular installation.

In general, a chlorohydrin plant converted from ethylene oxide to propylene oxide production will have the same tonnage capacity, for even though a higher capacity would be expected for propylene oxide because of its higher molecular weight, this is counterbalanced by the requirement that the chlorohydrin towers be operated at lower chlorohydrin concentration to obtain equivalent yields.

Other Processes for Propylene Oxide. Propylene oxide is potentially available from several other processes, some of which may become of importance.

For many years small amounts of propylene oxide have been obtained as by-product in the vapor-phase oxidation of propane–butane feed stocks (10,11). The process operates in the temperature range of 350–400°C at 100 psig pressure with 10% conversion per pass. The propylene oxide is a minor part of the products obtained and for this reason the process is not a potential source for large quantities of propylene oxide. See Hydrocarbon oxidation.

Numerous other noncatalytic vapor-phase oxidation processes have been reported in the patent literature (2,3,71,72). These are operated on propylene or propylene–propane mixtures and are usually characterized by formation of considerable amounts of by-product such as propionaldehyde, acrolein, and allyl alcohol. Low conversion rates and low yields would indicate that the processes are not yet commercially feasible.

Announcements in 1967 indicate that two commercial plants were under construction for production of propylene oxide by a hydroperoxidation process (12). This process involves peroxidation of a hydrocarbon which is then reacted with propylene to produce propylene oxide and an alcohol.

Several routes have been suggested (73–75). For example,

$$(CH_3)_2CHCH_3 \rightarrow \quad (CH_3)_3COOH \xrightarrow{C_3H_6} \quad CH_3\overset{O}{\overset{\triangle}{CHCH_2}} + (CH_3)_3COH$$
isobutane   t-butyl hydroperoxide   t-butyl alcohol

$$C_6H_5C_2H_5 \quad \rightarrow \quad C_6H_5CH(CH_3)OOH \xrightarrow{C_3H_6} CH_3\overset{O}{\overset{\triangle}{CHCH_2}} + \quad C_6H_5CH(CH_3)OH$$
ethylbenzene   α-methylbenzyl hydroperoxide   α-methylbenzyl alcohol

$$C_6H_5CH(CH_3)_2 \rightarrow \quad C_6H_5C(CH_3)_2OOH \xrightarrow{C_3H_6} CH_3\overset{O}{\overset{\triangle}{CHCH_2}} + C_6H_5C(CH_3)_2OH$$
cumene   cumene hydroperoxide   cumyl alcohol

The by-product alcohol formed can be used in various ways. For example, in the ethylbenzene process, the α-methylbenzyl alcohol can be dehydrogenated to acetophenone or dehydrated to styrene for sale, or it can be dehydrated and hydrogenated to re-form the ethylbenzene for recycle to the process.

A related process (76) involves oxidation of a secondary alcohol to a hydroperoxide which converts to H_2O_2 and a ketone. The peroxide is used in situ to convert phthalic anhydride to monoperoxyphthalate, which in turn oxidizes propylene to propylene oxide. Isopropyl alcohol and cyclohexanol are two alcohols of choice. They yield acetone and cyclohexanone respectively as by-products. The ketone can either be sold as a by-product or hydrogenated to regenerate the alcohol for recycle.

The oxidation of olefins to alkene oxides by peroxyacids is an old process, first described by Prileschajew in 1909 (77). Preparation of propylene oxide by this method has been the subject of numerous patents (78–81). The rate of epoxidation of propylene by peracetic is twenty times as fast as the epoxidation of ethylene and pilot plant production of propylene oxide by this method has been reported (83).

Other processes for direct oxidation of propylene to propylene oxide involve liquid-phase oxidation in the presence of a solvent. Escambia Chemical Corp. (4) carries out the oxidation in benzene solution with manganese propionate catalyst; Shingu (5) proposes oxidation in dibutyl phthalate with supported silver catalyst and claims up to 87% yield. A detailed study of liquid-phase oxidation in benzene solution has also been reported by Lanos et al. (9) and by Brill (82).   None of these processes appear to be of commercial importance at present.

Production and Economics

Propylene oxide now ranks as one of the major synthetic organic chemicals. U.S. production is approaching 800 million lb/yr and world production is over 1 billion lb/yr (Tables 8 and 9) with growth continuing at 8–10%/yr. This rapid growth (as indicated in Table 7) is due largely to expansion of the market for polypropylene glycols for polyurethans, and for propylene glycol for polyester resins.   Production capacity has been maintained largely by the conversion of chlorohydrin process plants from ethylene oxide to propylene oxide production.   Ethylene oxide production is being maintained through the construction of new plants based on direct-oxidation processes.

Table 7. U.S. Propylene Oxide Production

Year	million lb
1958	160
1960	309
1962	446
1964	569
1965	607
1966	710
1967	780[a]

[a] Ref. 94; all other data from U.S. Tariff Commission Reports.

Table 8. U.S. Propylene Oxide Capacity for 1967 (94)

Producer	million lb/yr
Celanese Corp. of America	10
The Dow Chemical Co.	300
Jefferson Chemical Co.	120
Olin Mathieson Chemical Corp.	80
Union Carbide Corp.	200
Wyandotte Chemical Corp.	160
total	870

For the present, at least, this propylene oxide production will represent a major outlet for propylene and chlorine since it requires approx 1 lb propylene and 1.6 lb chlorine per lb of propylene oxide produced (Table 6).

Production capacities for propylene oxide are shown in Table 9 for the free-world countries.   These figures are flexible because some of the plants can be used for either ethylene oxide or propylene oxide depending on current demand.

The price of propylene oxide has been relatively stable over the last several years. Since 1952 prices have varied between 17.5 and 13.5 ¢/lb for tankcar quantities delivered in the east.   The 1967 price, which has not changed since 1960, is 14.5 ¢/lb on the same basis.

Table 9. Free-World Propylene Oxide Capacity

Country	million lb/yr	
	1964 (95,96)	1966 (97)
Belgium	44	55
Canada	7	
France	47	48
Germany	129	150
Italy	26	39
Japan	155	171
Sweden	7	7
United Kingdom	97	139
United States	600	780
total	1,112	1,389

Safety Precautions in Handling Propylene Oxide

Propylene oxide is a highly flammable liquid, in the same class as ethyl ether. Its flammability range in air is 2.9–30.5 vol % in open tube (16). Simon (84), and Wagner and Dugger (85) report flame velocities of propylene oxide in air compared to other flammable compounds. The flash point of propylene oxide is $< -20°F$ (13).

Oral toxicity of propylene oxide has been reported by Weil et al. (86), and by Smyth and Carpenter (87):

LD_{50} (oral)	0.63 ml/kg (86)
LD_{50} (single skin application)	1.50 ml/kg (86)

Toxic concentrations of propylene oxide vapor can readily occur when propylene oxide is handled in poorly ventilated areas because of its high vapor pressure. Maximum recommended vapor exposures are (13):

daily exposure up to 8 hours	100 ppm
single exposure, several hours	400 ppm
single exposure, one hour	1000 ppm

Due care must be taken in storage of propylene oxide and in carrying out reactions on a laboratory or commercial scale. Explosionproof electrical equipment is required and reactors and storage tanks must be properly grounded to prevent static sparks. Storage tanks and reactors should be blanketed with N_2 or another inert gas.

Propylene oxide is a very reactive intermediate. Reactions involving opening of the epoxide ring are highly exothermic and, once started, can quickly get out of control. An excellent description of procedures for carrying out reactions in a laboratory or pilot plant is available (13).

Specifications, Analytical Procedures, Shipping Data

Typical specifications for propylene oxide include those listed in Table 10.

Shipping restrictions require a Department of Transportation (ICC) red warning label except for exempt quantities (1 quart or less in metal containers; one pint or less in glass containers).

Table 10. Specifications for Propylene Oxide

distillation range at 760 mm Hg,[a] °C	33.0–37.0
specific gravity,[b] 20/20°C	0.829–0.831
acidity as acetic acid,[c] max, %	0.003
aldehydes as acetaldehyde,[d] max, %	0.01
chlorides as Cl,[e] max, %	0.008
water,[f] max, %	0.05
color, APHA,[g] max	10

[a] Essentially ASTM designation D86, modified by using a water bath and 300-W immersion heater as source of heat.

[b] Pycnometer method, ASTM D941 or method C of ASTM D891.

[c] By sodium hydroxide titration to phenolphthalein end point.

[d] By reaction of a sample with standard sodium bisulfite at 0°C and titration of excess bisulfite with standard I_2 solution.

[e] By combustion and potentiometric Volhard titration of chloride.

[f] By Karl Fischer titration method.

[g] By comparison to APHA platinum–cobalt color standards.

Uses of Propylene Oxide

All of the significant uses of propylene oxide employ it as a chemical intermediate. These uses are listed below, approximately in order of importance.

Propylene oxide is reacted with glycols, glycerol, sucrose, and other polyols singly or in conjunction with other epoxides to form a variety of polyglycols for manufacture of polyurethan foams and resins (see Urethan polymers). This presently represents the largest single use of propylene oxide and also one that is growing at a rapid rate.

Propylene oxide is readily hydrated with excess water to form propylene glycol and minor amounts of di- and higher glycols. See Glycols. The major use of the propylene glycol is for the production of polyester resins (qv). Other smaller, but important, uses of propylene glycol include use as a solvent in pharmaceutical and food formulations, plasticizer for films, and as a humectant (93). Its use in these applications is enhanced by its low toxicity compared to that of ethylene glycol.

Addition of propylene oxide or mixtures of ethylene oxide and propylene oxide to glycols, glycerol, alcohols, and phenols produces a series of polyglycols and polyglycol ethers which are useful as lubricants and hydraulic fluids. The heteric polymers (that is to say, those containing randomly distributed oxyethylene and oxypropylene groups) such as the Ambiflo fluids (88) (The Dow Chemical Co.) and Ucon fluids (Union Carbide Corp.) are of special interest because they can be made in a wide range of viscosities, can be made as either water-soluble or oil-soluble products, have high viscosity indexes (low change in viscosity with temperature), and do not form tarry or resinous residues. A related series of products are the propylene glycol ethers such as the Dowanol glycol ethers (The Dow Chemical Co.) (89). These are prepared by addition of propylene oxide to alcohols or phenols. They are especially useful as solvents and coupling agents in hydraulic fluids and in the coatings industry.

Propylene oxide is also used in the preparation of nonionic surfactants. See Surfactants. Excellent emulsifiers and wetting agents can be made by adding propylene oxide to a phenol or alcohol to form the hydrophobic portion of the chain, followed by addition of ethylene oxide to form a hydrophilic group (90). A related group of nonionics are the Pluronic surfactants (Wyandotte Chemical Co.), based on block polymers of propylene oxide and ethylene oxide (91.92).

Propylene oxide is also used to react with ammonia or amines to form the alkanol-amines (qv), which are used as reactive solvents in gas sweetening operations, and in soap, shaving cream, and polish formulations.

Propylene oxide can be isomerized almost quantitatively to allyl alcohol (qv). This is reported to be one of the steps in a commercial process for glycerol (qv) (57).

Propylene oxide is used in relatively minor amounts as a fumigant and soil sterilant. Table 11 summarizes some of the principal uses of propylene oxide (93).

Table 11. End Uses for Propylene Oxide, 1963 (93)

Product	Propylene oxide consumption, million lb
propylene glycol	160
polyethers for polyurethans	145
dipropylene glycol	20
lubricants	25
surfactants	20
oil demulsifiers	10
miscellaneous	40
total	420

Bibliography

"Propylene Oxide" treated in *ECT* 1st ed. under "Ethylene Oxide," Vol. 5, pp. 922–923, by R. S. Aries, Consulting Chemical Engineer, and Henry Schneider, R. S. Aries & Associates.

1. B. Oser, *Bull. Soc. Chim.* (*Paris*) 235 (1860).
2. Brit. Pat. 960,332 (1964), Farbenfabriken Bayer A.G.
3. U.S. Pat. 2,530,509 (1950), G. A. Cook (to The Linde Air Products Co.).
4. U.S. Pat. 2,780,635 (1957), J. H. Gardner and N. C. Robertson (to Escambia Chemical Corp.); U.S. Pat. 2,784,202 (1957), J. H. Gardner and T. I. Tewksbury (to Escambia Chemical Corp.).
5. U.S. Pat. 2,985,668 (1961), Haruo Shingu.
6. U.S. Pat. 3,071,601 (1963), R. S. Aries.
7. U.S. Pat. 3,275,662 (1966), V. W. Gash (to Monsanto Co.); U.S. Pat. 3,281,433 (1966), S. L. Reid (to Monsanto Co.).
8. A. C. Fyvie, *Chem. Ind.* (*London*) **1964** (Mar. 7), 384.
9. F. Lanos, G. M. Clement, and F. Pouliguen, *Chem. Ind.* (*Paris*) **91**, 47 (1964).
10. D. R. Keck, *Oil Gas J.* **50**, 159 (May 12, 1952).
11. L. F. Hatch, *The Chemistry of Petrochemical Reactions*, The Gulf Publishing Co., Houston, Texas, 1955, pp. 28, 67, 96–97.
12. Anon., *Chem. Eng. News* **45**, 17 (April 10, 1967); *Oil, Paint, Drug Reptr.* **190**, 3 (Aug. 1, 1966); *Oil, Paint, Drug Reptr.* **191**, 3 (March 13, 1967).
13. *Alkene Oxide Brochure*, The Dow Chemical Co., Midland, Michigan (1965).
14. R. A. McDonald, S. A. Shrader, and D. R. Stull, *J. Chem. Eng. Data* **4**, 311 (1959).
15. K. A. Kobe, A. E. Ravicz, and S. P. Vohra, *J. Chem. Eng. Data* **1**, 50 (1956).
16. J. H. Burgoyne and R. F. Neale, *Fuel* **32**, 5–16 (1953).
17. G. C. Sinke and D. L. Hildenbrand, *J. Chem. Eng. Data* **7**, 74 (1962).
18. J. R. Lacher, J. W. Pollock, and J. D. Park, *J. Chem. Phys.* **20**, 1047 (1952).
19. H. Hibbert and J. S. Allen, *J. Am. Chem. Soc.* **54**, 4115 (1932).
20. M. T. Rogers, *J. Am. Chem. Soc.* **69**, 2544 (1947).
21. G. O. Curme and F. Johnston, *Glycols*, ACS Monograph No. 114, Reinhold Publishing Corp., New York, 1952, Chap. 11.
22. J. N. Wickert, W. S. Tamplin, and R. L. Shank, *Chem. Engr. Progr. Symp. Ser.* **48** (2), 92 (1952).
23. L. H. Horsley, *Advan. Chem. Ser.* **6** (1952); **35** (1962).

24. E. Abderhalden and E. Eichwald, *Ber.* **51,** 1312 (1918).
25. C. C. Price and M. Osgan, *J. Am. Chem. Soc.* **78,** 4787 (1956).
26. B. Franzus and J. H. Surridge, *J. Org. Chem.* **31,** 4286 (1966).
27. J. H. S. Green, *Chem. Ind. (London)* **1961,** 369, 1218.
28. E. J. Gallegos and R. W. Kiser, *J. Am. Chem. Soc.* **83,** 773 (1961).
29. H. H. Kirchner, *Z. Physik. Chem.* **39,** 273–305 (1963).
30. J. E. Field, J. O. Cole, and D. E. Woodford, *J. Chem. Phys.* **18,** 1298 (1950).
31. O. D. Shreeve, M. R. Heether, H. B. Knight, and D. Swern, *Anal. Chem.* **23,** 277 (1951).
32. S. Winstein and R. B. Henderson in R. C. Elderfield, ed., *Heterocyclic Compounds,* Vol. 1, John Wiley & Sons, Inc., New York, 1950, Chap. 1.
33. F. Fischer, *Z. Chem.* **2,** 297 (1962).
34. H. C. Chitwood and B. T. Freuer, *J. Am. Chem. Soc.* **68,** 680 (1946).
35. A. R. Sexton and E. C. Britton, *J. Am. Chem. Soc.* **75,** 4357 (1953).
36. P. Ferrero, L. R. Flamme, and M. Fourey, *Ind. Chim. Belge* **19,** 113 (1954).
37. R. O. Colchough, G. Gee, W. C. E. Higginson, J. B. Jackson, and M. Litt, *J. Polymer Sci.* **34,** 171–179 (1959).
38. A. A. Petrov, *Chem. Tech. (Berlin)* **6** (12), 639–643 (1954).
39. A. R. Sexton and E. C. Britton, *J. Am. Chem. Soc.* **70,** 3606 (1948).
40. J. D. Malkemus, *J. Am. Oil Chemists' Soc.* **33,** 571 (1956).
41. H. Gilman and L. Fullhart, *J. Am. Chem. Soc.* **71,** 1478 (1949).
42. F. N. Woodward, *J. Chem. Soc.* **1948,** 1892.
43. W. Davies and W. E. Savige, *J. Chem. Soc.* **1950,** 317.
44. J. A. Durden, Jr., H. A. Stansbury, Jr., and W. H. Catlette, *J. Am. Chem. Soc.* **82,** 3082 (1960).
45. G. Froment, *Ind. Chim. Belge* **23,** 3–14 (1958); *Chem. Abstr.* **52,** 8544 (1958).
46. U.S. Pat. 2,819,213–2,819,220 (1958), M. De Groote and O. H. Pettingill (to Petrolite Corp.); *Chem. Abstr.* **52,** 10560 (1958).
47. C. A. Stewart and C. A. VanderWerf, *J. Am. Chem. Soc.* **76,** 1259 (1954).
48. N. I. Shuikin and I. F. Bel'skii, *Zhur. Obshchei Khim.* **29,** 2973 (1959); *Chem. Abstr.* **54,** 11971 (1960).
49. R. T. E. Schenck and S. Kaizerman, *J. Am. Chem. Soc.* **75,** 1636 (1953).
50. U.S. Pat. 2,453,062 (1948), E. L. Carpenter (to American Cyanamid Co.).
51. Brit. Pat. 496,264 (1938), Usines de Melle and H. M. Guinot; *Chem. Abstr.* **33,** 2904 (1939).
52. V. R. Likhterov and V. S. Etlis, *Zhur. Obshchei Khim.* **27,** 2867 (1957); *Chem. Abstr.* **52,** 8082 (1958).
53. W. J. Peppel, *Ind. Eng. Chem.* **50,** 767 (1958).
54. A. A. Petrov, *J. Gen. Chem. (USSR) Eng. Transl.* **16,** 61 (1946); *Chem. Abstr.* **41,** 118 (1947).
55. W. Ipatiew and W. Leontowitsch, *Ber.* **36,** 2017 (1903).
56. P. G. Sergeev, L. M. Bukreeva, and A. G. Polkovnikova, *Khim. Nauka i Prom.* **2,** 133 (1957); *Chem. Abstr.* **52,** 6150 (1958).
57. W. L. Faith, D. B. Keyes, and R. L. Clark, *Industrial Chemicals,* 3rd ed., John Wiley & Sons, Inc., New York, 1965, p. 407.
58. R. C. Huston and C. O. Bostwick, *J. Org. Chem.* **13,** 331 (1948).
59. A. B. Borkovic, *J. Org. Chem.* **23,** 828 (1958).
60. C. C. Price, M. Osgan, R. E. Hughes, and C. Shambelan, *J. Am. Chem. Soc.* **78,** 690 (1956).
61. T. Tsuruta, S. Inoue, N. Yoshida, and J. Turukawa, *Makromol. Chem.* **55,** 230 (1962).
62. J. F. Norris, *Ind. Eng. Chem.* **11,** 817 (1919).
63. U.S. Pat. 2,130,226 (1938), E. C. Britton, H. S. Nutting, and M. E. Huscher (to The Dow Chemical Co.).
64. U.S. Pat. 2,769,845 (1956), R. Knaus (to Olin Mathieson Chemical Corp.).
65. A. May and K. H. Franke, *Chem. Tech. (Berlin)* **12,** 59 (1960).
66. V. S. Etlis and L. N. Grolov, *J. Appl. Chem. (USSR) Eng. Trans.* **1959,** 891 (1952).
67. U.S. Pat. 2,622,060 (1952), M. O. Robeson and W. E. Tylor (to Celanese Corporation of America).
68. U.S. Pat. 2,868,806 (1959), A. A. Holzschuh (to The Dow Chemical Co.).
69. U.S. Pat. 2,949,413 (1960), D. E. Harmer and E. T. Heckeroth (to The Dow Chemical Co.).
70. U.S. Pat. 2,993,059 (1961), H. A. Bruson and D. W. Kaiser (to Olin Mathieson Chemical Corp.).

71. U.S. Pat. 2,689,253 (1954), N. C. Robertson and R. L. Mitchell (to Celanese Corporation of America).
72. U.S. Pat. 3,132,156 (1964), R. C. Lemon, P. C. Johnson, and V. J. M. Berty (to Union Carbide Corp.).
73. Belg. Pat. 657,838 (1964), Halcon International, Inc.
74. Belg. Pat. 665,117 (1965), Halcon International, Inc.
75. Fr. Pat. 1,421,285 (1964), Halcon International, Inc.
76. U.S. Pat. 3,251,862 (1966), R. E. Lidov (to Scientific Design).
77. N. Prileschajew, *Ber.* **42**, 4811 (1909).
78. Brit. Pat. 858,793 (1961), Union Carbide Corp.
79. Brit. Pat. 900,836 (1962), British Celanese Ltd.
80. Brit. Pat. 735,974 (1955), Union Carbide and Carbon Corp.
81. Brit. Pat. 963,430 (1962), Imperial Chemical Industries Ltd.
82. W. F. Brill and B. J. Barone, *J. Org. Chem.* **29**, 140 (1964).
83. J. A. John and F. J. Weymouth, *Chem. Ind. (London)* **1962**, 62.
84. D. M. Simon, *Ind. Eng. Chem.* **43**, 2718 (1951).
85. Paul Wagner and G. L. Dugger, *J. Am. Chem. Soc.* **77**, 227 (1955).
86. C. S. Weil, N. Condra, C. Haun, and J. A. Striegel, *Am. Ind. Hyg. Assoc. J.* **24**, 305 (1963); *Chem. Abstr.* **59**, 13253 (1963).
87. H. F. Smyth, Jr., and C. P. Carpenter, *J. Ind. Hyg. Toxicology* **30**, 63 (1948).
88. *Ambiflo Fluids and Lubricants Brochure*, The Dow Chemical Co., Midland, Mich.
89. *Dowanol Glycol Ether Solvents Brochure*, The Dow Chemical Co., Midland, Mich., 1964.
90. U.S. Pat. 2,915,559 (1959), L. H. Horsley and H. O. Seeburger (to The Dow Chemical Co.).
91. U.S. Pat. 2,674,619 (1954), L. G. Lunsted (to Wyandotte Chemicals Corp.).
92. U.S. Pat. 2,677,700 (1954), D. R. Jackson and L. G. Lunsted (to Wyandotte Chemicals Corp.).
93. Anon., *Chem. Eng. News* **41**, 101 (May 13, 1963).
94. *Oil, Paint, Drug Reptr.* **192**, 3 (July 24, 1967).
95. "Olefines in Europe" Parts 1, 2, and 3, in *Chem. Eng. News* **42**, 118, 132 (Aug. 3, 1964); *Chem. Eng. News* **42**, 76, 86 (Aug. 31, 1964); *Chem. Eng. News* **42**, 97, 101 (Sept. 28, 1964).
96. *Chemicals Economics Handbook*, Stanford Research Institute, Menlo Park, Calif. (1964).
97. *European Chem. News Suppl.* (Feb. 23, 1966), p. 65.

LEE H. HORSLEY
The Dow Chemical Company

n-**PROPYL ETHER,** $(CH_3CH_2CH_2)_2O$. See Vol. 8, p. 487.

2-PROPYN-1-OL, PROPARGYL ALCOHOL, $HC{\equiv}CCH_2OH$. See Vol. 1, p. 598.

PROTACTINIUM, Pa. See Actinides; Radioactive elements, natural.

PROTEINS

Since man has had a technology he has taken advantage of the differences, other than nutritional, which exist between one protein and another. Thus, baking depends on the physical properties of proteins from one or two cereal seeds being distinct from those of other seed proteins (see also Bakery processes). Brewing involves the use of proteins with specific properties (enzymes) to transform a raw material into a desired product (see Beer and brewing). The use of protein fibers for clothing is as old as history and, without them, much written history would not have survived in the form of parchment. In more recent years egg proteins were exploited as the base of tempera; gelatin (qv) came to serve not only as a glue (qv) but as a sizing and fining agent; and enzymes such as rennin began to be used in the form of extracts (rather than as whole organisms, as is the case for yeasts in fermentations or for lactobacillus in cheesemaking) (see Milk and milk products; Fermentation). All these processes arose and, to a varying degree, found application before there was any knowledge of the chemistry of proteins; in view of the ignorance then prevailing of the nature of the raw materials, it is not surprising that results proved variable and often unsatisfactory. This was, of course, particularly true of the most complex processes—those involving a living organism—as traditional cheesemaking, brewing, and baking. Manufacture of glue was simpler, for the raw material is almost invariable (collagens from different sources are very similar) and the manufacturing processes are more easily controllable than those depending on fermentation in an age when sterility was a concept applied only to man and his domestic animals. It is not surprising that many attempts were made to avoid the use of processes dependent on microorganisms (qv), although it was a long time before it was possible to distinguish between these and enzymic processes.

Examples of this avoidance are the use, in place of the lactobacillus, of the proteolytic enzyme extract, rennet, to clot milk or, if cows did not thrive or religious tenets interdicted the use of their products, the use of plant proteases for the same purpose; or the use of baking powder to avoid the necessity for yeast in baking. It is interesting that even now, when we know much more of yeast and its control, it is still worthwhile inventing new leavening agents such as diethylpyrocarbonate (which decomposes to carbon dioxide and ethanol) to avoid using it. Not until the chemistry of proteins began to be known some 120 years ago could the technology of their use become other than the purest empiricism.

History. Proteins were named proteins on July 10th 1838 (1) and at that time eight were recognized by Mulder (2), who first used the name in print at the suggestion of Berzelius. Four were animal (fibrin, serum albumin, casein, and crystallin) and four plant proteins (soluble albumin, coagulated albumin, legumin, and gluten). By 1871 animals had overhauled plants with 24 proteins to 12, though plant "proteins" included perhaps the most complex mixture ever categorized as a single substance—yeast (3) (see Microorganisms; Yeasts). In the 1860s major advances in the chemistry of proteins were made by Ritthausen, who also published the first table of the amino acid composition of proteins (4); he was followed by other distinguished workers among whom Osborne, Fischer, Vickery, and Chibnall were outstanding. Osborne's work at Connecticut Agricultural Experiment Station on seed proteins was remarkable in that not only did he transform our knowledge of the chemical composition of proteins by their meticulous analysis, often by methods developed by himself, but in that he also made studies of their behavior in solution and thus laid the foundation for much fruitful development of the physical chemistry of proteins. Emil Fischer's work on the manner in which amino acids are linked to form proteins was essential to our ideas of protein structure; his early synthesis of large polypeptides, tour de force though it was, was in advance of its time for it led nowhere for more than a generation. Vickery, also at Connecticut Agricultural Experiment Station, built on the heritage of Osborne; and Chibnall was one of the last of the "classic" protein chemists who brought our knowledge of protein chemistry to the limits of the old methods and then fostered the recent advances in protein chemistry, signalled by the first complete determination of the covalent structure of a protein by his pupil Sanger and collaborators in 1955 (5). At the same time, in the fifth decade of this century, Cohn and his collaborators (6) at Harvard were bringing to a peak the methods of protein separation based on differences in solubility induced by changes in temperature, pH, ionic strength, and dielectric constant and by the presence of specific divalent cations. Each variable and sometimes two or even three at once had been exploited in the past but the Harvard school was the first to undertake the labor (which proved completely rewarding) of systematically exploring the possibilities of varying all five factors in a rational manner. Their work, and the work of the analysts, were both to go into eclipse under the impact of the new methods of paper and ion-exchange chromatography in analysis, and of column and exclusion chromatography in the preparative fields. Nevertheless, it is probable that the methods of Cohn's school will be employed in commercial manufacture for some time to come, the knowledge gained by the newer methods applied on a small scale being used both to guide and then to monitor large-scale production.

Classification. The first universal classification of proteins was that laid down in Great Britain (1907) and America (1908) by the respective Physiological Societies (7,8). It was based in its initial divisions on chemistry—first, on the presence or absence of prosthetic groups and then, for finer distinctions, entirely on solubility properties. It was a useful pragmatic framework and served well for many years. Today a multitude of classifications are possible. The most thorough, because the most necessary, is that which codifies all known enzymes and which is designed to adapt itself continuously to new additions of enzymes (9). The classification uses as its only significant criterion the chemical nature of the reaction catalyzed by the enzyme. The properties of the enzyme, apart from its catalytic properties, are ignored as are the properties of the substrate apart from its chemical structure. Other classifications of proteins based on their structure or function have been advanced, but have not as yet proved useful or detailed enough for wide adoption. It is perhaps significant that a recent four-volume treatise on proteins contains neither a definition of its subject nor a classification of the compounds to be described.

Technological Uses. The proteins of early technology (other than food technology) were few in number and are dealt with in other articles. These include keratin (animal fibers), collagen (leather and its breakdown product gelatin), casein, gluten, and silk. (See Leather; Silk; Wool.) They are either insoluble, or complex interacting systems, and all have proved intractable subjects of investigation in one degree or another.

The principal technological interest in proteins at present lies in their use as food for man in a world of expanding population much of which is undernourished (10). (See the various articles on food, Vol. 10, pp. 1–76; see also Eggs; Fish and shellfish; Meat and meat products; Milk and milk products; Nuts.) In this situation problems of producing proteins and distributing them have come to have great humanitarian, political, and commercial importance and have eclipsed previous interest in their importance as fibers or as material from which fibers may be made. The possibilities of the industrial use of enzymes are becoming more promising with the development of techniques by which enzymes may be used in continuous rather than batch processes.

Finally, as our knowledge of protein chemistry burgeons, it begins to become possible to predict properties and uses (a process well advanced in nutrition and beginning in other fields). For long we shall be limited to the proteins nature provides, few of which are well known, but intelligent prospecting for enzymes and other proteins with desired properties is already possible by methods similar in some respects to those used in antibiotic searches. Synthesis of one protein, insulin (qv) has been achieved and it is possible that it may become economic in some instances to synthesize specific proteins of high biological activity, and thus required only in small quantities, for such highly valued purposes as saving or prolonging human life. A promising approach is that of Merrifield (10a) in which the first amino acid of the desired product is attached to an insoluble resin, protected, reacted with the second amino acid, and so on in sequence. Yields of each intermediate are very high and the process has been automated. High yields are essential in sequential syntheses of this nature. Even a 99% yield at every step will give only a 61% yield after fifty steps and 37% after 100 steps.

Current prices of well-purified proteins range from a few dollars a gram to one thousand times as much. Only a very few of the known proteins are available commercially.

The Structure of Proteins

Proteins are variations on a relatively simple theme—a linear mixed polymer of 15–20 different monomers (all α-amino or α-imino acids) with a chain length of fifty to several hundred. Proteins differ from synthetic polymers in two important ways: The molecules of a single protein species are believed to be generally identical in covalent structure and number of residues, so that the distribution of chain length and considerations of average particle weight important in considering the behavior of synthetic polymers are irrelevant. Secondly, the number and variety of monomers involved in their formation are much greater than those employed in the synthesis of industrial polymers.

Protein chemistry today is concerned with identifying the sequence of amino acids which form the covalently bound polymer chains (*primary* structure), with the results of weaker forces between the residues which determine the *secondary* structure (helix formation, regular alternation of residues on either side of an extended backbone or stretches of random arrangement), with association between chains, sometimes by covalent crosslinking, often by secondary forces, and their arrangement in space (*tertiary* structure), and finally with association of protein monomers into protein oligomers of varying size (*quaternary* structure). Figure 1 illustrates these levels of organization. Thus, total analysis and sequence studies on fragments of the chain are involved in studies of primary structure; interactions with radiation (x rays, ultraviolet, infrared, and polarized light) are used to gain an idea of secondary structure; while the determination of tertiary structure is dependent on both the diffraction studies of the x-ray crystallographer and the thermodynamic studies of the protein chemist. Indications of quaternary structure may be gained by electron microscopy, or by evidence derived from determination of both particle size and end groups.

The chemistry and biochemistry of the amino acids occurring in proteins have been discussed by Vigneron (see Amino acids) and will therefore be referred to only in so far as they assist in understanding the nature and structure of proteins. In the polymerization of amino acids the reactive groups common to them all, the α-NH_2 and COOH groups (in the instances of proline and hydroxyproline, the ring —NH groups in place of the α-NH_2 groups), combine with elimination of water in the peptide linkage, resulting in a polymer backbone structure of $(-NHCHRCO-)_n$, varied only by the occasional interpolation of proline or hydroxyproline giving a sequence such as

$$-NHCHRCON\overset{\diagdown\diagup}{\underset{R}{\quad}}CHCO$$

The *side chains* (R) projecting from the backbone determine the properties each protein is capable of exhibiting; the variety of side chains and their sequence form the basis of the extraordinary richness and variety found in the entire protein group. It will be seen from Table 1 that the side chains vary in properties and reactivity though not perhaps enough, at first sight, to explain the varied properties of the polymers. Briefly, most side chains are predominantly hydrocarbon in character, modified in some instances by the presence of —OH groups, in others by the possession of —NH_2 or —COOH groups (the latter sometimes modified in turn by amide formation). None of these is particularly reactive at physiological pH values, though those capable of ionization are of course able to take part in salt formation either within the molecule or with external ions. The only side chains normally regarded as capable of taking part in the formation of covalent links are those of cysteine, which can and do form —S—S— links with other cysteine side chains (either in the same polypeptide chain or another) to form cystine. The important division in the properties of the side chains appears to be between those which are polar and capable of interaction with water (hydrophilic groups) and those of a purely hydrocarbon nature which are "insoluble" in water and tend to shun it (hydrophobic groups). Evidence has been produced (12) which indicates that the simple requirement that polar groups must be on the outside of the molecule in contact with water while the nonpolar groups must lie in an anhydrous interior, determines both the shape of the molecule (spheres with a low hydrophilic/hydrophobic ratio for a given molecular unit; cigar-shaped molecules with a greater surface/volume ratio if the proportion of hydrophilic groups is too high for a spherical shape) and its tendency to aggregate (if there are not enough hydrophilic groups to form a "skin" over the surface of a spherical molecule it will tend to aggregate with others by apposition of hydrophobic patches).

The *protein backbone* is flexible and capable of rotation at the —CR—CO— and —NH—CR— bonds though not at the —CO—NH— bonds. As a consequence polypeptide chains have considerable configurational freedom; the energetically most stable form is a resultant, within the limitations imposed by the shape and size and consequent spatial demands of the projecting side chains, of their energetically preferred environment—away from the surface and from water for the nonpolar, hydrophobic groups and projecting into water for the polar hydrophilic residues.

There are opportunities for *hydrogen bonding* to occur not only between the —CO— and —NH— groups of the peptide bond and water but also, in the absence of water, between themselves. As a result, hydrogen bonding between chains or between parts of the same chain occurs in the anhydrous interior of the globular proteins and

Val– His–Leu–Thr–Pro–Glu–Glu - Lys–Ser– Ala– Val–Thr– Ala–Leu–Try–Gly–Lys– Val– Asn–Val–
10   20

Asp–Glu–Val– Gly– Gly–Glu–Ala– Leu–Gly–Arg–Leu–Leu–Val–Val–Tyr– Pro–Try–Thr–Gln–Arg–
30   40

Phe–Phe–Glu–Ser– Phe–Gly–Asp–Leu–Ser– Thr–Pro–Asp–Ala– Val–Met–Gly–Asn–Pro–Lys–Val–
50   60

Lys–Ala– His–Gly– Lys–Lys–Val–Leu–Gly–Ala– Phe–Ser–Asp–Gly–Leu–Ala–His– Leu–Asp–Asn–
70   80

Leu–Lys–Gly–Thr– Phe–Ala–Thr–Leu–Ser– Glu–Leu–His– Cys–Asp–Lys–Leu–His– Val–Asp–Pro–
90   100

Glu–Asn–Phe–Arg– Leu–Leu–Gly–Asn–Val–Leu–Val–Cys–Val– Leu–Ala–His– His– Phe–Gly–Lys–
110   120

Glu–Phe– Thr–Pro– Pro–Val– Gln–Ala– Ala–Tyr–Gln–Lys–Val– Val– Ala–Gly–Val– Ala– Asn–Ala–
130   140

Leu–Ala– His–Lys–Tyr–His
146

(**a**)

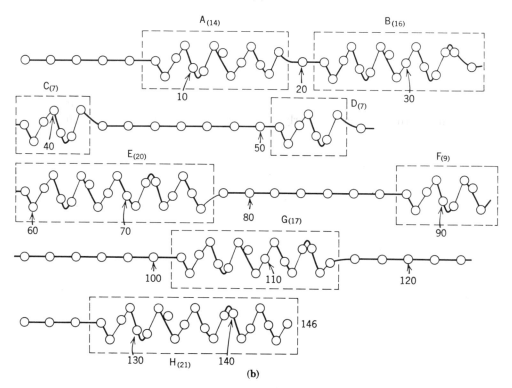

(**b**)

Fig. 1. The four structural levels of human hemoglobin.

(**a**) The primary structure of the β chain of human hemoglobin (abbreviations as in Table 1). Note that in some proteins there may be intrachain —S—S— bridges between cysteine residues in the same chain. Interchain covalent S—S bridges between distinct chains also occur in some proteins. It is conventional to number residues from the amino terminal end.

(**b**) The secondary structure of the β chain of human hemoglobin. The sectors of the chain which are hydrogen-bonded in the α helix form in the hemoglobin crystal are outlined.

(**c**) The tertiary structure of the β chain of human hemoglobin (11). Views of two β chains are given showing their relation to each other in the crystal. The position of the disc-shaped heme molecule is indicated. It is linked to the polypeptide chain via secondary forces involving histidine residues (residues 63 and 92). Lettering of regions of the chain corresponds with that in (b). Courtesy Drs. Muirhead and Peretz and the editors of *Nature*.

(**d**) The quaternary structure of human hemoglobins. The hemoglobin molecule is an association

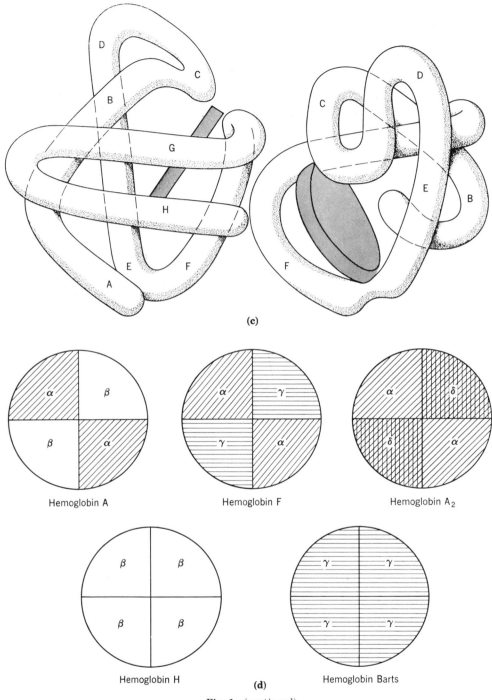

(c)

Hemoglobin A   Hemoglobin F   Hemoglobin A$_2$

Hemoglobin H   **(d)**   Hemoglobin Barts

Fig. 1. (*continued*)

of four polypeptide chains. In two of those illustrated the four chains are identical (hemoglobin H and hemoglobin Barts), the others are composed of two pairs of chains differing in amino acid composition and sequence yet with considerable overall similarity. Hemoglobin A is the form normally present in adults. The molecule is a spheroid 690 nm long, 500 nm high, and 550 nm wide.

Table 1. Amino Acid Residues Occurring in Proteins

Amino acid	CA abbreviations	Bonding nature(s)	Compatibility with helix formation	Residue in proteins
glycine	Gly			$.H$
alanine	Ala	Hpb		$.CH_3$
valine	Val	Hpb		$.CH(CH_3)_2$
leucine	Leu	Hpb		$.CH_2.CH(CH_3)_2$
isoleucine	Ile	Hpb		$.CH(CH_3).CH_2CH_3$
cysteine	Cys	Cov		$.CH_2.SH$
methionine	Met	Hpb		$.CH_2.CH_2.S.CH_3$
phenylalanine	Phe	Hpb		$.CH_2-$ (cyclohexyl)
proline	Pro	Hpb	incompatible	(ring structure)
tryptophan	Trp	Hpb		$.CH_2C$ (indole structure)
asparagine	Asn	Cov C Hd Ha		$.CH_2.CONH_2$
glutamine	Gln	Hd Ha		$CH_2.CH_2.CONH_2$
serine	Ser	Cov CP (Cov) Hd S		$.CH_2OH$
threonine	Thr	Cov P (Cov) Hd S		$.CHOH.CH_3$

Name	Abbrev.	Structure	Cov	Hd	Ha	E	S	Notes
hydroxyproline	Hyp	CHOH·CH₂·CH₂·CH₂·(N)	(Cov)	Hd			S	incompatible
tyrosine	Tyr	⟨OH ring⟩ .CH₂	(Cov)	Hd	Ha		S	
aspartic acid	Asp	.CH₂.COO⁻	(Cov)	Hd	Ha	E	S	usually incompatible
glutamic acid	Glu	.CH₂.CH₂.COO⁻	(Cov)	Hd	Ha	E	S	usually incompatible
histidine	His	⟨imidazole ring⟩				E	S	usually incompatible
arginine	Arg	.CH₂CH₂CH₂NHC(NH₂)=NH₂⁺	Cov E (Cov)			E	S	
lysine	Lys	.CH₂.CH₂.CH₂.CH₂.NH₃⁺	(Cov)			E	S	
hydroxylysine	Hyl	.CH₂.CH₂.CHOH.CH₂NH₃⁺		Hd		E	S	

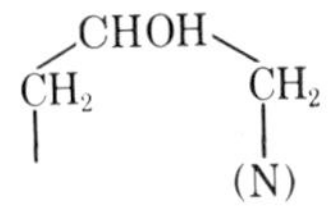

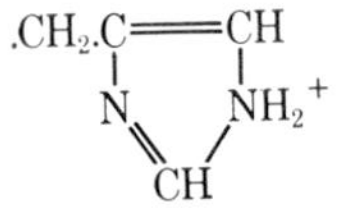

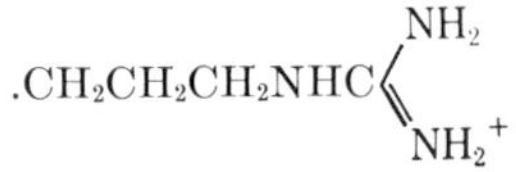

LEGEND:

Cov = covalent bond with another cysteine

(Cov) = residues perhaps involved in covalent links in some proteins, eg, collagen and other structural proteins

Hpb = hydrophobic bond

Hd = donor in hydrogen bonding

Ha = acceptor in hydrogen bonding

E = electrostatic bonding

S = normally at surface

Cov C = may form covalent bonds with carbohydrate

Cov P = may form covalent bonds with phosphate

Cov E = may form covalent bonds (eg, in elastin)

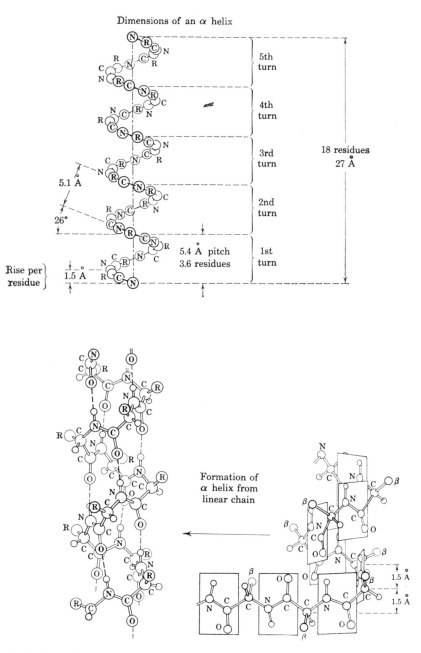

Dimensions of an α helix

Formation of
α helix from
linear chain

Fig. 2. A schematic representation of the process of coiling an extended polypeptide chain into the α-helical configuration. Redrawn from reference 14 (15).

very extensively in the insoluble proteins such as silk and keratin. It was shown in 1951 by Pauling and Corey (13) that an energetically favorable result of hydrogen bonding between consecutive portions of a polypeptide chain was a hydrogen bonded helix stabilized by *intra*chain H bonds (Fig. 2) (14,15), a structure typically found in keratin. *Inter*chain hydrogen bonding occurs if the chains are stretched to the extended form.

A high proportion of hydrogen bonding between peptide links is characteristic of the insoluble fibrous proteins but the α configuration (helical form) occurs to some extent in the interior of many soluble proteins.

The important forces determining *configuration* are electrostatic interactions, hydrogen bonding, and hydrophobic bonding, and it is remarkable how specific the results of these forces are in any particular protein. The proteins with accurately measurable, specific properties known to depend on their precise tertiary structure, such as the enzymes and protein hormones (see Hormones, Vol. 11, pp. 45–77), have been used to illustrate the remarkable specificity of secondary forces in determining total structure. It has, for example, been shown that the change of configuration induced by altering the energetically favorable configuration by adsorption at an air/water interface usually abolishes catalytic activity and that return to bulk solution sometimes restores that activity (16).

More remarkable is the fact that some enzymes such as ribonuclease and taka amylase A have been completely reduced with loss of secondary and tertiary structure, yet much activity may be restored on oxidation and reformation of S—S bonds (17). Both the secondary and the tertiary structure of the original enzyme appear to be restored in a large proportion of the protein—a much larger proportion than could be expected as a result of random reformation of S—S bonds. Anfinsen and others (18) have shown that ribonuclease oxidized under conditions in which "wrong" linkages have been formed may regain activity in the presence of an enzyme which catalyzes disulfide interchange in proteins.

Properties. The properties of proteins are, as would be expected, very varied. Most proteins are water-soluble or soluble in solutions of moderate ionic strength, though some are insoluble under all normal conditions and others are soluble in organic solvents either in their natural state or as a result of salt formation with organic acids. Most are denatured by heat, that is, they lose their solubility in water and their specific properties, though some are apparently unaffected by heating when in solution, even up to 100°C and for considerable periods. The solubility of some proteins increases with temperature, that of others decreases. Most enzymes show a high substrate specificity; in others it is very broad. Some proteins have unusual amino acids as part of their structure, for example one residue of *O*-tyrosine sulfate per molecule in fibrinogen (19), but most are confined to the usual 18 or 20 amino acids in their makeup.

All proteins are ampholytic, as they bear groups that vary in pK from close to 4 to 13. These groups by their presence modify the ionic environment of neighboring groups and, in turn, are affected by them. The dissociation constant of a carboxyl group, for example of a glutamic acid residue, will therefore not have the same value as that of the γ-COOH of the free amino acid, nor necessarily that of other glutamic acid carboxyl groups in the same or another protein. The values of the dissociation constants are in fact "smeared" over a range on either side of the expected value; as a consequence of the overlap that may occur between the ranges of dissociation constants of the different groups responsible for the charge on the surface of a protein, there are seldom any marked discontinuities in the titration curve of a protein. In acid media of pH 2.0 the positive charge is at a maximum and all negative charges (except for rare substituents such as phosphate and sulfate) are suppressed. Conversely, at a strongly alkaline pH, the negative charge is at a maximum. Between these extremes, at a pH depending on the amino acid makeup of the protein, there will be a

Table 2. Subunit Composition of Proteins. Determined by 1967[a] (20)

Protein	Molecular weight	Subunits	
		No.	Molecular weight
insulin	11,466	2	5,733
thrombin	31,000	(3)	(10,000)
β-lactoglobulin	35,000	2	17,500
avidin	53,000	3	18,000
hemoglobin	64,500	4	16,000
glycerol 1-phosphate dehydrogenase	78,000	2	40,000
alkaline phosphatase	80,000	2	40,000
enolase	82,000	2	41,000
liver alcohol dehydrogenase	84,000	2	42,000
procarboxypeptidase	87,000	1	34,500
		2	25,000
firefly luciferase	92,000	2	52,000
hexokinase	96,000	4	24,000
hemerythrin	107,000	8	13,500
tryptophan synthetase A	29,000	1	29,000
tryptophan synthetase B	117,000	2	60,000
mammary glucose 6-phosphate dehydrogenase	130,000	2	63,000
glyceraldehyde 3-phosphate dehydrogenase	140,000	4	37,000
aldolase	142,000	3	50,000
lactic dehydrogenase	150,000	4	35,000
yeast alcohol dehydrogenase	150,000	4	37,000
ceruloplasmin	151,000	8	18,000
threonine deaminase	160,000	4	40,000
thetin homocysteine methylpherase	180,000	3–4	50,000
fumarase	194,000	4	48,500
serum lipoprotein	200,000	6	36,500
tryptophanase	220,000	2	(125,000)
pyruvate kinase	237,000	4	57,200
catalase	250,000	4	60,000
phycocyanin	266,000	2	134,000
	134,000	3	46,000

point at which the *net* charge will be zero and the total number of charged residues at a maximum. At this isoelectric point solubility is normally at a minimum, for net electrostatic repulsion will not occur. As this pH is departed from, mutual repulsion due to like net charge will steadily increase, frequently with concomitant increased solubility.

Proteins vary in molecular weight from above 5000 (corresponding to 40 or so component amino acids) to ten million or more (proteins of very large size are normally stable associations of subunits (see Table 2) into which they may be dissociated by changes of pH or by high concentrations of solutes such as urea or guanidine). These molecular weights correspond roughly to spheres with diameters from 2.3 nm to 29 nm. The diameter of a water molecule, by comparison, is about 0.33 nm and of a "flickering cluster" of water molecules, about 1.4 nm. Normally water is associated with protein molecules in solution in amounts of about one third to one half their weight.

Sources of Proteins

Green plants use energy from the sun to synthesize over the surface of the earth about 200 billion tons of organic material per annum, of which some 10 billion (metric)

Table 2 (*continued*)

| Protein | Molecular weight | Subunits | |
		No.	Molecular weight
mitochondrial adenosine triphosphatase	284,000	10	26,000
aspartyl transcarbamylase	310,000	2	96,000
		4	30,000
lipovitellin	400,000	2	200,000
apoferritin	480,000	20	24,000
urease	483,000	6	83,000
phosphorylase	495,000	4	125,000
fraction I protein, carboxydismutase	515,000	24	22,000
β-galactosidase	520,000	4	130,000
	130,000	3–4	(40,000)
myosin	620,000	3	200,000
pyruvate carboxylase	660,000	4	165,000
	165,000	4	45,000
thyroglobulin	669,000	2	335,000
propionyl carboxylase	700,000	4	175,000
lipoic reductase–transacetylase	1,600,000	60	27,000
glutamic dehydrogenase	2,000,000	8	250,000
	250,000	5	50,000
hemocyanin	300,000–9,000,000		385,000
			70,000
			35,000
chlorocruorin	2,750,000	12	250,000
bromegrass mosaic virus	4,600,000	180	20,000
turnip-yellow mosaic virus	5,000,000	150	21,000
poliomyelitis virus	5,500,000	130	27,000
cucumber mosaic virus	6,000,000	185	21,500
alfalfa mosaic virus	7,400,000	160	35,000
bushy stunt virus	9,000,000	120	60,000
potato virus X	35,000,000	650	52,000
tobacco mosaic virus	40,000,000	2,130	17,500

Courtesy *Science* and I. M. Klotz. Copyright 1967 by the American Association for the Advancement of Science.

[a] Parentheses indicate doubt.

tons is protein. Since the total amount of organic matter on earth remains essentially constant, it may be assumed that this amount of protein is broken down in the course of a year, principally by the nonphotosynthesizing organisms (bacteria, fungi, and animals). Man diverts 1% or less of this protein flux for his own use: rather more than half of it for his nutrition, much of the rest in the waste associated with its conversion to forms suited better to his digestion and tastes than the original plant source.

Not long ago the only polymers available to industry were of natural origin and all the main groups of natural polymers except lignin and nucleic acids were used and valued in one way or another. The first attempts to develop new products depended on modifying the properties of natural polymers as in the production of celluloid and acetate "silk" from cellulose, and of other plastics from a casein protein base. (See Acetate fibers; Fibers, man-made, Vol. 9, p. 154.) For a time it seemed that proteins had a big future in the textile industry in the preparation of fibers (lanital or Aralac from casein, Ardil from peanut protein, and fiber from soybean protein were all brought to the stage of commercial feasibility). Three factors have aborted this originally promising development. Protein preparations tend to be variable in properties, availability and price; more important, synthetic fibers have been produced at a competitive price in ever-increasing variety over the last twenty-five years and, finally, a growing awareness of the present serious world shortage of protein for food has led to the increased use as food of protein formerly regarded as surplus. The only organisms raised or exploited by man primarily as a source of protein for industry are the silkworm and, in some countries, sheep. The protein arising as wastage or by-product from other animals or plants is increasingly used for animal feed—a method of upgrading inedible to edible protein with an efficiency of 10–30% at the most. In this category are slaughterhouse wastes, fish meal, and the protein-rich oil-seed cakes, though the latter are increasingly being exploited as a source of human food.

It is in the class of catalytically and biologically active products that the future industrial importance of proteins lies. The biologically active proteins include those normally circulating in the plasma, some in very low concentrations (protein hormones), and the protein toxins. Albumin has an important role in the body in maintaining plasma colloid osmotic pressure and hence total plasma and circulating blood volume. Albumin levels are lowered by a grossly inadequate diet and must be restored as a matter of urgency after blood loss. If whole blood is not available for transfusion, freeze-dried plasma proteins or albumin may be reconstituted and infused. An alternative method of restoring plasma colloid osmotic pressure is the use of solutions of neutral, osmotically active polymers such as dextran or polyvinylpyrrolidone. The only protein hormone prepared in large amounts today is insulin (qv) from the pancreas of slaughtered animals. The preparation of some of the protein and polypeptide hormones of the pituitary gland is beginning, but serious problems of separation still remain. It is in this field, if any, that synthesis of proteins may become economically feasible. Means of defense against pathogenic organisms in the form of human gamma globulins or antibodies produced by other animals (principally the horse) have a wide use in medicine.

The other group of proteins with biological activity is that of the protein toxins about which much is known, but little published. Their activity is extraordinary, for the lethal dose of botulinus toxin is one hundred thousand times less than that of the most toxic nonprotein organic substance known and 3×10^8 times less than that of cyanide. Methods for the large-scale preparation of such proteins have been worked out but fortunately they have not yet found a use.

The use of enzymes in the food industry is very old; more recently they have begun to be used in industrial processes (see Enzymes, industrial). Amylases, for example, have a wide use in desizing and in the preparation of glucose from starch. They have the inherent disadvantages of being readily inactivated by heat (though this may provide a method of stopping their action when required) and of being active only in an aqueous solution within a limited range of pH. Since they are used in solution they are normally only suitable for batch processes.

A very promising future appears likely for the exploitation in industrial processes of enzymes used in an insoluble or readily separable state for continuous processes. Several methods have been explored to modify soluble enzymes for this purpose (21). The enzymes may either be physically trapped within an insoluble hydrophilic polymer or encapsulated within semipermeable microcapsules of polymer, or they may be bound to an insoluble support by either ionic or covalent bonds (see Microencapsulation). Some enzymes may also be crosslinked in a microcrystalline form with the production of an insoluble crystalline derivative. Enzymes immobilized in these ways may be used as column packings or as reagents which can be added to substrate and subsequently removed by filtration or centrifugation. Some activity is frequently lost in the process of preparation but in many instances the stability of the enzyme is greatly increased. There may also be marked changes in other properties; for example, the enzymes' affinity for substrate may be altered and the optimum pH of activity changed by one or more units.

Enzymes which have been modified in this manner include proteases (trypsin, ficin, papain), glycosidases (invertase, β-glucosidase), choline esterase, and carboxypeptidase. Methods of attachment to an insoluble support include the use of charged cellulose derivatives (carboxymethylcellulose, diethylaminoethylcellulose) and covalent linking to a cellulose support. For example, benzoylaminocellulose may be diazotized and then coupled with the tyrosyl and histidyl residues of the enzyme. An alternative chemical method successfully used involves the preparation of the azide of carboxymethylcellulose and coupling to the protein amino groups. Enzymes have been entrapped in crosslinked dextrans (Sephadex) and in polyacrylamide gels and retained activity. Glutaraldehyde has been used to form covalently linked three-dimensional networks of enzyme molecules by the treatment of small crystals. If the crystals were less than 5 nm in size (carboxypeptidase) they had a constant specific activity; diffusion into the crystals was not limiting. As would be expected, the native enzyme in crystalline form is much less active (by a factor of 300) than in solution, while in amorphous form it is seventy times less active. Crosslinking reduced the activity by a further factor of four for the amorphous material. The considerable loss in activity is balanced to some extent by a remarkable stability of the product, no change in activity being observed over a period of three months (22). Chemical coupling of ficin to carboxymethylcellulose (23) gave a product in which much more of the enzyme's activity was preserved (a tenth). Only small losses of activity were found on storage for four months at 2°C. Protein solutions may be encapsulated with semipermeable polymer membranes of 1 to 100 nm diameter. Chang showed (24) that red-cell carbonic anhydrase encapsulated in 10-nm nylon microcapsules does not leak out and is nearly as active in this form as it is within the red blood cells from which it is prepared. Enzymes encapsulated in this way are of course effective only on substrates of low molecular weight. The use of membrane materials with a negative charge results in improved dispersibility in aqueous media. Such products may, in the future, be of therapeutic as well as industrial use.

Protein Purification

Purity is a Platonic concept and must be qualified and diluted in dealing with real systems. The most usual meaning in chemistry is that a pure preparation is one containing particles identical in weight (within the limits set by normal isotope abundance), chemical composition, and structure. In the case of proteins it is usually necessary to add the qualification that the identity in structure required extends beyond covalent linkage to spatial conformation and, if this requirement is met, it may be assumed that there is no variation in biological activity between particles. None of these identities can be shown to exist for a protein preparation by methods at present available. With some preparations it may be possible to produce evidence that 90–95% of the material consists of particles of the same size and having the same activity. Differences in chemical composition such as the substitution of one amino acid for another at a particular position in the polypeptide chain or differences in sequence in a small proportion of the particle population must frequently elude detection with present methods. For pure proteins, therefore, as for other substances, methods of preparation are methods that will produce proteins that are *not demonstrably impure* by whatever tests may be applied for their examination. The properties of proteins, however, are such that tests for purity are not as yet capable of the refinement of the methods appropriate for small molecules.

In purifying proteins much time and effort can be saved by taking advantage, where possible, of the properties of the starting material. A whole organism is likely to contain a thousand or more proteins, of which, necessarily, very few will be present as an appreciable fraction of the whole. One third of a man's protein is muscle protein and almost half of this is myosin. Obviously, muscle is likely to be a much better starting material for the preparation of myosin than is whole minced man. This principle applies also to many other proteins and organisms—thus, wheat germ is a better source of lipase than is wholemeal flour—it would be tedious to multiply examples. Exactly the same principle applies at the cellular level. The cell contains many organelles and many of the cell proteins are confined to one or another of these. Care taken to preserve the integrity of these subcellular structures and to separate them from the rest of the cell contents is well repaid by the elimination of many of the possible contaminating proteins and the consequent provision of an enriched starting material. It is also important to remember that the concentration of an individual protein in a tissue may vary with the physiological age of the organism or with its nutritional regime. Thus the concentration of a microbial enzyme may be enormously enhanced by growing the organisms in the presence of their substrate and urease is abundant in jack-bean seeds but not in the mature plant. The balance of inorganic nutrients supplied to green plants may affect enzyme levels over a ten- or twentyfold range (25).

Selection and isolation of the starting material is followed by extraction of the desired protein together with contaminating proteins. A few proteins are soluble in organic solvents (the prolamines in 70% ethanol and in chloroform/methanol, some exceptionally low molecular weight proteins, such as catalase, in 33% ethanol) and where possible advantage may be taken of this property to effect separation. Other proteins may not be readily soluble in water or aqueous salt solutions, owing to their association with lipids. These may often be brought into solution after exposure to butanol-saturated water or any one of a number of surface-active agents. Structural proteins (ordinarily extracellular proteins that are concerned with the structural integrity of an organism) are normally insoluble as a result of their specific and often limited amino acid composition (sericin, collagen) or as a result of covalent crosslinking between polypeptide chains (resilin, collagen, and probably keratin). In extreme instances they can only be brought into solution in the form of *S*-carboxymethyl or other derivatives which have the effect of increasing the number of ionizing groups while breaking intrachain and perhaps interchain —S—S— bridges. Collagen is more readily degraded, for heat in the presence of water is enough to transform it to gelatin. Once a protein is available in aqueous solution a varied battery of methods may be used by which fine differences in properties may be exploited to obtain an enrichment of the desired protein. The principal methods employed or available are listed in Table 3.

It must be emphasized that the purification of most proteins is still primarily confined to small-scale operations in research laboratories. The methods used are

Table 3. Methods of Exploitation of Protein Properties

Solubility

1.[a] Differential precipitation of desired product or impurity by changing solution properties in terms of the following:
    a. Ionic strength (ammonium sulfate precipitation, etc).
    b. Dielectric constant (lowered by many organic miscible solvents, ethanol, acetone; raised by others, eg, formamide).
    c. pH.
    d. Temperature.
2.[a] Differential precipitation by specific cations (Zn^{2+}, Ca^{2+}).
3. Using solubility of protein complex, eg, solubility of plasma albumin–trichloroacetic acid precipitate in ethanol.
4. Phase distribution using immiscible aqueous/nonaqueous phases. Countercurrent distribution methods of L. C. Craig (25a) appropriate.
5. Phase distribution using immiscible *aqueous* phases. P.-A. Albertsson (25b) used, for example, polyethylene glycol–water phase in equilibrium with methylcellulose–water phase.

Molecular Size

6. Centrifugation at high speeds. Also may give information on molecular size and shape.
7. Dialysis (qv). Mainly used for separation of proteins from small molecules.
8. Ultrafiltration. Clogging of membrane a frequent trouble.
9. Gel filtration. Separates classes of different molecular weight. Range of gels (dextran, acrylamide, agarose) in bead form commercially available can give information on molecular weight.

Charge

10. Change in pH as in 1c.
11. Gel electrophoresis. Migration through gel due to electrical field depends on *size* as well as charge. Preparative gel electrophoresis is feasible on small scale but method is primarily useful for monitoring progress of other methods.
12. Free electrophoresis (moving boundary). Can only separate slowest-moving and fastest-moving components from mixture.
13. Stabilized electrophoresis, as follows:
    a. Gel electrophoresis (see 11).
    b. Stabilization by density gradient (eg, sucrose).
    c. Paper or cellulose acetate membranes. Primarily analytical. Difficulties due to adsorption may arise.
    d. Column electrophoresis. As in b, but density-gradient stabilization replaced by inert powder packing (cellulose, glass bead, polyvinyl chloride, etc). As in c adsorption difficulties may arise.
14. Continuous stabilized electrophoresis, as follows:
    a. Curtain electrophoresis. Buffer solution flows evenly down paper sheet or thin bed of inert packing. Electric field applied at right angles to direction of flow causes separation of components of protein solution applied at one point of starting edge of paper or packed bed. Collection at multiple points at bottom of sheet or bed.
    b. Formally similar to 14a, but in place of paper or packing, buffer and solution to be separated flow in very thin layer between temperature-controlled glass plates. Multiple collection points.
15. Ion exchange (qv). Ion-exchange resins are seldom suitable owing to low porosity and hence low capacity. Substituted celluloses (carboxymethylcellulose, diethylaminoethylcellulose) or dextrans are widely used. Hydroxyapatite in highly hydrated, very finely divided state is also effective.

Specific Properties

16. Immunological. Antibodies may be adsorbed on columns in which the packing has been substituted with the antigen.
17. Enzymic. Column of insoluble substrate (eg, chitin, or substrate bound to cellulose or other packing).

[a]All the methods described in 1 and 2 were used in conjunction, by Cohn and co-workers (6), in separation of blood proteins.

seldom capable of handling more than a few grams of material at a time and are often restricted to the milligram scale.   Methods that seem likely to be employed on a larger scale include gel filtration and electrodecantation.   The former is being used for the removal of nonprotein constituents from milk.   In *gel filtration* (see also Table 3, item 9) a solution containing molecules of a range of sizes is passed through a column packed with beads of gel.   Small molecules can enter the interstices of the beads, very large molecules cannot, while molecules of intermediate size appear to penetrate the beads partially.   As a consequence the effective column volume is small for very large molecules (equal to the volume of liquid outside the beads) and almost equal to the empty column volume for small molecules.   Thus the excluded large molecules leave the column in advance of smaller, partially permeating molecules, and molecules to which the gel is completely permeable leave it last.   The mixture of solutes thus leaves the column in order of decreasing molecular size.   (In the case of milk, for example, large molecules such as proteins and dispersed fats will emerge at the front, followed some time later by the small molecules, such as lactose and salts.)   Columns of Sephadex dextran gel, 1 m in diameter, are used in a batch process.   Sterilization, which is essential, may be carried out by washing the column daily with hot (60°C) alkali with no change to the packing.   The product consisting entirely of the proteins and dispersed fats of the milk may be used to formulate products resembling human milk more closely than unmodified cow's milk or to prepare milk free of lactose or sodium for special diets.   *Electrodecantation* is being used increasingly in the preparation of highly purified enzymes and has the advantage of being a continuous process.   In any attempt to use essentially laboratory methods on a large scale, attention to sterility is of course of the utmost importance.

Purified proteins are normally preserved dry, after freeze drying from solution. Many are stable in the dry state at room temperature but others, including many enzyme preparations, must be stored at low temperatures.

Proteins as Food

Man cannot synthesize in his body some of the amino acids that are essential components of the proteins of which he is made, although these are essential to the function of his cells and therefore a condition of his life.   Without a constant external source of these amino acids he must die.   (For a discussion of the biosynthesis of amino acids and other facts concerning them, see Amino acids.)

Rose (26) in 1957 reviewed the results of his outstanding work on the amino acid requirements of adult men and summarized the results of ten years of "extraordinarily laborious, time consuming and costly" experimentation on a group of young men together with work by others on young women.   A set of accepted, authoritative figures for the essential amino acid requirements of young adults and children is shown in Table 4.   In giving these requirements the assumption is made that *total* amino acid intake is adequate to fulfil the needs of the body, for the nonessential amino acids are nonessential only in that they are interconvertible and hence do not have to be supplied individually, in their specific forms.   Moreover, it must be assumed that calorie needs are adequately met, for, if they are not, protein may be catabolized to satisfy energy requirements.   In principle then, it is possible to specify the requirements of an adult for total protein intake if we know how much protein he has to replace per day, if we know the amino acid composition of the protein he eats, and if we know with what

Table 4. Essential Amino Acid Requirements of Young Adults and Children[a]

	Adolescents (27)		Children (28)	
	Absolute requirements, mg/kg	In terms of tryptophan	Absolute requirements, mg/kg	In terms of tryptophan
tryptophan	7.2	1.0	30	1.0
phenylalanine	31	4.3	169	5.6
lysine	23	3.2	170	5.6
threonine	14	1.9	87	2.9
valine	23	3.2	161	5.4
methionine	31	4.3	85	2.8
leucine	31	4.3	425	14
isoleucine	20	2.8	90	3.0

[a] See also Vol. 2, p. 183.

efficiency he can use the fed protein. In practice such a specification cannot be made, for men vary one from the other in their needs, and our knowledge of protein nutrition in man is adequate at present only to serve as the basis of informed guesses. These guesses must however be made. In a situation of world protein shortage it is of the utmost importance whether political and other planning is based on, for example, a requirement of 65 g of protein or of 42 g of protein per day for a "reference adult" weighing 65 kg. Both of these figures have been advanced authoritatively in the last ten years (29). The difference between them, applied to the present world population, is approximately equal to the total world supplies of animal proteins. Differences of this magnitude make it possible to predict, with equal sincerity, that mankind is face to face with disaster or that there is little cause for alarm in the next decade or so. Since decisions made on unreliable data (in the confident belief that they have a status similar to that of physical constants) may have long-term effects of the greatest magnitude, it is essential to examine in some detail the way in which nutritional recommendations can be formulated.

Three Ways of Determining Protein Requirements. Three approaches to the problem are possible. The *first*, and in many ways the most desirable, is to determine the physiological needs for protein, using man as an experimental subject. The most satisfactory method is to feed volunteers diets of accurately known protein content that contain adequate amounts of the essential amino acids and that are adequate also in other respects (vitamins and calories). Protein levels are chosen to be near what is believed to be requirements and, by altering the levels fed to each subject, the level is determined at which nitrogen balance is reached (when there is neither a loss nor a gain in total body nitrogen). Unfortunately, such experiments are costly, time-consuming, and difficult to interpret. There is evidence, for example, that nitrogen balance can be reached at different intake levels in the same subject and there is no good reason to suppose that a value determined for one experimental subject in terms of grams of protein per kilogram of body weight will be applicable to another. It is known, for example, that vitamin C requirements of healthy guinea pigs may vary twentyfold and Rose (26), using a small number of young healthy men, found that the requirements for an essential amino acid may vary by up to 100%. If protein requirements vary in the healthy adult they are likely to vary still more in the diseased adult—often in the direction of increased demand.

A *second* approach is to use, in place of individuals, populations as the experimental subject. There is a very wide range in protein intake among different economic classes within nations. Surveys determining the amount of protein eaten per head by populations have been carried out, based on trade and agricultural statistics and the analysis of the foodstuffs consumed. Similar surveys at the family level have also been made. It is possible to judge from the results of such surveys, using figures for growth rate, life expectancy, and the incidence of those diseases believed to be connected with protein deficiency, what protein levels are necessary to ensure adequate protein intake for a population as a whole. Obviously it is necessary in any attempt to apply such a figure to a different population to allow for differences in population age structure and in the quality and amino acid composition of available protein.

Finally it may be desired to determine not the minimal requirements of protein intake but the optimal requirements and at this level people's preferences must be taken into account. There is no doubt that as the standard of living of a people rises so does the proportion of protein, particularly meat protein, in their diet.

Three levels can then in theory be set: (*1*) a minimal subsistence level based on evidence inevitably inadequate due to the impossibility of determining it on enough subjects to get a reasonable estimate of variability; (*2*) a level based on practice and depending for its adequacy on clinical impressions of population health and estimates of food actually consumed by a population of known structure existing near subsistence level; and (*3*) similar estimates based on populations or socioeconomic classes with high living standards. Which is chosen as a standard must depend on the use to which the results are to be put and, at the higher levels of decision, the choice will be made on grounds rather far removed from the objective considerations of nutritional science. As if choice were not sufficiently complicated there is evidence that choice of a plane of nutrition may inadvertently imply choice of particular disease patterns to which the population subject to that choice will be exposed. Thus the differences between incidence of types of cancer of African and American Negroes is best explained on the basis of dietetic differences which result in a high incidence of liver cancer in the former and of gastrointestinal cancer in the latter (30). Whether or not this particular instance proves entirely the result of dietary differences there seems little doubt that as Trowell (30) has pointed out "we may find that there is no such thing as a good or a bad diet, but that there are certain dietary ranges that produce certain disease patterns, particularly later in life." This statement must be qualified of course as applying only to diets adequate for maintenance over a reasonable life span.

Desirable Levels. Supplementation of a diet inadequate in protein with no care for the balance of the diet as a whole carries its own dangers. In a report of a joint FAO/WHO expert group (31), ". . . the group depreciated programs which overemphasize the provision of individual nutrients (with certain exceptions such as iodine and fluorine). In particular, it drew attention to the potential harm inherent in the provision of protein supplements, which may stimulate growth and hence increase the requirements for other nutrients, unless due consideration is given to the need for ensuring adequate intakes of other nutrients at the same time." The paucity of our knowledge of human nutrition is well illustrated by the definition of "recommended intakes" put forward by the same group for vitamins: "The recommended intakes . . . are the amounts considered sufficient for the maintenance of health in nearly all people."

In view of all these uncertainties and in view of the fact that most published figures include a "margin of safety," commonly of 50%, added to minimal estimates (this is particularly true of estimates of demands for the essential amino acids) it will be seen that any recommendations for minimal protein contents of human diets can be regarded as little more than inspired guesses with a very large uncertainty. All that is certain is that levels can be too low, for man must eat protein to survive; whether they can be too high (apart from consideration of wasting a product in short supply) we do not know though some suggest persuasively that this might be so. Animal experiments have been done for example on cows and other animals which indicate that diets suboptimal for growth result in an increased life expectancy and, in some instances at least, in a body composition changed in respect to that of the controls. Brozek (32) has said that there are few problems in human biology that call more urgently for the attention of research workers than does the relation between early growth rate and adult morbidity and longevity. Yet nothing is known of the relation in man though studies on animals would suggest that a diet in childhood designed to ensure optimal growth rate may have consequences which later may prove undesirable.

Whatever levels are believed, on available evidence, to be desirable they must obviously be expressed in terms of some standard. It is plain that proteins vary in composition and in their content of the essential amino acids and that even proteins of similar overall composition may vary in digestibility. Some vegetable-seed proteins are inhibitors of digestive enzymes; processing may render an essential amino acid unavailable (particularly lysine); or proteins may be unavailable to the digestive enzymes by physical segregation in unbroken plant cells or may simply be indigestible (as is keratin). All these factors result in a wide variation in protein quality from a nutritional point of view and quality must be measured quantitatively in order to judge, by whatever standards, the adequacy of a diet from a consideration of its composition.

Standards. The most useful biological measures of protein quality are (*1*) the *protein efficiency ratios* (PER), (*2*) the *biological value* (BV), and (*3*) the *net protein utilization* (NPU). The simplest to determine of these, since it needs only a balance, is the PER, the gain in weight per unit of protein intake. Its determination requires (a) that growing animals be fed an adequate diet in respects other than protein, and (b) that the protein be not supplied in any excess (which would give low PER values). Unfortunately there is no certainty that weight gain in such experiments will be proportional to gain in body protein, for body composition may vary in terms of fat and water in particular.

The determination of BV and NPU each require the correction of observed values for loss of urinary, dermal, and fecal nitrogen by subtraction of the amounts which would be lost on a proteinfree diet. This cannot be done with great accuracy. In the calculation of average nitrogen requirements of children and adults for example, the Joint FAO/WHO Expert Group (31) assumed a urinary nitrogen loss of 2 mg per basal kilocalorie and added to this arbitrary allowances of 20 mg N/kg of body weight for fecal N loss and the same amount for dermal N loss. The allowance for loss through the skin (mostly in the form of nitrogenous compounds in the sweat) is the equivalent of 8 g of protein metabolized per day for a 65-kg man. This is 21% of the estimated mean requirement of protein of NPU 100. The few figures available (29) indicate that dermal loss of N may vary in the adult from the equivalent of 1.6 g of NPU 100 protein per day to 28 g (for a man living in an environment of 100°F, resting 18 hr a day and sweating profusely 6 hr a day). There is of course no doubt that fecal N loss will also be found very variable and particularly high in some disease conditions.

The BV is the ratio between the amount of dietary protein nitrogen retained by the body and that which passes into it through the gut wall. Its determination therefore takes into account the varying digestibility of the fed protein. NPU is the ratio of retained nitrogen to protein nitrogen entering the intestine and is equivalent to the BV corrected for digestibility. Both methods require nitrogen balance experiments carried out at protein levels below maintenance levels. The difficulties of performing such experiments in man and the uncertainty in deciding on the significance of the results are well described by Holmes (29). Table 5 lists average requirements of nitrogen for children and adults; Table 6, the requirements of protein at three different

Table 5. The Average Nitrogen Requirements of Children and Adults (33)

			mg N per kg per day		
Age, years		Weight,[a] kg	Basal urinary N[b]	Total basal N loss[c]	Requirement for growth[d]	Total requirement[e]
children						
both sexes	1	11.3	74	114	20	148
	2	13.5	70	110	13	136
	3	15.5	68	109	13	134
	4–6	18	66	106	13	130
	7–9	27	59	99	13	123
	10–12	36	54	94	10	114
boys	13–15	49	50	90	10	110
	16–19	63	46	86	7	102
girls	13–15	49	49	89	10	110
	16–19	54	48	88	3	100
adults						
men		65	46	86		95
women		55	46	86		95

NOTE: The references cited below can be found in reference 33.

[a] The weights of children up to 4 years are taken from Table 9 in Waldo E. Nelson's *Textbook of Pediatrics* (W. B. Saunders Co., Philadelphia, Pa., 1959) and represent mean weights for the age intervals 1–2, 2–3, and 3–4 years for boys and girls, 50th percentile. The weights of older children are those given in the report *Evaluation of Protein Nutrition* (National Academy of Sciences—National Research Council, 1959). For adults the weights taken are those of the Reference Man and Woman given in the report of the FAO Second Committee on Calorie Requirements (FAO, 1957a).

[b] The basal urinary nitrogen loss has been taken as 2 mg N per basal kcal. The basal metabolic rate of children was computed from the formula given by Smuts (1935):

$$BMR = 70.4 \times W^{0.734}$$

where the BMR is in kcal and W is the weight in kg.

For adults the figures are those for the FAO Reference Man and Woman (FAO, 1957a).

[c] The figures are those for basal urinary nitrogen loss with the addition of 20 mg N/kg for endogenous fecal loss and 20 mg N/kg for dermal loss.

[d] For children up to 4 years, the nitrogen requirement for growth and maturation is taken from Table 1 in Holt et al. (1960). For older children, to calculate the nitrogen retained during growth it is assumed that 18% of the weight gain is protein, with a nitrogen content of 16%. The rates of gain at each age are those cited in the report *Evaluation of Protein Nutrition* (National Academy of Sciences—National Research Council, 1959).

[e] The figures are the sum of the basal requirement plus the requirement for growth, with an addition of 10% to cover the effects of everyday stresses.

Table 6. Protein Requirements of Children and Adults and the Effect of Protein Quality (33)

Age	NPU = 100			NPU = 90			NPU = 80			NPU = 70			NPU = 60			NPU = 50		
	I	II	III	I	II	III	I	II	III	I	II	III	I	II	III	I	II	III
infants, months																		
0–3			2.3															
3–6			1.8															
6–9			1.5															
9–12			1.2															
children, years																		
1–3[a]	0.70	0.88	1.06	0.78	0.98	1.18	0.88	1.10	1.32	1.00	1.25	1.50	1.17	1.46	1.75	1.41	1.76	2.11
4–6	0.65	0.81	0.97	0.72	0.90	1.08	0.81	1.01	1.21	0.93	1.16	1.39	1.07	1.34	1.61	1.30	1.62	1.94
7–9	0.62	0.77	0.92	0.69	0.86	1.03	0.77	0.96	1.15	0.88	1.10	1.32	1.02	1.28	1.54	1.23	1.54	1.85
10–12	0.58	0.72	0.86	0.64	0.80	0.96	0.72	0.90	1.08	0.82	1.03	1.24	0.96	1.20	1.44	1.15	1.44	1.73
adolescents																		
13–15	0.56	0.70	0.84	0.62	0.78	0.94	0.70	0.88	1.06	0.80	1.00	1.20	0.93	1.16	1.39	1.12	1.40	1.68
16–19	0.51	0.64	0.77	0.57	0.71	0.85	0.64	0.80	0.96	0.74	0.92	1.10	0.85	1.06	1.27	1.02	1.28	1.54
adults	0.47	0.59	0.71	0.53	0.66	0.79	0.59	0.74	0.89	0.67	0.84	1.01	0.78	0.98	1.18	0.94	1.18	1.42

CODE:

I Protein intakes considered inadequate for all but a very small fraction (2.5%) of the population.

II Estimated average protein requirement of a population.

III Protein intake considered adequate for all but a very small fraction (2.5%) of the population.

[a] The intake capacity of children of this age may not allow the provision of adequate protein of NPU below 60.

Table 7. Calculation of the Upper Level of Protein Requirements[a] (33)
(Level III of Table 6)

Age and other factors affecting human development	Population, 1000	Average body weight, kg	Requirement per kg body weight per day, g	Requirement per head per day, g	Total requirement, kg/day
infants, nonbreast-fed, 0–1 yr	36	9	1.70[b]	15.30	551
children, nonbreast-fed, 1–3 yr	231	12	1.06	12.72	2,938
4–6 yr	200.2	18	0.97	17.46	3,495
7–9 yr	184	27	0.92	24.84	4,571
10–12 yr	160.8	35	0.86	30.10	4,840
adolescents					
male, 13–15 yr	83.6	49	0.84	41.16	3,441
16–19 yr	113.6	63	0.77	48.51	5,511
female, 13–15 yr	84.6	46	0.84	38.64	3,269
16–19 yr	132	54	0.77	41.58	5,489
adults, men	670	65	0.71	46.15	30,920
women	705	55	0.71	39.05	27,530
allowance for pregnancy (59,400 women)				6.00	356
allowance for lactation	72			15.00	1,080
totals[c]	2,672.8				93,991

[a] The calculations apply to a country having a mean annual temperature of 30°C in which the duration of lactation is 8 months and the protein value of the diet 65.

[b] Average of four figures from Table 6.

[c] From these may be calculated the following requirements per person:

requirement for reference protein = 93,991/2,672.8 = 35.16 g per head per day

requirement for protein of NPU 65 = 35.16 × 100/65 = approx 54 g per head per day

levels assuming dietary protein of NPU from 50–100; Table 7, finally, shows a calculation of the amount of protein needed by a given population to ensure as far as can be estimated that intake will be adequate for at least 97.5% of that population (average values plus 20%, the 20% being roughly the equivalent of two standard deviations from the mean).

In considering the practical applications of figures such as these in Table 7 it is necessary to make some assumptions concerning the NPU value of a population's diet. For advanced countries and high-income groups the values lie probably in the range of 70–80. For developing countries, values of 60–70 are more likely. Calculated values refer, of course, to food eaten, and allowance for wastage in food preparation and food not eaten may be made by multiplying with a factor of 1.1. By this means a figure for a population of the structure used in Table 7 of 60 g per day per head of population may be arrived at, or 22 kg per annum per head. Protein production by world agriculture is estimated to have been about 1.67×10^8 tons in 1964—enough for a population of some seven billion assuming that all protein produced entered the retail level without loss and that distribution to each individual was perfect. In practice, however, some of the plant protein produced was used to feed animals, wastage in some areas may reach one third before food arrives at the retail level, and distribution is far from equitable.

In fact, much of the world's population suffers from a shortage of dietary protein and there seems no doubt that given the present socioeconomic world structure it is far easier to increase food production in order to reduce protein malnutrition than to organize effective distribution and significant reduction in wastage.

Future Sources of Edible Protein

There is no reasonable doubt that we must, as soon as may be, increase the amount of food available to mankind. In the immediate future this increase will be secured almost entirely by the expansion and exploitation of existing agricultural practice. New possibilities for expanding the total protein supply are however becoming more and more practicable and some will no doubt assume increasing importance in the near future.

Cereals. Of the 77 million metric tons of protein eaten by man annually more than half comes from cereals (40 million tons), 12 million tons from legumes, and 25 million tons from animals. An increase in quantity or quality of the cereal protein entering the diet must therefore be of major importance. Such an increase would be particularly effective in that the impact would be greatest in the areas of poorest nutrition where cereals are the major sources of calories—rice and wheat in Asia and North Africa and maize in Central and South America. Wheat protein has a slightly lower NPU value than has rice or corn protein but wheat contains a higher percentage of protein than these other cereals and thus is more than adequate as a protein source for adults (other than pregnant and nursing women) getting most of their calorie requirements from it (34). See also Wheat and other cereal grains.

One method by which both rice and maize might be greatly improved would be by the breeding of *varieties of higher protein content* even if quality remained otherwise unchanged. In effect, if most of the calorie needs are met from either rice or maize, increasing the amount of rice or maize protein in the diet is an inefficient but nevertheless effective method of increasing the amounts of the limiting amino acids, lysine and tryptophan, in the diet. Obviously it would be better to alter the *quality of the protein* by selecting for varieties with an increased proportion of lysine or tryptophan in the seed protein, and this is being done for maize. Already maizes have been selected with protein of much higher NPU values, resulting from increased proportions of the first and second limiting amino acids.

The first 'high lysine' maize to be found, tested, and publicized was discovered in 1935. Recognition of its exceptional nutritional value however was delayed until 1963 when it was first analyzed for lysine (35). This example illustrates in two ways the influence of techniques on the rate of advance. First, the recognition of the value of high-lysine maize came only when automatic methods of analysis of effluents from ion exchange columns had made amino acid analyses of hydrolyzates rapid and almost routine. Secondly, maize has been recognized as having a primary deficiency in tryptophan since the pioneer work of Osborne and Mendel showed that rats lost weight on zein, were able to maintain weight on zein plus tryptophan, and gained weight if lysine were added as well. Tryptophan unfortunately is destroyed to a variable extent during protein hydrolysis by acid and the usual methods of analysis do not give a reliable figure. It is certain that if it were not for the difficulty still encountered in estimating tryptophan our knowledge of the nutritional value of many products would be more advanced.

Though high-lysine varieties of maize have a much enhanced nutritional value, their yields are not as yet comparable to those of normal commercial varieties, and not until yields have been increased will high-lysine types successfully replace the high-yielding varieties of lower protein quality. Work along these lines—to produce rice, wheat, and soybean of greater nutritional value for man—is proceeding actively. The production of new varieties capable of adequate agronomic yields coupled with improved nutritive quality is inevitably a slow process. A similar result can be achieved *immediately* by *supplementing a cereal* with the appropriate limiting amino acid or acids. Thus wheat grains scarified lightly and soaked in lysine hydrochloride solutions have been shown after drying to have taken up 10% by wt of lysine (36). When mixed with bulk wheat in a proportion of 1:100 by wt, lysine is no longer limiting in flour milled from the enriched wheat and the PER is raised from 1.1–1.3 to 1.8–1.9. Table 8 shows the amount of lysine desirable for enriching cereal grains and the esti-

Table 8. Lysine Supplementation of Cereal Grains[a]

Cereal	Nutritive value[b]		Lysine added,[c] %	Estimated cost,[d] ¢
	Original	After supplementation		
whole wheat	1.3	1.7	0.1	28
wheat flour	0.7	1.6	0.25	70
rice	1.5	1.8–2.2	0.05	14
corn	1.5	1.9–2.2	0.1	28
millet	0.7	2.1	0.3	84
sorghum	0.7	2.2	0.3	84
casein		2.5		

[a] Courtesy Dairy and Food Industries Supply Association and E. E. Howe (37). Courtesy *Science* and A. M. Altschul (38). Copyright 1967 by the American Association for the Advancement of Science.
[b] In terms of protein efficiency ratio (PER) determined on rats.
[c] Added as L-lysine HCl.
[d] Cost of supplementing cereal per child per year based on its assumed cost of $1/lb.

mated cost of enrichment. Further improvement is possible by adding other limiting amino acids to maize (0.05–0.07% tryptophan), wheat (0.15% threonine), and rice (0.2% threonine); the improvement will be economically practical with a decrease in the price of threonine below about $2/lb (37). Measures such as these depend on a great expansion of present facilities for the manufacture of a few amino acids but have the very great advantage of increasing the value of familiar foodstuffs already accepted as diet staples in the areas where improved protein intake is most needed. Supplementation need not, of course, be necessarily limited to the addition of amino acids, for protein concentrates from other sources may be used. Examples are fish and oil-seed proteins, which may not only complement cereal protein in composition but may also add to the total protein intake. Used discreetly these additives need not change existing food use patterns.

It has been suggested by Howe, Jansen, and Anson (39) that the optimal approach to the immediate amelioration of the protein shortage in nutrition should employ two methods, the first adapted to the very large proportion of the undernourished whose diet is based on cereal grains (perhaps half the world's population), and the second to the much smaller proportion (about 100 million) whose diet consists predominantly of cassava and root crops. The first group has an adequate quantity of protein of in-adequate quality. In the second, both quantity and quality are deficient. Amino acid supplementation of the cereal diet (certainly with lysine, preferably with threonine and tryptophan as well) may be enough to solve the protein demands of the first group. This would not be enough for the second group, and supplementation of the diet by additional high-quality protein in the form of fish flour or seed proteins (soy, peanut, cottonseed, etc) would be necessary. This very valuable review concludes with specific proposals which, if implemented, could well redress the world imbalance in protein nutrition in a very short time.

New Food Forms. Technology has made available many protein-rich concen-trates which are not readily acceptable, often through unfamiliarity, in the form in which they are normally produced. Examples are soybean curd, fish flour, and protein-rich residues from seed-oil manufacture. The problem of acceptability is not however restricted to protein sources new to mankind—the same difficulties of acceptance arise if the food is unfamiliar to those to whom it is presented. Hence many efforts have been made to make wheat look and taste like rice so that it may be accepted and eaten by traditional rice eaters. On the other hand, wheat has also been processed into food forms hitherto known only to certain localities.

The great influence of habit and tradition as against purely nutritional factors is well illustrated by the world market prices of wheat and rice in 1967. One ton of rice very similar in nutritional value to wheat though with a slightly lower protein content and quality, sold at the same price as 2.7 tons of wheat.

The modification of vegetable and animal products to make them more palatable, more digestible or more easily preserved is, of course, the oldest aim of food technology, but appears to have been governed largely by the exploitation of accidental observa-tions. The processes used have often remained largely local and only recently have conscious efforts been made to apply the principles underlying many of these processes. Thus milk protein keeps better as cheese, soybean protein (see Soybeans) is more digestible after fungi have been encouraged to grow on the beans or allowed to ferment the protein curd, and autolysis is employed (as in cassava) to destroy toxins. Owing to the ubiquity of microorganisms, preservation was largely a matter of reducing water activity by drying or by the addition of solutes such as salt and sugar; only recently did the exclusion of microorganisms by sterilization and canning become possible. Canning, refrigeration, and the more sophisticated methods of drying (spray-, drum- and freeze-drying) have helped to make protein more readily available through storage and transport, but the application of our knowledge of food processing has been largely restricted to conventional raw products.

New Food Sources. New forms of conventional food are the province of food technology but the concern of the protein chemist is to investigate new sources of protein for human and animal nutrition. Perhaps the most immediately important, and obvious, of these are animal and plant products hitherto regarded as inedible and treated as wastes. Residues from oil seeds after oil extraction have long been used for animal feeding but are now assuming importance for human nutrition. Many formulations have been developed successfully in which mixtures of seed protein are incorporated in proportions designed to make the components complement each other in amino acid composition. The composition of many such mixtures and the PER values obtained are given by Parpia (40). Fish meal (see Vol. 9, p. 330) derived from trash fish and offal has long served as a protein-rich supplement in animal feeds;

in a more refined form—*fish protein concentrate* (see Vol. 9, p. 329)—it has now been widely accepted as a suitable material with which to fortify diets. The process is essentially simple in that whole fresh fish of little commercial value (for example, the red hake, *Urophycis chuss*) are ground up immediately after catching and extracted at once with a solvent such as isopropyl alcohol. The insoluble residue has a high protein content and a very low bacterial count, is stable and odorless, and is easily stored and transported.

Radically New Protein Sources. The edible parts of an animal are readily separated from the inedible protective and supporting tissues (skin, bone, or carapace). This process is not feasible with the vegetative mass of a plant for each cell is enclosed in cellulose which is not digestible by man. It is not surprising then that the seeds of the cultivated grasses (rice, wheat, and other cereals) have proved so successful as foods, for not only is their protein content high but the cell walls of the endosperm contain no cellulose. The greatest yield of protein per acre is supplied by green leaves but the amount of 'roughage' in the form of cellulose, hemicellulose, and lignin that must be consumed and the barriers to efficient digestion formed by the indigestible cell walls make green leaves an unsuitable source of protein for man, unless used at second hand by taking advantage of the superior digestive abilities of ruminants such as cows and sheep, and of kangaroos. Simple mechanical means have, however, been developed by Pirie (41) for preparing leaf protein in a concentrated form free from fiber in a yield of 50% or more. Leaf protein concentrate has a satisfactory amino acid composition and has been used successfully in conjunction with milk in the treatment of acute protein deficiency in children. Its use on a large scale is still hampered by problems of keeping quality, taste, and acceptability. Its future may well lie primarily in small-scale production and immediate use as a supplement to flavored dishes. In this way preservation is not necessary and the capital costs of the process are much reduced.

The lower plants—fungi, algae, and bacteria—have been little exploited as protein sources for a variety of reasons. The fungi present the difficulties of an indigestible cell wall (of chitin, not cellulose, in nearly all instances) and the frequent occurrence of toxins. The larger marine algae have been used to some extent but are difficult to harvest and generally of low nutritive value. Attention has recently been focused on the single-celled organisms—green unicellular algae, yeasts, and bacteria. All have the characteristic that methods of mass culture are known by which they can be produced in high yield in a short time. The photosynthesizing algae have the apparent advantage of needing only light as an energy source but suffer from the disadvantage of cellulose cell walls. Besides, higher plants may well be just as efficient converters of the sun's radiant energy and are considerably easier to raise in pure culture as weedfree crops and to harvest.

Yeast and Bacteria as Protein Sources (see also Microorganisms; Yeast). With the possible exception of blue-green algae, said to have been eaten by the Aztecs, yeast is the only single-celled organism hitherto used as food by man. (Regarding the possible future use of algae as human food or animal feed see Algal cultures, Vol. 1, p. 660.) The use of yeast grown on cheap carbohydrate sources such as molasses was patented in Britain in 1913. Since that time, particularly during world wars, the possibilities of growing yeasts as protein sources from a variety of waste materials have been explored. Such a process has proved commercially successful only when used for the production of animal feed from a waste otherwise expensive to dispose of.

Wastes from citrus-processing plants, from paper mills, and from timber mills have been used to grow fodder yeast—normally *Torula utilis*. Fodder yeast grown on paper-mill waste sulfite liquors costs about 18¢/lb to produce with no charge made for the sulfite liquor. The corresponding price for soybean meal of about the same protein content is 11¢/lb. Fodder yeast can command a higher price than soy meal owing to its high vitamin content. It has been estimated that yeast grown on oil may cost 14¢/lb or less.

A number of microorganisms will grow on hydrocarbons as an energy source if provided with an inorganic supplement which must include sources of nitrogen, sulfur, and phosphorus, as well as trace elements. Fungi, bacteria, and yeasts have been investigated as means of producing protein from crude oil or its fractions and inorganic nitrogen. *Fungi* are more difficult to grow in mass culture than are bacteria or yeasts, as the mycelial habit of growth makes aeration difficult; moreover, the product obtained with fungi normally contains less protein than that from bacteria or yeasts. *Bacteria* are more versatile than yeasts and can use a greater range of the compounds present in crude oil. Among their disadvantages, however, is the fact that they are more difficult to harvest from the culture medium because of their small size; that maintaining a pure culture is not as easy as for yeasts; and that their greater content of purines and pyrimidines may be a possible drawback in nutrition.

Yeasts grow at a relatively acid pH (so that fewer precautions are necessary to avoid infection with other organisms) and are easy to harvest. They utilize only the straight-chain alkanes, about C_{10}–C_{20}, in crude oil (normally 15–20% of the total). These alkanes are a nuisance to the refiner and have to be removed from fuel fractions; although they find some application as paraffin wax, that market is diminishing. Thus, the use of yeasts to make protein from one of the less desirable fractions of crude oil is attractive.

There are, however, a number of difficulties inherent in such a process. If the oil is not completely utilized by the organisms (as it will never be if crude oil is the energy source) the unused portion contaminates the product and must be completely removed for economic, esthetic, and probably toxicological reasons. Removal costs money and inevitably reduces the nutritional value of the harvested organisms by simultaneously removing fats and other lipids from them. This step can be obviated—or greatly simplified—by using purified fractions of oil as the starting material. One way of avoiding contamination completely is to use methane from natural gas as the the energy source. Two other difficulties arise from the fact that the hydrocarbons used as energy source contain no oxygen whereas the classical energy source, carbohydrate, contains almost one atom of oxygen for every carbon atom. This difference in composition means (a) that much more oxygen is required to grow a given weight of yeasts or bacteria from hydrocarbons than from carbohydrates and (b) that much more heat is evolved in the process. In the commercial production of baker's yeast the need for provision of oxygen is indeed one of the limiting factors, because 100 ml of water will dissolve less than a milligram of oxygen at 20°C, an amount that diminishes further as the temperature is increased. Some 10–20% of the cost of yeast production lies in the provision of energy to compress air for aerating the culture vats, and it has been calculated that production of yeast from oil would require three times as much oxygen as production of the same amount (by wt) from waste carbohydrate. In the process using oil, moreover, twice as much heat would be liberated, and this may result in greater expense for cooling.

Table 9.

Company	Energy source	Organism	Yield of protein
Shell Research Ltd.	methane[a]	bacterium	approx 25% of wt of methane
Esso Research and Engineering Co. in association with Nestlé Alimentana, S.A.	C_{13}–C_{19} alkane fraction	bacterium (*Micrococcus cerificans*)	approx 60% of wt of alkanes
Société Française des Pétroles B.P.	gas oil	yeast (*Candida lipolytica*)	more than 50% of oil used[b]
Mobil Oil Co.	. . . . active but no details published		

[a] Price of methane is 2.2¢/kg.

[b] Two semicommercial plants (France, U.K.) in operation. Unused fraction is dewaxed and consequently saleable as No. 2 feed oil.

In spite of these difficulties it seems that production of protein from oil is perfectly feasible, just as is the production of protein from a number of other sources such as industrial wastes or coal via the Fischer-Tropsch process. A favorable feature of production from oil is that the raw material could be expected to be in constant supply and to have constant properties at a refinery and that the supply of a suitable form of inorganic nitrogen should provide no difficulty. The only new feature is the use of an energy source for the organisms that is different from the sources used hitherto. In order to be economic such a process must be embarked on only after the most thorough survey of possible processes and of the long-term acceptability of the product as a food. Previous attempts to use yeast as human food (as for example by British Colonial Food Yeast Ltd. in Jamaica in 1944) have not been successful both for economic reasons and because the product caused marked digestive unease in human consumers.

Research is actively going on at present (1968) by four major oil companies. What is known of their approach to the problem and results is summarized in Table 9.

Bibliography

"Proteins" in *ECT* 1st ed., Vol. 11, pp. 226–248, by H. B. Vickery, The Connecticut Agricultural Experiment Station.

1. H. Hartley, *Nature* **168,** 244 (1961).
2. G. J. Mulder, *Bull. Sci. Phys. Naturelle Néerlande* **1,** 104 (1838).
3. L. Gmelin, *Handbook of Chemistry*, transl. H. Watts, Vol. 12, Harrison, London, 1871.
4. H. Ritthausen, *Die Eiweisskörper der Getreidearten, Hülsenfrüchte und Ölsamen*, Cohen & Sohn, Berlin, 1872.
5. F. Sanger and H. Tuppy, *Biochem. J.* **49,** 463, 481 (1951).
6. E. J. Cohn, "The Formed and the Fluid Parts of Human Blood: Their Discovery, Characterization, and Separation by Virtue of Their Physical Properties and Chemical Interactions," in J. L. Tullis, ed., *Blood Cells and Plasma Proteins*, Sect. I, Academic Press, Inc., New York, 1953, Chaps. 1–4.
7. Anon., *J. Physiol.* **35,** xvii (1907).
8. Anon., *Am. J. Physiol.* **21,** xxvii (1908).
9. International Union of Biochemistry, *Enzyme Nomenclature*, Elsevier Publishing Co., Amsterdam, Netherlands, 1965.
10. A. M. Altschul, *Proteins: Their Chemistry and Politics*, Chapman and Hall, London, and Basic Books, Inc., New York, 1965.

10a. R. B. Merrifield, *Endeavour* **24**, 3 (1965).

11. H. Muirland and M. F. Perutz, *Nature* **199**, 633 (1963).

12. H. F. Fisher, *Proc. Natl. Acad. (U.S.)* **51**, 1285 (1964); *Biochim. Biophys. Acta* **109**, 554 (1965).

13. L. Pauling, R. B. Corey, and H. R. Branson, *Proc. Natl. Acad. (U.S.)* **37**, 205 (1951).

14. L. Pauling and R. B. Corey, *Proc. Intern. Wool Textile Res. Conf.*, B, 249 (1955).

15. C. B. Anfinsen, *The Molecular Basis of Evolution*, John Wiley & Sons, Inc., New York, 1959.

16. L. K. James and L. G. Augenstein, *Advan. Enzymol.* **28**, 1 (1966).

17. T. Isemura, T. Takagi, Y. Maeda, and K. Ytani, *J. Biochem. (Tokyo)* **53**, 155 (1963).

18. S. Fuchs, F. de Lorenzo, and C. B. Anfinsen, *J. Biol. Chem.* **242**, 398 (1967).

19. F. R. Jevons, *Biochem. J.* **89**, 621 (1963).

20. I. M. Klotz, *Science* **155**, 697–698 (1967).

21. E. M. Crook, *Biochem. J.* **107**, 1P (1968).

22. F. A. Quiocho and F. M. Richards, *Biochemistry* **5**, 4062 (1966).

23. W. E. Hornby, M. Lilly, and E. M. Crook, *Biochem. J.* **98**, 420 (1966).

24. T. M. S. Chang, *Science* **146**, 524 (1964).

25. E. M. Holden and M. V. Tracey, *Biochem. J.* **43**, 147, 151 (1948).

25a. L. C. Craig, "Partition," in P. Alexander and R. J. Block, eds., *A Laboratory Manual of Analytical Methods of Protein Chemistry*, Vol. I, Pergamon Press, London, 1960, pp. 121–160.

25b. P.-A. Albertsson, *Partition of Cell Particles and Macromolecules*, John Wiley & Sons, Inc., New York, 1961.

26. W. C. Rose, *Nutr. Abstr. Rev.* **27**, 631 (1957).

27. W. C. Rose, *Federation Proc.* **8**, 546 (1950).

28. A. A. Albanese, "Protein and Amino Acid Requirements of Man," in A. A. Albanese, ed., *Protein and Amino Acid Requirements of Mammals*, Academic Press, Inc., New York, 1950, pp. 115–147.

29. E. G. Holmes, *World Rev. Nutr. Dietet.* **5**, 237 (1965).

30. H. C. Trowell, in G. Wolstenholme, ed., *Man and His Future*, J. & A. Churchill Ltd., London, 1963, p. 63.

31. *Joint FAO/WHO Expert Group Report on Requirements of Vitamin A, Thiamine, Riboflavine and Niacin, 1965*, Food and Agriculture Organization of the United Nations, Rome, Italy, 1967.

32. J. Brozek, *Science* **134**, 920 (1961).

33. *Protein Requirements: Report of a Joint FAO/WHO Expert Group*, FAO *Nutr. Meet. Rept. Ser. No. 37* (WHO Tech. Rept. Ser. No. 301), Food and Agriculture Organization of the United Nations, Rome, Italy, 1965.

34. T. Moran and J. Pace, *J. Food Technol.* **2**, 17 (1967).

35. E. T. Mertz, in *Proc. High Lysine Corn Conf., Purdue Univ., 1966*, Corn Refiners Assoc., Inc., Washington, D.C., 1966, p. 12.

36. F. R. Senti, in *International Agricultural Development*, No. 31, Intern. Agr. Develop. Serv., U.S. Dept. of Agriculture, Washington, D.C., May 1967, p. 8.

37. E. E. Howe, "World Protein Needs and How They May Be Implemented," *Proc., The Technology of the Food Supply: Management Looks at Current Resources, Oct. 25, 1966*, p. 60 (sponsored by Dairy and Food Industries Supply Association, Washington, D.C., 1967).

38. A. M. Altschul, *Science* **158**, 221–226 (1967).

39. E. E. Howe, G. R. Jansen, and M. L. Anson, *Am. J. Clin. Nutr.* **26**, 1134 (1967).

40. H. A. B. Parpia, "Novel Protein Foods and Their Protein Sources," in D. J. Tilgner and A. Borys, eds., *Proc. Intern. Congr. Food Sci. Technol., 2nd, Warsaw, Poland, 1967*, p. 51.

41. N. W. Pirie, *Science* **152**, 1701 (1966).

General References

Short Articles, Reviews:

Advances in Protein Chemistry, Academic Press, Inc., New York, yearly.

Relevant entries in R. J. Williams and E. M. Lansford, eds., *Encyclopedia of Biochemistry*, Reinhold Publishing Corp., New York, 1967.

A considerable body of information is available in booklet form from FAO/WHO and from the U.S. Dept. of Agriculture on the present and future protein needs of mankind.

Books:

A. A. Albanese, ed., *Protein Amino Acid Nutrition*, Academic Press, Inc., New York, 1959.

P. Alexander and R. J. Block, eds., *A Laboratory Manual of Analytical Methods*, Vols. 1–3 of *Protein Chemistry*, Pergamon Press, London, 1960.

A. M. Altschul, *Processed Plant Protein Foodstuffs*, Academic Press, Inc., New York, 1958.

R. S. Harris and H. von Loesecke, eds., *Nutritional Evaluation of Food Processing*, John Wiley & Sons, Inc., New York, 1960.

M. Joly, *A Physico-chemical Approach to the Denaturation of Proteins*, Academic Press, London, 1965.

H. Neurath, ed., *The Proteins*, Academic Press, London, 1963–1966.

H. A. Scheraga, *Protein Structure*, Academic Press, London, 1961.

C. Tanford, *Physical Chemistry of Macromolecules*, John Wiley & Sons, Inc., New York, 1963.

Michael V. Tracey
CSIRO (Commonwealth Scientific and
Industrial Research Organization)
Division of Food Preservation, Australia

PROTOZOAL INFECTIONS, CHEMOTHERAPY. See Therapeutic agents, protozoal infections.

PRUSSIAN BLUE. See Iron compounds; Pigments, inorganic.

PSYCHOPHARMACOLOGICAL AGENTS

Recent revolutionary advances in the study and treatment of mental disease have produced a nomenclature that is rather complex and unsystematic. The action of drugs used to treat mental illness has been described as psychotherapeutic, phrenotropic, neuroleptic, ataractic, or tranquilizing. It should be noted that the so-called tranquilizing drugs differ from the classical barbiturate depressants in that the tranquilizers can alter certain aspects of behavior or anxiety while producing only minimal incapacitating neurological effects.

Recently there has been a tendency to classify psychopharmacological agents according to the therapeutic expectations of the clinician: Thus, antipsychotic drugs are the agents used to treat psychoses; antineurotic drugs are the agents used to treat neuroses; and antidepressant drugs are the agents used to treat neurotic or psychotic depressions. In addition to these classifications, a number of other designations, such as psycholytic, psychosolytic, etc have been employed.

This discussion is restricted essentially to those psychopharmacological agents which are already on the market; any discussion of experimental agents still under development would be too extensive for this volume. A number of drugs which are not, strictly speaking, psychopharmacological agents are treated in this review. These classes include several psychotomimetic agents, antinauseants, and classical sedatives and stimulants.

History. Two agents—reserpine, an alkaloid of *Rauwolfia* species, and chlorpromazine, a synthetic drug related to the antihistamines—gave impetus to the systematic chemotherapeutic approach to mental disorders. The use of *Rauwolfia* (as the ground root) began in Western medicine in 1953; the use of chlorpromazine dates from 1954. Their discovery stimulated an intensive investigation in this field.

It is interesting that, in the long history of mental disease, enthusiasm has been generated for each treatment that has been proposed; each new remedy aroused a great deal of enthusiasm, which gradually waned until the new therapy settled into its proper place in medicine. For example, electroshock, insulin shock, prefrontal lobotomy, etc, were thought to be the answer when they were first introduced. But the relative undesirability of these treatments can be judged by the fact that in some hospitals today they are virtually no longer employed as routine measures in psychotherapy. Dr. Nathan S. Kline of the Rockland State Hospital, Orangeburg, New York, has pointed out that, as a result of the introduction of chlorpromazine and reserpine and the resulting constructive attitude toward mental disease, mental institutions have been converted from custodial establishments to true therapeutic hospitals (24). The personnel in these institutions also have had their function changed from that of custodian to that of therapist. In modern institutions today there is a marked absence of the restraining devices, cold packs, noise, agitation, and confusion that have always characterized the mental disease wards.

One of the psychopharmacological agents, reserpine, has a very old history. The roots and leaves of at least two *Rauwolfia* species, *Rauwolfia serpentina* Benth and *R. canescens* L., have long been used in Indian medicine as remedies for various ailments. The roots of *R. serpentina* are mentioned in the Charak (1000–800 BC), one of the old books of Hindu medicine, as an antidote for the bites of snakes and the stings of insects. However, this use has not been supported scientifically. The roots have, nevertheless, been employed more recently in the relatively modern medicine of India as a hypnotic and sedative in insomnia and insanity, and for the treatment of hypertension. Between 1931 and 1939, Siddiqui and Siddiqui (42–45) carried out extensive chemical studies on the roots of *R. serpentina* native to Dihar, and these workers isolated weakly and strongly basic groups of alkaloids. Undoubtedly, reserpine is the most important and one of the most pharmacologically active among the *Rauwolfia* alkaloids. It was first isolated by Müller, Schlittler, and Bein (32) in 1952. This isolation and identification was quickly confirmed by a number of other groups in this country and abroad.

It is of interest that L. Rauwolf, for whom the genus *Rauwolfia* was named, was born in Augsburg in the first half of the sixteenth century. He studied medicine and later botany at the then famous University of Montpelier. In order to study certain medicinal plants, he undertook a trip to the Orient in 1573, and in 1582 published a book on medicinal plants. The French botanist Plumier, some one hundred years later, named a new genus of the Apocynaceae in his memory. Hence, the name of this Indian shrub is of German origin. More than a hundred different *Rauwolfia* species have been botanically identified, and reserpine has been isolated from perhaps a dozen of these to date (53).

The hypotensive properties of reserpine were slow to be recognized by Western medicine because of their somewhat delayed onset in man. It was often necessary to administer reserpine for several days or weeks to produce significant effects. However, the lowered blood pressure that is obtained is prolonged in nature, as is the sedative effect. The latter effect was the basis for an investigation of reserpine as a psychotherapeutic agent.

Following limited previous use in France and England, chlorpromazine (first investigated as a hypothermic agent) was introduced in the United States, first as an antiemetic and then as an antipsychotic; its introduction as a psychopharmacological agent occurred at about the same time as that of reserpine.

Chlorpromazine had its origin in the antihistamines. It had been noted that a number of the antihistamines produced sedation as one of their undesirable side effects. A study of structure–activity relationships in the phenothiazine antihistamines showed that the sedative activity could be increased by chemical modification. These efforts led to chlorpromazine. It is therefore of great interest that two drugs, widely divergent both from the standpoint of their origin and history, and from the standpoint of structure, should have been introduced simultaneously to treat the same pathological condition.

As an indication of the revolutionary change that has been produced by the new drugs for mental disease, we can quote some figures from New York's twenty-seven state hospitals. In these institutions admissions had been increasing at a rate of 3000 per year over a period of many years. In 1957, the Department of Mental Hygiene reported a 19% increase in discharges and a net drop in admissions. The reason for this improvement was that mentally disturbed patients were being treated earlier, and more effectively, with chlorpromazine and reserpine. Thus, many illnesses were being arrested or alleviated so that the victims did not require commitment. Under the influence of the tranquilizing drugs, a certain percentage of patients not only become more manageable, and therefore more amenable to classical psychiatric treatment, but actually "recover" without the aid of any other treatments.

At the national level, statistics gathered by the National Institute for Mental Health show that the resident mental patient population dropped from 475,202 in 1965 to 452,000 in 1966, a decline of 4.8% and the largest annual reduction during an 11-yr period in which there was a decline every year. Between 1955 and 1966 the patient population in mental institutions dropped 19% while the national population rose 20%. If the mental hospital population had grown at the pre-1955 rate, there would have been 702,000 patients in hospitals last year instead of 452,000, a decrease that saved more than $1 billion in patient-care cost.

Biochemical Basis of Mental Disease

Mental disease has always been a puzzling, frightening thing, quite different, apparently, from the other ills of mankind which one could attack rationally, in one way or another. However, the possibility that there might be a biochemical basis for mental derangement has raised new hopes for drug therapy on a rational basis. Even the originator of psychotherapy, Sigmund Freud, speculated that a biochemical basis for mental disease would be found one day.

One of the great discoveries in this area was the finding that certain chemical agents could produce temporary model psychoses which greatly resembled certain chronic forms of mental diseases, like schizophrenia. This finding raised two fascinating possibilities.

1. If mental diseases were the result of biochemical lesions in the brain, or elsewhere, drugs might be found which would arrest or even reverse these pathological conditions.

2. The model psychoses produced by hallucinogenic compounds might be used in test procedures for finding new drugs.

A corollary to these considerations is the possibility that the hallucinogenic substances responsible for spontaneous mental diseases are abnormal metabolites of normal body components; this subject has been reviewed by Greenberg et al. (77).

These relationships are supported by the use of chlorpromazine in the treatment of mental disorders, since chlorpromazine antagonizes the effects of LSD. However, it must be admitted that the discovery of their impact on mental diseases was rather empirical, and resulted from the tranquilizing effects (antianxiety, etc) observed when the drugs were used for other purposes. The continued improvement of a certain fraction of patients, even after therapy was discontinued, was an unexpected and welcome discovery, but hardly a rational one. Thus, the probable involvement of chlorpromazine and reserpine in the fundamental biochemistry of the brain was suggested after their clinical usefulness had become fairly well established.

It is not unreasonable to hope that, in addition to the empirical success with chlorpromazine and reserpine, medicinal chemistry may be on the threshold of being able to employ all the above considerations in a rational search for new psychotherapeutic agents. Basic biochemical discoveries have virtually paralleled the relatively nonsystematic discovery of chlorpromazine and reserpine. Now that the direction has been indicated, the rational approach may be the more fruitful. Undoubtedly new agents will be developed which, in their selectivity and freedom from side effects, will overshadow today's drugs. Nonetheless, historically, chlorpromazine and reserpine mark a new era in the chemotherapy of mental diseases, and the former continues to be one of the outstanding agents in the field of psychotherapy. Reserpine is still employed in combination with other drugs as a hypotensive agent, but its use in psychiatry is now small.

Many factors have been considered in the context of mental disease:

1. Gaddum and associates (1,17) first identified serotonin (**1**) in the brain; Woolley and Shaw suggested that mental illness might be the result of a serotonin deficiency (56); and Fabing (14) suggested that bufotenine (**2**) might be found as an abnormal metabolite of serotonin.

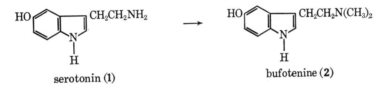

serotonin (**1**)   bufotenine (**2**)

2. Osmond (19,36) postulated that a derangement in the metabolism of epinephrine (**3**) could lead to the formation of the psychotomimetic agents adrenolutin (**4**) and adrenochrome (**5**). However, negative evidence for these proposals has been found.

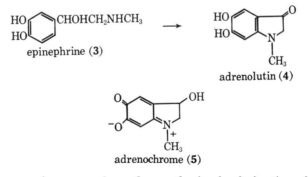

epinephrine (**3**)

adrenolutin (**4**)

adrenochrome (**5**)

3. In the course of some work on the synthesis of a derivative of one of the ergot alkaloids, Hofmann (6,90) noted that he experienced hallucinogenic symptoms. These effects were found to be caused by the inhalation of minute amounts of diethylamide of lysergic acid (LSD) (**6**). Except for the fact that LSD, like bufotenine and adrenolutin,

contains the indole nucleus, the possible relationship of LSD to spontaneous schizophrenic syndromes is obscure. Another compound capable of producing so-called model psychoses is mescaline (**7**), often used in tribal rites. (See also Vol. 4, pp. 877–878.)

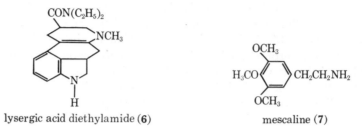

lysergic acid diethylamide (**6**)   mescaline (**7**)

Mescaline could conceivably be cyclized to an indole in vivo, but the possible relationships here are highly tenuous. Virtually none of the existing psychotherapeutic agents could be considered as specific antagonists of any of the above psychotomimetic agents. Hence, the empirical nature of our present efforts is emphasized.

4. Since about 1954, an interesting body of data on reserpine–serotonin relationships, as well as on LSD–serotonin antagonisms, has been accumulated. The exact role of serotonin in mental disease, however, if indeed it does play a role, is still obscure. Brodie and co-workers have found that small doses of reserpine produce a rapid and prolonged drop in brain serotonin. However, inasmuch as measures taken to delay the oxidation of serotonin to 5-hydroxyindoleacetic acid (see Scheme 1) lead to pharmacologically obscure results, and attempts to demonstrate the presence of reserpine in the brain by radioisotope techniques have failed (35,40,41), one is led to believe that the evidence for serotonin's involvement in psychoses and the action of reserpine is inconclusive, if not negative. It is of interest that monoamine oxidase inhibitors, which prolong the biological half-life of serotonin and other aralkylamines, do exacerbate schizophrenia. The biochemistry of serotonin has been studied and its principal pathway is shown in Scheme 1 (8).

Scheme 1

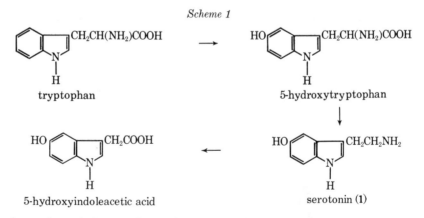

tryptophan   5-hydroxytryptophan

5-hydroxyindoleacetic acid   serotonin (**1**)

5. A number of abnormal protein factors have been postulated to be involved in mental disease. Thus Akerfeldt (72) reported on a factor called ceruloplasmin and stated that it might be involved in the serum of patients with mental disease. However, this could not be confirmed by Frank and Wurtman (73). Heath (74) claimed that a protein factor called taraxein was peculiar to the blood of schizophrenic patients.

This, too, is controversial (75). An α-globulin factor has been postulated by Frohman et al. (76) to be present to a greater degree in schizophrenics than in normals, and many other factors have been reported (77).

6.   Several investigators have isolated 3,4-dimethoxyphenethylamine (DMPEA), a so-called "pink spot," from the urine of schizophrenics (78,79). Reinjected into man, however, DMPEA does not appear to produce psychoses.

7.   Other theories of mental disease involve considering sympathetic nerve endings as "neurochemical transducers" and speculating that interference with adrenergic transmission could cause mental derangements (80).

Cerebral agents like γ-aminobutyric acid, glutamine, glutamic acid, etc, are involved in brain metabolism, and abnormal levels could lead to behavioral anomalies (77).

Mechanism of Action

As mentioned above, the evidence concerning the relationships of serotonin to psychotherapeutic and psychotomimetic agents is controversial. With the confusion that exists at the theoretical level, it is not surprising that there is little knowledge about the clinical aspects of the mechanism of action of psychopharmacological agents. It seems fairly clear that reserpine releases serotonin, norepinephrine, and other substances from the brain, and that the serotonin is metabolized to 5-hydroxyindoleacetic acid and excreted as such in the urine. However, it is not known whether reserpine also acts directly on the brain as well as through an intermediary substance.

Since reserpine acts partly through serotonin depletion, and chlorpromazine may act via norepinephrine (but not through depletion), it is possible that there are interrelationships between serotonin, norepinephrine, and the psychotherapeutic and psychotomimetic agents.

Some recent studies by Tedeschi et al. (116,117) showed that a good correlation exists between the potency of neuroleptics in causing ptosis in rats and their potency as neuroleptics as measured by behavioral techniques. These researchers suggest that the ptosis induced by neuroleptics in rats is centrally mediated and is referable to a somatic component as well as to a component of decreased central sympathetic outflow.

Hallucinogenic Drug Abuse

In recent years there has been extensive use and abuse of hallucinogenic drugs by alienated members of society (84,85). The most dangerous form of abuse probably involves LSD (86), although narcotics, stimulants, and depressants are abused as well. The term psychedelic has been used for psychotomimetic drugs, deriving from the Greek *psyche* (soul) and *delos* (visible or manifest). The major psychotomimetic agents are listed in section J of Table 1 (see p. 663). Bufotenine has been studied much less extensively than LSD. It is a constituent of the seeds of *Piptadenia peregrina* and other species of *Piptadenia*. Early reports on the hallucinogenic properties of these materials, as used by natives in Brazil, did not identify the active principle. Later (94) the active principles were found to be N,N-dimethyltryptamine (82) and bufotenine, and their psychotomimetic effect in man was demonstrated (95).

Harmala alkaloids like harmine and harmaline have not been readily available and their abuse has been minimal (96). They occur in *Peganum harmala, Passiflora incarnata,* and *Banisteriopsis caapi* (97).

The iboga alkaloids of the African shrub *Tabernanthe iboga* have been reported to be hallucinogenic, but their activity is equivocal and they have not become drugs of abuse (98).

Lysergic acid diethylamide (LSD-25) has been reported to be an aid in psychotherapy. However, the extensive abuse of this drug has inhibited research in this country and, especially in view of the recent reports of its chromosome-breaking effects, it is unlikely that LSD will achieve a permanent place in psychotherapy (89). Synthetic work on LSD and related compounds has been reported by Woodward et al. (87).

Peyote, or mescal, derived from the cactus plant *Lophophora williamsii*, has been used by American Indians for the production of hallucinogenic episodes during religious rituals. Mescaline, the active ingredient in peyote, is much less potent, however, than is LSD, and ritual use of the former has been sanctioned by various governments. Its abuse in the United States tends to be a local phenomenon in the Western states. It is of interest that some of the central effects of mescaline are reported to last for several months (88).

The hallucinogenic effects of certain Mexican mushrooms have been known for centuries. In the last ten years the active principle was identified as psilocybin (90), accompanied by psilocin (see Vol. 4, p. 878). These are rather exotic substances and are not sufficiently available or well-known to be widely abused in the United States.

Marihuana (*Cannabis*) is probably the most extensively abused of the hallucinogenic principles. Known to the smoking community as "pot" or "grass" it grows widely in temperate zones and is difficult to eradicate. It, along with opium, is one of the oldest known CNS(central nervous system)-active agents. In Asia the plant goes by a wide variety of local names such as "kif," "dagga," "hashish," "bhang," etc. Although investigation of the active principles of *Cannabis* had been undertaken in the 1930s, the structure of tetrahydrocannabinol was not fully elucidated until 1965 (91–93,99–108) (see Table 1).

Pharmacological Testing Procedures

One of the first procedures employed in the evaluation of tranquilizing agents measured aggressive behavior in monkeys. The tranquilizing action produced by reserpine or chlorpromazine is different from that produced by barbiturates or other hypnotics. The animals given tranquilizers are readily aroused from a sleepy state and are capable of carrying out essential functions such as eating, drinking, escaping from noxious situations, etc. When the classical sedatives or hypnotics are used, the action of the drug either is insufficient to permit easy handling of the animals, or produces sedation so complete that the animals sleep deeply and cannot readily be aroused.

It should be emphasized that medicinal chemical research in the psychopharmacological field is much more complex than in the more classical areas like chemotherapy, primarily because the physiology of behavior is so poorly understood. Often, assay procedures must measure some indirect effect of a tranquilizing drug. The mouse ptosis assay for reserpine is an example. In this procedure the effect of reserpine on sympathetic tone is reflected by a characteristic drooping of the eyelids in mice. By giving a series of graded doses to a large group of mice, it is possible to select the dose at which there is an onset of the ptotic activity and thus to assay the activity of reserpine (38). In addition, certain psychopharmacological agents are evaluated in regard to the protection they may confer against electric shock, or the convulsant shock produced by metrazole. Other procedures utilize the measurements of centrally mediated muscle-relaxant activity, inhibition of apomorphine-induced vomiting, depression of motor activity, etc.

Conditioned response tests, as exemplified by the conditioned avoidance-escape response test, play an important part in the testing of psychopharmacological agents. According to a typical early procedure, a test animal is conditioned to respond to an auditory stimulus which accompanies an unpleasant stimulus such as shock. After he has been duly trained, the animal will respond to the sound alone, without the shock being applied. Drugs are then tested for their ability to block the response to a bell, buzzer, or other stimulus in an animal which has been trained to give an avoidance response in this situation. In essence, this is the basis for all conditioned response blocking experiments. In recent times, however, the tests have been greatly refined so that a large variety of them are available to correlate the effect of drugs on situational anxiety, in addition to the conditioned response itself (9).

Dr. B. F. Skinner of Harvard University has pioneered one aspect of the study of the behavior of experimental animals, and has used this approach to assess alterations in the functioning of the nervous system which are not grossly observable. The first step in this approach is to bring a simple response of an animal under the control of the experimenter. This can be done in one of two ways: either by positive reinforcement (reward) or by negative reinforcement (punishment). A positive reinforcement or reward is defined as an event for which the animal will perform a response; food, water, sexual contact, etc, under appropriate conditions of deprivation, are the more common positive reinforcements employed. A negative reinforcement is defined as an event which will cause an animal to perform a response to avoid or escape the stimulus; electrical shock, noise, excessive light, etc are the more common negative reinforcements used. Once this response is brought under the control of the experimenter, the relationship between the reinforcement schedule and the frequency with which the response is made can be studied. From the work of Skinner and his associates, a large body of experimental evidence has been gathered and general principles have been established. These provide an excellent baseline upon which to assess the effects of pharmacological agents (9).

The apparatus most generally used with this approach is the Skinner box. The animal (rat, pigeon, or monkey) stands on a grid floor suitably wired for the presentation of an electric shock. A lever protrudes from the wall of the box at a height appropriate for the species being studied. For pigeon experiments, a plastic key is mounted in the wall and this can be pecked by the bird. A tray in which the animal is given food or water reinforcement is raised into position by the operation of a lever or key. This entire unit is placed in a soundproof chamber to avoid outside distractions. Observations of the animal's behavior are made through a window in the side of the box. An electronic programmer controls the reinforcement schedule—that is, the relationship between reinforcement and response rate. A cumulative recorder is used to record the number of lever presses per unit time. The number of reinforcements and the onset and duration of cues given to the animal are similarly recorded.

There are two basic types of reinforcement schedules. The first is the interval reinforcement, in which the reinforcement is dependent upon the passage of an interval of time controlled by the experimenter. This time interval may be either variable or fixed and the resulting behavior is significantly different for the two types of intervals.

In the variable-interval schedule, the animal will be rewarded at irregular intervals and therefore cannot anticipate when the reward is to come; hence he works steadily in anticipation of reward and a moderate response rate develops. Since the behavior which appears under this schedule is especially stable, this procedure is useful in studying the effects of other variables. In the fixed-interval schedule, an animal learns not to respond during the early stages of the time period, since these early responses are never reinforced. However, as the payoff time approaches, the response rate increases sharply. Essentially, this technique measures the animal's ability to discriminate time passage. In other words, the animal receives one reward every 30 sec (regardless of how often the lever is pressed), and will respond only just before the 30-sec interval expires.

The second basic type is the ratio reinforcement schedule, in which a definite number of responses must be made by the animal in order to obtain the reinforcement. In other words, he obtains a reward for every five lever presses. This schedule generates a very high response rate. It is also possible to study mixed schedules by training an animal to respond appropriately to a cue indicating that it will be paid off on a particular schedule of reinforcement. By associating different cues with the different schedules of reinforcement described above, it is possible to train an animal to show combinations of different forms of behavior. For example, the animal may be trained to recognize that it will be on a variable-interval reinforcement with a red light, and on a fixed-ratio reinforcement with a green light, and it will respond appropriately to these visual cues.

It is possible to apply the various schedules of reinforcement to a study of the conditioned emotional response situation. For example, it has been shown that a cue (buzzer associated with electric shock) elicits a stereotyped anxiety reaction in trained rats. If a cue is presented while the animal is lever pressing for food reinforcement, the animal typically responds with a complete cessation of lever pressing for the length of time the cue is presented. When the cue is stopped the animal returns to lever pressing for food reinforcement.

It is also possible to use intracranial electrodes for self-stimulation as a positive or negative reinforcement of lever-pressing behavior. In this procedure, electrodes are sealed into separate areas of the brain, and pressing of the lever stimulates these areas, causing an apparently pleasurable or unpleasant sensation to the animal. Rates of response to intracranial stimulation exceed those obtained from food and water reinforcement and are stable during a single session and over a period of months.

Because the testing in animals for antidepressant activity is complex and not well defined, only a brief discussion will be given here. In the case of antidepressants of monoamine oxidase (MAO) inhibitor type (see Table 1, section G) (ie, isocarboxazide, nialamide, phenelzine, and tranylcypromine), testing depends on demonstrating potentiation of other amines. For example, tryptamine, an excellent substrate for MAO, produces tremors when administered to mice. Tedeschi et al. (118) have shown that these tremors are potentiated by MAO inhibitors.

In the case of non-MAO-inhibitor antidepressants, test methods are complex and controversial. The first antidepressant of this type, imipramine (Table 1, section C), was clinically tested because of its structural resemblance to chlorpromazine. Its antidepressant activity was actually discovered in man. In fact, in laboratory animals, imipramine causes slight sedation. On the other hand, when the interaction of imipramine and reserpine is studied, the antidepressant nature of the former is revealed.

For example, imipramine will reverse reserpine-induced ptosis, will prevent reserpine-induced ptosis in animals pretreated with imipramine, will antagonize reserpine-induced hypothermia, etc. Various antidepressant candidates will exhibit one, or the other, or all of the above effects.

Principal Psychopharmacological Agents

In the relatively short space of time that these compounds have been under investigation, a rather large number of psychopharmacological agents have come to be commercially available throughout the world. The plethora of trade names and generic names, as well as chemical names, has led to a good deal of confusion in this area, and an attempt has been made to categorize this subject in Table 1, as follows: A, Phenothiazines; B, Thiaxanthenes; C, Dibenzazepines; D, Dibenzcycloheptanes; E, Benzodiazepines; F, Butyrophenones; G, Antidepressants; H, Stimulants; I, Miscellaneous depressants and antinauseants; and J, Psychotomimetic agents.

Chlorpromazine. In the years since its introduction, chlorpromazine has been used in a wide variety of conditions. A partial listing of the indications for this compound includes nausea and vomiting, mental and emotional disturbances in outpatients, treatment of hospitalized psychiatric patients, alcoholism (18), drug addiction, relief of pain and anxiety in cancer patients, hiccups, obstetrics, pediatrics, surgery, neurodermatitis, etc. The application of chlorpromazine in these areas has been documented quite well. For example, its use in nausea and vomiting depends mainly on the selective depression on the chemoreceptor trigger zone or the vomiting center or both. Because of this specific effect, there is often dramatic control of nausea and vomiting from a wide variety of causes. The use of chlorpromazine in mental and emotional disturbances in every-day practice depends on the tranquilizing or ataractic activity of this drug; this produces a calm detachment without clouding of consciousness or depression of mental faculties (81).

The synthesis of chlorpromazine from *m*-chlorodiphenylamine is shown below (70).

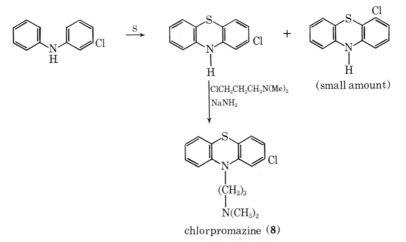

chlorpromazine (**8**)

Reserpine. Although reserpine (**9a**) is commercially the most important *Rauwolfia* alkaloid, two other compounds found in a number of species have almost identical pharmacological activity. These are rescinnamine (**9b**) (26,27) and deserpidine (**10**) (canescine, recanescine, etc) (30,39,46,47).

Table 1. Representative Psychopharmacological Agents of Various Types

A. Phenothiazines

Structure	Chemical name	Nonproprietary name	Proprietary name
(structure: phenothiazine with COCH$_3$; CH$_2$CH$_2$N(CH$_3$)$_2$)	10-(γ-dimethylaminopropyl)-2-acetylphenothiazine	acetylpromazine	Plegicin (Clin-Byla) Soprontin (Knoll)
(structure: phenothiazine with COCH$_2$CH$_3$; CH$_2$CH$_2$CH$_2$N⟨piperazinyl⟩NCH$_2$CH$_2$OH)	2-propionyl-10-[3'[4-(2-hydroxyethyl)-1-piperazinyl]propyl]-phenothiazine	carphenazine	Proketazine (Wyeth)
(structure: phenothiazine with Cl; CH$_2$CH$_2$CH$_2$N(CH$_3$)$_2$)	10-(γ-dimethylaminopropyl)-2-chlorophenothiazine	chlorpromazine, USP, NNR	Thorazine (SK&F) Largactil (Rhône-Poulenc) Megaphen (Bayer)
(structure: phenothiazine; CH$_2$CH$_2$N(C$_2$H$_5$)$_2$)	10-(β-diethylaminoethyl)phenothiazine	diethazine	Diparcol (May & Baker) Casantin (Rhône-Poulenc) Antipar (Farmitalia) Latibon (Bayer)
(structure: phenothiazine with CF$_3$; CH$_2$CH$_2$CH$_2$N⟨piperazinyl⟩NCH$_2$CH$_2$OH)	2-trifluoromethyl-10-[3'-[4-(2-hydroxyethyl)-1-piperazinyl]-propyl]phenothiazine	fluphenazine	Prolixin (Squibb) Trancin (Schering)

Structure	Chemical name	Generic name	Trade names
	2-methoxy-10-(3-dimethylamino-2-methylpropyl)phenothiazine	levomepromazine	Levoprome (Lederle); Nozinan (Rhône-Poulenc); Neuractil (May & Baker); Neurocil (Bayer)
	10-[N-methyl-(β-piperidylmethyl)]-phenothiazine	mepazine, pecazine	Pacatal (Promonta; Warner-Chilcott); Lacumin (Lundbeck)
	10-(1'-methyl-3'-pyrrolidino-methyl)phenothiazine	methdilazine	Tacaryl (Mead Johnson); Dilosyn (British Drug Houses)
	10-(3-dimethylaminopropyl)-2-methoxyphenothiazine	methopromazine	Tentone (Lederle); Mopazine (Specia)
	2-chloro-10[3'-(N'-2-hydroxyethyl-piperazinyl)propyl]phenothiazine	perphenazine	Trilafon (Schering); Decentan (E. Merck)

(continued)

Table 1 (*continued*)

Structure	Chemical name	Nonproprietary name	Proprietary name
	10-[3-(4-carbamoylpiperidino)-propyl]-2-chlorophenothiazine	pipamazine	Mornidine (Searle)
	2-chloro-10-[3′-(N-methylpiper-azinyl)propyl]phenothiazine	prochlorperazine	Nipodal (Bayer) Compazine (SK&F) Stemetil (Rhône-Poulenc)
	10-(γ-dimethylaminopropyl)-phenothiazine	promazine	Sparine (Wyeth) Prazine (Wyeth) Verophen (Bayer)
	10-(2-dimethylaminopropyl)-phenothiazine	promethazine, NF, NNR	Phenergan (Rhône-Poulenc) Atosil (Bayer)
	2-propionyl-10-(2′-dimethylamino-propyl)phenothiazine	propiomazine	Dorevan (Clin-Byla) Largon (Wyeth)
	10-[2-(1-pyrrolidyl)ethyl]pheno-thiazine	pyrathiazine, USP, parathiazine	Pyrrolazote (Upjohn)

Chemical name	Generic name	Trade name (company)
2-ethylmercapto-10-[3'-(4-methyl-1-piperazinyl)propyl]phenothiazine	thiethylperazine	Torecan (Sandoz) Toresten (Sandoz)
2-chloro-10-[3'-[4-(2-acetoxyethyl)-1-piperazinyl]propyl]phenothiazine	thiopropazate	Dartal (Searle)
2-methylmercapto-10[2-(N-methyl-2-piperidyl)ethyl]phenothiazine	thioridazine	Mellaril (Sandoz)
2-trifluoromethyl-10-[3'-(1-methyl-4-piperazinyl)propyl]phenothiazine	trifluoperazine	Stelazine (SK&F) Eskazinyl (SK&F) Jatroneural (Rohm and Haas)
2-trifluoromethyl-10-(3'-dimethylaminopropyl)phenothiazine	triflupromazine	Vesprin (Squibb) Adazine (Upjohn)

(continued)

Table 1 (*continued*)

Structure	Chemical name	Nonproprietary name	Proprietary name
(phenothiazine) $CH_2CH(CH_3)CH_2N(CH_3)_2$	10-(3'-dimethylamino-2'-methyl-propyl)phenothiazine	trimeprazine, alimemazine	Temaril (SK&F) Theralene (Rhône–Poulenc) Repeltin (Bayer) Vallergan (May & Baker)
B. Thiaxanthenes			
(thiaxanthene, Cl) $CHCH_2CH_2N(CH_3)_2$	9-(3-dimethylaminopropylidene)-2-chlorothiaxanthene	chlorprothixene	Taractan (Roche) Truxal (Lundbeck)
(thiaxanthene, Cl) $CHCH_2CH_2N$—(piperazine)—NCH_2CH_2OH	4'[3-(2-chlorothiaxanthenyl)-propyl]piperazine-1-ethanol	clopenthixol	Ciatyl (Troponwerke) Sordinol (Lundbeck)
C. Dibenzazepines			
(dibenzazepine) $CH_2CH_2CH_2NHCH_3$	5-(3-methylaminopropyl)-10,11-dihydro-5H-dibenz[b,f]azepine	desipramine	Norpramin (Lakeside) Pertofrane (Geigy)
(dibenzazepine) $CH_2CH_2CH_2N(CH_3)_2$	5-(3-dimethylaminopropyl)-10,11-dihydro-5H-dibenzo[b,f]azepine	imipramine	Tofranil (Geigy)

Structure	Name	Common name	Trade name (Company)
	4-[3-(5H-dibenz[b,f]azepin-5-yl)propyl]piperazine-1-ethanol	opipramol	Insidon (Geigy) Ensidon (Geigy)

D. Dibenzcycloheptanes

Structure	Name	Common name	Trade name (Company)
	5-(3-dimethylamino-2-methyl-propyl)-10,11-dihydro-5H-dibenz[b,f]azepine	trimeprimine, trimipramine	Surmontil (Specia) Stangil (Specia)
	5-(3-dimethylaminopropylidene)-10,11-dihydro-5H-dibenzo[a,d]-cycloheptadiene	amitriptyline	Elavil (Merck) Laroxyl (Roche) Saroten (Lundbeck)
	5-(3-methylaminopropylidene)-10,11-dihydro-5H-dibenzo[a,d]-cycloheptadiene	nortriptylene	Aventyl (Lilly) Nortrilen (Lundbeck)

E. Benzodiazepines (antineurotic sedatives)

Structure	Name	Common name	Trade name (Company)
	7-chloro-2-methylamino-5-phenyl-3H-1,4-benzodiazepine-4-oxide	chlordiazepoxide	Librium (Roche)

(continued)

Table 1 (*continued*)

Structure	Chemical name	Nonproprietary name	Proprietary name
	7-chloro-1,3-dihydro-1-methyl-5-phenyl-2*H*-1,4-benzodiazepine-2-one	diazepam	Valium (Roche)
	7-nitro-1,3-dihydro-5-phenyl-2*H*-1,4-benzodiazepine-2-one	nitrazepam	Mogadon (Roche)
	7-chloro-3-hydroxy-5-phenyl-2*H*-1,4-benzodiazepine-2-one	oxazepam	Serax (Wyeth) Adumbran (Thomae)
	F. Butyrophenones (*antipsychotics*) 1-(*p*-fluorophenyl)-4-(4-phenyl-4-acetamidomethylpiperidino-1-butanone	aceperone	Acetabutone (Janssen)

Structure	Chemical name	Common name	Trade name (manufacturer)
	1-[1-[3-(p-fluorobenzoyl)propyl]-4-piperidyl]-2-benzimidazolinone	benzperidol	Frenactyl (Clin-Comar)
	1-[1-[3-(p-fluorobenzoyl)propyl]-1,2,3,6-tetrahydro-4-pyridyl]-2-benzimidazolinone	droperidol	Leptofen (Janssen) Inapsin (McNeil)
	1-[3-(p-fluorobenzoyl)propyl]-[1,4'-bipiperidine]-4'-carboxamide	floropipamide, pipamperone	Dipiperon (Janssen) Propitan
	4'-fluoro-4-[4-(o-methoxyphenyl)-1-piperazinyl]butyrophenone	fluanisone, haloanisone	Haloanisone (Janssen) Sedalande (Delalande)
	4-[4-(p-chlorophenyl)-4-hydroxy-piperidino]-4'-fluorobutyro-phenone	haloperidol	Haloperidol (Janssen) Haldol (Leo) Serenace (Searle)

(continued)

Table 1 (*continued*)

Structure	Chemical name	Nonproprietary name	Proprietary name
	p-fluoro-4-(4'-hydroxy-4'-*p*-tolyl-piperidino)butyrophenone	methylperidol, moperone	Luvatrene (Cilag)
	8-[3-(*p*-fluorobenzoyl)propyl]-1-phenyl-1,3,8-triazaspiro[4,5]-decan-4-one	spiperone	Spiroperidol (Janssen)
	4'-fluoro-4-[4-hydroxy-4-(α,α,α-trifluoro-*m*-tolyl)piperidino]-butyrophenone	trifluperidol, flumoperone	Triperidol (Janssen) Psicoperidol (Luso)
	G. Antidepressants		
	1-benzyl-2-(5-methyl-3-isoxazolyl-carbonyl)hydrazine	isocarboxazide	Marplan (Roche)

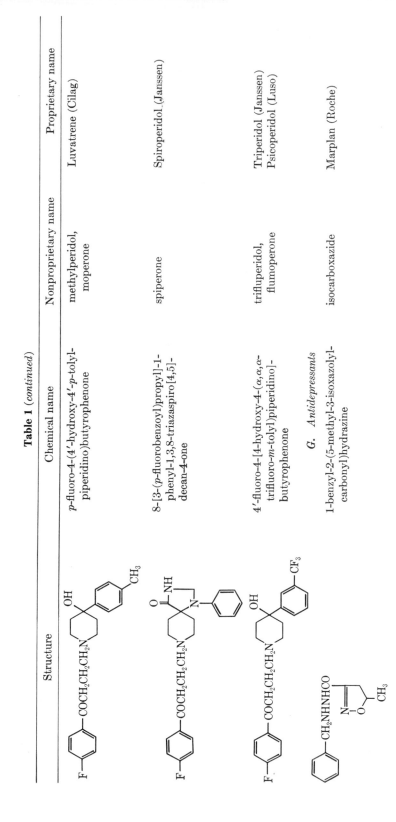

Structure	Name	Chemical name	Trade name (Manufacturer)
phenyl–CH₂NHCOCH₂CH₂NHNH–CO–pyridine	nialamide	isonicotinic acid 2-[2-(benzyl-carbamoyl)ethyl]hydrazide	Niamid (Pfizer)
phenyl–CH₂CH₂NH₂NH₂	phenelzine	phenethylhydrazine	Nardil (Warner-Chilcott), Stinerval (Wander)
phenyl–cyclopropyl–NH₂	tranylcypromine	2-phenylcyclopropylamine	Parnate (SK&F), Jatrosom (Rohm and Haas)

H. Stimulants

Structure	Name	Chemical name	Trade name (Manufacturer)
phenyl–CH₂CH(CH₃)NH₂	d-amphetamine, USP, NNR	d-α-methylphenethylamine	Dexedrine (SK&F), Benzedrine (SK&F)
cyclopentane–CH₂CHCH₃ / NHCH₃	cyclopentamine	N,α-dimethylcyclopentaneethyl-amine	Clopane (Lilly)
phenyl–CH₂CH(CH₃)NHCH₃	methamphetamine, desoxyephedrine	N,α-dimethylphenethylamine	Desoxyn (Abbott), Drinalfa (Squibb), Amphedroxyn (Lilly)

(continued)

Table 1 (*continued*)

Structure	Chemical name	Nonproprietary name	Proprietary name
	α-phenyl-2-piperidineacetic acid methyl ester	methylphenidate	Ritalin (Ciba)
	6,7,8,9-tetrahydro-5*H*-tetrazolo-azepine	pentylenetetrazole	Metrazol (Novocol) Cardiazol (Knoll)
	α,α-diphenyl-2-piperidinemethanol	pipradrol, NNR	Meratran (Merrell) Leptidrol (Kabi)
$CH_3CH_2CH_2CH_2CH_2CH(NH_2)CH_3$	1-methylhexylamine	tuaminoheptane	Tuamine (Lilly)

I. Miscellaneous depressants and antinauseants

Structure	Chemical name	Nonproprietary name	Proprietary name
	α,α-diphenyl-4-piperidinemethanol	azacyclonol	Frenquel (Merrell)
	benzylic acid β-diethylaminoethyl ester	benactyzine	Suavitil (Glaxo) Parason (Medix) Cevanol (ICI)

Structure	Chemical name	Generic name	Trade name (Company)
	α-5-norbornen-2-yl-α-phenyl-1-piperidinepropanol	biperiden	Akineton (Knoll)
	2-[p-(butylthio)-α-phenylbenzyl-thio]-N,N-dimethylethylamine	captodiamine	Covatin (Lundbeck) Suvren (Ayerst)
	1-diphenylmethyl-4-methyl-piperazine	cyclizine, NNR	Marezine (Burroughs-Wellcome)
	2-(benzhydryloxy)N,N-dimethyl-ethylamine 8-chlorotheophyll-inate	dimenhydrinate, USP, NNR	Dramamine (Searle)
	2,2-diisopropyl-1,3-dioxolane-4-methanol	dimethylyn, promoxolan	Dimethylane (National Drug)

(continued)

Table 1 (*continued*)

Structure	Chemical name	Nonproprietary name	Proprietary name
(α,α-diphenyl-1-piperidine butanol structure) $CHCH_2CH_2CH_2N$ / OH, two phenyl rings and piperidine	α,α-diphenyl-1-piperidine butanol	diphenidol	Vontrol (SK&F)
CH_3 / $CH_3CH_2CCH_2CH_3$ / $OCONH_2$	1-ethyl-1-methylpropyl carbamate	emylcamate	Nuncital (Kabi) Striatran (Merck)
(piperazine structure) NCH_2CH_2O—CH_2CH_2OH, CHN, phenyl, p-chlorophenyl, Cl	1-(p-chloro-α-phenylbenzyl)-4-(2-hydroxyethoxyethyl)piperazine	hydroxyzine, NNR	Atarax (Pfizer; Union Chimique Belge) Vistaril (Pfizer) Paxistil (Pfizer)
(piperazine structure) NCH_2—(m-methylphenyl, CH_3), CHN, phenyl, p-chlorophenyl, Cl	1-(p-chloro-α-phenylbenzyl)-4-(m-methylbenzyl)piperazine	meclizine, USP, NNR	Bonamine (Pfizer) Navicalm (Squibb) Ancolan (British Drug Houses)
H_3C, $CH_3CH_2CH_2$ — C — CH_2OCONH_2 / CH_2OCONH_2	carbamic acid 2-methyl-2-propyl-trimethylene ester	meprobamate	Miltown (Carter Products) Equanil (Wyeth-American Home Products) Oasil (Simes (Milan))

Structure	Chemical name	Name	Trade name
	2-methyl-3-o-tolyl-4(3H)-quinazolinone	methaqualone	Tuazole (Strasenburgh) Revonal (E. Merck)
	5,6-dimethoxy-2-methyl-3-[2-(4-phenyl-1-piperazinyl)ethyl]-indole	oxypertine	Equipertine (Winthrop)
	2-(p-chlorophenyl)-3-methyl-2,3-butanediol	phenaglycodol	Ultran (Lilly) (3) Sinforil (Roussel) Acalamid (Lilly)

J. Psychotomimetic agents

Structure	Chemical name	Name	Trade name
	3-(2-dimethylaminoethyl)indol-5-ol	bufotenine (82)	
	4,9-dihydro-7-methoxy-1-methyl-3H-pyrido[3,4-b]indole	harmaline (83)	

(continued)

Table 1 (*continued*)

Structure	Chemical name	Nonproprietary name	Proprietary name
	7-methoxy-1-methyl-9*H*-pyrido-[3,4-*b*]indole	harmine (84)	
		ibogaine (85)	
	ysergic acid diethylamide	lysergide (86,87), LSD	Delysid (Sandoz)
	3,4,5-trimethoxyphenethylamine	mescaline (88)	
	3-(2-aminopropyl)indole	α-methyltryptamine (89)	

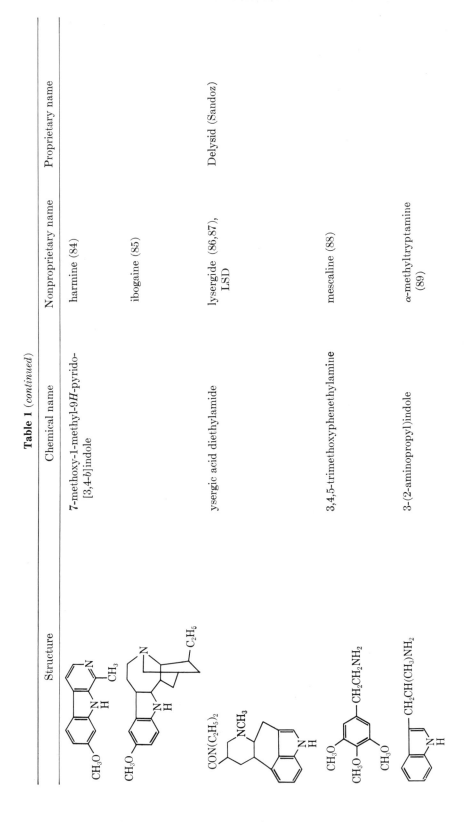

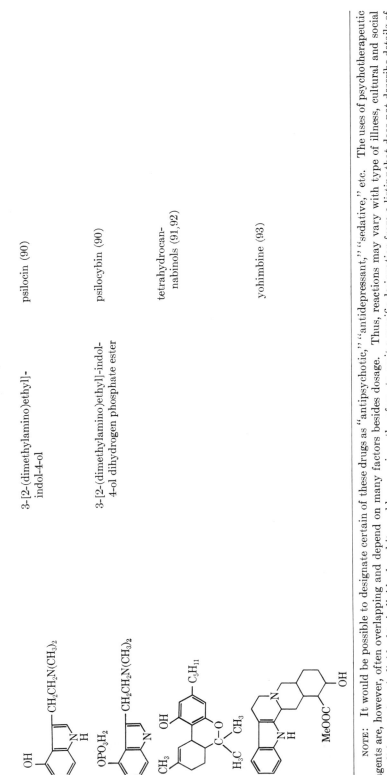
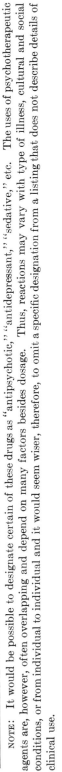

3-[2-(dimethylamino)ethyl]-indol-4-ol   psilocin (90)

3-[2-(dimethylamino)ethyl]-indol-4-ol dihydrogen phosphate ester   psilocybin (90)

tetrahydrocan-nabinols (91,92)

yohimbine (93)

NOTE: It would be possible to designate certain of these drugs as "antipsychotic," "antidepressant," "sedative," etc. The uses of psychotherapeutic agents are, however, often overlapping and depend on many factors besides dosage. Thus, reactions may vary with type of illness, cultural and social conditions, or from individual to individual and it would seem wiser, therefore, to omit a specific designation from a listing that does not describe details of clinical use.

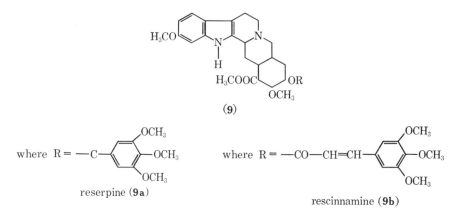

(9)

where R = —C— (reserpine (9a))

where R = —CO—CH=CH— (rescinnamine (9b))

It is interesting that two isomeric alkaloids, raunescine (**11**) and isoraunescine (**12**) (20) have been isolated from *Rauwolfia canescens* L.; raunescine apparently differs in structure from deserpidine (**10**) only in having a hydroxyl in place of a methoxyl group at C-17.

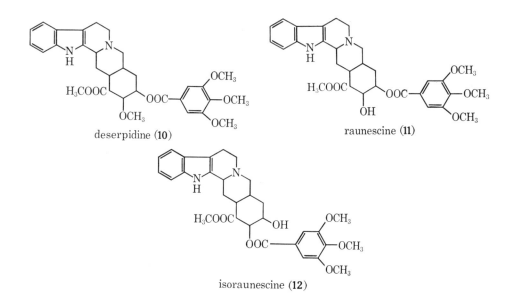

deserpidine (**10**)

raunescine (**11**)

isoraunescine (**12**)

Work on the elucidation of the structures of reserpine has been reviewed (11, 21,28,31,34,49) and will not be considered here. The total synthesis of reserpine (according to Scheme 2) was published by Woodward and co-workers (54).

The 1-isomer of isoreserpine (**18**) was isolated as the di-*p*-toluyl-1-tartaric acid salt (sparingly soluble). The *O*-acetyl ester was hydrolyzed by potassium hydroxide in methanol followed by hydrochloric acid to give the isoreserpic acid; this gives the isoreserpic acid lactone with *N,N'*-dicyclohexylcarbodiimide in pyridine. This lactone is isomerized by pivalic acid in boiling xylene to reserpic acid lactone. The methanolysis of reserpic acid lactone to methyl reserpate and the coupling with trimethoxybenzoyl chloride in pyridine is routine.

In a later report Woodward et al. (55) stated that (**20**), which contains all five asymmetric carbon atoms of ring E properly oriented, is prepared from the *p*-benzoquinone methylvinyl acrylate adduct in two simple operations.

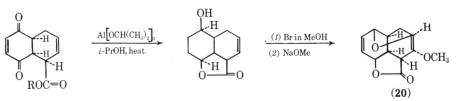

(**20**)

Reserpine has been used for the treatment of anxiety, tension states, insomnia, asthma, dermatological disorders, headache, and infant hyperactivity. The principal use of reserpine is in the treatment of hypertension. Among the side effects observed are lethargy, nasal congestion, flushing, and, in some cases, nausea, vomiting, and serious depressions.

OTHER PHENOTHIAZINES

Prochlorperazine. Alkylation of 2-chlorophenothiazine with *N*-methyl-*N'*-piperazino-3-chloropropane gives prochlorperazine (**21**).

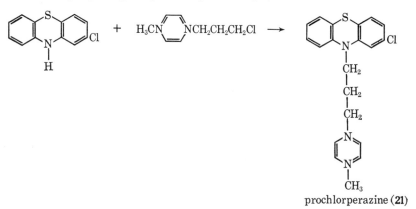

prochlorperazine (**21**)

The side chain can be prepared as follows:

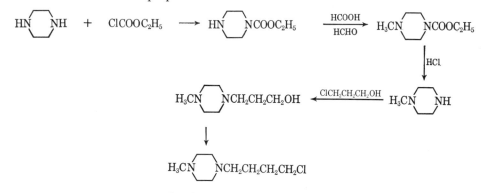

Prochlorperazine is a psychopharmacological agent which is also widely used as an antiemetic. In common with other phenothiazines it has been shown to be of value in mild neurotic disturbances as well as in mild to severe psychotic disturbances.

Scheme 2

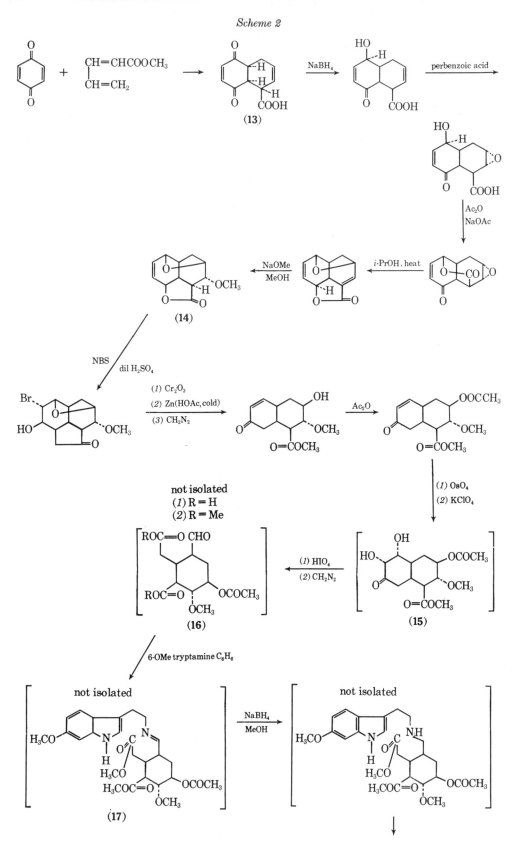

Scheme 2 (continued)

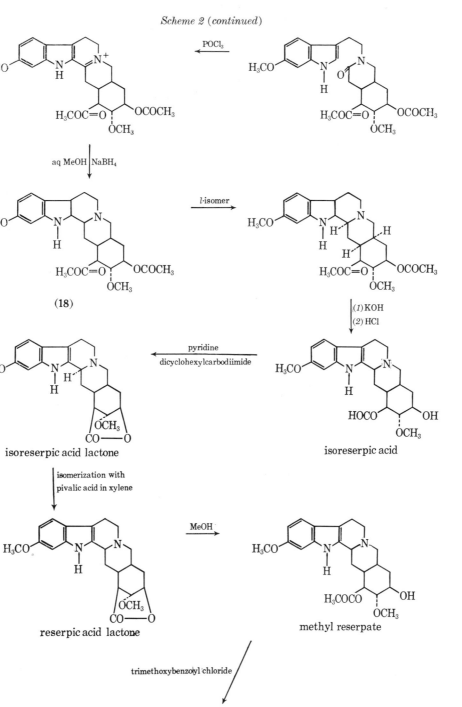

(18)

isoreserpic acid lactone

isoreserpic acid

reserpic acid lactone

methyl reserpate

reserpine (19)

Promethazine. Alkylation of phenothiazine with 1-chloro-2-dimethylamino-propane in the presence of sodamide in xylene gives promethazine (**22**) (66).

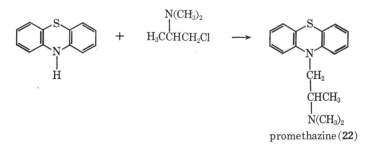

promethazine (**22**)

The product distills at 190–192°C at 3 mm Hg. The hydrochloride salt melts at 203–204°C. The picrate has mp 164°C and the methyl benzenesulfonate melts at 275°C. Promethazine is primarily an antihistamine compound. Its application in the psychotherapeutic area is primarily an exploitation of its prominent sedative effects.

Promazine. Treatment of phenothiazine with 3-dimethylamino-1-chloropropane and sodamide in xylene gives promazine (**23**) (65).

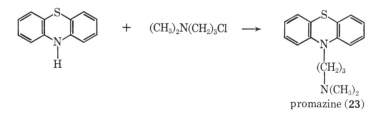

promazine (**23**)

The free base boils at 208–210°C at 3 mm Hg and the hydrochloride melts at 181°C. Promazine has been used for the management of the withdrawal syndrome of drug addiction and acute alcoholism, tremulousness, and the management of disturbed psychotics.

Mepazine. The alkylation of phenothiazine with 1-methyl-3-bromomethyl-piperidine and sodamide in xylene gives mepazine (**24**), bp 230–235°C at 4 mm Hg, mp of hydrochloride 180–181°C (19, 61).

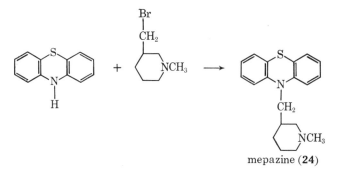

mepazine (**24**)

Mepazine is promoted in Germany for potentiation of narcosis, premedication in surgery, controlling hypothermia, and shock prophylaxis and therapy. Kline (25) tested mepazine in psychiatric patients and found little therapeutic effectiveness, but a number of side effects, including hyperthermia, postural difficulty, and marked anticholinergic activity.

More recent reports have indicated that some of the side effects observed in the earlier therapy were due to impurities in the mepazine. Bowes (5) has reported good results with mepazine in preliminary experiments with 250 patients. It is of interest that Bowes reports that chlorpromazine and mepazine act synergistically and antagonize each other's side effects.

Pyrathiazine. A solution of phenothiazine in dry toluene in which sodamide has been suspended is alkylated with 2-pyrrolidylethyl chloride to give pyrathiazine (**25**). The hydrochloride of the product has mp 200–201°C (37).

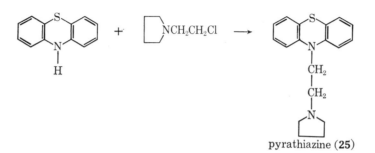

pyrathiazine (**25**)

This compound is primarily antihistaminic in its activity, but it has been used to some extent as a tranquilizing drug.

Diethazine. Alkylation of phenothiazine is accomplished by first forming the Grignard adduct with methyl magnesium iodide; this is reacted with β-diethyl-aminoethyl chloride in benzene to give diethazine (**26**). The product boils at 165–167°C at 0.05 mm Hg. The hydrochloride has mp 184–186°C (68). Obviously the more conventional alkylation with sodamide could also be used.

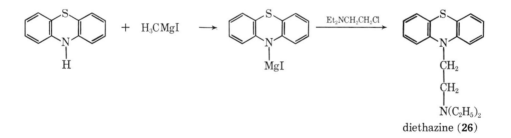

diethazine (**26**)

This compound is reported to have both parasympatholytic and sympatholytic activity. It may have applicability in the treatment of parkinsonism (10).

BENZODIAZEPINES

This is an important group of sedative, muscle-relaxant, and anticonvulsant substances (see also Hypnotics, sedatives, anticonvulsants), members of which have found wide use in the treatment of anxiety, alcoholism, and a variety of other disorders (109).

Synthesis. The synthesis of the first member of this series, *chlordiazepoxide* (**27**), is shown below (110).

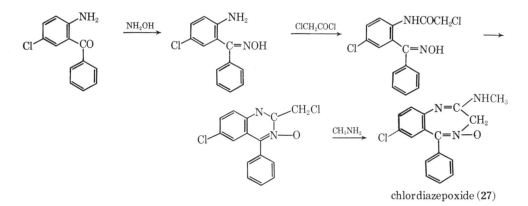

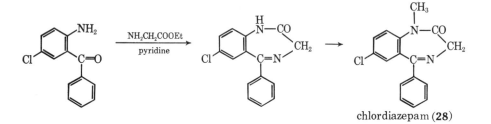

chlordiazepoxide (27)

The rearrangement of the quinazoline to the benzodiazepine is an unusual and interesting reaction. One of the methods of synthesizing *chlordiazepam* (**28**) uses the same starting material as does the chlordiazepoxide synthesis (111).

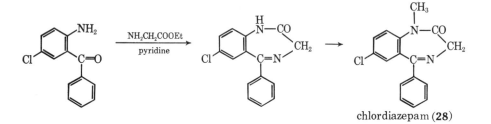

chlordiazepam (**28**)

Chlordiazepoxide (**27**). The most prominent effects of chlordiazepoxide seen in animals are its ability to antagonize convulsions produced by pentylenetetrazole (112) and to block the footshock-induced fighting behavior of mice (113). Hypnotic effects were not seen with chlordiazepoxide except at very high doses. This compound caused a decrease in spontaneous motor activity and, at higher doses, a muscle relaxation. Chlordiazepoxide showed no consistent activity in conditioned avoidance situations where chlorpromazine was active. A major difference also is its amelioration of passive avoidance behavior and the relative absence of locomotor depressant effects.

The activity of chlordiazepoxide in man parallels that in animals inasmuch as this compound shows antianxiety and anticonvulsant effects, but little or no antipsychotic properties. Structure-activity reviews have been published by Sternbach et al. (109,114) and by Childress (115).

CENTRAL–NERVOUS–SYSTEM STIMULANTS

d-**Amphetamine** (**29**). A synthesis of amphetamine from phenylacetic acid is shown below. The optical isomers are resolved by standard methods (63,64).

Amphetamine is a centrally acting stimulant which is widely used in the treatment of chronic fatigue, depressed states, hyperactivity in children, and obesity. It has weak peripheral activity and a large margin of safety. A variety of other drugs having related structures and properties are also on the market.

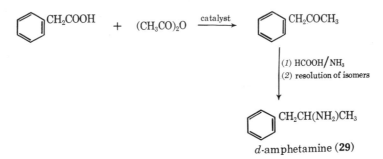

d-amphetamine (**29**)

Methyl Phenidylacetate. The reaction of benzyl cyanide with 2-chloropyridine in toluene in the presence of sodamide gives α-phenyl-2-pyridylacetonitrile. The latter compound is hydrolyzed to the amide and then esterified. Hydrogenation with platinum catalyst gives methyl phenidylacetate (**30**), bp 135–137°C at 0.6 mm Hg; hydrochloride salt, mp 208°C (62).

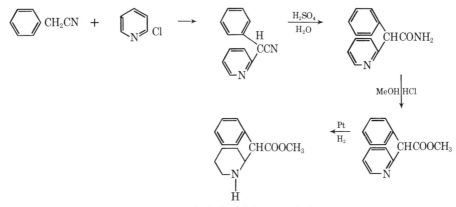

methyl phenidylacetate (**30**)

This drug has been employed as a stimulant for the treatment of chronic fatigue and depressed states.

Azacyclonol. Reaction of phenylmagnesium bromide with phenyl γ-pyridyl ketone in ether (15,48) gives the aromatic analog of the desired product, mp 235°C; chloroplatinate, mp 203°C; picrate, mp 101–103°C. Catalytic reduction yields azacyclonol (**31**).

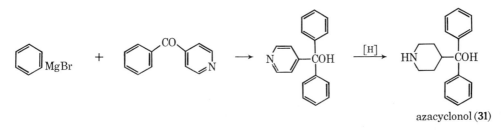

azacyclonol (**31**)

This drug has been reported to be useful in the treatment of hallucinations, postoperative confusion, alcoholic psychoses, and certain senile delusions.

Pipradrol. The reaction of phenyl α-pyridyl ketone with phenylmagnesium bromide gives α-diphenyl-2-pyridylmethanol, mp 104°C; picrate, mp 173°C. Reduction with Adams platinum catalyst gives pipradrol (**32**), mp 308–309°C with decomposition (12,13,15,48,69).

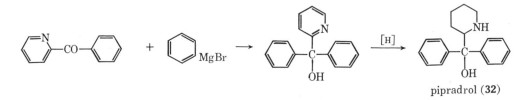

pipradrol (**32**)

Pipradrol has been used against functional fatigue, and menopausal, alcoholic, postoperative, and postpartum depression.

ANTIHISTAMINES USED AS ANTIEMETICS

Cyclizine. The reaction of benzhydryl chloride with *N*-methylpiperazine in benzene gives cyclizine (**33**). It is isolated as the dihydrochloride, mp 250°C with decomposition (60).

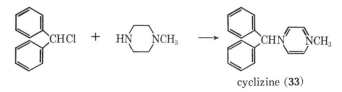

cyclizine (**33**)

This compound is being used for the prophylaxis and relief of nausea and vomiting resulting from motion sickness, pregnancy, vertigo, radiation sickness, or the postoperative period.

Meclizine (34). This synthesis does not seem to have been published, but there are indications that it is carried out as shown below.

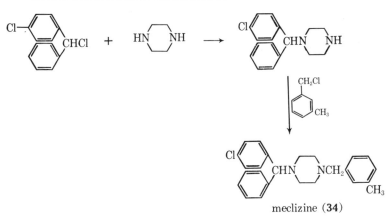

meclizine (**34**)

Meclizine is used as a motion-sickness preventive by virtue of its relatively long-acting antinausea activity.

Dimenhydrinate (35) (58,67). Finely cut sodium metal is added to a solution of β-dimethylaminoethanol in dry xylene, and this is reacted with benzhydryl bromide in xylene to give β-dimethylaminoethyl benzhydryl ether, mp 138–140°C; hydrochloride salt, mp 166–168°C. To convert it to the chlorotheophyllinate, the benzhydryl ether is dissolved in hot alcohol with 8-chlorotheophylline and the sodium bromide salt crystallizes out, mp 103–104°C.

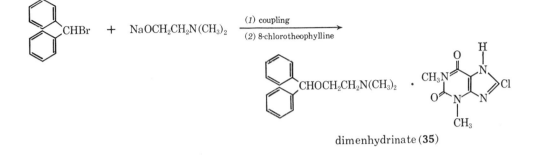

dimenhydrinate (**35**)

Dimenhydrinate has been used for control of the nausea and vomiting of motion sickness, pregnancy, drug therapy, electroshock, or the postoperative period. It has also been employed for the treatment of vertigo resulting from radiation sickness, hypertension, and migraine.

MISCELLANEOUS PRODUCTS

Captodiamine (or Covatin) (50,51). The synthesis of captodiamine (**36**) which is given below is described in Brit. Pat. 729,619 (59).

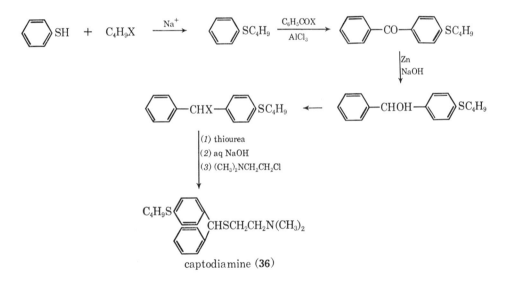

captodiamine (**36**)

Captodiamine is reported to have sedative and spasmolytic properties in animals. Clinically it is reported to be an excellent nonhypnotic sedative. In some patients it produces nausea and restlessness (31).

Hydroxyzine. There does not appear to be a published synthesis for this compound, but there are indications that hydroxyzine (**37**) is made with the same intermediates as is meclizine.

Hydroxyzine has been promoted for the nonhypnotic sedation of psychoneurotic individuals and for the treatment of tension, anxiety, isomnia, senile excitation, etc.

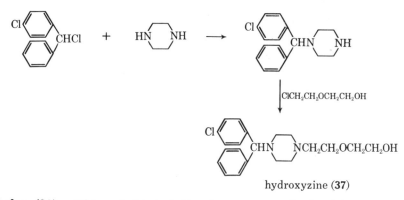

hydroxyzine (37)

Dimethylyn (38). This substituted dioxolane was synthesized by Boekelheide et al. (4) from diisopropyl ketone and glycerol in the presence of an acid catalyst in a hydrocarbon solvent and with continuous removal of the water formed.

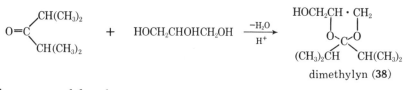

dimethylyn (38)

This compound has been recommended for the treatment of nervous tension, muscle spasm, and generally agitated states.

Benzactyzine (39). This compound was first synthesized in 1943 by Burtner and Cusic (7) from benzilic acid, mp 177–178°C.

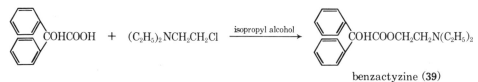

benzactyzine (39)

Benzactyzine has been recommended for the treatment of situational anxiety and other agitated states (22,23,52).

Meprobamate. Meprobamate diol has been synthesized by the following two procedures (16,29,57,71):

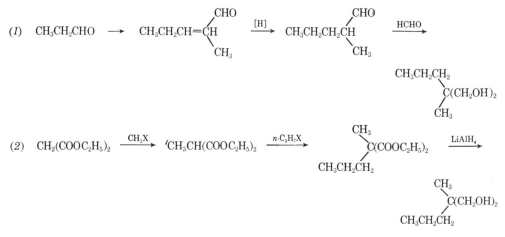

The diol is converted to the dicarbamate (**40**) as follows:

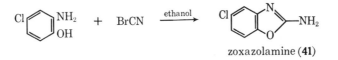

$$CH_3CH_2CH_2\text{-}C(CH_2OH)_2 + 2\ COCl_2 \rightarrow CH_3CH_2CH_2\text{-}C(CH_2OCOCl)_2 \xrightarrow{NH_3} CH_3CH_2CH_2\text{-}C(CH_2OCONH_2)_2$$

meprobamate (**40**)

Meprobamate is primarily an antineurotic agent. It has been employed in all types of tension and anxiety states and in the treatment of muscle spasm, to control certain forms of petit mal, and to relax spasticity in cerebral palsy (3).

Zoxazolamine. The reaction of cyanogen bromide with 2-amino-4-chlorophenol has been used to prepare 2-amino-5-chlorobenzoxazole (**41**) (32).

zoxazolamine (**41**)

Combinations of zoxazolamine and chlorpromazine have been reported to exhibit muscle-relaxant activity (2). However, zoxazolamine has been withdrawn from the market.

Bibliography

"Psychopharmacological Agents" in *ECT* 1st ed., Suppl. 1, pp. 720–743, by Maxwell Gordon and G. E. Ullyot, Smith, Kline & French Laboratories; "Stimulants and Depressants of the Nervous System" in *ECT* 1st ed., Vol. 13, pp. 1–45, by Mark Nickerson and E. F. Domino, University of Michigan.

1. A. H. Amin, T. B. B. Crawford, and J. H. Gaddum, *Abstr. Commun. XIX Intern. Physiol. Congr., Montreal, 1953*, p. 165.
2. W. Amols, *J. Am. Med. Assoc.* **160**, 742 (1956).
3. F. M. Berger, *J. Pharmacol. Exptl. Therap.* **104**, 229 (1952).
4. V. Boekelheide et al., *J. Am. Chem. Soc.*, **71**, 3303 (1949).
5. H. A. Bowes, *Am. J. Psychiat.* **113**, 530 (1956).
6. B. B. Brodie, A. Pletscher, and P. A. Shore, *J. Pharmacol. Exptl. Therap.* **116**, 9 (1956).
7. R. R. Burtner and J. W. Cusic, *J. Am. Chem. Soc.* **65**, 262 (Feb. 1943).
8. C. T. Clark, H. Weissbach, and S. Udenfriend, *J. Biol. Chem.* **210**, 139 (1954).
9. L. Cook and E. Weidley, "Behavioral Effects of Some Psychopharmacological Agents," in "The Pharmacology of Psychotomimetic and Psychotherapeutic Drugs," *Ann. N.Y. Acad. Sci.* **66**, 740 (1957).
10. F. W. J. DeMaar, *Arch. Intern. Pharmacodyn.* **105**, 349 (1956).
11. L. Dorfman et al., *Experientia* **9**, 368 (1953).
12. B. Emmert and E. Asendorf, *Ber.* **B72**, 1188 (1939).
13. B. Emmert and E. Pirot, *Ber.* **B74**, 714 (1941).
14. H. D. Fabing, *Neurology* **5**, 603 (1955).
15. H. D. Fabing et al., *Diseases Nervous System* **16**, 10 (1955).
16. A. Franke, *Monatsh. Chem.* **34**, 1893 (1913).
17. J. H. Gaddum and K. A. Hameed, *Brit. J. Pharmacol.* **9**, 240 (1954).
18. H. E. Himwich, ed., *Alcoholism: Basic Aspects and Treatment*, Am. Assoc. Advan. Sci. (AAAS), Washington, D.C., 1957; *Tranquilizing Drugs*, AAAS, Washington, D.C., 1957.
19. A. Hoffer, H. Osmond, and J. Smithies, *J. Mental Sci.* **100**, 29 (1954).
20. N. Hosansky and E. Smith, *J. Am. Pharm. Assoc., Sci. Ed.* **44**, 639 (1955).
21. C. F. Huebner and E. Wenkert, *J. Am. Chem. Soc.* **77**, 4180 (1955).
22. E. Jacobsen et al., *Acta Psychiat. Neurol. Scand.* **30**, 627 (1955).

23. E. Jacobsen and E. Sonne, *Acta Pharmacol. Toxicol.* **11,** 135 (1955).
24. N. S. Kline, ed., *Psychopharmacology*, AAAS, Washington, D.C., 1956.
25. N. S. Kline et al., *Am. J. Psychiat.* **112,** 63 (1955).
26. M. W. Klohs, M. D. Draper, and F. Keller, *J. Am. Chem. Soc.* **76,** 2843 (1954).
27. *Ibid.*, **77,** 2241 (1955).
28. M. W. Klohs et al., *J. Am. Chem. Soc.* **75,** 4867 (1953).
29. B. J. Ludwig and E. C. Piech, *J. Am. Chem. Soc.* **73,** 5779 (1951).
30. H. B. MacPhillamy et al., *J. Am. Chem. Soc.* **77,** 1071 (1955).
31. *Ibid.*, 4335 (1955).
32. J. M. Müller, E. Schlittler, and H. J. Bein, *Experientia* **8,** 338 (1952).
33. T. Nagano, M. Itow, and K. Matsumura, *J. Am. Chem. Soc.* **75,** 2770 (1953).
34. N. Neuss, H. E. Boaz, and J. W. Forbes, *J. Am. Chem. Soc.* **75,** 4870 (1953).
35. P. Numerof, M. Gordon, and J. M. Kelly, *J. Pharmacol. Exptl. Therap.* **115,** 427 (1955).
36. H. Osmond and J. Smithies, *J. Mental Sci.* **98,** 309 (1952).
37. W. B. Reid, Jr. et al., *J. Am. Chem. Soc.* **70,** 3100 (1948).
38. B. Rubin and J. C. Burke, *Federation Proc.* **13,** 400 (1954).
39. E. Schlittler et al., *Experientia* **11,** 64 (1955).
40. H. Sheppard and W. H. Tsien, *Proc. Soc. Exptl. Biol. Med.* **90,** 437 (1955).
41. H. Sheppard, R. C. Lucas, and W. H. Tsien, *Arch. Intern. Pharmacodyn.* **103,** 256 (1955).
42. S. Siddiqui and R. H. Siddiqui, *J. Indian Chem. Soc.* **8,** 667 (1931).
43. *Ibid.*, **9,** 539 (1932).
44. *Ibid.*, **12,** 37 (1935).
45. S. Siddiqui, *J. Indian Chem. Soc.* **16,** 421 (1939).
46. I. H. Slater et al., *Proc. Soc. Exptl. Biol. Med.* **88,** 293 (1955).
47. A. Stoll and A. Hofmann, *J. Am. Chem. Soc.* **77,** 820 (1955).
48. A. E. Tschitschibabin and S. W. Benewolenskaja, *Ber.* **B61,** 547 (1928).
49. E. E. Van Tamelen and P. D. Hance, *J. Am. Chem. Soc.* **77,** 4692 (1955).
50. H. Weidmann and P. V. Petersen, *J. Pharmacol. Exptl. Therap.* **108,** 201 (1953).
51. H. Weidmann, *Arch. Exptl. Pathol. Pharmakol.* **214,** 497 (1952).
52. A. Werenberg, *Ugeskrift Laeger* **117,** 381 (1955).
53. R. E. Woodson et al., *Rauwolfia: Botany, Pharmacognosy, Chemistry and Pharmacology*, Little, Brown & Co., Boston, 1957.
54. R. B. Woodward et al., *J. Am. Chem. Soc.* **78,** 2023 (1956).
55. *Ibid.*, 2657 (1956).
56. D. W. Woolley and E. Shaw, *Science* **119,** 587 (1954).
57. H. L. Yale et al., *J. Am. Chem. Soc.* **72,** 3716 (1950).
58. Brit. Pat. 605,915 (Aug. 3, 1948), E. P. Newton (to Searle).
59. Brit. Pat. 729,619 (May 11, 1955), H. Lundbeck and Co. (to Medicinalco).
60. Can. Pat. 514,437 (July 5, 1955), R. Baltzly and J. C. Castillo (to Wellcome).
61. Ger. Pat. 12p.4.C7333 (Sept. 9, 1954), W. Schuler (to Promonta).
62. Swiss Pat. 269,338 (Oct. 2, 1950) (to Ciba A.G.).
63. U.S. Pat. 1,879,003 (Sept. 27, 1932), G. A. Alles (to Smith, Kline & French).
64. U.S. Pat. 2,015,408 (Sept. 24, 1935), F. Nabenhauer (to Smith, Kline & French).
65. U.S. Pat. 2,519,886 (Aug. 22, 1950), P. Charpentier (to Rhône-Poulenc).
66. U.S. Pat. 2,530,451 (Nov. 21, 1950), P. Charpentier (to Rhône-Poulenc).
67. U.S. Pat. 2,534,235 (Dec. 19, 1950), J. W. Cusic (to Searle).
68. U.S. Pat. 2,607,773 (Aug. 19, 1952), S. S. Berg and J. Nicholson (to Rhône-Poulenc).
69. U.S. Pat. 2,624,739 (Jan. 6, 1953), H. W. Werner and C. H. Tilford (to Merrell).
70. U.S. Pat. 2,645,640 (July 14, 1953), P. Charpentier (to Rhône-Poulenc).
71. U.S. Pat. 2,724,720 (Nov. 22, 1955), F. M. Berger and B. J. Ludwig (to Carter Products).
72. S. Akerfeldt, *Science* **125,** 117 (1957).
73. M. M. Frank and R. J. Wurtman, *Proc. Soc. Exptl. Biol. Med.* **97,** 478 (1958).
74. R. G. Heath, *J. Neuropsychiat* **3,** 1 (1961).
75. T. F. Redick, *Science* **141,** 646 (1963).
76. C. E. Frohman, E. D. Luby, G. Tourney, P. G. S. Beckett, and J. S. Gottlieb, *Am. J. Psychiat.* **117,** 401 (1960).
77. M. Gordon, ed., *Psychopharmacological Agents*, Vol. 2, Academic Press, Inc., New York, 1967, p. 249.

78. A. J. Friedhoff and E. Van Winkle, *Am. J. Psychiat.* **121**, 1054 (1965).

79. R. E. Bourdillon, C. A. Clarke, A. P. Ridges, P. M. Shepperd, and P. Harper, *Nature* **208**, 453 (1965).

80. E. Costa and B. B. Brodie, in H. E. Himwich and W. A. Himwich, eds., *Biogenic Amines,* American Elsevier Publishing Co., New York, 1964, p. 168.

81. Reference 77, p. 159.

82. I. J. Pachter, D. E. Zacharias, and O. Ribeiro, *J. Org. Chem.* **24**, 1285 (1959).

83. I. D. Spenser, *Can. J. Chem.* **37**, 1851 (1959).

84. D. F. Downing, in M. Gordon, ed., *Pharmacological Agents,* Vol. 1, Academic Press, Inc., New York, 1964, p. 566.

85. V. D. Raymond-Hamet, *Compt. Rend. Soc. Biol.* **154**, 2223 (1960).

86. R. C. DeBold and R. C. Leaf, *LSD, Man and Society, a Symposium,* Wesleyan University Press, Middletown, Conn., 1967.

87. E. C. Kornfeld, E. J. Fornefeld, G. B. Kline, M. J. Mann, R. G. Jones, and R. B. Woodward, *J. Am. Chem. Soc.* **76**, 5256 (1954).

88. I. Stevenson and T. W. Richards, *Psychopharmacologia* **1**, 241 (1960).

89. H. B. Murphree, E. H. Jenney, and C. C. Pfeiffer, *Pharmacologist* **2**, 64 (1960).

90. A. Hofmann, *Experientia* **14**, 107, 397 (1958).

91. F. Korte and H. Sieper, *Ann. Chem.* **630**, 71 (1960).

92. S. Loewe, *Arch. Exptl. Pathol. Pharmakol.* **211**, 175 (1950).

93. S. Gershon and W. J. Lang, *Arch. Intern. Pharmacodyn.* **135**, 31 (1962).

94. V. L. Stromberg, *J. Am. Chem. Soc.* **76**, 1707 (1954).

95. H. D. Fabing and J. R. Hawkins, *Science* **123**, 886 (1956).

96. S. Kety, *Intern. J. Psychiat.* **1**, 409 (1965).

97. J. Lutomski, *Bull. Inst. Roslin Leczniczych* **6**, 209 (1960).

98. J. A. Schneider and E. B. Sigg, *Ann. N.Y. Acad. Sci.* **66**, 765 (1957).

99. R. Mechoulam and Y. Shvo, *Tetrahedron* **19**, 2073 (1963).

100. Y. Gaoni and R. Mechoulam, *J. Am. Chem. Soc.* **86**, 1646 (1964).

101. R. Mechoulam and Y. Gaoni, *J. Am. Chem. Soc.* **87**, 3273 (1965).

102. E. C. Taylor, K. Lenard, and Y. Shvo, *J. Am. Chem. Soc.* **88**, 367 (1966).

103. R. L. Hively, W. A. Mosher, and F. W. Hoffman, *J. Am. Chem. Soc.* **88**, 2079 (1966).

104. T. Petrzilka et al., *Helv. Chim. Acta* **50**, 719 (1967).

105. *Ibid.*, 1416 (1967).

106. T. Y. Jen, G. A. Hughes, and H. Smith, *J. Am. Chem. Soc.* **89**, 4551 (1967).

107. R. Mechoulam, P. Braun, and Y. Gaoni, *J. Am. Chem Soc.* **89**, 4552 (1967).

108. H. G. Pars et al., *J. Am. Chem. Soc.* **88**, 3664 (1966).

109. L. H. Sternbach, L. O. Randall, and S. R. Gustafson, in reference 84, p. 137.

110. U.S. Pat. 2,893,992 (July 7, 1959), L. H. Sternbach (to Hoffmann-La Roche).

111. L. H. Sternbach, *J. Org. Chem.* **27**, 3788 (1962).

112. L. O. Randall, W. Schallek, G. A. Heise, E. F. Keith, and R. E. Bagdon, *J. Pharmacol. Exptl. Therap.* **129**, 163 (1960).

113. R. E. Tedeschi, D. H. Tedeschi, A. Much, L. Cook, P. A. Mattis, and E. J. Fellows, *J. Pharmacol. Exptl. Therap.* **125**, 28 (1959).

114. L. H. Sternbach (in press).

115. S. Childress and M. L. Gluckman, *J. Pharm. Sci.* **53**, 577 (1964).

116. D. H. Tedeschi, P. J. Fowler, T. Fujita, and R. B. Miller, *Life Sci.* **6**, 515 (1967).

117. D. H. Tedeschi, *Excerpta Medica Int. Congr. Ser. No.* **129**, *Washington, D.C., March 28, 1966,* p. 314.

118. D. H. Tedeschi, R. E. Tedeschi, and E. J. Fellows, *J. Pharmacol. Exptl. Therap.* **126**, 223 (1959).

MAXWELL GORDON AND GLENN E. ULLYOT
Smith, Kline & French Laboratories

PULP

Pulp is a manufactured fibrous cellulosic material used in the production of paper and in such cellulosic products and derivatives as viscose rayon, carboxymethyl cellulose, cellulose nitrate, cellulose acetate, etc. The North American production of pulp amounted to over 50,000,000 tons in 1966. Wood, which is the most abundant source of cellulose, is the principal raw material for the manufacture of pulp but cotton and linen rags, straws, and similar materials are also used. Because of the diversity of raw material and of end use, a very wide variety of pulps is now produced covering a wide spectrum of chemical composition and physical form. See also Cellulose; Paper; and Rayon.

Table 1. Pulp Production by Grade in the U.S. and Canada, 1966[a]

Type	Canada, 1000 a-d tons[b]	U.S., 1000 a-d tons	Total, 1000 a-d tons	U.S. price range[c] Jan. 1968, $/a-d ton
dissolving pulp and high-alpha pulp	428	1539	1967	170–200
sulfate pulp,				
unbleached	1428	12,749	14,177	115–130
semibleached	732	1439	2171	141–146
bleached	2466	8174	10,640	145–155[d]
soda pulp, bleached		190	190	135
sulfite pulp,				
unbleached	2147	481	2628	110–130
bleached	923	2322	3245	137–142
mechanical pulp	7286	3972	11,258	85–90
semichemical pulp	205	3231	3436	
screenings	57	297	354	
total	15,672	34,394	50,066	
paper and board produced	11,256	46,567	57,823	

[a] Production data from the Canadian Pulp & Paper Association.

[b] Pulp is marketed as "air-dry tons," defined as containing a theoretical 10% moisture. Thus an a-d ton contains 1800 lb actual moisturefree pulp.

[c] Prices from *Paper Trade Journal*, March 25, 1968.

[d] Hardwood bleached sulfate pulp—$134–137.

Wood pulps have been classified into four groups. *Mechanical pulp*, ie groundwood pulp, is produced by a mechanical disintegration of the wood in the presence of water and is obtained in a yield of approximately 95%. See p. 693. *Chemimechanical pulps* are obtained by softening the wood by a very mild chemical treatment, without involving any significant delignification, and then disintegrating by mechanical action. The yield range of such pulps is approximately 80–95%. See p. 697. *Semichemical pulps* are obtained by somewhat stronger cooking conditions involving partial delignification followed by defibering by mechanical treatment. The yield range of such pulps is about 55–80%. See p. 698. *Chemical pulps* are obtained by a chemical treatment sufficient to remove interfiber lignin thus allowing the fibers to separate with only minor, if any, mechanical treatment. The yield range of unbleached chemical pulps is about 42–58% depending on wood species and digestion chemicals. Chemical pulp can be bleached to high brightness. Chemical pulping comprises alkaline pulping (the sulfate or kraft process, see p. 702) and the acid pulping process (see p. 712).

The paper mill for which the wood pulp forms the raw material may be adjacent to the pulp mill and integrated with it or it may purchase market pulp which is normally shipped in dried and sheeted form. Most of the mechanical, chemimechanical, and semichemical pulps are produced and used in integrated mills. On the other hand very large quantities of chemical pulps are shipped as market pulp.

Statistics for pulp production for the year 1966 are shown in Table 1. The first four types listed are chemical pulps. Dissolving pulp and high-alpha pulp are high-purity chemical pulps used for manufacturing rayon, plastics, etc. They are produced by either the sulfite process or by the prehydrolysis sulfate process (see Cellulose, Vol. 4, pp. 606–609). Chemimechanical pulp, a relatively recent development, is produced only in small quantities and is not yet separately classified. The coarse low-quality by-product pulp separated from unbleached chemical pulps is known as "screenings" and is used in building boards.

Pulp production in Canada and the U.S. is approximately eight million tons less than the paper and board production. This results from a greater import than export of pulp, from the use of waste paper for some paper and board grades, and from the fact that paper contains other materials such as clay which is used as a filler, rosin which is used as a size, etc.

Wood

Although this subject will be more fully dealt with in a later volume (see Wood), certain aspects with regard to the morphology and chemistry of wood which are basic to an understanding of the pulping processes and pulp properties are reviewed here.

From a structural standpoint wood consists chiefly of hollow interconnected fibers axially oriented in the tree. These support the tree and also form the conduits for the transport of water from the roots to the leaves where, under the catalytic action of chlorophyll, the water reacts with carbon dioxide to form sugars and other organic materials. Growth of the tree results from the return of the solution of these substances through the inner bark to further react and polymerize at the cambium at the interface between wood and bark, thus forming new cells which in turn form a further ring in the fibrous conduit system.

Cellulose (qv) forms the principal constituent of the fiber wall while lignin (qv) is the principal interfiber bonding agent, this resulting in the relatively rigid composite structure known as wood. In the production of chemical pulps this same conduit system conveys the chemical solution through the wood where it can react and dissolve away the interfiber lignin thus allowing the fibers to separate one from the other. There is also a substantial portion of lignin embedded in the fiber wall, which is somewhat less accessible to the pulping reagents than that in the middle lamella (the interfiber zone). Its complete removal, considered essential to the production of high-brightness pulps, requires several stages of bleaching and will be discussed later.

A small block of softwood, greatly magnified, is shown diagrammatically in Figure 1. The major portion of the wood is made up of axially aligned fibers known as tracheids, and it is these that are involved in the main transport of water through the tree. There is a marked transition in tracheid appearance at the annual rings. Thick-walled, relatively small fibers constitute what is known as "summer wood" while relatively thin-walled large fibers form the "spring wood." There are approximately 650,000 tracheids per square inch of cross section in spruce. In spruce the tracheids are 2–3 mm long and 15–20 mm thick.   They have a hollow center known as the lumen and their tapered ends are closed.   The fiber wall is perforated with a number of small openings known as bordered pits, which are interconnected with the bordered pits of

Pinus echinata, shortleaf pine

Tracheid volume	90.8%
Ray volume	8.4%
Resin canal volume	0.8%

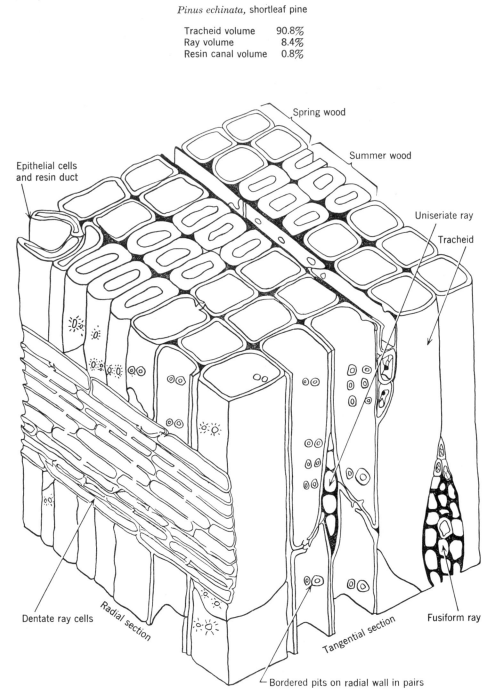

Fig. 1.   Diagram of softwood.

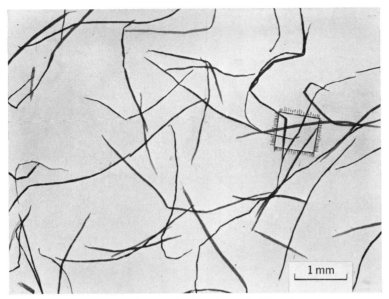

Fig. 2a. Photomicrograph of sulfate pulp fibers from spruce.

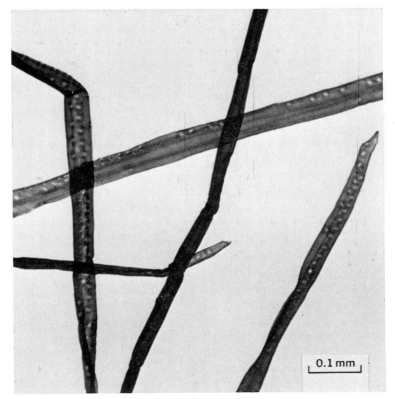

Fig. 2b. Detail of Figure 2a.

the next tracheid thus allowing the transport of fluid from the lumen of one tracheid to the next.   A diaphragm known as the torus is attached to the circumference of the bordered pit by a web of filaments and this can act as a "check valve."   There are also a relatively small number of vertical channels known as resin ducts which are surrounded by epithelial cells that contain rosin.   The radially aligned fibers are known as ray cells; they contain fats and fatty acids and serve as a food reservoir.   The ray cells have been botanically classified as dentate, uniseriate, and fusiform.   All of these diverse fibrous elements, when separated from one another in the pulping process form the constituents of the final pulp.   Figure 2a is a photomicrograph of sulfate pulp fibers from spruce, and Figure 2b is a detail at ten times the magnification of a portion of Figure 2a.   The bordered pits and lumen of the tracheid may be seen in the pulp fibers.

The conifers, of which spruce is an example, are generally referred to as softwoods. The broad-leafed deciduous woods which are morphologically and chemically distinct from the conifers are commonly referred to as hardwoods in spite of the fact that certain species, ie, basswood and poplar, have woods which are relatively soft.

In hardwoods, (Fig. 3) the axially aligned fibers play a relatively minor role in the vertical transport of sap which is carried out by the vessels.   The vessels are made up of relatively large cells with open ends or with grating-like structures referred to as scalariform plates.   The hardwood fibers have relatively thick walls and there is less differentiation in fiber appearance between spring and summer wood.   One or two layers of fibers laid down at the end of the summer (therminal parenchyma) can be used for showing the end of an annual ring.   Hardwood fibers are substantially shorter and finer than softwood tracheids; their length is about 1 mm.   Figures 4a and 4b, which illustrate sulfate pulp from American elm, are on the same scale as the corresponding Figures 2a and 2b thus illustrating the marked difference in size between hardwood and softwood pulp fibers.   A vessel element, which has a relatively large breadth-to-length ratio, is seen in the top center of Figure 2b.   It is a typical constituent of hardwood pulps and is absent from softwood pulps.

Major Constituents of Wood.   Wood, as might be expected from its biological origin, contains a number of chemically distinct constituents.   The nature of these, and the percentage present, may vary considerably from species to species.   Variations, particularly with regard to the percentage present, occur even in different trees of the same species.   Table 2 shows the approximate composition of the major constituents of balsam fir, a softwood, and trembling aspen, a hardwood.   In carrying out the analyses from which the table was compiled the wood had been pre-extracted with solvents to remove the minor nonpolymeric constituents.

In general the hardwoods contain more cellulose and less lignin than the softwoods. As a result chemical pulps are normally obtained in somewhat higher yields from hardwoods than from softwoods.   At least part of the lower lignin content of hardwoods results from a lower content in the cell wall; unbleached hardwood chemical pulps normally require less chemical for bleaching.   Hardwood lignin is chemically somewhat different from softwood and is characterized by a higher methoxyl content.   The hemicellulose of the hardwood carries less mannan and more xylan.

The detailed chemistry of cellulose and lignin is described in the specific articles dealing with these substances.   Cellulose (Vol. 4, pp. 593–616) is a linear polymer of D-glucose containing up to 10,000 monomer units (mol wt 1,500,000) linked together by 1,4-β-D-glucosidic links.

Table 2. Approximate Composition of Wood, Extractivefree Basis[a]

Constituent	Balsam Fir, %	Trembling Aspen, %
cellulose	42	48
lignin	29	21
hemicellulose components[b]		
galacto-glucomannan acetate	18	
glucomannan	9	3
4-O-methylglucurono-xylan acetate		24
total	27	27
pectin, starch, ash, etc	2	4
total	100	100

[a] From reference 7, p. 160, and T. E. Timell, *Wood Science and Technology*, Vol. 1, pp. 45–70, 1967, and T. E. Timell, private communications.

[b] Probable hemicellulose components as estimated from composition of individual sugars obtained on hydrolysis, % acetyl, % uronic anhydride, % methoxyl, etc.

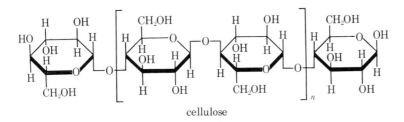

cellulose

Cellulose, which is white in color, has the same chemical structure, regardless of whether it occurs in softwoods, hardwoods, flax, cotton, etc, although its arrangement in microfibrils varies. As a result of chemical action in pulping, bleaching, etc, the native cellulose may be somewhat modified, ie, the molecular size is shortened and the terminal group may be converted to a carboxyl group. Certain groupings, such as carbonyl groups which may be formed under certain conditions of bleaching (hypochlorite at pH of about 8.0), result in an instability in the polymer which can result in subsequent yellowing and degradation on aging.

Lignin (Vol. 12, pp. 361–381) is a three-dimensional polymeric product based on the propylbenzene unit. Lignins in softwoods, hardwoods, and grasses are all chemically distinct and their structures are still not accurately known. All methods of its isolation from the plant material result in chemical modifications. The molecular weight is believed to be over 10,000. In softwoods the principal propylbenzene unit is dehydroconiferyl alcohol which has the following formula:

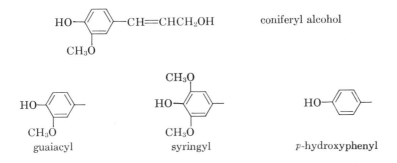

guaiacyl   syringyl   p-hydroxyphenyl

The polymeric reaction occurs in a variety of ways and at least twenty distinct units must be linked together in different ways to account for the various structures known to be present in lignin. (For a hypothetical structure see Lignin, Vol. 12, p.

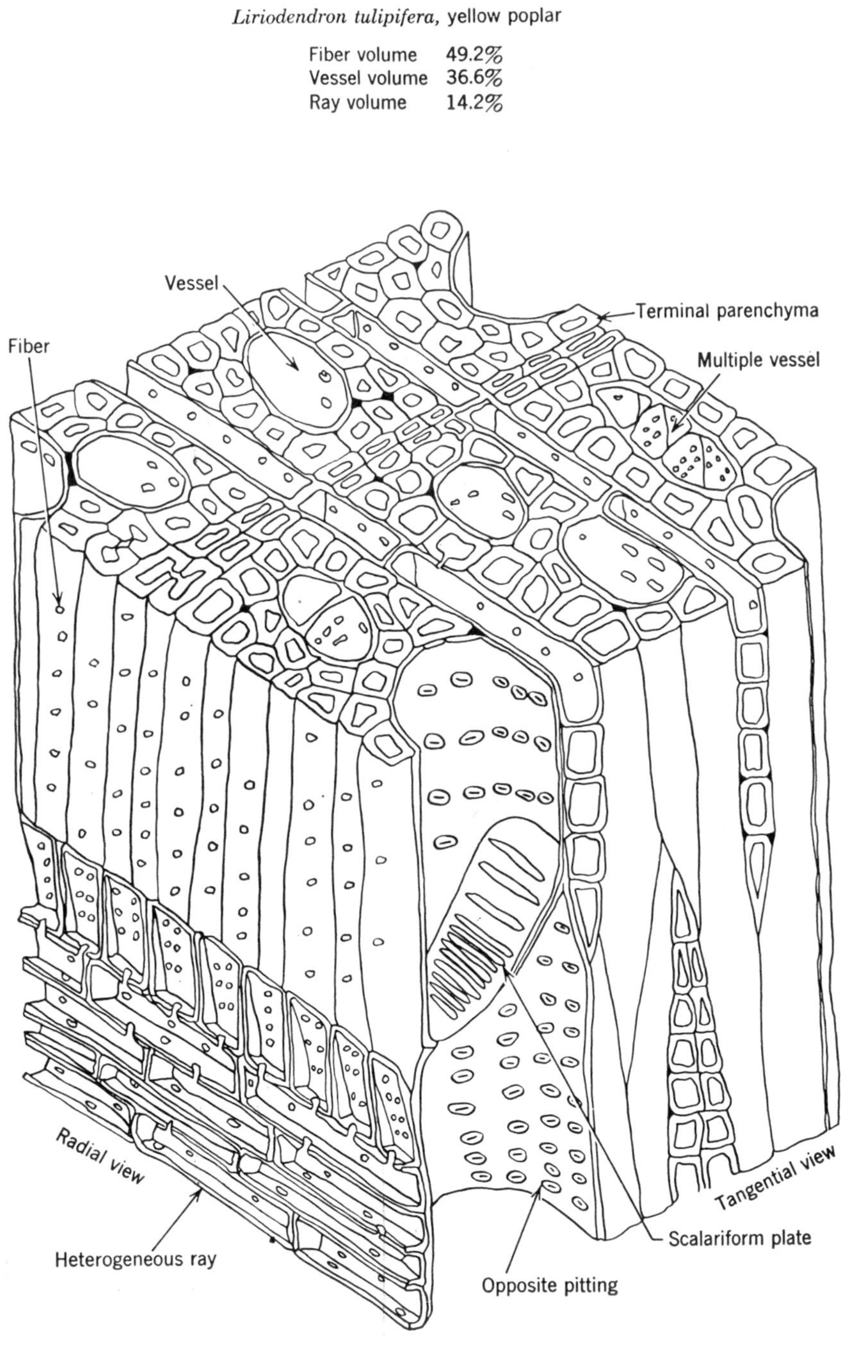
Liriodendron tulipifera, yellow poplar
Fiber volume 49.2%
Vessel volume 36.6%
Ray volume 14.2%
Vessel
Fiber
Terminal parenchyma
Multiple vessel
Radial view
Tangential view
Heterogeneous ray
Opposite pitting
Scalariform plate

Fig. 3. Diagram of hardwood.

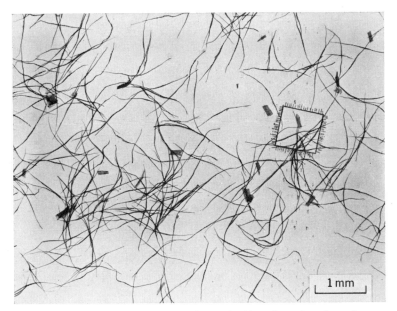

Fig. 4a. Photomicrograph of sulfate pulp fibers from American elm.

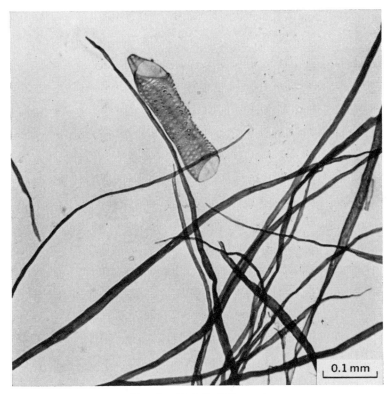

Fig. 4b. Detail of Figure 4a.

347, Fig. 1.)   In addition to the dehydroconiferyl alcohol subunit shown above, which is characterized by the guaiacyl grouping, lignin also contains syringyl and *p*-hydroxyphenyl groupings.

In softwood lignin the guaiacyl grouping predominates, and the other groupings are present in only minor proportions.   However, in hardwood lignin the syringyl grouping is a major constituent while in straw lignins the *p*-hydroxyphenyl grouping is important.   It is possible that the lignin component in any given species is made up of two or more closely related polymers as is the case with the hemicellulose component discussed below.

The hemicellulose constituents consist of a number of relatively complex, generally branch-chained polysaccharides, of lower molecular size than the cellulose.   The same molecule may contain two or more different sugars.   One of these sugars may be present in an oxidized state as its uronic acid and certain of the hydroxyl groups may be methylated, acetylated, etc.   The precise structure of these products has not yet been definitively established.

In softwoods galacto-glucomannan acetate forms the principal component, about 18% of the weight of balsam fir.   It contains at least 150 hexose units.   Glucose and mannose are both present in a main linear chain being connected through 1,4-β-D-bonds similar to those in cellulose, the ratio being 1 glucose to about 3 mannose units. In addition 1 galactose unit is present as a side chain for about every 10 glucose units; the bond is between the 6-carbon of the mannose and the 1-carbon of the galactose. The acetate groups are located on the 2- or 3-carbons of some of the mannose units.

In hardwoods the principal hemicellulose is 4-*O*-methylglucurono-xylan acetate. This is made up of 1 part 4-*O*-methyl-α-D-glucuronic acid, 10 parts β-D-xylose and 7 parts *O*-acetyl-β-D-xylose.   The molecule contains approx 200 xylose units.   Zinbo and Timell (1) have assigned to this the following formula:

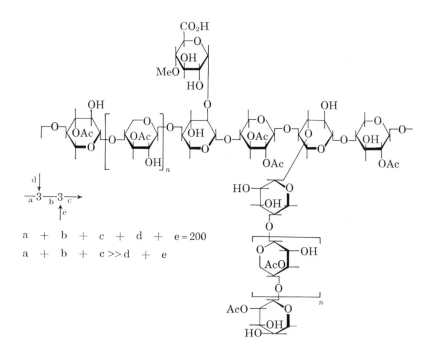

Table 3. Minor Constituents of Wood of Interest in Pulping

Constituent	Formula
palmitic acid (**1**)	$CH_3(CH_2)_{14}COOH$
stearic acid (**2**)	$CH_3(CH_2)_{16}COOH$
oleic acid (**3**)	$CH_3(CH_2)_7CH{=}CH(CH_2)_7COOH$
linoleic acid (**4**)	$CH_3(CH_2)_7CH{=}CHCH_2CH{=}CH(CH_2)_7COOH$
linolenic acid (**5**)	$CH_3CH_2CH{=}CHCH_2CH{=}CHCH_2CH{=}CH(CH_2)_7COOH$

gallic acid (**6**)

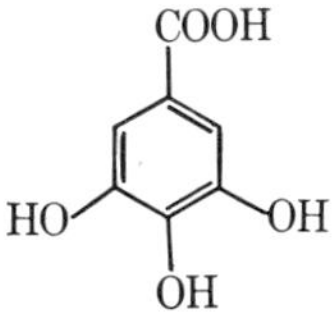

pinosylvin (**7**)

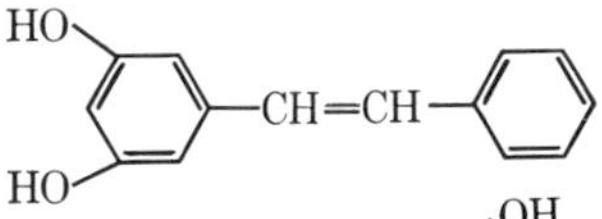

dihydroquercetin (**8**)

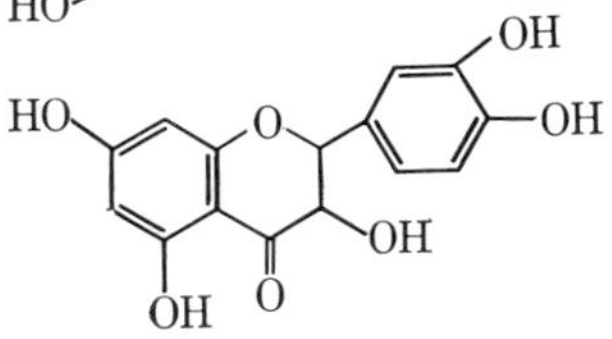

α-pinene (**9**)

thujic acid (**10**)

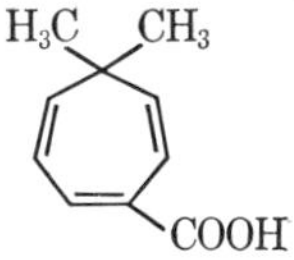

abietic acid (**11**)

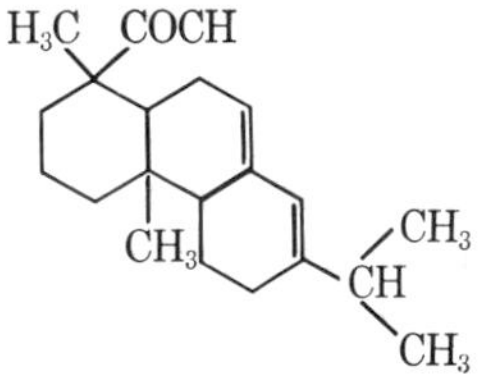

The hemicellulose constituents, which are colorless, are largely located in the cell wall and are retained in modified form and to a somewhat lesser extent than the cellulose in the final pulp; normally deacetylation occurs during pulping. Their amorphous nature and relatively low molecular size increase the water-swelling properties of the fibers and affect their bonding in the papermaking operation.

Minor Constituents of Wood. Wood contains about 3–10% of nonpolymeric constituents and these, often referred to as the extractives, vary markedly in composition and quantity from species to species and, in the case of certain constituents, with the seasons. The presence of one or more of these substances in certain wood species has caused major problems with regard to the pulping of the wood, and the developing knowledge about their structure and function in the tree is of importance to pulping technology. The structure of certain extractives, illustrating the different types, is shown in Table 3. (The bold-face number shown in the text after the specific substance refers to the formula number in Table 3.)

The fatty acids and their glycerides act as food reserves and are largely concentrated in the ray cells. They are formed from sugars by a series of reversible reactions. Palmitic (**1**) and stearic acids (**2**) are examples of the saturated fatty acids while oleic (**3**), linoleic (**4**), and linolenic (**5**) are examples of the unsaturated acids. These products, which form sodium soaps in the sulfate pulping process as a result of saponification of the fats and neutralization of the fatty acids, cause foaming in the residual black liquors. Their calcium salts are insoluble and are present in the characteristic "pitch" that forms on the walls of piping and equipment in the pulp mill. Seasoning of wood normally results in a marked reduction of the fats and the unsaturated linolenic and linoleic acids. This accounts for the lowered pitching tendency of pulps produced from seasoned wood. Oxidation and/or autooxidation, ie redox processes amongst the constituents, is involved in the breakdown of these acids during seasoning.

Certain of the minor constituents are involved in the preservation of the tree from insect and fungal attack. The tannins are concentrated largely in the bark, but, being water soluble, will migrate into the outer portion of the wood when the logs are floated. Certain species, eg redwood and oak, normally contain tannins in the wood. Gallic acid (**6**) is a hydrolysis product of tannin. Certain phenols develop in the heartwood as the tree ages. One of these, pinosylvin (**7**) which is present in certain pines, causes problems in the sulfite process. At the low pH of the acid sulfite process pH (1.0–1.5) pinosylvin reacts more rapidly with lignin (to form a phenol lignin) than the bisulfite, thus blocking the solubilizing sulfonation reaction. Tannin also has a similar reaction. The reaction of these phenols with lignin is markedly slower at the higher pH (3.0–4.0) of the bisulfite process thus allowing sulfonation and therefore pulping to proceed. The presence of dihydroquercetin (**8**), a heartwood and bark phenol of Douglas fir, prevents the pulping of this species by the acid sulfite process but not by the bisulfite process. The lignins, present in both heartwood and sapwood of some wood species, apparently have no deleterious effect on the pulping reaction. The lignins are characterized by the presence of a furan and two guaiacol rings.

The terpenes and resin acids are associated with the epithelial cells surrounding the resin ducts. The terpenes, the constituents of turpentine, are volatilized during the cooking process, α-pinene (**9**) being an example. Western red cedar contains a group of volatile 7-carbon ring compounds (tropolones) such as thujic acid (**10**). These compounds necessitate special corrosion-resistant alloys for the digester when this species is being cooked.

Abietic acid (**11**), the principal constituent of rosin (qv), is a resin acid. Its tacky consistency can create problems in groundwood produced from species such as pine, which contain large quantities of rosin. The resin acids together with the fatty acids form the principal constituent of the tall oil (qv) produced as a by-product of the sulfate pulping process.

In addition to the products discussed above, wood contains plant hormones such as phytosterol. Certain woods also contain specific attractants for different insect species; these probably have little effect on the pulping reactions.

Extraction of wood with water removes sugars and gums, ether removes the fats, fatty acids and resin acids, while alcohol or alcohol–benzene removes phenols such as the lignins, pinosylvin, tannin, etc.

Harvesting. Until about 1930 the commercially significant wood species used in pulping were limited to spruce, balsam, hemlock, and poplar. Since that time methods for the utilization of the pines, Douglas fir, and the dense hardwoods have been established and today virtually every species of significance in the temperate regions is used.

Methods of wood harvesting can be characterized by three distinct phases. Until the late 1940s muscle power prevailed—the man, with axe and cross-cut saw, harvested and cut the wood to 4-ft lengths, and the horse skidded it to the road or stream. This was followed by a second phase which involved the use of the chain saw and the wheeled, articulated skidder. A third method of harvesting, widely used in the 1960s, involves felling and branching with a chain saw, and tree-length skidding in which ten to twelve trees, each attached to a cable, are dragged to the road behind an off-road vehicle, known as a skidder. Here they are slashed to length and mechanically loaded on trucks for forwarding to the mill.

Productivity is dependent on a number of factors including tree size and terrain. In a northern Canadian spruce–jackpine forest, productivity would amount to 100–140 trees felled and branched per man per eight hour shift, while skidding productivity amounts to approximately 15 cunits per skidder per shift when the average distance of skidding is about 800 ft from roadside (1 cunit = 100 cu ft solid wood, barkfree). The wood recoverable from a single tree is largely dependent on diameter as can be seen for spruce in Table 4.

Table 4. Black Spruce: Relationship of Wood Volume to Tree Size

Diameter at breast height, in.	Total height of tree, ft	Marketable volume[a]	Trees/cunit
6	40	3.2	31.0
8	50	7.5	13.4
12	70	23.9	4.2
16	80	48.4	2.1

[a] When the top diameter equals 3 inches.

The forest worker has traditionally been subject to the vagaries of the weather. However, a third phase of forestry techniques is moving the operator into a cab with the result that forest operations can take place around the clock throughout the year.

It now appears that several different systems will be developed. The Beloit Harvester (Beloit Box Board Co.) for example, removes the branches and the top, severs the tree at its base with shears and lays it on the ground. The tree-lengths can then be picked up by a modified front-end loader and forwarded to the road. Because of the high cost of such large equipment, productivity is all-important. Equipment is under development (the Domtar Spruce Combine) that automatically and sequentially processes the tree through the operation of delimbing, topping, and bunching while the operator is clipping the next tree and bringing it to the vehicle with a fast-action boom. The bunches of 30 to 40 trees are then picked up by a separate vehicle which takes them to the road.

In another system under development, the tree is slashed to 8-ft lengths as part of the processing at the stump. A second unit such as the Waterous Forwarder (Koehring Company), equipped with a loading boom, will then place the wood previously stacked in 8-ft lengths on a platform and transport it in 3–4-cunit loads to the road where it is off-loaded on trucks.

Where tree-length delivery to the mill is not possible, or where the tree is not already slashed to the appropriate length, the wood will be slashed to 4-, 8-, or 16-ft lengths at the road. Roadside debarking and chipping is also a possibility, and units such as the Nicholson Utilizer (Nicholson Mfg. Co.) have been developed for this purpose.

Movement of the wood to the mill is very dependent on distance and other factors. Initially many mills were located downstream from the forest so that the wood could be floated to the mill. This involved large inventories because the water course was only available at certain seasons. Over relatively short and medium distances direct trucking is now normally preferred, with rail or ship being used on longer distances. The movement of chips suspended in water through pipelines has been proposed for distances of about 20–50 miles but this has not yet been adopted.

Barking. Bark removal has been considered a prerequisite for most pulping processes. Drum barkers are large open-ended cylinders which are rotated on an axis which is at such a slope that logs entering at one end will move towards and out the other. The bark which is broken off by rubbing and pummelling between the logs themselves and between the logs and the cylinders, drops out through slots in the cylinder. These units have a relatively high capacity. "In-line" barking units, that remove the bark from one log at a time, are either of the hydraulic or mechanical friction type. With the former, the bark is removed by jets of water at pressure in excess of 1000 psi. This system is used only with very large logs like those available on the west coast of North America. With friction debarkers, such as the Cambio debarker, special tools pressed against the log are rotated around it as it is passed through. This unit will process the logs at a linear throughput of about 150–180 ft/min.

Chipping. The purpose of chipping is to reduce the wood to a size that will allow penetration and diffusion of the chemicals needed for digestion. The chips, which are about ¾ in. long, are relatively free-flowing and can be transported pneumatically or on belts and then stored in piles or bins. The cost of moving chips in and out of storage is normally less than that of logs, so that a chip pile may form the primary storage for the mill.

In the Norman (Carthage Machine Co.) chipper, the cutting knives are mounted on the face of a large disc which is rotated on a horizontal axis. The log enters via a chute so arranged that the knives will sequentially cut across the log at an angle (approximately 37°) to the fiber axis; the chips which form pass through slots in the disc. The knife severs the fibers as it enters the wood and, because of its wedgelike shape, places an increasing edge compression on the cut fibers until this is relieved by shear along the grain. The thickness of the chip is thus related to the shearing forces at which the wood will yield and is therefore in turn related to the length of the chip which is normally specified in the range of ⅝–1 in. and which is set by the arrangement of knives.

Clark (1a) established the advantage of cutting the wood with the edge of the knife parallel to the fiber axis while directing the cut approximately at right angles to the fiber axis. This is essentially the "peeling" action involved in cutting veneer and gives chips or wafers of uniform thickness. The Söderhamn Company is now building chippers that have this type of action. In the Anglo drum chipper logs of fixed length are fed from a magazine to a large rotating drum where the wafers are cut passing through the drum. In the H.P. chipper, logs are fed endwise and sequentially engaged by a series of winged knives with the main knife edge peeling and the wing knife cutting across the fibers. These techniques result in chips of uniform length and thickness and with less compression damage. The uniform thickness results in more even penetration of pulping liquors and therefore less "screenings" in the resultant pulp.

Mechanical Pulps

Groundwood pulp was first produced experimentally about 1840 by independent inventors in Germany and in Canada and went into initial commercial production in Germany a few years later. Essentially it involved pressing wet wood against a wetted rotating grindstone with the axis of the wood parallel to the axis of the wheel. Over the years certain improvements have been made in the composition and speed of the grinding wheel, in methods of feeding the wood and pressing it against the stone, and in the size and capacity of the units. The original sandstone wheel has been replaced by mechanically stronger synthetic composite stones produced from fine grits of silicon carbide or alumina embedded in a softer ceramic matrix; the harder grit particles thus project from the surface of the wheel (see Abrasives). The synthetic stones have the mechanical strength to handle peripheral surface speeds of the order of 4000–4500 ft/min under conditions which consume from 500–5000 hp per stone.

In the magazine hydraulic grinder the logs are fed from above and pressed against the stone by a hydraulically operated pressure foot. The logs caught between the foot and the stone wear away, and when the foot reaches the end of its travel it rapidly moves back, allowing more logs to drop down which are then pressed against the stone repeating the cycle. Two magazines are provided on either side of the stone, and pulp from the first magazine is removed by showers ahead of the second. The period of interrupted pressure, when the foot is reset, amounts to about 20 seconds. Grinders have been designed which eliminate this interruption.

The feeding of logs to the individual grinders has traditionally involved considerable labor. The Kone automated feeding line developed in Finland allows one operator to handle a complete line of grinders. The logs are delivered by a series of belts and pushing devices so that they are available in bunches of appropriate size at each grinder; they are dropped to the magazine when required.

The quality of pulp is dependent on a number of variables. Grinder variables involve peripheral stone speed, grit size and number per unit area, stone surface, etc. Wood variables include species and moisture content. Process variables include grinding pressure, pit consistency, temperature, etc. The combination of moisture and raised temperature tends to soften the thermoplastic lignin binding the fibers together.

The grit diameter is about 8 mils, approximately ten times the fiber diameter, and Atack and May (2) have found that this relationship in size is important. The repeated compression–decompression cycles generate heat and soften the wood matrix before it reaches the grinding surface, where the loosened fibers are carried from the wood. The movement of the water and the removal of pulp controls and dissipates the heat, thus preventing charring of the wood. This action is very different from the simple mechanical cutting action which is characteristic of such processes as the grinding of metal.

The improvements in groundwood machines have been largely engineering ones relating to the size of the unit, the character of the stone, its speed and the method of feeding the wood. Very substantial progress has been made in this direction thus allowing relatively low-cost production of a pulp from softwood.

The concept of first reducing the wood to chips, which would then be ground, rather than grinding the log directly, opened a new avenue of approach during the 1950s. The operation of grinding chips is referred to as refining. Actually the double-disc refiner which can be used for this purpose had been previously used for producing semichemical pulps for corrugating medium (the inner ply in corrugated boxes), and, using steamed chips, for crude coarse groundwoods for building board. The mechanical pulp initially produced by this technique contained considerable "chop" or short chunky fiber bundles. The free-vortex centrifugal cleaners, which were developed at about this time, gave efficient removal of this "chop" thus establishing the possibility of such production. The action of the refiner was found to be somewhat different from that of the grinder and, in fact, it was proved possible to produce a paper-grade mechanical pulp with considerably greater average fiber length, tear resistance, and tensile strength than had previously been possible with the conventional method. Initially a higher specific energy requirement was indicated for these high-strength chip groundwoods but certain improvements have reduced this requirement to a value approaching that of conventional groundwood.

In a Bauer double-disc refiner two discs with alternating bars and depressions on the surface are rotated in opposite directions by directly connected motors, arranged so that the clearance between the plates of the discs can be adjusted. The chips are fed through channels near the shaft in one of the discs, and the chips, while undergoing attrition, move towards the periphery of the discs where the product emerges as fiber. The chips enter at a moisture content of about 50% and water is added at the eye of the discs to give a consistency of about 15–25%, ie 15–25 lb pulp per 100 lb slurry. At this consistency considerable water is evaporated, and leaves the unit as steam. Relative peripheral speeds are materially higher than those of the grinding wheel, being in the range of 12,500–30,000 ft/min. Whereas the attrition in stone grinding results from the rapidly moving high and low profile provided by the grits, the action of the disc refiner results from the alternating high and low zones provided by the bars and the intervening pulp-packed areas. In chip groundwood, the chips first break down into matchsticklike fragments near the center of the disc. These, in turn, break down into smaller fiber bundles as they move towards the periphery of the discs where they emerge as single fibers or fiber fragments including ribbons and fibrils which have been formed by the unravelling of the spiral fiber walls of individual fibers. Although it is possible to make chip groundwood in a single stage, normally two or even three refining units are used in series.

Conditioning the chips before grinding has been found desirable. The Pressafiner (The Bauer Bros. Co.), a modified screw press, subjects the chips to high pressure which squeezes out a portion of the water initially present including its soluble contents along with some of the rosin. The chips are then expanded into fresh water which is immediately imbibed. The dimensions of the Pressafiner are such that it carries a relatively large amount of wood at any given time and subjects it to the relatively

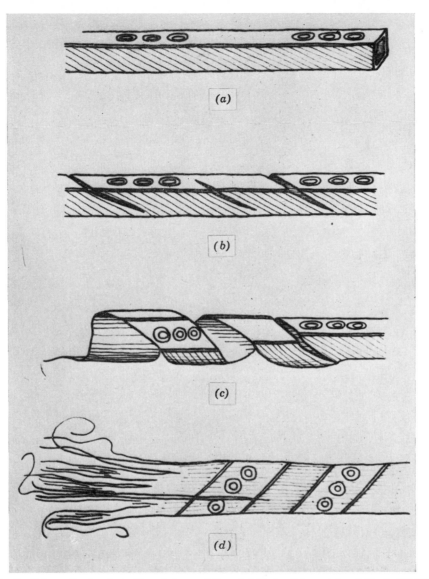

Fig. 5. Schematic drawing of breakdown of fiber (**a,b**) into ribbons (**c**) and fibrils (**d**) (3).

slow action of the screw as contrasted to the disc where the quantity of wood between the discs is small and the time extremely short. This pretreatment is thus desirable when chips initially are relatively dry or contain a relatively high amount of extractives.

It is possible to pressurize the refiner and thus operate at a higher temperature than is possible with normal atmospheric pressure. In this way one can adjust conditions at about 20–30 psi so that essentially only whole fibers are obtained. If the pressure is too high, for example 100–150 psi, the fibers, although intact, show relatively poor bonding in a paper sheet.

With groundwood and chip groundwood, as normally prepared, a substantial amount of fiber breakdown usually occurs. Forgacs (3) has shown that the strength

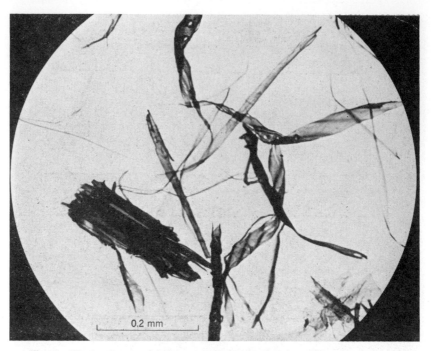

Fig. 6. Photomicrograph of groundwood pulp showing ribbons and chunk.

of the pulp is quite dependent on the nature of the fiber breakdown and can be predicted with surprising accuracy from measurements of fiber length and external specific
surface.   Figure 5 shows schematically how fiber fracture can follow a spiral pattern to
produce flexible ribbons and fibrils.   Either of these are desirable from the standpoint of
ultimate paper strength.   Rupture of wood into chunks containing short lengths of
several fibers is undesirable (Fig. 6).   Although stronger pulps can be obtained from
chip groundwood, the differences obtained to date are not sufficient to warrant scrap-
ping of grinders that are in good condition.   However, potential economies in wood
handling, together with improved quality and control, suggest that the long-term trend
will be entirely to chip refining.

Since mechanical pulps are obtained in yields of nearly 100% their cost is relatively low.   The major direct cost, other than wood, is power which is in the range of 65 to
100 hp per 24-hr day per ton for normal paper grades.   Somewhat less power is used in
producing pulps for hardboard and low-density wallboards which contain somewhat
coarser fiber than paper grade pulps.   Paper grade pulps find their principal use in
newsprint, magazine papers including coated publication grades, board for folding and
molded cartons, wallpapers, tissue, and similar products.   The pulp has high bulk,
excellent opacity, but relatively low mechanical strength.   All of these properties stem
from the presence of lignin which results in a lower paper bond than would otherwise
be obtained with the hemicellulose and cellulose.   The pulp can be partially bleached
with peroxide or hydrosulfite without significant loss in yield.   However the paper,
either bleached or unbleached, has relatively poor brightness stability, particularly in
the presence of ultraviolet radiation, so that it is not suited for fine papers.   Where
stability is significant the more expensive bleached chemical pulps are normally used
for such grades.

Chemimechanical Pulps

When hardwood chips are first impregnated with sodium hydroxide they can be refined in a disc refiner to produce pulps in the yield range of 85–90% which compares favorably in strength with spruce groundwood. Impregnation can be at temperatures in the range of 30–80°C. In either event the applied friction in the refiner will generate steam in the disc mill thus giving an instantaneous temperature at the boiling point (about 103°C) and above. Addition of sodium sulfite to the caustic reduces the tendency for the pulp to darken. Liquors of lower pH such as bisulfite (pH 3.5) or bisulfite–sulfite mixtures (pH 6) can also be used but pressure digestion, at a temperature of 125–135°C, normally is required.

The chemical treatment can be carried out in equipment such as the Bauer M & D digester (Fig. 7) in which the chips are mechanically conveyed through a pool of liquor and are then lifted from the liquor and discharged from the vessel. Where a mild effect is desired the Impressafiner, which compresses the chips and then expands them in the impregnating solution, has been found satisfactory.

As the yield is reduced (as a result of higher chemical concentration and/or longer treating time) the strength properties of paper produced from the pulp increase while the bulk, opacity, and brightness decrease, these changes resulting largely from the greater interfiber bonding obtained.

Peroxide bleaching will increase the brightness to the 65–70 G.E. range without loss in yield as a result of the bleaching. (The G.E. brightness is the percent reflectance of light of 457 mμ wavelength on the basis of a scale in which MgO gives reflectance of 100%.)

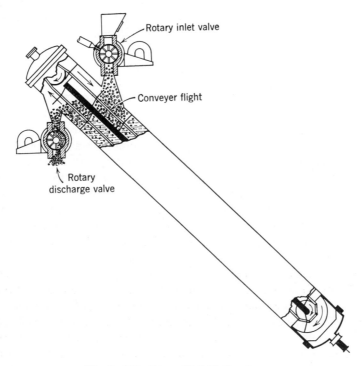

Fig. 7. The Bauer M & D digester.

The use of chemimechanical processing appears to be most attractive with hardwoods because of greater gains in strength in relation to those obtainable in the absence of pretreatment. In fact the quality of groundwood from the dense hardwoods is so low that without chemical pretreatment they are essentially worthless for paper production. Thus the use of the process allows the use of species which could not otherwise be used for papers requiring the high bulk and opacity characteristic of softwood groundwood. Unlike softwood groundwood, the fiber length of the chemimechanical hardwood pulp is preserved.

When wood is impregnated with sodium hydroxide solution it becomes swollen and its tensile strength is drastically reduced. Lagergren, Rydholm and Stockman (4) have shown that the tensile strength of birch wood is decreased from 1400 to 360 kp/cm² (kp = kilopond; 1 kilopond = 1 kilogram force) on soaking with cold caustic. This is a greater reduction than with spruce where the corresponding reduction is from 1480 to 1230 kp/cm² under similar conditions. Tarkow (5) has noted that with hardwoods the hemicellulose becomes deacetylated under these conditions and that the fiber saturation point of the wood is markedly increased, indicating increased accessibility of the cell wall for water. (The fiber saturation point is the point at which free moisture first appears in the cell lumen, ie approx 30% for untreated wood.) The decreased wood strength obtained with the caustic treatment allows a lower power input to the refiner and therefore less heat generation while the greater accessibility to water has the effect of increasing the internal water needed for plasticizing and cooling the fibers, which in the absence of such pretreatment would become brittle and even charred. It has been shown (6) that fiber rupture after cold caustic treatment is largely between the so-called S_1 and S_2 layers of the fiber wall, ie between the outer and main layers of the secondary wall rather than in the middle lamella. Thus the evidence suggests that changes in hemicellulose rather than lignin are responsible for the improved fiber separation obtained in refining hardwoods treated with cold caustic soda.

Semichemical Pulps

Semichemical pulping involves two stages: a preliminary treatment of wood with chemical which results in partial delignification and softening of the middle lamella and a subsequent mechanical treatment to isolate the fibers from the softened wood.

Although the general concept of semichemical pulping was well established in the period of 1930–1940, the technique then used of refining with rod mills was unsatisfactory. Thus the development of the precision disc refiner in the postwar period has allowed the development of this important pulping method. Since wood cost is normally the largest item in pulp production cost, an increase in yield has obvious economic attraction. However, this may be accompanied by certain increased problems such as disposal of effluent. Also, because of the different composition of pulps, different qualities result, these normally involving lower brightness. The following are the principal products which have reached commercial significance and of those listed, (1), (3), and (5) have become well established as economically viable processes, and are likely to remain so for some time: (1) hardwood neutral sulfite semichemical (NSSC) pulp in yields of 70–80% for corrugating medium, (2) hardwood neutral sulfite semichemical (NSSC) pulp in unbleached yields of 60–65% which may be bleached for fine papers, (3) softwood bisulfite high-yield pulp in yields of approximately 60–65% for newsprint and board, (4) softwood acid sulfite high-yield pulp in yields of approximately 65% for newsprint, and (5) softwood sulfate pulp in yields of approximately 55% for liner board.

The reagent initially used for semichemical pulping was neutral sodium sulfite (Na₂SO₃ buffered with Na₂CO₃) but it later became apparent that semichemical pulps could also be produced with any of the reagents suitable for full chemical pulping by applying somewhat milder conditions than would otherwise be used and by stopping

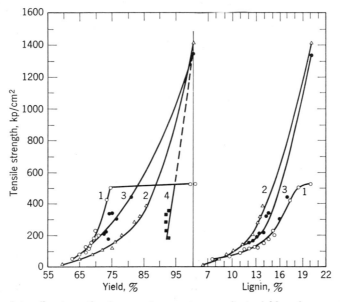

Fig. 8. Graphs of tensile strength at room temperature against yield and percentage lignin for birchwood after removal of material by (*1*) sulfate, (*2*) sulfite, (*3*) NSSC, and (*4*) cold soda process (*4*).

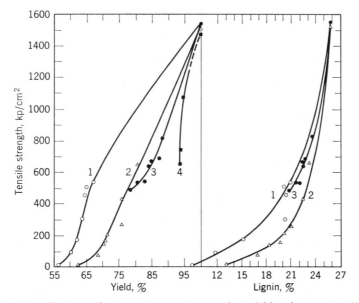

Fig. 9. Graphs of tensile strength at room temperature against yield and percentage lignin for spruce after removal of material by (*1*) sulfate, (*2*) sulfite, (*3*) NSSC, and (*4*) cold soda process (*4*).

the digestion before any major delignification occurred. Thus acid sulfite ($Ca(HSO_3)$ + H_2SO_3), bisulfite ($NaHSO_3$ or $Mg(HSO_3)_2$), and sulfate ($NaOH$ and Na_2S) (see below under Alkaline pulping) disgestion liquors are used.

The degree of softening is dependent on the wood species, the cooking liquor used, and the yield to which the digestion is carried. Lagergren et al. (4) have measured the strength of woods under varying digestion conditions. Figure 8 shows their results for birch and Figure 9, their results for spruce. These investigators digested thin speci-mens of wood with each of several reagents under conditions chosen to give varying yields; the specimens were then washed by diffusion and, while still wet, their tensile strength was measured. The strength values which were obtained in this way indicated the degree of softening of the wood structure by the various treatments, these values being approximately proportional to the power requirements for disintegrating the softened wood to a pulp. It can be seen that alkaline liquors such as cold soda or sulfate cooking liquor have a very marked softening action on birch (Fig. 8) in the very high yield range. However, at lower yields of about 70–75% and less, birch treated with sulfate liquor is less readily disintegrated than birch treated with neutral sulfite and acid sulfite liquors at the same yield.

It can be seen from Figure 9 for spruce that in the yield range of 60–75%, sulfate liquors have a markedly lower softening action than do acid sulfite liquors. Bisulfite liquors which were not included in this study have an even greater softening action in this same yield range.

NSSC Pulps

Neutral sulfite liquor has not been found to offer any special advantage over other liquors with softwoods and its use is largely limited to hardwoods. The major applica-tion of such liquor is in the production of pulp for corrugating medium. At one time this commercially important product was largely produced from straw using a caustic or lime–caustic liquor; such use of straw is now essentially obsolete in North America. Its successor, NSSC pulp, is obtained in 70–80% yields from hardwoods, including the dense hardwoods.

The digestion liquor consists of sodium sulfite and sodium carbonate or bicarbon-ate. Digestion liquor may be produced by treating sodium carbonate with sulfur dioxide. The carbon dioxide liberated reacts with excess sodium carbonate to produce sodium bicarbonate. This latter acts as a buffer during digestion, reacting with acetic acid liberated by deacetylation of hemicellulose. The sodium sulfite reacts with lignin, a portion of which dissolves as a water-soluble sulfonate. The digestion itself is carried out in a pressure vessel at a pressure of 125–150 psi. Continuous digesters are now normally used for this process (7). The chips may be fed to the digester through either a rotary pocket valve, such as the Bauer Grenco valve or through a screw feeder such as the Pandia valve (The Black Clawson Co.), where they are sufficiently compressed to form a plug against the digester pressure. On entering the digester the chips are flooded with liquor and a number of schemes have been used for maintaining continu-ous internal flow of the digesting chips. In one scheme the chips are advanced through a horizontal tube by means of a screw and on reaching the end drop to a similar tube set at a lower level. A sufficient number of these tubes are arranged to allow adequate dwell time for the production required. The semicooked chips are then discharged through an outlet valve to atmospheric pressure. Digesters of the multiscrew type are the Black-Clawson Pandia, the Asplund defibrator (American Defibrator, Inc.) and the Sprout-Waldron (Sprout, Waldron & Co., Inc.). Another digester used for this purpose is the Bauer M & D in which the chips are carried through by chain conveyor. A number of semichemical digester designs involve a vertical downflow. These include the improved Asplund Defibrator, the Excher-Wyss, and the Kamyr instant heating (Kamyr Inc.) digesters.

Following digestion, the softened chips will typically go to a screw press for removal of a portion of the liquor, then through disc refiners (normally two in series) and next to a rotary washer system to remove the balance of the liquor. The washed pulp then passes through a final refining stage and vortex cleaners to the paper machine.

One of the most serious problems in NSSC pulping is the economic disposal of the residual digestion liquor. Whereas similar liquors from the production of sulfate chemical pulps can be economically evaporated and burned with recovery of fresh digestion chemical, the residual liquor from NSSC pulping has appeared to be an economic liability.

From a chemical standpoint, acetic acid and other minor ingredients can be recovered but such recovery results in only partial removal of the organic constituents. Considerable effort has been devoted to establishing methods for its evaporation and combustion and several plants have been built in which techniques similar to those which are described in the following section on sulfate pulping are used. These involve multiple-effect evaporation of the residual liquor and firing in a special furnace, where the inorganic constituents are discharged as a smelt. The smelt which consists of sodium carbonate and sodium sulfide is dissolved in water. In the Mead process (8) the clarified smelt solution is treated with a gas containing carbon dioxide which converts the sodium sulfide to sodium bicarbonate while expelling hydrogen sulfide. This latter is burned to sulfur dioxide and, together with the sulfur dioxide-containing flue gas from the liquor recovery process, is contacted with the carbonated liquor to produce fresh cooking liquor containing sodium sulfite and sodium bicarbonate. In the Institute process (developed at the Institute of Paper Chemistry at Appleton, Wisconsin) (9), the clarified green liquor (see p. 711) is treated directly with flue gas but this has the disadvantage that a portion of the sulfide is converted to sodium thiosulfate, which is not desirable.

An alternate route involves combustion in a fluidized bed, and plants designed by Copeland (10) and by Dorr (11) are now in operation. By this technique the fluidized bed is maintained under oxidizing conditions to produce sodium sulfate together with a small amount of sodium carbonate. The temperature of the combustion is held to a value of about 660°C, below the melting point of the inorganics, by spraying the liquor into the combustion zone at a relatively low solids content, about 35%. The inorganic residue forms pellets which maintain the fluidized bed; a portion is continuously withdrawn to balance the incoming feed. This inorganic residue cannot be reused for producing the digestion liquor and is therefore sold to a sulfate mill. The reduced temperature, used in the fluidized bed, not only avoids the problems usually associated with the handling of a smelt, including the risk of explosions from some accidental uncontrolled contact with water, but also minimizes the amount of sodium salts volatilized which otherwise form a fume in the flue gas.

Because of the low heat content of NSSC liquors (about 5200 Btu/lb liquor solids) insufficient heat is generated during combustion to make the total processing, including evaporation, self-contained from a heat standpoint. This, in addition to the relatively low value of the recovered chemicals, requires that capital, operating, and maintenance costs be kept at a minimum.

Other methods of approach, including ion-exchange and pressure oxidation, have been considered. Another route involves changing the cooking process to obtain somewhat similar pulp using a magnesia base (12), for which a simple recovery system is available (see below under Acid pulping, p. 712). Still another route involves the use of ammonia base since the liquor can be burnt without smelt or ash, the ammonia being largely destroyed.

Chemical Pulps

In chemical pulps, sufficient lignin is dissolved from the middle lamella to allow the fibers to separate with little, if any, mechanical action. However, a portion of the lignin is retained in the fiber wall and an attempt to remove this during digestion would result in excessive degradation of the pulp. For this reason about 3–4% lignin is normally left in hardwood chemical pulps and 4–10% lignin in softwood chemical pulps. This is subsequently removed by bleaching in separate processing when completely bleached pulps are produced.

The concentration of the cooking liquor in contact with the wood has an important bearing on the rate of delignification. Because of the time required for diffusion of the chemical through the wood structure, and the fact that the reagent concentration becomes depleted as it penetrates the chip, delignification proceeds more slowly at its center. This is particularly apparent in the case of oversize chips which are normally present. In order to prevent overcooking of the major portion of the pulp, the digestion is normally stopped before the centers of these larger chips are adequately delignified. The resultant pulp thus contains a portion of nondefibered wood fragments which are separated from it by screening.

The different chemical pulping processes may be considered as follows: (1) alkaline pulping—(a) the soda process now essentially replaced by the sulfate process, (b) the sulfate or kraft process; (2) acid pulping—(a) the acid sulfite process, (b) the bisulfite process, (c) multistage sulfite processes.

ALKALINE PULPING

The Soda and Sulfate Processes. The original process for chemical pulping of wood, developed in 1851–1865, involved the use of caustic soda and was known as the soda process. Because of the cost of the reagent, it was necessary to recover and reuse the alkali in the residual liquor. This was done by separating and evaporating the black liquor, burning it, dissolving the resultant sodium carbonate, which is obtained as a smelt, in water and treating it with calcium hydroxide which regenerated the sodium hydroxide. It was subsequently found that the presence in the cooking liquor of sodium sulfide, in addition to the sodium hydroxide, allowed the dissolution to proceed more readily and that this gave a less degraded pulp. By using sodium sulfate to make up for the soda losses and adding it to the residual liquor before furnacing, the makeup sulfate is reduced to the desired sodium sulfide. The use of sodium sulfate, rather than caustic soda, for chemical makeup has given rise to the name for this process, ie the sulfate process. In the total cycle, substantial amounts of sulfur are normally lost, independently of the sodium base, in the form of gases such as thiols (mercaptans), hydrogen sulfide, etc so that the ratio of sulfur to sodium in the cycling system is substantially less than that in the makeup saltcake. The net effect is that only about one third of the sulfur input is retained by the recycling inorganic chemical. Thus the digestion reagent consists of approximately two thirds caustic soda and one third sodium sulfide, ie the sulfidity is about 33%. This reagent, which is obtained when sodium sulfate is used as makeup, is considerably more active than pure caustic soda, and in view of the stronger pulp obtained with this reagent, the sulfate or kraft process has essentially taken over as a new generation process and the initial soda process is now becoming obsolete.

Since sodium sulfide is a relatively expensive chemical, the change to the sulfate process increased the dependency of the pulping operation on the recovery process which was initially very inefficient. Thus the development in the 1920s and 1930s of the black liquor recovery furnace, which allowed simultaneous recovery of chemicals and steam, together with the use of continuous processing for brown stock (unbleached pulp) washing, causticizing, and lime reburning, markedly reduced processing costs for the production of high-strength pulp, thus paving the way for the tremendous expansion which followed.

The excellent strength of sulfate pulp, when used in linerboard, led to a major expansion of the corrugated carton industry thus replacing wooden cases; similarly its use in bags and multiwall sacks led to the replacement of cotton and, to a large extent, jute bags. The demand for these packaging papers was largely responsible for the development of the sulfate pulping industry in the southern U.S., based on pine, and later, on the West Coast, based primarily on Douglas fir. A further wave of expansion started in the 1950s when nondegrading chlorine dioxide bleaching techniques became available, thus increasing the use of sulfate pulps in the fine paper and printing paper field. The continuous building of new plants over a thirty-year period has resulted in an accumulation of experience which is reflected in the efficiency of the plants being built today.

The Sulfate Digesting Liquor and Digestion. The active chemical constituents of sulfate digestion liquor, which is known as *white liquor* and is regenerated from the residual liquor from previous digestions, are sodium hydroxide and sodium sulfide, about one third of the sodium being combined as sulfide. In addition to these chemicals, the liquor contains significant amounts of sodium carbonate and sulfate and minor amounts of sulfite and thiosulfate, these having essentially no pulping action and being incidental to the recovery process. The composition of the cooking liquor is customarily calculated in terms of its Na_2O equivalent. A typical analysis of the white liquor is as follows:

Compound	Na_2O content, g/l	Compound	Na_2O content, g/l
NaOH	73.0	Na_2SO_4	0.6
Na_2S	31.4	$Na_2S_2O_3$	0.4
Na_2CO_3	18.2	Na_2SO_3	0.2

The sodium sulfide present in the liquor is largely hydrolyzed to form sodium hydroxide and sodium hydrosulfide by the following reversible reaction:

$$Na_2S + H_2O \rightleftharpoons NaOH + NaHS$$

Thus the sodium hydroxide content of the liquor available for reaction includes not only that formed by causticizing the sodium carbonate from the smelt but also that which may be formed by hydrolysis of sodium sulfide. This is known as the "effective alkali," ie the NaOH plus one half Na₂S, expressed as Na₂O, while the term "active alkali" is the NaOH plus Na₂S, also expressed as Na₂O.

Although historically the analyses of white liquors have been expressed in terms of NaOH and Na₂S, it would be more desirable to express them in terms of "effective NaOH" and NaHS, since it is in these forms that reaction with the wood substances occurs. The detailed reactions with the lignin and carbohydrate have yet to be fully explained but the probable pattern is clear. The lignin molecule is partially depolymerized by hydrolysis of phenol ether bonds while the hydrosulfide reacts independently with the carbon in the α position to the benzene ring. The latter promotes the solubility of the lignin fragment and therefore accelerates delignification. Whereas the hydrosulfide reacts only with the lignin, only a minor portion of the sodium hydroxide reacts with the lignin, the major reaction being with carbohydrate. Of the 15–16 lb of effective alkali (as Na₂O) used for pulping 100 lb dry weight of spruce, about 3.1 lb is consumed in delignification where it forms the sodium salt of the phenol groups resulting from these reactions, 0.9 lb reacts with the acetic acid formed by deactylation of hemicellulose, and 6.8 lb is largely consumed by the sugar acids and other degradation products of the hemicellulose. A further small portion is consumed in miscellaneous reactions with fatty acids, etc while the balance is left as unreacted excess in the residual liquor. A large excess of alkali over that required for delignification is avoided since it has a strong degrading effect on the remaining cellulose. The effect of hydrosulfide is to accelerate the alkaline pulping of wood so that the digestion can be brought to a given degree of delignification in a short period of time. As the sulfidity is increased from a zero value to a value of about 30%, which is in the normal range for white liquor, the cellulose and hemicellulose are subjected to diminished alkaline degradation because of the shortened digestion time required, this resulting in better yields and strength. When the sulfidity is further increased from about 30 to 100%, and the digestion conditions are appropriately shortened, a further small gain in strength is obtained but there is little, if any, gain in yield over that at 30%.

The yield of alkaline pulps at a given degree of delignification is somewhat lower than that of acid sulfite and bisulfite pulps. This results from the relative instability of certain polysaccharides in the alkali which undergo end-group peeling reactions. The terminal glucose residue of the polysaccharides normally contains an aldehyde group and this end group can react with alkali in two ways. The main "peeling" reaction results in a molecular rearrangement with the result that the terminal glucose unit of the cellulose or hemicellulose splits off from the molecule. Since the glucose unit which was next to the terminal group now in its turn becomes the new terminal unit, and contains an aldehyde group, this reaction proceeds again. Fortunately a competing reaction will stabilize the end group by converting the aldehyde to a carboxyl, preventing further reaction (13). The tendency for this stopping reaction is much less than for the peeling reaction and Franzon et al. (14) have concluded that approximately 65 glucose units in cellulose will peel off before the molecule is stabilized. The initial cellulose contains approximately 3500 to 10,000 glucose units. With xylans, the stopping reaction is believed to be more favorable and with mannans, less favorable. This accounts for the relatively high xylan content and low glucomannan content of sulfate pulps.

It would, of course, be highly desirable to prevent end-group peeling and, at least from the theoretical standpoint, this is possible. For instance, when sodium borohydride is added to the liquor in sufficient quantity, the terminal aldehyde groups are

Table 5. Chemical Composition and Paper Properties of Kraft Pulps Cooked in the Absence and Presence of Polysulfide or Borohydride to the Same Degree of Delignification, Roe #5[a]

Wood species	Pulping process	Yield		Hemicellulose content		Paper properties at 45° SR[b]			
		Unbleached, %	Bleached, %	Gluco-mannan, %	Gluco-ronoxylan, %	Beating time, min	Tensile strength, km	Burst strength	Tear strength
spruce	kraft	50	46	7	10	76	11.1	112	133
	polysulfide	54	50	16	6	82	12.0	105	110
	borohydride	57	53	22	6	65	10.8	95	99
birch	kraft	54	51	1	27	29	9.0	78	75
	borohydride	61	58	4	30	32	9.6	70	62

[a] The Roe number of a pulp gives the percentage of Cl_2 that will react with it under standardized conditions. The Roe number thus gives a readily determined index of the residual lignin content.

[b] °SR indicates the pulp slurry drainage rate as determined by the standardized Schopper Riegler test. The value obtained characterizes the degree of bearing to which the pulp was subjected before conversion to paper sheets.

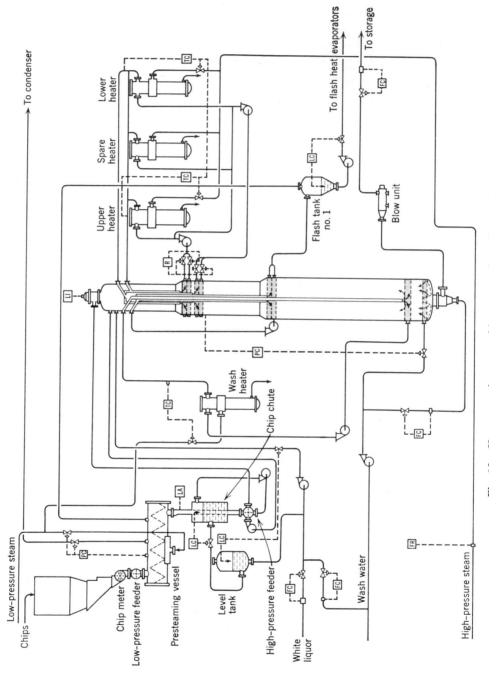

Fig. 10.   Kamyr continuous cooking system for sulfate pulp.

reduced to alcoholic groups and the pulp yield is therefore materially increased. However, this does not seem to offer a commercially practical answer because of the high cost of this reagent.

A more attractive possibility involves the use of sodium polysulfide a reagent that will not only produce an increased yield but that may also be more readily accommodated in the recovery system. When sulfur is added to sodium sulfide it takes up the sulfur to form polysulfide. Polysulfide reacts with the aldehyde group of cellulose to form a carboxylic group, thus stopping the peeling reaction. Unfortunately, the polysulfide itself is unstable since it also reacts with sodium hydroxide to form sodium thiosulfate and substantial amounts are therefore required in order to obtain an appreciable increase in yield. The presence of this added sulfur creates problems in the liquor recovery cycle and, although several methods for dealing with this have been proposed, no method has yet reached the commercial stage. Table 5 indicates the increase in yield that can be obtained in the laboratory by stabilizing the carbohydrate aldehyde group. With softwood, the gain is largely in glucomannan, this being accompanied by a small loss in glucuronoglucxylan. Whereas there is some decrease in pulp strength associated with the increased yield, the strength is still suitable for most purposes. The development of techniques for establishing yield gains on an economic commercial basis is a major challange for the industry in the 1960s.

The Digestion Vessel. Initially the digestion was carried out as a batch operation. The digester for batch operations commonly consists of a vertical cylindrical vessel with a conical bottom, about 9–12 ft in diameter and 30–60 ft in height. It is fitted with a recirculating system which includes a steam-heated heat exchanger. The chips are charged through a manhole at the top and are heated with steam as the digester is being filled, this materially reducing the air in the fiber cavities. The cover is closed and a quantity of white liquor sufficient to give the desired alkali ratio (approximately 16 lb effective alkali per 100 lb dry wood) together with a portion of recycled black liquor to give a liquor-to-wood ratio of about 4:1 is added. The digester is then heated to a temperature of about 170°C in about $1\frac{1}{2}$ hours and held at that temperature for $1\frac{1}{2}$ hours to produce a bleachable pulp. A valve at the base of the digester connected to a "blow tank" is then opened; the digester empties and the digestion is terminated.

Many recently built mills carry out the digestion in a continuous digester; the Kamyr digester (Fig. 10) is the most widely used. The chips are first continuously steamed and are then brought to digester pressure (about 150 psi) where they are picked up in a stream of recycled liquor to which white and black liquor makeup have been added. This stream carries through to the top of the digester where the recycling feed liquor is extracted from the chips. The chips, together with the balance of the liquor, flow continuously down through the digester, their temperature being raised to about 170°C in a top heating zone. This requires about $1\frac{1}{2}$ hours. They are then held at this temperature for $1\frac{1}{2}$ hours while passing through a second zone. At this point the digestion is essentially complete and they next pass continuously through a counter-current washing and cooling zone, with the black liquor leaving the digester from the top of this zone while the digested and partially washed chips leave the bottom of the digester through a "blow" valve to the blow tank.

A method of producing bleachable sulfate pulp by continuous vapor-phase cooking has been described (15). This allows more rapid pulping with lower chemical change.

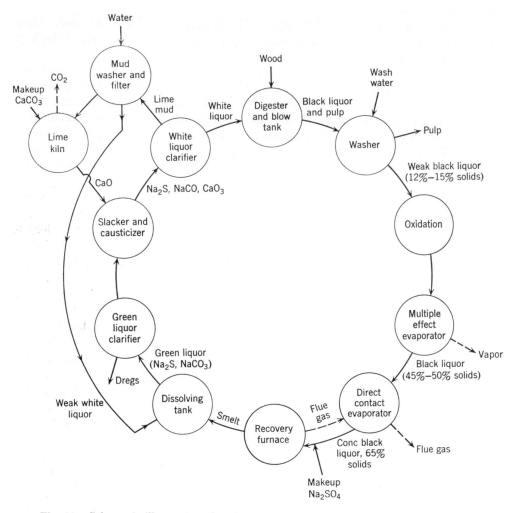

Fig. 11. Schematic illustration of cyclic recovery system for the sulfate pulp process.

The Cyclic Recovery System. As previously pointed out, sulfate pulping is dependent on its recovery process for producing the digestion liquor. This recovery is schematically illustrated in Figure 11. The chemical recovery cycle involves the separation of the black liquor from the pulp, its evaporation, and combustion for the recovery of the inorganic chemicals as a smelt which is subsequently converted to the white liquor for the next digestion. The recovery system together with its heat and material balance has been described in some detail in *Pulp and Paper Manufacture* (26).

Much of the equipment used in the recovery system is identical with or closely related to similar equipment used in other chemical industries. This includes the rotary filters used for brown stock washing, the multiple-effect evaporators, the causticizing equipment and the lime kiln. The following discussion will therefore concentrate on the function and nature of equipment essentially unique to this process, namely the oxidation tower, the black liquor recovery furnace, and its related equipment.

Black Liquor Processing. The black liquor is normally separated from the pulp by washing on rotary filters, two to four countercurrent stages being employed. After this separation it is subjected to evaporation, the last stage of which is by contact with the recovery furnace flue gas. Under these conditions residual sodium hydrosulfide will partially hydrolyze to form hydrogen sulfide and sodium hydroxide while sodium methanethiolate will partially hydrolyze to form methanethiol (methyl mercaptan) and sodium hydroxide. In order to prevent the escape of the volatile hydrogen sulfide and methanethiol the black liquor may be oxidized with air, leading to dimethyl disulfide (16). The following reactions occur during oxidation:

$$2 \text{ NaHS} + 2 \text{ O}_2 \rightarrow \text{Na}_2\text{S}_2\text{O}_3 + \text{H}_2\text{O}$$

$$2 \text{ CH}_3\text{SNa} + \tfrac{1}{2} \text{ O}_2 + \text{H}_2\text{O} \rightarrow \text{CH}_3\text{SSCH}_3 + 2 \text{ NaOH}$$

Although the inclusion of this stage is not essential to the total process it allows better control of the sulfide level in the liquor and also reduces the odor which is characteristic of sulfate pulp mills.

Black liquor oxidation is normally carried out by passing a stream of liquor and a stream of air to a tower fitted with perforated plates or with suitable packing to allow repeated intimate contact of liquor and gas. Due to the presence of fatty acid sodium salts, ie soaps, a considerable problem may result from foam, particularly when unseasoned pine is used and a number of designs have served to deal with this problem. With any given design, less foaming is obtained when operating at a higher solids concentration and this may be obtained by recycling a portion of the evaporated liquor through the oxidation tower.

As the solids concentration of black liquor is increased as a result of evaporation, it becomes increasingly viscous. For this reason the evaporation is conducted in two separate operations. Multiple-effect evaporation is used to bring the liquor to a concentration of about 45–50% solids while direct-contact evaporation is used to bring it to about 65–70% solids, the concentration at which it is fired in the recovery furnace. At the upper range of concentration it is extremely viscous and heat exchange is more readily obtained by direct contact with hot flue gas available from the recovery furnace than by indirect heating through heat exchange tubes. In the cascade evaporator, which may be used for direct evaporation, rotating vertical discs are partially submerged in the black liquor over which the furnace flue gas is passed. As a result of the contact the liquor is concentrated and a portion of the sulfur dioxide present in the gas is absorbed. The gas which still contains a colloidal fume consisting largely of sodium sulfate is then passed to an electrical precipitator where the fume particles are charged and collected for subsequent return to the concentrated black liquor ahead of the recovery furnace.

In the *venturi scrubber*, which is alternatively used for evaporating the concentrated black liquor, the liquor is sprayed into a stream of gas at a venturi throat. By operating the venturi at high gas velocities of the order of 300 ft/sec not only evaporation takes place but the liquor is broken down into a very large number of small droplets which capture the colloidal sodium sulfate fume which is carried in the gas from the furnace. Sulfur dioxide present in the gas is also absorbed. The droplets are then separated from the gas in a cyclone of special design which has its walls continually washed by a stream of black liquor. With this system electrical precipitation is not required. However, because of the high velocity required for efficient recovery of sodium salts in the venturi scrubber, considerably more power is required at the fan than when the cascade evaporator is used.

The Black Liquor Recovery Furnace. The function of the recovery furnace is to burn off the organic matter, to recover the chemical in the form of sodium carbonate and sodium sulfide, and to generate steam through utilization of the heat which is liberated. The steam may be generated at about 200 psi for direct use as process steam or as superheated steam at pressures up to 1200 psi for driving a turbine for electrical power generation with turbine exhaust steam being used as process steam.

In the B & W recovery furnace the evaporated liquor, after addition of makeup sodium sulfate, is heated to about 120°C and fired through one or more special oscillating nozzles (spray oscillators) in the front of the furnace which throws the droplets to the far and side walls. The remaining water is quickly evaporated at the high temperature in the furnace. The dried liquor builds up to a certain depth on the wall and then drops off from its own weight in chunks and falls towards the hearth which is covered with a mass of char. Primary air is admitted through a series of ports which controls the depth of the charred mass by burning it away. Reducing conditions are maintained in this zone so that the sodium- and sulfur-containing compounds will be largely reduced to sodium sulfide as indicated by the following reaction:

$$Na_2SO_4 + 2\,C \rightarrow Na_2S + 2\,CO_2$$

The inorganic residue melts at a temperature of about 990–1020°C depending on its exact composition and continuously runs from the furnace through smelt spouts placed at the lower end of a sloping hearth. Secondary air is admitted at a higher level to limit the height of the bed and also to carry out gas-phase reactions, ie conversion of CO to CO_2, H_2 to H_2O, and H_2S to SO_2. Tertiary air is added at a still higher point at a relatively high velocity to ensure mixing of the gases and to complete their oxidation. A small excess of oxygen is required to ensure complete combustion of the gases; a large excess is avoided because it favors conversion of SO_2 to SO_3. The furnace temperature is approximately 1250°C. A portion of the sodium salts, about 10%, is volatilized in the form of Na_2O which quickly reacts with CO_2 to form Na_2CO_3 and this further reacts in the upper portion of the furnace with SO_3 and SO_2 to form Na_2SO_4 and Na_2SO_3. The walls of the furnace are water cooled by an arrangement of fin-tubes connected to the water circulation of the boiler. The unit is so designed that the combustion gases will be cooled to a temperature below the melting point of the inorganic constituent during the upward passage through the furnace, so that when they condense on the closely spaced boiler tubes at the top and back of the furnace they will be present as a dustlike solid which can be blown off, rather than as a slag which would block the gas passage. Automatically timed soot blowers which impinge jets of steam (or compressed air) on the tubes traverse the boiler banks to blow them clean. The released ash falls either towards the hearth or to a special hopper where it is collected and added to the black liquor for return to the furnace.

Proper control of the reactions in the furnace is important. Reducing conditions are necessary at the base of the furnace if the smelt is to contain sodium sulfide rather than the inert sodium sulfate. Slightly oxidizing conditions are needed above the bed so that volatile sulfur compounds are converted to sulfur dioxide which will not only react with the fume but will be absorbed in the direct contact evaporator. Strongly oxidizing conditions in the upper portion of the furnace are undesirable since sulfur trioxide is formed in large amounts. This will react with the sodium sulfate fume to form sodium pyrosulfate which melts at 400°C and forms a glasslike corrosive covering on the boiler tubes. The reaction for its formation is as follows:

$$Na_2SO_4 + SO_3 \rightarrow Na_2S_2O_7$$

A major hazard in connection with recovery furnace operation is that accidental introduction of water into the smelt can result in serious explosions. Furnace explosions have occurred when, through mistakes, weak rather than strong black liquor has been fired to the furnace and reached the pool of smelt on the hearth. Explosions have also occurred when one or more of the tubes in the wall is ruptured thus allowing water to flow into the unit. This can occur if the furnace is relighted after a "blackout" which has resulted from an interruption of fuel or air and if the furnace is not first purged of the explosive gas mixture which may be present. If the primary explosion results in rupture of a tube a major secondary explosion results. Thus great care is needed in handling this equipment.

Preparation of White Liquor. The smelt is continuously run from the furnace to the dissolving tank. The liquor is strongly agitated in order to dissipate the heat. The temperature in the tank is readily controlled when the hot smelt is added to the water as opposed to the explosive mixture resulting when water is added to a pool of hot smelt. Weak white liquor obtained from washing the lime mud in the causticizing plant is used for dissolving the smelt.

The green liquor, ie the solution obtained on dissolving the smelt, carries an insoluble residue known as the dregs which gives it a dark green appearance. The dregs contain a small amount of carbon plus a number of inorganic constituents including iron sulfide, manganese dioxide, calcium carbonate, magnesium aluminum silicate, etc which have their origin in the wood and the process water or from corrosion of equipment. The liquor is separated from the dregs by continuous decantation, the separated dregs in turn are mixed with water and the decanted solution is used for washing the lime mud at a subsequent stage.

The clarified green liquor is used for slaking the lime. The causticizing reaction starts at this stage but additional time of one to two hours is provided in a series of tanks equipped with agitators through which the mixture is passed to allow equilibrium to take place. The causticizing reaction is as follows:

$$Na_2CO_3 + Ca(OH)_2 \rightleftharpoons 2\,NaOH + CaCO_3 \downarrow$$

The white liquor is separated from the calcium carbonate by decantation in a clarifier, and is then available for a new cycle. The underflow from the clarifier containing the calcium carbonate, which is known as lime mud, is diluted with water and goes to a second clarifier known as the lime mud washer. The clarified weak white liquor then goes to the dissolving tank while the residue goes to a rotary filter and then to the lime kiln where calcium carbonate is converted back to calcium oxide thus completing the lime cycle.

Recovery of By-Products from the Sulfate Process. *Turpentine* (qv) is usually present in the digester relief gas and is separated when this is condensed. Turpentine recovery amounts to about 20 lb/ton pulp when pine is used but the quantity is substantially less with spruce.

Tall Oil. The soaps present in the liquor are "salted out" as the liquor is evaporated and these can be suitably separated when the liquor is at a concentration of about 25–28%. When the liquor reaches this concentration in the multiple-effect evaporator it is transferred to a continuous settling vessel where the soap is skimmed off; the liquor is then returned to the evaporator to complete the evaporation. The soap is acidified with sulfuric acid, which may be waste acid from the generation of chlorine dioxide required for the bleaching step. The resultant product, known as tall oil, is separated from the aqueous phase which in turn is returned to the black liquor system. On distillation the crude tall oil yields fatty acids (see Vol. 8, p. 845), resin acids, and a pitch residue. The fatty acids are used for the production of soap and drying oils while the resin acids are used for sizing paper. The yield of tall oil is about 20–200 lb/ton pulp, the higher value being obtained from pine. Tall oil does not normally separate in commercially significant quantities from spruce or hardwoods. See Tall oil.

Lignin. A portion of the alkali lignin (qv) can be obtained from the black liquor by carbonating it to a pH of about 9.0–9.4. The crude lignin melts and settles as a viscous tar at a temperature of about 90°C and the decant liquor is returned to the recovery cycle. The separated lignin is then reprecipitated with acid to obtain a purified product. The lignin may be used as a resin or phenolic resin extender for the production of plastic laminates. The economies of this process are dependent on the price of phenol, the principal alternate raw material for this use. Alkali lignin has also been used in the preparation of asphalt emulsions, for entraining air in cement, for reinforcing rubber, etc.

Dimethyl Sulfide. If further caustic is added to the black liquor and it is heated to 250–285°C about 85 lb methyl sulfide and 10 lb methanethiol (methyl mercaptan) are produced as a result of demethylation of the lignin (17). This operation is now being carried out commercially in a mill in the southern U.S. The dimethyl sulfide is further converted at this location to dimethyl sulfoxide (DMSO). See Thiols; Sulfoxides.

ACID PULPING

Chemical pulps are also produced under acid conditions; the wood breakdown results from the reaction of bisulfite with lignin to form water-soluble ligninsulfonates. For successful pulping the bisulfite ion must be combined with a base such as calcium, magnesium, sodium, or ammonium and, in addition to the bisulfite, either sulfurous acid or sulfite may be present. Until the late 1950s the digestion liquor used for producing chemical pulps was of one type only, ie a bisulfite with a substantial excess of sulfurous acid. The process was traditionally known as the sulfite process. To avoid confusion with the recently developed bisulfite pulps produced with true bisulfite digestion liquor, ie without excess sulfurous acid, the old sulfite process is now referred to as the acid sulfite process.

The relationship between the composition of the digestion liquor and its pH as measured at room temperature, is shown in Figure 12. It will be seen that bisulfite and sulfite are in highly unbuffered regions, that is to say, a slight change in composition will markedly change the pH value. Sulfite solutions have a pH of 8.5–9.5, while bisulfites have a pH of 3.0–4.5. There are also relatively highly buffered regions, ie sulfurous acid–bisulfite mixtures with a pH of about 1.7 and sulfite–bisulfite mixtures with a pH of about 6.3–6.5.

Calcium bisulfite is in equilibrium with calcium sulfite and sulfurous acid as shown in the following reaction:

$$Ca(HSO_3)_2 \rightleftharpoons CaSO_3 + H_2SO_3$$

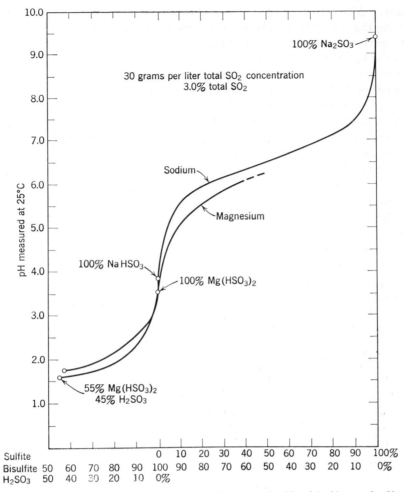

Fig. 12. The pH of solutions containing various combinations of sulfite, bisulfite, and sulfurous acid.

When calcium bisulfite solutions are heated the reaction goes to the right and the highly insoluble calcium sulfite is precipitated. This can be prevented by the presence of an excess of sulfurous acid which drives the reversible reaction to the left and for this reason only sulfurous acid–bisulfite liquors are possible with a calcium base, ie the liquor traditionally used for acid sulfite digestion. Approximately two-thirds of the SO_2 is present at sulfurous acid, the balance being in the form of bisulfite.

Magnesium sulfite has limited solubility but bisulfite and bisulfite–sulfite liquors with a pH of 6 or lower are stable and can be used as pulping liquors. The solubility of sodium and ammonium salts is such that the full pH range is available.

The acid sulfite process first came into commercial production about 1880. The raw materials for this process consist of approximately 325 lb limestone and 225 lb sulfur per ton of pulp, these having a total cost of about $4.00 to $6.00 per ton of pulp depending on the location of the mill. No satisfactory process has yet been found for recovering and recycling the calcium base. However, in view of the relatively low cost of the digestion chemicals, this initially presented no disadvantage since the sulfite mill was relatively easy to operate compared with the kraft mill where recovery was mandatory. Also, the cost of makeup chemical in the alkaline mill was probably greater than the cost of the total chemical requirement in the sulfite mill which operated without recovery. However this situation changed during the 1930s with the rationalization of the kraft recovery system already referred to. Thus the absence of a satisfactory recovery system made the sulfite process unattractive for new mills because of the potential pollution problems. Actually a relatively simple process based on a magnesium base liquor was developed in the late thirties (18), but because of the war it was not until 1948–1949 that the first plant went into operation and a further six years before the second mill started. In addition to the magnesia base recovery system a number of methods for recovery of sodium and ammonia base liquors have been proposed and two of these, the Sivola (19) and the Stora processes (20), which are both based on soda base, have reached commercial fruition.

The use of bases other than calcium has materially extended the available range of pH for sulfite pulping. Initially attention to bases other than calcium was directed to the neutral sodium sulfite liquors which were used to produce semichemical pulps from hardwoods for use in corrugating medium. It was subsequently found that sodium bisulfite could be used for producing softwood semichemical pulps (21).

The use of bisulfite for chemical pulping was initially confined to multistage pulping where acid sulfite cooking was used for one stage. With the Stora process a sodium bisulfite–sulfite liquor of pH 5.5–6.0 was used for the first stage while an acid sulfite liquor in the buffered 1.5 pH range was used for the second stage. Subsequently, techniques were developed for producing chemical pulp with true bisulfite liquor, ie the Magnefite process in which a magnesium bisulfite liquor is used and the pH is held at a value of 3–4 during the digestion (22).

Thus the use of soda and magnesia bases has not only allowed a cyclic recovery process but by widening the pH range available for pulping has greatly extended the usefulness of the acid pulping processes.

The Acid Sulfite Process. Unlike unbleached soda and sulfate pulps which are brown in color, unbleached sulfite pulp has a relatively light color and it can be bleached by comparatively simple means. It therefore finds its chief application in printing and fine papers. It is also used, after special bleaching, for pulps which are converted to rayon, cellulose acetate, etc.

The calcium base digestion liquor is prepared by burning sulfur to sulfur dioxide, cooling the gas and passing it through Jenssen towers which are packed with limestone. Two or three towers are connected in series and cold water is run countercurrent to the gas. The resultant bisulfite solution is fortified in one or more pressurized accumulators by absorption of sulfur dioxide relieved from a previous cook. The final digestion liquor will have a composition of approximately 1% "combined SO_2" and 6% total SO_2. By definition "combined SO_2" is the quantity of SO_2 theoretically equivalent to the monosulfite, ie $CaSO_3$. Thus the "bisulfite SO_2" is twice the combined sulfur.

The digestion is carried out in batch digesters lined with acid-resistant brick or with molybdenum-containing stainless steels such as 316 or 317. The digesters range in diameter from 10–18 ft and are 30–60 ft high. Before carrying out the digestion the chips are steamed to purge the air. Forced penetration of liquor is obtained by filling the digester and applying a hydraulic pressure of about 100 psi. During the heating period surplus liquor is withdrawn (and mixed with fresh liquor for the next digestion) thus reducing the liquor to wood ratio to about 1:4. The initial liquor concentration and the quantity withdrawn are adjusted so that approx 4 lb combined SO_2 per 100 lb dry wood are left in the digester. The complete digestion cycle requires about 6–10 hr with a relatively slow heating period and a maximum temperature of about 135–145°C. Due to the vapor pressure of the sulfurous acid the total pressure established in the digester is 30–40 psi higher than the vapor pressure of water, ie about 90–100 psi total pressure. During the last one to two hours the digester is heavily relieved, and the sulfur dioxide gas obtained is dissolved in fresh liquor for the subsequent digestion. Approximately two thirds of the total sulfur dioxide is recycled in this way.

The time, final temperature and acid concentration are normally selected in relation to the final product. Dissolving pulps, which are subsequently converted to rayon, etc, should have a low hemicellulose content and this is obtained by higher temperature and time and lower combined SO_2. At the other extreme are pulps which are used for glassine and greaseproof papers where high hemicellulose is desirable; these are obtained by use of lower temperature, higher time and higher combined SO_2. Intermediate conditions are chosen for pulps for fine papers and newsprint.

Bases such as ammonium, sodium, and magnesium can be used instead of calcium for the acid sulfite solution, these normally giving marginally better qualities. Several large magnesium acid sulfite mills with chemical recovery plants have been built on the west coast of North America for producing dissolving pulps and paper-grade pulps. The recovery systems will be described after discussion of other modifications of the pulping process.

The Bisulfite Process. Although many attempts were made over the years to produce chemical pulps using true bisulfite liquors, a practical understanding of the important factors involved was only established about 1956 and this method of pulping dates from that time.

Bisulfite reacts with certain constituents of the wood to form thiosulfate, the reaction with sugars resulting from the conversion of the aldehyde group to an aldonic acid as follows:

$$2\ C_5H_{11}O_5.CHO + 2\ HSO_3^- \rightarrow 2\ C_5H_{11}O_5COOH + S_2O_3^{2-} + H_2O \tag{1}$$

Thiosulfate acts as a catalyst for the disproportionation of bisulfite to thiosulfate and sulfuric acid:

$$4\ HSO_3^- \xrightarrow{(S_2O_3^{2-})} 2\ SO_4^{2-} + S_2O_3^{2-} + 2\ H^+ + H_2O \tag{2}$$

Since this reaction produces its own catalyst, the bisulfite is soon consumed, after which the thiosulfate itself breaks down to form bisulfite and elemental sulfur.

$$S_2O_3^{2-} + H^+ \rightarrow HSO_3^- + S \tag{3}$$

These reactions can occur with acid sulfite and bisulfite liquors. However, reaction 2 is highly dependent on the temperature and the quantity of bisulfite present. With bisulfite pulping the temperature used is approx 30°C higher than that for acid sulfite pulping while the quantity of bisulfite is twice as great and thus the risk of an uncontrolled reaction is more acute. Fortunately these reactions can be kept under control by avoiding too great an excess of bisulfite so that it will be largely consumed by reaction with lignin before the digestion reaches temperature. About 8–9 lb combined SO_2 per 100 lb dry wood is a suitable amount for chemical pulp; if the bisulfite is depleted as a result of too little or too much being added, sulfur can precipitate as a result of reaction 3 and the pulp is ruined.

With true bisulfite pulps the situation can be further complicated unless the pH is under strict control. Whereas acid sulfite liquors have a low pH of about 1.5 and are therefore little affected by the formation of the less strongly acidic acetic and other wood acids formed during the cook, bisulfite liquors which are at higher pH are un-buffered and these acids can result in a rapid decrease in pH as cooking proceeds. Delignification at any given temperature is strongly dependent on pH, and with a changing pH it is difficult to balance conditions so as to avoid what is called a "burnt cook." However a satisfactory method was developed for holding the pH in the range of 3–4 by adjusting the pressure in the digester to 5–10 psi above the vapor pressure of water at digester temperature. The acetic acid formed from the wood reacts with the bisulfite to form sulfurous acid and by relieving the digester, as just described, SO_2 will be relieved as it is formed once an equilibrium is established thus preventing the serious drop in pH that would otherwise occur. The slight over-pressure of 5–10 psi is desired since otherwise SO_2 would be partially stripped from the bisulfite bringing the pH to a value of about 5 which is in a pH range where the cooking proceeds very slowly. Using this technique the Magnefite (magnesium bisulfite) pulp can be pre-pared in not only high yield but also in bleachable range and it was found that the pulp showed marked strength and yield improvement over the corresponding conven-tional acid sulfite pulp (22). Certain woods, including pine, which cannot be pulped by the acid sulfite process, can be pulped by this technique.

Most bisulfite pulping operations use batch digesters similar to those in the acid sulfite process. In the newer installations chip filling and closing of the digester is automated. In one Magnefite installation producing chemical pulp at about 58% yield, a Kamyr continuous digester is used.

Sodium bisulfite pulps can also be prepared in this manner. Hartler et al. (23) compared sodium bisulfite pulp and calcium acid sulfite pulp from the standpoint of defibration, in other words the maximum yield at which only 1% screenings were obtained using a water-jet defibrator. The following results were obtained:

Time to reach digester temperature, hr	Yield at defibration point	
	Sodium bisulfite, %	Calcium acid sulfite, %
½	59	
2	60	51
5	60.5	57

It is apparent that the heating time, the time required for the diffusion of chemical into the chip, is much less critical with the bisulfite pulp and that even with a one-half-hour heating time the yield, at the defibration point, is substantially better than with five hours for the acid sulfite. At still higher yields, about 65%, less mechanical refining power is required for bisulfite pulps. Semichemical bisulfite pulps are now being widely used for newsprint.

Sulfite–Bisulfite Pulps. Whereas it is apparently not possible to produce a satisfactory chemical pulp when the pH is held at 6.0 throughout the complete cook, it is possible to carry out a portion of the digestion in this range. When the cook is started at a pH of about 6, as in the Stora process, the glucomannan acetate is de-acetylated before pulping occurs. This reaction appears to stabilize the glucomannan so that when the pulping is completed at a lower pH as a second stage, the gluco-mannan is retained in the pulp rather than dissolved as it largely would be other-wise. This results in a substantial gain in yield when softwoods are being pulped.

Bleached neutral sulfite–bisulfite two-stage pulps can be obtained in yields up to 54% compared with 49–50% for one-stage bisulfite pulps. These two-stage pulps refine rapidly to give glassine-type pulps. However their physical strength properties are somewhat lower than those of the bisulfite pulp. There is no corresponding yield gain for hardwoods which contain relatively little glucomannan acetate. The glucurono-xylan which results from deacetylation of the 4-O-methylglucurono-xylan acetate contained in hardwoods is not strongly retained in the pulp.

Bisulfite–Sulfite Pulps. When two-stage magnesium or sodium base cooks are initiated in the bisulfite range and completed at pH 6.0, the pulp is stronger than obtained with one-stage bisulfite treatment and the yield is essentially unchanged.

In the Sivola process, which uses a sodium base, an acid sulfite stage is followed by an alkaline stage at pH of about 9.0, this being achieved by adding sodium carbonate to the liquor part way through the cook. Using this technique it is possible to produce pulps of high-alpha cellulose content suitable for rayon. The recovery process used will be later described.

Recovery Processes. *Calcium Base.* A number of mills, especially in Europe, have installed equipment for collecting residual calcium base liquor, evaporating it to about 55% and burning it under self-sustaining conditions with the recovery of steam. The resultant fly-ash consists of about 50% calcium sulfate and 50% calcium oxide. No method for returning the calcium salts to the process has been developed so the ash must be discarded. Thus heat recovery, but not base recovery, is obtained. Special evaporators have been developed for concentrating the liquor which scales badly because of the calcium salts. With the Rosenbladt evaporator the liquor and steam sides of the heat exchanger are interchanged at frequent periodic intervals; the condensate which has a low pH dissolves the scale which is formed from the liquor.

Ammonia Base. Heat recovery can also be obtained by burning ammonia base liquor. However base recovery is not possible because the ammonia breaks down to form nitrogen and water in combustion.

Soda Base Recovery. A flowsheet for the Stora recovery process (20) is shown in Figure 13. Following the digestion and blow the residual liquor is separated from the pulp and concentrated by multiple-effect evaporation. The liquor is burned in a recovery furnace similar to that used in the sulfate process. The smelt is dissolved in water and clarified. The green liquor, which contains Na_2S and Na_2CO_3, is carbonated with pure CO_2; H_2S is stripped off leaving a solution of $NaHCO_3$. The effluent H_2S is combined with pure SO_2 in a Claus reactor which converts the two gases to elemental sulfur. Thus sulfur, together with makeup sulfur is burned in air, a portion being concentrated to 100% SO_2 (by dissolving in cold water and then stripping with steam) for use in the Claus reactor while the other portion is used directly for converting a sodium sulfite solution to sodium bisulfite. The sodium bisulfite is mixed with the $NaHCO_3$ solution referred to above and, as a result, sodium sulfite is formed and pure CO_2 is evolved which is used for carbonation at the previous stage. A portion of the sulfite solution is recycled for absorbing the burner gas SO_2 as described above. The balance, after absorbing sulfur dioxide from the recovery furnace flue gas, is converted to sodium bisulfite. After the absorption of SO_2, relieved from the digester, this becomes the regenerated cooking liquor, which is recycled to the digester. The flue gas, prior to sulfiting of the liquor, is passed through an electrostatic precipitate to remove the sublimed sodium sulfate fumes.

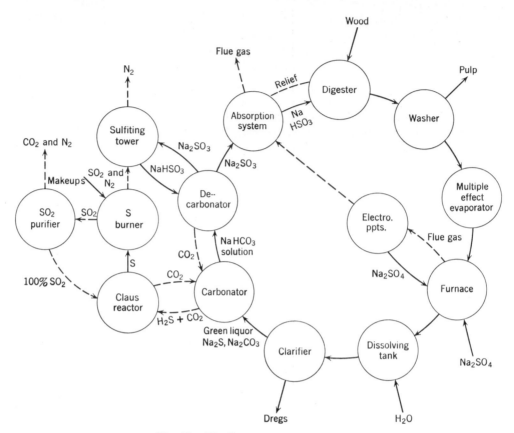

Fig. 13. The Stora recovery process.

The Stora process is somewhat more complex than the Mead process previously described in connection with NSSC pulping. In the Stora process, pure CO_2, rather than flue gas, is used for stripping the sulfide in order to prevent excess O_2 in the gas from oxidizing the sulfide to thiosulfate. With chemical pulping, which requires relatively high bisulfite concentrations, longer cooking times, and higher temperature, a low initial thiosulfate content in the digestion liquor is essential because of its auto-catalytic effect on the decomposition of bisulfite.

In the Sivola recovery process (19), the other soda base system being used commercially, the sulfide is also stripped from the clarified green liquor but in this case multistage carbonation, including pressure carbonation at two atmospheres, is used. The concentration of the green liquor is carried at a relatively high level so that the sodium bicarbonate is precipitated from the liquor. The major portion of the bicarbonate crystals, which are filtered off, are used for preparing the cooking liquor by first mixing with a recycling bisulfite solution in order to evolve CO_2. The resultant sodium sulfite solution is then treated with flue gas to prepare the regenerated cooking liquor. This liquor should have very low thiosulfate content as a result of the bicarbonate purification stage.   The balance of the bicarbonate slurry, together with the bicarbonate filtrate, is stripped of a portion of its CO_2 with steam to prepare the neutralizing solution, which is required for addition to the digester in the final stage in the Sivola cooking process. Thiosulfate, which may have formed from oxidation of the

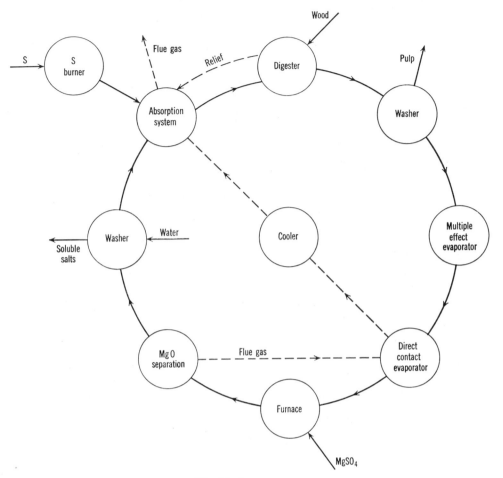

Fig. 14. The MgO recovery process.

sulfide in the green liquor, during the dissolving process, has a less serious effect at the end of the digestion, particularly at a high pH.

Magnesia Base. With magnesia base liquors recovery is somewhat simpler. Figure 14 shows the essential stages of this process (22). Liquor separation and evaporation are similar to those used for sodium base liquors. However, the magnesia base recovery furnace and its operation are substantially different from those for alkaline liquors. Atomizing nozzles are provided to give burning of the liquor in flight. The magnesium compounds are converted essentially to MgO while the sulfur compounds are converted to sulfur dioxide. At the furnace temperature, approximately 1250°C, magnesia is a nonvolatile solid which carries as small particles through the boiler and heat economizer sections of the furnace to a cyclonic separator. The separated magnesia is slurried in water thus hydrating to form Mg(OH)$_2$. The slurry is filtered and washed to remove water-soluble salts which enter the process as inorganic constituents of the wood. After removal of the magnesia, the gas passes through the direct heat evaporator and a cooler where its saturated temperature is reduced to about 145°F. The gas is then contacted with the magnesium hydroxide which is reslurried following the purification stage; the resultant magnesium bisulfite solution is filtered to remove insoluble impurities and, after addition of sulfur dioxide released during the cooking operation, forms the digestion liquor. Losses of magnesia and sulfur can be replenished by the addition of magnesium sulfate to the liquor before combustion and/or by the addition of purchased MgO or Mg(OH)$_2$ and sulfur dioxide obtained by burning purchased elemental sulfur.

Special features of this process are the absence of smelt and fume and the fact that no magnesium sulfide or thiosulfate is formed in combustion. This latter greatly simplifies the subsequent absorption stage.

Acid Pulping By-Products. Although a number of by-products are produced, none have found sufficient market and/or economic advantage to be adopted by the industry as a whole. Ethyl alcohol can be produced by fermentation of the residual liquors from softwood pulps and this process has been in commercial operation since early in the century. The liquor is partially neutralized to pH 5.0 and fermented with baker's yeast which is recycled. This allows fermentation of the glucose, mannose and galactose but not the pentoses nor aldonic acids. Approximately 25–30 U.S. gal of 95% alcohol per ton acid sulfate pulp can be produced. See Vol. 8, p. 438.

The ligninsulfonates also find a limited market either as a crude dried waste liquor or after partial purification such as is obtained after removal of sugars by alcohol fermentation. Ligninsulfonates will reduce the viscosity of clay slurries and are used in the production of ceramics, as dispersants for oil-well drilling muds, etc (see Lignin).

Vanillin, which is used in flavoring, is produced by alkaline oxidation of sulfite liquor. The yield is about 5–8% of the lignin present. The total world supply of vanillin is now produced from sulfite liquors.

Chemical Pulps from Cellulosic Products Other Than Wood

At least 2000 years ago rags were used for the production of pulp in China. Cotton rag pulps are still used for top quality fine papers and the limit on this production is the scarcity and relatively high cost of suitable rags. The rags, usually clippings from garment manufacture, are cut into small pieces and treated with sodium hydroxide solution in a digester for approx 3–4 hr at 25 psig pressure. No delignification is involved; the alkali treatment gives a controlled cellulose degradation that facilitates the subsequent mechanical breakdown of the cloth. The digested product is washed and subjected to the mechanical action of a beater which breaks the rags down to a fibrous pulp known as half-stuff. After mild bleaching and washing, the pulp is ready for conversion to papers. Cotton linter, the short staple left on cotton seed after ginning, is pulped and used as a substitute for rag pulps.

Straws and grasses are also used for pulp production. Flax straw, a by-product from linseed, contains bast fiber which after mechanical separation from the short lignified fiber, also contained in the straw, is cooked with sodium hydroxide and sodium sulfide to give a product used for cigarette paper, bank note paper and other specialty uses. Hemp pulp, having somewhat similar properties, can be made in the same mill. Cereal straws, esparto, bagasse and bamboo are cooked by the alkaline process for the production of pulps. Straw pulps are also produced by the Pomilio process. This involves a mild alkaline cook followed by chlorination, a second alkaline treatment and a hypochlorite bleach. This gives a pulp in about 42% yield, this requiring about 25% caustic and 18% chlorine based on the pulp.

The storage and handling of annual straws and grasses adds greatly to the cost of production, and added to this is the uncertainty of the crop from year to year. Most straw pulp operations have been relatively small, they therefore are not able to take advantage of the economies now available in the large scale wood pulp operation. Most straws have a high silicate content which complicates the alkaline recovery process. Special situations exist in which a premium pulp is prepared, such as that from flax straw, and here the decorticated straw will be held for at least two years to guarantee a continuing supply. Although bamboo is a grass it is not an annual and thus has the advantage that it can be harvested throughout the year. The fiber length is somewhat longer than that of cereal straws and hardwoods and therefore the pulp is useful in areas where hardwood is plentiful but softwood is scarce. Certain other fast-growing cellulosic materials such as kenaf are being considered as a crop for pulp production.

Treatments

Washing and Cleaning. Chemical pulps must be washed to free them from residual chemical, solubilized lignin, etc. When the residual liquor is evaporated and burned it is desirable to obtain as high a concentration as possible. Thus a high removal of soluble impurities and a minimum of dilution, two opposing factors, are desired. A continuous washing system is now always used. A normal three-stage washing system uses three rotary filters. The pulp, suspended in recycled black liquor, is pumped to the first filter where it forms a cake and is washed by means of sprays with dilute liquor from No. 1 filter. The partially washed cake is dispersed in recycled dilute liquor from No. 2, and then, in turn is filtered and washed on No. 2, using the effluent from No. 3 filter for washing and redispersing. Finally, it is filtered and washed in No. 3 using hot water for the final wash. This gives three countercurrent diffusion washes with three intermediate dilution-extraction washing stages. Approximately 96–99% of the chemical will be removed with a black liquor dilution of 2–5 lb water per lb of pulp.

A portion of the washing or even the complete washing is alternatively carried out by countercurrent diffusion in the outlet section of a continuous digester. This has the advantage that the residual liquor carries a substantial portion of the heat from the digestion thus reducing the quantity required for its subsequent evaporation. The pulped chips remain in chip form while still in the digester. The washwater passes between the cooked chips rather than through them so that the diffusion rate is controlled by the migration of soluble matter through the chip as a result of the concentration differential between the center of the chip and the liquor surrounding it. Thus several hours are required for complete washing in this manner.

A new method of continuous diffusion washing of pulp in separated fiber form has been recently developed by Kamyr (24). A unit of this type is shown in Figure 15. The pulp suspension at about 10–12% consistency moves up a tower between a series of closely placed two-sided concentric screen rings. Washwater is distributed between the rings by rotating streamlined fin nozzles thus displacing the liquor which passes through the screen rings. The screen rings intermittently travel up at a rate equal to that of the pulp, then rapidly drop down. This reciprocating motion repeats continuously and the washed pulp is scraped from the top of the tower.

The pulp should also be free of insoluble impurities such as incompletely pulped coarse fiber bundles, bark dirt, and sand. Normally three separate types of equipment are sequentially used, the knotter screen for removing large uncooked fragments, the rotary screen for shives, and the centrifugal vortex cleaner for miscellaneous dirt.

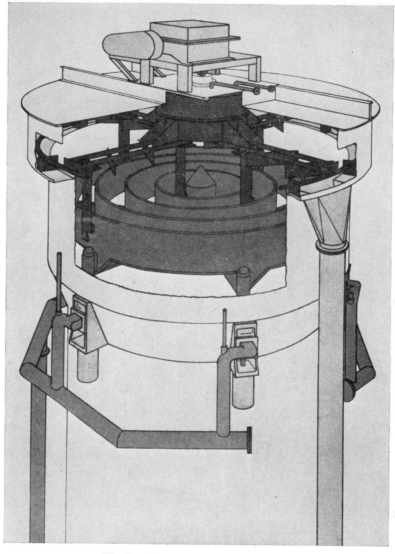

Fig. 15. The Kamyr diffuser washer.

Knotting and Screening. With standard chipping techniques a certain number of thick chips are formed, particularly so at and in the vicinity of the knots which occur in the log. It has been found impractical to choose a digestion liquor concentration and a digestion time and temperature suitable for the largest chips and wood fragments, since this would overly degrade the pulp formed from the normal chips. Thus, with the conditions used there is a spectrum of sizes of undefibered partially cooked wood particles. The largest, the knots, are normally removed before pulp washing since their presence in the pulp cake prevents the normal flow of wash water through the portion of the mat where the fragment is located.

In the Jönnson knotter the pulp slurry is passed down through a vibrating screen plate set at an angle to the horizontal and arranged so that only the lower section is submerged. The plate has perforations of about ⅜ in. The vibration of the plate

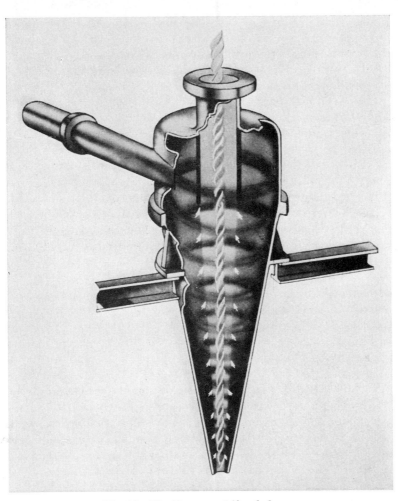

Fig. 16. The Bauer centrifugal cleaner.

moves the oversize material out from the submerged area of the plate so that it is separately discharged. Following the washing of the pulp the smaller fragments known as shive are removed. A rotary screen may be used for this purpose. It consists of a stationary perforated cylindrical screen set on the horizontal. The pulp is axially fed at one end while an internal rotating baffle moves the reject material to the far end where it is discharged while the cleaned pulp passes through the screen. The rejected material is rescreened in order to recover fiber that is carried with the shive. In order to maintain a reasonable throughput the holes are relatively large, about $\frac{1}{16}$–$\frac{1}{8}$ in. in diam. This removes the major portion of the long shive but chunky material and grit pass through.

Centrifugal Cleaners. Bark particles, chunky shive, sand, and so on may be efficiently removed with centrifugal cleaners (25). The pulp slurry is pumped to a battery of units such as that shown in Figure 16. The centrifugal cleaner consists of a stationary "cyclone" having a tangential inlet to an essentially conical vessel fitted with axial outlets; the apex outlet at the bottom is relatively small while that at the upper end is larger. As a result of the tangential inlet and the configuration a free vortex motion is established in the cone. The spinning velocity of the pulp suspension increases as it approaches the axis where a liquidfree core forms. The apex opening is slightly larger than the diameter of this core and thus only a relatively small amount of material is discharged at this point, the major portion being discharged at the other end. The material in suspension is subjected to high shear and to centrifugal force. The fiber, which has a high length to diameter ratio is drawn towards the center by the shear while the more chunky material is thrown towards the cone wall by centrifugal force. The motion of the fluid in the unit carries the reject material to the apex where it is discharged while the main portion of the fiber carries with the main flow. The rejected material carries a certain amount of fiber; this is diluted and sent to a secondary unit to minimize fiber loss. The action of the cleaners with regard to material which will be accepted or rejected is dependent on conditions of centrifugal force and of shear, and these can be independently varied by the choice of dimensions of the unit, the relative size of the inlets and outlets, etc. Thus different units will be chosen depending on fiber length and the type of dirt to be removed.

BLEACHING

Groundwood and Chemimechanical Pulps. The high bulk and opacity of groundwood and chemimechanical pulps make them suited for printing papers. However, they have relatively low brightness values, ie 50–65 G.E. It is therefore desirable to increase the brightness using techniques which will bleach rather than destroy the lignin. This can be accomplished with sodium peroxide (Na_2O_2) which oxidizes the lignin or with sodium or zinc hydrosulfite ($Na_2S_2O_4$ or ZnS_2O_4) which reduces the lignin. These can be used sequentially if desired since the results are to some extent additive. Heavy metal ions, such as iron or copper, which are often present in the pulp, will decompose the bleaching agent so that sequestrants such as tetrasodium ethylenediaminetetraacetate (EDTA) should be first added to the pulp.

For peroxide bleaching the pH should be 10.5–11.0, and 1–3% peroxide is used. In addition, sodium silicate and magnesium sulfate are normally added. About three hours' retention time at 40°C and 12% consistency are used. The use of 1% peroxide, based on pulp weight, will give a brightness gain of about 5 points for spruce groundwood and 15 points for the somewhat darker cold caustic pulp. With 3% peroxide the gains are about 12 points and 25 points, respectively.

Hydrosulfite bleaching is carried out at pH 6–7. Sodium tripolyphosphate is added with the hydrosulfite, the treatment requiring about 2 hours at 55°C. The use of 0.5–1.0% hydrosulfite, based on pulp weight, will give a 6–10 point increase in brightness for spruce groundwood.

Unfortunately the brightness of bleached pulps of this type is relatively unstable to ultraviolet radiation so that bleached chemical pulp must be used for papers where stability is important.

Chemical Pulp Bleaching. Chemical pulps can be brought to about 90–92 brightness and this involves complete removal of the lignin as well as incidental removal of some hemicellulose. Continuous multistage treatment, with intermediate wash, is now standard. Acid sulfite and bisulfite pulps can be completely bleached by sequential treatment involving *chlorination*, caustic soda *extraction*, and chlorine *dioxide* bleaching. This treatment is referred to as CED. With sulfate pulps an additional caustic extraction and chlorine dioxide stage is necessary, ie, the sequence is CEDED. In some cases a hypochlorite stage precedes the first chlorine dioxide stage to give the sequence CEHDED. Most recently built bleach plants work on one or other of these sequences.

Delignification by bleaching is more selective and less degrading to the cellulose than is the delignification occurring in the final stages of the digestion. Since about 1.5 lb chlorine are required per pound of lignin, the more lignin that is left at the end of the digestion the more expensive is the bleaching stage. However, delignification to low lignin content in the digester is accompanied by a high carbohydrate loss and within a certain range the increase in cost for bleaching chemicals may be offset, or nearly so, by increased final yield. The lignin content is normally measured indirectly by its oxidizing requirement, under standard conditions of chlorine (Cl_2 number) or permanganate (Kappa number). The molecular weight of the cellulose is measured indirectly by the viscosity of a chlorite-bleached sample dissolved in a standard cupriethylenediamine solution and is expressed as the disperse viscosity. The balance between Kappa number and viscosity is important; the higher the viscosity for any given Kappa number, the less degraded the pulp. In bleaching pulps for use in paper, conditions are chosen so as to give a minimum viscosity loss and thus maintain maximum strength characteristics in the final pulp.

Bleaching is a topochemical reaction. The lignin is distributed throughout the cell wall and it is necessary to break it down into fragments sufficiently small so that they will diffuse out. Thus several stages are required for complete bleaching of the pulp. Washing is provided between each stage.

The chlorination is carried out at relatively low temperature, 25°C or below, and for relatively short times, 30–60 min. Reactions with the lignin involve substitution of chlorine for hydrogen in the 5 and 6 positions of the benzene ring, partial demethylation and at least a partial depolymerization by fission of the aryl alkyl ether bonds. With acid sulfite and bisulfite pulps the fragments thus formed are largely water soluble while with sulfate pulps a somewhat smaller portion of the lignin is dissolved. In the alkali extraction reaction which follows, further quantities of partially depolymerized chlorinated lignin are removed as the sodium salt. With sulfite pulps the extraction is carried out at 20–40°C while with sulfate pulps a higher temperature, 50–60°C, is used. The quantity of NaOH used is about 1.5–3.5% of the weight of the pulp.

The introduction of chlorine dioxide bleaching in about 1950 resulted in a major advance since it is essentially nondegrading to cellulose and is capable of producing very bright pulps. Chlorine dioxide is a gas and its use was delayed by the fact that it is explosive at high concentration, toxic, and highly corrosive. Techniques for handling it are now well established; these involve generating it at point of use at low concentration and the use of proper vents and corrosion-resistant equipment including such metals as titanium for the mixer where it is introduced to the pulp. The temperature used for reaction with pulp is 60–80°C, the consistency 12–15%, the pH about 4, and the time, from 2 to 6 hours. In addition to the ability to demethylate the lignin, chlorine dioxide will also break down the aromatic ring. With sulfite and bisulfite pulps a brightness of 90–92 can be reached at the end of this stage. With sulfate pulps the brightness is only about 85 and a second caustic extraction followed by a second chlorine dioxide stage is required to bring it to the same level.

Hypochlorite is sometimes used following the first extraction stage. The pH should be held at about 11 and an excess should be avoided. Unlike chlorine dioxide, hypochlorite can have a marked degrading effect on cellulose, not only lowering its molecular size but also changing its chemical nature. If the pH is allowed to drop during hypochlorite bleaching, an increase in carbonyl content (as measured by copper number) is obtained. A pH of 7.0 during hypochlorite bleaching results in a very high copper number. This pulp has very poor stability; it yellows and loses further strength on aging. The high carbonyl content obtained with such treatment also results in an increased alkali solubility and therefore a loss of yield at the extraction stage, no doubt in part from the end-group peeling reaction described under Alkaline pulping.

An increase in carboxyl content (as measured by methylene blue absorption) is obtained when bleaching is carried out at high pH. This increase in carboxyl does not result in the undesirable effects obtained from increased carbonyl; in fact, conversion of carbonyl to carboxyl has a stabilizing effect.

Sodium borohydride will reduce the carbonyl groups to alcohol groups thus giving brightness stability to the pulp. Unfortunately the present cost of this reagent makes such use impractical. It is apparent, however, that not only lignin reactions but carbohydrate reactions are involved in bleaching.

In the production of dissolving pulps, for subsequent conversion to viscose and acetate, removal of hemicellulose is desired. In this case the alkali extraction stage is carried out at higher temperature, 70–120°C. At the higher temperature pressure treatment is required.

Bleaching Equipment. Each stage in the bleaching sequence requires continuous processing equipment which will allow: (*1*) adequate mixing of the pulp with bleaching chemicals and where necessary, steam; (*2*) sufficient retention times; and (*3*) adequate washing. For low-consistency operation, such as in the chlorination, a pump can be used for mixing. For higher consistency, specialized equipment such as a double-shaft mixer is required.

A tower is normally provided for retention time and care is taken in the design to promote plug flow. When a gas is the reactant an up-flow tower for all, or a portion of the reaction, is normally desirable. With the extraction stage up- or down-flow towers can be used. Rotary washers have been conventionally used, with the final wash spray preparing the pulp for the next stage. That is, hot water is used if the next stage is to operate at high temperature. As an alternative to the rotary washer, the new Kamyr pulp diffusion washer is now being mounted on the top of up-flow towers; this naturally simplifies the layout.

Pulp Drying. Where the pulp is prepared for market it must be dried and baled, The pulp is partially dewatered on a cylinder or a fourdrinier wire, pressed and dried. the drying taking place by contact with heated rotating cylinders or by hot air while the sheet is conveyed or floated through a drying chamber. Recently some mills have used flash drying systems where the dewatered and pressed pulp is shredded and then simultaneously conveyed and dried in a hot air system. The dried pulp is then pressed and baled for shipment.

Bibliography

"Pulp" in *ECT* 1st ed., Vol. 11, pp. 250–277, by R. S. Hatch, Hudson Pulp & Paper Corporation.

1. M. Zinbo and T. E. Timell, *Svensk Papperstid.* **68,** 647 (1965).
1a. U.S. Pat. 2,735,762 (Feb. 21, 1956), James d'A. Clark.
2. D. Atack and W. D. May, *Tech. Sect. Proc. Can. Pulp Paper Assoc.* **T10** (1962).
3. O. Forgacs, *Pulp Paper Mag. Can.* **64,** 100–115 (1963).
4. S. Lagergren, S. Rydholm, and L. Stockman, *Svensk Papperstid.* **60,** 632–644 (1957).

5. H. Tarkow and William C. Feist, *Tappi* **51** (2), 80–83 (1968).

6. C. A. Carlsson and S. Lagergren, *Svensk Papperstid.* **60**, 664–670 (1957).

7. S. Rydholm, *Pulping Processes*, Interscience Publishers, a division of John Wiley & Sons, Inc., New York, 1965, pp. 343–355.

8. H. P. Markant, *Tappi* **43**, 699–702 (1960).

9. R. P. Whitney, S. T. Han, and J. L. Davis, *Tappi* **40**, 587–594 (1957).

10. G. G. Copeland and J. E. Hanway, Jr., *Tappi* **41** (6), 175–184A (1964).

11. Anon., *Chem. Eng.* **72**, 74–76 (1965).

12. N. Sanyer and E. L. Keller, *Tappi* **48**, 99–105 (1965).

13. G. Machell, G. N. Richards, and H. H. Stephton, *Chem. Ind., London* **1957**, 467–469.

14. O. Franzon and O. Samuelson, *Svensk Papperstid.* **60**, 872–877 (1957).

15. L. Munk, Z. Todorski, J. R. G. Bryce, and G. H. Tomlinson II, *Pulp Paper Mag. Can.* **65** (10), 411–414 (1964).

16. G. H. Tomlinson, G. H. Tomlinson II, J. H. Swartz, H. D. Orloff, and J. H. Robertson, *Pulp Paper Mag. Can.* **47**, 71–77 (1946).

17. W. M. Hearon, W. S. MacGregor, and D. W. Goheen, *Tappi* **45** (1) 28A–34A (1962).

18. G. H. Tomlinson and L. S. Wilcoxson, *Paper Trade J.* **110**, 209 (1940).

19. T. A. Pasoce, J. S. Buchanan, E. H. Kennedy, and G. Sivola, *Tappi* **42**, 265–281 (1959).

20. R. Söderquist, *Svensk Papperstid.* **58**, 706–712 (1955).

21. J. H Ross, J. S. Hart, R. K. Strapp, and W. Q. Yean, *Pulp Paper Mag. Can.* **55**, 192–199 (1954).

22. G. H. Tomlinson, G. H. Tomlinson II, J. R. G. Bryce, N. G. M. Tuck, *Pulp Paper Mag. Can.* **59**, 247–252 (1958).

23. N. Hartler, L. Stockman, and O. Sundberg, *Svensk Papperstid.* **64**, 67–85 (1961).

24. J. Richter, *Tappi* **49** (6), 48A–49A (1966).

25. U.S. Pat. 3,096,275 (July 2, 1963) G. H. Tomlinson.

26. J. N. Stephenson, ed., *Pulp and Paper Manufacture*, Vol. 1, 1st ed., McGraw-Hill Book Co., Inc., New York, 1950, pp. 403–429 and 499–662.

G. H. Tomlinson, II
Domtar Limited

PULP COLORS. See Pigments, Vol. 15, p. 603.

PULVERIZING. See Size reduction.

PUMICE, PUMICITE. See Vol. 1, p. 26.

PUMPS AND COMPRESSORS

PUMPS

Pumps, in their many types and classifications, represent the second most widely used industrial machine in the chemical industry today. Only electric motors find greater usage.

Pumps are most commonly classified according to the method employed in moving the fluid. The two broad categories of pumps have definite advantages and disadvantages for their use, depending primarily on the nature of the liquid and, to some degree, the nature of the pumping system. The first category, *kinetic pumps*, increase the energy of the liquid as it enters the eye of the impeller and travels through the pump casing. *Positive displacement* pumps achieve liquid transfer by forcing the liquid from suction to discharge through voids created by a rotating device, or by means of a reciprocating device, or by means of another fluid (pistonless pump). Chart 1 shows a further breakdown of pump types within the two main categories.

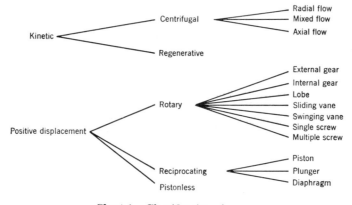

Chart 1. Classification of pumps.

Even though the pump may represent only a small fraction of the total cost of the system, its work is vital, and downtime is so costly that the primary selection factor for a chemical pump is normally *reliability*. The chemical process engineer, however, should not as a rule become too involved with pump selection. He should rather give full information to the specialist, who will then help him make the decision.

Figure 1 shows the *approximate* ranges for the fields suitable for the main types of pumps. It must be emphasized that there are no strict boundaries for the fields shown. According to the figure, in many ranges more than one type of pump can be applicable; the choice will be made according to factors such as the characteristics of the liquid to be moved (corrosiveness, or viscosity), the process requirements, net positive suction head, or other considerations.

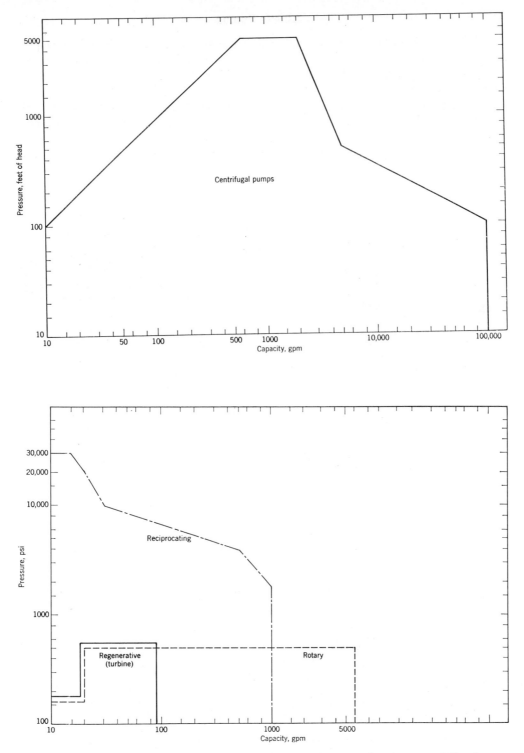

Fig. 1. Approximate ranges for the fields suitable for the main types of pumps: centrifugal pumps (top), and positive displacement pumps (bottom).

Kinetic Pumps

This type of pump imparts energy, mainly kinetic energy, to the liquid, principally by the action of centrifugal force. The most common type of pump in use today is the centrifugal pump. Figure 2 is a schematic diagram of a typical single-stage, single-suction centrifugal pump.

The rotation of the impeller (Fig. 3) within the liquid imparts velocity to the liquid by centrifugal force. The liquid is accelerated and most of the velocity is converted to pressure or, saying it another way, kinetic energy in the form of velocity head is converted to pressure head. The casing surrounding the impeller collects the

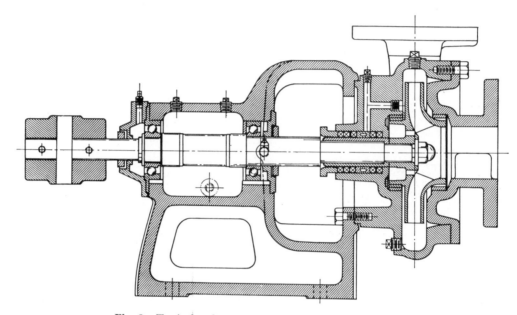

Fig. 2. Typical end-suction, single-stage centrifugal pump.

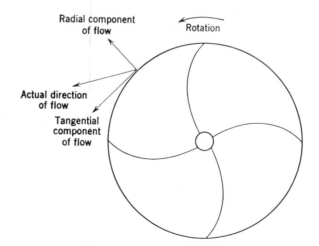

Fig. 3. Flow tendencies of liquid leaving the tip of the pump impeller. The actual direction which the liquid takes is a result of the radial and tangential flow directions.

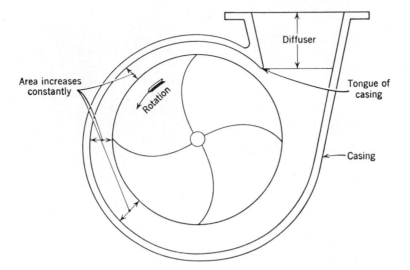

Fig. 4. Volute casing design showing increasing area of space between the impeller tip and casing inner wall. As liquid is being discharged in increasing quantities from every point on the impeller, the ever-increasing area keeps fluid velocity constant.

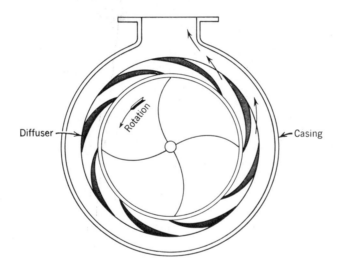

Fig. 5. Concentric casing with individual diffuser vanes.

liquid being discharged from all points around the circumference of the impeller and channels the liquid to a point of discharge.

Some method must be employed to reduce the velocity (and thus increase the pressure energy) before the liquid leaves the pump. Centrifugal pumps achieve this by a diffuser action. Volute pumps (Fig. 4) contain a straight diffuser ending at the discharge flange. These pumps may have more than one volute-shaped passage, all ending in a common discharge stream. Figure 5 shows a diffuser pump where individual diffuser vanes reduce fluid velocity.

Centrifugal pumps are further classified by flow direction. Figure 2 shows a pump with a radial-flow impeller where liquid flow is directed primarily radially outward from

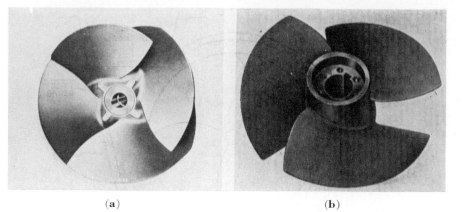

(a)   (b)

Fig. 6. (a) Axial-flow impeller; (b) end view of a mixed-flow impeller.

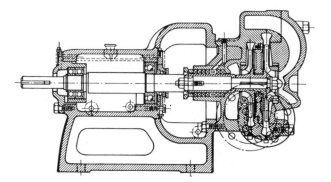

Fig. 7. Diagram of a frame-mounted, two-stage, end-suction pump.

the axis of rotation. As the component of radial flow is decreased and the axial component of flow is increased a propeller action is achieved. The surfaces of the impeller vanes thrust and lift the liquid primarily in an axial direction. This axial flow wheel is shown in Figure 6.

Since the vanes of an axial-flow impeller are large in comparison to a radial-flow wheel, and axial-flow impellers impart considerably less energy to the liquid, this type of pump is used for large volumes of liquids pumped against low head requirements. By reducing the axial width of the impeller vane and increasing the diameter a combination of axial and radial flow is achieved. This is called a mixed-flow impeller. Most centrifugal pumps used today are of radial-flow design, especially those used for the chemical process industries.

Multistage Pumps. When high pressures at low or moderate capacities are required, the addition of one or more impellers can achieve this purpose. Figure 7 shows an end-suction, radially split case, multistage pump. Figure 8 shows a multistage axially split case pump. Axially split case units generally handle higher capacities and pressures than the radially split case pump, which is designed with a cantilever shaft. One advantage is the ease of inspecting or repairing the pump without breaking the pipe connections located in the lower half of the casing. The complete rotating element can be lifted out of the casing when the upper half is removed. Under normal conditions the axially split pump has a longer life because of heavier construction.

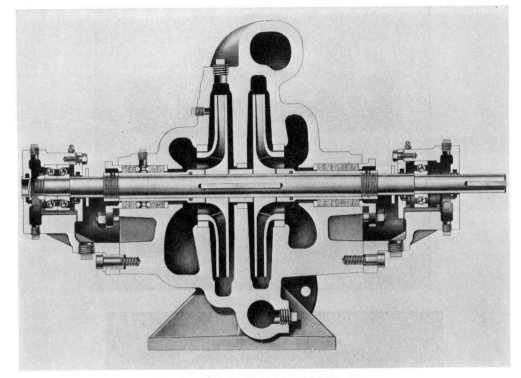

Fig. 8. Axially split case, multistage pump.

Very heavy duty service pumps, capable of pressures up to 3000 psi, with 12 or more stages, are not uncommon today. This design finds applications from general plant water through desuperheating, boiler feed, makeup water, hydraulic systems, auxiliary nuclear generator feed, and secondary feed.

Centrifugal pumps can be even further refined by several distinct features. Impellers can be of an open or closed design (Figs. 9, 10). Open impellers are not bound by shrouds over the vanes and are less expensive to manufacture than closed impellers. For this reason open impellers are normally made in alloy steel or stainless steel and see wider use on corrosive and erosive service than closed-impeller pumps. Figure 10 shows typical liquid-end schematics for closed and open or semiopen impellers.

The conventional method of mounting the pump liquid-end to the frame assembly was shown in Figure 2. This is commonly referred to as a "frame-mounted" pump. The liquid end can also be directly mounted on the motor bracket. This close-coupled unit (Fig. 11) has a space-saving advantage over a frame-mounted unit. However, it has the inherent limitation that if it becomes worn by corrosive chemicals considerable cost is incurred in replacing the shaft.

The in-line unit (Fig. 12) is gaining wider acceptance in the chemical process industry. Recently introduced for general chemical plant service, it eliminates a baseplate and since it can be mounted vertically it saves valuable floor space. On larger sizes some form of support for both pipe and pump is required to eliminate vibration and hold the unit in place.

Several types of vertical pumps other than in-line units are available for capacities up to 15,000 gpm and heads to 5000 ft. Some of the common configurations are

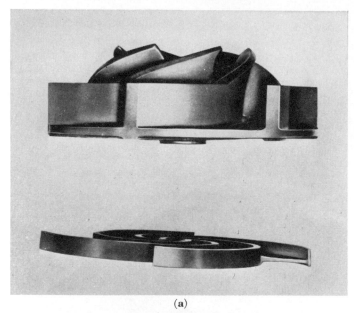

(a)

(b)

Fig. 9. (**a**) Open or semiopen impeller;   (**b**) closed impeller.

shown in Figures 13a–c. A vertical unit for space saving has solved many a process problem. Such units find many applications for transfer and booster service, LPG (liquefied petroleum gas) (qv), filter service, and spray booths.

In recent years, a standard for chemical process pumps has been introduced by the American Standards Association and is widely used in the chemical process industry today. The ASA proposed a dimensional standard pump with a rear pull-out design. It has the advantage of removal of the rotor assembly and bearing frame from the rear of the casing without disturbing the suction or discharge connections or driver position.

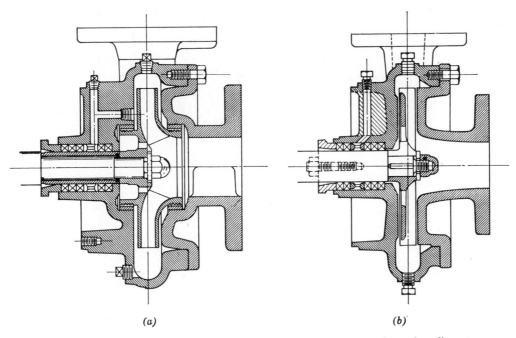

Fig. 10. Liquid-end schematics for (**a**) closed and (**b**) open or semiopen impellers.

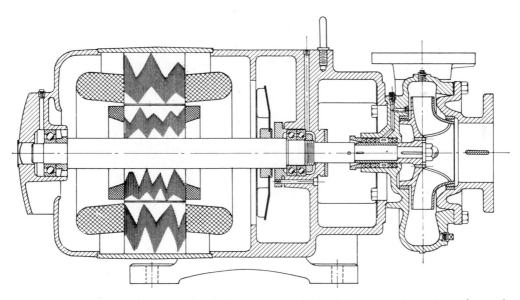

Fig. 11. Motor-mounted, end-suction, single-stage pump (note shaft common to motor and pump).

Regenerative Pumps. The regenerative pump (sometimes called a turbine pump) is basically a centrifugal pump. It operates on the principal of pressure regeneration by which a multivaned impeller engages and re-engages the liquid to develop high heads in a single stage. The liquid follows a spiral path as it enters and re-enters the impeller while it is carried around the casing (Fig. 14a).

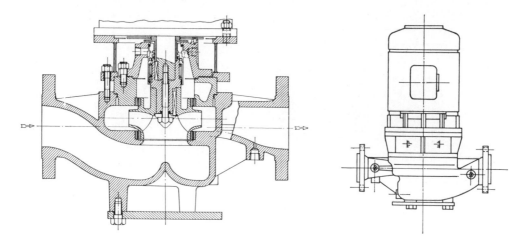

Fig. 12. Vertical in-line pump configuration.

As the liquid enters the pump, it is evenly divided by a separator and each half passes through an opening in the plates to reach the impeller (Fig. 14b). As the liquid passes around through the plates, it is thrown outward due to centrifugal force. However, the flow is contained by the plates and turned inward again until the liquid again enters the impeller. This cycle is repeated many times as pressure is built up in the pump (Fig. 14c). Finally, when the liquid reaches the discharge opening, it is allowed

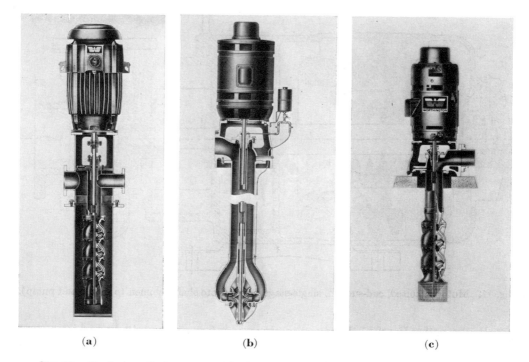

(a)   (b)   (c)

Fig. 13. Typical vertical pumps. (**a**) Can-pump with built-in NPSH (net positive suction head); the liquid is completely enclosed. (**b**) Vertical double-suction pump used for wet-pit application. (**c**) Vertical industrial pump; single- and multistage for wet-pit, tank, and sump service.

to escape and a close-clearance stripper in the plates prevents the flow from continuing to the suction area (Fig. 14d).

Because of the close-clearance stripper, the self-priming turbine pump can handle liquids with large amounts of gas or vapor. As long as sufficient liquid is trapped in the

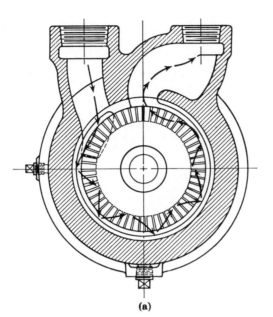

(a)

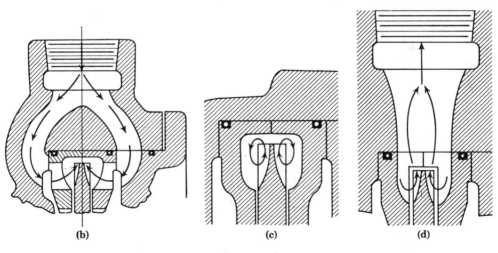

(b)   **(c)**   **(d)**

Fig. 14. Regenerative pump.

casing, the pump will mix the liquid with the gas in the suction pipe and separate the gas on the discharge side.

Regenerative pumps have an advantage over those with an end-suction design since the regenerative pump is, in effect, a double-suction pump. This results in balancing axial hydraulic thrust.

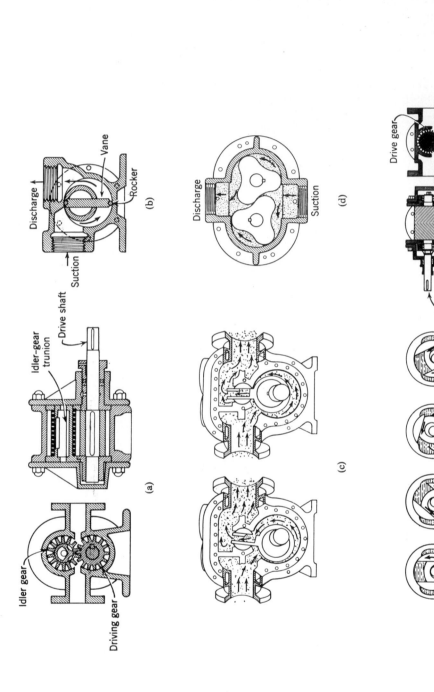

Fig. 15. Rotary displacement pumps: (**a**) spur gear, (**b**) rotary plunger, (**c**) rotary piston, (**d**) three-lobe rotary, (**e**) single-vane, and (**f**) herringbone gear.

Positive Displacement Pumps

Rotary Displacement Pumps. Some of the better-known types are shown in Figure 15. All of these pumps employ the following operating cycle: (*1*) space opens at the inlet to receive liquid, (*2*) liquid is entrapped and conveyed to the outlet, (*3*) space closes at the outlet forcing the liquid out.

Rotary pumps are suitable for liquids which are clean, more viscous than water, and have lubricating characteristics; they are particularly useful for supplying a fixed rate of flow without auxiliary controls. In the simpler types, these pumps are relatively small and low in initial cost. Nearly all types produce a flow that is freer from pulsations than that from a reciprocating pump, and a more constant volume against variable head than that from a centrifugal pump. External timing-gears and bearings are employed to control the clearance of mating parts and to reduce rotor wear in pumps designed for handling nonviscous or nonlubricating liquids at appreciable pumping heads. Rubber rotors, vanes, or liners are useful for the antifriction and abrasion-resistance qualities of rubber when pumping dirty water and abrasive slurries. Several types are inherently designed or easily adapted for variable-displacement operation of the pumping element; this obviates the necessity for an adjustable-speed drive or external by-pass controls in order to secure any desired flow or pressure within the capacity of the pump.

For pumping very viscous liquids, it is usually necessary to operate a rotary displacement pump at reduced speed in order to allow time for the liquid to flow into the spaces where it is entrapped, and to flow out as fast as it is displaced, without the development of excessive local pressure, that is, between gear teeth. Herringbone-gear wheels, and other special provisions, often permit a pump to be operated at much higher speeds with liquid of a given viscosity before it becomes strained by excessive pressure or loses capacity due to cavitation. The small size and compact arrangement of most types of rotary displacement pumps facilitate the construction of heated jackets, which enable the pump to handle extremely viscous liquids or molten solids without risk of freezing of the rotors. Rotary displacement pumps, like reciprocating pumps, have the ability to handle gases with the liquid without loss of prime. This enables a rotary pump to remove gas from the suction line and permits liquid to flow to the pump under barometric pressure, even when the pump is located above the liquid level.

Reciprocating Pumps. These employ a plunger, piston, or diaphragm to displace the pumped fluid and provide the most positive means for maintaining a constant volume of flow against a variable discharge head. The ability to handle compressible fluids dictates their selection when operating with variable suction conditions where air or gas is apt to enter the pump suction to an extent that would cause a centrifugal pump to cease pumping. The liquid velocities in a reciprocating pump are usually low; this makes them particularly suitable for viscous liquids. Reciprocating pumps may be designed to produce the highest heads, and to handle the smallest flows that may be required.

The cost of reciprocating pumps of standard design is moderate to low. It is especially low when direct drive by steam power is contemplated and the drive cost is included with the pump. Specially designed pumps for exceptionally high pressure or small flows are more readily available as reciprocating pumps than any other type of pump. The normal life of a reciprocating pump is long, maintenance and repair are fairly simple, hence reliability is good. Continuous maintenance is required for good performance, however, and the flow is intrinsically pulsating. For electric-motor drive at constant speed, a rotary or centrifugal pump is to be preferred. Steam-driven reciprocating pumps are extremely valuable for stand-by service where electric power failures must be contemplated.

Slip and Volumetric Efficiency. Displacement-type pumps do not discharge a volume of liquid equal to the volume displaced by the solid element, because of internal leakage of the liquid past valves, pistons, or rotors. The ratio of the volume of liquid discharged to the volume displaced by the pump element is called the *volumetric efficiency*. The amount of internal leakage, called the *slip*, results in a decrease in the hydraulic efficiency of the pump.

When the pumping pressure increases, the internal leakage or slip of the pump increases. At low pumping rate or high pressure, the slip of a pump may increase until it equals or exceeds the displacement of the pumping element, especially in pumping a liquid of low viscosity. When pumping a compressible fluid, the volumetric efficiency of the pump is decreased due to the decrease in volume of the fluid during pumping. This effect increases the apparent slip of the pump and is particularly important in gas compressors. When reciprocating pumps are employed in handling dirty, abrasive, or corrosive liquids, or when the pump is used to meter a liquid, the internal leakage must be kept to a minimum. One means for reducing slip, due to valve leakage, is to employ two or more sets of suction and discharge valves through which the liquid must flow successively. If the valves do not often fail to close, the coincidental failure of both valves during the same stroke is unlikely.

Pistonless Pumps. Liquids may be transported from one vessel to another, through piping of various lengths, under the influence of the pressure of an auxiliary fluid usually immiscible with the liquid transported. Air or gas may be employed (or water, to displace oil), for example. Heating a volatile liquid in the original vessel, or cooling the vapor in the receiving vessel, or both, results in a "pumping" pressure differential which will cause the desired flow. In this case, the liquid transported is displaced by its own vapor.

When the displacement chamber is made small compared to the supply or receiving vessel, and is arranged for automatic and cyclic operation, the device is called a *pistonless pump*. Any fluid appropriate for a blow-case operation is suitable for a pistonless pump, provided a supply is maintained under sufficient pressure, and that the fluid is expendable or easily recoverable after use. One arrangement uses steam for the motive fluid. The pressure discharges the pumped fluid, and the reduction in pressure which is induced cyclically by injection of the cold liquid, or water, allows the pumped fluid to refill the chamber from the supply vessel. This device is known as the *pulsometer*. It is a low-cost device, requires little operating attention, and achieves a discharge pressure close to that of the supply steam.

Bibliography

"Pressure Technique (Pumps)" in *ECT* 1st ed., Vol. 11, pp. 123–126, by L. H. Garnar, Worthington Corp.

Tyler G. Hicks, *Pump Selection and Application*, McGraw-Hill Book Co., Inc., New York, 1957.
A. J. Stepanoff, *Centrifugal and Axial Flow Pumps*, 2nd ed., John Wiley & Sons, Inc., New York, 1957.
Austin H. Church, *Centrifugal Pumps and Blowers*, John Wiley & Sons, Inc., New York, 1944.

Sigar J. Karassic and Roy Carter, *Centrifugal Pumps, Selection, Operation, and Maintenance,* Mc-Graw-Hill Book Co., Inc., New York, 1960.

American Institute of Chemical Engineers, *Pump Manual,* The Science Press, Inc., New York, 1960.

F. A. Holland and F. S. Chapman, *Chem. Eng.* **73** (Feb. 14, 1966).

F. A. Holland and F. S. Chapman, *Chem. Eng.* **73** (July 4, 1966).

ROBERT KOBBERGER
Worthington Corporation

COMPRESSORS

The purpose of compression equipment is to raise the energy level of air or gas to a useful level as economically and efficiently as possible. Compression plays an important role in the chemical process industries.

The higher energy level of the air or gas is mandated by the requirements of the process. In some cases the compressed medium is used to promote chemical reactions, an example being the conversion of hydrogen and nitrogen to ammonia at high pressure. In other cases the compressed medium may be used to perform work such as that done by the wide and varied assortment of air-operated equipment that may be needed in any plant.

General Classification of Compressors. The increase in pressure achieved by compression may be accomplished (*1*) by physically reducing the initial volume of gas in a closed chamber to the terminal volume, or (*2*) by a dynamic effect brought about by a change in gas velocity.

The first type of compression is accomplished by *positive displacement compressors* and the second by *dynamic compressors.* Positive displacement units include *reciprocating* and *rotary compressors.* The reciprocating compressor admits and exhausts the gas through pressure-actuated valves which open and close as the piston moves through one revolution. The gas admitted to the cylinder in the suction stroke is reduced in volume by movement of the piston and an increase in pressure accompanies the reduction in volume. In the rotary compressor the gas is admitted directly to the compressor chamber. The decrease in volume with accompanying increase in pressure is accomplished by eccentricity of a rotating element or by intermeshing of rotors.

Dynamic compressors, *centrifugal* and *axial,* increase the pressure of the gas by means of changes in velocity. The operation of a centrifugal-type compressor can be compared to that of a centrifugal pump. Structurally, it consists of an inlet duct, impeller, diffuser, and volute. The inlet duct directs the medium to be compressed from the suction pipe to the impeller. The impeller transmits kinetic or velocity energy to this medium by centrifugal action. The medium is accelerated in the impeller to a speed approaching the impeller tip speed. The diffuser decelerates the high-velocity fluid, changing kinetic energy to pressure energy, and causes the pressure to rise.

The limits for the various types of compressors are shown in Figure 1. This is not an ironclad delineation but merely a general representation of areas for each category. There is, of course, some overlapping and the final decision on the unit to be used may be influenced by other considerations such as the nature of the medium being compressed. The economic factors to be considered include initial cost, installation costs, operation costs, and maintenance costs.

Terminology. The following is a list of definitions important in compressor terminology:

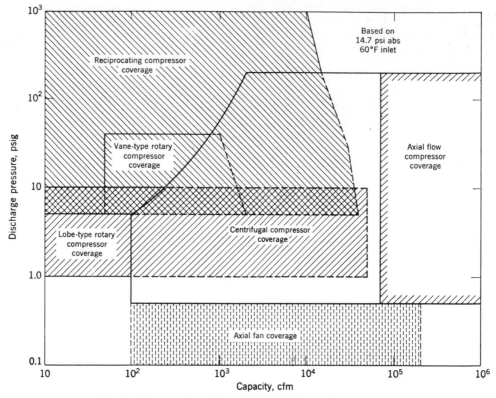

Fig. 1. Ranges of usefulness of various types of compressors.

1. Piston displacement (PD)—the volume swept by the compressor piston, usually expressed in cfm derived by dividing the cylinder area (ft²) by the piston speed (ft/min).

2. Piston speed—the average linear velocity of the piston, expressed as feet per minute. It is equal to $(2 \times \text{stroke})/(12 \times \text{rpm})$ since the stroke or linear travel of the piston is commonly expressed in inches.

3. Ratio of compression—$R_c = \dfrac{\text{discharge pressure, abs } (P_d)}{\text{suction pressure, abs } (P_s)}$

4. Actual capacity—the volume of gas, measured at the suction pressure and temperature, and expressed in cfm, that the compressor will deliver to the specified conditions. If units other than cfm are used, this is regarded as the *equivalent capacity*.

5. Volumetric efficiency (VE)—equal to the actual capacity divided by the piston displacement.

6. Valve velocity—the average velocity of the gas through the compressor valves expressed in ft/min; equal to $144 \times \text{PD}$ divided by the valve area in square inches.

7. Clearance—the volume in the cylinder over and above that swept by the piston. The clearance ratio equals the clearance volume divided by the swept volume.

8. Compression efficiency—reflects the gas losses that take place within a cylinder, that is, slippage past the piston rings, and the losses in getting the gas in and out of the valves.

9.   Indicated hp—equals the theoretical hp divided by the compression efficiency.

10.   Friction hp—the hp consumed by the compressor due to heat generated by the moving parts.

11.   Brake hp or shaft-required hp—the sums of ihp and fhp.

12.   Mechanical efficiency—the ratio of ihp to bhp.

Reciprocating Compressors

Of the positive-displacement-type units, the one most widely used because of its great versatility is the reciprocating compressor. It is used for pressures from vacuum to the hyper range in the area of 50,000 psi, and also can accommodate wide ranges of capacity. Basically, any reciprocating compressor consists of three major components: the frame, cylinder and driver.

The frame can be of many different forms; however, it must be of sufficient strength to withstand the loads that will be imposed on it, and rigid enough to support and maintain alignment of the crankshaft. For small capacities and horsepowers to approx 150 hp, the single, center-crank frame is used (Fig. 2). To accommodate a range of horsepowers the frame is built in a variety of strokes with corresponding speeds. For slightly higher horsepower rating, vertical or angle units are used (Fig. 3). They are also built in several stroke sizes with corresponding speeds. For the greatest range of horsepower capability, up to 15,000, a multicylinder frame is available (Fig. 4). This class of reciprocating compressor is also built in a number of stroke sizes with corresponding speeds.

Fig. 2. HB type of compressor.

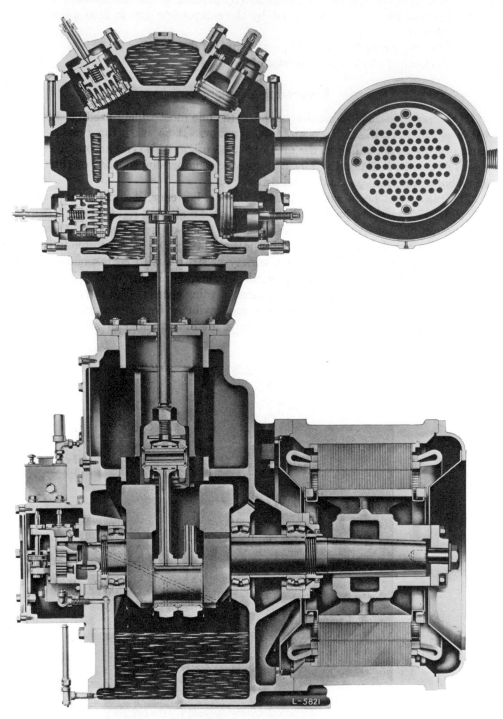

Fig. 3. Y type of compressor.

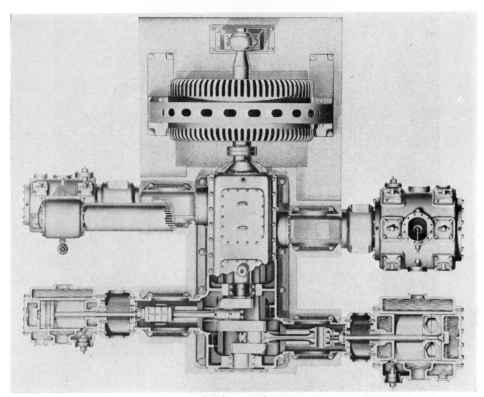

Fig. 4. BDC type of compressor.

Fig. 5. Transverse section of a BDC compressor.

The crankcase or frame is most commonly a casting made of gray iron. The frame consists of the running gear including the crankshaft, connecting rod, crosshead, and crosshead guide (Fig. 5). Frame size and type, as indicated previously, vary from single-cylinder units to those that have positions for as many as ten individually mounted compressor cylinders to meet the many requirements of the chemical process industry.

The crankshaft is a forged-steel element normally supported by sleeve bearings except for high-speed, low-horsepower units. The rotating motion of the crankshaft is converted to reciprocating motion by the forged-steel connecting rod terminating in the crosshead. The reciprocating crosshead is contained and guided in the crosshead guide.

Fig. 6. Typical compressor cylinder.

The compressor cylinder includes valves, piston, and piston rod, and is normally double-acting with compression occurring at both ends of the cylinder (Fig. 6). Some small-diameter, high-pressure applications and the higher stages of a multistage compressor are sometimes made single-acting. In the single-acting cylinder, compression occurs in either the crank end or head end, whichever best suits the design. The cylinders are normally water jacketed to remove some of the heat of compression and also the friction heat generated by the piston rings. The jacket coolant also serves to equalize temperature distribution, reducing thermal stress and possible distortion. The piston rod opening in the cylinder is effectively sealed with a stuffing box with floating segmental metallic packing.

Pressure-actuated valves, which open and close as the piston moves through its stroke, ensure correct suction and discharge of medium in the cylinder.

The compressor cylinder is, without question, the most important part of a compressor. It is the component which requires most careful consideration of materials and finishes to be compatible with the service for which it will be used. The compressor cylinder must be individually considered for each application from the viewpoint of strength, resistance to corrosion, and bore surface finish compatible with service.

The pressure to which the cylinder will be subjected normally dictates the material. Generally, cast iron is used for pressures up to 1000 psig; nodular iron, up to 1500 psig; cast steel, up to 2500 psig; and forged steel for pressures over 2500 psig. Cylinder liners, when used, are cast iron and, for some high-pressure cases, a steel liner is used. A cast-iron or cast-steel cylinder is cast with an integral cooling-medium jacket and its design must be such that circulation completely around the bore is assured. The cooling jacket space must also have large accessible openings to permit cleaning of jacket space, as very often cooling water is not clean and free of solids. For the forged-steel cylinder, the mass of metal is such that cooling water is circulated merely for equalization of thermal stresses in the forging.

High-pressure cylinder design, in the area of 5000 psig, must take into account the cyclic change in stress which is a cause of fatigue failure at areas of stress concentration. On some cylinders the cyclic tensile stress can be overcome by using heavy bolts to place the cylinder under a compressive load. On larger cylinders at higher pressures, it is desirable to eliminate stress concentration areas in the cylinder barrel. This can be accomplished by using a single-acting cylinder with the valves as well as the suction and discharge ports located in the cylinder head.

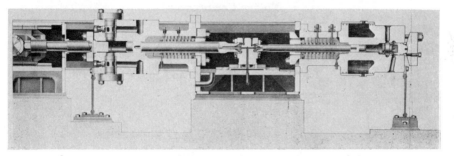

Fig. 7. Opposed-plunger construction.

A dominant consideration in high-pressure compressor design is assurance of load reversal; that is, the algebraic sum of the gas pressure load should go from plus to minus in a complete revolution. As the piston moves in one direction, compressing the gas, the gas pressure exerts a force on the piston which is transmitted through the piston rod to all the running gear components. As the piston moves in the other direction, the loads should reverse. This reversal of loads assures that lubrication will be uniform around the complete bearing surfaces, and will eliminate premature wear and possible malfunction. This load reversal may be accomplished with a balanced tandem cylinder design or opposed-plunger construction (Fig. 7). Further, in some cases, load reversal is obtained by use of a tail rod which is an extension of the piston rod through the piston. This gives an equalized piston area for compression on both ends of the piston, resulting in equal and reversing loads on the frame. (Admittedly it does introduce an additional high-pressure packing.)

The opposed-plunger construction is well suited for high-pressure applications. Although each cylinder is single acting, they perform in unison as a double-acting cylinder. Also, with this construction, it is possible to utilize the head of the cylinder to house a combination suction and discharge valve and suction and discharge ports, eliminating the need for boring in the cylinder barrel. The supporting structure of this design must be very rigid to maintain the alignment necessary for trouble-free operation.

Although oil has always been considered a necessity for operating reciprocating compressors, it can be a serious or undesirable contaminant for many chemical processes. Its removal from the gas stream is costly and the degree of cost increases with the degree of oil removal required.   In recent years there has been a trend toward the reduction or complete elimination of the oil required to lubricate the compressor cylinder and rod packing.   This trend has been accelerated with the development of polytetrafluoroethylene, PTFE, whose slippery surface or low coefficient of friction permits operation either with reduced quantities of oil or with none at all.   Further, the strength of the PTFE has been greatly increased without sacrifice of its desirable characteristics by use of bonding agents such as glass, carbon, or bronze.

The cost saving that results from elimination of oil-removal equipment must be evaluated against the higher maintenance cost of non-lube compression.   A popular compromise is nominal lubrication utilizing PTFE construction.   With this construction, oil is supplied to packing only.   The lubricant will travel along the piston rod and to the cylinder, supplying a bare minimum at that point.

Rotary Compressors

Another type of positive displacement compressor is the rotary.   There are three variations of the rotary compressor: the sliding vane, the lobe, and the rotary screw. Each type has its limitations in capacity and pressure.   See Table 1.

Table 1. Comparison of the Three Types of Rotary Compressor

Type	Capacity, cfm	Single-stage, pressure range, psig	Multistage, pressure, max, psig
screw	120–20,000	10–50	300
sliding vane	50–2000	10–50	120
lobe	50–15,000	0–10	25

Of the rotary types, the rotary screw is the most commonly used because of its greater range of capacities and pressures.   The sliding vane and lobe types are less frequently used because of a low pressure ratio limit for the lobe and a low capacity for the sliding vane.

In the *sliding vane compressor* the rotor is eccentric to its casing and has vanes mounted in radial slots in the rotor.   Rotation causes the vanes to move in and out of their slots;   as they move out, they are held against the casing by centrifugal force. Gas is trapped between the casing and vanes and is compressed as the rotor turns and the vanes move back into their slots.

The *lobe compressor* has two rotating elements, each shaped like a figure eight. One of the meshing lobes rotates clockwise and the other counterclockwise.   The suction may be at the top of the casing and the discharge at the bottom, or they may be at the side;   both are radial to the lobes.   As the lobes rotate, they scoop in a given volume and transport it at constant volume to the discharge side.

The *rotary screw compressor* consists of a casing which houses two meshing rotors with helical lobes, one concave and the other convex.   The helical lobes do not make contact and are kept apart by timing gears at one end (Fig. 8).   Gas is admitted axially at one end of the casing.   The male lobe acts as a piston, moving and compress-

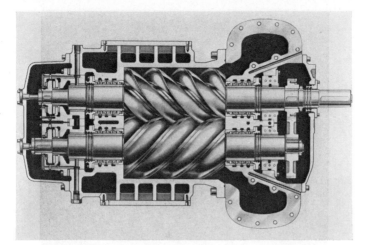

Fig. 8. Rotary section.

ing the gas along the mating female lobe to the other end of the casing where it is discharged radially. The compression ratio is determined by the length of the rotors, the helix angle of the lobes, and the configuration of the discharge port. The casing is water jacketed to prevent thermal distortion. As the gas is passing through the unit at relatively high velocities, little heat is removed from the gas by the casing cooling medium. For compression ratios over 4.5, the units are multistaged by connecting in series and intercooling between stages.

The casings for any of the rotary-type units are normally cast iron. For the rotary screw and the sliding vane, the rotors are carbon steel. The lobe-type rotors are cast-iron.

Centrifugals

Of the dynamic compressors, the axial flow type has very little application in the chemical process industry. Therefore, this discussion will be limited to centrifugal units only.

The centrifugal may be of a variety of configurations depending on the job to be done. A *single-stage centrifugal compressor* is a single-impeller unit that is built for pressure ratios from 1.35 to 5. The *multistage* centrifugal compressor is a multi-impeller unit for pressure ratios above 2. *Multicasing* centrifugal compressors are machines having several casings driven by a single driver; these compressors can be single- or multistage. The *integral gear* centrifugal compressor is a machine having one or several casings, all directly geared to a single-speed increaser and driven by a single driver. Integral gear compressors can be single- or multistage. *In-line* centrifugal compressors have one or more impellers on a single shaft operating in a single case. In-line compressors may be single- or multistage.

For a centrifugal compressor the fluid-handling parts are in contact with the fluid to be compressed. The impeller is the rotating fluid-handling part. The casing, diffusers, inlet guide vanes, and return channels are the stationary fluid-handling parts.

The impeller is the pressure-producing rotating part of the centrifugal compressor. It accelerates the flowing medium as it enters the inlet of the impeller and travels to the outer periphery. In an open impeller, the blades are mounted directly on the hub

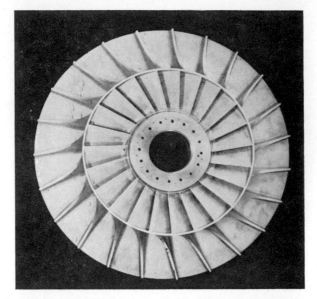

Fig. 9. Semiclosed centrifugal compressor impeller with cast-in inducer section.

Fig. 10. Closed or shrouded centrifugal compressor impeller with front cover removed.

without a front or rear cover. Open impellers are either cast in one piece, milled from a solid forging, or built up from forgings, castings, or plates. They are used on low-pressure blowers, superchargers, and single-stage centrifugal compressors. This type of impeller provides a scraping action on the casing wall which is quite effective in preventing dirt buildup and, in addition, the blades are accessible for cleaning. Although relatively inexpensive to manufacture, open impellers require close clearance between the stationary parts of the impeller and compressor.

Figure 9 shows a semiclosed impeller; it has a rear cover to add structural support to the blades. Semiclosed impellers are fabricated by the same methods as those used for open impellers. They are used on multistage centrifugal compressors, gas pipeline

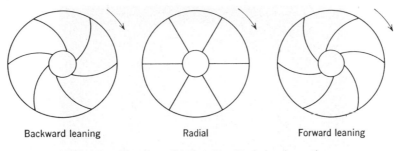

Backward leaning   Radial   Forward leaning

Fig. 11. Three possible impeller blade configurations.

booster compressors, and integral gear compressors. This type of impeller is capable of high tip speeds, up to 1500 ft/sec. It is ideally suited for single, radially split case compressors. Figure 10 shows a closed or shrouded impeller; it has a front and a rear cover. Closed impellers are normally fabricated by welding or riveting the blades to the front and rear covers. For high tip speeds the blades and rear cover are cast or milled integrally from a single piece, then the front cover is either welded or riveted to the blades. They are used on most multistage in-line centrifugal compressors, both axially and radially split case and integral gear types. This type of impeller does not require a close clearance between the stationary parts of the impeller and compressor and it is capable of high tip speeds, up to 1200 ft/sec.

The impeller is the most efficient pressure-producing element in the compressor; however, its pressure-producing ability is largely due to its blade configuration. Figure 11 shows the three possible blade configurations: radial, having straight blades extending radially; backward leaning, having straight or curved blades leaning at an angle away from the direction of rotation; and forward leaning, having straight or curved blades leaning at an angle in the direction of rotation.

The casing is the pressure-containing stationary part of the compressor which houses the rotating elements. Two types are being manufactured in the 1960s: an axially split case and a radially split case. Axially split cases are used on

Fig. 12. Axially split casing.

Fig. 13. Radially split barrel compressor.

multistage process compressors with up to 700 psig discharge pressure. The axially split case is divided through the horizontal axis of the machine. By removing the upper half of the case, all components are readily accessible. A single case will incorporate as many as nine stages of compression. Figure 12 shows an axially split in-line casing. For discharge pressures above 700 psig or with low-molecular-weight gases, such as hydrogen or helium, sealing along the horizontal casing halves and around the compressor shaft requires expensive manufacturing and assembly procedures. To alleviate these problems radially split or barrel-type casings are used.

Barrel construction was originally developed and used on high-pressure, boiler-feed pumps. It consists of an inner and outer assembly. The inner assembly consists of the rotor, axially split diaphragms, and guide vanes. The outer assembly consists of the cylinder or barrel with end covers. Figure 13 shows a radially split barrel compressor. High-pressure, multistage centrifugal process compressors and gas pipeline booster compressors use this type of construction. Single-stage pedestal-type compressors and integral gear compressors use a radially split casing arrangement somewhat simpler than the dual assembly barrel units. Figure 14 shows this radially split casing construction.

The following stationary, fluid-handling parts are either part of the casing or inserted into it. The *diffuser* is the stationary part surrounding the impeller. Its function is to convert the velocity energy of the fluid leaving the impeller into pressure energy. Diffusers can be either of a vaneless or free-vortex type, or provided with aerodynamic airfoils or vanes. Vaneless diffusers offer a flat, wide efficiency performance curve. Vaned diffusers permit more rapid diffusion and give a higher efficiency at the design point. The physical size of a vaned diffuser is much smaller than that of a vaneless one for the equivalent velocity reduction.

Diaphragms are separating walls between impellers or stages. They form the dynamic flow path of the gas within the stationary part of the compressor. Diaphragms are divided into three types: suction, interstage, and discharge. The suction diaphragm guides the gas into the eye of the first-stage impeller. It can be fitted with stationary or adjustable inlet guide vanes to alter the angle of introduction of the in-

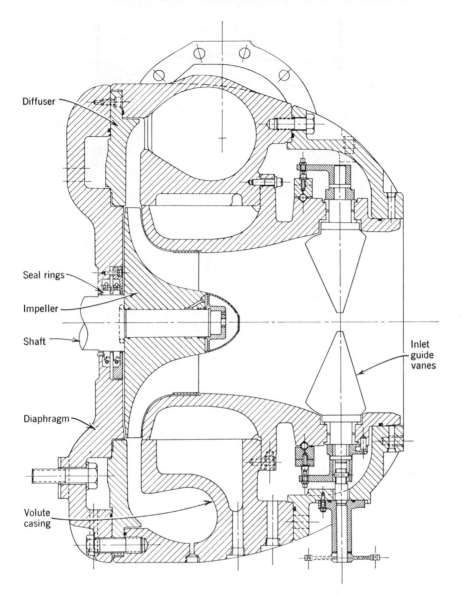

Diffuser

Seal rings

Impeller

Shaft

Inlet guide vanes

Diaphragm

Volute casing

Fig. 14. Radially split construction.

coming gas. The interstage diaphragms normally contain the return channels or interstage passages to channel the gas to the eye of the next impeller. Diffuser diaphragms
are interstage diaphragms containing the diffuser (vaned or vaneless) of that particular
stage. The discharge diaphragm guides the gas from the last-stage diffuser to the
discharge nozzle.

Return channels are smoothly machined return bends to turn the flow from a
peripheral to a radial direction.

Inlet guide vanes are located at the eye or entrance of each impeller. Their purpose is to direct the gas from the diaphragm into the eye of the impeller at the correct
angle.

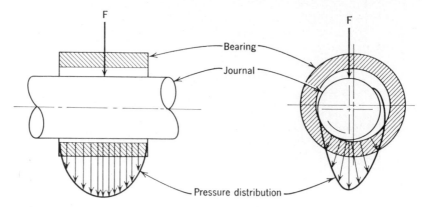

Fig. 15. Lubrication principle of centrifugal compressor journal bearings.

The *discharge volute* or *scroll* is a spiral-shaped passage which collects the gas leaving the final discharge diffuser and directs it to the compressor-discharge flange.

The stationary fluid-handling parts are generally made from castings, but fabricated steel parts have been used successfully. In some designs the stationary fluid-handling parts are machined integrally with the compressor casing.

All fluid-handling parts, either stationary or rotating, control the overall size, weight, and efficiency of a compressor. The compressor designer must compromise among these factors. For example, a multistage in-line compressor could be designed with optimum inlet guide vane angles, return bends, and diffusers, for high efficiency, but its overall length may introduce vibration problems or critical speed problems. In other words, the compressor rpm coincides with the natural frequency of the rotor system. Operation at the critical speed of the compressor imposes stresses, bearing loads, and vibrations sufficient in magnitude to destroy the machine. To reduce overall length, impeller spacing may be reduced, but the sharp turns at the impeller inlets and abrupt changes in the return channels penalize efficiency.

Impellers are normally made from steel, either cast steel, steel forgings, or fabricated from steel plate. For corrosive gases, stainless-steel or chrome-plated steel impellers are used. Aluminum or magnesium alloy impellers are used on several industrial air compressors and superchargers with tip speeds of up to 1300 ft/sec. With a given impeller construction the permissible tip speed is dependent on the ratio of the specific weight of the impeller material to the material yield strength. An aluminum or magnesium alloy impeller with 45,000 psia yield strength and 0.09 lb/cu in. specific weight is just as useful as a steel impeller with 140,000 psia yield strength and 0.28 lb/cu in. specific weight.

Casings are made from materials to suit the particular application and may be cast iron, ductile iron, cast steel, or fabricated steel. The casing thickness, corrosion allowance, and allowable stresses conform to safety standards outlined in "Unfired Pressure Vessels" of *ASME Boiler and Pressure Vessel Code*. Cast-iron casings are used for air or nonflammable gas applications where the operating pressure and temperature, at any point within the case, do not exceed 250 psig and 450°F, respectively. If the gas is flammable or toxic, the operating pressure and temperature limits are reduced to 75 psig and 350°F for cast iron. For operating pressures and temperatures exceeding the above limits, cast-steel cases are used. Nickel alloy steel cases are used for low-temperature operation below $-20°F$. The stationary fluid-handling parts are made from cast iron, nodular iron, alloy cast steel, or stainless steel, depending on the type of service and gas to be compressed.

Centrifugal compressors use hydrodynamic journal- and thrust-bearing designs. Hydrodynamic journal bearings operate with a pressure distribution shown in Figure 15. In a properly lubricated journal bearing, as a result of shaft rotation, lubricant is drawn into the converging region formed by the displacement of the shaft in the bearing. Because of the viscosity of the lubricant, fluid pressure is generated in the lubricant film separating the shaft and the bearing. This fluid pressure provides the load-carrying capacity in the bearing.

THERMODYNAMICS

For positive displacement compressors, the theoretical thermodynamics are essentially the same in that compression is isentropic. A typical indicator card (plot of pressure in the cylinder vs travel of the piston) (Fig. 16) shows the relative events in one revolution for a reciprocating compressor as they would occur in either end of a double-acting cylinder.

For rotary compressors the cycle from suction to discharge is a continuous one and an indicator card as shown in Figure 16 for reciprocating compressors cannot be obtained. However, a pressure–volume relation can be established to denote the work performed (Fig. 17).

A centrifugal compressor performs work on a compressible fluid. The amount of work performed by the compressor is the product of the work performed on a unit

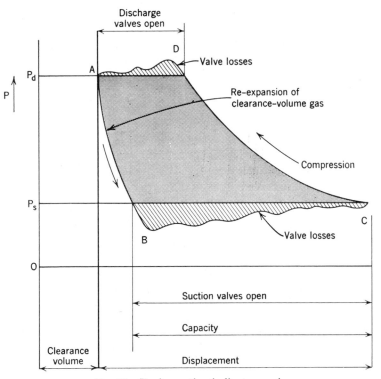

Fig. 16. Reciprocating indicator card.

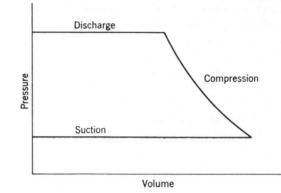

Fig. 17. Pressure–volume diagram for a rotary compressor.

weight of fluid, and the total number of units upon which the work is performed. In a practical sense, this involves raising a given volume flow of gas from one pressure level to a higher pressure level. Therefore, centrifugal compressor work is a function of two factors: first, the volume flow; and second, the pressure rise. The volume flow is expressed in cubic feet per minute (cfm); the pressure rise in terms of "head."

The first factor (volume flow) is equivalent, in all cases, to the volume rate of flow of gas at the temperature, pressure, and composition prevailing at the compressor inlet.

The second factor (head) is a measurement of the work output of the centrifugal compressor expressed in foot-pounds per pound of fluid handled (ft-lb/lb). Head is fundamentally defined by the following:

$$H = 144 \int V \, dp \qquad (1)$$

where V is the specific volume in cu ft/lb and p is the pressure, psia.

For a centrifugal pump, where the specific volume is constant, equation 1 is readily integrated to

$$H = 144V(P_2 - P_1) \qquad (2)$$

For a centrifugal compressor where the specific volume of the fluid handled is variable, a somewhat more complex relation is obtained. If reference is made to Figure 18 which shows various compression cycles on a pressure–volume diagram, it can be seen that the slope of the compression curve is a function of the value of the exponent N. If the compressor is not cooled and if compression takes place with 100% efficiency, the compression process will be adiabatic and may be represented by the equation

$$PV^K = \text{constant}$$

where K is the ratio of specific heats, C_p/C_v.

Equation 1 may be integrated and rearranged to the form

$$H = \frac{144P_1V_1}{(K-1)/K} \left[(P_2/P_1)^{(K-1)/K} - 1 \right] \qquad (3)$$

If the compressor is cooled (all heat of compression is removed) and if compression takes place with 100% efficiency, the compression process will be isothermal and may be represented by the equation

$$PV = \text{constant}$$

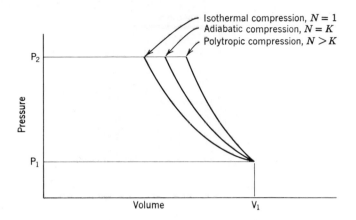

Fig. 18. Pressure–volume diagram showing various compression cycles.

Equation 1 may then be integrated and rearranged to the form

$$H = P_1 V_1 \ln_e P_2/P_1 \tag{4}$$

However, the actual compressor cycle results in the addition of heat during compression (no longer adiabatic) and the temperature of the gas changes (no longer isothermal). As a result, the actual compression cycle is polytropic, and may be represented by the equation

$$PV^N = \text{constant}$$

Equation 1 may now be integrated and rearranged to the familiar form

$$H^1 = \frac{144\ P_1 V_1}{(N-1)/N} \left[(P_2/P_1)^{(N-1)/N} - 1 \right] \tag{5}$$

where H^1 is the polytropic head developed by the compressor and N is the polytropic exponent of compression.

The relationship between the polytropic exponent N and K is

$$\frac{N-1}{N} = \frac{K-1}{K} \times \frac{1}{N_p}$$

where N_p is the compressor polytropic efficiency and is established by tests.

Either adiabatic, isothermal, or polytropic relations can be used by the compressor designer as a basis for calculating compressor performance. Polytropic relationships have generally replaced adiabatic and isothermal ones because the actual compression process is closer to polytropic with a value of N greater than K. In addition, application of existing performance information to gases with different K values is simplified with polytropic relations.

Compressor efficiency is the ratio of the theoretical power to the shaft power. With known values of polytropic efficiency, polytropic head in feet, and weight flow in lb/min, the theoretical power or gas horsepower (ghp) demand of the compressor can be calculated

$$\text{ghp} = H^1 W/(33{,}000 N_p)$$

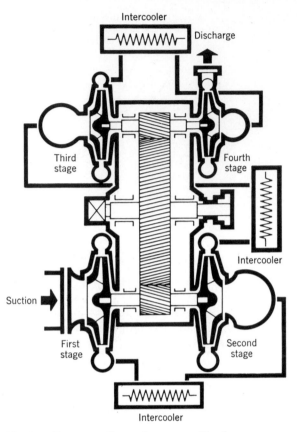

Fig. 19. Four-stage integral gear centrifugal compressor.

where H^1 is the polytropic head developed by the compressor, W is the weight flow, and N_p is the polytropic efficiency.

Shaft power is greater than gas horsepower by an increment that includes the external compressor losses and is calculated by

$$\text{shaft power} = \text{ghp} + \text{bearing losses} + \text{leakage losses} +$$
$$\text{disk friction losses} + \text{gearing losses}$$

Intercooling between stages with shell- and tube-type heat exchangers reduces the total power requirement of the compressor and the total number of compressor stages. For example, the unit shown in Figure 19 is a four-stage centrifugal with shell and tube intercooling between each stage. The machine is rated at 22,000 cfm with a final discharge pressure of 125 psig. Because of intercooling, this machine achieves in four stages the same compression ratio that formerly required nine.

Direct liquid injection cools the compressed fluid by injecting a coolant directly into the gas stream. The coolant, either water or some other substance compatible with the gas, is injected through spray nozzles into the discharge side of the compressor. Liquid injection is highly effective; practically all the heat of compression can be removed before the fluid enters the next stage.

Diaphragm cooling removes heat from the flowing medium by the circulation of a coolant in passages built inside the compressor diaphragms. Diaphragm cooling is still used in modern centrifugals. In compressing certain unsaturated hydrocarbons it affords a good method to control hydrocarbon polymerization without contaminating the gas stream. Diaphragm cooling also permits maximum compression ratios in a single case.

Direct-injection and diaphragm cooling are primarily used to permit high compression ratios, to control the discharge temperatures and polymerization of the gas, and to reduce the total number of stages of compression.

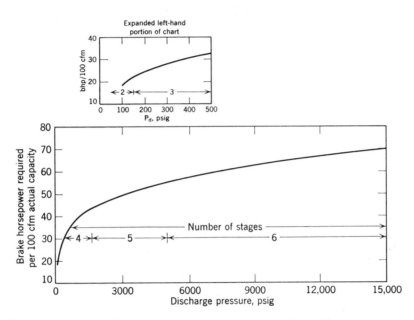

Fig. 20. Approximate brake horsepower requirement of a reciprocating compressor applicable to machines above 300 bhp. Basis of figure: nitrogen; sea level pressure, 14.7 psia; suction pressure, 0 psig; suction temperature, 80°F; suction relative humidity, 0%; multistage compression with perfect intercooling (number of stages as indicated).

There are many factors that affect compressor performance. Compressibility, or the deviation from ideal gas laws for many gases, has a very pronounced effect on actual performance. Properties of the gas, such as molecular weight, and ratio of specific heats also have bearing on performance. The pressure level to which it is being compressed, the ratio of compression, is also a significant consideration. Multistaging with cooling between stages effects savings in horsepower. A very rough determination of staging and horsepower for reciprocating units can be derived from Figure 20.

CONTROL

In many chemical processes that use compressors, there is a need for some variation in the compressor output. This may be accomplished in many ways, depending on the desired objectives and the type of compressor.

For reciprocating compressors, clearance may be added to the cylinder by means of a pocket. Compression will not occur in a cylinder until all the clearance volume is filled. It is conceivable, therefore, that sufficient clearance can be added to a cylinder so that no gas would be delivered from the discharge. This may be a fixed volume

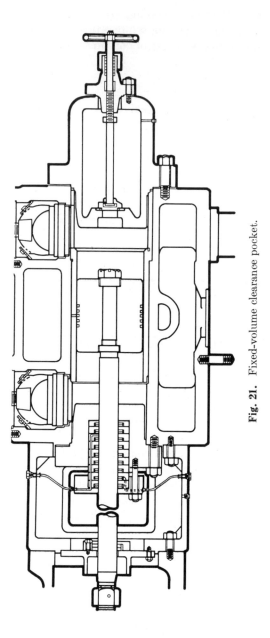

Fig. 21. Fixed-volume clearance pocket.

(Fig. 21) so that it is either opened or closed, or it may be a variable-volume type which may be opened in infinite steps. The fixed volume type is most commonly used.

While clearance pockets may be used to unload an end of a compressor cylinder completely, the physical size of the pocket should be considered as it may well require the same or greater dimensions as the cylinder it is to unload. This can be done but it is impractical. For complete unloading of a cylinder end, suction-valve unloaders are used. The suction valves in a compressor cylinder, after admission of gas, are held closed by the gas pressure in the cylinder. If the suction valve is held open by some mechanical means, the gas will not remain in the cylinder but will be moved back into the suction line. In other words, no compression will take place in that end of the cylinder in which the suction valves are held open by unloaders. The valve unloaders hold the suction valve open so that the gas passes in and out; no compression takes place in that end of the cylinder.

Clearance pockets and valve unloaders may be operated manually or automatically. Suction throttling is used for capacity control much more with rotary than with reciprocating compressors because rotary compressors have no suction valves and hence no valve unloaders. Clearance pockets are not possible in a rotary compressor with its continuous compression cycle.

Any of the positive displacement-type units can use bypass control for capacity variation, bypassing discharge gas back to suction. This, of course, wastes horsepower and is used when other methods are impractical or to give infinite steps between fixed points of clearance pockets and/or unloaders on reciprocating compressors. If the driver is such that its speed can be varied, this may be used for capacity control as capacity is directly proportional to speed.

Centrifugal compressors use speed control for the majority of applications. When speed control is not practical, control may be accomplished by throttling the suction pressure, bypassing the discharge, or inlet guide vane control. Guide-vane control adjusts capacity of the compressor by prerotation of the inlet gas. Speed or inlet guide vane modulation can be made directly from the process controller.

DRIVERS

Many choices of drivers for a compressor are available depending on the type of compressor, horsepower requirements, energy available, and plant requirements.

For reciprocating compressors the most commonly used driver is the slow-speed, engine-type synchronous electric motor. This class of motor has higher efficiencies than comparable induction motors, gives power factor correction, and operates at constant speed. A rough rule of thumb, all things being equal, is if the horsepower required exceeds the rotative speed economics of initial cost, favor the slow-speed, engine-type synchronous motor.

When conditions require, induction motors are used, either slow-speed, direct-connected, or high-speed with reduction gear. Very often, for small reciprocating units, high-speed induction motors are used with belt drive. For other than a reciprocating unit, high-speed induction and synchronous motors are used with speed increasers. Power engines are also used either direct-connected or with gear, depending on the unit being driven. In some cases the power unit and compression end are integrated in a single machine with power cylinders vertical and reciprocating compressor cylinders horizontal on the same frame.

Where suitable steam is available, turbines and either a speed increaser or reducer are used, depending on the type of driven unit. Since centrifugal compressors operate at speeds exceeding those of available drivers, step-up gearing must be employed. In-line compressors use separate gear units, not mounted directly on the compressor casing. Gears are normally commercially available helical speed-increaser types. Integral gear compressors combine the compressor and gearing to form a single unit. The gear unit has one to four pinion shafts driven by a large bull gear operating at driver speed.

Bibliography

"Pressure Technique (Compressors)" in *ECT* 1st ed., Vol. 11, pp. 115–123, by E. L. Case and J. Charls, Jr., Worthington Corp.

Compressed Air and Gas Handbook, 3rd ed., Compressed Air and Gas Institute, New York, 1961.
L. S. Marks and T. Baumeister, eds., *Marks Standard Handbook for Mechanical Engineers*, 7th ed., McGraw-Hill Book Co., Inc., New York, 1967.
Centrifugal Compressors for General Refinery Services, API Standard 617, 2nd ed., American Petroleum Institute, New York, 1963.
Centrifugal Compressors, Tech. Progr. Ser., Vol. 3, Gas Turbine Subcommittee, Society of Automotive Engineers, New York, 1961.
Compressors and Vacuum Pumps and Their Lubrication, The Shell Petroleum Company, Ltd., London, 1958.
CAGI Technical Digest, Vol. 1, No. 1, Compressed Air and Gas Institute, New York, 1968.

JAMES J. JULIAN AND JAMES F. HENDRICKS
Worthington Corporation

PURGATIVES. See Cathartics.

PURINE. See Caffeine.

PVC, PVP. See Poly(vinyl chloride), polyvinylpyrrolidone under Vinyl compounds and polymers.

PYRAZOLES, PYRAZOLINES, AND PYRAZOLONES

Pyrazoles are heterocyclic compounds having five-membered doubly unsaturated rings with two adjacent nitrogen atoms. (See Heterocyclic compounds.) Pyrazolines have a similar ring system, but only one double bond is present. Pyrazolones, more properly termed pyrazolinones, are oxopyrazolines. The structure of representative compounds of these classes are given by (**1**), pyrazole; (**2**), Δ^2-pyrazoline; (**3**), 5-pyrazolone; and (**4**), 3-pyrazolone, and the usual numbering systems are indicated.

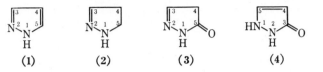

(1)   (2)   (3)   (4)

Pyrazoles and pyrazolines are capable of existing in a number of isomeric forms depending upon the positions of the double bonds. Such isomerism is also possible for pyrazolones, but, in addition, pyrazolones may be isomeric with respect to the position of the oxygen atom and also may exist as keto–enol tautomers. The enol tautomers of pyrazolones are hydroxypyrazoles, but in this discussion they will be considered as pyrazolones. Neither pyrazoles nor pyrazolines have found extensive uses, but pyrazolones have been widely utilized as fabric dyes and pigments, as food coloring agents, in color photography, as photographic developing agents, and as pharmaceuticals. (See Analgesics and antipyretics; Azo dyes; Color photography; Colors for foods, drugs, and cosmetics; Photography, Vol. 15, p. 355; Pigments, organic.) These uses will be discussed more fully in subsequent sections.

Pyrazoles

The pyrazole ring system can exist in several tautomeric forms. In two of the tautomers, double bonds are attached to both nitrogen atoms. Such compounds — called pyrazolenines — will not be discussed here because of their minor importance scientifically and commercially. Pyrazoles (see Vol. 10, p. 910) have either hydrogen or a substituent on one of the nitrogen atoms and possess aromatic character due to a six-π-electron system. In pyrazoles having no substituent on nitrogen and a substituent at either C-3 or C-5 or at both, there are two possible structures, (**5**) and (**6**) (1–3). Only one form of such compounds has ever been isolated, and it is generally

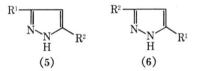

(5)   (6)

considered that the two forms exist in tautomeric equilibrium. Recent investigations (4) using NMR techniques are in agreement with such conclusions. It has been demonstrated that pyrazoles unsubstituted on nitrogen are associated into cyclic dimers such as (**7**), and analogous cyclic trimers and linear polymers. Such association would greatly facilitate tautomerism.

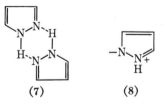

(7)   (8)

Ehrlich (5) has reported, on the basis of crystallographic studies, that pyrazole exists as the zwitterion indicated in (**8**). Tautomerism could occur in such a molecule by a simple proton transfer from a positively charged nitrogen to a negatively charged nitrogen. However, it is probable that strongly polar substituents may result in one tautomer being the predominant form. In pyrazoles having a nitrogen substituent such tautomerism cannot occur, and a single form represents the structure. It is only recently that a naturally occurring pyrazole has been discovered. β-Pyrazol-1-ylalanine has been isolated from the seeds of cucurbits (6).

Three excellent recent reviews of pyrazoles are available (1–3).

PHYSICAL PROPERTIES

Pyrazoles are very stable compounds with high boiling points. Pyrazole itself boils at 187–188°C and melts at 70°C. Increasing substitution on the carbon atoms causes higher boiling points, but substitution on nitrogen lowers both melting and boiling points. For example, 3-methylpyrazole boils at 205°C, but 1-methylpyrazole boils at 127°C (7). These properties reflect an association of pyrazoles having hydrogen on nitrogen.

Pyrazole and its lower homologs are soluble in water and most organic solvents. Increasing molecular weight decreases water solubility. The specific gravities of pyrazoles are usually 0.89–1.02, and the refractive indexes are 1.46–1.48 (2). The low dipole moments of pyrazoles (2.4 D for pyrazole) have been the subject of considerable discussion and are usually attributed to strong association. Pyrazoles having hydrogen on nitrogen are weakly acidic and weakly basic, forming salts with strong acids and giving metal salts by replacement of the hydrogen on the nitrogen atom (2). The pK_a of pyrazole is 2.53. *N*-Substituted pyrazoles are not acidic.

The ultraviolet spectra of pyrazoles have been thoroughly studied (8,9). Alkylpyrazoles have maxima at 210–225 mμ (log ϵ 3.5–4.0), but arylpyrazoles absorb at 250–280 mμ (log ϵ 3.4–4.2). Electronegative substituents give rise to a bathochromic shift of 25–40 mμ. The infrared spectra of pyrazoles show the expected bands (2). Absorption occurs at 3500–3100 cm^{-1} if NH is present. The C=N system gives rise to a strong band at 1590 cm^{-1}; weak bands at 1660 and 1550 cm^{-1} are attributed to C=C.

The NMR spectra of pyrazoles have been studied extensively (4,10). Pyrazoles having no substituents on nitrogen exhibit identical chemical shifts for protons on C-3 and C-5. In the cases of alkyl substitution on nitrogen, the chemical shift of a proton on C-3 in a 1,5-dialkyl isomer differs slightly from that of a proton on C-5 in a 1,3-dialkyl isomer with the signal due to the former being downfield from that due to the latter. *N*-Acylpyrazoles have the chemical shift for the proton on C-5 substantially downfield from that of the proton on C-3 and markedly different from the chemical shift of the proton on C-5 in other types of pyrazoles. The proton on C-4 gives rise to a normal signal for an olefinic proton.

CHEMICAL PROPERTIES

Pyrazoles are five-membered ring systems having aromatic character due to the fact that the nitrogen atom in position 1 can contribute an electron pair to form, with the π-electrons of the remaining atoms, an aromatic sextet of π-electrons. The nitrogen atom at position 2 retains its free electron pair, and as a consequence is basic. The aromatic character of pyrazoles confers great stability on the ring system and the property of undergoing aromatic-type reactions such as halogenation. Theoretical considerations indicate that the 3- and 5-positions, being adjacent to nitrogen, would be less liable to electrophilic attack than position 4. In agreement with such views molecular orbital calculations predict that position 4 should have the greatest electron density (11), and electrophilic substitution tends to occur at that position. Under acidic conditions pyrazoles are less readily susceptible to electrophilic attack due to protonation at N-2. In N-1 substituted pyrazoles nucleophilic reaction takes place at position 5.

Halogenation of pyrazoles having no substituent on C-4 usually occurs at that position. However, further reaction may follow depending upon reagents used and

substituents present in the pyrazole. Chlorination of 3(5)-methylpyrazole in nonpolar solvents leads to a 4-chloro compound, but the use of more polar solvents yields 4,5-dichloro-3-methyl- and 4,5-dichloro-3-trichloromethylpyrazole. Bromination of pyrazoles in nonpolar solvents gives the 4-bromo compounds, but catalysts, such as iron, cause formation of di- and tribromopyrazoles. Pyrazoles with electronegative substituents can give 1-bromopyrazoles. Iodination of pyrazoles at C-4 occurs readily with elemental iodine if bases are present to neutralize the hydriodic acid formed. Pyrazoles can also form quite stable 1-iodo derivatives in the presence of metal salts such as silver nitrate.

Electrophilic substitution under acidic conditions, such as sulfonation, nitration, nitrosation, and azo coupling, are much less facile than are halogenations because of protonation of the basic nitrogen. Nitration of 3-methylpyrazole gives the 4-nitro compound, but the reaction is quite slow and rather drastic conditions must be employed. Substituents, such as a phenyl group, which reduce the basicity of the pyrazole, lead to much easier nitration. Electronegative substituents on pyrazoles make nitration virtually impossible. Sulfonation of pyrazoles is very similar to nitration, occurring only with difficulty and giving substitution at C-4. Direct nitrosation of pyrazoles occurs only if an activating substituent, such as ethoxy, is present.

Alkylation or acylation of pyrazoles by the Friedel-Crafts reaction takes place at C-4. The reaction occurs more readily if there is a substituent on the 1-position particularly if the substituent is an aryl group. 4-Formylpyrazoles can be prepared by the Vilsmeier procedure (see Polymethine dyes, p. 297), using dimethylformamide and phosphorus oxychloride.

Halogen atoms attached to a pyrazole are very unreactive unless an electronegative substituent is present at C-4. In such cases halogens at the C-5 position are activated but not those at C-3. Halogen substituents are removed by chemical reduction with such agents as red phosphorus–hydriodic acid, sodium–ethanol, and zinc–hydrochloric acid. Replacement of halogen occurs with nucleophilic reagents, but usually activation of the ring is required.

A variety of reactions occur at the nitrogen atoms of pyrazoles. Most of these take place on N-1 and only if there is no 1-substituent. Hydrogen is readily replaced by reaction with bases to give metal salts such as sodium, potassium, and silver. Treatment of 1-NH pyrazoles with alkylating agents in the presence of base forms 1-substituted pyrazoles which can then quaternize. If the pyrazole is unsymmetrically substituted, two products are frequently obtained, but quaternization by the same reagent gives only one product. Pyrazoles without a 1-substituent are readily alkylated to give 1-dialkylaminomethylpyrazoles by means of the Mannich reaction.

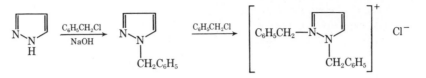

Replacement of hydrogen on N-1 occurs readily with acylating agents such as acid chlorides and anhydrides to form 1-acylpyrazoles. Unsymmetrically C-substituted pyrazoles usually give only the more stable of the two possible products as acyl migration occurs under the influence of heat. The 1-acyl groups are easily replaced by other groups and can be removed by acidic or basic hydrolysis.

The NH group of pyrazoles adds readily to α,β-unsaturated acids, esters, ketones, and nitriles. This reaction is reversible.

The pyrazole ring is quite resistant to reduction and oxidation. Under most conditions of catalytic or chemical reduction various substituents can be reduced without destroying the pyrazole ring. Such oxidizing agents as permanganate and chromic acid leave the pyrazole ring untouched. However, it is destroyed by ozonization and electrolytic oxidation. Fusion of quaternary salts with potassium hydroxide or other strong bases brings about the cleavage of the pyrazole ring, and the formation of dialkylhydrazines.

SYNTHESIS

A tremendous number of pyrazoles have been synthesized by an extensive array of synthetic methods which can be classified under three headings. Perhaps the most widely used procedure has been the reaction of a hydrazine with a ketone or ketone derivative containing a functional group in a position that will permit cyclization to occur at the 3 position. Conversion of a variety of heterocyclic systems to pyrazoles, most frequently involving a pyrazoline-to-pyrazole oxidation, has been employed extensively. The third method is the reaction of an appropriate acetylenic or olefinic compound with a diazo compound.

From a Ketone or Ketone Derivative and Hydrazines. The reaction of 1,3-diketones with hydrazine is typical of the first method as illustrated by the reaction leading to 3,5-dimethylpyrazole.

$$CH_3COCH_2COCH_3 \;+\; N_2H_4 \;\longrightarrow\;$$

The most commonly used synthesis of pyrazole itself is a variation of this method. 1,1,3,3-Tetraethoxypropane (malonaldehyde bisacetal) is condensed with hydrazine in an acidic medium allowing generation of carbonyl groups during the course of the reaction. The reaction is an extremely general one, occurring with almost all linear 1,3-diketones and with β-ketoaldehydes. Alkylhydrazines, arylhydrazines, sulfonylhydrazides, acylhydrazides, semicarbazides, and aminoguanidine have all been used successfully as the hydrazine in this procedure. The use of appropriate ketones or ketone derivatives and hydrazines makes possible the synthesis of a very large number of pyrazoles substituted in all possible positions. The principal difficulty with the 1,3-diketone–hydrazine method is that the use of unsymmetrical hydrazines usually results in two products:

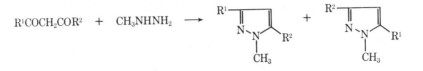

$$R^1COCH_2COR^2 \quad + \quad CH_3NHNH_2 \quad \longrightarrow$$

Even a considerable difference in the carbonyl groups of the reactant, as is the case with β-ketoaldehydes, frequently leads to two products.

A closely allied procedure for the preparation of pyrazoles is the reaction of α,β-unsaturated ketones with hydrazines. The α,β-unsaturated ketones may be ethynyl ketones or they may be olefinic ketones having an α,β-substituent which may be readily eliminated as a small molecule. These two variants are illustrated in the following equations:

$$CH_3COC\equiv CC_6H_5 \quad + \quad N_2H_4 \quad \longrightarrow$$

$$CH_3COCH=CHCl \quad + \quad C_6H_5NHNH_2 \quad \longrightarrow$$

These reactions are not as general as are the 1,3-diketone reactions because they require somewhat more basic hydrazines, and the starting ketones are not as readily available. However, they have the advantage of giving rise to only one product.

From Heterocyclic Compounds. The preparation of pyrazoles from other heterocyclic compounds is most frequently achieved by aromatization of pyrazolines which are readily available. The reaction, which can be brought about in several ways, is shown in the following equation:

$$\xrightarrow{-2H}$$

The most general dehydrogenation procedure is the use of sulfur or selenium. Oxidation can be used, but most oxidizing agents give rise to other products. The most satisfactory oxidative procedures are those starting with a pyrazoline containing a carboxyl, cyano, or sulfonic acid substituent and oxidizing with bromine. Elimination of a smaller molecule from a pyrazoline, as shown by the following equation, has been successful in many instances.

$$C_6H_5CH=CHC=NNHSO_2C_6H_5 \quad \longrightarrow$$

A number of other heterocyclic systems have been converted to pyrazoles. A procedure based on the use of heterocyclics called sydnones (12) may become an important method for the synthesis of pyrazoles.

$$C_6H_5-N \overset{\pm}{\underset{N-O}{|}} \overset{O}{|} \quad + \quad CH_2{=}CHCN \quad \longrightarrow \quad \underset{\underset{C_6H_5}{|}}{N\text{-}N} \quad + \quad CO_2 \quad + \quad HCN$$

The use of olefins as well as various other acetylenic compounds in this reaction gives rise to pyrazoles.

From Acetylenic Compounds and Diazoalkanes. Acetylenic compounds react with diazoalkanes to form pyrazoles. The use of acetylene, alkylacetylenes, and arylacetylenes usually requires pressure. When the acetylenic compound is activated by

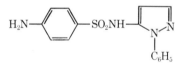

$$HC{\equiv}CH \quad + \quad CH_2N_2 \quad \longrightarrow \quad \underset{H}{N\text{-}N}$$

an electronegative substituent, such as a ketone or a carboxyl group, the reaction occurs under milder conditions. This preparative procedure is limited by the availability of acetylenic compounds and diazoalkanes. The same result can be achieved by the use of a compound such as β-chlorovinyl methyl ketone, which can form a pyrazoline followed by loss of a small molecule.

USES

A considerable number of uses for various pyrazoles have been suggested in publications and patents (2), most of which have been related to the biological activities of pyrazoles. Although many pyrazoles have pharmacological activities, those which have found practical application owe their activity more to substituents than to inherent activity of the pyrazole ring iteslf. Furthermore, those which are in use have not been employed extensively. A sulfonamide containing a pyrazole ring, sulfaphenazole, is in clinical use and is sold under the trade names Orisul (Ciba Pharmaceutical Co.) and Sulfabid (The Purdue Frederick Co.). Three esters of 5-hydroxypyrazoles,

$$H_2N-\!\!\!\!\!\bigcirc\!\!\!\!\!-SO_2NH-\underset{\underset{C_6H_5}{|}}{N\text{-}N}$$

sulfaphenazole

Isolan (see Vol. 11, p. 711), Pyrolan, and Pyrazoxon, have found some applications as systemic insecticides acting, no doubt, as choline esterase inhibitors. These compounds are not sold in the United States.

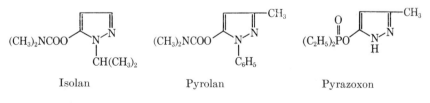

Isolan   Pyrolan   Pyrazoxon

Indazoles

Indazoles are benzopyrazoles and like the pyrazoles exist in a number of isomeric ring systems. The only two of any importance are 1 H-indazole (**9**) and 2 H-indazole

(10); in the earlier literature these are commonly referred to as isoindazole and indazole, respectively. Indazoles having no substituents on nitrogen can be isolated only

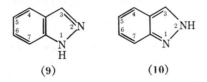

(9)   (10)

in one form, but *N*-substituted isomers corresponding to the two structures are readily
prepared.   Indazoles are usually synthesized by cyclization of an appropriately
o-disubstituted benzene derivative in which the substituents contain two nitrogen
atoms and one carbon atom that are arranged so as to complete the pyrazole ring
(see also Vol. 10, p. 911). The three types of indazole synthesis that are most widely
employed are illustrated in the following equations:

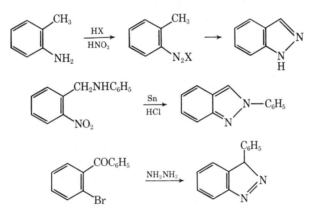

Since indazoles may be regarded as azo analogs of indoles a number of indazoles
have been investigated as antimetabolites of indoles having biological activity such as
tryptophan. In a number of cases antimetabolite activity has been demonstrated.
However, no commercial uses have arisen from such properties, and they are of no
industrial importance. Indazoles are discussed exhaustively in a recent review (3).

Pyrazolines

The chemistry of pyrazolines has not been of great interest and has not been
investigated nearly as extensively as that of pyrazoles (see Vol. 10, p. 911). Pyrazolines lack the aromatic character and ring stability of pyrazoles and behave more as
unsaturated aliphatic compounds. The number of tautomers possible in pyrazolines
due to differing double bond positions is large. In the case of pyrazoline three isomers,
(11), (12), and (13), are possible. The isomers are named as Δ^1-, Δ^2-, and Δ^3-pyrazo-
lines, respectively, or as 1-, 2-, and 3-pyrazolines. Those pyrazolines having one
substituent on nitrogen have three possible tautomers derived from (12) and (13), but

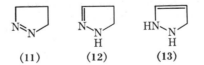

(11)   (12)   (13)

lack of substituents on nitrogen combined with one substituent on carbon makes possible five tautomeric forms.   More complex substitution may diminish the number of possible forms.   In many cases of pyrazoline synthesis very little consideration has been given to the structure of the product.   The structure has been assumed from the method of synthesis.   There seems to be no extensive commercial use for pyrazolines, and none of these products occur naturally.   However, a number of patents have reported the effectiveness of pyrazolines as bleaching agents and for their use in dyes.

PHYSICAL PROPERTIES

Pyrazolines are colorless high-boiling liquids or low-melting solids.   Substitution on nitrogen tends to lower the melting point.   Low-molecular-weight pyrazolines are quite water-soluble, but as the molecular weight increases, water solubility decreases and solubility in organic solvents increases.   Pyrazolines are weakly basic compounds forming salts which, in some cases, are subject to hydrolysis by hot water (7).   The position of protonation varies depending upon the structure of the pyrazoline. Δ^2-Pyrazolines are protonated on N-1 (13), but Δ^3-pyrazolines may be protonated on carbon (14).

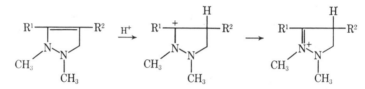

The spectral properties of pyrazolines have not been studied extensively although in recent years there has been considerable interest in the use of NMR to establish structures when tautomers are possible.   Very little has been published about the ultraviolet spectra of pyrazolines, and most of what has appeared concerns pyrazolines with aromatic substituents.   As would be expected Δ^2-pyrazolines with no aromatic substituents absorb at about 330 mμ with very low extinction coefficients (15).   In aryl-substituted Δ^2-pyrazolines two maxima appear at 220–245 mμ and 275–290 mμ (13,16,17). Δ^1-Pyrazolines with aromatic substituents have a single maximum at 327–329 mμ (18).   The infrared spectra of pyrazolines are those expected for the various saturated and unsaturated systems (16,18).   The NMR spectra of Δ^1- and Δ^3-pyrazolines have been reported (14,18,19).   In the Δ^3-pyrazolines, hydrogen on carbon adjacent to nitrogen gives a chemical shift of 6.18 τ, and hydrogen on olefinic carbon gives a signal at 4.77 τ.   (For an explanation of the τ scale see Vol. 14, p. 47.) Hydrogen on C-3 and C-5 in Δ^1-pyrazolines gives signals at 4.2–5.8 τ, depending upon substitution, while hydrogen on C-4 appears at 7.9 τ.

CHEMICAL PROPERTIES

The outstanding chemical property of pyrazolines is the ready loss of nitrogen from Δ^1-pyrazolines to give cyclopropanes and olefins (1–3,7).   This occurs under a variety of conditions and has frequently been used as a method for the preparation of cyclopropanes.   Simple pyrolysis may be effective or a variety of basic catalysts such as potassium hydroxide, dipotassium hydrogen phosphate, and triethanolamine may be

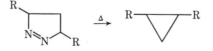

used. In some cases olefin formation is the predominant reaction, and occasionally a pyrazole is obtained.

As already mentioned, mild, controlled oxidation of pyrazolines can be used to convert them to pyrazoles, but more commonly oxidizing agents disrupt the ring with formation of a variety of products. Oxygen reacts readily with most pyrazolines in such a complex reaction, and permanganate usually destroys the pyrazoline ring.

Reduction of pyrazolines catalytically or with chemical agents usually gives pyrazolidines. However, vigorous reduction with chemical agents or high-pressure catalytic reduction tends to disrupt the ring with nitrogen–nitrogen bond cleavage and formation of 1,3-diamines.

The double bond of pyrazolines shifts readily, and one tautomer may be converted into another under the influence of such reagents as acids, bases, or acylating agents; in some cases, conversion occurs spontaneously.

The pyrazoline ring is relatively resistant to substitution, but 1-arylpyrazolines with no substituent at C-3 couple with aryldiazonium salts. The products lose the azo nitrogen easily, giving a 3-arylpyrazoline and other products. Pyrazolines that have a

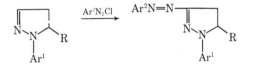

hydrogen on nitrogen react with acylating agents such as acyl chlorides and isocyanates to form 1-acylpyrazolines.

SYNTHESIS

There are three general methods for the synthesis of pyrazolines (1,3,7). The most useful method is the condensation of a hydrazine with an α,β-unsaturated aldehyde or ketone. This reaction appears to proceed through a hydrazone,

$$R^1CH{=}CHCOR^2 \quad + \quad R^3NHNH_2 \quad \longrightarrow$$

which can frequently be isolated, and acid usually serves to bring about cyclization. Condensations using ketones proceed much more readily than those using aldehydes ($R^2 = H$), although many of the latter can be employed if sodium hydroxide is present. Both aliphatic and aromatic ketones react readily unless steric hindrance is prohibitive. Hydrazine, alkylhydrazines, and arylhydrazines all condense quite easily.

A very similar synthesis is the reaction of hydrazines with β-substituted carbonyl compounds. The β-substituent may be chloro, hydroxyl, mercapto, or dialkylamino. β-Dialkylaminoketones are particularly useful in this reaction because of their ready

$$XCH_2CH_2COR^1 \quad + \quad R^2NHNH_2 \quad \longrightarrow$$

availability from Mannich reactions. An interesting method (16), somewhat akin to the β-substituted ketone condensation, is the use of a symmetrical dialkyl-hydrazine in a Mannich reaction, followed by cyclization to give a 1,2-dialkyl-Δ^3-pyrazoline.

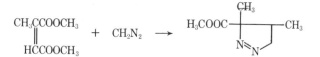

$$C_6H_5COCH_3 \;+\; CH_2O \;+\; CH_3NHNHCH_3 \;\longrightarrow\; C_6H_5COCH_2CH_2NNHCH_3 \;\longrightarrow$$

The synthesis of Δ^1-pyrazolines is usually achieved by reaction of a diazoalkane with an olefin. This reaction proceeds most readily if the olefin is activated by an

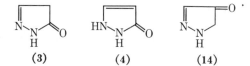

electronegative substituent such as carbalkoxy, although ethylene does react under appropriate conditions. Most diazoalkanes add to olefines quite easily. A complication of this synthetic method is that frequently the product loses nitrogen and forms a cyclopropane or an olefin.

Pyrazolones

Pyrazolones can exist in a number of isomeric forms, but the three structures (**3**), (**4**), and (**14**) are those usually assigned.

The older chemical literature refers to these structures as 5-pyrazolones, 3-pyrazolones, and 4-hydroxypyrazoles, respectively. *Chemical Abstracts* prefers the names 2-pyrazolin-5-one, 3-pyrazolin-5-one, and 2-pyrazolin-4-one. Compounds having structures of type (**14**) are of little scientific and commercial importance and will not be considered further. The 5-pyrazolones and 3-pyrazolones can exist in a number of tautomeric forms, and a great deal of effort has been devoted to a study of the exact structures. The question has not been satisfactorily settled, but it appears that many, if not most, pyrazolones can exist in different tautomeric forms, depending upon their environment. Pyrazolones have been by far the most commercially important members of the pyrazole type, having been widely used as pharmaceuticals, as dyes, and in color photography. A comprehensive review of pyrazolones has recently appeared (20) (see also Vol. 10, p. 911).

STRUCTURE

One of the intensively studied problems of heterocyclic chemistry for many years has been the study of the structures of pyrazolones capable of existing in various tautomeric forms. It has been generally agreed that, at least in *N*-substituted pyrazolones, the structures must be of types (**3**), (**4**), and (**15**), or mixtures of these. There is no agreement, however, as to the structures of various compounds in different environments (20–23).

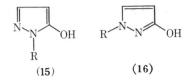

(15)   (16)

A report published in 1964 reviews previous data and conclusions and attempts to establish structures on the basis of pK_a's and of ultraviolet and NMR spectra (21). As this review represents the most thorough, comprehensive, and compelling appraisal of pyrazolone structures to date, its conclusions are those presented here. Pyrazolones having nitrogen substituents only on the amide-type nitrogen exist in the solid state as 3-pyrazolones (4). In nonpolar solvents, only the 5-pyrazolone form, (3), is present. In aqueous solutions such pyrazolones exist as an equilibrium of the 3-pyrazolone tautomer, (4), and the enol form, (15), but (4) constitutes the major component. Those 3-pyrazolones having only N-1 substituted exist in aqueous solutions as mixtures of the oxo form, (4), and the enol form, (16), but in nonpolar solvents and in the solid state, they are solely in the enol form, (16).

PHYSICAL PROPERTIES

Most pyrazolones are solids, although many can be distilled, but some are high-boiling liquids. Substitution on N-1 and N-2 tends to lower the melting and boiling points. The solubilities of the enormous number of pyrazolones known varies so greatly that widespread generalizations are not possible. However, pyrazolones tend to be more soluble in polar solvents than in nonpolar ones, and are frequently water-soluble. 5-Pyrazolones are both acidic and basic, readily dissolving in strong acids and bases. The pK_a's are in the range 6–11 while the pK_b's are 10–13. The acidic properties appear to be a result of hydrogen at C-4, as disubstitution at this position results in loss of acidity. The 3-pyrazolones are weakly basic, readily forming stable salts, but they are very weakly or not at all acidic. The absence of substitution at N-1 enhances acidity.

The ultraviolet, infrared, and NMR spectra of pyrazolones have been studied extensively (20,21), mostly in connection with studies of the structures of pyrazolones. The spectra are frequently quite complex due to mixtures of tautomeric forms and there is also considerable variation, depending upon whether solutions or solids were studied and upon variation in solvent. The uv spectra of pyrazolones usually have a maximum in the 245–300 mμ region with extinction coefficients of 5000–20,000. It has been reported that 3-pyrazolones absorb at longer wavelengths than do 5-pyrazolones (20), but this has been challenged (21). In some cases two maxima were reported and considered to be due to a mixture of 3- and 5-pyrazolones. From the literature data it seems that the type of substitution affects the uv spectrum more than does the position of the double bond. The ir spectra of pyrazolones having a carbonyl group show characteristic bands for carbonyl and C=N or C=C. In the case of the 5-pyrazolones the bands are at 1690–1710 cm^{-1} and at 1600–1630 cm^{-1}, respectively. The 3-pyrazolones have carbonyl bands at 1650–1670 cm^{-1} and olefinic bands at 1585–1600 cm^{-1}. Pyrazolones existing in the enolic form exhibit absorption bands at 2400–3300 cm^{-1} and do not absorb in the 1500–1700 cm^{-1} region. The NMR spectra of 5-pyrazolones have chemical shifts of 6.25–6.82 τ due to the 4-H, of 7.8–8.1 τ arising from methyl at C-3, and of 8.7–8.9 τ from methyl at C-4. Protons on the olefinic system of 3-pyrazolones have chemical shifts of 4.6–4.9 τ and methyl groups of about 7.8 τ. In all cases methyl groups substituted on nitrogen have signals at 6.4–7.0 τ.

CHEMICAL PROPERTIES

5-Pyrazolones are very reactive at C-4, and most of the important reactions they undergo occur at that position. Alkylation at C-4 by means of alkyl halides occurs under appropriate conditions, although this is not a very satisfactory reaction as a rule because of the greater tendency to react at N-2. Usually some alkylation occurs at both positions. Acylation takes place at C-4 with acyl chlorides, anhydrides, and esters. Condensation with aldehydes and ketones forms 4-alkylidene and bispyrazolones.

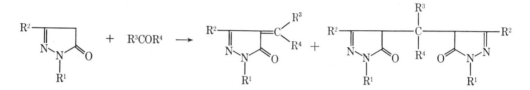

Halogenation at C-4 occurs with such reagents as bromine, phosphorus tribromide, and phosphorus pentachloride. Both the monobromo and dibromo compounds can be prepared. Nitrous acid reacts at C-4 to give an oxime, and nitric acid reacts to form 4-nitro derivatives. Substituents such as sulfonic and cyano groups can be introduced directly at C-4.

The reaction of 5-pyrazolones with diazonium salts is an important commercial process as it serves to synthesize the widely used 4-arylazo-5-pyrazolone dyes (see Vol. 2, pp. 871, 902). This reaction is an extremely general one, occurring with almost

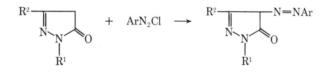

all 5-pyrazolones having no C-4 substituent. The nitrogen substituent is usually, although not necessarily, aryl, and the C-3 substituent may be of the alkyl, aryl, aralkyl, heterocyclic, carboxyl, sulfonic, or other type.

Another class of compounds having commercial importance and synthesized by introduction of a group at C-4 in 5-pyrazolones is the 4-arylimino derivatives used as color couplers. Aromatic nitroso compounds condense with 5-pyrazolones at C-4 to form such compounds. Another procedure for introducing the same type of group is

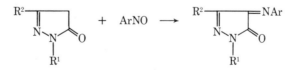

reaction of 5-pyrazolones with aromatic diamines in the presence of such oxidizing agents as silver salts, potassium ferricyanide, and sodium hypochlorite. The synthesis of a number of merocyanine dyes (see Polymethine dyes, p. 285) which include

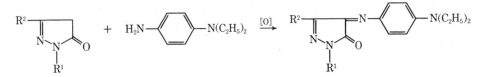

the pyrazolone ring system is illustrated by the following equation:

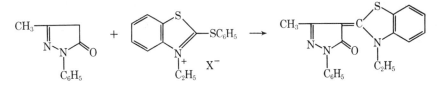

If 5-pyrazolones have hydrogen at N-1, acylation occurs readily at this position. The carbonyl group of 5-pyrazolones reacts with phosphorus oxychloride to form 5-chloropyrazoles and with phosphorus pentasulfide to give the 5-thiono analog.

Strong oxidizing agents completely destroy the 5-pyrazolone ring, but mild oxidizing agents cause dimerization to bispyrazolones coupled at the C-4 positions. Under certain conditions oxygen and peroxides form 4-hydroxy-5-pyrazolones. Reduction of 5-pyrazolones occurs in a variety of ways depending upon the reagents and conditions used. Sodium and amyl alcohol or lithium aluminum hydride reduce the carbonyl group to hydroxyl. Some chemical reagents completely remove oxygen and give pyrazoles and pyrazolines. Catalytic reduction usually has no effect on pyrazolones.

The characteristic reactions of 3-pyrazolones occur at C-4. Such reagents as nitrous acid, nitric acid, and halogens introduce, respectively, the nitroso group, the nitro group, and halogen at C-4. Alkylation and acylation also take place at C-4. Aldehydes react at C-4 and form either 4-(α-hydroxyalkyl)-3-pyrazolones or, with two moles of pyrazolone, a bispyrazolone. 4-Arylazo-3-pyrazolones are the product of 3-pyrazolones and diazonium salts.

3-Pyrazolone systems are stable to mild catalytic reduction, but vigorous conditions result in rupture of the ring.

SYNTHESIS

A very large number of syntheses of 5-pyrazolones have been reported, but only a few of these are generally applicable. By far the most important synthetic procedure has been the condensation of β-ketoesters with hydrazines. The R groups may be hydrogen, alkyl, aralkyl, aryl, and heterocyclic, although R^2 is commonly a small alkyl

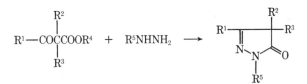

group and R^3 is usually either hydrogen or methyl. However, this reaction is so general that it has been used as a diagnostic test for β-ketoesters. Modifications of this procedure have utilized β-thionoesters, β-oximinoesters, and β-ketoamides. If an acyl hydrazide is used, the acyl group is lost and N-1 has no substituent.

Appropriately substituted α,β-unsaturated esters condense with hydrazines to form pyrazolones. The esters used are usually either α,β-acetylenic esters or β-substituted α,β-unsaturated esters in which the β-substituent is halogen, alkoxy, alkylthio, or acylthio. A variety of heterocyclic systems, such as isoxazolin-5-ones, various α-pyrones, and pyrimidines, condense with hydrazines to give pyrazolones. 5-Alkoxypyrazoles can be hydrolyzed to pyrazolones and pyrazolidines and readily oxidized to pyrazolones.

Pyrazolones substituted on N-1 as numbered in (**4**) are always called 3-pyrazolones. These are usually synthesized by alkylation of 5-pyrazolones, using the common alkylating agents. The alkylating agents most frequently used have been alkyl

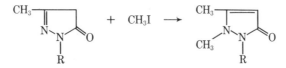

halides, alkyl sulfates, and alkyl sulfonates. The formation of a 5-alkoxypyrazole and alkylation at C-4 may be important side reactions, although yields are moderately good. If there is no N-1 substituent, alkylation usually occurs there also. Synthesis of 3-pyrazolones can also be achieved by condensation of a β-ketoester with disubstituted hydrazines.

If one of the hydrazine substituents is an acyl group, N-2 of the product has no substituent. A modification of this synthesis gives rise to 3,5-pyrazolidinediones, which exist chiefly in their enolic form as hydroxypyrazolones. Such compounds are prepared by reaction of malonic esters with disubstituted hydrazines.

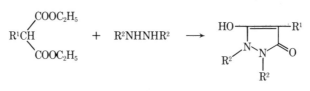

USES

A number of pyrazolones have been of commercial importance because of their extensive use as antipyretics and analgesics. Most of these have been 3-pyrazolones, of which antipyrine (**17**) (also called phenazone) is the best known and was the earliest. Antipyrine (see Vol. 2, p. 391) is not used in the United States at present (1968), but its world use is still very extensive; world production is in the neighborhood of 50,000 lb annually. Its synthesis has already been mentioned. Bulk drug is available at about $6.50/lb. Various analogs have been synthesized in an attempt to retain the same activity as, but eliminate some of the undesirable side effects of, antipyrine. Aminopyrine (**18**) (see Vol. 2, p. 391), marketed under a number of trade names, has been the most successful of these. As in the case of antipyrine, it is no longer used in the United States, but world production is about 250,000 lb/yr. Market price in bulk is $11–12/lb. Aminopyrine can be synthesized by the reduction of 4-nitro-, 4-nitroso-, or

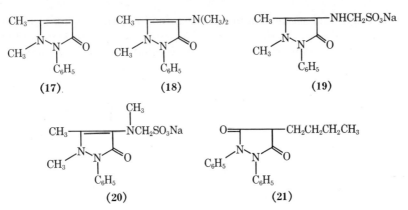

(17)   (18)   (19)

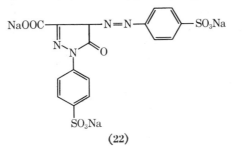

(20)   (21)

4-phenylazo-2-phenyl-1,5-dimethyl-3-pyrazolone to the 4-amino compound, followed by methylation with formaldehyde and formic acid. Similar compounds which have had some, but not extensive, use are sulfamipyrine (**19**) and dipyrone (**20**).

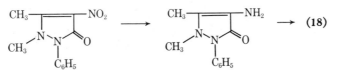

Phenylbutazone (see Vol. 2, p. 391), marketed as its sodium salt, Butazolidin (**21**), by Geigy Chemical Corporation, is usually considered to be a 3,5-pyrazolidine-dione, but, as it probably has the 5-hydroxy-3-pyrazolone structure, it will be discussed here. Because phenylbutazone is a very active inhibitor of inflammatory action, its principal use is in the treatment of arthritis. In spite of numerous undesirable side effects of phenylbutazone, its use has continued to grow, and at present, its sales in the United States are about $10 million per year at producers' prices. Synthesis is by the reaction of a malonic acid derivative with *sym*-diphenylhydrazine, followed by condensation with butyraldehyde and subsequent reduction. A few analogs of phenylbutazone have been marketed, but none have achieved wide use.

A large number of pyrazolone derivatives have been marketed for use as dyes and pigments (see Pigments, organic). The 4-phenylazopyrazolones have been most widely used, but merocyanine dyes derived from pyrazolones have also found commercial applications. An allied use has been employment of pyrazolones as color couplers in color photography (see Vol. 5, p. 824). A few relatively simple pyrazolones are manufactured in fairly large quantities for use as intermediates in the synthesis of drugs, dyes, and pigments. Of all the commercial pyrazolone derivatives tartrazine (**22**) (CI Acid Yellow 23; 19140) (see Vol. 2, p. 881) is produced on the largest scale.

(22)

It is used as a dye and pigment and also as a food coloring agent (see Vol. 5, pp. 867, 871, 873). Synthesis is by the reaction of diethyl oxaloacetate with *p*-sulfophenyl-hydrazine followed by coupling with diazotized sulfanilic acid. Table 1 lists U.S. production and sales as well as unit price for several pyrazolone products (24).

Table 1. U.S. Production and Sales of Some Pyrazolone Derivatives (24)

Product	Year	Production, lb	Sales Quantity, lb	Sales Value, $	Unit value, $/lb
Developer Z (3-methyl-1-phenyl-2-pyrazolin-5-one)	1965	281,000	216,000	353,000	1.63
	1964	279,000	218,000	355,000	1.63
	1960	385,000	264,000	464,000	1.76
	1957	282,000	172,000	320,000	1.86
Pyrazolone T (5-oxo-1-(*p*-sulfophenyl)-2-pyrazoline-3-carboxylic acid)	1965	40,000			
	1964	54,000			
	1957	29,000			
Pyrazolone G (*p*-(3-methyl-5-oxo-2-pyrazolin-1-yl)benzenesulfonic acid)	1965	203,000			
	1964	125,000	36,000	66,000	1.83
	1960	78,000			
	1957	62,000			
Tartrazine[a] (CI Acid Yellow 23; 19140)	1965	387,000	334,000	728,000	2.18
	1964	385,000	280,000	592,000	2.11
	1960	274,000	209,000	447,000	2.14
	1957	271,000	228,000	429,000	1.88
Xylene Light Yellow 2G and 3G (CI Acid Yellow 17; 18965)	1965	461,000	472,000	1,011,000	2.14
	1964	482,000	445,000	972,000	2.18
	1960	225,000	198,000	442,000	2.23
	1957	111,000	97,000	239,000	2.46
Pyrazolone Red[a] (CI Pigment Red 38; 21120)	1965	157,000	127,000	576,000	4.54
	1964	144,000	131,000	594,000	4.53
	1960	126,000	115,000	519,000	4.51
	1957	189,000	178,000	729,000	4.10
Benzidine Orange[a] (CI Pigment Orange 13; 21110)	1965	172,000	160,000	520,000	3.25
	1964	155,000	145,000	487,000	3.36
	1960	74,000	68,000	221,000	3.25
	1957	102,000	63,000	202,000	3.21

[a] See also Pigments, organic.

Indazolones

Indazolones are benzo analogs of 3-pyrazolones. The commonly accepted structure is indicated in formula (**23**), although indazolones commonly exhibit phenolic properties suggesting existence in an enolic form. If both nitrogens are substituted, only the keto form is possible. The usual synthesis of indazolones is by cyclization of an *o*-hydrazinobenzoic acid.

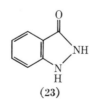

(**23**)

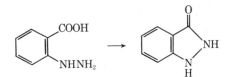

Indazolones have been reported to have analgesic, sedative, and spasmolytic properties (3). A class of magenta couplers (see Color photography, Vol. 5, p. 825) derived from indazolones has been reported to be of value in color photography. In spite of the useful properties reported for a number of indazolones, it appears that their commercial utilization has been insignificant. (See reference 3 for a recent review of indazolones.)

Bibliography

1. T. L. Jacobs, in R. C. Elderfield, ed., *Heterocyclic Compounds*, Vol. 5, John Wiley & Sons, Inc., New York, 1957, p. 45.
2. A. N. Kost and I. I. Grandberg, in A. R. Katritzky and A. J. Boulton, eds., *Advances in Heterocyclic Chemistry*, Vol. 6, Academic Press, Inc., New York, 1966, p. 347.
3. L. C. Behr, R. Fusco, and C. H. Jarboe, in R. H. Wiley, ed., *Pyrazoles, Pyrazolines, Pyrazolidines, Indazoles, and Condensed Rings*, Vol. 22 of A. Weissberger, ed., *The Chemistry of Heterocyclic Compounds*, Interscience Publishers, a division of John Wiley & Sons, Inc., New York, 1967.
4. J. K. Williams, *J. Org. Chem.* **29,** 1377 (1964).
5. H. W. W. Ehrlich, *Acta Cryst.* **13,** 946 (1960).
6. P. M. Dunnill and L. Fowden, *Biochem. J.* **86,** 388 (1963).
7. J. D. Loudon, in E. H. Rodd, ed., *Chemistry of Carbon Compounds*, Vol. 4, Part A, Elsevier, Amsterdam, 1957, pp. 245, 261.
8. D. Del Monte Casoni, A. Mangini, and R. Passerini, *Gazz. Chim. Ital.* **86,** 797 (1956).
9. I. I. Grandberg, *Zh. Obshch. Khim.* **33,** 518 (1963).
10. C. L. Habraken and J. A. Moore, *J. Org. Chem.* **30,** 1892 (1965).
11. L. E. Orgel, T. L. Cottrell, W. Dick, and L. E. Sutton, *Trans. Faraday Soc.* **47,** 113 (1951).
12. V. R. Vasil'eva, V. G. Yashuvskii, and M. N. Shchrikina, *Zh. Obshch. Khim.* **31,** 1501 (1961).
13. J. Elguero and R. Jacquier, *Tetrahedron Letters* **1965,** 1175.
14. J. L. Aubognac, J. Elguero, and R. Jacquier, *Tetrahedron Letters* **1965,** 1171.
15. J. Elguero and R. Jacquier, *Bull. Soc. Chim. France* **1965,** 769.
16. R. L. Hinman, R. D. Ellefson, and R. D. Campbell, *J. Am. Chem. Soc.* **82,** 3988 (1960).
17. G. L. Duffin and J. D. Kendall, *J. Chem. Soc.* **1954,** 408.
18. C. G. Overberger, J.-P. Anselme, and J. R. Hall, *J. Am. Chem. Soc.* **85,** 2752 (1963).
19. D. E. McGreer, R. S. McDaniel, and M. G. Virje, *Can. J. Chem.* **43,** 1389 (1965).
20. R. H. Wiley and P. Wiley, *Pyrazolones, Pyrazolidines, and Derivatives*, Vol. 20 of A. Weissberger, ed., *The Chemistry of Heterocyclic Compounds*, Interscience Publishers, a division of John Wiley & Sons, Inc., New York, 1964.
21. A. R. Katritzky and F. W. Maine, *Tetrahedron* **20,** 299, 315 (1964).
22. R. Jones, A. J. Ryan, S. Sternhell, and S. E. Wright, *Tetrahedron* **19,** 1497 (1963).
23. V. S. Troitskaya, I. I. Grandberg, and Yu. A. Pentin, *Tr. Soveshch. po Fiz. Metodam Issled. Organ. Soedin. i Khim. Protsessov Akad. Nauk Kirg. SSR, Inst. Organ. Khim., Frunze* **1962,** 84–93; *Chem. Abstr.* **62,** 2691 (1965).
24. U.S. Tariff Commission, *Synthetic Organic Chemicals, United States Production and Sales, 1957,* Rept. No. 203, 2nd ser., 1958, U.S. Govt. Printing Office, Washington, D.C.; *ibid. 1960,* TC Publ. 34, 1961; ibid. *1964,* TC Publ. 167, 1965; *ibid. 1965,* TC Publ. 206, 1967.

PAUL F. WILEY
The Upjohn Company

PYRETHRUM, PYRETHRINS. See Vol. 11, pp. 684, 685, 734.

PYRIDINE AND PYRIDINE DERIVATIVES

Pyridine (**1**), C₅H₅N (RI 277), is the parent ring system of a large number of naturally occurring products and important industrial, pharmaceutical, and agricultural chemicals. Vitamin B₆ (pyridoxine (qv)); nicotinamide (niacinamide) (see Vitamins); and coenzymes I and II (see Vol. 8, p. 175) are of the greatest biochemical importance. The pyridine nucleus is also found in members of several alkaloid families such as the pomegranate, lobelia, hemlock, areca, and tobacco (nicotine) alkaloids. Pyridine and many of its homologs are found in the light- and middle-oil fractions of coal tar and are known as the *pyridine bases*.

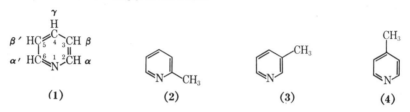

(1)   (2)   (3)   (4)

Pyridine is an aromatic compound and, like benzene, gives rise to a large number of substituted homologs and derivatives. Unlike benzene, however, in which all the nuclear positions are identical, pyridine can give rise to three isomeric monosubstituted compounds. For example, there are three methyl homologs of pyridine, the *picolines*, namely 2- (**2**), 3- (**3**), and 4-picoline (**4**), (also known as α-, β-, and γ-picoline, respectively). The dimethyl compounds are the *lutidines* (six isomers possible), and the trimethyl derivatives are the *collidines*. Ethylpyridines have sometimes been called lutidines and 5-ethyl-2-methylpyridine has been called "aldehyde collidine" (after its method of synthesis) but, though the latter usage may be excused, the former is deplored.

2-Picoline was the first pure coal-tar base to be isolated (Anderson, 1846). The parent base, pyridine, was isolated and characterized by Anderson in 1851 from bone oil (Dippel's oil), which also yielded some pyridine homologs. It was later isolated from coal tar by Goldschmidt and Constam, as well as from petroleum, peat, shale oil, commercial amyl alcohol, and roasted coffee. The basic components of coal tar can be conveniently resolved by gas chromatography and, in addition to simple pyridine homologs, include indoles, anilines, quinolines, isoquinolines, and more complex ring systems (1).

Preparation of Pyridine and its Homologs

The pyridine bases have been available since the original procedure for condensing the volatile products from the commercial coking process was developed in 1860. Since that time, a very large number of methods have been devised for the preparation of pyridine derivatives and these have been reviewed (2). The present discussion is divided into what may be conveniently called laboratory syntheses and manufacturing processes. Reactions involving the preformed pyridine ring system are discussed below under Chemical properties (see p. 787).

LABORATORY SYNTHESES

From Open-Chain Compounds. There are a very large number of syntheses of this type (2). The original synthesis of pyridine (Ramsay, 1876) involved passing acetylene and hydrogen cyanide through a red-hot tube; the yields are low and the method has little practical value.

Aldehydes and ketones condense with ammonia to give pyridines. Both saturated and unsaturated aldehydes may be used. This is a versatile reaction which has found wide industrial application (see below). Thus, crotonaldehyde ((5), R = CH₃) and aqueous NH₃ at 250°C in the liquid phase under pressure and in the presence of ammonium acetate gives 5-ethyl-2-picoline ((6), R = CH₃) (18% yield). The use of acrolein ((5), R = H), at 350°C in benzene vapor as a diluent gives a yield of 56% 3-

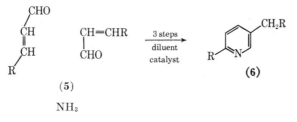

picoline and 1% pyridine. On the other hand, the reaction of crotonaldehyde with ammonia in the vapor phase over alumina at 340°C gives mainly 3-ethyl-4-picoline in low yield. A much better yield (90%) of 5-ethyl-2-picoline may be obtained by the liquid-phase condensation of acetaldehyde or paraldehyde with an excess of ammonia

in the presence of a catalyst (ammonium acetate or fluoride, cobalt chloride, and others) at high temperatures. In the vapor phase at 450°C over a catalyst composed of 82% silica, 15% alumina, and 3% thoria, the products were 2-picoline (34%), 4-picoline (32%), 5-ethyl-2-picoline (10%), and 3-ethyl-4-picoline (3%). A mechanism involving the self-condensation of acetaldimine, CH₃CH=NH, has been proposed to account for these products (2).

The use of ketones is illustrated by the conversion of acetone and ammonia to 2,4,6-trimethylpyridine (*sym*-collidine) (7) with loss of a methyl group, probably during the aromatization step (2a).

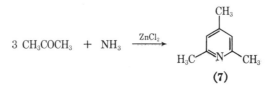

In the presence of a suitable catalyst, acetylenes and ammonia also condense in the vapor phase or in solution under pressure to give products similar to those obtained when the aldehydes corresponding to the hydration products of the acetylene are used. For example, acetylene itself (which would correspond to acetaldehyde) with aqueous ammonia in the presence of CoCl₂ at 140°C gives ((6), R = CH₃) in 75% yield (3). The condensation of acetylene (or acetaldehyde), ammonia, and methanol over a fluidized bed of silica–alumina catalyst at 500°C gives a mixture of pyridine and 3-picoline; the yields are greatly improved by the use of methanol *and* formaldehyde in equimolar proportions (4).

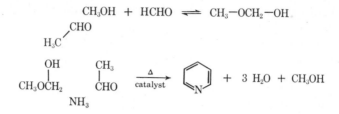

Probably the most important of the laboratory syntheses of pyridine derivatives is that of Hantzsch (5), mainly because of its versatility and flexibility which have permitted wide variations in the nature of the starting materials and hence the products obtained. In its original form the synthesis involved the condensation of 2 moles of a β-keto ester and 1 mole of an aldehyde with ammonia under mild conditions to give a 1,4-dihydropyridine, which is easily oxidized, eg with dilute nitric acid, to the fully aromatic compound.

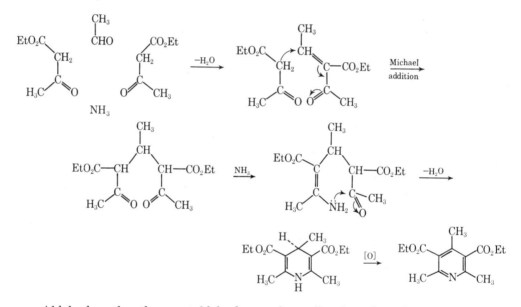

Aldehydes other than acetaldehyde may be used to introduce different functional groups at C-4. β-Diketones may be used instead of β-keto esters. A variation involves the use of 1 mole of β-dicarbonyl compound and 2 moles of an aldehyde of the type RCH₂CHO. Here an excess of the aldehyde may act as the oxidizing agent.

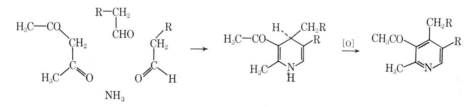

Nitriles may also be used, as can suitable amides. For instance, ethoxyacetylacetone (**8**) and cyanoacetamide give a 3-cyano-2-pyridone (**9**) which is an intermediate in a synthesis of pyridoxine (6).

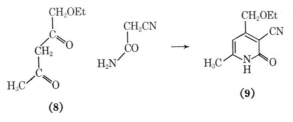

(8)   (9)

An interesting synthesis of substituted 2-pyridones is that of Thesing and Müller (7). Here, the active methylene group required in the second step of the Hantzsch synthesis (see above) is attached to the nitrogen atom of a pyridinium salt. For example, 4-*o*-nitrophenyl-2-pyridone (**10**) may be synthesized in this way (8).

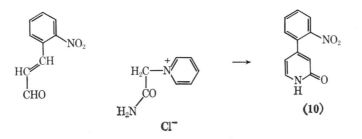

(10)

Diels-Alder additions have been used to obtain pyridines. For example, trifluoro-acetonitrile adds 1,4 to butadiene at 350–520°C, the product undergoing dehydrogenation at this high temperature, to give (**11**) (9).

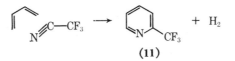

(11)

From Other Heterocyclic Systems. The pyrones react with ammonia readily to replace the ring oxygen with nitrogen and give pyridones.

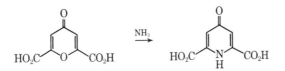

The Diels-Alder reaction has been combined with the oxygen-replacement method in a new synthesis of 3-alkoxypyridines (10).

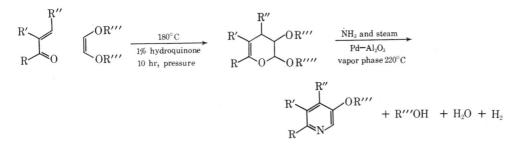

Pyrroles may be ring-expanded to the pyridines in reactions which are more of academic than of practical interest. Treatment of pyrrole with chloroform and sodium ethoxide (in effect, with dichlorocarbene, Cl₂C) gives a low yield of 3-chloropyridine. A much better yield (33%) is obtained if chloroform and pyrrole are heated together in the vapor phase at 550°C; some 2-chloropyridine is also formed (11).

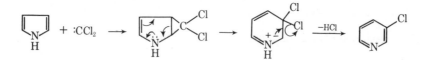

The diene addition has also been used in a novel synthesis of an intermediate (**12**) in the preparation of 2-norpyridoxal 5′-phosphate (12).

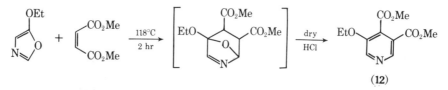

(**12**)

A large number of pyridine derivatives have been obtained by the dehydrogenation of suitable piperidines (2).

From Naturally Occurring Compounds. The degradation under drastic conditions of alkaloids containing hydropyridine or fused pyridines often yields pyridine derivatives in low yield. For instance, zinc dust distillation of nortropane hydrochloride (from tropine) gives 2-ethylpyridine, and distillation of cinchonine with caustic potash gives 3-ethylpyridine and 3-ethyl-4-picoline. Selenium dehydrogenation of corynantheine gives alstyrine (**13**), which proved of value in establishing the structure of the alkaloid.

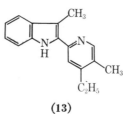

(**13**)

MANUFACTURE

Now that the petroleum industry supplies so many aromatics and fuel gas, the chief incentive in distilling coal is to supply coke for steel. About 75 million tons of coal were coked in the U.S. in 1962 and in 1964 the pyridine crude bases obtained in this way amounted to 464,000 gal. Every ton of coal carbonized produces from 0.07 to 0.21 lb pyridine bases. Thus, no large-scale expanding industry can be based exclusively on pyridine or picolines from the coking process. Fortunately, synthetic processes have been developed which are capable of supplying the increasing demand for these products.

From Coal Chemicals. Coking procedures and methods for recovery of the noncondensable gas and coal tar have been described in detail (13). The noncondensable gas contains ammonia and approx 60% of the pyridine bases formed during coking.

The other 40% remains with that portion of the gas which is condensed and becomes a part of the tar. The noncondensable gas is passed into sulfuric acid, and the water-soluble pyridinium sulfate and ammonium sulfate are formed (ammonia saturator liquor). Pyridine and its homologs are reclaimed by treating these sulfates with ammonia vapor. The pyridine bases thus obtained consist of approx 70% pyridine and 30% higher homologs, mainly picolines. The layer of crude bases contains approx 15–20% water.

The coal tar is distilled in pipe stills to give (1) a "light-oil fraction" (distillation end-point of about 210°C) which contains tar acids, some naphthalene, and the crude pyridine bases, and (2) a "middle-oil" (up to bp 270°C, approx) which contains naphthalene, tar acids, quinolines, and higher-boiling pyridine homologs. The pyridines are recovered from the light oil by circulating aqueous sulfuric acid through the oil after it has been extracted with caustic soda to remove the phenols. The solution of the water-soluble pyridinium sulfates is decanted and, if necessary, boiled to volatilize small amounts of oil which may have been carried over into the water layer. The pyridine bases are "sprung" from their sulfates by treatment with caustic soda or ammonia. Of the pyridine bases thus obtained 35–40% is pyridine, over 10% is 2-picoline, and the remainder consists of higher homologs (14). See also Tar.

The crude pyridine bases are dried by azeotropic distillation with benzene and then separated by fractional distillation. The crude dried pyridine is distilled and sold in the following grades: (1) technical-grade (denaturing-grade) pyridine, bp 115–145°C; (2) refined-grade, 2° pyridine (bp 113.5–115.5°C—some commercial products have a narrower boiling range); (3) and further-refined grades—reagent, cp, and medicinal—which are required for special purposes. The next distillation cut, bp 128–129°C, consists of 2-picoline. The fraction with a bp of 143–146°C is primarily a mixture of 3-picoline, bp 143.8°C (ca 40%); 4-picoline, bp 144°C (ca 45%); and 2,6-lutidine, bp 144.4°C (ca 15%). These proportions may vary greatly, however, depending on the source of the coal. This mixture (ca 4–8% of the crude), which cannot be separated by simple fractionation, is known as the "β-picoline fraction." A mixture of higher alkylated pyridines is separated up to 184–185°C, at which temperature aniline (about 4% of the crude) distills over, and a residue of quinoline bases (ca 15%) remains behind.

Separation of the β-picoline fraction has been effected by both physical and chemical methods, which are costly, and which have been carried out in up to pilot-plant quantities only. 2,6-Lutidine is separated from 3- and 4-picoline as its crystalline urea addition compound. The β-picoline fraction may be separated into its components by azeotropic distillation with aliphatic acids or phenols (15,16), countercurrent extraction with hexane and water (17), or steam distillation with sulfur dioxide (18), to name but a few methods. A number of chemical methods of separation of 3- from 4-picoline take advantage of the reactivity of the methyl group in the latter; it is condensed with a suitable reagent, or oxidized to a carboxylic acid function, leaving 3-picoline intact (2). In view of these difficulties, pure 3- and 4-picoline are manufactured in the United States by synthetic processes only.

Synthetic Processes. Synthetic pyridine is produced from acetaldehyde and ammonia as described on p. 781 above. Acetylene may be used instead of acetaldehyde, and the addition of formaldehyde and methanol is advantageous (4). A mixture of equal parts formaldehyde and methanol (formaldehyde hemiacetal) is treated with acetaldehyde (or acetylene), vaporized, and mixed with ammonia. The vapors are passed through a fluid-catalyst-type reactor containing a fluidized catalytic bed of silica–alumina catalyst at 500°C. The crude dry bases are fractionated to recover pyridine (35%) and 3-picoline (27%). Little or no 4-picoline is formed (4). A catalyst consisting of silica–alumina–cadmium oxide (or zinc oxide) has also been used in the synthesis of pyridine and 3-picoline (19). 2-Picoline and 4-picoline are prepared by the vapor-phase reaction described above under Laboratory syntheses from open-chain compounds, involving acetaldehyde and ammonia over a silica–alumina–thoria catalyst at 450°C (20).

5-Ethyl-2-picoline (MEP, aldehyde collidine) is produced in high yield from paraldehyde (the trimer of acetaldehyde) and ammonia *in the liquid phase* in the presence of a catalyst. Small amounts of 2- and 4-picoline are also formed (21). 2,4,6-Trimethylpyridine (*sym*-collidine) is manufactured by the reaction of acetone with ammonia.

Physical Properties and Structure

Pyridine is a very hygroscopic, colorless (when pure) liquid, mp −42°C, bp 115.3°C, d_4^{25} 0.9780, n_D^{25} 1.5073, vapor density (air = 1) 2.73, flash point (closed cup) 68°F, ignition temperature 900°F. Explosive limits (% by volume of air) are: lower 1.8, upper 12.5. It has a somewhat unpleasant smell. Its ultraviolet spectrum is similar to that of benzene: λ_{max} 170, 195, and 250 mμ. In acid solution, the pyridinium ion exhibits a strong absorption maximum at 255 mμ (log ε 3.75). The infrared spectrum exhibits bands at 3070–3020, 1660–1590, 1500, 1200, 750, and 710 cm^{-1}, among others (22). The NMR spectrum is that expected for an AB_2X_2 system (23), the α-protons absorbing at 1.40 τ, the β-protons at ca 3.00 τ, and the γ-proton at 2.40 τ. Pyridine is completely water-soluble and forms an azeotrope with atmospheric moisture, corresponding to $C_5H_5N \cdot 3H_2O$, which boils at 92–93°C; it may be dried by azeotropic distillation with benzene or over potassium hydroxide or, preferably, barium oxide.

Table 1. Physical Properties of Pyridine Bases

Pyridine base	Mp, °C	Bp, °C	d_4^{20}	n_D^{20}	$pK_a{}^a$	Picrate mp, °C
pyridine (C_5H_5N)	−42	115.3	0.9819	1.5095	5.17	164
2-picoline	−64	128–129	0.9455	1.5020	5.97	169–171
3-picoline	−17.7	143.8	0.9564	1.5049	5.68	149–150
4-picoline	+4.3	145.3	0.9546	1.5040	6.02	167–168
2,3-dimethylpyridine		162–164			6.57	183–184
2,4-dimethylpyridine		157–158	0.9332	1.5012	6.63	184–185
2,5-dimethylpyridine		157			6.40	170
2,6-dimethylpyridine	−5.9	144.4	0.9237	1.4971	6.72	163–164
3,4-dimethylpyridine		163.5–164.5			6.46	163
3,5-dimethylpyridine		172			6.15	235–236
2-ethylpyridine		148–149	0.9347		5.97	107.0–107.5
3-ethylpyridine		165	0.9421	1.5030	5.70	128–130
4-ethylpyridine		169.6–170.0	0.9417	1.5022	6.02	169–170
2,4,6-trimethylpyridine	−46	170.3	0.9142	1.4981		156
5-ethyl-2-methylpyridine (MEP)	−70.3	178.3	0.9208	1.4970		167–168
2-*n*-propylpyridine		166–168			5.97	65

^{a} In water at 25°C.

Its basicity is intermediate (K_b 2.3 $\times$ 10^{-9}; pK_a 5.17 in water at 25°C) between that of piperidine (K_b 1.6 $\times$ 10^{-3}; pK_a 11.1) and aniline (K_b 3.8 $\times$ 10^{-10}; pK_a 4.58). Pyridine is an excellent solvent for many organic compounds and gives conducting solutions of many inorganic substances such as silver bromide, silver nitrate, cuprous and cupric chlorides, ferric chloride, mercuric chloride, lead nitrate, and lead acetate. It forms complexes at the nitrogen with most inorganic salts, many of which remain in solution in excess pyridine or in a suitable solvent but a number of which precipitate out. The dipole moment of pyridine is 2.23D.

A summary of some physical properties of the more important pyridine homologs is given in Table 1.

The resonance energy of pyridine (from heat-of-combustion data) was found to be 35 kcal/mole (24), and the molecular dimensions, as calculated from microwave measurements, are as shown in Figure 1 (25).

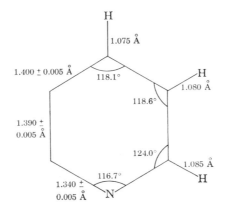

Fig. 1. Dimensions of pyridine.

Chemical Properties

The chemical properties of pyridine may be fairly well predicted qualitatively on the basis of molecular-orbital (MO) calculations of the electron densities around the ring or of valence-bond (resonance theory) considerations. With the MO method it is important to know something about the transition state before deciding which parameters are to be used in predicting the behavior of the molecule in aromatic substitution. Thus, if the transition state resembles the ground state, the order of π, or preferably $\pi + \sigma$, electron densities at the various possible nuclear-reaction sites will give a reasonably good correlation with relative reactivities, whereas if the transition state resembles a Wheland or σ-complex, atom localization-energy data give better agreement. For free-radical substitution, calculations of the free valences have given useful results. In Table 2 are summarized some of the more recent values calculated (26) for π and $\pi + \sigma$ electron densities in pyridine and the pyridinium ion (C$_5$H$_5$NH) using Extended Hückel Theory; the values of the localization energies are given in Table 3. It should be noted that the numbers obtained in such calculations depend greatly upon the choice of parameters and the approximations involved, and no emphasis should be placed on their absolute magnitudes since there are many other calculated values available in the literature (27).

Table 2. Electron Densities in Pyridine and Pyridinium Ion (26)

	Position	π^a	$\pi + \sigma$
pyridine	1	1.43 (1.063)	5.92
	2	0.84 (0.981)	3.63
	3	1.01 (0.994)	4.05
	4	0.87 (0.981)	3.89
pyridinium ion	2	0.84 (0.977)	3.66
	3	1.01 (0.887)	4.04
	4	0.87 (0.822)	3.89

[a] Values in parentheses are taken from ref. 27.

Table 3. Localization Energies for Electrophilic (A_e), Nucleophilic (A_n), and Homolytic (A_r) Substitution in Pyridine and Pyridinium Ion (27), in units of $-\beta$, the resonance integral

	Position	A_e	A_r	A_n
pyridine[a]	2	2.67	2.51	2.35
	3	2.54	2.54	2.54
	4	2.70	2.54	2.37
pyridinium ion[b]	2	2.71	2.28	1.86
	3	2.56	2.56	2.56
	4	3.07	2.54	2.01

[a] Values for pyridine are based on inductive parameter $h = 0.5$.
[b] Values for pyridinium ion are based on inductive parameter $h = 2.0$.

According to resonance theory, the valence structure of pyridine may be represented as a hybrid of five canonical structures:

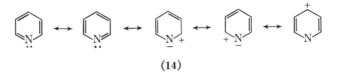

(14)

The electronegative nitrogen atom (**14**) should also polarize the σ-bonds inductively to a certain extent. On the basis of these considerations and of the MO calculations summarized above, one might expect the pyridine ring, like nitrobenzene, to be less susceptible than benzene to electrophilic attack at carbon and, when electrophilic substitution did take place, that it would take place more readily at C-3 and C-5 than at the other carbon atoms. On the other hand, one would expect pyridine to undergo nucleophilic substitution readily at C-2 and C-4, the order of reactivity being 2->4->3-. The lone pair of electrons of nitrogen is in an sp^2 orbital orthogonal to the π-system so that it is not involved in the resonance and is available for donation to an acid. On the other hand, since it is present in an sp^2 hybrid orbital it is easy to see why pyridine will be a much weaker base than a tertiary aliphatic amine in which the lone pair is in an sp^3 orbital (which has less s character) and is, therefore, less tightly bound to the nitrogen atom. Upon the addition of a strong acid, the pyridinium ion, which is much more resistant to electrophilic attack than is pyridine itself, is formed. It has been estimated that substitution of $=N-$ for $=CH-$ in benzene is deactivating by a factor of at least 10^{-6}, but substitution of $=\overset{+}{N}H-$ results in considerably greater deactivation of the nucleus towards electrophilic attack, with estimates varying from

$<10^{-12}$ to 10^{-18} (28).   This is understandable in terms of the valence-bond structures (**15**), in which the canonical forms bearing a positive charge on carbon contribute much more to the resonance hybrid than do those in (**14**), since, unlike in the latter, there is no charge separation here.   Attack by a positively charged species (eg NO_2^+) would now lead to a doubly positively charged intermediate whose formation would require a great deal of energy.

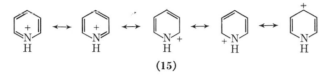

(**15**)

Salt Formation.   Pyridine forms salts (pyridinium salts) not only with Brønsted-Lowry acids but also with Lewis acids (see Acid–base systems).   With hydrogen chloride, pyridine hydrochloride (pyridinium chloride, $C_5H_5N \cdot HCl$ or $C_5H_5\overset{+}{N}H\ Cl^-$) is formed; with boron trichloride, a coordination complex (**16**) is formed.   Similar complexes are formed with a vast number of salts, eg $2C_5H_5N \cdot LiCl$ and $2C_5H_5N \cdot BeCl_2$.

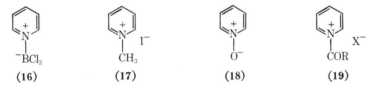

(**16**)　　　　　(**17**)　　　　　(**18**)　　　　　(**19**)

Pyridine, as a tertiary amine, forms typical quaternary ammonium salts.   For example, pyridine and methyl iodide react with the evolution of heat to give pyridine methiodide (N-methylpyridinium iodide) (**17**) as a water-soluble white crystalline solid, mp 116°C.   Also, an N-oxide (**18**) is formed on reaction of pyridine with peroxyacids; this is an important compound and its chemistry is discussed later.   With an acid chloride or anhydride, pyridine yields N-acylpyridinium salt (**19**), which is a powerful acylating agent, hence the use of pyridine as a catalyst or solvent for acylations.

Reduction (29).   As expected from the fact that the pyridine nucleus has a higher electron affinity than has the benzene ring, it is more readily reduced than the latter. Predictably, reduction of the pyridinium ion is still more facile.   Catalytic reduction of pyridine as the neutral molecule takes place at 200°C and 150–300 atm over Raney nickel to give the hexahydro derivative, piperidine (qv) (**20**).   In an acidic

(**20**)　　　　　　　　　　　　　　(**21**)

medium pyridine may be reduced at 25°C and 2 atm using a platinum catalyst. Other catalysts that have been used for the reduction of the free base include rhenium, ruthenium, and rhodium; palladized charcoal has been used for the reduction of pyridinium salts.

Electrolytic reduction of pyridine (in sulfuric acid at a lead cathode) to piperidine is carried out industrially, but the product contains small amounts of 1,2,5,6-tetrahydropyridine (3-piperideine) (**21**).   Dissolving metals are also a source of electrons, and sodium in dry ethanol reduces pyridine to the 1,4-dihydro stage. Vigorous treatment of pyridine with lithium aluminum hydride in boiling di-*n*-butyl ether gives piperidine.

The relative ease of reduction of pyridine and benzene is illustrated by the fact that the reduction of 2-phenylpyridine (**22**) gives 2-phenylpiperidine (**23**).

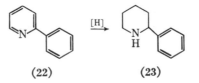

(**22**)   (**23**)

Oxidation (29).   As mentioned above, the oxidation of pyridine with peroxyacids leads to pyridine *N*-oxide. The ring, however, is more resistant to oxidation than is the benzene ring under ordinary conditions, since it is very reluctant to donate electrons. Thus, the oxidation of quinoline (**24**) under vigorous conditions gives, almost entirely, quinolinic acid (pyridine-2,3-dicarboxylic acid) (**25**) in which the benzene ring

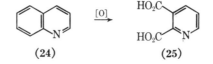

(**24**)   (**25**)

has been destroyed but the pyridine ring is intact. Indeed, pyridine has occasionally been used as a solvent in which to carry out permanganate oxidations.

Pyridine homologs give the corresponding pyridinecarboxylic acids on oxidation, eg, with neutral potassium permanganate at 90°C, 2-picoline gives *picolinic acid* (**26**), 3-picoline gives *nicotinic acid* (**27**), and 4-picoline gives *isonicotinic acid* (**28**). The catalytic vapor-phase oxidation of the picolines is an important industrial route to the

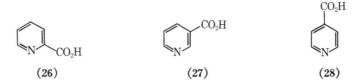

(**26**)   (**27**)   (**28**)

pyridinecarboxylic acids. Vapor-phase oxidation in the presence of ammonia gives cyanopyridines, probably via an amide which is dehydrated to the nitrile.

Electrophilic Substitution (28).   Nuclear substitution of pyridine by electrophilic reagents usually requires very stringent conditions, conditions under which nitrobenzene undergoes polysubstitution. Under the conditions used for the reaction the pyridine nitrogen is usually quaternized, and it is the pyridinium ion that is undergoing substitution. Many electrophilic substitution reactions of pyridine (such as sulfonation and chlorination) are catalyzed by salts such as mercuric sulfate and aluminum chloride. Coordination of the metal ion to the ring-nitrogen atom and back-donation of electrons from the metal atom to the ring occur, thus decreasing the formal positive charge on the ring and facilitating electrophilic attack. Alkyl substituents activate the nucleus towards electrophilic substitution, and more powerful electron-donating substituents render substitution relatively easy (see discussion below under Effects of substituents upon chemical properties).

Nitration of pyridine under even very vigorous conditions gives very poor yields of product. With potassium nitrate in fuming sulfuric acid at 300°C, only a 5% yield of 3-nitropyridine is obtained, together with smaller amounts of 3,5-dinitropyridine; ie substitution does take place at the β-position as predicted, albeit with great difficulty. 2-Picoline undergoes nitration at 160°C to give a low (3.6%) yield of a mixture of 3- and 5-nitro-2-picoline, and *sym*-collidine is mononitrated at 100°C to give a 90% yield of 3-nitro-2,4,6-trimethylpyridine. With NO_2^+ the *N*-nitropyridinium salt is formed.

Sulfonation of pyridine also requires vigorous conditions, but pyridine-3-sulfonic acid is obtained in good yield when pyridine is heated in fuming sulfuric acid (20% SO_3) with mercuric sulfate for 24 hr at 220–230°C. If protonation of the ring nitrogen is prevented sterically, as with 2,6-di-*t*-butylpyridine, the 3-sulfonic acid is obtained under relatively mild conditions (SO_3 in liquid SO_2 at -10°C).

Halogenation of pyridine and its homologs is complicated by competition between two different mechanistic pathways. Chlorination in the gas phase at 200°C gives 3,5-dichloro- and 3,4,5-trichloropyridine by electrophilic attack. At 270°C, chlorine atoms appear to be reactive species and 2-chloropyridine is the main product. Pyridine reacts with cold bromine to form an addition complex, pyridine perbromide, $C_5H_5N.Br_2$ which is used as a mild brominating agent. It forms a hydrobromide which on heating to 200°C is transformed into a mixture of 3-bromo- and 3,5-dibromopyridine. Bromination of pyridine in the vapor phase at 300°C also gives the same compounds in good yield, but at 500°C bromine atoms are involved (30) and the products are primarily 2-bromopyridine (45–50%) and 2,6-dibromopyridine (15–20%). Chlorination and bromination of pyridine and its homologs may be effected under relatively mild conditions (80–100°C) in the presence of an excess of aluminum chloride or of thionyl chloride (28). The light-catalyzed chlorination of 2-picoline with chlorine water eventually

(29)   (30)

gives 3,4,5-trichloro-2-trichloromethylpyridine (**29**). Iodination of pyridine can be brought about with fuming sulfuric acid and iodine at 300°C, 3-iodopyridine being formed in low yields.

Mercuration can be effected by mercuric acetate at 155°C to yield 3-pyridylmercuric acetate, (**30**) but the *Friedel–Crafts alkylation* or *acylation* has not been successful with pyridine and its homologs.

Nucleophilic Substitution (28). In contrast to the electrophilic replacement of a proton, nucleophilic attack upon the pyridine nucleus often takes place with ease, and eventual replacement of a hydride ion results if a powerful enough nucleophile is used.

Amination (the Tschitschibabin reaction) takes place when pyridine is heated with sodium amide in boiling toluene or in *N,N*-dimethylaniline at 180°C. See Vol. 2, p. 367. The main product is 2-aminopyridine (**31**). At 170°C, in the presence of a twofold excess of sodamide, 2,6-diaminopyridine is obtained. Potassium amide can also be used in these aminations but lithium amide gives complex results and virtually no (**31**). Sodium alkylamides and sodium hydrazide–hydrazine give the corresponding 2-substituted pyridines.

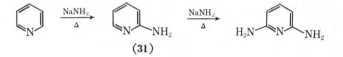

(31)

Alkylation and *arylation* can be effected by reaction with a suitable Grignard reagent or, more readily, using organolithium compounds. Substitution takes place exclusively at C-2 and C-6 with organolithium reagents, except if the attacking carbanion is particularly stable, eg benzyllithium, in which case attack takes place at C-4 to give 4-benzylpyridine.

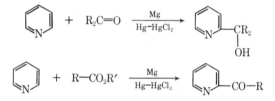

Hydroxyalkylation as well as acylation may be effected by means of the *Emmert reaction*, wherein pyridine is heated with a ketone or an ester in the presence of magnesium and mercuric chloride:

Although the latter reaction formally resembles a Friedel-Crafts acylation it is, in fact, a nucleophilic substitution by the $R\!-\!\overset{\_}{C}\!-\!OR'$ carbanion.

$\quad\quad\quad\quad\quad\quad\quad\quad\quad\quad\quad\quad\quad\;$ |
$\quad\quad\quad\quad\quad\quad\quad\quad\quad\quad\quad\quad$ OMg

Homolytic Substitution (28). The free-radical alkylation of pyridine can be effected with diacyl peroxides. For example, when pyridine and acetyl peroxide are heated together, 2-, 3-, and 4-picoline are formed in the ratio of 3.5:1.2:1. Homolytic arylation can be effected either with diaryol peroxides or better with aryldiazonium salts (Gomberg-Hey reaction). When pyridine and benzenediazonium salts are heated at 40°C, 2-, 3-, and 4-phenylpyridine are obtained in the ratio of 54:29:17.

Effects of Substituents Upon Chemical Properties. Alkyl substituents exert the expected base-enhancing effect as can be seen from Table 1. With large substituents at both the α-positions, eg *t*-butyl groups, steric hindrance to coordination of Lewis acids at the ring nitrogen is marked.

As expected, electron-donating substituents facilitate, and electron-attracting ones retard, electrophilic attack upon the nucleus. A sufficiently strong electron-donating substituent takes over the directive influence from the nitrogen atom if the two are acting in opposition. For example, whereas 3-picoline undergoes sulfonation at C-5, 3-methylaminopyridine gives an *N*-nitro derivative which rearranges to 3-methylamino-2-nitropyridine. Chlorination of 3-aminopyridine at 80°C with hydrochloric acid and hydrogen peroxide gives 3-amino-2-chloropyridine (88%) together with a small amount of 3-amino-2,6-dichloropyridine. Under suitable conditions 3-hydroxy-2-methylpyridine yields, on nitration, a mixture of the 4- and of the 6-nitro derivatives. Nitration of 2-aminopyridine proceeds in two distinct steps: The first, the formation of 2-*N*-nitraminopyridine, is followed on warming by an exothermic rearrangement to give a mixture of 3-nitro- and 5-nitro-2-aminopyridine in the ratio of 1:8. The nitration of 2-pyridone (2-hydroxypyridine, structure discussed below) gives a mixture of 3-nitro- and 3,5-dinitro-2-pyridone in which the former predominates.

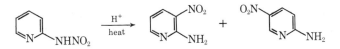

Substituent effects in nucleophilic substitution of pyridines have been studied (28,31). A 3-alkyl group directs the entering nucleophile mainly to the 2-position, though some 6-substituted product is also formed, the extent depending largely on the size of the 3-alkyl group.

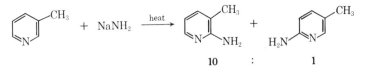

10 : 1

3-Amino and 3-alkoxy substituents behave similarly. The effects of substituents upon orientation and reactivity have been reviewed (28), and though much is known, a great deal more has to be learned before the state of the art reaches the same level of knowledge as that about the effects of substituents in benzene.

Effect of Pyridine Nucleus Upon the Properties of Substituent Groups. *Alkyl Groups.* Although a methyl group attached to the β-position is unreactive and similar in properties to that in toluene, it is quite reactive if attached to the α- or the γ-position of the pyridine nucleus. This is caused by the presence of a partial positive charge at these positions (contributing structures (**32b**) and **33b**)) which is not present at C-3.

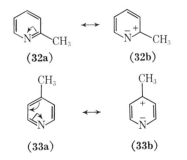

This positive charge is relayed by induction to the methyl group, thus facilitating the removal of a proton. Thus, both 2- and 4-picoline condense with benzaldehyde in the presence of acetic anhydride or zinc chloride to give azastilbene derivatives. They are

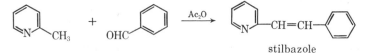

stilbazole

also metalated with ease in the side chain by *n*-butyllithium or by sodamide in liquid ammonia, whereas 3-picoline only undergoes metalation with the latter reagent with difficulty and in poor yield. 2-Picoline undergoes the Mannich reaction with formaldehyde and dimethylamine giving 2-β-dimethylaminoethylpyridine. The 2- and 4-picolines react with paraformaldehyde at 200°C to give the β-hydroxyethylpyridines, which can be dehydrated to the important vinylpyridines (see below). As mentioned before, oxidation of all three picolines gives the corresponding carboxylic acids.

Halogen Derivatives. The 2- and 4-halopyridines compare in reactivity towards nucleophilic reagents with *o*- and *p*-halonitrobenzenes, whereas 3-halopyridines are much less susceptible to nucleophilic substitution of the halogen atom. This, again, is due to dipolar contributing structures such as (34b); nucleophilic attack at C-2 and

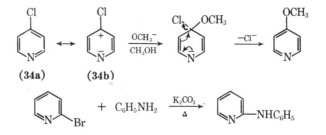

C-4 is greatly facilitated by the presence of the partial positive charges at these positions. Substitution of a 3-halogen atom requires much more drastic conditions and usually the presence of a copper catalyst. For fluoropyridines see Vol. 9, p. 798.

Hydroxy Derivatives. 3-Hydroxypyridine, prepared by fusing pyridine-3-sulfonic acid with potassium hydroxide, behaves as a normal phenol. On the other hand, 2- and 4-hydroxypyridines (prepared by diazotization of the corresponding amine or by the hydrolysis of the desired halopyridine) exhibit lactim–lactam tautomerism. As indicated by infrared, NMR and ultraviolet spectroscopy and by pK_a measurements, these compounds exist predominantly in the pyridone form ((35b), (36b)), both in the solid state and in solution, and should, therefore, be referred to as such and not as hydroxy-

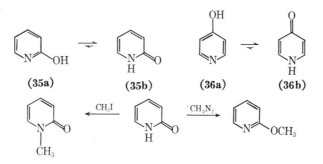

pyridines. They can react in either form. 2-Pyridone and phosphorus oxychloride yield 2-chloropyridine. With diazomethane, (35) gives 3-methoxypyridine but with methyl iodide it gives *N*-methyl-2-pyridone.

Amino Derivatives. Here again, although 3-aminopyridine behaves like an ordinary primary aromatic amine, the 2- and 4-aminopyridines can exhibit amine–imine tautomerism. Unlike the hydroxy compounds, however, these aminopyridines exist mainly in the amine form. For a long time it was thought that a diazonium salt could

be prepared only from a 3-aminopyridine. 3-Pyridyldiazonium salts behave normally, undergoing the Sandmeyer, Gattermann, and Gomberg-Hey reactions. Diazotization of 2- and 4-aminopyridines was effected in concentrated acid and the diazonium salt was not obtained; instead, the corresponding pyridone was formed. It has now been found (32) that diazotization of 2- and 4-aminopyridine in dilute mineral acid

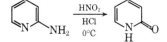

does lead to the formation of diazonium ions, which hydrolyze rapidly to the corresponding hydroxy compounds but which may be trapped by coupling with alkaline β-naphthol.

Pyridinium Salts

These are of importance, not only in themselves, but also because of their relationship to coenzymes I and II, which are pyridinium salts in which the quaternizing group is a phosphorylated ribose derivative. N-Alkyl- and N-arylpyridinium salts are more reactive towards nucleophilic reagents than are the pyridines themselves. Thus, nicotinamide methiodide (37) reacts with cyanide ion to give the 1,4-dihydropyridine derivative (38).

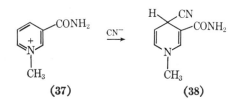

Reduction of pyridinium salts also takes place reversibly under mild conditions (33), a process of fundamental importance in the mode of action of the coenzymes **I** and **II**.

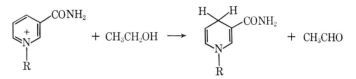

Ferricyanide oxidation of pyridinium salts under strongly alkaline conditions takes place at 5–10°C to give the corresponding pyridones, presumably via a very small concentration of the *pseudo*-base (39) present in equilibrium with the pyridinium hydroxide. The in vivo counterpart of this process in plants may be an important

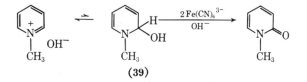

biosynthetic pathway to alkaloids such as nudiflorine.

One-electron reductions of pyridinium ions are of interest. For example, the herbicidal activity of the bisquaternary salts of 2,2'- and 4,4'-dipyridyls results from a one-electron reduction; a relationship exists between the reduction potential (ease of radical formation) and herbicidal activity. Stable free radicals have been obtained by the one-electron reduction of suitably substituted pyridinium salts (34).

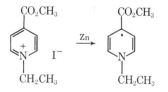

Pyridinium salts have been put to many synthetic uses (35). The pyridinium ring will undergo cleavage under suitable conditions if the quaternizing group is strongly electron-attracting (R in (40) = 2,4-dinitrophenyl or CN) to give glutacondialdehyde (41) or its derivatives, which are normally used in situ to carry out further

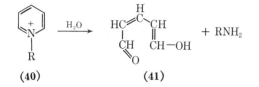

(40)   (41)

reactions. For example, reaction with cyclopentadienylsodium at 200°C gives azulene:

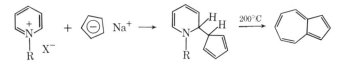

The pyridinium ring can also activate a methylene group attached to the ring nitrogen. A useful aldehyde synthesis via a nitrone is illustrated in Scheme 1.

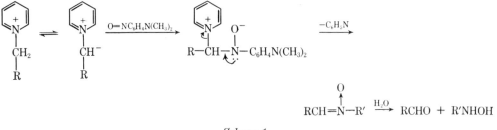

Scheme 1.

Pyridinium salts undergo base-catalyzed proton abstraction under very mild conditions; the C-2 proton is the most acidic one. An *N*-methyl-group proton undergoes abstraction much more slowly than does a ring α-proton.

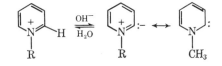

Pyridine *N*-Oxide

Pyridine *N*-oxide has acquired great importance since about 1950, as it was found (in contrast to pyridine) to undergo many electrophilic substitutions with ease and to give products having a different orientation than those obtained from pyridine itself. As the *N*-oxide group can be readily eliminated, this provides a convenient route to a variety of substituted pyridines not previously available. The chemistry of pyridine *N*-oxides has been reviewed (36).

Pyridine *N*-oxide is prepared in high yield by oxidation of pyridine with peroxyacetic acid. It is a hygroscopic white solid, mp 66°C and bp 138–140°C/15 mm; it gives a hydrochloride, mp 180–181°C and a picrate, mp 179.5°C. Its dipole moment is 4.24D. It retains some basic properties but the drop in basicity on passing from pyridine (pK_a 5.17) to the *N*-oxide (pK_a 0.79) is large. In ethanol solution it absorbs light at λ_{max} 213, 265 mμ ($\epsilon \times 10^{-3}$ 16.7, 12.9). In the infrared the *N*-oxide group exhibits a band at 1240–1270 cm^{-1}. The chemical shifts in the NMR spectrum depend greatly upon the proton-donating ability of the solvent used. In nonpolar solvents such as carbon tetrachloride, the spectrum of the neutral molecule is observed; as proton donation from the solvent increases, the spectrum gradually shifts to that of the *N*-hydroxypyridinium salt (37).

The molecule is considered to be a resonance hybrid of various canonical structures (**42a–e**):

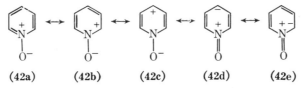

(42a)   (42b)   (42c)   (42d)   (42e)

The first three correspond to the canonical structures written for pyridine itself. Structures (**42d**) and (**42e**) indicate appreciable *back-donation* of electrons from oxygen to the ring, thereby increasing the electron densities at C-2 and C-4 and also indicating that electrons are available there by an electromeric (polarizability) mechanism. The importance of all these canonical structures has been amply demonstrated by dipole moment and NMR studies as well as by the chemical reactivity of pyridine *N*-oxide and its derivatives.

Chemical Properties. In acid solution, pyridine *N*-oxide is protonated at oxygen and an equilibrium mixture of the protonated and unprotonated forms exists. In

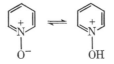

acidic media, therefore, the molecule can react in either form, the protonated species behaving like a typical pyridinium salt. The oxygen atom will also react with Lewis acids (SO$_3$, BF$_3$, PCl$_5$, POCl$_3$ etc), and with alkyl halides or sulfates to give *N*-alkoxypyridinium salts.

Nitration of pyridine *N*-oxide occurs readily with nitric acid and sulfuric acid under mild conditions and in high yield to give 4-nitropyridine *N*-oxide, thus permitting the introduction of a host of substituents at C-4 of the pyridine ring. Nitration of the free base takes place. *Sulfonation,* on the other hand, is about as difficult as that of pyridine itself, and gives the 3-sulfonic acid, via the salt.

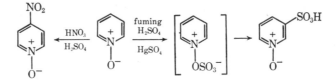

Pyridine *N*-oxides are very susceptible to nucleophilic substitution, and the *N*-alkoxypyridinium salts even more so. For instance, pyridine *N*-oxide will react with phenylmagnesium bromide to give an *N*-hydroxy-1,2-dihydropyridine derivative which can be dehydrated to the pyridine.

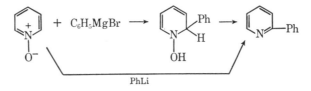

Reaction of *N*-alkoxy salts with cyanide ion occurs readily:

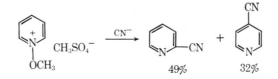

Chlorination of pyridine *N*-oxide can be effected with phosphorus pentachloride or phosphorus oxychloride to give a mixture of 2- and 4-chloropyridine. The former arises mainly by intramolecular attack whereas the latter results mainly from intermolecular attack by chloride ion and the relative proportions of the two products can be varied according to the proportions of PCl₅ and POCl₃ used (Scheme 2).

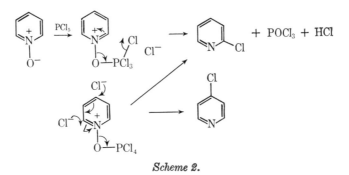

Scheme 2.

Pyridine *N*-oxides undergo nuclear deprotonation at the α-positions at low temperatures (−65°C) and in nonprotic solvents when treated with *n*-butyllithium. The carbanions so formed react with a variety of electrophiles, thus providing a convenient entry to a number of 2- or 6-substituted pyridine *N*-oxides. With cyclo-hexanone, for example, (**43**) and (**44**) are obtained.

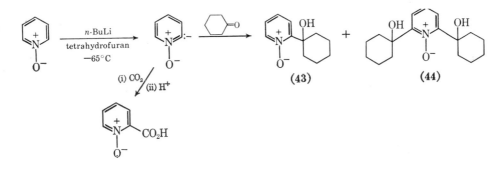

The nitro group in 4-nitropyridine *N*-oxide can be reduced to the corresponding amine, or displaced by halogen donor to give the 4-halopyridine *N*-oxide or the de-oxygenated species.

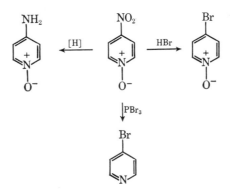

The deoxygenation of pyridine *N*-oxides can be effected with a variety of rea-gents, by means of catalytic hydrogenation, heating with PCl_3, ferrous oxalate, thio-urea, triethyl phosphite and oxygen, or triphenyl phosphine.

Halogen substituents attached to C-2 and C-4 are even more easily displaced by nucleophilic reagents than are the corresponding ones in pyridine itself. For example, 2-bromopyridine *N*-oxide reacts with potassium methoxide in methanol at 110°C, 760 times faster than does 2-bromopyridine itself under the same conditions. The 2- and 4-hydroxy compounds exhibit lactim–lactam tautomerism and in solution exist in both forms. Strong intramolecular hydrogen bonding is evident in the 2-hydroxy

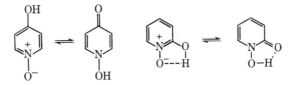

compound which is a cyclic hydroxamic acid and forms metal chelates very readily. In fact 1-hydroxypyridine-2-thione is used as a bactericide.

Economic Aspects

With the advent of commercial syntheses of pyridine and the picolines, the supply of these substances, previously limited by the coking process, has become plentiful. This is reflected in their prices; the price of a pound of refined pyridine rose steadily from $0.40 in 1942 to $1.05 in 1953, and after some fluctuation in 1961–1962, was down to $0.58 in 1965. Production of 2° pyridine (see p. 785) in the U.S. went from 884,000 lb in 1954 to 6,488,000 lb in 1965. Similar statistics are indicated for other countries which depend for their supply of tar bases on coal tar; the total amount of tar bases produced from this source in, eg, Japan and Germany (the production of pure pyridine in West Germany has fluctuated from 122 tons in 1950 to 167 tons in 1966, with a high of 279 tons in 1962), has remained relatively constant, but synthetic pyridine plants have now been built in the U.K., Japan, and Italy. Estimated (14) production of pyridine outside the United States in 1965 was believed to be (in million lb): U.K., 3.8; Western Europe, 1.5; U.S.S.R. and Eastern Europe, 2.5; Japan, 0.7 (production of pure pyridine from tar bases alone in Japan in 1965 amounted to 169,325 kg).

The U.S. production of pyridine (crude and refined) is given in Table 4, and that of 2-picoline, 3-picoline and 4-picoline, and mixtures of the latter two, is given in Table 5

Table 4. U.S. Production of Pyridine (Crude and Refined)

Year	Crude (natural) pyridine bases		Refined (natural and synthetic) 2° pyridine	
	Production, gal	Unit value, $/gal	Production, lb[a]	Unit value, $/lb
1955	226,000	1.11	1,554,000	0.67
1956	1,348,000		1,260,000	0.70
1957	1,351,000	0.92	1,820,000	0.71
1958	1,034,000	1.18	1,382,000	0.73
1959	808,000	1.03	2,175,000	0.69
1960	761,000	1.09	2,359,000	0.67
1961	836,000		3,176,000	0.77
1962	730,000		3,183,000	0.75
1963	[b]		3,053,000	0.68
1964	464,000		5,503,000	
1965	[b]		6,488,000	0.58

[a] Pyridine can be shipped in drums, barrels, cans, and bottles; a red ICC shipping label is required.

[b] Data not supplied separately.

(data from U.S. Tariff Commission Report for 1967). Production data are understated; they exclude those quantities which were captively consumed. Data for crude pyridine bases can be converted from gallons to pounds using a factor of approx 8.1 lb/gal.

It is more than likely that markets for pyridine and its derivatives will grow, in view of the greater uses being made of these starting materials in the pharmaceutical and rubber industries and with the expanding consumption of herbicides and bactericides. This is particularly so since commercialization of synthetic processes for the manufacture of pyridine and its homologs has freed these chemicals from dependence upon a traditionally erratic supply of raw material.

Table 5. U.S. Production of Picolines

Year	2-Picoline Production, lb	2-Picoline Unit value, $/lb	3-Picoline, 4-picoline, and mixtures of both[a] Production, million lb	3-Picoline, 4-picoline, and mixtures of both[a] Unit value, $/lb	Total picolines Production, lb	Total picolines Unit value $/lb
1956	446,000	0.41	0.57	0.56	1,018,000[b]	0.49
1957	641,000		0.74		1,386,000	0.57
1958					1,474,000	0.61
1959	891,000	0.35	1.34	0.71	2,234,000	0.56
1960	1,435,000	0.40	0.98	0.70	2,414,000	0.57
1961	2,214,000	0.43		0.64		0.57
1962	3,201,000	0.44				
1963		0.40				
1964	3,297,000	0.36				
1965	2,332,000	0.34	2.45	0.44	4,779,000	0.41

[a] Taken from ref. 14.

[b] In 1956, includes mixture of picolines but excludes separated 3- and 4-picoline isomers.

Uses and Important Derivatives

Pyridine and the pyridine bases, especially in the unrefined form from coal tar, have a disagreeable odor and have been used for the denaturing of ethyl alcohol (see Vol. 8, p. 450). *2° Pyridine* (see p. 785) is valuable as a solvent, eg in drug manufacture, and as a reagent, eg Karl Fischer moisture determinations (see Aquametry). It is an intermediate in the manufacture of (*1*) pharmaceuticals, eg steroids, sulfa drugs, and 2-aminopyridine for antihistamine manufacture; (*2*) textile water-repellent agents, eg Zelan (see p. 804); (*3*) rubber chemicals, eg piperidine; (*4*) piperidine for uses such as hardening agents for epoxy resins; (*5*) bactericides such as 1-hydroxypyridine-2-thione and cetylpyridinium bromide; and (*6*) herbicides such as Diquat (9,10-dihydro-8a,10a-diazoniaphenanthrene dibromide).

2-Picoline is used in the manufacture of 2-vinylpyridine (see p. 803), herbicides such as Tordon (see p. 803), and pharmaceuticals such as Methyridine (2-(2'-methoxyethyl)pyridine) and Amprolium (1-[(4'-amino-2'-propyl-5'-pyrimidinyl)methyl]-2-picolinium chloride hydrochloride).

3-Picoline is an intermediate in the manufacture of 3-cyanopyridine and nicotinic acid (niacin) and hence niacinamide (see Vitamins). The crude β-picoline fraction is used as a solvent and as a surface-active agent.

4-Picoline is an intermediate in the manufacture of isonicotinic acid hydrazide, a tuberculostatic drug, and Niamid, a monoamine oxidase inhibitor.

The *collidines* are used as solvents for the manufacture of anthraquinone.

Piperidine is hexahydropyridine, $CH_2.CH_2.CH_2.CH_2.CH_2.NH$.

Nicotinic acid (pyridinecarboxylic acid, niacin, pellagra-preventive factor) (**27**), $C_6H_5O_2N$ (see Vitamins); mp 236.6°C, pK_a 4.76, λ_{max} 263 mμ, mp of picrate 216–219°C; is prepared commercially by the vapor-phase oxidation of 3-picoline or 5-ethyl-2-methylpyridine (MEP), or by hydrolysis of 3-cyanopyridine. Under milder conditions, hydrolysis of 3-cyanopyridine yields *nicotinamide* (niacinamide, pyridine-3-carboxylic acid amide, vitamin PP, vitamin B$_3$), $C_6H_6ON_2$, mp 128–131°C, bp 150–

160°C/5 × 10⁻⁴ mm. It is a component of coenzymes I and II. *Nicotindiethylamide*, bp 280°C, prepared from nicotinic acid and diethylamine in the presence of phosphorus pentachloride, is used extensively as a respiratory stimulant under the trade name Coramine.

Isonicotinic acid (pyridine-4-carboxylic acid), mp 305–307°C, is important because of the antitubercular action of its hydrazide (Nydrazid, Cotinazin, Isoniazid, Rimifon, Marsilid). The acid is prepared by the oxidation of 4-picoline; it can also be obtained from citric acid via the triamide.

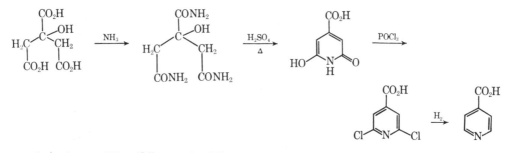

2-Aminopyridine (**31**) mp 57.5°C, bp 204°C, prepared as described above, is used in the preparation of 2-pyridone and of sulfapyridine (**45**). The activating influence

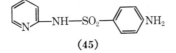

(**45**)

of the amino group is used to introduce a variety of other substituents into the pyridine nucleus. It is the starting material for the preparation of a number of antihistamines, such as pyrilamine (**46**), R = OCH₃, and pyribenzamine (**46**), R = H. (See Histamine and antihistamine agents.)

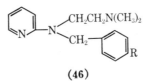

(**46**)

2,6-Diamino-3-phenylazopyridine hydrochloride (pyridium, Mallophene) (**47**) (see Vol. 2, p. 640) is a red crystalline dye obtained by coupling 2,6-diaminopyridine with benzenediazonium chloride, and is used as a urinary antiseptic. Neotropin, used as a bactericide, is prepared by coupling 2,6-diaminopyridine with diazotized 2-butoxy-5-aminopyridine.

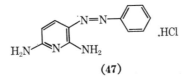

(**47**)

3-Aminopyridine, mp 64.5–65°C, bp 250–252°C, is prepared in 60% yield by heating 3-bromopyridine with concentrated ammonia in the presence of copper sulfate, or by the Hofmann degradation of nicotinamide.

2-Bromopyridine, bp 193.5–194°C/764 mm, can be prepared (together with 2,6-dibromopyridine) by the bromination of pyridine at 300–400°C in the presence of cuprous bromide. It can also be obtained from 2-aminopyridine using the Craig perbromide method (2-aminopyridine in hydrobromic acid is treated with bromine and then with sodium nitrite).

3-Bromopyridine, bp 173.7–174°C/762 mm, may be prepared by the gas-phase bromination of pyridine at 300°C, or at lower temperatures in the liquid phase in the presence of thionyl chloride or an excess of aluminum chloride. It can also be obtained by the Sandmeyer or Gattermann reactions on 3-aminopyridine, or by the Craig perbromide procedure.

5 - Ethyl - 2 - picoline (2 - methyl-5-ethylpyridine, aldehyde collidine, MEP), fp −70.3°C, bp 178.3°C, picrate mp 164–165°C, is produced from paraldehyde and ammonia. It may be oxidized with nitric acid to the dicarboxylic acid. At elevated temperatures the α-carboxyl group is lost as CO_2 to give nicotinic acid in high yield. This provides an alternate industrial source of this acid. MEP may be catalytically dehydrogenated at an elevated temperature in the presence of an inhibitor to give *2-methyl-5-vinylpyridine* (MVP) (**48**), which is used as a dye assistant in acrylic fiber manufacture, and can give a terpolymer with styrene and butadiene. One plant in the United States has a capacity (1967) of 5.4 million lb MVP per year (14).

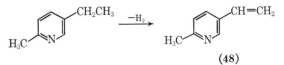

(**48**)

2-Vinylpyridine (**49**), C_7H_7N, bp 159°C, d_4^{20} 0.976, is a pyridine analog of styrene and has an activated olefinic double bond of the type that is present in acrylonitrile (C=C—C=N). The condensation of 2-picoline with formaldehyde gives 2-ethanolo-pyridine which is subsequently dehydrated to give (**49**). It has been used as a monomer

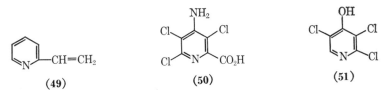

(**49**)   (**50**)   (**51**)

for copolymerization with acrylonitrile, butadiene, and styrene. It may be copolymerized with acrylonitrile to improve the dyeing properties of the resulting acrylic fiber. The availability of synthetic 2-picoline has resulted in the increasing use of 2-vinylpyridine. It is also a component of a terpolymer latex adhesive, used in heavy-duty tire cord and V-belts. Polyvinylpyridine is used as an element in photographic film. 2-Vinylpyridine undergoes nucleophilic addition reactions at the olefinic double bond readily. For example, methoxide ion adds to give the β-pyridylethyl ether.

(**49**) + MeO⁻ ⟶ [pyridyl]—CH₂CH₂OMe

4-Amino-3,5,6-trichloropicolinic acid (Tordon, Picloran) (**50**) is probably the most powerful herbicide known at present. It is prepared from 2-picoline by chlorination, hydrolysis, and amination. It is a broad-spectrum herbicide and gives good control of broad leaves (75–91.8% at ¼ lb/acre) (38). It has found extensive use as a defoliating agent. See Weed killers.

2,3,5-Trichloro-4-pyridinol (Daxtron) (**51**) is effective against oat plants and weeds and has also been used as a pesticide.

Diquat dibromide (Reglone) (**52**) and Paraquat (**53**) (39) are used as specific herbicides.

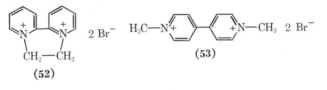

(52)   (53)

Cetylpyridinium chloride (Ceepryn) $[C_5H_5\overset{+}{N}C_{16}H_{33}]Cl^-$ is useful as an antiseptic for skin and wound disinfection and for the sterilization of surgical instruments. See also Quaternary ammonium compounds. Hospital blankets impregnated with a dilute solution of the compound retain their bactericidal power for at least three months (40).

Zelan, $(C_5H_5\overset{+}{N}CH_2NHCOC_{17}H_{33})Cl^-$, prepared by the reaction of stearamide, formaldehyde, and pyridine hydrochloride, is used in an important water-repellent process for textiles. The fabric is treated with Zelan compound, dried, and baked at 150°C for less than 4 min. The Zelan compound dissociates, evolving pyridine, and leaves the fabric water-repellent. See Waterproofing.

2,2'-Dipyridyl (α,α'-dipyridyl) (**54**) is prepared by heating 2-bromopyridine with

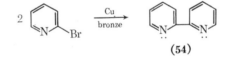

(54)

copper bronze. It forms colored complexes with divalent metallic ions and is used in the colorimetric determination of ferrous iron. It is an important complexing agent in coordination chemistry.

Pyridoxine. See p. 806.

2-Pyridine aldoxime methiodide (2-PAM) (**55**), $C_7H_9ON_2I$, mp 214°C, is prepared from 2-pyridine aldehyde (obtained by the controlled oxidation of 2-picoline either with selenium dioxide or in the gas phase at 350–450°C in the presence of water vapor and a catalyst consisting of vanadium pentoxide–molybdenum trioxide–silica gel) by treatment with hydroxylamine, followed by methyl iodide. It has been developed as an antidote for nerve gases and cholinesterase-inhibitor-type insecticides such as Parathion.

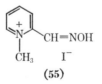

(55)

N-Hydroxy-2-pyridinethione (pyridine-*N*-oxide-2-thiol), C_5H_5NOS, mp 68–70°C, pK_a − 1.95, is prepared from 2-chloropyridine *N*-oxide and sodium sulfide and sodium hydrosulfide (41). It has important antifungal and antibacterial activity (42) and has found application, for example, in antidandruff shampoo. Heavy-metal complexes also exhibit bactericidal and fungicidal activity (43).

Bibliography

"Pyridine and Pyridine Bases" in *ECT* 1st ed., Vol. 11, pp. 278–293, by Harry S. Mosher, Stanford University.

1. R. Oberkobusch, *Brennstoff-Chem.* **40,** 145 (1959); D. L. West, M.Sc. Thesis, Saskatchewan, Canada, 1960.
2. F. Brody and P. R. Ruby, in E. Klingsberg, ed., *Pyridine and Its Derivatives*, Part 1, Interscience Publishers, Inc., New York, 1960, pp. 99–589.
2a. U.S. Pat. 2,796,421 (June 18, 1957), Robert J. Zellner.
3. Ger. Pat. 858,399 (Dec. 8, 1952), W. Reppe, H. Krzikalla, and E. Woldon (to Badische Anilin- und Soda-Fabrik); *Chem. Abstr.* **48,** 12810 (1954).
4. U.S. Pats. 2,744,904 (May 8, 1956) and 2,807,618 (Sept. 24, 1957), F. E. Cislak and W. R. Wheeler (to Reilly Tar and Chemical Corp.).
5. A. Hantzsch, *Ann.* **215,** 1 (1882).
6. S. A. Harris and K. Folkers, *J. Am. Chem. Soc.* **61,** 1245 (1939).
7. J. Thesing and A. Müller, *Ber.* **90,** 711 (1957).
8. R. N. Seelye and D. W. Stanton, *Tetrahedron Letters* **1966,** 2633.
9. G. J. Janz and M. A. DeCrescente, *J. Org. Chem.* **23,** 765 (1958).
10. Yu. I. Chumakov and V. P. Sherstynk, *Tetrahedron Letters* **1967,** 771.
11. H. L. Rice and R. E. Longeran, *J. Am. Chem. Soc.* **77,** 4678 (1955).
12. V. L. Florentiev, N. A. Drobinskaya, L. V. Ionova, and M. Y. Karpersky, *Tetrahedron Letters* **1967,** 1747.
13. R. N. Shreve, *Chemical Process Industries*, 3rd ed., McGraw-Hill Book Co., New York, 1967, pp. 70–80.
14. M. G. Erskine, "Pyridine and Pyridine Bases," in *Chemical Economics Handbook*, Stanford Research Institute, California, 1967, 691–7030A.
15. E. A. Coulson and J. I. Jones, *J. Soc. Chem. Ind.* **65,** 169 (1946).
16. W. Mathes, *Die Chemie* **58,** 65 (1945); *Brennstoff-Chem.* **32,** 69 (1951); *Chem. Abstr.* **45,** 8014 (1951).
17. A. E. Karr and E. G. Scheibel, *Ind. Eng. Chem.* **46,** 1583 (1954).
18. Brit. Pat. 734,812 (Aug. 10, 1955), (to Stamicarbon NV); *Chem. Abstr.* **50,** 7147 (1956).
19. Japan. Pat. 21,536 ('61) (Nov. 9, 1958), M. Yamada, A. Tamano, J. Hashimoto, and Y. Wada (to Koei Chemical Co.); *Chem. Abstr.* **57,** 13735 (1962).
20. U.S. Pat. 2,698,849 (Jan. 4, 1955), R. S. Aries; *Chem. Abstr.* **50,** 1088 (1956).
21. U.S. Pat. 2,615,022 (Oct. 21, 1952), J. E. Mahan (to Phillips Petroleum Co.); *Chem. Abstr.* **48,** 8270 (1954).
22. L. J. Bellamy, *The Infrared Spectra of Complex Molecules*, Methuen and Co., London, 1958.
23. J. A. Pople, W. G. Schneider, and H. J. Bernstein, *High-Resolution Nuclear Magnetic Resonance*, McGraw-Hill Book Co., New York, 1959. R. F. M. White, "Nuclear Magnetic Resonance Spectra," in A. R. Katritzky, ed., *Physical Methods in Heterocyclic Chemistry*, Vol. 2, Academic Press, Ltd., New York, 1963, p. 141.
24. J. D. Cox, A. R. Challoner, and A. R. Meetham, *J. Chem. Soc.* **1954,** 265.
25. B. Bak, L. Hansen, and J. Rastrup-Andersen, *J. Chem. Phys.* **22,** 2013 (1954).
26. W. Adam, A. Grimison, and G. Rodriguez, *Tetrahedron* **23,** 2513 (1967).
27. J. Ridd, "Heteroaromatic Reactivity," in A. R. Katritzky, ed., *Physical Methods in Heterocyclic Chemistry*, Vol. 1, Academic Press Inc., New York, 1963, p. 109.
28. R. A. Abramovitch and J. G. Saha, "Substitution in the Pyridine Series: Effect of Substituents," in A. R. Katritzky and A. J. Boulton, eds., *Advances in Heterocyclic Chemistry*, Vol. 6, Academic Press, Inc., New York, 1966, pp. 229–345.
29. R. F. Evans, *Rev. Pure Appl. Chem.* **15,** 23 (1965).
30. E. C. Kooyman, "Vapour Phase Halogenation of Aromatic Compounds," in G. H. Williams, ed., *Advances in Free Radical Chemistry*, Vol. 1, Logos Press, London, 1965, p. 137.

31. R. A. Abramovitch and C. S. Giam, *Can. J. Chem.* **42,** 1627 (1964), and references cited therein.
32. E. Kalatzis, *J. Chem. Soc.* **B1967,** 273.
33. R. E. Lyle and P. S. Anderson, "The Reduction of Nitrogen Heterocycles with Complex Metal Hydrides," in A. R. Katritzky and A. J. Boulton, eds., *Advances in Heterocyclic Chemistry*, Vol. 6, Academic Press Inc., New York, 1966, pp. 45–93.
34. E. M. Kosower and E. J. Poziomek, *J. Am. Chem. Soc.* **85,** 2035 (1963).
35. F. Kröhnke, *Angew. Chem. Intern. Ed. Engl.* **2,** 380 (1963).
36. E. N. Shaw, "Pyridine *N*-Oxides," in E. Klingsberg, ed., *Pyridine and Its Derivatives*, Part 2, Interscience Publishers, Inc., New York, 1961, pp. 97–153.
37. R. A. Abramovitch and J. B. Davis, *J. Chem. Soc.* **B1966,** 1137.
38. W. R. Arnold and P. W. Santelmann, *Proc. Southern Weed Conf.* **18,** 56 (1965).
39. U.S. Pat. 3,332,959 (July 25, 1967), J. T. Braunholtz; U.S. Pat. 3,340,041 (Sept. 5, 1967), R. F. Homer and J. E. Downes.
40. P. M. Rountree, *Med. J. Australia* **33,** 539 (1946); *Chem. Abstr.* **40,** 6550 (1946).
41. U.S. Pat. 3,159,640 (Dec. 1, 1964), R. E. McLure and D. A. Sherner.
42. F. Leonard, F. A. Barkley, Ellis V. Brown, F. E. Anderson, and D. M. Green, *Antibiot. Chemotherapy* **6,** 261 (1956).
43. U.S. Pat. 2,809,971 (Oct. 15, 1957), J. Bernstein and K. A. Losee.

R. A. Abramovitch
University of Alabama

PYRIDOXINE

The IUPAC (1) has suggested that the term pyridoxine be used to designate the naturally occurring pyridine derivatives (see also Pyridine) with vitamin B_6 activity (see also Vitamins). The three common forms of pyridoxine are pyridoxol (**1**) (formerly called pyridoxine), pyridoxal (**2**), and pyridoxamine (**3**). (The CA names for (**1**), (**2**), and (**3**), respectively, are 5-hydroxy-6-methyl-3,4-pyridinedimethanol, 3-hydroxy-5-(hydroxymethyl)-2-methylisonicotinaldehyde, and 4-(aminomethyl)-5-hydroxy-6-methyl-3-pyridinemethanol.) Pyridoxal 5-phosphate (**4**) (codecarboxylase) is the

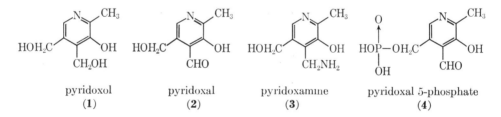

| pyridoxol | pyridoxal | pyridoxamine | pyridoxal 5-phosphate |
| (**1**) | (**2**) | (**3**) | (**4**) |

coenzyme for many enzymes of amino acid metabolism including transaminases, decarboxylases, and racemases. Pyridoxine is required by all species of animals which have been studied, including man.

During an investigation of the vitamin B complex, György (2) found that rats fed a diet free of a source of B complex but supplemented with adequate amounts of pure B_1 (thiamine) and riboflavin showed a reduced rate of growth. A characteristic dermatitis of the extremities developed, which was described as "pellagra-like." The additional factor in the B complex was designated vitamin B_6. The term "pellagra-like dermatitis" was later changed to "rat acrodynia" (3). The isolation of pure crystalline vitamin B_6 was first reported by Lepkovsky (4) and shortly thereafter independently by four other groups (5–8). The structure was shown to be 2-methyl-3-hydroxy-4,5-dihydroxymethylpyridine (**1**) (9,10). In 1942 Snell et al. (11) found that pyridoxol had very little vitamin B_6 activity for certain lactic acid bacteria, but that natural materials contained related compounds of high activity. These were subsequently identified and named pyridoxal and pyridoxamine (12).

Occurrence and Isolation

Vitamin B_6 is found in nature in the three forms, pyridoxol, pyridoxal, and pyridoxamine as well as their 5-phosphate esters which may be bound more or less tightly to protein. The vitamin has a broad distribution throughout both the plant and animal kingdoms. As shown in Table 1, grains and meats are relatively rich sources of vitamin B_6, while vegetables are intermediate in their content, and fruits (except banana) are relatively poor sources. Brewer's yeast contains up to 50 $\mu g/g$ of vitamin B_6 and is the only natural source from which pyridoxamine has been isolated (13). Although pyridoxol has been isolated from several natural sources, chemical synthesis of the vitamin is far more efficient and economical.

Table 1. Vitamin B_6 Content of Representative Foodstuffs[a] (14)

Foodstuff	Pyridoxol·HCl, $\mu g/g$	Foodstuff	Pyridoxol·HCl, $\mu g/g$
cereal grains		banana	5.00
barley meal	3.00	cherry	0.45
corn flour	0.05	grape	0.40
wheat flour	0.85	orange	0.50
rice	1.50	peach	0.30
vegetables		meats, dairy products, and fish	
asparagus	0.60	beef	4.50
brussels sprout	2.80	chicken	5.50
cabbage	1.10	lamb	2.00
celery	0.90	calf liver	9.00
carrot	0.65	pork	3.30
pea	1.60	veal	4.00
potato	1.40	whole milk	0.50
spinach	2.20	egg	1.20
tomato	1.00	cod	2.00
fruits		flounder	2.50
apple	0.45	salmon	9.75

[a] The values are expressed as micrograms (μg) of pyridoxol hydrochloride per gram fresh weight of material. The *Saccharomyces carlsbergensis* assay was used (14).

Physical and Chemical Properties

Pyridoxol (1), 2-methyl-3-hydroxy-4,5-bis(hydroxymethyl)pyridine, or 5-hydroxy-6-methyl-3,4-pyridinedimethanol, has the empirical formula $C_8H_{11}NO_3$, mol wt 169.28, mp 160°C; its hydrochloride, mol wt 205.64, forms platelets or thick, birefringent rods from alcohol which melt with decomposition at 205–212°C. See Table 2 for the ultraviolet absorption spectrum. A characteristic shift in the ultraviolet absorbance maximum with increasing pH (Table 2) is ascribed to successive proton removals from (**5**) in acid to (**6**) (zwitterion) in neutral solution to (**7**) in base (15). One gram of the hydrochloride dissolves in about 4.5 ml of water or 90 ml of ethanol; the pH of a 10% solution in water is 3.2. Pyridoxol hydrochloride is soluble in propylene glycol, sparingly soluble in acetone, and insoluble in ether or chloroform. Acidic solutions

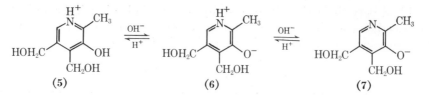

(5)   (6)   (7)

of pyridoxol hydrochloride are stable and may be heated for 30 min at 120°C without decomposition.   Neutral solutions of pyridoxol in water dimerize and even polymerize when autoclaved at 120°C (16), due to the high activity of the 4-hydroxymethyl group.   This polymerization may be inhibited by the addition of borate, which ties up the hydroxyl groups in the 3 and 4 positions of pyridoxol (17); see formula (8).

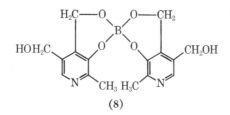

(8)

Table 2. Ultraviolet Absorptions of Vitamin B_6 Family[a]

	0.1N HCl		pH 7.0		0.1N NaOH	
Compound	λ_{max}, mμ	ϵ_{max}, liter/ (mole) (cm)	λ_{max}, mμ	ϵ_{max}, liter/ (mole) (cm)	λ_{max}, mμ	ϵ_{max}, liter/ (mole) (cm)
pyridoxol hydrochloride[b]	291	8700	254	3760	244	6700
			324	7100	309	6950
pyridoxol 5-phosphate	290	8700	253	3700	245	6500
			325	7400	310	7300
pyridoxal hydrochloride[c]	288	9100	317	8800	240	8300
					300	6100
			390	200	390	1700
pyridoxal 5-phosphate monohydrate[c]	293	7200				
	334	1300	388	5500	389	6600
pyridoxamine dihydrochloride	293	8500	253	4600	245	5900
			325	7700	308	7300
pyridoxamine 5-phosphate dihydrate	293	9000	253	4700	245	6700
			325	8300	308	8000

[a] Some of these values are taken from the table published by Peterson and Sober (14a).

[b] See Firestone, Harris, and Reuter (14b).

[c] The values given by Mühlradt, Morino, and Snell (14c) for pyridoxal and its phosphate differ slightly from those given by Peterson and Sober (14a).

The various forms of pyridoxine are destroyed by prolonged heating in the presence of protein, and by ultraviolet radiation in neutral or alkaline solutions.

Pyridoxal (2) hydrochloride, 3-hydroxy-5-(hydroxymethyl)-2-methylisonicotinaldehyde hydrochloride, or 2-methyl-3-hydroxy-4-formyl-5-hydroxymethylpyridine hydrochloride, $C_8H_9NO_3 \cdot HCl$, has a mol wt of 203.63; rhombic crystals, mp about

165°C.   One gram dissolves in 2 ml of water; 1.7 g, in 100 ml of ethyl alcohol.   The pH of a 1% aq soln is 2.65; its ultraviolet absorption is given in Table 2.   This compound is not as stable as pyridoxol hydrochloride; aqueous solutions are adversely affected by heat or sunlight at quite low pH levels.

Pyridoxal readily forms an oxime, $C_8H_{10}N_2O_3$, which is insoluble in water and crystallizes from ethyl alcohol; mp 225–226°C with decomposition.   It is reconverted to the aldehyde by treatment with sodium nitrite and hydrochloric acid.   This derivative was used for the isolation of pyridoxal after oxidation of pyridoxol with manganese dioxide (18).

Numerous amines (19) and amino acids (20) have been condensed with pyridoxal to give brightly colored Schiff bases (9) which are then catalytically reduced to the corresponding pyridoxylamine and pyridoxylamino acids (10).   Most of these amines display 50–100% activity when compared with pyridoxol in rats.

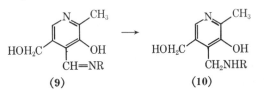

(9)   (10)

Pyridoxamine (3) **dihydrochloride,** 4-(aminoethyl)-5-hydroxy-6-methyl-3-pyridinemethanol dihydrochloride, or 2-methyl-3-hydroxy-4-aminomethyl-5-hydroxymethylpyridine dihydrochloride, $C_8H_{12}N_2O_2 \cdot 2HCl$, mol wt 241.12, forms platelets which decompose at 226–227°C.   For synthesis and structure see reference 18.   The free base melts at 193–193.5°C.   The dihydrochloride liquefies on exposure to the atmosphere at 80% rh.   One gram dissolves in 2 ml of water; 0.65 g, in 100 ml of 95% ethyl alcohol.   The pH of a 1% aq soln is 2.4.   See Table 2 for the ultraviolet spectrum.

The stability of pyridoxamine dihydrochloride is intermediate between that of pyridoxol hydrochloride and that of pyridoxal hydrochloride.   Aqueous solutions kept in the dark show no decomposition after 10 days at 60°C.   The crystalline substance should be kept in amber bottles or ampuls.

Pyridoxamine 5-phosphate (11), 2-methyl-3-hydroxy-4-aminomethyl-5-pyridylmethylphosphoric acid, was synthesized from pyridoxamine and phosphorus oxychlo-

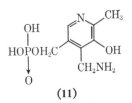

(11)

ride (21) and was characterized as a crystalline compound (14a,14c,22).   Air-dried crystals have the composition of $C_8H_{13}N_2O_5P \cdot 2H_2O$, mol wt 276.34.   Negligible hydrolysis occurs in 3 weeks if the solutions are stored at or below room temperature, even in $1N$ NaOH or $1N$ HCl.

Pyridoxal 5-phosphate (4), codecarboxylase, or 2-methyl-3-hydroxy-4-formyl-5-pyridylmethylphosphoric acid, $C_8H_{10}NO_6P \cdot H_2O$, mol wt 265.15, is colorless in acid solution and bright-yellow in alkaline solution.   See Table 2 for the ultraviolet spectrum.

The oxime, $C_8H_{11}N_2O_6P$, mp 229–230°C with decomposition, is practically insoluble in water, alcohol, and ether; the *O*-methyloxime, $C_9H_{13}N_2O_6P$, melts at 212–213°C with decomposition (21).

Pyridoxal 5-phosphate is oxidized with hydrogen peroxide to replace the 4-formyl group with a hydroxyl group to give 2-methyl-3,4-dihydroxy-5-pyridylmethyl-phosphoric acid, $C_7H_{10}NO_6P$, mp 233–234°C with decomposition.

Solutions of pyridoxal 5-phosphate show only 2–3% hydrolysis in 3 weeks when stored in the cold and only 4–6% at room temperature in this time even in $0.1N$ NaOH or $0.1N$ HCl. In $6N$ H_2SO_4 at 100°C there is 50% hydrolysis in 4 hr, but only 6% hydrolysis in $0.1N$ NaOH after 15 hr at 100°C.

Pyridoxol 5-phosphate, 2-methyl-3-hydroxy-4-hydroxymethyl-5-pyridylmethyl-phosphoric acid, $C_8H_{12}O_6NP$, mol wt 249.13, crystallizes from conc aq sol in white needles which are insoluble in ethyl alcohol. It was prepared (14a) by treatment of pyridoxamine 5-phosphate with sodium nitrite. See Table 2 for the ultraviolet spectrum. Pyridoxol 5-phosphate is hydrolyzed very slowly in $1N$ HCl at 25°C (1% in 54 days), and in $1N$ NaOH at 25°C (2.6% in 54 days). At 100°C, in $0.05N$ HCl, it loses 30% of its phosphate in 15.3 hr; in $1N$ HCl, 35% in 15.3 hr; while in $1N$ NaOH, it loses only 11% of its phosphate.

4-Pyridoxic acid (12), 3-hydroxy-5-hydroxymethyl-2-methylisonicotinic acid, or 2-methyl-3-hydroxy-4-carboxy-5-hydroxymethylpyridine, $C_8H_9NO_4$, mol wt 183.16, is the chief metabolic product of all forms of pyridoxine. It forms wedge-shaped crystals, mp 247–248°C. It has a characteristic blue fluorescence, with a maximum at pH 3–4. Its lactone (13) β-pyracine, $C_8H_7NO_3$, mp 263–265°C, exhibits strong fluorescence at pH 10.

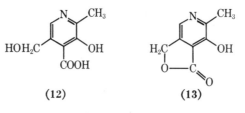

(12)   (13)

Assay Methods

Chemical assay methods of vitamin B_6 in all its forms are fairly simple in pure solutions containing no other vitamins or organic materials. The phenolic nature of pyridoxol has been made the basis for chemical determinations through coupling reactions with 2,6-dichloro-*p*-quinone chlorimide, or *N*,2,6-trichloro-*p*-quinone imine (14) (23), to yield a blue-colored product (15). Also diazotized sulfanilic acid (24), ferric chloride (7,25), and diazotized *p*-aminoacetophenone (26) have been used.

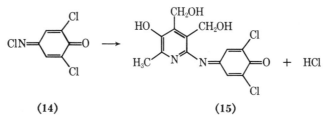

(14)   (15)

The 2,6-dichloro-*p*-quinone chlorimide method (27) has been perfected for use with relatively pure mixtures or solutions of pyridoxol. In the presence of borate, pyridoxol forms a complex (8), which does not react with the chlorimide, allowing the determination of a blank.

However, the greatest use for an assay for vitamin B₆ is in foodstuffs, tissue, blood, urine, etc. Because much of the vitamin is found in a bound form, it is necessary to liberate and extract it in a form suitable for analysis. A general review of these problems is given by Storvick and Peters (28).

A chemical method which measures all forms of vitamin B₆ involves their isolation and conversion to a common degradation product. Such a product is the lactone of 4-pyridoxic acid (13), for which a fluorometric method has been developed (29). This method is based on the oxidative conversion of pyridoxol and pyridoxal to 4-pyridoxic acid (12), which upon heating in acid forms the highly fluorescent lactone. Pyridoxamine must first be converted by deamination to pyridoxol and must then be oxidized. This lactone method is highly specific and is more sensitive than other spectrophotometric or colorimetric methods.

Pyridoxal and pyridoxal phosphate form cyanohydrins which can be measured fluorometrically (30).

The principal metabolite of vitamin B₆, 4-pyridoxic acid (12), can be determined fluorometrically (31) after conversion to the lactone. Although this acid does not have vitamin activity, its assay is important in the determination of the nutritional fate of vitamin B₆.

Biological assays for vitamin B₆ have been developed based on the growth response of rats (32,33) and chicks (34) which have been fed purified diets. These assays are probably the most meaningful since they measure the content of nutritionally available vitamin B₆. A modified rat diet (33) based on sucrose and blood fibrin gives a linear growth response with up to 75 µg pyridoxol per 100 g of diet. Pyridoxal and pyridoxamine are slightly less active when incorporated into the diet, but they are as active as pyridoxol when given separately by mouth or by intraperitoneal injection. Animal assays are rarely used because of their cost and slowness.

Microbiological assays for vitamin B₆ are not entirely satisfactory. Much of the difficulty arises from sample preparation and selection of the test organism (35). As in the large-animal assays, vitamin B₆ is measured by growth response in a defined medium supplemented with the vitamin. Growth is determined by turbidity, acid production, or dry weight.

The method recommended by The Association of Vitamin Chemists, Inc. (36) uses *Saccharomyces carlsbergensis* 4228 as the test organism. This yeast is generally considered to respond equally to all three forms of the vitamin, although MacArthur and Lehmann (36a), after careful study, concluded that the response to pyridoxamine is lower than that to the other forms. Growth is measured turbidimetrically. Bound forms of the vitamin are released by autoclaving at 120°C for 4 hr in 0.055N HCl, but errors may be introduced by the formation of growth-stimulating materials by the action of acid on carbohydrates present in the material being assayed. The assay has been performed on a wide variety of animal and plant tissues, and on many foodstuffs (37).

Many of the lactic acid bacteria respond much more readily to pyridoxamine and pyridoxal than to pyridoxol. Snell and Rabinowitz made this the basis of a differential assay for the three forms (38). *Streptococcus faecalis* responds to both pyridoxamine and pyridoxal (using either to racemize L-alanine and possibly to synthesize certain polypeptides), while *Lactobacillus casei* responds only to pyridoxal. *S. carlsbergensis* was used to measure the total vitamin B₆. Some materials, especially blood, cannot be assayed since the hydrolysis leads to the formation of D-alanine and polypeptides, which will partially or totally fulfill the requirement for pyridoxal by *L. casei* and *S. faecalis* or *faecium* (39). It was suggested that a chromatographic separation of the three forms of the vitamin (40), followed by assay of each form separately should be considered. An x-ray-induced mutant of *Neurospora sitophila* has been used to measure total vitamin B₆ (41).

Synthesis

Pyridoxol. Shortly after the elucidation of its structure, two different total syntheses of pyridoxol were reported almost simultaneously by independent groups. The route of Harris and Folkers (9,42) (Scheme 1) became the basis of a commercial synthesis. Condensation of ethoxyacetplacetone (**17**) with cyanoacetamide (**16**) in the presence of piperidine yields 3-cyano-4-ethoxymethyl-6-methyl-2(1*H*)-pyridone (**18**). Nitration to the derivative (**19**) is effected in acetic anhydride, and treatment with phosphorus pentachloride in chlorobenzene affords the chloro derivative (**20**). Catalytic hydrogenation in two steps reduces the nitro group, then attacks the nitrile and the chlorine to yield the diamino derivative (**21**). Diazotization affords the 4-ethyl ether (**22**) of pyridoxol, which is cleaved to the product (**1**) initially with hydrobromic acid by way of the dibromide (**23**), followed by treatment with silver chloride, and later by direct hydrolysis at high temperature and pressure in dilute hydrochloric acid (43). Modifications of a number of the details of this route have been described by the original workers (44) and by others (45), and a very similar path was reported from E. Merck A.G. in Germany (46), and by Morii and Makino (47).

Scheme 1

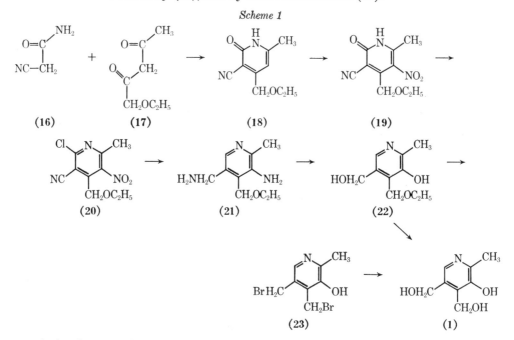

A closely related synthesis, which also acquired some commercial importance, was reported by Mowat, Pilgrim, and Carlson (48) (Scheme 2), and by Itiba and Emoto (49) in Japan. The ester (**24**), ethyl acetylpyruvate, instead of the ether (**17**) em-

Scheme 2

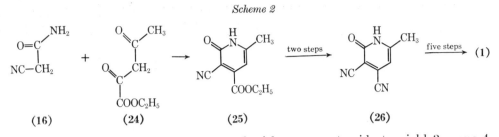

(16)   (24)   (25)   (26)

ployed by the Merck group, is condensed with cyanoacetamide to yield 3-cyano-4-ethoxycarbonyl-6-methyl-2-pyridone (**25**). The difficult reduction of this ester is effected by the method of Kuhn (Scheme 3, below) by way of the amide and nitrile (**26**); other functionalities are introduced and altered by the Harris and Folkers procedure (Scheme 1).

The second of the original syntheses was reported by Kuhn and co-workers in Germany (10) (Scheme 3), and subsequently by Itiba and Miti (50), Szabo (51), and Suzuki (52). The known 4-methoxy-3-methylisoquinoline (**27**) is oxidized to 5-

Scheme 3

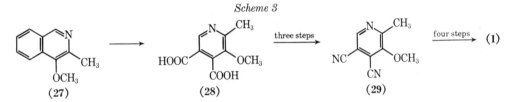

(27)   (28)   (29)

methoxy-6-methylcinchomeronic acid (**28**), the carboxyls reduce to hydroxymethylenes by way of the diamide, dinitrile (**29**), hydrogenation to the diamine, and diazotization; the methyl ether is cleaved with hydrogen bromide through the dibromo intermediate (**23**). This lengthy reduction scheme has been a problem with a number of pyridoxol syntheses; the only satisfactory alternative has been the reduction of the diester directly to the diol with complex metal hydride reducing agents (53–57).

A number of syntheses appeared in the 1950s in which the pyridine ring was assembled from totally different fragments. Jones (58) (Scheme 4) condensed ethyl hydroxymethyleneoxalacetate (**30**) with imino acetylacetone (**31**) in two steps to the

Scheme 4

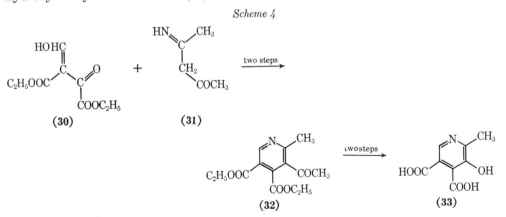

(30)   (31)

(32)   (33)

pyridine (**32**), converted the 5-acetyl functionality to the amine by a Schmidt reaction, and diazotized to the familiar 5-hydroxy-6-methylcinchomeronic acid (**33**). Reduction to pyridoxol was effected with lithium aluminum hydride (LAH). Cohen and co-workers (54) (Scheme 5) in Britain formed the pyridine from dimethyl α-formyl suc-

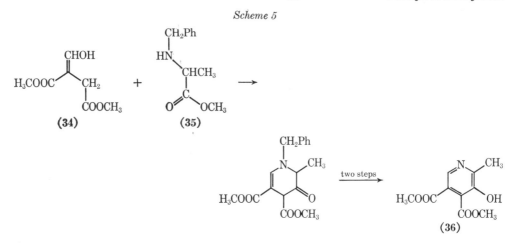

Scheme 5

cinate (**34**) and *N*-benzylalanine ester (**35**), oxidizing and catalytically debenzylating to the same hydroxymethylcinchomeronate (**36**); benzylation tied up the nitrogen to prevent pyrrole formation. Elming and Clauson-Kaas (59) (Scheme 6) effected a reductive methoxylation of 2-(α-acetaminoethyl)-3,4-bis(acetoxymethyl)furan (**37**) to the intermediate (**38**), deacetylated with base to the free amine, and rearranged

Scheme 6

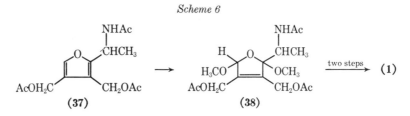

with acid directly to pyridoxol (**1**). They prepared the starting material from furan and acetylene dicarboxylic ester by a series of steps which included LAH reduction of the ester groups during this early portion of the sequence. Stevens (60) has reported syntheses from fragments (**39**) and (**40**), and Pollak (61) from fragments such as (**41**).

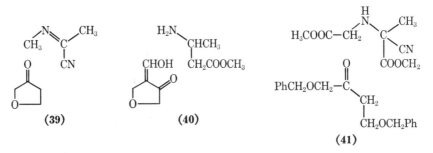

In 1962, variations of an important new and significantly shorter pathway to pyridoxol were reported independently by three groups. Kondrat'yeva (62) in the U.S.S.R. had found that alkyl oxazoles react as dienes in Diels-Alder condensations with maleic anhydride, with cleavage of the adducts, to afford alkylcinchomeronic acids. Based on this reaction, she treated (63) 4-methyl-5-acetyloxazole (**42**) (Scheme 7) with maleimide to obtain 5-acetyl-6-methylcinchomeronimide (**43**), the imide

Scheme 7

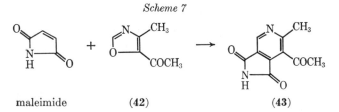

maleimide   (**42**)   (**43**)

of the Jones intermediate (**32**), and carried it on to pyridoxol by much the same route. E. Harris and co-workers, at Merck, introduced the phenolic functionality directly (14b,64) (Scheme 8) by employing 4-methyl-5-ethoxyoxazole (**45**), readily formed from *N*-formylalanine ester, as the diene. A variety of dienophiles could be employed —diethyl maleate gave a high yield of 5-hydroxy-6-methylcinchomeronate (**46**) (where $X = COOC_2H_5$); fumaronitrile gave cinchomeronitrile (**46**) (where $X = CN$), the unmethylated form of Kuhn's dinitrile (**29**); and even the unactivated dienophile 2-butene-1,4-diol (**44**) (where $X = CH_2OH$) produced pyridoxol directly, in low yield. A host of variations on this procedure have been described (65,66), among them the substitution, as the diene, of 4-methyl-5-cyanooxazole (66), which forms the phenolic hydroxyl with loss of HCN rather than of ethanol as in Scheme 8, and of 5-ethoxy-

Scheme 8

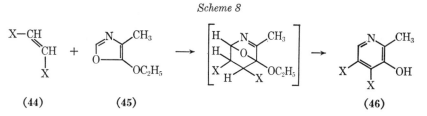

(**44**)   (**45**)   (**46**)

oxazole-4-acetic ester (67), which proceeds through an easily decarboxylated pyridine-2-acetic acid. Finally, a group at Hoffmann-La Roche Inc. (68) employed 4-methyloxazole (**47**) with a range of dienophiles (Scheme 9), avoiding loss of the phenolic

Scheme 9

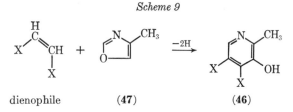

dienophile   (**47**)   (**46**)

hydroxyl by running the reaction in the presence of hydrogen acceptors such as chloronitrobenzenes. A modified use of this oxazole is reported in the Japanese patent literature (69).

Pyridoxal and Pyridoxamine. *Pyridoxal* (**2**) is prepared by the oxidation of pyridoxol with manganese dioxide and sulfuric acid, isolation as the oxime, and regeneration of the aldehyde with sodium nitrite and hydrochloric acid (12,18b,70). An alternative has been described in the patent literature (71).

Pyridoxamine (**3**) may be obtained by treatment of the 4-methyl ether of pyridoxol with ammonia under heat and pressure (18) or, better, by catalytic hydrogenation of pyridoxal oxime over platinum oxide (18b) or variations of this procedure (72,73).   A direct preparation by the reaction of an oxazole with γ-hydroxycrotononitrile has been reported (74).

5-Phosphates of Pyridoxol, Pyridoxal, and Pyridoxamine. *Pyridoxol 5-phosphate* was first prepared by direct treatment of pyridoxol with phosphorus oxychloride and water (21), but is better obtained by phosphorylation of 3,4-isopropylidenepyridoxal with phosphoric acid–phosphorus pentoxide (75) or by diazotization of pyridoxamine 5-phosphate (14a).

Pyridoxal 5-phosphate (**4**) has been synthesized from pyridoxal in poor yield by phosphorylation with phosphorus oxychloride in water (76) and isolation as the calcium salt (21) or, better, by manganese dioxide oxidation of pyridoxamine 5-phosphate (14a,77).   Direct phosphorylations of pyridoxal with protection of the aldehyde function have been described (78,79), as has the conversion of the amine 5-phosphate by means of pyruvic acid and metal catalysis (80).

Pyridoxamine 5-phosphate can be obtained by the action of phosphorus oxychloride and water (81) or, better, of phosphoric acid–phosphorus pentoxide on pyridoxamine (14a,14c,22,82).

Production and Prices

Table 3 shows the bulk selling price of pyridoxine (pyridoxol) hydrochloride in $/kg.   The Department of Commerce published U.S. production figures from 1944 to 1959, then suspended publication because the number of producers had been reduced to two, namely Hoffmann-La Roche Inc. and Merck & Co., Inc.   The vitamin was imported in substantially increasing quantities from 1959 to 1967.   These figures, in kilograms, are also shown in Table 3.

Table 3.   U.S. Production and Imports of Pyridoxine Hydrochloride

Year	Bulk selling price, $/kg	Reported[a] production, kg	Reported[b] imports, kg
1940	7,600		
1944	1,000	1,900	
1947	670	5,900	
1950	515	8,000	
1955	460	13,600	
1959		27,000	4,662
1960	80		4,142
1963	65		8,269
1964	65		5,768
1965	55		11,410
1966	45		15,691
1967	30		15,129

[a] U.S. Tariff Commission Reports (*Synthetic Organic Chemicals*), U.S. Department of Commerce (published at frequent intervals).
[b] Bureau of Census—Department of Commerce—Monthly Report.

Clinical Evaluation

Vitamin B$_6$ is probably necessary for the growth of all animal species.   Requirements have been shown for protozoa, insects, fish, chickens, turkeys, ducks, mice, rats, hamsters, rabbits, cats, dogs, pigs, calves, monkeys, and man.   Although the symptoms of deficiency vary from species to species, and even within the same species, depending upon age, the most characteristic symptoms are anemia and nervous disorders. Rats exhibit a dermatitis which has been termed "rat acrodynia" (3). Swine and dogs develop microcytic hypochromic anemia and epileptiform convulsions. Monkeys have been found to develop arteriosclerotic lesions, dental caries, and hepatic cirrhosis (83), as well as anemia and nervous symptoms.

It has been only in recent years that vitamin B_6 deficiency has been demonstrated in humans. The rarity of B_6 deficiency is probably due to the ubiquitous occurrence of the vitamin in foods and to its synthesis by the intestinal flora (84). Snyderman et al. (85), in 1953, described the first instance of nervous disorder in infants kept on a diet devoid of pyridoxine. This observation was soon confirmed when large numbers of infants fed a commercial formula containing only 60 μg of pyridoxine per liter developed similar nervous symptoms and convulsions (86,87). Harris et al. (88) described a case of hypochromic microcytic anemia which responded to 50 mg of pyridoxol hydrochloride per day orally. This pyridoxine-responsive anemia has been described in detail (89,90) and documented by a further seventy-two cases.

An interesting case of vitamin B_6 dependency was described by Hunt et al. (91). It was that of a mentally retarded child requiring 10 mg/day of pyridoxol hydrochloride to prevent the occurrence of epileptiform convulsions. Since these requirements as well as those in pyridoxine-responsive anemia are unusually large, it may be assumed that a defect in B_6 metabolism is responsible for these diseases.

Symptoms of vitamin B_6 deficiency have been induced in man by isonicotinic acid hydrazide therapy (92). Many carbonyl-reactive reagents will combine with pyridoxal in vivo and in vitro and lead to symptoms of B_6 deficiency. McCormick and Snell (93) showed that such derivatives of pyridoxal were extremely potent inhibitors of pyridoxal kinase.

In vitamin B_6 deficiency, many of the enzymes which require pyridoxal phosphate as a cofactor are present in significantly reduced concentrations. Kynureninase, an enzyme involved in tryptophan degradation, seems to be especially susceptible and B_6 deficiency is often accompanied by increased excretion of xanthurenic acid. The tryptophan load test is widely used as an indicator of vitamin B_6 deficiency (94).

The minimum daily adult requirement for vitamin B_6 is still subject to considerable controversy. The Food and Nutrition Board of the National Academy of Sciences—National Research Council (95) estimates that 1.5–2.0 mg/day is a reasonable allowance although there is some feeling that this is too low (96).

Metabolism of Vitamin B_6

Biosynthesis. Essentially, nothing is known of the biosynthesis of vitamin B_6. Recent work indicates that Krebs cycle intermediates and glyoxylic acid may contribute to the carbon skeleton of pyridoxol synthesized by the yeast *Candida albicans* (97).

Interconversion and Phosphorylation. The primary functional form of vitamin B_6 is pyridoxal 5-phosphate although pyridoxamine 5-phosphate will act as the coenzyme for transaminases. Kinases that will transfer a phosphate group from adenosine triphosphate (ATP) to the 5-hydroxymethyl group of the three forms of vitamin B_6 (98) have been found in various tissues. A divalent metal ion, Zn^{2+} or Mg^{2+}, is required for maximum activity. An oxidase in rabbit liver will oxidize pyridoxol 5-phosphate or pyridoxamine 5-phosphate to pyridoxal 5-phosphate (99).

Degradation. The major excretion product of vitamin B_6 in man other than unchanged vitamin is 4-pyridoxic acid (**12**) (100). Johannson et al. (101) published data on the turnover and rate of excretion of small amounts of tritium-labeled pyridoxol. About 20% was excreted in the first 24 hr. The remainder was eliminated with a half-life of 18–38 days. From 20 to 40% of the vitamin was excreted as 4-pyridoxic acid.

Soil pseudomonads have been isolated which degrade vitamin B_6 through a novel series of reactions (102). Pyridoxol was degraded through Scheme 10 by one isolate, and pyridoxamine through Scheme 11 by another isolate.

Scheme 10

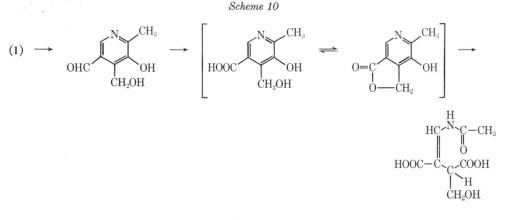

Scheme 11

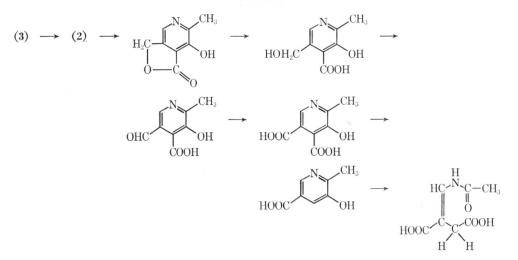

Biochemical Function

Pyridoxal 5-phosphate is the coenzyme for many enzymes which participate in the intermediary metabolism of amino acids. Pyridoxal itself was found to catalyze these same reactions nonenzymatically. This finding has greatly facilitated the study of the reaction mechanisms (103,104). The initial step is the formation of a Schiff base between pyridoxal and the amino acid. A metal ion (Fe^{3+}, Cu^{2+}, or Al^{3+}) also participates and enhances the rate of reaction. As shown in proposed structure (**48**) (104), the shift of electrons toward the electrophilic pyridine nitrogen labilizes the bonds to the α carbon of the amino acid.

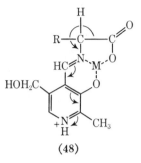

(48)

Amino Acid Decarboxylation. Decarboxylases or carboxylases are found in all organisms. In higher animals, many of the resulting amines are either important intermediates or have pharmacologic activity themselves. Aromatic L-amino acid decarboxylase (105) will decarboxylate 3,4-dihydroxyphenylalanine (to give dopamine, a precursor of epinephrine), 5-hydroxytryptophan (to give serotonin), phenylalanine, tyrosine, tryptophan, and histidine (to give histamine). A specific histidine decarboxylase is found in mast cells (106). Glutamic decarboxylase yields γ-aminobutyric acid. This compound plays an important role in neuronal functions which may explain the neural symptoms of vitamin B_6 deficiency.

Transamination. The reversible transfer of an amino group from an amino acid to an α-keto acid to form the respective α-keto and α-amino acids is mediated through pyridoxal 5-phosphate and pyridoxamine 5-phosphate. The most common transaminases are glutamate–aspartate and glutamate–alanine aminotransferases. However, transaminations in animal tissues of twenty-two other amino acids have also been described (107).

β Elimination and Addition. Pyridoxal 5-phosphate acts as the cofactor for enzymes catalyzing the elimination of a substituent from the β position of an amino acid. Examples of such reactions are the elimination of indole from tryptophan, hydrogen sulfide from cysteine, and water from serine. In each case, the other products are pyruvic acid and ammonia.

Racemization. Pyridoxal 5-phosphate acts as the coenzyme for the enzyme-catalyzed racemization of L- to D-amino acids. D-Amino acids are important constituents of the cell walls of many bacteria.

Miscellaneous. Pyridoxal 5-phosphate has been found to be a constituent of rabbit muscle phosphorylase (108). It has since been shown that it is an essential cofactor for all known phosphorylases, including potato phosphorylase, although its specific role is not known. It is interesting that most of the vitamin B_6 in muscle can be accounted for by that contained in phosphorylase (109).

The role of vitamin B_6 in fat metabolism has been a subject of controversy. Wakil has obtained evidence that vitamin B_6 may be involved in the elongation of fatty acids (110).

Antimetabolites of Pyridoxine

Antimetabolites are compounds which compete with the natural substance in certain vital reactions. They are usually produced by a slight modification of the natural structure. The effectiveness of antimetabolites is often expressed as the *inhibition index*, which is the ratio of analog to natural compound that will permit half maximal growth.

A great number of analogs of vitamin B_6 have been synthesized. Interest in anti-B_6 compounds has been stimulated by the finding that some of them have antitumor activity (111). The first analog which was found to have antivitamin activity was 4-desoxypyridoxol (**49**). Ott showed that two moles of this analog antagonized one

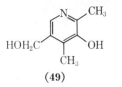

(**49**)

mole of pyridoxol in chicks (112). As little as 0.001% added to the diet of B_6-deficient mice had a marked inhibitory effect on a variety of tumors (113). 4-Desoxypyridoxol has been used to enhance the effect of vitamin B_6 deficiency in man (114). The 4-methyl ether of pyridoxol, an analog of structure (**22**), also was markedly active in chicks (114a).

A third antimetabolite is ω-methylpyridoxol (**50**) (115) which is an antagonist of pyridoxol for *S. carlsbergensis*, having an inhibition index of 43 with respect to pyri-

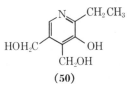

(**50**)

doxol. The 5-phosphate ester of ω-methylpyridoxal was shown to act as a cofactor for glutamate–aspartate apotransaminase of pig heart and apotryptophanase of *E. coli* (14c).

Korytnyk et al. (116) reported the synthesis of pyridoxol analogs modified by extension of the 5-hydroxymethyl side chain. One of these, the *n*-butanol analog, had an inhibition index of 2 against pyridoxol in *S. carlsbergensis*. The *n*-propanol analog had an index of 7.

Toxopyrimidine, 2-methyl-4-amino-5-hydroxymethylpyrimidine, a thiamine degradation product, is a potent convulsant in rats and mice (117). Its inhibitory action on the growth of rats and *S. carlsbergensis* is reversed by pyridoxol (118).

Bibliography

"Pyridoxine, Pyridoxal, and Pyridoxamine" in *ECT* 1st ed., Vol. 11, pp. 293–307, by S. A. Harris, G. E. Sita, and P. G. Stecher, Merck & Co., Inc.

1. Commission on the Nomenclature of Biological Chemistry, *J. Am. Chem. Soc.* **82**, 5575 (1960).
2. P. György, *Nature* **133**, 498 (1934); *Biochem. J.* **29**, 741 (1935).
3. T. W. Birch, P. György, and L. J. Harris, *Biochem. J.* **29**, 2830 (1935).
4. S. Lepkovsky, *Science* **87**, 169 (1938); *J. Biol. Chem.* **124**, 125 (1938).
5. P. György, *J. Am. Chem. Soc.* **60**, 983 (1938).
6. J. C. Keresztesy and J. R. Stevens, *Proc. Soc. Exp. Biol. Med.* **38**, 64 (1938); *J. Am. Chem. Soc.* **60**, 1267 (1938).
7. R. Kuhn and G. Wendt, *Ber.* **71B**, 780, 1118 (1938).

8. A. Itiba and K. Miti, *Sci. Papers, Inst. Phys. Chem. Res. (Tokyo)* **34,** 623 (1938); *Chem. Abstr.* **32,** 7534 (1938).

9. S. A. Harris and K. Folkers, *J. Am. Chem. Soc.* **61,** 1245 (1939).

10. R. Kuhn, K. Westphal, G. Wendt, and O. Westphal, *Naturwissenschaften* **27,** 469 (1939); *Chem. Abstr.* **33,** 8201 (1939).

11. E. E. Snell, B. M. Guirard, and R. J. Williams, *J. Biol. Chem.* **143,** 519 (1942).

12. E. E. Snell, *J. Am. Chem. Soc.* **66,** 2082 (1944).

13. K. D. Lunan and C. A. West, *Arch. Biochem. Biophys.* **101,** 261 (1963).

14. H. Lieck and H. Søndergaard, *Intern. Z. Vitaminforsch.* **29,** 68 (1958).

14a. E. A. Peterson and H. A. Sober, *J. Am. Chem. Soc.* **76,** 169 (1954).

14b. R. A. Firestone, E. E. Harris, and W. Reuter, *Tetrahedron* **23,** 943 (1967).

14c. P. F. Mühlradt, Y. Morino, and E. E. Snell, *J. Med. Chem.* **10,** 341 (1967).

15. S. A. Harris, T. J. Webb, and K. Folkers, *J. Am. Chem. Soc.* **62,** 3198 (1940).

16. S. A. Harris, *J. Am. Chem. Soc.* **63,** 3363 (1941).

17. J. V. Scudi, W. A. Bastedo, and T. J. Webb, *J. Biol. Chem.* **136,** 399 (1940).

18. S. A. Harris, D. Heyl, and K. Folkers, (a) *J. Biol. Chem.* **154,** 315 (1944); (b) *J. Am. Chem. Soc.* **66,** 2088 (1944).

19. D. Heyl, E. Luz, S. A. Harris, and K. Folkers, *J. Am. Chem. Soc.* **70,** 3669 (1948); **74,** 414 (1952).

20. D. Heyl, S. A. Harris, and K. Folkers, *J. Am. Chem. Soc.* **70,** 3429 (1948).

21. D. Heyl, E. Luz, S. A. Harris, and K. Folkers, *J. Am. Chem. Soc.* **73,** 3436 (1951).

22. E. A. Peterson, H. A. Sober and A. Meister, *J. Am. Chem. Soc.* **74,** 570 (1952); in E. E. Snell, ed., *Biochemical Preparations*, Vol. 3, John Wiley & Sons, Inc., New York, 1953, pp. 29, 34.

23. E. T. Stiller, J. C. Keresztesy, and J. R. Stevens, *J. Am. Chem. Soc.* **61,** 1237 (1939); J. V. Scudi, *J. Biol. Chem.* **139,** 707 (1941).

24. M. Swaminathan, *Nature* **145,** 780 (1940).

25. R. D. Greene, *J. Biol. Chem.* **130,** 513 (1939).

26. E. B. Brown, A. F. Bina, and J. M. Thomas, *J. Biol. Chem.* **158,** 455 (1945).

27. M. Hochberg, D. Melmick, and B. L. Oser, *J. Biol. Chem.* **155,** 109, 119, 129 (1944).

28. C. A. Storvick and J. M. Peters, *Vitamins Hormones* **22,** 833 (1964).

29. A. Fujita, K. Matsuura, and K. Fujino, *Vitaminology* **1,** 267 (1955); A. Fujita, D. Fujita, and K. Fujino, *Vitaminology* **1,** 275, 279 (1955); A. Fujita and K. Fujino, *Vitaminology* **1,** 290 (1955); *Chem. Abstr.* **50,** 2722 (1956).

30. V. Bonavita and V. Scardi, *Experientia* **14,** 7 (1958); *Chem. Abstr.* **52,** 11991 (1958); *Anal. Chim. Acta* **20,** 47 (1959); *Chem. Abstr.* **53,** 21428 (1959); *Arch. Biochem. Biophys.* **82,** 300 (1959).

31. J. W. Huff and W. A. Perlzweig, *J. Biol. Chem.* **155,** 345 (1944).

32. T. W. Conger and C. A. Elvehjem, *J. Biol. Chem.* **138,** 555 (1941).

33. P. S. Sarma, E. E. Snell, and C. A. Elvehjem, *J. Biol. Chem.* **165,** 55 (1946).

34. G. M. Briggs, Jr., R. C. Mills, D. M. Hegsted, C. A. Elvehjem, and E. B. Hart, *Poultry Sci.* **21,** 379 (1942).

35. E. E. Snell and P. György, *Vitamin Methods*, Vol. I, Academic Press, Inc., New York, 1950, p. 406.

36. The Association of Vitamin Chemists, Inc. (M. Freed, Chairman of the Methods Committee), *Methods of Vitamin Assay*, 3rd ed., John Wiley & Sons, Inc., New York, 1966, p. 209.

36a. M. J. MacArthur and J. Lehmann, *J. Assoc. Offic. Agr. Chemists* **42,** 619 (1959).

37. E. E. Snell and C. S. Keevil, Jr., in W. H. Sebrell, Jr., and R. S. Harris, *The Vitamins*, Vol. 3, Academic Press, Inc., New York, 1954, p. 255.

38. J. C. Rabinowitz and E. E. Snell, *J. Biol. Chem.* **169,** 631 (1947).

39. B. E. Haskell and U. Wallnöffer, *Anal. Biochem.* **19,** 569 (1967).

40. E. W. Toepfer and J. Lehmann, *J. Assoc. Offic. Agr. Chemists* **44,** 426 (1961).

41. J. L. Stokes, A. Larson, C. R. Woodward, Jr., and J. W. Foster, *J. Biol. Chem.* **150,** 17 (1943).

42. S. A. Harris and K. Folkers, *Science* **89,** 347 (1939); U.S. Pats. 2,422,617, 2,422,621, 2,422,-622, and 2,422,195 (June 17, 1947), S. A. Harris (to Merck & Co., Inc.).

43. U.S. Pat. 2,422,619 (June 17, 1947), S. A. Harris (to Merck & Co., Inc.).

44. U.S. Pats. 2,399,347 (April 30, 1946), 2,422,618, and 2,422,620 (June 17, 1947), S. A. Harris (to Merck & Co., Inc.).

45. Brit. Pat. 626,368 (July 14, 1949) (to American Cyanamid Co.); E. Testa and A. Vecchi, *Gazz. Chim. Ital.* **87**, 467 (1957); *Chem. Abstr.* **52**, 1163 (1958); U. Schmidt, *Ann. Chem.* **657**, 156 (1962).

46. U.S. Pat. Appls. 346,568 and 346,569 (vested in Alien Property Custodian) *Offic. Gaz. U.S. Pat. Office*, **549**, xxxiii (1943).

47. S. Morii and K. Makino, *Enzymologia* **7**, 385 (1939).

48. J. H. Mowat, F. J. Pilgrim, and G. H. Carlson, *J. Am. Chem. Soc.* **65**, 954 (1943); U.S. Pats. 2,310,167 (Feb. 2, 1943), G. H. Carlson (to Lederle Laboratories, Inc.); 2,417,541 (March 18, 1947) and 2,431,463 (Nov. 25, 1947), G. H. Carlson and F. J. Pilgrim (to American Cyanamid Co.).

49. A. Itiba and S. Emoto, *Sci. Papers, Inst. Phys. Chem. Res. (Tokyo)* **38**, 347 (1941); *Chem. Abstr.* **35**, 6960 (1941).

50. A. Itiba and K. Miti, *Sci. Papers, Inst. Phys. Chem. Res. (Tokyo)* **36**, 173 (1939); *Chem. Abstr.* **33**, 8201 (1939).

51. U.S. Pat. 2,359,260 (Sept. 26, 1944), L. J. Szabo (to S. M. A. Corp.).

52. Y. Suzuki, *Yakugaku Zasshi* **81**, 792 (1961); *Chem. Abstr.* **55**, 24746 (1961).

53. R. G. Jones and E. C. Kornfeld, *J. Am. Chem. Soc.* **73**, 107 (1951).

54. A. Cohen, J. W. Haworth, and E. G. Hughes, *J. Chem. Soc.* **1952**, 4374.

55. U.S. Pat. 2,918,471 (Dec. 22, 1959), J. H. Mowat and J. S. Webb (to American Cyanamid Co.).

56. H. M. Wuest, J. A. Bigot, T. J. deBoer, B. van der Wal, and J. P. Wibaut, *Rec. Trav. Chim.* **78**, 226 (1959).

57. U.S. Pats. 2,590,841 (April 1, 1952), A. Cohen (to Hoffmann-La Roche Inc.); 2,744,114 (May 1, 1956), R. G. Jones (to Eli Lilly & Co.); Brit. Pat. 804,236 (Nov. 12, 1958) (to N. V. Phillips Gloeilampen Fabrieken); 839,583 (June 29, 1960) (to Chas. Pfizer & Co., Inc.); Fr. Pat. 1,441,497 (June 10, 1966) (to Merck & Co., Inc.); Neth. Pat. 6,613,567 (April 7, 1967) (to Merck & Co., Inc.).

58. R. G. Jones, *J. Am. Chem. Soc.* **73**, 5244 (1951).

59. N. Elming and N. Clauson-Kaas, *Acta Chem. Scand.* **9**, 23 (1955).

60. U.S. Pats. 2,680,743 (June 8, 1954) and 2,734,063 (Feb. 7, 1956), P. G. Stevens (to General Aniline & Film Corp.).

61. U.S. Pats. 2,904,551 (Sept. 15, 1959), 2,948,733 (Aug. 9, 1960), and 3,024,244 (March 6, 1962), P. I. Pollak (to Merck & Co., Inc.).

62. G. Ya. Kondrat'yeva, *Khim. Nauka i Promy.* **2**, 666 (1957); *Chem. Abstr.* **52**, 6345 (1958); *Izv. Akad. Nauk SSSR, Otd. Khim. Nauk* **1959**, 484; *Chem. Abstr.* **53**, 21940 (1959).

63. C. N. Huang and G. Ya. Kondrat'yeva, *Izv. Akad. Nauk SSSR, Otd. Khim. Nauk* **1962**, 525; *Chem. Abstr.* **57**, 15064 (1962).

64. E. E. Harris, R. A. Firestone, K. Pfister, III, R. R. Boettcher, F. J. Cross, R. B. Currie, M. Monaco, E. R. Peterson, and W. Reuter, *J. Org. Chem.* **27**, 2705 (1962).

65. U.S. Pat. 3,227,721, 3,227,722, and 3,227,724 (Jan. 4, 1966), K. Pfister, III, E. E. Harris, and R. A. Firestone (to Merck & Co., Inc.); T. Naito and T. Yoshikawa, *Chem. Pharm. Bull.* **14**, 918 (1966); Neth. Pat. 6,614,801 (April 24, 1967) (to Merck & Co., Inc.); Fr. Pat. 1,400,843 (May 28, 1965) (to Takeda Chemical Industries, Ltd.).

66. S. African Pat. Appl. 63/4849 (April 15, 1964) (to Hoffmann-La Roche Inc.); U.S. Pat. 3,250,778 (May 10, 1966), W. Kimel and W. Leimgruber (to Hoffmann-La Roche Inc.); U.S. Pat. 3,296,275 (Jan. 3, 1967), S. F. Schaeren (to Hoffmann-La Roche Inc.).

67. Fr. Pat. 1,449,952 (Aug. 19, 1966) (to Takeda Chemical Industries, Ltd.); Belg. Pat. 671,385 (Feb. 14, 1966) (to Tenabe Seiyaku Co., Ltd.); T. Miki and T. Matsuo, *Yakugaku Zasshi* **87**, 323 (1967); *Chem. Abstr.* **67**, 32549 (1967).

68. Belg. Pat. 626,620 (June 28, 1963) (to Hoffmann-La Roche Inc.); S. African Pat. Appl. 62/5308 (May 15, 1963) (Derwent 7574) (to Hoffmann-La Roche Inc.).

69. Japan. Pat. 2705/67 (June 2, 1967) (to Daiichi Seiyaku, Ltd.).

70. D. Heyl, *J. Am. Chem. Soc.* **70**, 3434 (1948).

71. Brit. Pat. 852,398 (Oct. 26, 1960) (to E. Merck A.G.).

72. O. Manonsek, *Coll. Czech. Chem. Comm.* **25**, 2250 (1960); *Chem. Abstr.* **55**, 174 (1961).

73. Brit. Pat. 915,451 (Jan. 16, 1963) (to E. Merck A.G.).

74. Belg. Pat. 648,226 (Sept. 15, 1964) (to Takeda Chemical Industries, Ltd.).

75. J. Baddiley and A. P. Mathias, *J. Chem. Soc.* **1952**, 2583.

76. I. C. Gunsalus, W. W. Umbreit, W. D. Bellamy, and C. E. Foust, *J. Biol. Chem.* **161,** 743 (1945).
77. A. N. Wilson and S. A. Harris, *J. Am. Chem. Soc.* **73,** 4693 (1951).
78. M. Viscontini, C. Ebnother, and P. Karrer, *Helv. Chim. Acta* **34,** 1834, 2198 (1951).
79. U.S. Pat. 3,124,587 (March 10, 1964), G. Schorre (to E. Merck A.G.).
80. U.S. Pat. 2,755,284 (July 17, 1956), R. F. Long (to Hoffmann-La Roche Inc.).
81. D. Heyl, E. Luz, S. A. Harris, and K. Folkers, *J. Am. Chem. Soc.* **73,** 3436 (1951).
82. M. Viscontini, C. Ebnother, and P. Karrer, *Helv. Chim. Acta* **34,** 2199 (1951).
83. L. D. Greenberg, *Vitamins Hormones* **22,** 677 (1964).
84. C. W. Denko, W. E. Grundy, N. C. Wheeler, C. R. Henderson, G. H. Berryman, T. E. Friedemann, and J. B. Youmans, *Arch. Biochem.* **11,** 109 (1946).
85. S. E. Snyderman, L. E. Holt, Jr., R. Carretero, and K. Jacobs, *J. Clin. Nutr.* **1,** 200 (1953).
86. E. M. Nelson, *Public Health Repts.* (*U.S.*) **71,** 445 (1956).
87. D. B. Coursin, *Am. J. Diseases Children* **90,** 344 (1955).
88. J. W. Harris, R. M. Whittington, R. Weisman, Jr., and D. L. Horrigan, *Proc. Soc. Exp. Biol. Med.* **91,** 427 (1956).
89. J. W. Harris and D. L. Horrigan, *Vitamins Hormones* **22,** 721 (1964).
90. D. L. Horrigan and J. W. Harris, *Advan. Internal Med.* **12,** 103 (1964).
91. A. D. Hunt, J. Stokes, W. W. McCrory, and H. H. Stroud, *Pediatrics* **13,** 140 (1954).
92. R. W. Vilter, *Vitamins Hormones* **22,** 797 (1964).
93. D. B. McCormick and E. E. Snell, *J. Biol. Chem.* **236,** 2085 (1961).
94. D. B. Coursin, *Am. J. Clin. Nutr.* **14,** 56 (1964).
95. *Food and Nutrition Board 1964. Recommended Dietary Allowances,* 6th revised ed., Natl Acad. Sci-Natl. Res. Council, Publ. 1146.
96. H. Borsook, *Vitamins Hormones* **22,** 855 (1964).
97. K. Sato, T. Suzuki, and Y. Sahashi, *Bitamin* **33,** 355, 357 (1966); *Chem. Abstr.* **64,** 18063 (1966).
98. D. B. McCormick, M. E. Gregory, and E. E. Snell, *J. Biol. Chem.* **236,** 2076 (1961).
99. H. Wada and E. E. Snell, *J. Biol. Chem.* **236,** 2089 (1961).
100. J. C. Rabinowitz and E. E. Snell, *Proc. Soc. Exp. Biol. Med.* **70,** 235 (1949).
101. S. Johannson, S. Lindstedt, U. Register, and L. Wadström, *Am. J. Clin. Nutr.* **18,** 185 (1966).
102. E. E. Snell, R. W. Burg, W. B. Dempsey, E. J. Nyns, T. K. Sundarum, and D. Zach, in E. E. Snell, P. M. Fasella, A. Braunstein, and A. Rossi Fanelli, eds., *Chemical and Biological Aspects of Pyridoxal Catalysis,* The Macmillan Company, New York, 1963, p. 563.
103. D. E. Metzler, M. Ikawa and E. E. Snell, *J. Am. Chem. Soc.* **76,** 648 (1954).
104. E. E. Snell in E. E. Snell, P. M. Fasella, A. Braunstein and A. Rossi Fanelli, eds., *Chemical and Biological Aspects of Pyridoxal Catalysis,* The Macmillan Co., New York, 1963, p. 1.
105. W. Lovenberg, H. Weissbach, and S. Udenfriend, *J. Biol. Chem.* **237,** 89 (1962).
106. H. Weissbach, W. Lovenberg, and S. Udenfriend, *Biochem. Biophys. Acta* **50,** 177 (1961).
107. P. S. Cammarata and P. P. Cohen, *J. Biol. Chem.* **187,** 439 (1950).
108. T. Baranowski, B. Illingworth, D. H. Brown, and C. F. Cori, *Biochem. Biophys. Acta* **25,** 16 (1957).
109. E. G. Krebs and E. H. Fischer, *Vitamins Hormones* **22,** 399 (1964).
110. S. J. Wakil, *J. Lipid Res.* **2,** 1 (1961).
111. F. Rosen, E. Mihich, and C. A. Nichol, *Vitamins Hormones* **22,** 609 (1964).
112. W. H. Ott, *Proc. Soc. Exp. Biol. Med.* **61,** 125 (1946).
113. E. Mihich, F. Rosen, and C. A. Nichol, *Cancer Res.* **19,** 1244 (1959).
114. R. W. Vilter, J. F. Mueller, H. S. Glazer, T. Jarrold, J. Abraham, C. Thompson, and V. R. Hawkins, *J. Lab. Clin. Med.* **42,** 335 (1953).
114a. W. H. Ott, *Proc. Soc. Exp. Biol. Med.* **66,** 215 (1947).
115. J. C. Rabinowitz and E. E. Snell, *Arch. Biochem. Biophys.* **43,** 408 (1953).
116. W. Korytnyk, B. Paul, A. Bloch, and C. A. Nichol, *J. Med. Chem.* **10,** 345 (1967).
117. R. Abderhalden, *Arch. Ges. Physiol.* **242,** 199 (1939); *Chem. Abstr.* **33,** 9377 (1939).
118. T. Sakuragi and F. Kummerow, *Arch. Biochem. Biophys.* **71,** 303 (1957).

General References

F. A. Robinson, *The Vitamin Co-factors of Enzyme Systems,* Pergamon Press, New York, 1966, pp· 328–405.

Vitamins Hormones **22**, 359–885 (1964) (*International Symposium on Vitamin B₆, New York, July 23–24, 1964*). (Excellent series of reviews with extensive bibliographies.)

E. E. Snell, P. M. Fasella, A. Braunstein, and A. Rossi Fanelli, eds., *Chemical and Biological Aspects of Pyridoxal Catalysis*, The Macmillan Co., New York, 1963.

W. H. Sebrell, Jr., and R. S. Harris, *The Vitamins*, Vol. III, Academic Press, Inc., New York, 1954, pp. 219–298.

A. F. Wagner and K. Folkers, *Vitamins and Coenzymes*, Interscience Publishers, a division of John Wiley & Sons, Inc., New York, 1964, pp. 160–193.

E. E. Snell, A. E. Braunstein, E. S. Severin, and Yu. M. Torchinsky, eds., *Pyridoxal Catalysis: Enzymes and Model Systems*, John Wiley & Sons, Inc., New York, 1968.

STANTON A. HARRIS,
ELBERT E. HARRIS, AND
RICHARD W. BURG
Merck & Co., Inc.

PYRITE, FeS_2. See Iron compounds; Pigments (inorganic); Sulfur; Sulfuric acid.

PYROCATECHOL (1,2-BENZENEDIOL), $C_6H_4(OH)_2$. See Hydroquinone, pyrocatechol and resorcinol.

PYROGALLOL (1,2,3-BENZENETRIOL), $C_6H_3(OH)_3$. See (Polyhydroxy)benzenes.

PYROLUSITE, MnO_2. See Manganese; Manganese compounds.

PYROMETRIC CONES. See Vol. 4, pp. 786, 787.

PYROMETRY. See Temperature measurement.

PYROTECHNICS

Historically, modern pyrotechnics, the "fire-art" (from the Greek words *pyr*, fire, and *techne*, an art) derives from fireworks for pleasure (1–3) and from crude military incendiarism of earlier periods (4,5). At present, military pyrotechnics encompasses a large array of light effects for illumination and signaling, noisemakers for troop training, and numerous specialized heat sources. In addition, minor rocketry, production of nonspecific gases for pressurization and inflation or for dispersion of aerosolized agents (smokes and chemical-warfare agents), as well as production of specific gases (oxygen candle), belong in the realm of military pyrotechnics (6–9). Civilian pyrotechnics comprises all types of fireworks items as well as certain warning signals such as railroad fusees and railroad torpedoes. Some military and civilian items are quite similar except for the more rugged construction and protection against adverse environmental conditions that military items require; others, such as flares of 1 million candlepower or more, are specific for military purposes. It must be understood that pyrotechnics has largely remained an empirical practical discipline and technique and that the strictly scientific and theoretical approach to solid/solid reactions is only gradually and very slowly gaining in importance.

Principles of Pyrotechnics

The usefulness of pyrotechnic items derives from the properties of a class of pyrochemical reactions that pyrotechnics shares with rocketry and explosives technology. The specific and typical functionality of these reactions can be expressed briefly as *exothermic, self-sustaining,* and *self-contained.* When two or more substances interact chemically, or if only one substance decomposes, this may take place because of an input of external energy (endothermic reaction), or because the mixture or compound will spontaneously release energy (exothermic reaction). The latter type of reaction will normally occur only after the chemical system has been initiated, ie elevated locally to an incipient reaction temperature by a relatively small energy input. Combustion in air is a typical example of an exothermic reaction. However, in order to qualify as pyrotechnical, such a reaction must be completely or predominantly independent of the presence of ambient air. It must also be self-sustaining, ie it must complete its course until all the active material present has been reacted.

Another characteristic of the typical pyrotechnic process, one that distinguishes it from the behavior of propellants or explosives, is that all the major components are solids and the products are not, or are only partly, gaseous at ordinary temperature. Thus, the released energy is concentrated in a small volume and this creates extremely high temperatures that are maintained over a relatively long reaction period. In contradistinction, the typical explosive reaction for destructive purposes derives from the decomposition of a single substance, solid or liquid, and produces only or predominantly gaseous products within an extremely short time interval; in propellants intermediate conditions prevail, the materials being of either the interacting or decomposing kind, solid or liquid, and the speed of reaction brisk but not extremely fast. The reaction products are gaseous.

The independence of many exothermic pyrochemical reactions from the surrounding air permits the operation of the flare, cartridge, etc under a variety of conditions other than at ground level in the open, such as in a highly rarefied atmosphere at high altitude, under water, and within completely sealed containers. The last is important when the advancing glow front of a powder train is used as a timing device, which thus will allow a predetermined sequencing of events under varying external conditions. This has become important in the complex systems that culminate in the ejection of a pilot from an aircraft; in separation systems in astronautics; and in safe activation of nuclear devices. Although the timing thus achieved is not of high accuracy compared with mechanical or electronic devices, the delay columns have the great advantage of smallness, extreme ruggedness, and low cost. They share these properties with other pyrotechnic items and all have the added advantage that, if properly designed, they are completely stable over many years of storage. Another point in their favor is that pyrotechnic devices contain no moving parts (with the possible exception of the initiation system, and this may be of the simplest kind as in the well-known hand grenade fuse). Thus, pyrotechnic ordnance is ready for use without any special preparation even after years of storage. Setting up assembly lines for the production of hundreds of thousands of flares, cartridge-type devices, or accessory items can be performed with short lead times, simple equipment, and a majority of unskilled labor, all of which are strategically significant when a sudden demand arises for large numbers of these items.

Uses of Pyrotechnics

A number of processes and devices based on pyrotechnical principles are treated or touched upon in another context. This is the case with the pyrochemical dispersion of obscuring and signaling *smokes* and of irritating and toxic substances (see Chemical warfare); the rapid production of metals and their alloys by the Goldschmidt process (see the articles on the various metals); and the closely related application of this thermite reaction to the welding of rails, repair of machinery, and similar purposes (see Welding). The production of flame by the modern match, another pyrochemical and in the wider sense pyrotechnical phenomenon, has been described in the article Matches.

It has been thought neither practical nor advisable to furnish more than the essentials of fireworks information in order not to encourage the activities of amateurs. Pyrotechnics is a hazardous field and no one should engage in it without a thorough study of the extant literature and the advice of experts. General safety rules are given below, but they do not suffice for individual operations.

Materials of Pyrotechnics

The chemical ingredients for pyrochemical reactions can be divided into fuels, oxidizers, binders (adhesives), and accessory materials. Fuels are those elements and compounds that enter into strongly exothermic reactions with oxygen or, occasionally, with halogens (fluorine, chlorine) or the chalcogens (sulfur, selenium, tellurium). Fuels are, chemically speaking, reducing agents or electron donors.

Prior to the nineteenth century, *charcoal* and *sulfur* were the only major fuels, used in the form of black powder (gunpowder)—then the jack-of-all-trades of pyrotechnics. It was varied in the ratio of components and used as ignition material, illuminant, driving force, and explosive for dispersion and sound effects. Black powder was still an important accessory ingredient in many devices up until World War II, but it is now used mainly in fireworks. *Magnesium* powder is unsurpassed for high-intensity light effects; *aluminum* in coarse-grained form is an important heat producer and, as a fine powder, is preferred in flash compositions and noisemakers. The nonmetals *silicon* and *boron* and the metals *zirconium* and *titanium* have excellent fire-transfer properties and are used for these purposes in ignition mixtures ("first fires"). Zirconium–nickel alloys, manganese, molybdenum, and tungsten, all as fine powders, are used in delay columns for military items. Various forms of steel and cast-iron fragments create special fireworks effects. Lead powder and selenium are used in pyrotechnic delays for blasting caps. All binders act incidentally as fuels and some other organic compounds such as gallic acid, picrates, carbohydrates, oils, solid chlorinated hydrocarbons, waxes, and even the lowly wood flour appear in certain formulations.

Oxidizers fall into the following three categories: (*1*) salts that easily give off oxygen; (*2*) oxides and some pyrochemically related compounds such as chromates; and (*3*) oxygenfree elements such as sulfur and selenium, also fluorine or chlorine, the last two always in the form of compounds.

Useful oxidizer salts are the *nitrates* of sodium, potassium, strontium, and barium; and potassium *chlorate* and potassium *perchlorate*. Of these, sodium nitrate, formerly shunned because it attracts moisture, especially if of low purity, has become by far the most important one, and potassium chlorate has been used in primary ignition devices (matches), in colored smoke compositions, and also in many fireworks formulas. Calcium sulfate, surprisingly, has good oxidizing properties under some conditions and was used in World War II in Germany as a partial substitute for nitrates.

Oxides and chromates are restricted to special uses for the creation of high temperatures. The most important compounds of this class are black iron oxide (Fe_3O_4) and barium chromate ($BaCrO_4$).

Of halogen donors, the fluorocarbon polymers such as polytetrafluoroethylene, PTFE (Teflon (Du Pont), and Halon (Allied Chemical Corporation)) are newcomers to the field and are used in certain types of military flares and in ignition mixtures. Useful chlorinated organic compounds include hexachloroethane, "HC," in smoke formulations; others, such as hexachlorobenzene of World War II—now already obsolete—and polyvinyl chloride, serve as color intensifiers and would function only incidentally as oxidizers. Because of their pyrochemical reactivity, chlorinated solvents are by no means "inert" in contact with fuel-type metals such as aluminum or magnesium.

Binders, which hold together the ingredients of exposed beads, rods (sparklers), and "star" pellets, and increase the mechanical strength of flare candles, can be dextrins and gum arabic, lacquer-type cellulose nitrate, and various synthetic, cold-polymerizing plastics such as unsaturated polyesters (Laminac). In fireworks, several natural gums and resins such as shellac and red gum (gum accroides), are also used.

Minor ingredients include processing aids that make powdery substances free-flowing in order to promote intimate mixing; volatile liquids that desensitize a mixture prior to pressing into pellets; and some additives that are meant to prevent influx of moisture such as oils and waxes. The effectiveness of the latter is limited since they merely slow down the diffusion of water vapor. Easily corroded metal powders or hygroscopic oxidizer salts will eventually succumb to even the slowest penetration of moisture, the only real protection being hermetic sealing from ambient atmosphere after thorough predrying of all chemical and structural components.

Siliceous materials such as diatomaceous earth sometimes play a minor part in adjusting the properties of a formula. Neutralizers (zinc oxide, calcium carbonate) are important in the prevention of destructive internal decomposition reactions promoted by the influx of moisture.

Techniques

The interaction of finely powdered chemical components in a typical device, in the manner indicated above, requires three essential steps: mixing, pressing, and fusing. If the ingredients of a formulation do not tend to agglomerate, mere tumbling in an inclined, open barrel-like container (Globe mixer) or in a V-shaped rotating tubular vessel ("twin shell blender") is sufficient. Rubber-coated metal balls or plain bronze balls are sometimes added to break up a tendency of some fine powders to "ball up." Smaller quantities can be effectively mixed by forcing the stirred-together materials repeatedly, with gentle rubbing, sometimes with a gloved hand, through a fairly coarse sieve. Some mixtures require a more forceful alternate squeezing and "shoveling" action as performed in a wheel mill or "mix muller" (Simpson mixer). This is the specific method for black powder and, on a smaller scale, for producing batches of illuminating formulations that contain a sizable amount of a liquid (polymerizing) binder.

Although those powder mixtures used for the creation of a flash or a sharp noise are always used as loose powders, the typical pyrotechnic composition is consolidated more or less strongly to form a pellet, a substantial cylindrical column, or an elongated narrow train. In military devices, strong hydraulic consolidation forces, mostly in the range of 6000 to 30,000 psi, are exerted on the material within a steel or brass mold. Except when a bare, overall-burning pellet is desired, the composition is directly pressed into a strong cardboard tube or steel canister, the powder mixture being consolidated in several increments, each of a final height not exceeding its diameter. For the top layer, a more sensitive, easier-igniting composition, called a "first fire," is added in order to assure proper initiation of the main charge. In fireworks, consolidation forces generally are small and a hand-tamping or ramming process is resorted to though more modern production methods with arbor or hydraulic presses are now used for mass-produced items. All pyrotechnic candles, stars, etc are arranged with additional fuse trains, ejection charges, and ignition squibs depending on design and functionality. Thus, an air-launched parachute flare will undergo a succession of timed steps, namely release from the launcher, ejection and unfolding of the parachute, and ignition of the flare candle. Star signals ejected from a pyrotechnic pistol ("Very pistol") are propelled into the air with delayed ignition and display their light at and near the apex of the trajectory. Delay timing is critical in explosive items such as photoflash cartridges or hand grenades where a certain distance prior to explosion from the dispenser or from the person throwing the grenade is imperative. All photoflash cartridges avail themselves of pyrotechnic delay columns, ignited by the ejection charge, whereas in the hand grenade the release of the safety lever actuates a striker on a percussion primer, which then initiates in sequence a first fire, a delay column, and a detonator.

Hazards of Pyrotechnics

In explosives technology, it is fairly easy to assess the degree of hazardousness because one deals mostly with individual chemicals or with mixtures in which a certain chemical such as a primary explosive predominates. These compounds can be characterized by their sensitivity to impact, friction, and ignition by flame or static electricity. In addition, changes in formulas and introduction of new materials are rare so that the manufacturer acquires an extensive background of statistical information. In contradistinction, the pyrotechnic formulas are of infinite varieties, not only by percentage but also by particle-size distribution. New materials are frequently introduced. Thus, the degree of hazardousness of these compositions is always difficult to assess. Mixtures may react slowly and in orderly fashion in small amounts but become explosive in somewhat larger quantities. All mixtures are more hazardous in loose, powdered form than when consolidated, and are more likely to become explosive in confinement than when reacting in the open. However, under some circumstances, even a single strongly consolidated flare candle can become explosive, and the term "confinement" can become meaningless when "open burning" is just not open enough, as, for example, if a tremendously rapid buildup of pressure occurs owing to an unfavorable pressure coefficient of the speed of reaction.

Disregarding prime-explosive-type mixtures such as the extremely hazardous and unpredictable combinations of potassium chlorate and red phosphorus, it can be said that the potential hazard diminishes with increase of particle size of the fuel, especially with the absence of sub-sieve size (less than about 10 μ diameter) metal particles; with the presence of liquid vehicles and lubricants; and with the exclusion of ingredients of specific sensitivity or sensitizing action such as the metal zirconium and the oxidizers potassium chlorate and perchlorate, lead dioxide, and also PTFE. However, every mixture in powdered form in more than gram quantities must be considered able to undergo, without assignable cause, an unexpected ignition causing a searing flash or a damaging explosion.

In order to avoid grievous injuries to persons and damage to equipment and buildings, the following essential lines of approach are taken by the manufacturer: Materials known to cause frequent accidents are avoided (if they are not irreplaceable because of a functional advantage such as in an igniter composition); the more potentially hazardous and destructive the mixture, the smaller is the amount processed in one batch; sensitivity to accidental impact or friction during mixing is attenuated wherever possible by the presence of a liquid vehicle such as water or a volatile organic liquid, or sometimes a small amount of a thin oil; and the more dangerous phases of an operation are performed by remotely controlled starting and stopping with adequate barricading or, if small experimental quantities are involved, by mere shielding and the wearing of protective clothing.

Thus, pyrotechnics cannot be regarded as a harmless amusement and hobby for the amateur. Only if the processor *always* acts under the assumption that his mixture can spontaneously "go off" without discernible cause will he avoid grievous injuries and damage. Unfortunately, the beginner will often pass through an initial period of caution and anxiety followed by an optimistic feeling of relaxation and subsequent carelessness, culminating in an accident.

Toxic hazards from the materials themselves and from the fumes of reacted mixtures are not very great except when certain unusual materials such as selenium and tellurium and the products from fluorine-containing mixtures are involved. Several of the dyes used in colored smokes have been found to possess carcinogenic properties.

Military Pyrotechnics

The literature of military pyrotechnics is widely dispersed and much of it is inaccessible to the general reader even though it may not bear the label "confidential" or "secret." However, a few books give a comprehensive survey of the whole field with large numbers of references and formulas. These are the second (6) and especially the third (7) edition of Shidlovsky's *Fundamentals of Pyrotechnics* written in the Russian language. Both have been translated into English by U.S. Government effort but only the translation of the second edition is purchasable; the other is available to qualified persons on a "need to know" basis. Ellern's *Modern Pyrotechnics* (8) is similar in scope and treatment to Shidlovsky's, and his newer *Military and Civilian Pyrotechnics* (9) is in the same vein but much more detailed. The *Aerospace Ordnance Handbook* (10), a collection of monographs on special phases and accessory devices of pyrotechnic interest, contains much specific information, especially on the subject of delay powder formulations. Faber's three-volume work (11) treats of military pyrotechnics at the time of World War I.

Flares for Illumination. During night engagements in the field or for purposes of visual reconnaissance, it is often necessary or desirable to provide powerful illumination from the air. Such lighting is done by flares that are either ejected from an artillery (mortar or howitzer) shell or dropped from an airplane. The former are smaller and operate at a lower altitude than the latter; for both, descent is slowed down by a parachute. The candlepower varies from 500,000 to 2 million and the burning time from 1 to 5 min, the lower figures pertaining to illuminating shells, the higher ones to airplane flares. The result in either case is a minimum useful illumination of the ground of 0.025 foot-candles or better.

Table 1 gives Formulas 1 and 2 and other pertinent data on one of either kind of flare candles. The formulas differ only slightly in composition. Experience has shown that these combinations furnish optimal amounts of light at the present state of the art. The reaction between the magnesium and the nitrate is highly exothermic and the resulting magnesium oxide is a strong emitter of "gray-body" radiation. However, the sodium of the nitrate displays luminescent properties that contribute significantly to white-light emission as can be easily proved experimentally by the use of other nitrates. (Under different conditions, sodium, used as the oxalate, furnishes a strong yellow light.) The binder, mixed with a small amount of an organic peroxide and applied to the mixture in liquid state, polymerizes without external heating and creates strong bonding forces between particles and to the wall of the container. Because an artillery shell is subjected to severe mechanical stresses, twice as much binder is used in the formulation than in aircraft flare candle formulations. The larger candles, ejected from a projectile, are pressed into steel containers whereas the smaller ones and all aircraft flares use sturdy cardboard casing. The flame is so large and powerful that its gradual partial recession into the steel cases does not cause obscuration of the emitted light. When cardboard casing is used, it will burn off and the ash disappears as the candle burns down.

Table 1. Typical Formulas for and Properties of the Parachute Flare Candle
(Formula 1) and the Mortar Shell (Formula 2)

Ingredients and properties	Parachute flare Formula 1	Mortar shell Formula 2
Ingredients		
magnesium, atomized, %	58	55
sodium nitrate, %	37½	36
binder,[a] %	4½	9
Properties		
candle diameter, in.	4.25	2.835
burning area, in.^{2}	14.2	6.3
candle length, in.	16.75	4.0
candle weight, g	6804	622
burning time, sec	170	60
burning time, sec/in.	10.0	15
candlepower (million)	1.77	0.50
candlepower-sec (million)	300	30
candlepower-sec/g	44	48
candlepower/in.^{2} (thousand)	125	79

[a] Laminac #4116 (Am. Cyanamide Co.) or equivalent, a polyester resin with added cold-curing catalyst.

The formulas presented contain a considerable excess of magnesium beyond the stoichiometric relation between fuel metal and oxidizer. Such metal burns in the surrounding air coincidental with the fuel/oxidizer interaction. The binder also burns in air and thus adds to flame formation. The burning time per unit length of this type of flare candle varies with the particle size and shape (ie with the total surface area) of the major ingredients. Increased fineness of the magnesium powder means faster reaction and hence shorter burning time. Another significant factor is the ratio of fuel metal to oxidizer salt; the greater the excess of metal powder (at least up to a point), the faster the pyrochemical reaction progresses, probably on account of the greater heat conductivity. Increased compaction lowers the rate of reaction up to a certain point, but the regulation of burning time by varying the compression on the powder mixture is rarely practical. The major difficulty for the manufacturer is the fact that he cannot predict the burning time well enough on the basis of prior tests and must rely on the evaluation of actual samples from the line. Even then, the freshly made candles may not show the properties the item exhibits after some additional time has elapsed. This may be due to incomplete polymerization of the binder in fresh samples or to some still obscure phenomenon as when a freshly made item without resin binder changes its burning time on exposure to a higher temperature and then remains constant. It should be mentioned only in passing that a flare candle will burn much faster when in violent spinning motion than it will when stationary; turntables have been employed to simulate field conditions in the testing of flares for light output and burning time.

    Signal Flares. Relatively small end-burning flares or overall burning "stars" serve a variety of tactical military uses. A few of these emit white light, but the majority burn with a clearly distinguishable color—red, green, or yellow (amber). Formulas mentioned in this section are given in Table 2. The purpose of such lights is not to illuminate but to be seen and thus to convey a message. This message (using the term in a general way) may be that a training device has been involuntarily set off (Booby-Trap Simulator (low-energy white flare), Formula 3); that an air-dropped light signal marks the initial contact point with an enemy submarine (Marine Location Marker, formerly Float or Drift Signals (combined light and smoke signal), Formula 4);

Table 2. Formulas for Signal Flares

Ingredients	%	Ingredients	%
Formula 3—Low-energy white flare		*Formula 7—yellow star*	
red gum	21	magnesium	19
dextrin	6	gilsonite	9
potassium perchlorate	73	hexachlorobenzene	7
		sodium oxalate	15
Formula 4—combined light and smoke signal		potassium perchlorate	50
magnesium	8		
red phosphorus	51	*Formula 8—red artillery tracer*	
manganese dioxide	35	magnesium	28
zinc oxide	3	strontium nitrate	40
linseed oil	3	potassium perchlorate	20
		strontium oxalate	8
Formula 5—red star		calcium resinate	4
magnesium	23		
gilsonite	8	*Formula 9—red artillery tracer*	
hexachlorobenzene	6	magnesium	28
strontium nitrate	41	strontium nitrate	55
potassium perchlorate	22	polyvinyl chloride	17
Formula 6—green star			
magnesium	15		
oil	2		
hexachlorobenzene	15		
copper powder	2		
barium nitrate	66		

that an incoming aircraft is friendly (precoded "color of the day" of World War II using multiple star signals, Formulas 5–7). Other uses are as distress or alarm signals or to outline an emergency landing strip in clandestine operations.

Small arms and artillery ammunition provided with a *tracer* in the base create a red trail of light (Formulas 8 and 9), thus showing the trajectory of the projectile. This may be the most frequent use of a "signal" light in military pyrotechnics.

Colored lights owe their selective light emission to the presence of the elements strontium (red), barium (green), copper (green or blue), and sodium (yellow). There are some others such as lithium (red) and thallium (green), but they have no practical use because of cost, hygroscopicity of their compounds, or toxicity. As far as the most desirable and most frequently used red and green lights are concerned, it is necessary to bring a maximum of the elements strontium and barium into the flame as the relatively volatile chlorides. This is indirectly done by employing the nitrates as oxidizers and converting the residual alkaline earth into the chlorides by admixture of potassium chlorate (in commercial fireworks only), potassium perchlorate, or certain highly chlorinated organic compounds. Unfortunately, depth and purity of color and high luminosity exclude each other. It is also necessary to operate within certain temperature intervals in order to create the most desirable type of spectrum for the color-producing compound. Greater visibility at a distance is achieved by addition and, therefore, superimposition, of white light. This dilutes the color effect and may make it unrecognizable at a greater distance or in haze or rain. The most difficult to produce and the least effective is the color blue, though it is quite acceptable for fireworks purposes.

In modern pyrotechnics, the useful selective spectral emission of flames extends into the infrared (ir) range even though it is not possible or at least not practical to create an efficient radiant emitter devoid of visible light. Special flares with a relatively larger percentage of ir emission are used for the augmentation of the heat radiation from the exhaust gas of propellants on small unmanned airplanes (drones). They serve the purpose of testing ir seeking devices such as the Sidewinder missile (10).

Flash Charges. An important part of reconnaissance such as in the assessment of bomb damage is night photography from an aircraft. By releasing the energy from light-producing pyrotechnic mixtures in a time interval of less than $1/10$ sec, extremely high light concentration can be achieved. Smaller units, called photoflash cartridges, furnish a peak candlepower of 100 million–400 million from only $1/2$ to $1\frac{3}{4}$ lb of a suitable mixture, and photoflash bombs, such as one with an 85-lb charge weight, reach a peak of about 3000 million candles. The standard formula, identical in both cases, is as follows:

Formula 10—photoflash

Ingredients	%
aluminum, atomized	40
potassium perchlorate	30
barium nitrate	30

Its mixing and filling into bombs is done entirely under remote-control operation, a power blender being located above the open bomb body and its contents emptied into the bomb in an armored processing bay. The dispersion of the powder is aided by explosive action in order to create an effective fireball with more or less uniform distribution of the glowing particles. Even so, the light output in proportion to the weight and to the released heat energy is very small, much inferior to the light output from a flare. Coordination of the light with the opening and closing of the photographic shutter is a difficult problem. The actual period of useful light emission starts within a few milliseconds (msec) after initiation and is completed in about 40 msec. Because not only the preparation of the powder mixture but its mere presence in an aircraft is hazardous, certain schemes, such as the dispersion of metal powders by themselves, which then burn in the ambient air, have been employed, but their main drawback is inefficiency and also slowness of the development of the light compared with pyrotechnic mixtures.

Flash charges are also used as simulating and spotting devices; special formulations exist for effective light emission at high altitude for the purpose of plotting the trajectory of a missile. On the ground, such flash charges that simulate a gunflash or the explosion of a booby trap pose a problem, since they might cause unintended injuries. All explosive flash charges are also sound signals and are used in guerrilla warfare as a means to create confusion or diversion.

Smokes. Although this subject has been treated in the article Chemical warfare in Vol. 4, the strictly pyrotechnic aspect must be given some additional consideration. Smokes serve two purposes, obscuration and daytime signaling, paralleling the functions of light-production at night time. Obscuration, such as the hiding of advancing or retreating troops or the envelopment of a ship, requires such large amounts of aerosolized particles that it is not normally done by pyrotechnic means. An exception is the so-called HC smoke, which can serve small-scale screening action. Its formula is as follows:

Formula 11—HC smoke

Ingredients	%
aluminum	9.0
hexachloroethane (HC)	44.5
zinc oxide	46.5

Besides its advantage of needing no mechanical equipment and auxiliary power sources to develop and disperse the smoke, it is only slightly irritant and barely toxic under the conditions of short-time and occasional exposure. HC derives its signature from the compound hexachloroethane (C_2Cl_6). By reacting aluminum powder, zinc oxide, and hexachloroethane primarily in a thermitic reaction and secondarily with the organic compound, a grayish-white gas-colloidal mixture of aluminum oxide particles and zinc chloride droplets is produced. The color is caused by the presence of carbon, the amount of which depends on the ratio of the components, specifically the percentage of aluminum.

Signal smokes may be white or colored. Because all pyrotechnic flares or flashes are more or less smoky, a light signal may also be useful as a smoke signal. Spotting charges, which mark the impact of a practice bomb or projectile, may use merely the smoky flash from some black powder. The previously mentioned Marine Location Marker with phosphorus as the major fuel (Formula 4) is specifically designed to serve both as a white light and a white smoke signal. Most typical signal smokes are, however, brilliantly colored. They owe their existence to the fact that certain organic dyestuffs can be evaporated and recondensed, though not without partial decomposi-

Table 3. Formulas for Colored Smokes

Ingredients	%	%
	Formula 12	*Formula 13*
potassium chlorate	22–30	20–35
sulfur	8½–12	
confectioner's sugar		23–35
dye[a]	38–47	30–54
sodium bicarbonate	18–31½	0–15

[a] Examples of smoke dyes used most frequently, singly or in combination, are as follows:

auramine hydrochloride (yellow)	1-methylamino-4-*p*-toluidino-
1-aminoanthraquinone (red)	anthraquinone (blue)
1,4-diamino-2,3-dihydroanthra-	1,4-di-*p*-toluidinoanthraquinone
quinone (violet)	(green)

tion. The heat sources are relatively cool-burning, high-gassing mixtures of potassium chlorate and either sulfur (Formula 12, Table 3) or sugar (Formula 13, Table 3), often with a sizable amount of diluent added in the form of sodium bicarbonate. The best and most frequently used colors are yellow, orange, red, and violet; blue and green are less desirable.

Chlorate is needed in these mixtures as an oxidizer because it decomposes and reacts below red heat. The processing of those smoke mixtures that contain sulfur is hazardous but the large excess of potential fuel material in the form of the dye seems to mitigates this hazard. The sucrose-containing mixtures are relatively safe to process. Smoke dyes can also be dispersed by explosive action. Smoke mixtures containing inorganic pigments are known. Compositions quite similar to the sugar-containing colored smoke mixtures are used for the dispersion of irritants such as the formidable type CS. (See Vol. 4, p. 877.)

Miscellaneous Items. Military pyrotechnics embraces a variety of minor devices and applications, some on the borderline of pyrotechnics proper. Examples are destructive heat sources for incendiarism, sabotage, and the destruction of documents and "black boxes" (electronic devices) to prevent the material from being captured by hostile elements (12). Certain "gasless" (actually low-gassing) heat sources can be used to

Table 4. Formulas for a First Fire for High-Intensity Flares
(Formula 14) and Delay Mixtures (Formulas 15–17)

Ingredients	%	Ingredients	%
Formula 14—first fire		*Formula 16—delay time 9 sec/in.*	
silicon	20	manganese	37
zirconium hydride	15	barium chromate	20
tetranitrocarbazole (TNC)	10	lead chromate	43
barium nitrate	50		
Laminac	5	*Formula 17—delay time 40 sec/in.*	
		tungsten	27
Formula 15—delay time 2½ sec/in.		barium chromate	58
70% zirconium–30% nickel alloy[a]	54	potassium perchlorate	10
barium chromate	31	Superfloss[b]	5
potassium perchlorate	15		

[a] Alloys with different ratios of components are also useful for this type of formula.

[b] Trade name for calcined diatomaceous earth (Johns-Manville).

activate solid electrolyte batteries. (These, in contradistinction to ordinary galvanic cells, are entirely dormant in storage and thus become important stable "one-shot" power sources, which deliver current only when the solid salt mixture that forms the electrolyte is melted. See Vol. 3, p. 134.)

Igniters and delay columns are important accessories to pyrotechnic devices, rockets, and explosives (8–10). As examples, four formulas are given in Table 4; Formula 14 is the standardized first fire pressed on the above-described high-intensity candle whereas Formulas 15, 16, and 17 each represent a type of a low-gassing ("gasless") delay mixture. The ratio of components in these formulas can be varied to permit a certain range of burning times for each type. The linear burning times for delay mixtures are from about 1 to 40 sec/in. if tested in vented columns, but compositions exist for the millisecond range.

Civilian Pyrotechnics

Since military pyrotechnic devices and accessories are now extensively and routinely manufactured by private contractors to the government, the term "commercial pyrotechnics" has become somewhat ambiguous; the term "civilian pyrotechnics" is more descriptive. This is a quite limited field and is surrounded by secrecy entirely out of proportion to its commercial value and importance. The industry is divided into *fireworks manufacture*, concerning items for enjoyment, and *warning signals*. To these may be added certain novelties and minor items of insignificant sales volume such as enclosed "one-shot" heat cartridges for a soldering iron. One might also include here the photoflash bulb.

As a rule, civilian items are made with the least expensive materials in order to be competitively salable. Most of them are more vulnerable to atmospheric extremes and to physical abuse than are corresponding military devices. Certain chemicals that are shunned in military items except when unavoidably needed, such as potassium chlorate, are used in civilian items. (Chlorate mixtures are highly sensitive to explosive reaction by impact and become dangerous in the field because a bullet impact may destroy them and their surroundings.) The commercial value of utilitarian items is not known, but a survey of the fireworks industry (13) in 1960 for the United States disclosed a total value of $16 million of which $13 million was domestic, the remainder imported. Great Britain spends about 4 million pounds (sterling) annually, and Germany spends in excess of 30 million marks. A troublesome feature of the business is that consumption is always strongly concentrated in certain short periods of the year, in the U.S. on the Fourth of July and, in the South, on the days from Christmas to New Year's Day, in England on Guy Fawkes Day (5th of November), and in Germany on New Year's Eve (Silvester).

A cross between fireworks for amusement and utilitarian devices is the "special effects" in the motion picture and television industries—battle noises, conflagrations, volcanic activities, etc. They are a highly specialized branch of the fireworks industry.

Fireworks. The engravings of fireworks displays that have come to us from the eighteenth century and earlier (1) show vast stationary outlines of buildings as well as a profusion of rocketing and whirling light trails and stars, and, if any color effects were displayed, they must have been faint and limited in variety. The reason is that black powder was then the mainstay of the art and the now common brilliant color effects were unknown prior to the development of modern chemistry, ie the discovery of the elements strontium and barium and their salts, as well as other pure chemicals.

Only a highly condensed description of the fireworks art and a few representative formulas can be given here. The literature of fireworks, at least that which gives concrete and useful information rather than historical subject matter, is not large. Since the basic devices have to a large extent remained the same, even older works are of interest but not much of practical use has been published in the twentieth century. Davis' book on explosives (14) has a chapter on fireworks, and the monumental work on military pyrotechnics up to World War I by Faber (11) contains, surprisingly, extensive information on fireworks for pleasure. Weingart's book (2) is the one most strongly devoted to chemical and technical details. Long out of print, it is again (1967) available. Formulas 18–25 discussed below (given in Table 5) are from reference 9 but have actually been furnished by the Reverend Ronald Lancaster, a British fireworks expert. The newcomer to the field will find that to one part available information he has to add at least nine parts experience and tricks of the trade.

Basically, the fireworks art can be divided into light effects, sound effects, and miscellaneous novelties. Light can be characterized by its color and by its kinematic aspects—stationary, in linear motion, or whirling; steady flames or stars or those that disintegrate into a shower of sparks.

Tableau fires and *Bengal* illumination are stationary quiet-burning loose or lightly tamped powder mixtures that are used to illuminate actual buildings while the source of the light is hidden from the viewer. Formulas 18 and 19 show one example each of the red and the green variety. *Lances* are similar but faster burning. Arranged on a framework, they can outline pictures or letters. *Torches* are hand-held, larger lances, mostly white burning (Formula 20). They were formerly popular for parades and must be adjusted to safe and proper performance, eliminating sputtering, irregular burning, excessive smoke, or noxious fumes.

Stars are cylinders or cubes of more or less well-compacted and in general overall-burning compositions. They are propelled into the air singly or in clusters from black-powder rockets or successively from a tube containing propelling powder (roman candle). An ascending rocket displaying the simultaneous emission and ignition of a large number of stars sometimes followed by secondary clusters is probably the most impressive spectacle of the modern fireworks art and undoubtedly requires great care and skill in the manufacture. The largest of these displays are fired from mortars, some of which are of remarkable size. Formulas 21–24 are for a variety of colored stars.

Although colored lights for military purposes must be unequivocally identifiable as to the color designation, no such restriction pertains to fireworks for pleasure. Quite a large array of delicate shades such as lavender or purple are possible through the combination of color-producing compounds, and since the viewer is seldom very far from the emitting item and ordinarily views it on a clear night, the depth and variety of color add to the enjoyment.

No fireworks display is complete without the impressive spectacle of the brilliantly scintillating imitation of a waterfall. This requires setting up banks of tubes filled with a suitable composition (Formula 25). Safer mixtures, wherein the potassium chlorate is replaced by barium nitrate, are sometimes used.

Under the names of fountains, saxons, pinwheels, flower pots, and gerbs, various spark-expelling revolving pieces are found. The driving force as well as the light source is always a modified black powder with additives such as extra charcoal or lampblack for gold-spark effects.

Table 5. Typical Fireworks Formulas

Ingredients	%	Ingredients	%
Formula 18—tableau fire (red)		*Formula 22—green star*	
strontium nitrate	65	potassium chlorate	29
potassium chlorate	20	barium chlorate	53
shellac (powdered)	15	red gum	9½
		charcoal	4½
		dextrin	4
Formula 19—Bengal illumination (green)			
barium nitrate	70	*Formula 23—red star*	
potassium chlorate	16	potassium perchlorate	70
red gum	13	red gum	9
paraffin oil	1	charcoal	2
		dextrin	4
Formula 20—torch (white)		strontium carbonate	15
barium nitrate	76	*Formula 24—yellow star*	
sulfur	4	potassium perchlorate	70
petrolatum	2	red gum	6
aluminum (fine dark pyro)	18	shellac	6
		dextrin	4
Formula 21—blue star		sodium oxalate	14
potassium chlorate	68		
rosin	6	*Formula 25—waterfall[a]*	
dextrin	4	potassium chlorate	72
paris green	22	aluminum	28

[a] The mixture is "damped" with a solution of 10% shellac in alcohol.

Noisemakers. To heighten the excitement of a fireworks display, noisemakers are used. Such items are also sold to and used by children, often illegally, and are not infrequently the cause of accidents. Because of the hazards of these items, both in manufacture and in use, no formulas are given here so as not to encourage youthful amateurs. The moderately large "salute" firecracker and other varieties not only serve as items of amusement but also can be employed to simulate real military skirmishes in the field, make maneuvers more realistic, or provide the proper illusion in battle scenes in motion pictures.

A different kind of noisemaker is the pyrotechnic *whistle*, which is attached to some fireworks but has also found military use as a shell-approach simulant. The effect is based on the fact that certain organic compounds can decompose with development of much gas but in a manner of rapidly alternating decrepitation and suppression of decomposition when reacted with an oxidizer (14a). Because this oxidizer is generally potassium chlorate, the mixtures are hazardous to manufacture, but the pyrotechnic whistle normally behaves properly, at least in its customary small size. The mixture is compacted in a narrow, short, cardboard tube. The manufacture of the item so that it functions properly is rather tricky. The formula is as follows:

Formula 26—whistling compound

Ingredients	%
potassium chlorate	73
gallic acid	24
red gum	3

Table 6. Two Formulas for Sparklers

Ingredients	%
Formula 27	
potassium perchlorate	60
aluminum	30
dextrin	10
Formula 28	
barium nitrate	50
aluminum	8
dextrin	10
steel (filings)	30
charcoal	$\frac{1}{2}$
neutralizer	$1\frac{1}{2}$

Miscellaneous Devices. In order to start display fireworks devices at the proper moment, the older way was to ignite a black-powder-impregnated cotton thread leading to the ignition mixture of the device. This fuse train (quickmatch) burns steadily at a rather slow rate but if enveloped in a narrow paper tube (piped match), fire transfer is nearly instantaneous, thus permitting several effects to be initiated at the same time. The same goal can be achieved with a so-called electric match or squib when electric circuitry is provided.

Of minor devices, one of the least harmful is the popular *sparkler* for which two formulas are given in Table 6 (Formulas 27 and 28). Since, however, sparklers may contain the toxic barium nitrate aside from the presence of moderately toxic potassium salts, they should not be regarded as entirely innocuous for small children.

Finally, a few minor items, such as *Pharaoh's Serpents*, are generally treated in connection with civilian pyrotechnics. This is a small pellet that on ignition smolders and leaves a prodigiously expanded residue. It is prepared from a certain type of nitrated pitch. Formerly, mercuric thiocyanate, $Hg(CNS)_2$, was used, but this compound is highly toxic and also expensive.

Special *matches* with elongated bulbs appear occasionally on the market. They may display a colored flame (Bengal matches), emit a perfume of sorts, or provide a prolonged wind-resistant flame and glow. Technically, these are true miniature fireworks items with an added match tip, not matches.

Utilitarian Devices. As ground warning signals for an approaching railroad train and also on the highway to indicate the proximity of a temporary obstruction, the red-burning *railroad* or *highway fusee* is a standard item. It is manufactured in a variety of burning times from 5 to 30 min, the intermediate sizes being the most popular. A specification issued by the Bureau of Explosives of the Association of American Railroads (15) covers numerous requirements of performance, eg, ability to withstand exposure to short immersion in water, to elevated temperature, etc.

The fusee consists of a slender cardboard tube closed with a bottom plug that often contains a spike in order to emplace the flare by sticking it into the ground. It functions best when in a slightly inclined position with the flame pointing upward, but more recently flares without spikes have been sold to be placed flat on the ground or used as hand-held devices, eg over water. A button-shaped safety-match mixture is embedded into the top layer of the composition, which is similar to the flare mixture but of easier ignitability. The whole tip is covered by a cardboard cap whose top is a wooden plug on which the match-striker mixture is painted. This surface as well as

Table 7. Formulas for Railroad Fusee and Railroad Track Torpedo

Ingredients	%	Ingredients	%
Formula 29—railroad fusee		*Formula 30—railroad track torpedo*	
strontium nitrate	74	potassium chlorate	40
potassium perchlorate	6	sulfur	16
sulfur	10	sand	37
grease or wax	2–6	binder	5
sawdust	4–8	neutralizer	2

the juncture of flare body and cap is protected by a paper sleeve in which is embedded a black cambric tear strip.

The candle composition, Formula 29 (given in Table 7), is an inexpensive metal-free mixture. It burns slowly with a moderately luminous (required minimum 70 candlepower) flame and leaves a large molten residue. The latter drops off during burning or is ejected with slight sputtering. Under unfavorable conditions, the ash builds up in such a way as to form a chimney (or "scoria"). This causes partial obscuration of the bright-red flame until the sintered tubular residue breaks off.

The *railroad* or *track torpedo* is an auditory warning device set off by the impact of a railroad engine wheel. In its American version it consists of a tablet of an explosive pyrotechnic mixture wrapped in water-resistant paper. A lead or aluminum strip permits affixing the device to the rail.

Certain conditions of sensitivity limits have to be met so that the item performs reliably but is not too hazardous on ordinary handling. Its explosion must create a minimum sound level of 105 dB at a distance of 20 ft. The whole device must be so designed that no damaging pieces or particles are dispersed by the explosion. These and other conditions are spelled out in a commercial specification (16).

Formula 30 (Table 7) shows that the explosive mixture consists essentially of potassium chlorate and sulfur. An adhesive, which may be a cellulose nitrate lacquer or a hydrophilic binder, aids in forming and strengthening the pellet, the fine sand increases impact sensitivity, and a neutralizing agent such as ground limestone counteracts any tendency of the mixture to self-destructive decomposition under the influence of moisture. There are some formulas that contain sawdust as a cushioning additive to prevent accidental explosion during transportation and other handling.

Flare and *smoke signals* similar to the ones for military uses are being sold as distress signals for hikers and boat owners. Recently, some miniaturized red-light signals shot from a small cartridge with the help of a fountain-pen-size launcher have been marketed and have also attracted the interest of the military. The U.S. Coast Guard has standardized certain fairly large orange *smoke canisters* as daytime distress signals.

An interesting newer item is a hand-held *underwater flare*. Its major distinguishing feature is a battery-operated and hence completely self-contained electric initiator protected by a rubber diaphragm.

One might also mention here the commercial *photoflash bulb* as a borderline case of a pyrotechnic device and an unusual one at that. It employs shredded thin aluminum or zirconium foil or wire and pure oxygen at less than atmospheric pressure within a glass bulb that for safety's sake is coated with heat-resistant lacquer. Electric current initiates a first-fire mixture, which then sets off the instantaneous combustion of the metal in oxygen.

Miscellaneous Civilian Items. Pyrotechnic mixtures as fire starters have appeared in the patent literature but undoubtedly their storing and handling creates enough undesirable features to forbid their commercial exploitation, the more so since easily ignitable fuel-type materials are just as useful.

A more desirable item is a completely enclosed cartridge that can be inserted in a special soldering iron.   On retracting and releasing a spring-loaded firing pin, a percussion primer on the cartridge actuates its thermitic "heat powder" content whereupon the copper tip of the soldering iron becomes heated for several minutes to about 800°F.   The cartridge is claimed to release 10,000 cal and is relatively inexpensive.

Formerly frequently used were vulcanizing patches containing a cool-burning mixture of potassium nitrate, sugar, and a binder whose smoldering reaction gave adequate heat for the quick vulcanization of freshly repaired automobile inner tubes.

Small smoke cartridges claimed to be nontoxic and suitable for indoor use are sold commercially for the purpose of detecting leaks in air ducts or for following visually the airflow from an air-conditioning or heating system.   Such smoke generators burn from 1 to 5 min and are claimed to emit from 8000 to 100,000 ft^3 of smoke.

Bibliography

"Pyrotechnics" in *ECT* 1st ed., Vol. 11: "Military Pyrotechnics," pp. 322–332, by David Hart, Picatinny Arsenal; "Commercial Pyrotechnics," pp. 332–338, V. C. Allison, Aerial Products, Inc.

1. A. St H. Brock, *A History of Fireworks*, George G. Harrap & Co., Ltd., London, 1949.
2. G. W. Weingart, *Pyrotechnics*, 2nd ed., Chemical Publishing Co., Inc., New York, 1947.
3. Colonnello Dott. Attilio Izzo, ed., *Pirotecnia e Fuochi Artificiali*, Ulrico Hoepli, Milan, 1950.
4. J. R. Partington, *A History of Greek Fire and Gunpowder*, W. Heffer & Sons, Ltd., Cambridge, 1960.
5. Vannoccio Biringuccio, *The Pirotechnia* (Engl. trans.), Basic Books, Inc., New York, reissued 1959 (originally printed in Venice in 1540).   Also available in paperback edition from MIT Press, Cambridge, Mass., 1966.
6. A. A. Shidlovsky, *Osnovy Pirotekhniki*, 2nd ed., Moscow, 1954 (available in translation, as *Foundation of Pyrotechnics*, AD 602687, from Wright Patterson Air Force Base, Ohio (1964)).
7. A. A. Shidlovsky, *Osnovy Pirotekhniki*, 3rd ed., Moscow, 1964 (translated by U.S. Joint Publication Research Service, Feltman Research Laboratories, Picatinny Arsenal, Dover, N.J., as *Fundamentals of Pyrotechnics*, Technical Memo 1615 (May 1965)).
8. Herbert Ellern, *Modern Pyrotechnics*, Chemical Publishing Co., Inc., New York, 1961.
9. Herbert Ellern, *Military and Civilian Pyrotechnics*, Chemical Publishing Co., Inc., New York, 1968.
10. Frank B. Pollard and Jack H. Arnold, Jr., eds., *Aerospace Ordnance Handbook*, Prentice-Hall, Inc., Englewood Cliffs, N.J., 1966.
11. Henry B. Faber, *Military Pyrotechnics*, 3 vols., U.S. Government Printing Office, Washington, D.C., 1919.
12. H. Ellern, "Destruction by Pyrochemical Action," *Weapons Technology*, (Nov. 1960).
13. "Fireworks: No Boom," *Chem. Week* **87**, 55 (July 2, 1960).
14. T. L. Davis, *The Chemistry of Powder and Explosives*, John Wiley & Sons, Inc., New York, 1941.
14a. W. R. Maxwell, *Paper, Fourth Symposium on Combustion, Cambridge, Mass., 1952*, Williams & Wilkins, Baltimore, Md. (1953).
15. *Specification for Red Railroad Fusees or Red Highway Fusees*, Bureau of Explosives of the Association of American Railroads, revised May 1, 1959.
16. *Specifications for Standard Track Torpedoes*, Bureau of Explosives of the Association of American Railroads, revised Feb. 1, 1949.

HERBERT ELLERN
Pyrotechnic Consultant
formerly UMC Industries, Inc.

PYRRHOTITE, FeS.   See Vol. 12, p. 6.

PYRROLE AND PYRROLE DERIVATIVES

Runge, in 1834, first reported (1) the existence of pyrrole (azole), as the product obtained from the distillation of coal tar, bone oil, or proteins. This material was presumed responsible for imparting a red color to pine shavings previously dipped in hydrochloric acid. Because of this bright red color Runge called this substance *pyrrole* (Greek, "red oil"). In 1858 Anderson (2) characterized this substance and in 1870 Baeyer (3) determined its composition.

A description of the various positions in the pyrrole ring is based on numbers or on Greek letters, with the numbering system supplanting the older system of Greek letters.

pyrrole

Interest in the chemistry of pyrrole and its derivatives was originally stimulated by the discovery that indole (qv), which is benzopyrrole, is the fundamental nucleus in indigo (see Dyes, natural; Indigoid dyes). The pyrrole nucleus is of biological importance because it is the building block of several natural pigments, such as heme, chlorophyll (qv), and bile pigments (see Vol. 3, p. 481), as well as of certain amino acids (qv), namely proline and hydroxyproline, and of many alkaloids (qv) and enzymes (qv).

Health and Safety Factors. The acute oral toxicity of pyrrole is not excessive. Tests indicate that it has a moderate cumulative toxicity. Workers with abnormal respiratory, circulatory, or liver conditions should not be exposed to pyrrole. Contact with the skin should be avoided (4). When heated in air to decomposition, pyrrole, much as all nitrogen-containing organic materials, emits highly toxic fumes of oxides of nitrogen. Pyrrole can also react violently with oxidizing agents (5).

Physical Properties of Pyrrole

Pyrrole is a colorless liquid with an odor often described as suggestive of chloroform. However, many feel the musty smell is more reminiscent of an old tobacco pipe. Pyrrole darkens on standing in air, finally producing a dark-brown resin. It may be preserved by storage under ammonia.

Pyrrole has a high degree of "aromatic character" by virtue of its "aromatic sextet" of electrons and is isoelectronic with the cyclopentadienyl anion. Pyrrole is a weaker base than pyridine. The aromatic character is destroyed by the addition of acids and the resultant diene polymerizes. This extreme reactivity requires special conditions for many of the common electrophilic substitution reactions with pyrrole. Pyrrole is also a weak acid whose conjugate base is stabilized by delocalization of negative charge through the ring. This anion is probably an intermediate in a number of nucleophilic substitution reactions of pyrrole.

Pyrrole can be represented by several resonating formulas to explain its lack of basicity, its acidity, and its pronounced aromatic character.

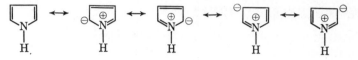

The resonance energy of pyrrole has recently been calculated from thermochemical data (6). These data, however, were not corrected for the formation of oxides of nitrogen during combustion. Simonetta derived a more exact value (24.7 kcal/mole) from a molecular orbital calculation (49). The resonance energy value generally accepted today is 24.5 kcal/mole (50).

Some other physical properties of pyrrole are given in Table 1.

Table 1. Physical Properties of Pyrrole

melting point, °C	-24
boiling point, °C	130–131
specific gravity, 20/4°C	0.9691
refractive index, n_D^{20}	1.5085
dipole moment, μ as a gas	1.84
in benzene	1.80
Reid modified vapor pressure, psi	0.25 (± 0.05)
flash point (Tag closed cup), °C	39
dielectric constant, ϵ, at 20°C	8.00

The dielectric constant has also been measured as a function of temperature in the range 16–84°C (7). The critical temperature (T_c) of pyrrole has been determined by the sealed-tube method; T_c and T_c/T_{bp} are 639.7°K and 1.59, respectively (8). Vapor-pressure data and critical data have been determined at a pressure of up to 60 atm (9). The viscosities of pyrrole and pyrrolidine have been measured over a temperature range from their freezing points to about 70°C. Viscosity plotted against temperature indicates that the degree of association increases gradually with a decrease in temperature (10).

The pK_a of pyrrole has been determined spectrophotometrically by the Hammett H_0 indicator method and was found to be -0.27 (11).

Numerous spectroscopic studies have been carried out on the pyrrole nucleus. For a detailed description of these data the reader is directed to the general references at the end of this article.

Pyrrole is only slightly soluble in water (8 g in 100 g H_2O at 25°C) but is readily soluble in most organic solvents. Pyrrole is insoluble in aqueous alkali; it dissolves slowly in acids with polymerization. The picrate melts at 69°C (dec) and the trinitrobenzene adduct at 95°C.

Synthesis of Pyrroles

One of two general approaches to the pyrrole nucleus involves formation of one or both of the carbon–nitrogen bonds starting with a four-carbon-chain compound. This approach is limited in its general application and in the availability of appropriate starting materials. The more useful and general syntheses involve formation of one of the carbon–carbon bonds and a carbon–nitrogen bond.

Knorr Synthesis. One of the broadly applicable ring closures leading to the pyrrole nucleus is the Knorr synthesis (12), which involves condensation of an α-aminoketone with a ketone having a reactive methylene group alpha to the carbonyl.

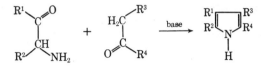

The limitations of the Knorr synthesis may be summarized as follows:

1. R^1 may be alkyl, aryl, acyl, or carbalkoxy without seriously affecting the yield.

2. When R^2 is hydrogen or alkyl or aryl, however, the reaction may be useful but the yields may be unsatisfactory. When R^2 is acyl or carbalkoxy, the yields are excellent.

3. When R^3 is alkyl, the yields are poor or negligible. When R^3 is acyl or carbalkoxy the yields are excellent.

4. When R^4 is alkyl, aryl, acyl, or carbalkoxy, the yields are excellent. The tendency of α-aminoketones toward self-condensation to pyrazines is overcome by reducing an α-oximinoketone in the presence of a suitable ketone.

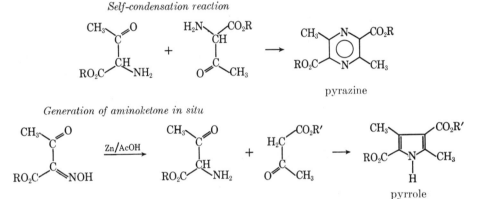

The course of this condensation can be controlled by controlling the pH of the condensing medium.

Paal-Knorr Synthesis. The Paal-Knorr pyrrole synthesis involves the condensation of 1,4-dicarbonyl compounds with primary amines and ammonia. A variety of amines have been successfully used, including hydrazine and hydroxylamine.

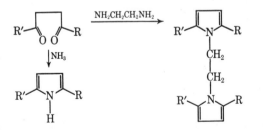

This reaction is not limited to dicarbonyl compounds. The appropriate monocarbonyl alcohol can be dehydrated over a palladium–alumina catalyst at 450°C in the presence of ammonia to give the corresponding pyrrole.

Hydroxypyrroles and Other Pyrrole Derivatives. In a similar condensation, monoacyl or hydroxymethylenesuccinic esters yield 2-hydroxypyrroles when heated with ammonia or amines (13).

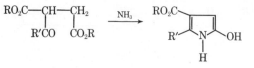

The 3-hydroxypyrroles can be prepared from the appropriate hydroxydicarbonyl compounds.   These 3-hydroxypyrroles usually exist as the 3-ketopyrrolines.

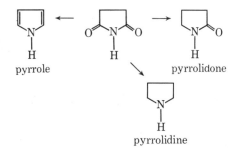

Derivatives of 3-hydroxy-1-phenylpyrrole, however, in which the 2 position is unsubstituted so that interannular conjugation is possible between the two rings, appear to exist in the hydroxypyrrole form (14).   Starting with succinimide it is possible to prepare various members in the pyrrole series.   On distilling succinimide with zinc dust, pyrrole is formed; reduction with sodium in alcohol gives pyrrolidine; while electrolytic reduction or catalytic hydrogenation produces pyrrolidone.

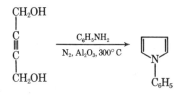

Miscellaneous Reactions.   A number of reactions involving acetylenic derivatives lead to pyrrole.   Thus vinylacetylene epoxides react with various amines to give the pyrrole ring (15).

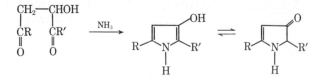

Another method similar to that developed by Reppe converts 2-butyne-1,4-diol into 1-phenylpyrrole by heating the acetylene to 300°C with aniline in the presence of alumina (16).

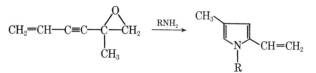

α-Aminoketones and acetylenedicarboxylic esters cyclize and dehydrate to give pyrroles in high yield (17).

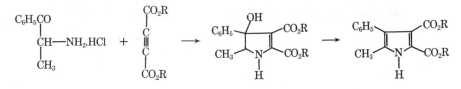

Acetylenedicarboxylic esters also react with phenylhydroxylamines to give pyrroles (18).

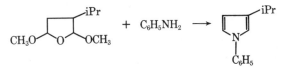

Pyrrole as well as 1,2-, 2,5-, and 1,2,5-substituted pyrroles also were prepared in good yields from butadiyne and mono- and disubstituted butadiynes by reacting the diacetylenes with ammonia or primary aliphatic and aromatic amines in the presence of catalytic amounts of cuprous chloride at 140–160°C (19).

An important set of reactions leading to pyrrole and the reduced pyrrole derivatives, pyrroline and pyrrolidine, is the conversion of furans and reduced furans (20) in the presence of a large excess of ammonia or an amine in the vapor phase over alumina at approx 400°C. Derivatives of tetrahydrofuran form pyrrolidine when treated with ammonia or amines at elevated temperatures. If the tetrahydrofuran contains labile substituents, aromatization of the pyrrolidine to pyrrole takes place. Thus, 2,5-dimethoxy-3-isopropyltetrahydrofuran gives 1-phenyl-3-isopropylpyrrole when refluxed with aniline in acetic anhydride.

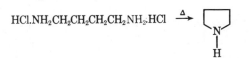

Pyrrolidines are also obtained from 1,4-dihydroxyalkanes by a similar pathway. When these are treated with dehydrating agents in the presence of ammonia or amines at elevated temperatures, pyrrolidines are formed, presumably through a tetrahydrofuran intermediate (21). Since furfural and furfuryl derivatives are 2-substituted furans they exhibit similar conversions to pyrroles.

Finally pyrroles can be prepared by dehydrogenation of pyrroline or pyrrolidine with various catalysts generally used for the dehydrogenation of cyclic amines. Pyrroles can also be hydrogenated to pyrroline and pyrrolidine. These reductions are discussed under Chemical reactions of pyrroles.

Pyrrolidines (tetrahydropyrroles) are prepared by the reaction of primary amines with 1,4-dihalides, or benzenesulfonic esters of 1,4-diols. The dry distillation of 1,4-diamine hydrochlorides also generates pyrrolidines.

$$\text{HCl.NH}_2\text{CH}_2\text{CH}_2\text{CH}_2\text{CH}_2\text{NH}_2\text{.HCl} \xrightarrow{\Delta}$$

The action of a Grignard reagent upon γ-halonitriles gives pyrrolines (dihydropyrroles).

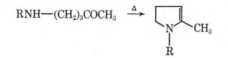

Pyrrolines are also produced from γ-aminoketones.

$$RNH-(CH_2)_3COCH_3 \xrightarrow{\Delta}$$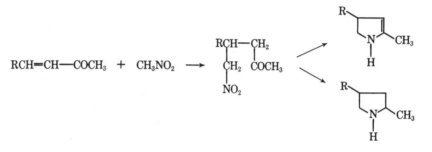

Reduction of the addition product of a nitroalkane and an α,β-unsaturated ketone leads to a pyrroline (22) or a pyrrolidine (23).

If an α,β-unsaturated ester is used in place of the ketone, a pyrrolidone is formed (24). It should be noted that 2-pyrrolidones are α-lactams, and therefore all reactions leading to lactams are pertinent.

Chemical Reactions of Pyrroles

Pyrrole is a highly reactive organic compound. In spite of this high reactivity, its character is decidedly aromatic. Typical olefin reactions do not occur; hydrogenation of the pyrrole nucleus is not easy; and in ordinary Diels-Alder reactions pyrrole does not act as a diene. N-Benzylpyrrole, however, has been condensed with acetylenedicarboxylic acid (45).

Pyrrole derivatives behave much like phenol or resorcinol in their substitution reactions, readily undergoing nitration, halogenation, diazo coupling, and such aromatic substitutions as the Gattermann, Hoesch, Reimer-Tiemann, and Mannich reactions.

Generally the α position is preferentially attacked; if the α position is blocked, substitution at the β position takes place without difficulty.

Alkylation. Alkylpyrroles are generally prepared by the Knorr synthesis, but there are also a number of direct alkylations involving the pyrrole nucleus. Pyrroles can be alkylated with methyl iodide, acyl or carboxyl groups may be reduced to alkyl groups, and alcoholic sodium alkoxides alkylate certain pyrrole derivatives (25).

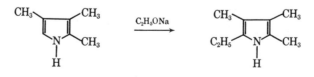

Diarylcarbinols and triarylcarbinols condense with pyrrole under mild conditions.

The lower alkyl halides give *N*-alkylation. The resulting *N*-alkyl- and *N*-aryl-pyrroles at a red heat give the 2 isomers. Allyl bromide and the potassium salt of pyrrole form 2-allylpyrrole, while propargyl bromide and the potassium salt give *N*-propargylpyrrole. As the number of alkyl groups increases, the pyrrole nucleus becomes more basic, less stable in air, and less rapidly polymerized by acids.

In general, to prepare *N*-derivatives of pyrrole it is first necessary to convert pyrrole to a metallic salt by the action of a basic reagent. Thus, in the presence of alkali, pyrrole unites with acrylonitrile to give β-*N*-pyrrylpropionitrile and with acetylene to give *N*-vinylpyrrole. An important class of compounds are those prepared by the action of Grignard reagents on pyrrole, the reaction not being confined to nitrogen.

Halogenation. Halopyrroles are prepared by the action of sulfuryl chloride, bromine in alcohol or acetic acid, or iodine in potassium iodide. It is difficult to stop the reaction until complete halogenation occurs. The halogen atom is usually firmly held by the pyrrole nucleus. In the bromination of pyrroles which have 2-methyl substituents dipyrrylmethenes are formed (26). This is one of the most frequently used preparative methods for these intermediates.

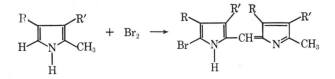

When the pyrrole ring is substituted with a sulfonic acid residue, treatment with halogen eliminates and replaces the sulfonic acid by a keto group (27).

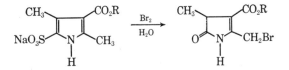

Iodopyrroles serve as convenient intermediates since the iodine is easily replaced by hydrogen, bromine, chlorine, aryl, azo, nitro, and CH_2R groups. Tetraiodopyrrole is the antiseptic Iodol (Winthrop Laboratories).

Oxidation. Pyrroles containing β substituents are oxidized by chromic–sulfuric acid mixtures to maleimides.

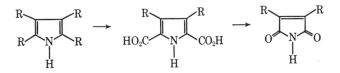

Under certain conditions β-alkyl substituents survive oxidations; substituents in the α position are oxidized to carboxyl and then eliminated with further oxidation. Peroxide and potassium dichromate oxidations cause ring openings. The peroxide oxidation product of pyrrole has recently been characterized (48).

Reductions. When pyrrole is treated with hydriodic acid and red phosphorus, some 3-pyrroline (2,5-dihydropyrrole) is formed and the main product is pyrrolidine (tetrahydropyrrole).

Treatment with zinc and hydrochloric acid gives a better yield of pyrrolidine. The 3-pyrrolines are usually obtained by direct reduction of pyrrole, while the 2-pyrrolines are usually formed by ring-closure reactions. Pyrrolines can be reduced to pyrrolidines by low-pressure hydrogenation over Raney nickel.

Ring Openings and Enlargements. The common ring openings of pyrrole involve the carbon–nitrogen bond. With hydroxylamine hydrochloride and sodium bicarbonate, pyrroles are converted to 2,5-dioximes.

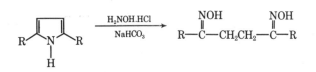

Phosphorus pentachloride opens isonitrosopyrroles to diamines. Oxidation of pyrrole with hydrogen peroxide in acetic acid yields aldehydes, acids, and lactones. Ultraviolet irradiation has been used to rearrange 2,3,5-triphenylpyrrole to a pyrimidine. The same rearrangement has been observed when pyrrole is allowed to stand for long periods of time in the presence of amines or ammonia. Pyridine is formed in 32% yields as a by-product in the Reimer-Tiemann reaction.

Detection of Pyrroles. Besides the physical methods available (infrared, ultraviolet, NMR, and mass spectroscopy) there are several chemical tests used to identify pyrrole.

The best-known test for pyrrole is the red-to-violet color produced when it is brought in contact with a wood splint moistened with acid. A light-colored wood generally provides better color contrast. Suitable furans also give a color change, but the resulting shade is of a greenish rather than a reddish hue.

When pyrrole is treated with an aqueous isatin solution containing dilute sulfuric acid, a deep-blue precipitate is formed. This precipitate is soluble in glacial acetic or concentrated sulfuric acid, giving a deep-blue solution. This reaction is also positive for thiophene and for vicinal dicarbonyl compounds.

Both pyrrole and indole react with selenium dioxide in the presence of nitric acid to give a deep-violet solution. This method can be used to detect 0.00004 g of pyrrole.

Important Derivatives of Pyrrole

HYDROXYPYRROLES

The hydroxypyrroles (see also p. 843) are an important class of compounds related to the bile pigments. Pyrroles with hydroxyl groups on side chains substituted on the nitrogen are best prepared by the Paal-Knorr cyclization (see p. 843). Pyrroles with hydroxyl groups on carbon side chains have been made by reducing the appropriate carbonyl compound with lithium aluminum hydride, by Grignard synthesis, by reaction with ethylene oxides, or with formaldehyde in alkaline solution.

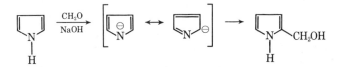

The hydroxymethylpyrroles do not behave as normal primary alcohols because any carbonium ion generated is resonance-stabilized.

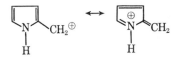

Hydroxyl groups substituted on the pyrrole nucleus in the α position are prepared from acylsuccinic esters or by the oxidation of pyrrole homologs. These 2-hydroxy-pyrroles do not behave as phenols.

The 3-hydroxypyrroles are prepared by the reaction of chloroacetyl chloride with β-aminocrotonates, or the Schiff bases of β-ketoesters (β-diketones or β-ketoaldehydes) with α-aminoesters. These 3-hydroxypyrroles are very reactive. From their reactions and physical properties they are best represented by a polar formula:

They give some reactions of alcohols but no ketone reactions. They are intermediates for dipyrryltrimethine dyes, pyrrolopyrrylium compounds, and α- and γ-pyranopyr-roles.

PYRROLE ALDEHYDES AND KETONES

Pyrrole aldehydes are prepared by the Gattermann, Houben-Hoesch, Reimer-Tie-mann, and Friedel-Crafts acylation reactions. The most common way of preparing pyrrole ketones is a ring-closure reaction. Other alternatives involve isomerization of N-acylpyrroles to 2-pyrrole ketones and reaction of pyrryl Grignard reagents with acid chlorides, anhydrides, or esters.

The pyrrole aldehydes are important synthetic intermediates in the pyrrole series. The formyl group is readily reduced to methyl. Sodium borohydride or lithium alumi-num hydride reduces the carbonyl to carbinol. Dilute sulfuric acid oxidizes the alde-hyde to the corresponding carboxylic acid. The aldoxime can be dehydrated to the nitrile. An important reaction of the pyrrole aldehydes is the preparation of dipyrryl-methenes and porphyrins.

Pyrrole ketones show normal carbonyl reactions. Some of the methyl ketones split off the acyl group in hot dilute acids.

PYRROLE CARBOXYLIC ACIDS AND DERIVATIVES

Pyrrole carboxylic esters are usually prepared by one of the general cyclization reactions of the appropriate compounds. The —$CONH_2$ group can be inserted by treatment with carbamyl chloride. The 2-methyl group can be halogenated and hydrolyzed to carboxyl. The N-substituted pyrroles are attainable through amino acids.

The acids easily lose carbon dioxide, the α compounds even on heating in water. Dilute base removes carboxyl and ester groups. Selective hydrolysis of carboxylic esters is possible owing to the difference in reactivity related to position. Esterification of acids and reduction of esters and amides has been described in the literature.

NITRO-, NITROSO-, AMINO- AND AZOPYRROLES

Mono- and dinitropyrroles are prepared by the classical method of nitration, with nitric and sulfuric acids or acetic anhydride. The nitropyrroles are colorless or pale yellow, fairly stable, and soluble in base.

Nitrosopyrroles are prepared with nitrous acid or amyl nitrite and sodium ethoxide. Controlled oxidation and reduction are possible as are alkylation and acylation.

Aminopyrroles are obtained from the nitropyrroles or nitrosopyrroles. The N-aminopyrroles are obtained from appropriate cyclization reactions. Mono- and dialkylaminopyrroles are obtained through the Mannich reaction. The amines are colorless bases which can be alkylated, acylated, and diazotized.

Azopyrroles are prepared by the azo coupling reaction. It has been shown that the 2 position is more reactive to coupling than the 3 position; the 2-azo dyes, however, are less stable to light and air than are the 3-azo dyes. The 2-azopyrroles can be distinguished from the 3-azopyrroles by testing with p-nitrobenzenediazonium salts.

PYRROLINE (DIHYDROPYRROLE) AND PYRROLIDINE (TETRAHYDROPYRROLE)

Pyrrolines are water-soluble bases which can exist in three isomeric forms.

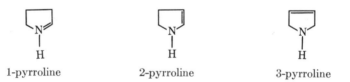

1-pyrroline   2-pyrroline   3-pyrroline

The 1- and 2-pyrrolines are unstable, forming resins on exposure to air or on distillation. The 3-pyrrolines are more stable. The ketopyrrolines are tautomeric with the hydroxypyrroles.

Physical Properties of 3-Pyrroline: bp, at 760 mm, 91°C; sp gr, 28/4°C, 0.9097; refractive index, n_D^{20}, 1.4664.

Pyrrolidines are stable, strong bases and have all the properties of secondary cyclic amines. Pyrrolidine, itself, is water-soluble with an odor like piperidine.

Physical Properties of Pyrrolidine: bp, at 760 mm, 88.5–88.9°C; sp gr, 22/4°C, 0.8520; refractive index, n_D^{15}, 1.4270.

Derivatives. The β-hydroxypyrrolidines are stable and behave like alcohols while the α-hydroxypyrrolidines readily lose water, forming pyrrolines. An important class of pyrrolidines are the α-ketopyrrolidines. These compounds are known as pyrrolidones.

PYRROLIDONES

The synthetic products of the pyrrolidine series which have found the greatest commercial utility are the derivatives of 2-pyrrolidinone (commonly called 2-pyrrolidone). These lactams have developed many large-scale uses and are available in the United States in tank-car quantities.

2-Pyrrolidone is a colorless, high-boiling polar solvent and chemical intermediate. It serves as a solvent for many organic compounds and is completely miscible with water, ether, alcohols, esters, ketones, and chlorinated and aromatic hydrocarbons. Physical properties are given in Table 2.

Table 2. Physical Properties of 2-Pyrrolidone

bp, °C, at 760 mm	245	refractive index, n_D^{25}	1.486
at 10 mm	122	viscosity, at 25°C, cP	13.3
mp, °C	25	flash point (Tag open	
sp gr, 25/4°C	1.107	cup), °C	129.4

Reactions. 2-Pyrrolidone forms alkali metal salts by direct reaction with alkali metals, or with their alkoxides, or even with their hydroxides under conditions in which the water of reaction is removed. Such salts have been suggested as catalysts for the polymerization of caprolactam (29). The mercuric salt also has been described, as has the *N*-bromo derivative (30).

2-Pyrrolidone can be polymerized to polypyrrolidone, "nylon-4," a high-molecular-weight linear polyamide of potential interest as a textile fiber, film former, and molding compound (31).

$$\underline{NHCH_2CH_2CH_2CO} \rightarrow \underline{+NHCH_2CH_2CH_2CO+}_n$$

It can be hydrolyzed, with strong acids or alkalis as catalyst, to 4-aminobutyric acid, an amino acid involved in the functioning of the brain and nervous system, and of considerable interest as a potential dietary supplement.

$$\underline{NHCH_2CH_2CH_2CO} \xrightarrow{H_2O} NH_2CH_2CH_2CH_2COOH$$

It can be alkylated by forming the alkali metal salt and reacting with an alkyl halide (32).

$$\underline{NaNCH_2CH_2CH_2CO} \xrightarrow{RX} \underline{RNCH_2CH_2CH_2CO}$$

It can be acylated by reaction with an acid anhydride or acyl halide (30).

$$\underline{HNCH_2CH_2CH_2CO} \xrightarrow{acetic\ anhydride} \underline{CH_3CONCH_2CH_2CH_2CO}$$

Alkali-catalyzed reaction with paraformaldehyde gives *N*-methylol-2-pyrrolidone (33).

$$\underline{HNCH_2CH_2CH_2CO} \rightarrow \underline{HOCH_2NCH_2CH_2CH_2CO}$$

Manufacture. 2-Pyrrolidone is manufactured by the reaction of butyrolactone and ammonia. It is produced domestically by GAF Corporation, and is also manufactured in Germany. The bulk price was listed at 62¢/lb, in October 1967.

Toxicity. 2-Pyrrolidone is a mild primary skin irritant with some fatiguing properties which are overshadowed by definite sensitizing properties. Prompt removal from the skin by washing with soap and water is advisable.

It is only very moderately toxic. Acute oral toxicity studies on white rats and guinea pigs gave the following values: LD_0, 4.0 ml/kg; LD_{50}, 6.5 ml/kg; and LD_{100}, 9.5 ml/kg.

N-Methyl-2-Pyrrolidone is a colorless, high-boiling liquid showing many valuable properties as a medium for chemical reactions and as an industrial solvent. It is completely miscible with water, ether, alcohols, esters, ketones, and chlorinated and aromatic hydrocarbons. For physical properties of N-methyl-2-pyrrolidone see Table 3.

Table 3. Physical Properties of N-Methyl-2-Pyrrolidone

bp, °C, at 760 mm	202	refractive index, n_D^{25}	1.469
at 10 mm	78	viscosity, at 25°C, cP	1.65
fp, °C	−24.4	flash point (Tag open	
sp gr, 25/4°C	1.027	cup), °C	95

Reactions.   N-Methyl-2-pyrrolidone behaves as a very weak base and forms a hydrochloride (mp 80–88°C) which can be recrystallized from absolute alcohol.

Although very stable to hydrolysis, it can be hydrolyzed with strong acids or alkalis as catalyst to 4-methylaminobutyric acid.

$$CH_3NCH_2CH_2CH_2CO \xrightarrow{H_2O} CH_3NHCH_2CH_2CH_2COOH$$

It gives, upon treatment with PCl_5, the amide chloride, which in turn autocondenses when treated with dimethylaniline to give 2,3'-dimethyl-2,3'-diaza-2'-oxodicyclopentylidene (34).

$$CH_3NCH_2CH_2CH_2CO \xrightarrow{PCl_5} CH_3NCH_2CH_2CH_2CCl_2 \xrightarrow{DMA}$$

$$CH_3NCH_2CH_2CH_2C=CCH_2CH_2N(CH_3)CO$$

Medium for Chemical Reactions.   N-Methyl-2-pyrrolidone is useful as a reaction medium because it is an excellent solvent for a wide variety of organic and inorganic compounds and has a high dielectric constant. It may also participate in the reaction mechanism, and frequently its effect is catalytic. Various reactions aided by the presence of N-methyl-2-pyrrolidone are described below.

Thus, alkali compounds of substituted acetylene are easily alkylated by alkyl halides, but sodium acetylide itself ordinarily is alkylated only in liquid ammonia. In the presence of N-methyl-2-pyrrolidone, however, sodium acetylide reacts with alkyl halides or sulfates, giving good yields of alkylacetylenes (35). N-Methyl-2-pyrrolidone has also been shown to be a suitable catalyst for the alkylation of malonates, acetoacetates, or cyanoacetates (36).

N-Methyl-2-pyrrolidone is a particularly effective solvent for the reaction of ketones with acetylene. Its use is said to give high yields of tertiary ethynylcarbinols at room temperature, with little diol or other by-product. N-Methyl-2-pyrrolidone is also a good solvent for the vinylation of difficultly vinylated compounds such as carbazole or allyl alcohol (37).

Alcohols, esters, ethers, and amines can be carboxylated with carbon monoxide and nickel or cobalt salts as catalysts and N-methyl-2-pyrrolidone as solvent. For example, methyl acetate has been described as giving a 95% yield of acetic anhydride (38).

A solution of cuprous cyanide in *N*-methyl-2-pyrrolidone can be reacted with aryl or heterocyclic halides to form aromatic nitriles, generally in high yields (39).

Many carbohydrates dissolve in *N*-methyl-2-pyrrolidone and can be treated with various reagents in such solutions (40). For example, sucrose can be reacted with stearyl chloride to give sucrose monostearate, a sugar-based surfactant.

Industrial Solvent. 1. Hydrocarbons. Because of high solvency coupled with good selectivity and easy recovery, *N*-methyl-2-pyrrolidone is used in a number of large commercial units for the separation of acetylene from other gases (41).

Pure butadiene can be recovered from dilute 4-carbon fractions by countercurrent scrubbing with *N*-methyl-2-pyrrolidone (42). This solvent is also suitable for decolorizing petroleum hydrocarbons (43). It is particularly effective for the extraction of asphaltic constituents from crude oil prior to distillation.

2. Polymer Solvent. *N*-Methyl-2-pyrrolidone is an efficient solvent for spinning, surface-coating, stripping, casting, and solvent-welding operations. Numerous resins, including many which are ordinarily difficult to dissolve, are readily soluble in this lactam. These include polyacrylonitrile, polyvinyl chloride, nylon, various cellulosics, various polyurethans, various polyesters, and polyvinylidene fluoride.

Manufacture. *N*-Methyl-2-pyrrolidone is manufactured by the reaction of γ-butyrolactone and methylamine. It is produced domestically by GAF Corporation, and is also manufactured in Germany. The bulk price was listed at 49.5¢/lb in October 1967.

Toxicity. *N*-Methyl-2-pyrrolidone is not a primary irritant when left in contact with the skin for less than 24 hr, although repeated and prolonged contact produces a mild, transient irritation. It is not a sensitizer.

In inhalation studies on white rats, all animals survived an uninterrupted 6-hr exposure to an atmosphere saturated with *N*-methyl-2-pyrrolidone.

Oral toxicity is low. Studies on white rats gave the following values: LD_0, 3 ml/kg; LD_{50}, 7 ml/kg; and LD_{100}, 10 ml/kg.

N-Vinyl-2-Pyrrolidone (see also Vol. 1, p. 205) is a versatile vinyl monomer which can readily be homopolymerized, or copolymerized with many other monomers, to give polymers with unusual properties. The monomer is miscible with water, ether, alcohols, esters, ketones, and chlorinated and aromatic hydrocarbons. Its physical properties are given in Table 4.

Table 4. Physical Properties of *N*-Vinyl-2-Pyrrolidone

bp, °C, at 400 mm	193	refractive index, n_D^{25}	1.511
at 14 mm	96	viscosity, at 25°C, cP	2.07
fp, °C	13.5	flash point (Tag open	
sp gr, 25/4°C	1.04	cup), °C	98.4

See also Vinyl compounds and polymers.

Copolymerization. The extent to which *N*-vinyl-2-pyrrolidone affects the properties of copolymers is in approximate proportion to its content in the product. Generally, desirable properties are imparted with as little as 1–20% in the copolymer. Reactivity ratios are given in Table 5.

Emulsifying and protective colloid properties which are imparted by *N*-vinyl-2-pyrrolidone are useful in such products as paints and lube-oil additives. Viscosity

Table 5. Reactivity Ratios for Free-Radical Copolymerization of N-Vinyl-2-Pyrrolidone (M_1)

Comonomer (M_2)	r_1	r_2
acrylonitrile	0.06 ± 0.07	0.18 ± 0.07
allyl alcohol	1.0	0.0
allyl acetate	1.6	0.17
maleic anhydride	0.16 ± 0.03	0.08 ± 0.03
methyl methacrylate	0.005 ± 0.05	4.7 ± 0.5
	0.02 ± 0.02	5.0
styrene	0.045 ± 0.05	15.7 ± 0.5
trichloroethylene	0.54 ± 0.04	<0.01
tris(trimethylsiloxy)-		
vinyl silane	4.0	0.1
vinyl acetate	3.30 ± 0.15	0.205 ± 0.015
	2.0	0.24
vinyl chloride	0.38	0.53
vinylene carbonate	0.4	0.7

index (VI) improvers based upon acrylates or methacrylates gain detergency when they contain small proportions of N-vinyl-2-pyrrolidone (44).

The hydrophilic character of the monomer imparts such characteristics as improved antistatic performance, higher moisture regain, and higher moisture permeability to copolymers. Improved printability and improved dyeability are also commonly obtained. N-Vinyl-2-pyrrolidone contributes to the adhesion of its copolymers to various substrates such as glass and metals.

Manufacture. N-Vinyl-2-pyrrolidone is manufactured by the vinylation of 2-pyrrolidone with acetylene. It is produced domestically by GAF Corporation, and is also manufactured in Germany. The bulk price was listed at 85¢/lb in October 1967.

Stability. Commercial N-vinyl-2-pyrrolidone is ordinarily stabilized with 0.1% flake caustic soda since the monomer polymerizes readily, especially in light and at high temperatures, unless it contains an inhibitor. The monomer can readily be filtered or decanted prior to use. Vacuum distillation can be carried out but exposure to temperatures above 120°C should be avoided. The unstabilized monomer should be used promptly or refrigerated.

Stabilized commercial samples, protected from light and heat, show no tendency to polymerize in over a year. Neutral or alkaline solutions of N-vinyl-2-pyrrolidone are stable, but acidic aqueous solutions gradually hydrolyze into 2-pyrrolidone and acetaldehyde.

Toxicity. N-Vinyl-2-pyrrolidone is neither a primary skin irritant nor a sensitizer and has very little fatiguing action. Normal hygienic practice is advocated, including prompt removal from the skin, and avoidance of ingestion or inhalation.

Studies on white rats gave the following oral toxicity values: LD_0, 1.0 ml/kg; LD_{50}, 1.5 ml/kg; and LD_{100}, 2.5 ml/kg.

PYRROLE DYES

The condensation reactions of pyrrole are important synthetic approaches to the pyrrole dyes as well as to the bile pigments and porphyrins. The importance of the condensation products of pyrrole is evident from the extensive literature covering this class of compounds. For a rather detailed account of the pyrrylmethane and pyrryl-methene dyes the reader is referred to Elderfield's *Heterocyclic Chemistry* (see under General references). A few important syntheses are discussed below.

Dipyrrylmethanes. One of the routes to dipyrrylmethanes is the condensation of pyrrole with an aldehyde or ketone.

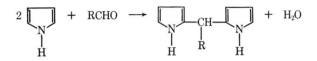

Unsymmetrical dipyrrylmethanes are obtained by condensing α-bromomethyl- or α-hydroxymethylpyrroles with a pyrrole having an unsubstituted α or β position. Pyrrole carbinols readily lose formaldehyde under acid conditions to give dipyrrylmethanes,

$$2\ RCH_2OH \xrightarrow{\text{acid}} RCH_2R + CH_2O + H_2O$$

where R is a pyrryl radical.

An example of a ketonic condensation is the acid-catalyzed reaction of pyrrole with acetone to give acetonepyrrole (46).

Tripyrrylmethanes. If a pyrrole aldehyde is used tripyrrylmethanes are prepared. The same or different pyrroles may be used to arrive at the desired substitutions. The tripyrrylmethanes closely resemble the triarylmethanes and may be regarded as leuco bases (see also Triphenylmethane dyes).

Dipyrrylmethenes. The tripyrrylmethanes dissociate in an acid medium to dipyrrylmethenes.

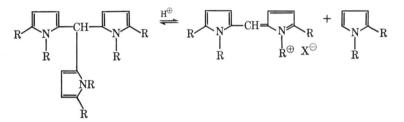

The dipyrrylmethenes can also be prepared by the oxidation of dipyrrylmethanes, or by the bromination of pyrroles (see under Halogenation, p. 847). The bromination products thus obtained are frequently used in porphyrin synthesis.

BILE PIGMENTS AND PORPHYRINS

The bile pigments are molecules containing a system of four pyrroles linked by methane or methene bridges. The porphyrin ring system has the same molecular linkage as the bile pigments, where the bile pigments are straight-chain molecules and the porphyrins are cyclic with a 16-membered ring. The bile pigments are obtained by condensation reactions analogous to those used in dipyrrylmethane synthesis. Further condensation leads to the porphyrin nucleus. One of the most spectacular syntheses carried out in the porphyrin field has been the synthesis of chlorophyll (qv) by Woodward (28). This synthesis employs many of the reactions of pyrrole discussed above. Another outstanding synthesis in the field of pyrrole chemistry was that of hemin, by Fisher and Zeile, in 1928 (47). In both of these porphyrin deriva-

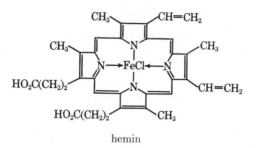

hemin

tives the pyrrole nitrogens are bound to metal: iron in hemin and magnesium in chlorophyll.

An important example of the bile pigments is bilirubin.

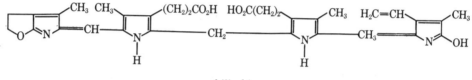

bilirubin

PHTHALOCYANINES

An important group of pigments which contain the pyrrole ring system are the phthalocyanines. These compounds have a 16-membered ring analogous to the porphyrin nucleus but contain four nitrogen atoms in place of the four methene groups.

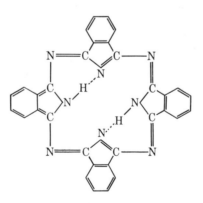

The first isolated member of this class of compounds was an iron complex reported in 1934. The metallic derivatives have the imino-hydrogen atoms replaced by metals. Metalfree phthalocyanine, first prepared in 1907, also has considerable utility in the pigment field. Phthalocyanines are not prepared from pyrroles but are produced by a strongly exothermic reaction between phthalonitrile or related compounds and a metal or metallic salt.

Bibliography

"Pyrrole and Pyrrole Derivatives" in *ECT* 1st ed., Vol. 11, pp. 339–353, by W. R. Vaughan, University of Michigan.

1. R. Runge, *Ann. Physik* **31,** 67 (1834).
2. T. Anderson, *Ann.* **105,** 349 (1858).
3. A. Baeyer and H. Emmerling, *Ber.* **3,** 517 (1870).
4. W. F. von Oettingen, *The Therapeutic Agents of the Pyrrole and Pyridine Group,* Edward Brothers, Ann Arbor, Mich., 1936.
5. N. Irving Sax, *Dangerous Properties of Industrial Materials,* 2nd ed., Reinhold Publishing Corp.. New York, 1963.
6. H. Zimmermann and H. Geisenfelder, *Z. Elektrochem.* **65,** 368 (1961).
7. P. Tuomikoski, *J. Phys. Radium* **16,** 347 (1955).
8. D. C.-H. Cheng, J. C. McCoubrey, D. G. Phillips, *Trans. Faraday Soc.* **58,** 224 (1962).
9. F. Glaser and H. Rüland, *Chem. Ingr. Tech.* **29,** 772 (1957).
10. R. K. Hind, E. McLaughlin, A. R. Ubbelohde, *Trans. Faraday Soc.* **56,** 331 (1960).
11. N. Naqui and Q. Fernando, *J. Org. Chem.* **25,** 551 (1960).
12. L. Knorr and H. Lange, *Ber.* **35,** 2998 (1902) (and general references).
13. W. O. Emery, *Ann.* **260,** 137 (1890).
14. J. Davoll, *J. Chem. Soc.* **1953,** 3802.
15. F. Ya. Perveer and E. M. Kuznetsova, *Zhur. Obshch. Khim.* **28,** 2360 (1958); *Chem. Abstr.* **53,** 3190 (1959).
16. Yu. K. Yurev, I. K. Korobitsyna, R. D. Ben-Yarik, L. A. Savina, and P. A. Akishin, *Vestn. Mosk. Univ.* **6,** No. 2, *Ser. Fiz.-Mat. i Estestven Nauk* No. 1, 37 (1951); *Chem. Abstr.* **47,** 124 (1953).
17. J. B. Hendrickson and R. Rees, *J. Am. Chem. Soc.* **83,** 1250 (1961).
18. E. H. Huntress, T. E. Lesslie, and W. M. Hearon, *J. Am. Chem. Soc.* **78,** 419 (1956).
19. K. E. Schulte, J. Reisch, and H. Walker, *Ber.* **98,** 98 (1965).
20. Yu. K. Yurev and I. S. Levi, *Vestn. Mosk. Univ., Ser. Mat., Mekh., Astron., Fiz. i Khim.* **11,** No. 2, 153 (1956); *Chem. Abstr.* **52,** 355 (1958).
21. "Process of Producing Pyrroles and Hydrogenated Pyrroles," U.S. Pat. 2,421,650 (June 3, 1947), W. Reppe, C. Schuster, and E. Weiss (to General Aniline & Film Corp.); "Production of Pyrrolidine," U.S. Pat. 2,525,584 (Oct. 10, 1950), C. Bordner and C. Kamin (to E. I. du Pont de Nemours & Co., Inc.); H. Adkins and J. Paden, *J. Am. Chem. Soc.* **58,** 2487 (1936); H. Adkins and R. Hill, *J. Am. Chem. Soc.* **60,** 1033 (1938).
22. A. Sonn, *Ber.* **68,** 148 (1935).
23. M. Kloetzel, *J. Am. Chem. Soc.* **69,** 2271 (1947).
24. R. Moffett and J. White, *J. Org. Chem.* **17,** 407 (1952).
25. J. Cornforth and R. Robinson, *J. Chem. Soc.* **1942,** 680.
26. H. Fisher and H. Scheyer, *Ann.* **434,** 237 (1923).
27. A. Triebs and H. Bader, *Ann.* **627,** 182 (1958).
28. R. B. Woodward et al., *J. Am. Chem. Soc.* **82,** 3800 (1960).
29. "Polymerization of Caprolactam," U.S. Pat. 2,727,017 (Dec. 13, 1955), G. H. Berthold (to Olin Mathieson Chemical Corp.).
30. J. Tafel and M. Stern, *Ber.* **33,** 2228–2229 (1900).
31. "Polymers from Pyrrolidone," U.S. Pat. 2,638,463 (May 12, 1953), W. O. Ney, Jr., W. R. Nummy, and C. E. Barnes (to General Aniline & Film Corp.); "Polymerization of Pyrrolidone and Piperidone," U.S. Pat. 2,739,959 (March 27, 1956), W. O. Ney, Jr., and M. Crowther (to Arnold, Hoffman and Co.).
32. J. Tafel and O. Wassmuth, *Ber.* **40,** 2835 (1907).
33. "Preparation of *N*-Hydroxymethylpyrrolidone," U.S. Pat. 3,073,843 (Jan. 15, 1963), S. R. Buc (to General Aniline & Film Corp.).
34. H. Eilingsfeld, M. Seefelder, and H. Weidinger, *Angew. Chem.* **72,** 836 (1960).
35. "Acetylene Hydrocarbons," Ger. Pat. 944,311 (June 14, 1956), M. Kracht and H. Pasedach (to Badische Anilin- & Soda-Fabrik A.-G.).
36. "Method of Alkylating Esters," U.S. Pat. 2,971,024 (Feb. 7, 1961), H. E. Zaugg, F. C. Garven, A. O. Geiszler, and E. Hamlin (to Abbott Laboratories).

37. "Vinyl Compounds," Ger. Pat. 940,981 (Mar. 29, 1956), K. Schuster and F. Hanusch (to Bad-ische Anilin- & Soda-Fabrik A.-G.).
38. "Acetic Anhydride," U.S. Pat. 2,789,137 (April 16, 1957), W. Reppe and H. Friederich (to Badische Anilin- & Soda-Fabrik A.-G.).
39. M. S. Newman and D. K. Phillips, *J. Am. Chem. Soc.* **81,** 3668 (1959); M. S. Newman and H. J. Boden, *J. Org. Chem.* **26,** 2525 (1961).
40. "Carbohydrate Reactions in 2-Pyrrolidone and *N*-Methyl-2-pyrrolidone Solvents," U.S. Pat. 2,853,485 (Sept. 23, 1958), J. Werner and F. A. Hessel (to General Aniline & Film Corp.).
41. "Acetylene Solution," U.S. Pat. 2,599,649 (July 10, 1952), L. Lorenz; "Absorption of Acetylene by *N*-Pyrrolidinone," U.S. Pat. 2,664,997 (Jan. 5, 1954), J. C. Eck (to Allied Chemical & Dye Corp.); "Recovery of Solvents Used for Removal of Acetylene from Gas Mixtures," U.S. Pat. 2,846,443 (Aug. 5, 1958), G. Malcusa and M. Rossoni (to Società Edison S.p.A.).
42. H. Kroper, H. M. Weitz, and V. Wagner, *Hydrocarbon Process. Petrol. Refiner* **41** (11), 191 (1962).
43. "Decolorization of Petroleum Hydrocarbons with Pyrrolidinones," U.S. Pat. 2,767,119 (Oct. 16, 1956), A. L. Forchielli (to General Aniline & Film Corp.).
44. "Lubricating Oils Containing Detergent and Thickening Additives," U.S. Pat. 2,977,304 (March 14, 1961), R. L. Ferm and A. D. Abbott (to California Research Corp.).
45. W. Blanchard and L. Mandell, *J. Am. Chem. Soc.* **79,** 6198 (1957).
46. A. Corwin et al., *J. Org. Chem.* **29,** 3207 (1964).
47. H. Fischer and K. Zeile, *Ann.* **462,** 210–230 (1929).
48. L. Chierici and G. Gardini, *Tetrahedron* **22,** 53–56 (1966).
49. M. Simonetta, *J. Chem. Phys.* **49,** 68 (1952).
50. L. Fieser and M. Fieser, *Advanced Organic Chemistry*, Reinhold Publishing Corp., New York, 1961, p. 673.

General References

A. H. Corwin in R. C. Elderfield, ed., *Heterocyclic Compounds*, Vol. I, John Wiley & Sons, Inc., New York, 1950, pp. 277–342.

E. Baltazzi, *Chem. Rev.* **63,** 511–550 (1963).

E. H. Rodd, ed., *Chemistry of Carbon Compounds*, Vol. IVA, Elsevier Publishing Co., New York, 1957, pp. 28–70.

A. Treibs, *Rev. Chim., Acad. Rep. Populaire Roumaine* **1** (2), 1345–1366 (1962) (in German).

Z. N. Nazarova, ed., *Ocherki Po Khimii Azolov* (Outlines of the Chemistry of Azoles), Rostov-on-Don, Izd. Rostovsk Univ., 1965, 107 pp.

EUGENE V. HORT AND RICHARD F. SMITH
GAF Corporation

PYRROLIDINE, PYRROLIDONES.   See Pyrrole and pyrrole derivatives.

Q

QUARTZ, SiO_2. See Silica.

QUATERNARY AMMONIUM COMPOUNDS

The reaction products of tertiary amines with alkyl halides are known as quaternary ammonium compounds. These compounds have four carbon atoms linked directly to the nitrogen atom through covalent bonds. The anion in the original alkylating agent is linked to the nitrogen through an electrovalent bond.

$$R^1-\overset{\overset{\displaystyle R^2}{|}}{\underset{\underset{\displaystyle R^4}{|}}{N}}{}^{+}-R^3 \quad X^-$$

The R groups may be alike or different and may be substituted or unsubstituted, branched-chain or unbranched, saturated or unsaturated. Alkyl halides and heterocyclic compounds such as pyridine or quinoline form compounds in which the nitrogen is linked by two carbon–nitrogen covalent bonds and one carbon–nitrogen double bond. These are also regarded as quaternary ammonium compounds. Originally reaction products of tertiary amines with alkyl halides were thought to be "complexes" formed by simple addition of the two reagents. Later work showed their true structure and led to a prominent part in the elucidation of the various valence states of nitrogen derivatives. One of the first quaternary ammonium compounds prepared was ethyltrimethylammonium iodide from trimethylamine and ethyl iodide. It could also be prepared from dimethylethylamine and methyl iodide. It was shown that regardless of which reactants were used, the product was the same. This proved that something more was happening than just "complex formation." Later the tetrahedral configuration was proved by a synthesis of an optically active quaternary ammonium salt (1), in which there were four different substituents: methyl, allyl, phenyl, and benzyl. However, the resolution of optically active quaternary ammonium salts is difficult because of the ease with which they undergo racemization at room temperature. This can be explained by their dissociation into an optically inactive tertiary amine and an alkyl halide,

$$[R^1R^2R^3R^4N]X \rightleftharpoons R^1R^2R^3N + R^4X$$

The introduction of high-molecular-weight, aryl-containing quaternary ammonium salts slows down the rate of dissociation and permits the resolution into the optical enantiomers.

Nomenclature. The quaternary ammonium salts are usually named as substituted compounds. The expressions "pyridinium" and "quinolinium" are used for the corresponding quaternaries; for example $C_5H_5N + C_{16}H_{33}.Cl^-$ would be named hexadecylpyridinium chloride.   The substituents may be cited, according to the IUPAC, either in alphabetical order (neglecting prefixes such as di- and tri-) or in order of increasing complexity, but the CA system is based on alphabetical order, since the "increasing complexity" rule can become exceedingly complicated and most difficult to apply.   Thus the expressions "methylethylpropylbutylammonium chloride" and "butylethylmethylpropylammonium chloride" are both satisfactory.   (The normal alkyl group is understood unless otherwise mentioned.)

Physical Properties

There are a great variety of quaternary ammonium salts and their physical state ranges from highly crystalline solids to viscous liquids.   The lowest-molecular-weight quaternary, tetramethylammonium chloride, is very soluble in water and insoluble in ether.   As the alkyl groups increase in molecular weight the solubility in water decreases and the solubility in organic solvents increases.   Thus trimethyloctadecylammonium chloride dissolves in water only up to about 27%.   Further increases in molecular weight of the alkyl units further decrease the solubility in water.   Thus dimethyl-dioctadecylammonium chloride has very limited solubility in water.   In this case dispersion in water is possible and, as a matter of fact, this is how most compounds of this type are used.

The quaternary ammonium compounds have rather indefinite melting points. Those that form crystalline solids decompose on heating, and the amount of water present and/or rate of heating will determine the decomposition points.   Some quaternaries form hydrates or other solvates and in some instances they can be crystallized in this form.

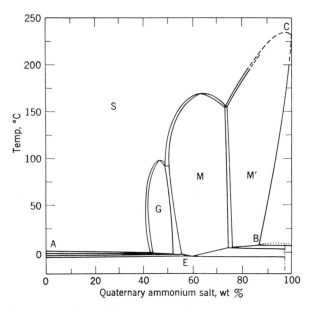

Fig. 1. The system dodecyltrimethylammonium chloride–water: A, freezing point of water; E, eutectic of water plus hydrate of the quaternary ammonium salt; B, incongruent melting point of the hydrate; C, melting point of the anhydrous salt; S, region of isotropic liquid; G, region of isotropic gel; M and M', liquid crystalline phases.

Quaternary ammonium salts in which one of the alkyl groups contains twelve or more carbon atoms are often referred to as *invert soaps*. See Surfactants. This is because the lypophilic portion of the molecule is now cationic instead of anionic as in sodium stearate. Figure 1 is an example of how this type of surfactant behaves in water (2). The diagram has been simplified by omitting the curves representing an unstable polymorph. These salts are surface-active colloidal electrolytes which form aggregates in solution. These aggregates or micelles are formed as a result of the hydrophilic nature of the ammonium group together with the hydrophobic nature of the hydrocarbon chain. The micelle is assumed to be made up of molecules with polar groups oriented toward the surrounding aqueous solution. The concentration at which micelle formation begins is termed the critical concentration for micelle formation and is a measure of the tendency for the specific compound to leave solution. This tendency is an important factor in surface activity. Having the lypophilic portion of the molecule positively charged is the reason for the greater part of the uses for these compounds. Most surfaces are negatively charged and solutions or emulsions made from these cationic surface agents are readily adsorbed to these negatively charged surfaces causing reaction, breaking of emulsions, and protection of these surfaces.

Reactions and Analysis

Quaternary ammonium salts are very reactive organic compounds. They will dissociate in solution and are sensitive to heat. Equations 1 and 2 are examples of the type of decomposition that may occur. The decomposition noted in equation 1

$$[RCH_2CH_2N(R^1)_3]X \rightarrow RCH{=}CH_2 + (R^1)_3N + HX \tag{1}$$

$$[R_4N]X \rightleftharpoons R_3N + RX \tag{2}$$

is irreversible. However, reaction 2 is reversible. In many cases both reactions may proceed simultaneously and both may follow first- or second-order kinetics. Reaction 1 was discovered by Hofmann in 1851 and has been used in rare instances for the preparation of olefins. It has been used a great deal in the elucidation of the structure of complex bases, particularly alkaloids. This reaction has become known as the Hofmann exhaustive methylation reaction. The following equation for the conversion of pyrrolidine to butadiene is an example of the use of this method:

Quaternary ammonium hydroxides decompose much more easily than quaternary ammonium halides. The hydroxides are easily prepared by treatment of the halides with silver oxide or alkyl potassium hydroxide. Later modifications of this synthesis route used ion-exchange resins. A free base is very seldom isolated but is used in solution. Quaternary ammonium compounds containing alkyl substituents in which there are negative groups on the carbon alpha to the nitrogen atom, cleave readily when subjected to conditions of catalytic hydrogenation. This propensity has been used as a synthetic tool. In the case of benzyltrimethylammonium chloride the products of this cleavage are toluene and trimethylammonium chloride.

$$[C_6H_5CH_2N(CH_3)_3]Cl \xrightarrow{H_2} C_6H_5CH_3 + [HN(CH_3)_3]Cl$$

Quaternary ammonium compounds of higher molecular weight, for example those with an aliphatic group with twelve carbon atoms, react with proteins, causing precipitation, denaturation, redispersion, and complex formation. Herein lies the reason for their bactericidal usage. Factors such as the ionic nature of the quaternary ammonium salt, the length of its paraffinic chain, pH, and the mass ratio of quaternary ammonium salt to protein, are governing variables. In general, the quaternary ammonium salts cause precipitation of protein in the pH region above the isoelectric point of the protein. There appears to be an equivalence point at which maximum precipitation occurs. When the protein is in excess, precipitation occurs to only a fractional degree; whereas when the surface-active material is in excess, redispersion occurs. Below the isoelectric point the quaternary ammonium salts form complexes with proteins. In most cases of precipitation, redispersion, and complex formation, denaturation of the protein takes place.

Quaternary ammonium compounds are subject to a large variety of very specific analytical techniques. The lower-molecular-weight members are difficult to analyze because it is hard to isolate them in a pure form. The halide portion of the molecule is frequently analyzed by titration with silver nitrate. The cationic portion is sometimes estimated from this titration. This of course assumes that there is no other halide ion present except that belonging to the quaternary ammonium salt. The higher-molecular-weight members of the series are analyzed by titration with various anionic indicators such as tetrabromofluorescein, bromothymol blue, and phenolsulfonephthalein to form colored complexes. Color intensity, as measured photometrically, thus becomes a determination of activity.

A new method of analysis has recently been developed. This method depends on the ability to titrate quaternary ammonium compounds with tetraphenylboron. This method has displaced other analytical tools as far as quaternary ammonium compounds are concerned (3).

Biological Properties

Quaternary ammonium compounds play an important part in the living process. The vitamin B complex contains two components which have the quaternary nitrogen atom. Vitamin B (thiamine) (qv) is a heterocyclic compound which contains a thiozolium ring and is part of the enzyme carboxylase which participates in carbohydrate metabolism. Choline (qv), $((CH_3)_3NCH_2CH_2OH)OH$, trimethyl(2-hydroxyethyl) ammonium hydroxide is important in fat metabolism in transmethylation reactions. Acetylcholine is involved in the transmission of nerve impulses.

Curare action, muscarinic-nicotinic action, and ganglia-blocking action are three general types of physiological actions attributed to quaternary ammonium compounds (4). The active substance in curare is capable of producing muscular paralysis without affecting the central nervous system or the heart. Curare has been used to induce muscular relaxation during surgery. A large number of similar-type quaternary ammonium compounds have been synthesized in attempts to optimize properties. Direct stimulation of smooth muscles is called muscarinic action, and primary transient stimulation and secondary persistent depression of sympathetic and parasympathetic ganglia is called nicotinic action. Many quaternary ammonium compounds cause these actions in varying degrees. All these effects must be considered when studying the clinical action of quaternary ammonium compounds.

The first report on the bactericidal action of quaternary ammonium compounds, published in 1916, dealt with derivatives of hexamethylenetetramine. Since that time there have been numerous and voluminous reports on structure versus bactericidal activity, chain length of the higher aliphatic group, total number of carbon atoms, ring substitution of phenyl-containing compounds, type of anion, and substitution on the aliphatic group. Generally speaking completely aliphatic compounds optimize their activity when the higher aliphatic group contains a normal chain of sixteen to eighteen carbon atoms, and benzyl quaternary compounds optimize their bactericidal activity when the higher aliphatic chain contains fourteen carbon atoms. The anion has little influence, except on the solubility.

The mechanism of the bactericidal action is closely related to the surface activity of the quaternary ammonium compound. This is why solubility is so important. Undoubtedly interaction of the bactericidal agent with the cell wall interferes with the metabolic process of the organism and this causes the inhibiting or killing action. Pharmacological and toxicological studies of certain higher aliphatic quaternary ammonium compounds have indicated that these compounds are innocuous in the concentrations required for germicidal effectiveness. See Vol. 2, pp. 632–635.

Preparation

Quaternary ammonium compounds are prepared by the alkylation of primary, secondary, or tertiary amines.

$$R^1R^2NH + R^3Cl \rightarrow R^1R^2R^3N + HCl$$
$$R^1R^2R^3N + R^4Cl \rightarrow R^1R^2R^3R^4N + Cl$$

When primary or secondary amines are used a base has to be used to neutralize the acid formed by the alkylation. Many alkylating agents are used, methyl halides, dimethyl sulfate, and benzyl chloride being used most frequently (see Alkylation). When dimethyl sulfate is used only one methyl group is available for alkylation. The resultant compound is a quaternary ammonium methylsulfate. Heterocyclic compounds such as pyridine or quinoline can be quaternized in a like manner.

$$R_3N + (CH_3)_2SO_4 \rightarrow R_3CH_3N + CH_3OSO_3{}^-$$

Alkoxylated amines (see Alkanolamines) can be used as the tertiary amine in quaternary production.

$$RN(CH_2CH_2OH)_2 + R^1X \rightarrow RR^1N(CH_2CH_2OH)_2X$$

Quaternary ammonium compounds containing hydroxyl groups may also be prepared by the reaction of alkylene oxides with amine salts.

$$RNH_3Cl + 3\ CH_2CH_2 \underset{O}{\overset{}{\diagdown\!\diagup}} \rightarrow RN + (CH_2CH_2OH)_3Cl$$

Quaternization of tertiary amines with alkyl halides is bimolecular. The rate of reaction is influenced by a number of factors including basicity of the amine, steric effects, reactivity of the halide, and the polarity of the solvent. Polar solvents promote the reaction by stabilizing the ionic products. The following data illustrate the effect of solvent on the reaction between pyridine and ethyl iodide (5):

Solvent	*Benzene*	*Ethanol*	*Methanol*	*Acetone*	*Nitro-benzene*
Relative rate	1	1.4	2.5	12.8	25.0

Uses

As stated above almost all of the uses for quaternary ammonium salts are based on their cationic nature which in turn allows them to be substantive to (that is, to be adsorbed on) negatively charged surfaces. The single largest use is in the fabric softener market, which uses 4–8% dispersions of high-molecular-weight quaternary ammonium salts. Additional benefits to the users of these fabric softeners are found in static resistance and ease of ironing the garment. The most widely used fabric softener base is dimethyldi(hydrogenated tallow)ammonium chloride which is sold "75% active" (that is to say as a preparation containing 75% of the quaternary salt) to formulators of bottled softeners. The estimated 1968 market for these bases is 25 million pounds of 75% active material (6).

Another large use for quaternary ammonium compounds is in the preparation of cationic emulsions. A notable example of this use is in cationic asphalt emulsions where quaternary ammonium compounds are used to prepare asphalt emulsions. These emulsions can be prepared to "break" on contact with the negatively charged aggregates used in road maintenance (7).

A very large variety of surface-active quaternary ammonium compounds are employed for germicidal use. The most popular types are those prepared by the reaction of benzyl chloride and a dimethylalkylamine wherein the alkyl group is in the C_{12} to C_{16} range. These compounds in high concentration are viscous liquids, but are usually sold as aqueous solutions. A very wide variety of these solutions are used as sanitizing agents in cleaning eating utensils and food processing equipment, and as cleaning compounds in restaurants, dairies, and hospitals. They have advantages over phenols and chlorine disinfectants in that they are nonirritating and odor free, and have relatively long activity.

Quaternary ammonium compounds containing three methyl groups and one long alkyl chain, such as trimethyloctadecylammonium chloride, also exhibit excellent germicidal activity. The only drawback may be found in formulating difficulty. Compounds containing two methyl groups and two alkyl groups such as those derived from coconut-oil fatty acids are most effective against anaerobic bacteria such as are found in oil wells. These bacteria are sulfate reducers and their growth frequently causes severe corrosion problems in oil wells plus plugging of formations. The surface-active property of the quaternary ammonium compound also helps in removing oil from the sandstone formation.

The substantive qualities of the higher aliphatic ammonium compounds make them effective antistatic agents; they also act as lubricants in textile spinning (see Antistatics). Their property of imparting a soft feel or "hand" to fabrics makes these compounds valuable in hair rinses where they act as conditioning agents. They are also useful in plastics.

1-Stearamidomethylpyridinium chloride, $[C_{17}H_{35}CONHCH_2NC_5H_5]Cl$, prepared by the reaction of stearamide with pyridine, formaldehyde, and hydrochloric acid, is used in the production of water-repellent fabrics. The fabric is impregnated with the quaternary ammonium salt; upon heating, a water-repellent film is deposited.

Reaction products of bentonite and quaternary ammonium compounds are useful as gelling or thickening agents for organic vehicles. Thixotropic paints, grease additives, drilling muds, foundry additives, and printing inks find application for these complexes.

Bibliography

1. W. J. Pope and S. J. Peachey, *J. Chem. Soc.* **1899**, 1127.
2. F. K. Broome, C. W. Hoerr, and H. J. Harwood, *J. Am. Chem. Soc.* **73**, 3350 (1951).
3. L. D. Metcalfe, R. J. Martin, and A. A. Schmitz, "The Titration of Long Chain Quaternary Ammonium Compounds Using Tetraphenylboron," *J. Am. Oil Chemists' Soc.* **43**, 355 (1966).
4. A. Burger, ed., *Medicinal Chemistry*, 2nd ed., Interscience Publishers, Inc., New York, 1960, Vols. 1 and 2.
5. L. P. Hammett, *Physical Organic Chemistry*, McGraw-Hill Book Co., Inc., New York, 1940, p. 215.
6. *Arquads*, Armour Industrial Chemical Company, Chicago, Ill., 1956.
7. *Redicotes*, Armour Industrial Chemical Company, Chicago, Ill., 1967.

RICHARD A. RECK
Armour Industrial Chemical Co.

QUENCHING OILS. See Vol. 15, p. 84.

QUINHYDRONE. See Quinones.

QUININE. See Alkaloids.

QUINOLINE AND ISOQUINOLINE

Quinoline (**1**) and isoquinoline (**2**) (see p. 876) are the two isomeric benzopyridines. They have the same relationship with pyridine (qv) that naphthalene has with benzene.

(**1**)   (**2**)

QUINOLINE

Quinoline (1-benzazine; benzo[*b*]pyridine) (RRI 1707), C_9H_7N, is a heterocyclic base, comparable to naphthalene with a methine group replaced by —N═. Quinoline derivatives are used as medicinals and as dyes, and many alkaloids are derivatives of quinoline. The *Ring Index* prints the formula as shown above, with the nitrogen at the top; hereafter, however, formulas will be given with the nitrogen at the base, as has been customary in this branch of chemistry.

The name quinoline was adopted after Hofmann had shown that "leukol" from crude tar bases and "chinolein" from drastic alkaline distillation of quinine were the same. The determination of its structure is based on methods of synthesis and degradation. The benzene ring of quinoline is destroyed by strong oxidizing agents with the formation of 2,3-pyridinedicarboxylic acid (quinolinic acid). The numbering of positions in the structural formula is shown in (**1**).

Physical and Chemical Properties

PHYSICAL PROPERTIES

Quinoline is a colorless, highly refractive liquid with a pungent odor. It is very hygroscopic, is more soluble in hot than in cold water, and distils in steam. A weak tertiary base (basic ionization constant, 3.2×10^{-10} (1)), quinoline dissolves in acids and forms characteristic salts such as the sparingly soluble dichromate, $2C_9H_7N \cdot H_2Cr_2O_7$. Quinoline is soluble in ethyl alcohol, ethyl ether, acetone, and carbon disulfide.

Quinoline has the following constants: bp, 237.10°C; mp, −15.6°C; d_4^{15}, 1.0978; d_4^{120}, 1.0150; n_D^{15}, 1.62928; saturated vapor pressure, 2.55 mm at 75.3°C, 10.65 mm at 104.3°C; heat of fusion, 19.98 cal/g. Data from heats of combustion give evidence for considerable resonance in the quinoline system (2). The uv spectrum of quinoline (in cyclohexane) has been reported (3). The Raman spectrum showed the strongest lines at 521 cm^{-1}, 758 cm^{-1}, and 1372 cm^{-1} (4).

REACTIONS

Quinoline and quinoline derivatives show the reactions which are well-known in the benzene and pyridine series. Electrophilic substitution occurs almost exclusively in the benzene ring. Nucleophilic substitution occurs in the pyridine ring.

Nitration. In the nitration of quinoline the position which the nitro group enters is determined by the conditions of the nitration. The nitration of quinoline in concentrated sulfuric acid gives a mixture of 5- and 8-nitroquinoline in about equal quantities. This orientation is in accordance with molecular orbital calculation of the positions of maximum electron density (5). Studies showed that in mixed acid the nitronium ion attacks the protonated quinoline molecule and this proton is still present in the transition state (6). 7-Nitroquinoline may be obtained through nitration of 1,2,3,4-tetrahydroquinoline followed by dehydrogenation (6a). Under less acidic conditions of nitration as, for example, when acetic anhydride with nitric acid or with dinitrogen tetroxide is used, the main product is 3-nitroquinoline. This orientation presumably results through the initial addition of the nitrating reagent to the heterocyclic ring (7). 3-Nitroquinoline N-oxide is produced when quinoline N-oxide methyl methosulfate is nitrated with potassium nitrate in dimethyl sulfoxide (8). The nitration of quinoline N-oxide with warm mixed acid gives 4-nitroquinoline N-oxide which is readily reduced to 4-nitroquinoline. 4-Nitroquinoline N-oxide undergoes substitution in the 3 position when treated with diethyl malonate and sodium ethylate (9).

Sulfonation. Sulfonation of quinoline at 220°C gives mainly the 8-sulfonic acid which when heated to 300°C rearranges to the 6-sulfonic acid.

1,2-Addition. Quinoline reacts with allylmagnesium chloride in tetrahydrofuran in the absence of air to form 2-allyl-1,2-dihydroquinoline in 80% yield (10). This is a labile compound and isomerizes to 2-n-propylquinoline when heated at 170°C in an inert atmosphere or is converted to 2-propenylquinoline when exposed to air or oxidizing agents. When quinoline is exposed to bromine and aqueous potassium cyanide (in effect, to cyanogen bromide, CNBr) it forms 1-cyano-2-hydroxy-1,2-dihydroquinoline which on heating with alcohols and boron trifluoride is converted to 1-cyano-2-alkoxy-1,2-dihydroquinoline (7). These compounds are useful as pesticides and particularly as a postemergence herbicide in the control of mustard (11). The "Reissert compounds" described below are also 1,2 adducts of quinoline.

Amination. 2-Aminoquinoline can be obtained in 80% yield by treating quinoline with barium amide in liquid ammonia (12). This compound together with 4-aminoquinoline is also obtained by amination of quinoline with sodium or potassium amide in such solvents as xylene, toluene, or dimethylaniline. The 2-, 3- and 4-aminoquinolines are formed by reaction of the corresponding chloro compounds with ammonia.

Halogenation. Halogenation is analogous to nitration of quinoline in that the 3 substitutions can be considered to involve electrophilic attack on the neutral quinoline molecule while the 5 and 8 substitutions involve attack on the protonated molecule. 3-Bromoquinoline is conveniently prepared in 82% yield by heating the quinoline–bromine adduct in an inert solvent with pyridine as the hydrogen bromide acceptor (13). 3-Chloroquinoline is prepared similarly. The treatment of quinoline in concentrated sulfuric acid containing silver sulfate with one mole of bromine results in a mixture of 5- and 8-bromoquinoline in about equal quantities together with some 5,8-dibromoquinoline (14). When the quinoline–aluminum chloride complex is heated with bromine 5-bromoquinoline is formed in 78% yield (15).

Further brominations in sulfuric acid or in the presence of aluminum chloride lead to 5,8-dibromo-, 5,6,8-tribromo-, and 5,7,8-tribromoquinolines. Quinoline with bromine at 450°C gives rise to 2-bromoquinoline. The 2- and 4-halogenated quinolines are readily obtained from the corresponding hydroxyquinolines by reaction with phosphorus oxychloride.

Oxidation. Oxidation of quinoline with alkaline permanganate or with boiling concentrated sulfuric acid in the presence of selenium dioxide or with ozone (15a) or electrolytically produces quinolinic acid (2,3-pyridinedicarboxylic acid). This can be easily decarboxylated by heating to nicotinic acid (3-pyridinecarboxylic acid). Oxidation with hypochlorous acid produces carbostyril (2-quinolinol or 2(1H)-quinolone). The tertiary nitrogen of quinoline may be converted to the N-oxide (16) by the action of peroxyacetic acid, monoperoxyphthalic acid, or peroxybenzoic acid. The N-oxide is also obtained by dissolving quinoline in acetic acid in the presence of 30% hydrogen peroxide and heating at 50°C for 24 hours. Quinoline N-oxide is chlorinated with sulfuryl chloride in good yields to 2- and 4-chloroquinolines; for the chlorination of substituted quinoline N-oxides a better reagent is phosphorus oxychloride.

Quaternary Salts. Quinoline forms quaternary salts with alkyl and with acyl chlorides. The reaction with acid chlorides leads to valuable quinoline intermediates known as "Reissert compounds" (17). Thus N-benzoylquinolinium chloride (**3**) reacts with aqueous potassium cyanide to give 1-benzoyl-2-cyano-1,2-dihydroquinoline (**4**) which on treatment with concentrated hydrochloric acid yields 2-carboxyquinoline (**5**) and benzaldehyde. If the Reissert compound (**4**) is treated with phosphorus penta-

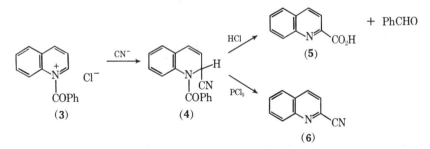

chloride 2-cyanoquinoline (**6**) is formed. 2-Cyanoquinoline (**6**) can be prepared in excellent yield by mixing quinoline N-oxide with benzoyl chloride and then treating the reaction mixture with alkali cyanide. The ability of the quinoline to form the Reissert compounds is greatly affected by the substituents present on the ring. The reaction has failed with a number of substituted quinolines. The reaction of N-alkylquinolinium salts with alkali cyanides follows a different course in that the cyano group ends up in the 4 position. Thus *N*-methylquinolinium iodide on treatment with cyanide yields *N*-methyl-4-cyano-1,4-dihydroquinoline which when heated with iodine in pyridine loses methyl iodide to form 4-cyanoquinoline.

Manufacture and Synthesis

PRODUCTION FROM COAL TAR

Quinoline is isolated from suitable coal-tar distillates which have an appreciable concentration of oils boiling in the range 235–240°C. In general, the tar bases are extracted with dilute sulfuric acid, liberated on making the sulfate solution alkaline, and recovered from the aqueous layer by decantation or steam distillation. A further refining process includes fractional distillation. For the market, refined quinoline of 95–97% purity is described with a maximum distillation range of 2° between 235 and 238°C (sp gr at 15.5°C, 1.092–1.098). See also Tar and pitch.

In the cruder fractions of tar bases (distilling at 230–251°C), earlier investigators identified isoquinoline, 2-methylquinoline, and 4-methylquinoline. Jantzen (18) carried out studies of carefully controlled fractional distillation and refractionation of 30 kg of such crude tar base (bp 230–265°C); he found, in addition to quinoline and isoquinoline, small or trace amounts of all the possible isomeric monomethylquinolines. Jantzen also isolated 2,8-dimethylquinoline, as well as homologs of isoquinoline. Both refined and semirefined isoquinoline and refined quinaldine are separated from tar distillates and quoted as market items; methods for isolation of these fractions are noted below (see pp. 873, 877) (19,20).

SYNTHESIS OF QUINOLINE AND QUINOLINE DERIVATIVES

Skraup Synthesis (Quinoline and Derivatives) (21). The Skraup synthesis is a general reaction and may be used for the synthesis of many quinolines. The method consists of heating a primary aromatic amine with glycerol, concentrated sulfuric acid, and an oxiding agent such as the nitro compound corresponding to the aromatic amine used, *m*-nitrobenzenesulfonic acid, arsenic acid, or ferric chloride. The reaction proceeds through a number of stages consisting of dehydration of glycerol to acrolein, reaction of acrolein with the amine to form β-anilinopropionaldehyde (7), cyclization of this to the 1,2-dihydroquinoline (8), and oxidation to the quinoline (1).

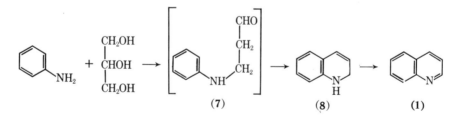

The vigor of this frequently violent reaction may be controlled by the addition of ferrous sulfate or boric acid or by the portionwise addition of the mixture of the amine, sulfuric acid, and glycerol to the oxidizing agent.

The original Skraup method which was designed for the synthesis of quinolines substituted in the benzene ring has been extended to the synthesis of quinolines substituted in the heterocycle. This is done by using substituted acroleins instead of glycerol. Thus β-methylacrolein (crotonaldehyde) and α-methylacrolein when used in place of glycerol yield 2- and 3-methylquinoline, respectively. In a similar manner 4-methylquinoline is obtained from methyl vinyl ketone, 4-methoxy-2-butanone, or 1,3,3-trimethoxybutane.

A meta-substituted aromatic amine can give rise to two isomeric quinoline derivatives. If the meta substituent is strongly ortho-para directing then the 7-substituted quinoline results. If the meta-substituent is meta-directing, a mixture of the 5- and 7-substituted quinolines is formed with the former predominating. 2-Naphthylamine gives only one product, the angular benzo(*f*)quinoline while 1-naphthylamine produces the isomeric benzo(*h*)quinoline. Aromatic diamines react twice in the Skraup reaction to form the phenanthrolines.

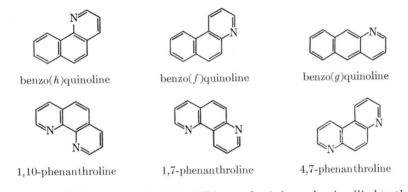

benzo(*h*)quinoline	benzo(*f*)quinoline	benzo(*g*)quinoline

1,10-phenanthroline	1,7-phenanthroline	4,7-phenanthroline

Döbner-von Miller Synthesis (22). This synthesis is so closely allied to the Skraup synthesis that it is sometimes difficult to distinguish between them. The original Döbner-von Miller synthesis consists of a reaction of one mole of an aromatic amine with two moles of acetaldehyde in the presence of hydrochloric acid or zinc chloride without using an oxidizing agent to form 2-methylquinoline (quinaldine). The mechanism has not been fully established but several by-products have been isolated which help to explain the reaction.

Crotonaldehyde is first formed by the self-condensation of acetaldehyde and under the acidic conditions condenses with the aromatic amine to form β-anilinobutyraldehyde (**9**). Cyclization yields the so-called "aldol bases" (**10**) which react with another molecule of the amine to form (**11**). Dehydration of the "aldol bases" or the loss of aniline from (**11**) results in dihydroquinaldine (**12**). This is then converted to quinaldine (**13**)

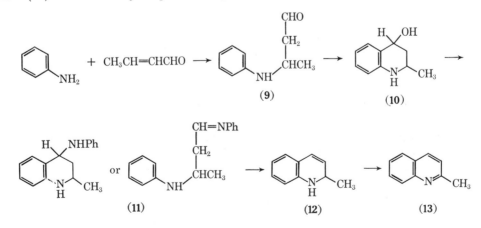

by dehydrogenation with the anils of acetaldehyde and crotonaldehyde (also formed during the reaction) acting as the hydrogen acceptors.

The scope of the Döbner-von Miller synthesis has been extended by using in place of two moles of acetaldehyde, a mixture of one mole each of two different aldehydes or a mixture of one mole of an aldehyde and one mole of a ketone. Thus an acetaldehyde–benzaldehyde mixture yields 2-phenylquinoline, a propionaldehyde–methylal mixture yields 3-methylquinoline, a methylal–acetone mixture yields 4-methylquinoline, an acetaldehyde–acetone mixture yields 2,4-dimethylquinoline, and a benzaldehyde–pyruvic acid mixture yields 2-phenyl-4-carboxyquinoline (cinchophen) (see Vol. 2, p. 391). The yields of these quinoline derivatives are usually poor.

Conrad-Limpach-Knorr Synthesis (23). The condensation of β-keto esters with aromatic amines has become an important reaction because it leads to 2- and 4-hydroxyquinolines which are intermediates for chemotherapeutic agents. When aniline is allowed to condense with ethyl acetoacetate (14) at temperatures below 100°C, ethyl 3-anilinocrotonate (15) is formed, which can be cyclized to 2-methyl-4-hydroxyquinoline (16) by adding it to paraffin or Dowtherm (see Heat transfer media) preheated to about 250°C. If, however, aniline is allowed to react with ethyl acetoacetate (14) at

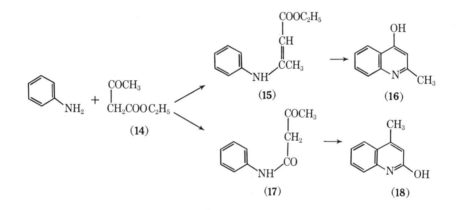

about 160°C, acetoacetanilide (17) is formed which may be cyclized to 2-hydroxy-4-methylquinoline (18) by treating with concentrated sulfuric acid. The factors which govern the course of the condensation of ethyl acetoacetate with aromatic amines have been studied by Hauser and Reynolds (24).

The Conrad-Limpach-Knorr reaction has wide scope and has been applied to the synthesis of many quinoline derivatives. This was made possible by the availability of many β-keto esters derived from acetoacetic ester. Thus 3-substituted 2-methyl-4-hydroxyquinolines and 3-substituted 2-hydroxy-4-methylquinolines are readily obtained from α-substituted ethyl acetoacetates. Condensations of aromatic amines with ethyl ethoxalyl acetate ($C_2H_5OOCCH_2COCOOC_2H_5$) (25), and with ethyl ethoxalyl propionate ($C_2H_5OOCCH(CH_3)COCOOC_2H_5$) lead to 2-carbethoxy-4-hydroxy- and 2-hydroxy-4-carbethoxyquinolines as well as their 3-methyl derivatives. A convenient route to 4-substituted quinolines with the 2 position free was developed by Price and Roberts (26). This comprises heating an aromatic amine with ethoxymethylenemalonic diethyl ester ($C_2H_5OCH=C(COOC_2H_5)_2$) and cyclizing the resulting β-anilino-α-carbethoxyacrylate ($ArNHCH=C(COOC_2H_5)_2$) to the 3-carbethoxy-4-hydroxyquinoline.

Other β-keto esters that have been applied to the synthesis of quinoline derivatives include ethyl β-ketocaprylate, ethyl acetonedicarboxylate, 2-carbethoxycyclopentanone, and 2-carbethoxycyclohexanone. In addition to these, 1,3-diketones, 1,3-ketoaldehydes, and 1,3-dialdehydes have been employed in the synthesis of quinoline derivatives.

Pfitzinger Reaction (27). The Pfitzinger reaction comprises the condensation of isatin (**19**) with carbonyl compounds (aldehydes, ketones, acids, and esters) (**20**) in alkaline medium to form 4-carboxyquinolines (**21**). Many ketonic compounds have been condensed with isatin, but some have failed in this reaction, the failure being attributed to steric hindrance of the R and R′ groups.

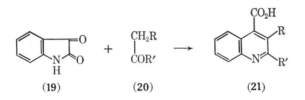

$$\text{(19)} \qquad\qquad \text{(20)} \qquad\qquad\qquad \text{(21)}$$

Friedländer, Camps, and V. Niementowski Reactions. In these syntheses an o-substituted aniline (**22**) is condensed in a basic medium with a carbonyl compound (**23**) to form the quinoline (**24**). The Friedländer method which employs o-aminobenzaldehyde ((**22**), R = H), yields quinolines without substituents in the 4 position. 4-Alkyl- and 4-arylquinolines are prepared from o-aminoacetophenones ((**22**), R =

$$\text{(22)} \qquad\qquad \text{(23)} \qquad\qquad\qquad \text{(24)}$$

alkyl) and from o-aminobenzophenones ((**22**), R = aryl) (Camps method). 4-Hydroxyquinolines are obtained through the condensation of anthranilic acids ((**22**), R = OH) with ketones (**23**) (V. Niementowski's method), usually in poor yields.

Miscellaneous Syntheses. A convenient method for the preparation of dimethyl quinoline-2,3-dicarboxylates involves the condensation of o-aminobenzaldehyde, o-aminoacetophenone, or o-aminobenzophenone with dimethyl acetylenedicarboxylates. In this way dimethyl 6,7-methylenedioxyquinoline-2,3-dicarboxylate was prepared in 52% yield (28) and dimethyl 4-phenylquinoline-2,3-dicarboxylate in 76% yield (29). When aniline and acetone are heated in the presence of iodine 1,2-dihydro-2,2,4-trimethylquinoline is formed in 68% yield (30). 6-Ethoxy-1,2-dihydro-2,2,4-trimethylquinoline which is prepared similarly from p-phenetidine is used as an antioxidant in rubber and as a fodder and feed stabilizer (31). These compounds lose methane on heating with hydrogen chloride, with aniline hydrochloride, or with the sodium salt of aniline to form 2,4-dimethylquinolines. 1,2-Dihydro-2,2,6-trimethylquinoline (**27**) has been obtained in 87% yield by heating p-toluidine with 3-chloro-3-methyl-1-butyne (**25**) in the presence of a silver chloride catalyst, followed by cyclization of the result-

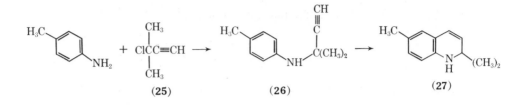

(25)   (26)   (27)

ing 3-*p*-methylanilino-3-methyl-1-butyne (**26**) by heating in ether with a copper catalyst (32). Quinoline can be obtained similarly from *N*-propargylaniline. It is claimed (33) that 3,4-dimethylquinoline is produced when α,β-dimethylcinnamaldehyde oxime is heated with acetic anhydride or with phosphorus oxychloride. The oxime of cinnamaldehyde itself does not produce quinoline when heated with phosphorus pentoxide because it undergoes the Beckmann rearrangement first and then dehydrates to form isoquinoline.

Economic Aspects

Table 1 gives selected figures from 1962 to 1966 on the production and sales of quinoline (dyes) and some quinoline derivatives. The price of quinoline in July 1967 was 51¢/lb and of isoquinoline 65¢/lb.

Table 1. Production and Sales of Quinoline and Some Derivatives in the United States

Year	Chemical	Production, 1000 lb	Sales Quantity, 1000 lb	Sales Value, $1000	Unit value per lb, $
1961	quinaldine	12			
1962	quinoline dyes	322	292	1224	4.19
	8-quinolinol deriv (medicinal)	325	145	496	3.42
	8-quinolinol copper salt (pesticide)	68	54	211	3.91
1963	quinaldine	24			
	quinoline dyes	464	392	1294	3.30
	8-quinolinol deriv (medicinal)	178	101	316	3.13
	8-quinolinol copper salt (pesticide)	56	58	212	3.66
1964	quinaldine	33			
	quinoline dyes	637	519	1658	3.19
	deriv (medicinal)	320	227	2905	12.80
	8-quinolinol copper salt (pesticide)	85	83	196	2.36
1965	quinaldine	38			
	quinoline dyes	576	507	1664	3.28
	deriv (medicinal)	536	152	495	3.26
1966	quinoline dyes	523	597	1934	3.24
	deriv (medicinal)	934			
	8-quinolinol copper salt (pesticide)	426	390	924	2.37

Derivatives of Quinoline

Alkylquinolines. Alkylquinolines are encountered in small amounts in tars from low-temperature and high-temperature carbonization of coal, and are found in the middle oil from liquid hydrogenation of coal. A patent (19) has been issued for the isolation of quinaldine from tar distillates through the formation of an addition complex of quinaldine with phenol or cresols. Jantzen (18) succeeded in isolating and identifying the methylquinolines from coal tar bases and gives characteristic constants for the methylquinolines and their sulfates. During the cracking of certain crude petroleum oils from California, Venezuela, etc, (34) quinoline and its homologs increase the catalysis problems by acting as catalyst poisons. Mills et al. (35) have used the sorption and desorption of quinoline from silica gel and silica–alumina gel at 315°C for the study of the properties of cracking catalysts.

Many alkyl derivatives of quinoline have been synthesized and characterized. The benzene-substituted alkyl derivatives of quinoline undergo reactions which are typical of alkyl groups. The pyridine-substituted alkyl derivatives of quinoline and especially *quinaldine* (2-methylquinoline) and *lepidine* (4-methylquinoline) are different in that the methyl groups possess enhanced reactivity. Thus quinaldine and lepidine condense with benzaldehyde to give the compound $C_9H_6NCH\!\!=\!\!CHC_6H_5$, as well as the corresponding diquinaldine and dilepidine derivatives, $(C_9H_6NCH_2)_2CHC_6H_5$. The condensation is brought about by heating the reactants together or by heating with acetic anhydride, hydrochloric acid, or zinc chloride. Other aldehydes react similarly (36). 3-Methylquinoline does not undergo these condensation reactions.

The cause of the enhanced reactivity of the 2- and 4-methylquinolines is not known. One postulate is that these compounds form reactive methylene intermediates (enamines) by a tautomeric shift of a methyl hydrogen to the nitrogen atom.

When quinaldine and lepidine are converted to the quaternary salts the reactivity of the methyl groups is further enhanced. Quinaldine methiodide (**28**) condenses with benzaldehyde at room temperature in the presence of a basic catalyst to form the styryl compound (**31**). The mechanism of this reaction comprises formation of the methylene base (**29**) from (**28**), condensation of this reactive intermediate with benzaldehyde and conversion of the resulting allene (**30**) to the styryl compound (**31**). Evi-

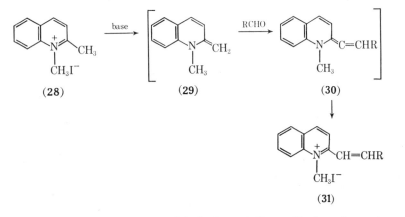

dence for this mechanism is the actual isolation of the methylene bases in a few instances. The methyl group of quinaldine can undergo metalation and also enters into condensations of the Claisen type. The oxidation of quinaldine and lepidine with selenium dioxide yields quinoline-2- and quinoline-4-aldehyde. These aldehydes undergo the benzoin type of condensation in the presence of cyanide ions to form quinoloin, $C_9H_6NCHOHCOC_9H_6N$, which is reduced in situ to $C_9H_6NCHOHCHOH$-C_9H_6N at the expense of the aldehyde which is converted to the corresponding acid (37). Quinaldine undergoes bimolecular dehydrogenation when heated with sulfur or with sulfuric acid to form 1,2-bis(2-quinolyl)ethane, $C_9H_6NCH_2CH_2$-C_9H_6N, along with other dehydrogenation products (38). Bimolecular reduction of a different nature occurs when quinaldine is reduced by zinc metal or electrolytically (39). In this case a dihydroquinaldine dimer is formed, containing 2,3'- and 4,4'-linkages. Quinaldine and lepidine react with benzyl alcohol in the presence of alkali to form 2- and 4-β-phenylethylquinoline, respectively, in high yields (40).

Hydroquinolines. The hetero ring of quinoline is much more readily hydrogenated than the benzene ring. The reaction of quinoline with sodium in liquid ammonia yields 1,2-dihydroquinoline (41). N-Methyl-2-phenyl-1,2-dihydroquinoline can be obtained from quinoline methiodide by reaction with phenylmagnesium bromide. Reagents such as sodium and alcohol, tin and hydrochloric acid, as well as mild catalytic hydrogenation, convert quinoline to 1,2,3,4-tetrahydroquinoline. The hetero ring of quinoline is progressively more difficult to hydrogenate as the number of alkyl substituents on the hetero ring increases.

1,2,3,4-Tetrahydroquinoline behaves like a monoalkylaniline. It forms an N-nitroso derivative which can be readily rearranged to 6-nitrosotetrahydroquinoline. Tetrahydroquinolines can be dehydrogenated by oxidation with chromic acid, silver acetate, iodine, or chloramil (42) or by heating with palladium or platinum. When quaternary salts of N-alkyl-1,2,3,4-tetrahydroquinoline are reduced with sodium amalgam and water, the ring opens to give N,N-disubstituted-3-phenylpropylamine (Emde degradation). Total hydrogenation of quinoline can be brought about by hydriodic acid and phosphorus or by vigorous catalytic hydrogenation over platinum catalyst to form cis- and trans-decahydroquinolines.

Hydroxyquinolines (Quinolinols). 2- and 4-Hydroxyquinolines show properties of both the enol and keto tautomers and hence are also called 2(1H)- and 4(1H)-quinolones. Thus 2-hydroxyquinoline (carbostyril) yields the O-methyl ether on methylation with diazomethane but with methyl iodide and alkali N-methylcarbostyril is the product. However, spectroscopic evidence (43) and that of ionization constants (44) indicate that 2- and 4-hydroxyquinolines exist predominantly in the 2- and 4-quinolone forms. On the other hand 3-carboxy-4-hydroxyquinoline is believed to exist entirely in the hydroxy form. It is claimed that the reaction of 2-hydroxyquinoline N-oxide in pyridine with one equivalent of p-toluenesulfonyl chloride yields mainly 8-tosyloxy-2-quinolone (45). 3-, 5-, 6-, 7-, and 8-Hydroxyquinolines do not exhibit the keto-enol tautomeric behavior.

8-Hydroxyquinoline (oxine) (46) can be prepared by sulfonation of quinoline with oleum and fusion of the sodium salt with sodium hydroxide at 225°C, from 8-chloroquinoline by hydrolysis, or from o-aminophenol by the Skraup method. It is an effective external antiseptic and on sulfonation and iodination produces the amebacidal drug chiniofon, principally 7-iodo-8-hydroxyquinoline-5-sulfonic acid. Vioform (Ciba), 5-chloro-7-iodo-8-hydroxyquinoline, is used in the treatment of gastrointestinal infections of bacterial origin. The copper salt of 8-hydroxyquinoline, $(C_9H_6NO)_2Cu$, possesses fungicidal activity and will completely inhibit mold growth in laboratory media at a concentration of 1–2 ppm. The structure of 8-hydroxyquinoline is such that it permits chelation of the hydroxyl group with the nuclear nitrogen and the formation of metallic chelates. In these metallic complexes or "oxinates," the metal replaces the hydrogen of the hydroxyl group and is also linked by a coordinate bond to the nuclear nitrogen. These chelate compounds are used in the determination of metals, particularly magnesium and aluminum.

Haloquinolines. *2-* and *4-Chloroquinolines* are prepared from the corresponding hydroxyquinolines by the action of phosphorus oxychloride (and phosphorus pentachloride), and have the unique properties shown by the corresponding halopyridines. Treatment of quinoline *N*-oxide with sulfuryl chloride or with phosphorus oxychloride provides another method of obtaining 4-chloroquinolines and small amounts of 2-chloroquinolines. 2- and 4-Quinolinethiols have been prepared from the halides by reaction with potassium hydrosulfide or thiourea (ref. 34, pp. 122, 135). Numerous other reactions of 2- and 4-chloroquinolines with nucleophilic reagents occur readily; see also reference 47.

A successful method for commercial production (26,48) of *4,7-dichloroquinoline* (mp, 85°C; lacrimatory and irritating to the skin) utilizes the action of formic acid on *m*-chloroaniline to produce *m*-chloroformanilide; further condensation with *m*-chloroaniline hydrochloride gives the formimide, $m\text{-ClC}_6\text{H}_4\text{NHCH}{=}\text{NC}_6\text{H}_4\text{Cl-}m$. On treatment with diethyl malonate the formimide is converted to an intermediate, $m\text{-ClC}_6\text{H}_4\text{NHCH}{=}\text{C(COOC}_2\text{H}_5)_2$, which promptly cyclizes to ethyl 4-hydroxy-7-chloro-3-quinolinecarboxylate. After saponification, the decarboxylation and treatment with phosphorus oxychloride are carried out in Dowtherm (The Dow Chemical Co.). 4,7-Dichloroquinoline is an important intermediate in the synthesis of antimalarials such as chloroquine and amodiaquin (Camoquin (Parke, Davis & Co.)).

Aminoquinolines. *3-Aminoquinoline* is best prepared by replacement of the bromine in 3-bromoquinoline by the use of a complex of copper sulfate with ammonia (ref. 34, p. 162).

4-Aminoquinolines. In the search for drugs to combat malaria during World War II, a large series of 4-alkylaminoquinolines (ref. 49, pp. 791–801) was made by a reaction of appropriate amines with the desired 4-chloroquinoline, often through the intermediate phenoxy derivatives. These products include chloroquine and amodiaquin (see Protozoal infections, chemotherapy). Trypanocydal activity has been shown by Surfen (I. G. Farbenindustrie), 1,3-bis(4-amino-2-methyl-6-quinolyl)urea, and analogs (ref. 49, pp. 847–849; ref. 50, pp. 295–296).

8-Aminoquinolines. A large number of 6-methoxy-8-dialkylaminoalkylaminoquinolines were synthesized for study as antimalarials, including pamaquine and primaquine (49,50). (See also Therapeutic agents, protozoal infections.) The general procedure is reduction of the 8-nitro group to an amine. Alkylation of the 8-amino compound is carried out with the selected alkyl halide, or the intermediate bromoalkylphthalimide may be used as an alkylating agent.

Aldehydes, Ketones, and Acids. *2-* and *4-Quinolinecarboxaldehydes* (quinaldaldehyde and cinchoninaldehyde, respectively) are most conveniently prepared by oxidation of the corresponding methyl derivatives with fresh selenium dioxide (51) in hot xylene. Quinaldaldehyde oxime forms chelated metal compounds and therefore has a cis configuration (52). The aldehydes condense with aromatic amines, nitromethane, or active methylene groups; they also undergo a benzoin condensation. *Ketones* are prepared by treating the aldehyde with diazoethane and other diazoalkanes (53). *Carboxylic acids* are obtained by chromic–sulfuric acid oxidation of methyl groups.

Hydrolysis of cyano groups gives rise to carboxylic acids. Conversion of 2- and 4-methylquinolines to styryl derivatives and subsequent cleavage of the double bond is also practical. Decarboxylation of 2-quinolinecarboxylic acid (quinaldinic acid) and of 4-quinolinecarboxylic acid (cinchoninic acid) occurs readily.

Biquinolines, $(C_9H_6N)_2$, and their derivatives, are generally obtained by application of standard quinoline syntheses to bifunctional molecules, or by the application of the Ullmann synthesis.

Benzoquinolines. Benzoquinoline nuclei characterize certain alkaloids (54); benzo[f]quinoline in the ergot alkaloids (see Vol. 1, p. 789); benzo[g]quinoline in a pigment from fungi; and benzo[h] quinoline in the chelidonine–sanguinarine group of alkaloids. The structures are designated as azaphenanthrenes and azaanthracenes in the German patent literature.

Uses

Quinoline derivatives are the parent substances of quinine and other plant alkaloids (see Alkaloids) and of synthetic medicinals; for example, local anesthetics (dibucaine, 2-butoxy-N-(2-diethylaminoethyl)cinchoninamide), antimalarials (4- and 8-aminoquinoline derivatives, 4-quinolinemethanols), and amebacides (hydroxyquinolines and their halogenated derivatives) (see Therapeutic agents, protozoal infections). In veterinary medicine in the tropics (50) Surfen and Antrycide (Imperial Chemical (Pharmaceuticals) Ltd.), 4-amino-6-(2-amino-6-methyl-4-pyrimidylamino)quinaldine-1,1'-dimetho salts, have been effective in the treatment of trypanosome infections in cattle. The copper derivative of 8-quinoline is used as a mildewproofing agent (see Vol. 10, p. 222). 8-Quinolinol is used in the analysis and separation of metallic ions. Some substituted quinolines are also used in perfumes.

The oxidation of quinoline affords a source of nicotinic acid (see Vitamins), which is used as a supplement in human and animal nutrition; however, in this field quinoline must meet competition from alkylpyridines (see Pyridine).

Quinoline cyanine dyes were among the first materials developed as agents for sensitizing photographic plates for color photography (see Cyanine dyes). For fabric dyes, quinaldine and other quinoline derivatives serve as intermediates in the preparation of quinoline dyes (qv).

Quinoline and isoquinoline are strong collectors of talc and serve some uses as flotation agents. In the dephenolization of waste liquors from the carbonization of coal (55), both the Holley-Mott and the Lowenstein-Lom processes take advantage of the favorable effects of additions of aromatic nitrogenous bases, such as quinoline and isoquinoline, on the distribution coefficient in liquid–liquid extraction of phenols.

ISOQUINOLINE

Isoquinoline (**2**) (2-benzazine; benzo[c]pyridine; leucoline) (RRI 1025), C_9H_7N, is a heterocyclic compound formed by the fusion of a benzene and a pyridine ring with nitrogen in the 2 position. The structure is assigned on the basis of synthesis and degradation studies. On treatment with alkaline permanganate, isoquinoline is oxidized to phthalic acid and cinchomeronic (3,4-pyridinedicarboxylic) acid.

The isoquinoline nucleus is found in plant alkaloids in the group of opium bases, such as papaverine, narcotine, and apomorphine (see Vol. 1, p. 767). In small amounts isoquinoline occurs in products from the hydrogenation of coal and in coal tar (56). Isoquinoline can be isolated from the coal tar by preparing hydrogen sulfate salts, $C_9H_7N \cdot HSO_4H$, from the mixed bases of the fraction boiling at 236–243°C. After repeated crystallization from 88% alcohol, the salt fraction (melting at 205°C) is decomposed to liberate isoquinoline. A patented method (57) removes isoquinoline as a complex with calcium chloride. More recently, Kjellman (20) has patented a procedure for separating isoquinoline from a crude fraction, melting at 8–12°C. The batch is cooled to approx −2°C and centrifuged to separate solid isoquinoline. In one operation an isoquinoline melting above 20°C can be obtained in 40–50% yield. Purification by repeated freezing and centrifuging yields an isoquinoline with a melting point of 24–25°C.

Physical and Chemical Properties

PHYSICAL PROPERTIES

Isoquinoline has an odor resembling that of benzaldehyde, is a stronger base than quinoline, and reacts vigorously with alkyl halides to form quaternary salts. The basic ionization constant of isoquinoline is 2×10^{-9} (1). It is sparingly soluble in water and volatile in steam. Isoquinoline dissolves readily in ethyl alcohol, ethyl ether, and the majority of organic solvents. Isoquinoline picrate, $C_9H_7N \cdot C_6H_3N_3O_7$, melts at 224–225°C; 2-methylisoquinolinium iodide monohydrate melts at 159°C.

Freiser and Glowacki (58) have described a very careful purification of isoquinoline and report the following physical properties: fp, 26.48 ± 0.1°C; bp, 243.25°C; dT/dp, 0.059°; d_4^{30}, 1.09101; d_4^{100}, 1.03540; viscosity, 3.2528 cP at 30°C, 1.0230 at 100°C; n_D^{30}, 1.62078; heat of fusion, 1.34 kg-cal/mole (59); heat of combustion, 1123 kg-cal/mole (59).

The ultraviolet spectrum of isoquinoline (in cyclohexane) has been determined (3). Freiser and Glowacki (58) also show the absorption curve of isoquinoline in cyclohexane and list maxima at 266, 304, 312, and 318 mm. The Raman spectrum (4) showed the strongest lines at 507, 523, 782, 1037, and 1381 cm^{-1}.

Reactions

In general isoquinoline undergoes electrophilic substitution reactions in the 5 position and nucleophilic substitution reactions in the 1 position. This is in accord with quantum-mechanical calculations of the highest and lowest electron densities at the carbon atoms. Nitration of isoquinoline with mixed acids gives mainly 5-nitro-isoquinoline along with some of the 8 isomer. Isoquinoline N-oxide also nitrates in the 5 position. The nitration of 1,2,3,4-tetrahydro- and 3,4-dihydroisoquinoline produces 7-nitro derivatives which on dehydrogenation yield 7-nitroisoquinoline (60). Sulfonation of isoquinoline results in a mixture of products with 5-sulfoisoquinoline predominating. Amination by the action of sodamide in neutral solvents gives 1-aminoiso-quinoline which may be converted to isocarbostyril, 1-hydroxyisoquinoline, by diazotization and decomposition.

Like quinoline, isoquinoline is oxidized by peracids to the N-oxide. Oxidation with alkaline permanganate or with hot concentrated sulfuric acid yields cinchomeronic acid (3,4-pyridinedicarboxylic) acid (**32**) and phthalic acid (**33**).

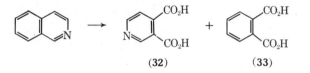

(32)   (33)

Mercuration of isoquinoline results in substitution in the 4 position. Direct bromination also leads to substitution in the 4 position. However, bromination of the isoquinoline–aluminum chloride complex with gaseous bromine gives 5-bromoiso-quinoline in 78% yield (15). Continued bromination leads to 5,8-di- and 5,7,8-tri-bromoisoquinoline. The same orientation of substitution occurs on chlorination of the aluminum chloride–isoquinoline complex.

Isoquinoline reacts vigorously with alkyl and acyl halides to give quaternary ammonium salts. Isoquinoline methiodide (34) upon treatment with alkali yields 1-hydroxy-2-methyl-1,2-dihydroisoquinoline (35) which can be oxidized with potassium ferricyanide to N-methylisoquinolone (N-methylisocarbostyril) (36).

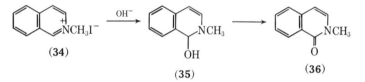

(34)   (35)   (36)

Like quinoline, isoquinoline forms the "Reissert compound" (17) when treated with benzoyl chloride and alkali cyanide. This compound, 1-cyano-2-benzoyl-1,2-dihydroisoquinoline, is converted to 1-carboxyisoquinoline upon treatment with hydrochloric acid. Isoquinoline reacts with Grignard reagents to form 1-substituted 1,2-di-hydroisoquinoline magnesium halide (37) which decomposes in water to the 1-substituted isoquinoline (38).

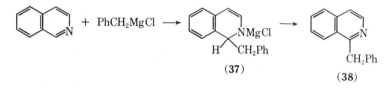

(37)   (38)

Isoquinoline reacts with peroxides to form isoquinoline N-oxide which rearranges to a mixture of 2- and 4-hydroxyisoquinoline derivatives on treatment with acetic anhydride (61) or with p-toluenesulfonyl chloride (62). Isoquinoline N-oxide forms a 1:1 adduct with ethyl acrylate in dimethyl formamide (DMF) which is believed to be 2-hydroxy-3-(1-isoquinolyl) propionate (63).

Synthesis of Isoquinoline and Derivatives

Synthetic procedures for the preparation of isoquinolines are important in estab-lishing the constitution of alkaloids. The 1-benzylisoquinoline system is found in many alkaloids. The three most important methods which have been used extensively are the Bischler-Napieralski, the Pictet-Spengler, and the Pomeranz-Fritsch reactions (64–66). These are based on ring closures of benzene derivatives of the type Ph—C—C—N—C and Ph—C—N—C—C.

Bischler-Napieralski Reaction (64). This reaction consists of the cyclization of acyl derivatives of 2-phenylethylamine (39) to 3,4-dihydroisoquinolines (40) with

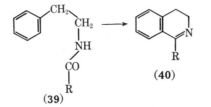

(39)   (40)

powerful dehydrating agents such as phosphorus pentoxide or zinc chloride in boiling toluene, xylene, or tetralin. The cyclization is aided by the presence of electron-donating substituents in the ethylamide (**39**) para to the position involved in cyclization. The acyl group, R, may be aliphatic or aromatic but the yields are poor with formyl derivatives. The 3,4-dihydroisoquinoline (**40**) can be dehydrogenated catalytically with palladium to the corresponding isoquinoline.

A modification of the Bischler-Napieralski reaction consists of the use of 2-hydroxy-2-phenylethylamines in place of (**39**) (Pictet-Gams synthesis). In this case isoquinolines are produced as a result of dehydration at one stage or the other of the reaction. The ketoamide (**41**) resists the Bischler-Napieralski cyclization. However, if the keto group is first protected as its ethylene ketal, then the ketal undergoes cyclization in the presence of phosphorus pentoxide and pyridine (67) to form the ketal (**42**). Hydrolysis

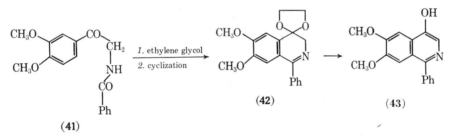

(41)   (42)   (43)

of this yields 1-phenyl-4-hydroxy-6,7-dimethoxyisoquinoline (**43**). The oximes of phenylethyl ketones and of cinnamaldehyde undergo the Beckmann rearrangement when treated with phosphorus pentoxide followed by the Bischler-Napieralski cyclization of the resulting amide to form the corresponding 3,4-dihydroisoquinolines.

Pictet-Spengler Synthesis (64). This synthesis is used in the preparation of 1,2,3,4-tetrahydroisoquinolines which may subsequently be dehydrogenated to the corresponding isoquinolines. 2-Arylethylamines (**44**) are heated with a slight excess of an aldehyde with strong hydrochloric acid to form the anil (**45**). This is then cyclized with or without isolation to the tetrahydroisoquinoline (**46**).

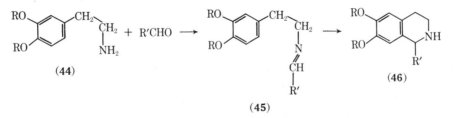

(44)   (45)   (46)

The biogenesis of the isoquinoline alkaloids is believed to follow a similar scheme.

Pomeranz-Fritsch Synthesis (66). This synthesis is represented by the ring closure of benzene derivatives of the type Ph—C—N—C—C. It permits the preparation of isoquinolines with substituent groups in the benzene nucleus in an orientation difficult to obtain by other methods. A Schiff base (**47**) is first formed from an aromatic aldehyde and aminoacetal and then cyclized to the isoquinoline (**48**) in the presence of sulfuric acid or phosphorus oxychloride.

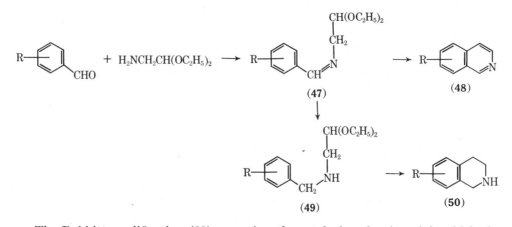

The Bobbitt modification (68) comprises the catalytic reduction of the aldehyde–aminoacetal condensate (**47**) to the amine (**49**), followed by cyclization to the tetrahydroisoquinoline (**50**) by treating with hydrochloric acid and hydrogenating over palladium catalyst. Good yields of the tetrahydroisoquinoline (**50**) are obtained which may be aromatized to (**48**). *N*-Methylation may be carried out as part of the first reduction step by the addition of formaldehyde to the reaction mixture containing (**49**) and then continuing the reduction. The *N*-methylated (**49**) may then be reductively cyclized to the *N*-methyltetrahydroisoquinoline. This synthesis seems to be limited to the preparation of 1,2,3,4-tetrahydroisoquinolines bearing an oxygen in the 7 position.

In the Schlittler and Müller modification (69) of the Pomeranz-Fritsch synthesis a benzylamine is condensed with glyoxal hemiacetal to form the imine (**51**) which is then cyclized to the isoquinoline (**52**). This method permits the synthesis of 1-substituted derivatives of isoquinoline.

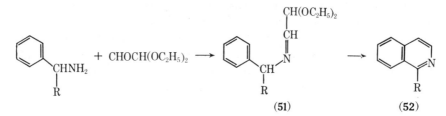

Other Syntheses. A number of syntheses of isoquinoline utilize ortho-disubstituted benzenes as starting materials. In the synthesis of 1,2,3,4-tetrahydro-2-methyl-4-isoquinolone (70) ethyl *o*-chloromethylbenzoate is condensed with the ethyl ester of sarcosine, $CH_3NHCH_2COOC_2H_5$, to form *N*-(*o*-ethoxycarbonylbenzyl) sarcosine, *o*-$COOC_2H_5C_6H_4CH_2N(CH_3)CH_2COOC_2H_5$, and this is then cyclized by heating with sodium ethylate in boiling benzene or with sodium in xylene followed by decarboxylation. 1,2,3,4-Tetrahydro-2-methyl-4-isoquinolone is readily dehydrogenated to the 4-hydroxy-2-methylisoquinolinium cation by treatment with cuprous chloride in alkaline suspension.

A general synthesis of *N*-substituted 1,2,3,4-tetrahydroisoquinolines consists of treating *o*-(2-bromoethyl)benzyl bromide, *o*-BrCH₂CH₂C₆H₄CH₂Br, with primary amines (71). Isocoumarins can be readily converted to the corresponding 1-hydroxy-isoquinolines by treatment with ammonia hydroxide. Homophthalimide, 1,3-iso-quinolinedione, is obtained in excellent yield by heating the diammonium salt of homo-phthalic acid, *o*-COOHC₆H₄CH₂COOH. This cyclic imide (homophthalimide) upon treatment with phosphorus pentachloride is converted to 1,3-dichloroisoquinoline from which isoquinoline may be obtained by dechlorination with hydriodic acid and red phosphorus or with zinc dust (72). Aminophthalides (**53**) undergo rearrangement to form 1-hydroxy-3-alkylisoquinoline derivatives (**54**) which can be dehydrated to the corresponding 1-hydroxyisoquinoline (73).

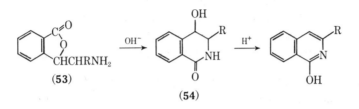

Alkylisoquinolines. 1-Methyl-, 3-methyl-, and 1,3-dimethylisoquinoline have been isolated in small amounts from coal-tar crudes. The methyl groups of 1- and 3-methylisoquinoline are more reactive than those of 4-, 5-, 6-, 7-, and 8-methyliso-quinoline and can be oxidized readily with selenium dioxide to form the corresponding isoquinolinaldehydes (74). These methyl groups will also condense with benzaldehyde in the presence of zinc chloride to form the corresponding 1- and 3-styrylisoquinolines, C₉H₆NCH=CHPh. 3-Methylisoquinoline is less reactive than the 1 isomer so that the formation of 3-styrylisoquinoline requires more drastic conditions than the formation of the 1 isomer. The reactivity of the methyl group is further enhanced when the methyl-isoquinoline is quaternized. Thus 3-styrylisoquinoline methiodide has been obtained in high yield by condensing 3-methylisoquinoline methiodide with benzaldehyde under mild conditions (75). Both 1-methyl- and 3-methylisoquinoline react with benzyl alco-hol in the presence of base to form 1- and 3-dihydrostyrylisoquinoline (40). 1-Alkyl-isoquinolines may be prepared through a series of reactions which comprise the formation of 1,2-dihydro-1-cyano-2-benzoylisoquinoline (Reissert compound) from isoquinoline, treating this with phenyllithium and alkyl halide, and hydrolyzing the resulting 1,2-dihydro-1-cyano-1-alkyl-2-benzoylisoquinoline to the 1-alkylisoquinoline (76). 1-Benzyl-3,4-dihydroisoquinolines, which have been encountered frequently in alkaloid studies, are labile and may be oxidized readily on exposure to air or by treatment with iodine to the corresponding 1-benzoyl-3,4-dihydroisoquinolines (77).

Hydroisoquinolines. The hydroisoquinolines are prepared by ring-closure reac-tions or by reduction of isoquinoline. Lithium aluminum hydride (78) or sodium in liquid ammonia (79) converts isoquinoline to 1,2-dihydroisoquinoline initially. 1,2,3,4-Tetrahydroisoquinolines may be obtained by further reduction of the 1,2-dihydroiso-quinolines, or of the isoquinolines, or of their methiodides (80) by sodium borohydride in aqueous alcohol, sodium and alcohol, tin and hydrochloric acid, or catalytically with hydrogen under pressure. The catalytic reduction of isoquinoline methiodide requires the presence of diethylamine for best results (81). Further reduction of the dihydro- and tetrahydroisoquinolines provides decahydroisoquinolines which exist in both the cis and trans forms. The hydroisoquinolines are readily dehydrogenated to the corresponding isoquinolines by heating with platinum or with chloranil (78).

The hydroisoquinolines are more susceptible to ring opening than the isoquinolines. Ring opening occurs with nitrogen elimination when 3,4-dihydroisoquinolines (55) are heated with alkali and dimethyl sulfate to form *o*-acylstyrenes (56) in good yield (82). When there is no substituent in the 1 position of the 3,4-dihydroisoquino-

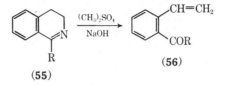

(55)   (56)

line, the product is an aldehyde ((56), R = H). Ring opening without loss of nitrogen occurs when the 3,4-dihydroisoquinoline is heated with formaldehyde, formic acid, and diethylamine or sodium formate (83) to form the *o*-substituted *N,N*-dimethylphenethylamine.

Exhaustive methylation of 1,2,3,4-tetrahydroisoquinoline yields *N*-methyl-1,2,3,4-tetrahydroisoquinoline methiodide (57) which undergoes cleavage at the 2–3 bond in the presence of alkali to *o*-dimethylaminomethylstyrene (58) (Hofmann degradation).

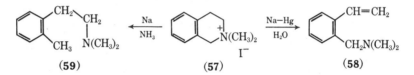

(59)   (57)   (58)

In the presence of sodium and liquid ammonia, (57) undergoes cleavage at the 1–2 bond to form *o*-dimethylaminoethyltoluene (59).

Hydroxyisoquinolines. Hydroxyl groups in the benzene nucleus undergo the characteristic reactions of phenols. The use of 7-hydroxyisoquinoline in the synthesis of homomeroquinene, 3-vinyl-4-piperidinepropionic acid (84), which was required for the total synthesis of quinine, presents an interesting cross section of the reactions of isoquinoline. The manufacture and utilization of 1,3-isoquinolinediols (85) in chromiferous monoazo dyes has been reported (86). 1-Hydroxyisoquinoline gives both *O*-methyl- and *N*-methyl derivatives on methylation, indicating the tautomeric existence of both forms (44). Spectral studies show that it exists predominantly in the isoquinolone (60) and zwitterion forms. Homophthalimide also exists predominantly in the nonaromatic amide form.

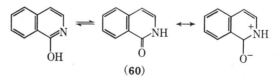

(60)

3-Hydroxyisoquinoline,   3-hydroxy-1-methylisoquinoline,   and   3-hydroxy-1-methyl-6,7-dimethoxyisoquinoline have been shown to exist by uv spectrometry as lactim (hydroxy) tautomers in nonhydroxylic solvents and as lactam tautomers in water (87). Like the naphthols, 5-, 6-, 7-, and 8-hydroxyisoquinolines undergo the Bucherer reaction to form the corresponding aminoisoquinolines.

Haloisoquinolines. Generally, chloroisoquinolines are prepared from aminoisoquinolines by the Sandmeyer reaction, or from isocarbostyrils by treatment with chlorides of phosphorus; or the chloro substituents may be present in the aromatic intermediates used in the initial synthesis. The action of phosphorus oxychloride on isoquinoline N-oxide furnishes the 1-chloro derivatives in good yield. The enhanced reactivity of chlorine in the 1 position is shown in the reaction of sodium ethoxide with dichloroisoquinolines to replace only the 1-chloro substituent, for example in the formation of 1-ethoxy-3-chloroisoquinoline (65).

Another example is the preparation of 1-diethylaminoethylamino-3-chloroisoquinoline (65). 4-Bromoisoquinoline is obtained by heating the perbromide of isoquinoline or of its salts. 5-Bromoisoquinoline is obtained by treating the isoquinolinealuminum chloride complex with gaseous bromine (15). Treatment of 3-methylisoquinoline with N-bromosuccinimide gives side-chain bromination.

Uses

Much of the chemistry of isoquinolines has been developed in studies of the structure of plant alkaloids, including papaverine, narcotine, berberines, and other benzyl- and bisbenzylisoquinolines (88) (see Alkaloids). Isoquinoline derivatives have been patented (86) as intermediates in the preparation of dyes for wool, cellulose, and nylon fabrics. Some benzylisoquinoline and bisbenzylisoquinoline alkaloids possess pharmacological activity. These include the "curare" alkaloids which were originally used as arrow poisons by the South American natives and later applied in purer form as anesthetics (see Curare).

1-(3,4-Dimethoxybenzyl)-6,7-dimethoxyisoquinoline (papaverine) has clinical use as an antispasmodic while 1-methyl-6-hydroxy-7-methoxy-1,2,3,4-tetrahydroisoquinoline (salsoline) has been used in the treatment of hypertension. 1-(p-Chlorophenethyl)-6,7-dimethoxy-2-methyl-1,2,3,4-tetrahydroisoquinoline, commonly known as Versidyne or Methopholine, is an effective and safe analgesic agent (89). It is claimed that compositions prepared with 1,2,3,4-tetrahydroisoquinoline hydrochloride are appetite reducing (90). 1,1'-Methylenebis(3-methyl-3,4-dihydroisoquinoline) is an effective amebacide (91). Isoquinoline has been used for the detection and identification of gold, platinum, iridium, and ruthenium (92) and also in the inhibition of corrosion of steel (93).

Bibliography

"Quinoline and Isoquinoline" in *ECT* 1st ed., Vol. 11, pp. 389–401, by Alice G. Renfrew, Mellon Institute.

1. I. M. Kolthoff and N. H. Furman, *Potentiometric Titrations*, John Wiley & Sons, Inc., New York, 1926, p. 329.
2. G. W. Wheland, *The Theory of Resonance*, John Wiley & Sons, Inc., New York, 1944, p. 70.
3. R. A. Friedel and M. Orchin, *Ultraviolet Spectra of Aromatic Compounds*, John Wiley & Sons, Inc., New York, 1951, pp. 270–271.
4. H. Luther and C. Reichel, *Z. Physik. Chem.* **195**, 103–115 (1950); *Chem. Abstr.* **44**, 9257 (1950).
5. M. J. S. Dewar and P. M. Maitlis, *J. Chem. Soc.* **1957**, 2521–2528; K. Schofield, "Nitration of Heterocyclic Nitrogen Compounds," *Quart. Rev.* **4**, 382 (1950).
6. M. W. Austin and J. H. Ridd, *J. Chem. Soc.* **1963**, 4204–4210.
6a. M. Kulka and R. H. F. Manske, *Can. J. Chem.* **30**, 720–724 (1952).
7. P. B. D. De la Mare, M. D. Johnson, and J. H. Ridd, *Chem. Ind.* (*London*) **1960**, 1505; *Chem. Abstr.* **55**, 24751 (1961).

8. E. Ochiai and A. Ohta, *Chem. Pharm. Bull. (Tokyo)* **10,** 349 (1962); *Chem. Abstr.* **58,** 2433 (1963).
9. H. J. Richter and N. E. Rustad, *J. Org. Chem.* **29,** 3381–3383 (1964).
10. H. Gilman, J. Eisch, and T. S. Soddy, *J. Am. Chem. Soc.* **81,** 4000–4003 (1959).
11. Fr. Pat. 1,470,433 (1967), Roussel-Uclaf.
12. F. W. Bergstrom, *Chem. Rev.* **35,** 77–277 (1944).
13. J. J. Eisch, *J. Org. Chem.* **27,** 1318–1323 (1962).
14. P. B. D. De la Mare, M. Kiamud-din, and J. H. Ridd, *Chem. Ind. (London)* **1958,** 361; *Chem. Abstr.* **52,** 16352 (1958); *J. Chem. Soc.* **1960,** 561–565.
15. M. Gordon and D. E. Pearson, *J. Org. Chem.* **29,** 329–332 (1964).
15a. U.S. Pat. 2,964,529 (1960), M. G. Sturrock, E. L. Cline, K. R. Robinson, and K. A. Zercher (to Koppers Co.); *Chem. Abstr.* **55,** 11443 (1961).
16. G. B. Bachman and D. E. Cooper, *J. Org. Chem.* **9,** 302–309 (1944).
17. W. E. McEwen and R. L. Cobb, "The Reissert Reaction," *Chem. Rev.* **55,** 511–549 (1955); R. L. Cobb and W. E. McEwen, *J. Am. Chem. Soc.* **77,** 5042–5048 (1955); R. F. Collins and T. Henshall, *J. Chem. Soc.* **1956,** 1881–1883; F. D. Popp and W. Blount, *Chem. Ind. (London)* **1961,** 550; *Chem. Abstr.* **57,** 3409 (1962).
18. E. Jantzen, *Das fraktionierte Destillieren und das fraktionierte Verteilen als Methoden zur Trennung von Stoffgemischen* (Dechema Monographie 48), Vol. V, Verlag Chemie, Berlin, 1932, pp. 117–142.
19. U.S. Pat. 2,432,064 (Dec. 2, 1947), F. E. Cislak and M. M. Otto (to Reilly Tar & Chemical Corp.).
20. U.S. Pat. 2,483,420 (Oct. 4, 1949), H. A. Kjellman, Jr. (to Koppers Co.).
21. R. H. F. Manske and M. Kulka, "The Skraup Synthesis of Quinolines," in R. Adams, et al., eds., *Organic Reactions,* Vol. 7, John Wiley & Sons, Inc., New York, 1953.
22. I. T. Millar and H. D. Springall, *Sidgwick's Organic Chemistry of Nitrogen,* 3rd ed., Clarendon Press, Oxford, England, 1966, Chap. 24.
23. R. H. Reitsema, *Chem. Rev.* **43,** 43–68 (1948).
24. C. R. Hauser and G. A. Reynolds, *J. Am. Chem. Soc.* **70,** 2402–2404 (1948).
25. G. F. Lisk and G. W. Stacey, *J. Am. Chem. Soc.* **68,** 2686–2688 (1946).
26. C. C. Price and R. M. Roberts, *J. Am. Chem. Soc.* **68,** 1204–1208, 1255–1256 (1946).
27. Ng. Ph. Buu-Hoi and René Royer, *J. Chem. Soc.* **1948,** 106.
28. J. B. Hendrickson and R. Rees, *J. Am. Chem. Soc.* **83,** 1250 (1961).
29. E. C. Taylor and N. D. Heindel, *J. Org. Chem.* **32** (5), 1666–1667 (1967).
30. I. W. Elliott, Jr. and P. Yates, *J. Org. Chem.* **26,** 1287–1289 (1961).
31. A. S. Taranenko, G. A. Belousova, and V. G. Vaidanich, *Sin. Issled. Eff. Stabil. Polim. Mater. Voronezh* **1964,** 180–184; *Chem. Abstr.* **67,** 281 (1967); U.S. Pat. 3,325,288 (1967), C. C. Tung (to Monsanto Co.).
32. N. R. Easton and D. R. Cassady, *J. Org. Chem.* **27,** 4713–4714 (1962).
33. C. Troszkiewicz and J. Glinka, *Roczniki Chem.* **36,** 1387–1388 (1962); *Chem. Abstr.* **59,** 2766 (1963).
34. R. C. Elderfield, ed., *Heterocyclic Compounds,* Vol. IV, John Wiley & Sons, Inc., New York, 1952, pp. 1–343.
35. G. A. Mills, E. R. Boedeker, and A. G. Oblad, *J. Am. Chem. Soc.* **72,** 1554–1560 (1950).
36. R. S. Tipson, *J. Am. Chem. Soc.* **67,** 507–511 (1945).
37. H. Andrews, S. Skidmore, and H. Suschitzky, *J. Chem. Soc.* **1962,** 3827–3828.
38. S. Skidmore and E. Tidd, *J. Chem. Soc.* **1961,** 1098–1102.
39. I. W. Elliott, E. S. McCaskill, M. S. Robertson, and C. H. Kirksey, *Tetrahedron Letters* **1962** (7), 291–294; H. C. Dunathan, I. W. Elliott, and P. Yates, *Tetrahedron Letters* **1961,** 781.
40. M. Avramoff and Y. Sprinzak, *J. Am. Chem. Soc.* **78,** 4090–4096 (1956).
41. W. Hückel and L. Hagedorn, *Chem. Ber.* **90,** 752–754 (1957).
42. T. Masamune, T. Saito, and G. Homma, *J. Fac. Sci. Hokkaido Univ. Ser. III* **5** (1), 55–58 (1957): *Chem. Abstr.* **52,** 11062 (1958).
43. G. W. Ewing and E. A. Stack, *J. Am. Chem. Soc.* **68,** 2181–2187 (1946).
44. A. R. Katritsky, ed., *Advances in Heterocyclic Chemistry,* Vol. 1, Academic Press, New York-London, 1963, pp. 339–437.
45. M. Hamana and K. Funakoshi, *Yakugaku Zasshi* **84,** 28–35 (1964); *Chem. Abstr.* **61,** 3068 (1964).

46. J. P. Phillips, "The Reactions of 8-Quinolinol," *Chem. Rev.* **56**, 271–297 (1956); R. G. W. Hollingshead, *Oxine and Its Derivatives*, Vols. 1–4, Butterworth & Co. (Publishers) Ltd., London, 1954–1956.

47. H. I. Thayer and B. B. Corson, *J. Am. Chem. Soc.* **70**, 2330–2333 (1948).

48. R. L. Kenyon, J. A. Wiesner, and C. E. Kwartler, *Ind. Eng. Chem.* **41**, 654–662 (1949).

49. A. Burger, ed., *Medicinal Chemistry*, 2nd ed., Interscience Publishers, Inc., New York, 1960.

50. W. A. Sexton, *Chemical Constitution and Biological Activity*, E. & F. N. Spon Ltd., London, 1949.

51. V. G. Ramsey, *J. Am. Pharm. Assoc. Sci. Ed.* **40**, 564–565 (1951).

52. T. W. J. Taylor, H. G. Winkles, and M. S. Marks, *J. Chem. Soc.* **1931**, 2778–2783.

53. A. Burger and L. R. Modlin, *J. Am. Chem. Soc.* **62**, 1079–1083 (1940).

54. L. P. Walls, "Benzoquinolines," in R. C. Elderfield, ed., *Heterocyclic Compounds*, Vol. IV, John Wiley & Sons, Inc., New York, 1952, pp. 625–661.

55. W. W. Hodge, in W. Rudolfs, ed., *Industrial Wastes*, Reinhold Publishing Corp., New York, 1953, pp. 402–403.

56. H. H. Lowry, *Chemistry of Coal Utilization*, John Wiley & Sons, Inc., New York, 1945, p. 1353.

57. U.S. Pat. 2,391,270 (Dec. 18, 1945), F. E. Reimers (to Allied Chemical & Dye Corp.).

58. H. Freiser and W. L. Glowacki, *J. Am. Chem. Soc.* **71**, 514–516 (1949).

59. F. K. Beilstein, *Handbuch der organischen Chemie*, 4th ed., Vol. 20, pp. 339, 380; 1st Suppl., pp. 134, 143; 2nd Suppl., pp. 222, 236.

60. A. McCoubrey and D. W. Mathieson, *J. Chem. Soc.* **1951**, 2851–2853; **1950**, 1833–1836.

61. M. M. Robison and B. L. Robison, *J. Org. Chem.* **21**, 1337–1341 (1956).

62. E. Ochiai and M. Ikehara, *Pharm. Bull.* (*Tokyo*) **3**, 454–458 (1958); *Chem. Abstr.* **50**, 15560 (1956).

63. H. Seidl and R. Huisgen, *Tetrahedron Letters* **1963** (29), 2023–2025.

64. W. M. Whaley and T. R. Govindachari, "The Preparation of 3,4-Dihydroisoquinolines and Related Compounds by the Bischler-Napieralski Reaction," and "The Pictet-Spengler Synthesis of Tetrahydroisoquinolines and Related Compounds," in R. Adams et al., eds., *Organic Reactions*, Vol. 6, John Wiley & Sons, Inc., New York, 1951, Chaps. 2, 3.

65. W. J. Gensler, "Isoquinoline," in R. C. Elderfield, ed., *Heterocyclic Compounds*, Vol. IV, John Wiley & Sons, Inc., New York, 1952, pp. 344–490.

66. W. J. Gensler, "The Synthesis of Isoquinolines by the Pomeranz-Fritsch Reaction," in R. Adams et al., eds., *Organic Reactions*, Vol. 6, John Wiley & Sons, Inc., New York, 1951, Chap. 4.

67. N. Itoh and S. Sugasawa, *Tetrahedron* **6**, 16–20 (1959).

68. J. M. Bobbitt, J. M. Kiely, K. L. Khanna, and R. Ebermann, *J. Org. Chem.* **30**, 2247–2250 (1965); J. M. Bobbitt, D. N. Roy, A. Marchand, and C. W. Allen, *J. Org. Chem.* **32**, 2225–2227 (1967).

69. E. Schittler and J. Müller, *Helv. Chim. Acta* **31**, 914–924 (1948).

70. I. G. Hinton and F. G. Mann, *J. Chem. Soc.* **1959**, 599–608.

71. E. G. Holliman and F. G. Mann, *J. Chem. Soc.* **1942**, 737–741; **1945**, 34–37.

72. G. Jones, *J. Chem. Soc.* **1960**, 1896–1899.

73. G. E. Ullyot, J. J. Stehle, C. L. Zirkle, R. L. Shriner, and E. J. Wolf, *J. Org. Chem.* **10**, 429–440 (1945).

74. C. E. Teague, Jr. and A. Roe, *J. Am. Chem. Soc.* **73**, 688–689 (1951).

75. L. G. S. Brooker and F. L. White, *J. Am. Chem. Soc.* **73**, 1094–1097 (1951).

76. V. Boekelheide and J. Weinstock, *J. Am. Chem. Soc.* **74**, 660–663 (1952); F. R. Popp and W. E. McEwen, *J. Am. Chem. Soc.* **79**, 3773–3777 (1957).

77. T. R. Govindachari and K. Negarajan, *Proc. Indian Acad. Sci. Sect. A* **42**, 261–266 (1955); *Chem. Abstr.* **50**, 8643 (1956).

78. L. M. Jackman and D. I. Packham, *Chem. Ind.* (*London*) **1955**, 360; *Chem. Abstr.* **50**, 1820 (1956); H. Schmid and P. Karrer, *Helv. Chim. Acta* **32**, 960–966 (1949); *Chem. Abstr.* **43**, 6631 (1949).

79. W. Hückel and G. Graner, *Chem. Ber.* **90**, 2017–2023 (1957); *Chem. Abstr.* **54**, 21122 (1960).

80. R. Mirza, *J. Chem. Soc.* **1957**, 4400–4401.

81. J. A. Barltrop and D. A. H. Taylor, *J. Chem. Soc.* **1951**, 108–110.

82. W. J. Gensler, E. M. Healy, J. Anshuus, and A. L. Bluhm, *J. Am. Chem. Soc.* **78**, 1713–1716 (1956).

83. J. Gardent, *Compt. Rend.* **243**, 1042–1043 (1956); *Chem. Abstr.* **51**, 6641 (1957).

84. R. B. Woodward and W. E. Doering, *J. Am. Chem. Soc.* **67**, 860–874 (1945).

85. U.S. Pat. 2,351,391 (June 13, 1944), H. A. Bergstrom and W. V. Wirth (to Du Pont); *Chem. Abstr.* **38,** 5228 (1944).
86. U.S. Pat. 2,508,404 (May 23, 1950), D. E. Kvalnes and B. G. Carson (to Du Pont); *Chem. Abstr.* **44,** 11108 (1950); Ger. Pat. 1,051,242 (1959), H. A. Dortmann, P. Schmitz, and J. Eibl (to Farbenfabriken Bayer A.G.); *Chem. Abstr.* **55,** 2126 (1961).
87. D. A. Evans, G. E. Smith, and M. A. Wahid, *J. Chem. Soc.* **B1967** (6), 590–595.
88. R. H. F. Manske and H. L. Holmes, eds., *The Alkaloids*, Vol. 9, Academic Press, Inc., New York-London, 1967, Chap. 4.
89. F. F. Foldes, J. More, and I. M. Suna, *Am. J. Med. Sci.* **242,** 682–693 (1961); *Chem. Abstr.* **57,** 14400 (1962); L. J. Cass and W. S. Frederik, *Am. J. Med. Sci.* **246** (5), 550–557 (1963); *Chem. Abstr.* **60,** 11854 (1964).
90. Belg. Pat. 632,520 (Nov. 18, 1963), C. H. Bohringer Sohn; *Chem. Abstr.* **60,** 15688 (1964).
91. T. N. Ghosh and S. K. Ganguly, *J. Indian Chem. Soc.* **39** (1), 28–32 (1962); *Chem. Abstr.* **57,** 4633 (1962).
92. H. F. Schaeffer, *Anal. Chem.* **31,** 1111–1112 (1959); *Chem. Abstr.* **53,** 13880 (1959).
93. R. Bartonicek and J. Nemcova, *Korose Ochrana Mater.* **1962,** 85–87; *Chem. Abstr.* **58,** 12233 (1963).

MARSHALL KULKA
Uniroyal (1966) Ltd.

QUINOLINE DYES

In 1856, C. Greville Williams prepared one of the earliest known synthetic dyes, Cyanine Blue (**1**), by heating a mixture of the ethiodides of lepidine and quinoline in an alkaline medium (1) (see also Cyanine dyes; Polymethine dyes). Jacobsen, in 1882, synthesized Isoquinoline Red (**2**), another cyanine dye, by heating "quinoline" and benzotrichloride (2). The quinoline was obtained from coal tar and must have contained quinaldine and isoquinoline, which are necessary reagents in the synthesis (3). (See also Quinoline and isoquinoline.) Most cyanines are too fugitive to light to have value as textile dyes but they do have important uses as photographic sensitizers.

Flavaniline (**3**) was prepared in 1881 by Fischer and Rudolph by heating acetanilide with zinc chloride (4). The hydrochloride was used as a basic yellow dye for

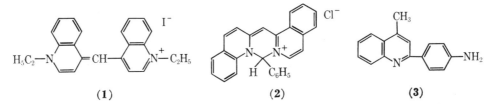

(**1**)   (**2**)   (**3**)

wool and silk, and the sulfonic acid derivative was marketed as Flavaniline S (5). The flavaniline dyes have poor lightfastness and tinctorial strength, and are now obsolete.

In addition to the compounds usually classified as quinoline dyes this review includes others which contain the quinoline nucleus, such as some azo and triarylmethane dyes (see also Azo dyes; Triphenylmethane and related dyes).

Quinophthalone (2-Quinolyl-1,3-indanedione) and Its Derivatives

Interest in this class of dyes has increased during the past ten years because of the rising demand for dyes for paper and synthetic fibers. Quinophthalone (D&C Yellow

No. 11, Solvent Yellow 33, CI 47000) was discovered by Jacobsen and Reimer in 1882 (6,7). They reacted two moles of quinoline with one mole of phthalic anhydride and one mole of zinc chloride at 200°C. Actually quinaldine, an impurity in the quinoline, is the nucleophilic reagent. An inert solvent such as *o*-dichlorobenzene facilitates the condensation (8).

The constitution of quinophthalone was investigated first by Jacobsen and Reimer, and then by Eibner, who proposed structure (4) (9). According to Dilthey and Wizinger (10), this structure lacks the necessary intramolecular resonance to

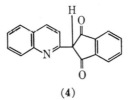

(4)

produce color. This theory is supported by the observation that bromoquinophthalone (5) and 2-phenylindandione (6) are colorless. Wizinger then proposed structures

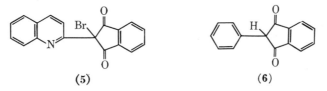

(5)   (6)

(7a) and (7b), which explain the color and other properties of quinophthalone (11,12). Support for (7) is found in the deep-red color of the 2-benzylideneindandione derivative (8). Structure (7) was later confirmed by Kuhn and Bär (13). They methyl-

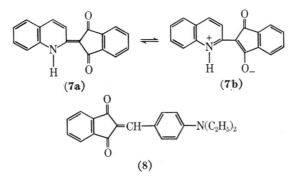

(7a)   (7b)

(8)

ated the sodium derivative of (7) with dimethyl sulfate in xylene at 100°C and oxidized the resulting *N*-methylquinophthalone to obtain phthalic acid and *N*-methyl-2-quinolone. *N*-Methylquinophthalone can also be prepared by condensing 2-phenylmercaptoquinoline-*p*-toluenesulfonate with 1,3-indandione (14). Pure quinophthalone can be crystallized as yellow needles (mp 220°C) from alcohol and acetic acid. The greenish-yellow pigment has low tinctorial power and poor lightfastness, but is used in cosmetics (D&C Yellow No. 11) and occasionally in spirit lacquers.

Quinophthalone dyes can be classified into three groups: anionic, nonionic, and cationic. The *anionic group* includes the sulfonic and carboxylic acid derivatives. Sulfonic acid groups can be introduced by treating quinophthalone and its derivatives with fuming sulfuric acid (oleum), the extent of sulfonation depending on the reaction temperature and the strength of the oleum (15). Alternatively, the addition products of sulfur trioxide and quinophthalone derivatives can be heated under reduced pressure (16). Also, the sulfonic acid groups can be introduced into anilines or naphthylamines which are then treated with paraldehyde and an oxidizing agent. The resulting sulfonated quinaldines are condensed with phthalic anhydride in dimethylformamide at 160–200°C to form quinophthalones with sulfonic acid groups in specific positions (17).

Sulfonation of a mixture of quinophthalone and its 6'-methyl derivative gives Quinoline Yellow (Acid Yellow 3, D&C Yellow No. 10, CI 47005). The 6'-methyl group adds tinctorial value to the quinophthalone nucleus (18). Also, when the addition products of sulfur trioxide and the quinophthalone mixture are heated to 170–190°C under reduced pressure, the products are the monosulfonic acids, which have higher tinctorial values than the mixed mono- and disulfonic acids which are obtained by treating the quinophthalones with 65% oleum at 58–62°C (16). Quinoline Yellow is used to dye wool, silk, and nylon in cases where good lightfastness is not required, and its barium lake is used as a pigment for printing inks (see also Pigments (organic)). The dye is used also as a drug and cosmetic color (see Colors for foods, drugs, and cosmetics), and the spectrophotometric determination of phthalic acid content has been described (19).

Sulfonation of 6'-chloroquinophthalone (1) produces Quinoline Yellow PN (Acid Yellow 2, CI 47010), which has better lightfastness than Acid Yellow 3. Quinoline Yellow GP (Direct Yellow 5, CI 47035), the disulfonic acid of 5',6'-benzoquinophthalone (15), is used to dye cotton, viscose rayon, and paper, and its heavy-metal lakes are used as pigments for inks (qv) and oil colors. Sulfonated 3'-hydroxyquinophthalone (CI 47020) (15) is now obsolete; however, the 3'-hydroxy group adds considerable lightfastness to the quinophthalone nucleus, and is the basis for the utility of most of the newer quinophthalone dyes for polyester and acrylic fibers.

When 2- or 4-aminobiphenyl is condensed with crotonaldehyde, the resulting 8- or 6-phenylquinaldine, respectively, forms a quinophthalone which gives a yellow acid dye after sulfonation (20). Benzidine and its derivatives condense with paraldehyde (21) and acetylacetone (22) to give 6,6'-biquinaldines which, when condensed with phthalic anhydride and sulfonated, yield yellow and orange dyes which are substantive to cotton (21–23). When 3- or 5-hydroxytrimellitic anhydride is condensed with quinaldine and sulfonated, the product can be afterchromed on wool to give fast yellow shades (24). Phthalic anhydride-4,5-dicarboxylic acid condenses with quinaldine derivatives to give reddish-yellow, unsulfonated dyes for wool and nylon (25). Another direct dye for wool and nylon is made by condensing trimellitic acid with 3-hydroxyquinaldine-4-carboxylic acid (26).

Certain sulfonated quinophthalones are used to dye paper, on which they have better lightfastness than the earlier dye, Auramine (Basic Yellow 2, CI 41000) (27). When dehydrothiotoluidinesulfonic acid is treated with paraldehyde and an oxidizing agent at 100°C, and then condensed with phthalic anhydride in dimethylformamide at 175–185°C, the product (9) dyes paper and cotton in greenish-yellow shades with high substantivity to paper pulp (28). Other paper dyes are made by condensing di-, tri-, and tetrachlorophthalic anhydrides with naphthoquinaldines and sulfonating in oleum (29). An unsulfonated paper dye is 3'-hydroxyquinophthalone-5-carboxylic acid (26).

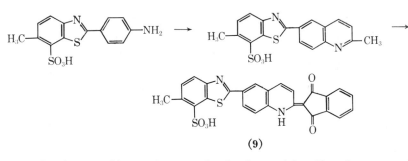

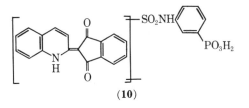

(9)

Aluminum oxide coatings can be dyed greenish yellow from a neutral solution of a sulfonated quinophthalone which contains a phosphoric acid group (**10**) (30).

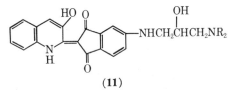

(**10**)

The *nonionic group* of quinophthalones is composed mostly of disperse dyes for polyester fibers. 3'-Hydroxyquinophthalone (Disperse Yellow 54), the first such dye to be described (31), is prepared by the condensation of 3-hydroxyquinaldine-4-carboxylic acid with phthalic anhydride. Decarboxylation takes place during the reaction (32). 3-Hydroxyquinaldine-4-carboxylic acid is obtained by condensing monochloroacetone and isatin (33). Disperse Yellow 54 dyes polyester fibers in greenish-yellow shades with good buildup and lightfastness, but with a sublimation fastness that is borderline. It has been necessary to improve the sublimation fastness in order to cope with recent dyeing processes which involve more severe conditions (the Thermosol process, for example).

Chlorination of Disperse Yellow 54 in an inert solvent gives a mixture of chloro compounds which has better sublimation fastness (34); bromination in a melt with excess phthalic anhydride gives the 4-bromo derivative (35). When 3-hydroxyquin-aldine-4-carboxylic acid is condensed with 3- or 4-nitrophthalic acid, the resulting 4- or 5-nitro-3'-hydroxyquinophthalone dyes polyester yellow shades with good fastness to sublimation and light (36). The nitro group can be reduced to an amine which, when treated with epichlorohydrin and a secondary aliphatic or aromatic amine, gives a yellow disperse dye (**11**) that has good properties on polyester (37). The amide

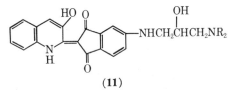

(**11**)

derivatives of 3'-hydroxyquinophthalone-5-carboxylic acid have good properties on polyester (26), and 3'-hydroxyquinophthalone-5-carboxylate esters are used for mass pigmentation of polyester (38). Pigments are obtained by condensing 3-hydroxyquin-aldine with tetrachlorophthalic anhydride (39), and by treating a quinophthalone carboxylic acid with an aromatic diamine (**12**) (40).

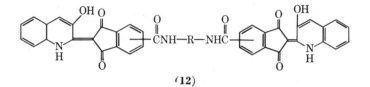

(12)

Quinophthalones which contain *cationic groups* serve as yellow dyes for polyacrylonitrile fibers. If compound (11) is made with a tertiary aliphatic or aromatic amine, the quaternary ammonium product is a yellow dye for acrylic fibers (37). When 5-nitro-3'-hydroxyquinophthalone is treated with N,N-dimethyl-1,3-propanediamine and then quaternized with dimethylsulfate, the product (13) dyes polyacrylonitrile in yellow

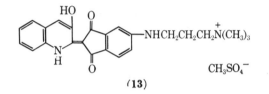

(13)

shades of good lightfastness (41). Treatment of 3'-hydroxyquinophthalone-5-carboxylic acid with thionyl chloride followed by condensation with N,N-dimethyl-1,3-propanediamine gives a dye whose hydrochloride (14) is yellow on polyacrylonitrile (26).

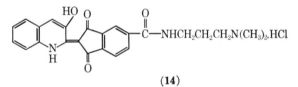

(14)

Condensation of paraformaldehyde with 3'-hydroxyquinophthalone and dimethylamine hydrochloride followed by quaternization with dimethyl sulfate gives the water-soluble yellow dye (15) (42).

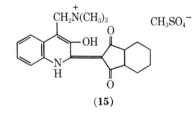

(15)

Azo Dyes (qv)

8-Quinolinol Derivatives. Diazonium salts can be coupled with 3-, 4-, 5-, 6-, 7-, and 8-quinolinols, and the 5- and 8-hydroxy derivatives form metal chelates (43–45). However, the quinoline nucleus usually gives weaker and duller azo dyes than the corresponding naphthalene intermediates (45), and only 8-quinolinol ("oxine") leads to dyes of practical value. In this case, the 8-hydroxyl group is able to chelate with the nuclear nitrogen atom, which gives mordant dyeing properties to the azo derivatives of 8-quinolinol (46). 8-Quinolinol also is a well-known analytical reagent, and its copper salt is used as a fungicide. Coupling in alkaline solution with diazonium salts normally takes place in the 5 position of 8-quinolinol, and the resulting azo dyes resemble the azosalicylic acids in the nonparticipation of the azo group in the formation of metal-dye complexes (1). Under extreme conditions of alkalinity and concentration, the coupling can be made to take place in the 7 position (47,48). The normal chelate compounds of 8-quinolinol have the formula $M(C_9H_6NO)_n$ in which n is the valence of the metal (M) ion (46). When the coupling takes place in the 7 position, the 8-hydroxyl group may chelate with either the nuclear nitrogen or the azo group (49).

Neutral-dyeing 1:1 chromium complexes of monoazo dyes which contain an 8-quinolinol group have been used to dye wool and silk in orange shades (15,50,51) (Acid Orange 61, CI 19320; Mordant Orange 26, CI 19325, both obsolete). Metalizable disazo dyes, mainly bluish- to yellowish-red in color, obtained by coupling a diazotized aminoazo compound with 8-quinolinol, are applicable to cotton, rayon, wool, and leather (52). Water-soluble direct dyes (orange to blue) in which the end component is 8-quinolinol can be applied to cotton, which is then aftercoppered to form insoluble 1:2 complexes (**16**) which have enhanced fastness to washing and light (53–57).

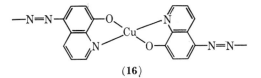

(**16**)

Metalizable azo compounds from 8-quinolinol have been proposed as dyes for premetalized polyolefin fibers (58). Also, derivatives of 8-quinolinol have been suggested as color formers in photography (59,60).

2,4-Quinolinediol Derivatives. Treatment of malonanilide with phosphoric acid at 140–150°C gives 2,4-quinolinediol in a yield of 86% (61). This intermediate can also be prepared in a yield of 83% by heating N-acetylanthranilic acid with sodium amide at 150–190°C (62). Other methods of synthesis have been described (63–66).

Nonionic monoazo dyes having a 2,4-quinolinediol group have been used as disperse dyes for cellulose acetate (67–69) (Disperse Yellow 4, CI 12770, obsolete) and as pigments for inks and prints (**15**) (Pigment Yellow 7, CI 12780, obsolete).

Quinazol Yellow (CI 19340), made by coupling diazotized sulfanilic acid with 2,4-quinolinediol, was formerly used as a paper dye (70), and Acid Orange 4, CI 28690, made from diazotized 4-aminoazobenzene-3,4-disulfonic acid and 2,4-quinolinediol (15), had limited use as a yellow lake pigment where good lightfastness was not required. Sulfonated trisazo compounds containing the 2,4-quinolinediol group have been used as chrome dyes for leather (Acid Black 70, CI 30355) (71) and as direct cotton dyes (Sirius Supra Brown RD, CI 34285) (18). Other direct dyes have been described in which the coupling component is 6,8-quinolinediol (72).

Azo dyes from 2,4-quinolinediol have found important application in the field of metal-complex dyes (see Azo dyes, Vol. 2, p. 888). Acid Red 179 (CI 19351) is the 1:1 chromium complex of the monoazo dye from diazotized 2-amino-4-chlorophenol-6-sulfonic acid and 2,4-quinolinediol; the complex is prepared by heating an aqueous solution of chromium sulfate and the dye in an autoclave at 115°C and salting out as the sodium salt (15). Other chrome dyes have been described (73,74). When *o*-hydroxy diazonium salts containing no sulfonic or carboxylic acid groups are coupled with 2,4-quinolinediol, the products can be used to dye wool by a metachrome (single-bath) process; these dyes give duller shades when applied by afterchrome processes (75). Dyes of this type become water-soluble when esterified with compounds such as benzoyl chloride disulfonic acid (76); the esters are saponified during the metalizing step. Pigment Green 10 (CI 12775) is the nickel complex of the azo dye from diazotized *p*-chloroaniline and 2,4-quinolinediol (77). Other lightfast nickel-complex pigments have been described (78) (see Vol. 15, p. 572). In the past several years, azo dyes from 2,4-quinolinediol have been proposed as dyes for premetalized polyolefin fibers (79,80). When diazonium salts containing quaternary ammonium groups are coupled with 2,4-quinolinediol, the products dye polyacrylonitrile fibers (81).

The metachrome dye (**17**) made from diazotized 2-aminophenol-4-sulfon-2-(2′-carboxyanilide) and 1,3-isoquinolinediol dyes wool in red shades having good lightfast-

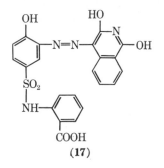

(17)

ness (82). 1,3-Isoquinolinediol can be made by treating homophthalic acid with ammonia (83).

4-Hydroxy-*N*-alkyl-2-quinolone Derivatives. Monoazo disperse dyes which contain a 4-hydroxy-2-quinolone group were used to dye cellulose acetate in yellow shades with good fastness to light, gas, washing, and sublimation (Disperse Yellow 10, CI 12795, obsolete) (84,85). Celliton Yellow 5GA (Disperse Yellow 5, CI 12790) is now used for polyester fibers (15). This bright greenish-yellow dye is made by coupling diazotized *m*-nitroaniline with 4-hydroxy-*N*-methyl-2-quinolone (4-hydroxy-1-methyl-carbostyril), the latter being obtained by the action of boiling acetic acid and acetic anhydride on *N*-methylanthranilic acid (15,62). Other disperse azo dyes from *N*-substituted derivatives of 4-hydroxy-2-quinolone have been described (85,86). Diazotized 2-aminophenolsulfonic acids couple with *N*-alkyl-4-hydroxy-2-quinolone derivatives to give afterchrome or metachrome dyes for wool (87–89). 4-Hydroxy-*N*-methyl-2-quinolone derivatives also are useful couplers in diazotype prints (90) (see Reprography).

1,2,3,4-Tetrahydroquinoline Derivatives. Diazonium salts couple with 1,2,3,4-tetrahydroquinoline and its derivatives in acid solution in the benzene ring, para to the nitrogen. With a given diazonium component, tetrahydroquinoline derivatives give dyes of much deeper color than the corresponding *N*-alkylanilines, and therefore are useful for obtaining blue shades. However, the lightfastness of these dyes is generally insufficient, and they have been used mainly as disperse dyes for cellulose acetate (91), especially in discharge printing (eg, Disperse Violet 7, CI 11410; Celliton Discharge Blue 3G, CI 11420, obsolete) (92). The most frequently used coupling components are *N*-alkyltetrahydroquinolines (**18**) (93) and 3-hydroxytetrahydroquinolines (for example (**19**), (**20**), and (**21**)) (94,95). Other tetrahydroquinoline intermediates have been described (96–98).

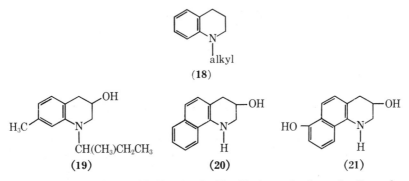

(18)

(19)   (20)   (21)

Disperse azo dyes from *N*-dicarboximidoalkyltetrahydroquinolines have been proposed for dyeing wool–polyester blends with the claims that they reserve wool (99). Other disperse azo dyes from tetrahydroquinoline derivatives have been described (100–103). The water-soluble red dye (**22**) is a cellulose acetate dye of the Solacet (ICI) type (104). Water-soluble acetate dyes can also be produced by coupling diazonium salts with 2,4-quinolinediolsulfonic acids (105).

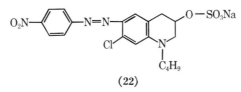

(22)

Methine dyes such as (**23**), made from tetrahydroquinoline-6-aldehydes, dye polyester, polyacrylonitrile, and cellulose acetate fibers in yellow shades (106).

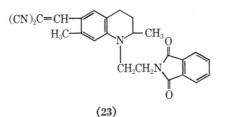

(23)

Aminoquinoline Derivatives. Most aminoquinolines can be prepared by reduction of the appropriate nitro compounds (see reference 107 for a review of preparative methods). Aminoquinolines in which the amino group is in the 5, 6, 7, or 8 position couple with diazonium salts in the same positions as the corresponding naphthylamines. 4-Aminoquinoline does not couple, while 3-aminoquinoline gives a small yield of the diazoamino derivative (108). The use of 5- and 8-aminoquinolines as end or middle components for metalizable dyes has been suggested (109).

The 3-, 5-, 6-, 7-, and 8-aminoquinolines can be diazotized and coupled (107,110). Such dyes are not commercially important, partly because of the unfavorable effect of the basic quinoline nucleus to lightfastness. When this basicity is reduced by electron-withdrawing substituents, or by positively charged metal complexes or quaternary ammonium groups, lightfastness improves. For example, nitro derivatives of 8-aminoquinaldine have been proposed as diazo components for disperse dyes for cellulose acetate (111). Azo derivatives of 8-aminoquinoline which contain *o*-hydroxyl groups (**24**) form 1:1 copper complexes which dye wool, tanned cotton, and polyacrylonitrile

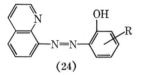

(24)

(112,113), and have been proposed as dyes for premetalized polyolefin fibers (114–117).

If cotton is padded with a naphtholic coupler and then treated with a solution of a diazotized 8-aminoquinoline derivative and a metal salt, a metal chelate dye is formed on the fiber (118). Other azoic dyes utilizing diazotized aminoquinolines have been described (119).

Water-insoluble metalized azo dyes from diazotized 8-aminoquinoline are proposed as lightfast pigments for paints and plastics (120). The condensation of 8-aminoquinoline with (25) gives a metachrome or afterchrome brown with good lightfastness (121,

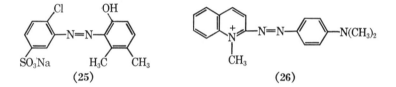

(25)   (26)

122). Aminoquinolines can be condensed with aromatic nitroso compounds and then quaternized to give cationic dyes for polyacrylonitrile (26) (123).

Miscellaneous Compounds

Hydrazone derivatives of 2- and 4-quinolinecarboxaldehydes can be quaternized with alkylating agents to produce cationic dyes for polyacrylonitrile (124–127). Other cationic dyes (27) are made by condensing N-alkylquinolones with indoles which are unsubstituted in the 3 position (128).

The products of the condensation of tetrahydroquinoline derivatives with chloronitrobenzenes are nitro dyes (28) for wool, silk, and rayon acetate (129). Oxindole and indoxyl condense with 4-chloroquinaldine to give orange to red dyes for cellulose acetate (130). Reactive dyes have been proposed whose active groups are 4-chloroquinoline oxide (29) (131) and 2,4-dichloroquinoline (132).

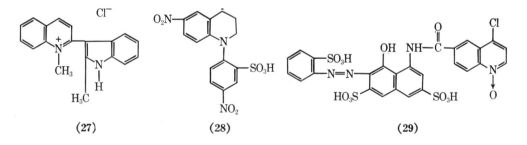

(27)   (28)   (29)

Triarylmethane dyes containing 8-quinolinol in place of salicylic acid have been described; thus, the leuco compound obtained by condensing two moles of 8-quinolinol with one mole of 4-dimethylamino-2-sulfobenzaldehyde gives, after chroming, a green dye of good washing and fulling fastness on wool (133). Basic triarylmethane dyes of the Malachite Green type have been prepared by condensing quinoline and tetrahydroquinoline with aromatic aldehydes (134), and by reacting 2-quinoline-carboxaldehyde with dialkylanilines (135). (See also Triphenylmethane and related dyes.) Quinoline analogs of the phthaleins have been prepared by condensing 2,3,4-quinolinetricarboxylic acid with aromatic amines or phenols (135).

In the course of research on substances which luminesce on activation by ultraviolet irradiation, I. G. Farbenindustrie A.G. (I.G.) found that 4,4′-di-2-quinolyl-biphenyl (**30**) had a blue-white fluorescence with very good lightfastness. This and other Lumogen (I. G.) dyes have been described (18).

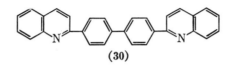

(30)

Alizarin derivatives such as (**31**) and their sodium bisulfite addition products were formerly used as chrome dyes for wool (eg, Alizarin Green S, CI 67405; Alizarin Blue ABI, CI 67410, now obsolete).

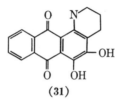

(31)

Economic Aspects

U.S. production, sales, and import figures for quinoline dyes (1965 and 1966), and dollar unit value per pound, are shown in Table 1.

Table 1. U.S. Production, Sales, and Imports of Some Available Quinoline Dyes[a] (136)

Dye (CI name)	Production, 1000 lb	Sales, 1000 lb	Imports, lb	Price, $
Acid Red 179	nf	nf	1,000	nf
Acid Yellow 2	nf	nf	nl	nf
Acid Yellow 3	nf	31	25	3.58
D&C Yellow No. 10	nf	nf	nl	nf
D&C Yellow No. 11	nf	nf	nl	nf
Direct Yellow 5	75	105	nl	2.88
Disperse Yellow 5	56	44	17,950	3.41
Disperse Yellow 54	185	155	nl	3.65
Pigment Green 10	nf	nf	2,300	nf
Solvent Yellow 33	nf	nf	nl	nf

[a] Import figures are for 1966; all others are for 1965.

LEGEND: nf, dye listed but no figures are given; nl, dye not listed.

Figures for total U.S. production and sales of quinoline dyes (1962–1966), and dollar unit value per pound, are shown in Table 1 of the article Quinoline and isoquinoline (p. 872).

Bibliography

"Quinoline Dyes" in *ECT* 1st ed., Vol. 11, pp. 401–410, by K. Venkataraman, University of Bombay.

1. K. Venkataraman, *The Chemistry of Synthetic Dyes*, Vols. I and II, Academic Press, Inc., New York, 1952.
2. Ger. Pat. 19,306 (Feb. 2, 1882), E. Jacobsen.
3. F. M. Hamer, "The Cyanine Dyes and Related Compounds," Vol. 18, in A. Weissberger, ed., *The Chemistry of Heterocyclic Compounds*, Interscience Publishers, a division of John Wiley & Sons, Inc., New York, 1964, pp. 300–301.
4. O. Fischer and C. Rudolph, *Chem. Ber.* **15**, 1500 (1882).
5. Ger. Pat. 19,766 (Dec. 10, 1881) (to Meister Lucius und Brüning).
6. E. Jacobsen and C. L. Reimer, *Chem. Ber.* **16**, 514 (1883).
7. Ger. Pat. 23,188 (Nov. 4, 1882), E. Jacobsen.
8. U.S. Pat. 1,963,374 (June 19, 1934), J. Ogilvie (to National Aniline & Chemical Co.).
9. A. Eibner and H. Merkel, *Chem. Ber.* **37**, 3009 (1904).
10. W. Dilthey and R. Wizinger, *J. Prakt. Chem.* **118**, 321 (1928).
11. E. H. Bottke, Thesis, Bonn, 1931; B. Melita, Thesis, Bonn, 1937.
12. W. Jenny, *Helv. Chim. Acta* **34**, 539 (1951).
13. R. Kuhn and F. Bär, *Ann. Chem.* **516**, 155 (1935).
14. L. G. S. Brooker and G. H. Keyes, *J. Am. Chem. Soc.* **73**, 5356 (1951).
15. *BIOS (British Intelligence Objectives Subcommittee) Report 961* (1945).
16. Brit. Pat. 445,201 (April 3, 1936) (to I. G. Farbenindustrie A.G.).
17. U.S. Pat. 3,108,109 (Oct. 22, 1963), R. A. Clark (to E. I. du Pont de Nemours & Co., Inc.).
18. "Dyestuffs Research," *Field Information Agency Tech. (FIAT), Final Report 1313*, Feb. 1948.
19. C. Graichen, *J. Assoc. Offic. Agr. Chemists* **34**, 407 (1951).
20. U.S. Pat. 2,211,662 (Aug. 13, 1940), L. P. Kyrides (to Monsanto Chemical Co.).
21. B. I. Ardashev and Z. V. Malina, *J. Gen. Chem. USSR (Eng. Transl.)* **21**, 1349–1354 (1951).
22. L. N. Goldyrev, *J. Gen. Chem. USSR (Eng. Transl.)* **27**, 2874 (1957).
23. U.S.S.R. Pat. 41,097 (Jan. 31, 1935), A. E. Porai-Koshitz.
24. Brit. Pat. 492,668 (Sept. 23, 1938), A. H. Knight (to Imperial Chemical Industries, Ltd.).
25. U.S. Pat. 2,592,370 (April 8, 1952), F. Zwilgmeyer (to E. I. du Pont de Nemours & Co., Inc.).
26. U.S. Pats. 3,023,212, 3,023,213, and 3,023,214 (Feb. 27, 1962), J. W. Richter (to E. I. du Pont de Nemours & Co., Inc.).
27. H. A. Lubs, ed., *The Chemistry of Synthetic Dyes and Pigments*, Reinhold Publishing Corp., New York, 1955.
28. U.S. Pat. 3,301,860 (Jan. 31, 1967), R. A. Clarke (to E. I. du Pont de Nemours & Co., Inc.).
29. U.S. Pat. 2,828,311 (March 25, 1958), E. C. Gifford (to American Cyanamid Co.).
30. Fr. Pat. 1,347,692 (Jan. 3, 1964) (to Durand & Huguenin A.G.).
31. Am. Dyestuff Reptr. **44**, 844 (1955).
32. *U.S. Dept. Comm. Office Tech. Serv. PB Rept. 70,256*, July 26, 1946, p. 9591.
33. U.S. Pat. 2,082,358 (June 1, 1937), H. Schlichenmaier and L. Schoernig (to General Aniline Works, Inc.).
34. U.S. Pat. 3,036,876 (May 29, 1962), A. Schoellig, K. G. Roessler, and R. Krallmann (to Badische Anilin- und Soda-Fabrik A.G.).
35. Ger. Pats. 1,229,663 (Dec. 1, 1966), 1,234,183 (Feb. 16, 1967), A. Schoellig, R. Schroedel, G. Doessler, and R. Krallmann (to Badische Anilin- und Soda-Fabrik A.G.).
36. U.S. Pat. 2,818,410 (Dec. 31, 1957), F. Zwilgmeyer (to E. I. du Pont de Nemours & Co., Inc.).
37. U.S. Pat. 2,818,409 (Dec. 31, 1957), F. Zwilgmeyer (to E. I. du Pont de Nemours & Co., Inc.).
38. Belg. Pat. 678,479 (Sept. 26, 1966) (to Imperial Chemical Industries, Ltd.).
39. Fr. Pat. 1,403,435 (May 10, 1965), E. Merian and H. Wasem (to Sandoz Ltd.).
40. Fr. Pat. 1,445,003 (June 23, 1965) (to Ciba Ltd.); U.S. Pat. 3,374,238 (March 19, 1968), A. Wick and C. Frey (to Ciba Ltd.).
41. U.S. Pat. 2,795,582 (June 11, 1957), A. W. Bauer and C. F. Belcher (to E. I. du Pont de Nemours & Co., Inc.).
42. U.S. Pat. 3,293,246 (Dec. 20, 1966), O. Fuchs and F. Ische (to Farbwerke Hoechst A.G.).
43. C. Courtot and H. Hartman, *Compt. Rend.* **194**, 1949 (1932).
44. Ger. Pat. 355,534 (May 23, 1915), R. Haugwitz (to Aktiengesellschaft für Anilin-Fabrikation).

45. A. Meyer and L. Silberstein, *Bull. Soc. Chim. France* **1948,** 590–593.

46. J. P. Phillips, *Chem. Rev.* **56,** 271 (1956).

47. K. Matsumura, *J. Am. Chem. Soc.* **52,** 4164 (1930).

48. A. Badrinas, *Talanta* **10,** 704–707 (1963).

49. A. I. Cherkesov, *Dokl. Akad. Nauk SSSR* **142,** 1098–1100 (1962).

50. U.S. Pat. 3,125,561 (March 17, 1964), F. Beffa and G. Schetty (to J. R. Geigy S.A.).

51. U.S. Pat. 1,991,808 (Feb. 19, 1935), H. Krzikalla and W. Limbacher (to General Aniline Works, Inc.).

52. U.S. Pat. 2,411,646 (Nov. 26, 1946), W. Anderau (to Ciba Ltd.).

53. H. R. Schweizer, *Künstliche organische Farbstoffe und ihre Zwischenprodukte,* Springer-Verlag, Heidelberg, 1964, p. 473.

54. Brit. Pats. 533,364 (Feb. 12, 1941), 695,330 (Aug. 5, 1953), 710,734 (June 16, 1954), 744,829 (Feb. 15, 1956), U.S. Pats. 2,475,265 (July 5, 1949), 2,671,775 (March 9, 1954), 2,762,793 (Sept. 11, 1956), 2,809,963 (Oct. 15, 1957), Swiss Pats. 251,583 (Aug. 2, 1948), 299,709 (Sept. 1, 1954), 302,402–302,404 (Dec. 16, 1954), 304,720 (April 1, 1955), 339,305 (Aug. 15, 1959) (to Ciba Ltd.).

55. Brit. Pats. 747,872 (April 18, 1956), 757,727 (Sept. 26, 1956), 761,776 (Nov. 21, 1956), 785,457 (Oct. 30, 1957), 786,567 (Nov. 20, 1957), U.S. Pat. 2,794,797 (June 4, 1957) (to Imperial Chemical Industries, Ltd.).

56. U.S. Pat. 2,856,396 (Oct. 14, 1958), R. Duerig (to J. R. Geigy S.A.).

57. Czech. Pat. 85,538 (Feb. 15, 1956), J. Proskočil and Z. J. Allan.

58. U.S. Pat. 3,317,272 (May 2, 1967), H. Wunderlich and M. Schwarz (to Farbenfabriken Bayer A.G.).

59. U.S. Pats. 2,524,725–2,524,741 (Oct. 3, 1950), R. F. Coles and V. Tulagin (to General Aniline & Film Corp.).

60. Neth. Pat. 71,530 (Jan. 15, 1953) (to Kodak N.V.).

61. Brit. Pat. 916,103 (Jan. 23, 1963) (to Cassella Farbwerke Mainkur A.G.).

62. *BIOS (British Intelligence Objectives Subcommittee) Report 1153,* 1951.

63. J. N. Ashley, W. H. Perkin, Jr., and R. Robinson, *J. Chem. Soc.* **1930,** 382.

64. L. G. S. Brooker and L. A. Smith, *J. Am. Chem. Soc.* **59,** 72 (1937).

65. F. J. Buckmann and C. S. Hamilton, *J. Am. Chem. Soc.* **64,** 1357 (1942).

66. E. H. Huntress and J. Bornstein, *J. Am. Chem. Soc.* **71,** 745 (1949).

67. Brit. Pat. 236,037 (June 20, 1924), J. Baddiley and J. Hill (to British Dyestuffs Corp.).

68. U.S. Pat. 1,690,900 (Nov. 6, 1929), K. Holzach and R. Metzger (to Grasselli Dyestuff Corp.).

69. U.S. Pat. 2,173,054 (Sept. 12, 1940), E. F. Hitch (to E. I. du Pont de Nemours & Co., Inc.).

70. Ger. Pat. 165,327 (Oct. 2, 1905) (to Badische Anilin- und Soda-Fabrik A.G.).

71. "Dyestuffs Research," *Field Information Agency Tech. (FIAT),* *764.*

72. Brit. Pat. 787,646 (Dec. 11, 1957), H. F. Andrew and R. R. Davies (to Imperial Chemical Industries, Ltd.).

73. U.S. Pat. 961,355 (June 14, 1910), J. Jansen and W. Neelmeier (to Farbenfabriken Bayer A.G.).

74. Ger. Pat. 821,977 (Nov. 22, 1951), H. Krzikalla and T. Toepel (to Badische Anilin- und Soda-Fabrik A.G.).

75. Ger. Pat. 208,498 (March 8, 1909) (to Farbenfabriken Bayer A.G.).

76. U.S. Pats. 2,496,386 (Feb. 7, 1950), F. Felix and A. Heckendorm (to Ciba Ltd.); 2,570,052 (Oct. 2, 1951), F. Felix, A. Heckendorm and W. Widmer (to Ciba Ltd.).

77. U.S. Pat. 2,396,327 (March 12, 1946), D. E. Kvalnes and H. E. Woodward (to E. I. du Pont de Nemours & Co., Inc.).

78. U.S. Pat. 3,132,140 (May 5, 1964), E. E. Jaffe (to E. I. du Pont de Nemours & Co., Inc.).

79. Fr. Pat. 1,406,537 (June 14, 1965), M. Jirou, C. Triquet, and J. Khachoyan (to Etablissements Kuhlmann).

80. Fr. Pat. 1,473,787 (March 17, 1967), P. L. Stright (to Allied Chemical Corp.).

81. U.S. Pat. 2,965,631 (Dec. 20, 1960), M. F. Sartori (to E. I. du Pont de Nemours & Co., Inc.).

82. U.S. Pat. 2,535,121 (Dec. 26, 1950), B. G. Carson (to E. I. du Pont de Nemours & Co., Inc.).

83. U.S. Pat. 2,351,391 (June 13, 1944), H. A. Bergstrom (to E. I. du Pont de Nemours & Co., Inc.).

84. Brit. Pat. 327,394 (Oct. 1, 1928), I. G. Farbenindustrie A.G.

85. U.S. Pat. 2,529,924 (Nov. 14, 1950), J. B. Dickey (to Eastman Kodak Co.).

86. Ger. Pat. 1,244,314 (July 13, 1967), J. Dehnert (to Badische Anilin- und Soda-Fabrik A.G.).
87. Swiss Pats. 261,368 (Aug. 16, 1949), 267,274–267,277 (June 1, 1950) (to Ciba Ltd.).
88. Ger. Pat. 1,058,172 (May 27, 1959) (to Farbenfabriken Bayer A.G.).
89. Brit. Pat. 804,766 (Nov. 19, 1958) (to Farbenfabriken Bayer A.G.).
90. U.S. Pat. 2,542,848 (Feb. 20, 1951), H. von Glahn and L. N. Stanley (to General Aniline & Film Corp.).
91. Brit. Pats. 446,745 (April 15, 1936), 474,678 (Nov. 4, 1937), I. G. Farbenindustrie A.G.).
92. U.S. Pat. 2,149,051 (Feb. 28, 1939), J. H. Helberger and C. Taube (to General Aniline Works, Inc.).
93. U.S. Pat. 2,342,678 (Feb. 29, 1944), J. G. McNally and J. B. Dickey (to Eastman Kodak Co.).
94. Brit. Pats. 449,089 (June 19, 1936), 456,824 (Nov. 16, 1936), 458,423 (Dec. 21, 1936), I. G. Farbenindustrie A.G.).
95. U.S. Pat. 2,194,399 (March 19, 1940), H. Lange (to General Aniline & Film Corp.).
96. U.S. Pat. 2,432,393 (Dec. 9, 1947), J. B. Dickey and J. G. McNally (to Eastman Kodak Co.).
97. Ger. Pat. 642,558 (Feb. 18, 1937), J. H. Helberger (to I. G. Farbenindustrie A.G.).
98. U.S. Pat. 2,102,593 (Dec. 21, 1937), J. H. Helberger and O. Bayer (to General Aniline Works, Inc.).
99. U.S. Pats. 3,206,452 (Sept. 14, 1965), 3,213,081 (Oct. 19, 1965), J. M. Straley and D. J. Wallace (to Eastman Kodak Co.).
100. U.S. Pats. 2,196,776 (April 9, 1940), 2,221,020 (Nov. 12, 1940), 2,773,054 (Dec. 4, 1956), 2,827,450 (March 18, 1958), 2,839,523 (June 17, 1958), 3,143,540 (Aug. 4, 1964), 3,213,080 (Oct. 19, 1965) (to Eastman Kodak Co.).
101. U.S. Pat. 2,067,726 (Jan. 12, 1937), H. Ohlendorf and E. Baumann (to General Aniline Works, Inc.).
102. Ger. Pat. 641,569 (Feb. 11, 1937), J. H. Helberger and H. Ohlendorf (to I. G. Farbenindustrie A.G.).
103. Ger. Pats. 951,525 (Oct. 31, 1956), 960,752 (March 28, 1957), W. Kruckenberg (to Farbenfabriken Bayer A.G.).
104. Brit. Pat. 492,668 (Sept. 23, 1938), A. H. Knight (to Imperial Chemical Industries, Ltd.).
105. Brit. Pat. 441,628 (Jan. 23, 1936) (to I. G. Farbenindustrie A.G.).
106. U.S. Pat. 3,240,783 (March 15, 1966), J. M. Straley, D. J. Wallace, and M. A. Weaver (to Eastman Kodak Co.).
107. R. C. Elderfield, *Heterocyclic Compounds*, Vol. 4, John Wiley & Sons, Inc., New York, 1952.
108. R. R. Renshaw, H. L. Friedmann, and F. J. Sajewski, *J. Am. Chem. Soc.* **61**, 3322 (1939).
109. Brit. Pats. 417,489 (Oct. 5, 1934), 443,163 (Feb. 24, 1936), 447,521 (May 14, 1936), 465,902 (May 19, 1937) (to I. G. Farbenindustrie A.G.).
110. H. Coates, A. H. Cook, I. M. Heilbron, D. H. Hey, A. Lambert, and F. B. Lewis, *J. Chem. Soc.* **1943**, 401.
111. U.S. Pat. 2,283,220 (May 19, 1942), J. G. McNally and J. B. Dickey (to Eastman Kodak Co.).
112. H. Iida and A. Ikegami, *Kogyo Kagaku Zasshi* **67** (1), 118 (1964).
113. Ger. Pat. 1,120,040 (Dec. 21, 1961), H. Pfitzner and J. Dehnert (to Badische Anilin- und Soda-Fabrik A.G.).
114. Belg. Pats. 643,554 (Feb. 2, 1964), 644,384 (June 15, 1964), P. L. Stright (to Allied Chemical Corp.).
115. Belg. Pats. 648,524 (Nov. 30, 1964), 652,720 (March 4, 1965), V. Ramanathan and D. Mäusezahl (to Ciba Ltd.).
116. Belg. Pat. 614,566 (Sept. 3, 1962) (Imperial Chemical Industries, Ltd.).
117. Fr. Pat. 1,439,286 (Dec. 4, 1966) (to Sumitomo Kagaku Kogyo Co.).
118. Ger. Pats. 1,136,034 (Sept. 6, 1962), R. Gross, H. Hertel, R. Mohr, and K. Schilling (to Farbwerke Hoechst A.G.); 1,150,471 (June 20, 1963), R. Gross, H. Hertel, R. Mohr, and W. Staab (to Farbwerke Hoechst A.G.).
119. U.S. Pats. 2,725,376 (Nov. 29, 1955), 2,754,293 (July 10, 1956), F. Brody, J. J. Leavitt, and R. S. Long (to American Cyanamid Co.).
120. Ger. Pat. 1,117,234 (June 14, 1961), K. Schilling (to Farbwerke Hoechst A.G.).
121. *BIOS (British Intelligence Objectives Subcommittee) Misc. Report 20.*
122. Ger. Pat. 748,913 (Nov. 23, 1944) (to I. G. Farbenindustrie A.G.).
123. U.S. Pat. 2,864,813 (Dec. 16, 1958), W. Bossard, J. Voltz, and F. Favre (to J. R. Geigy A.G.).

124. U.S. Pats. 2,774,757 (Dec. 18, 1956), E. Kuhle and R. Wegler (to Farbenfabriken Bayer A.G.), 3,158,608 (Nov. 24, 1964), 3,238,198 (March 1, 1966), R. Raue and E. H. Rohe (to Farbenfabriken Bayer A.G.).

125. Ger. Pats. 1,038,522 (Sept. 11, 1958) (to Badische Anilin- und Soda-Fabrik A.G.); 1,150,475 (June 20, 1963), 1,209,679 (Jan. 27, 1966), R. Raue and E. H. Rohe (to Farbenfabriken Bayer A.G.).

126. Brit. Pat. 885,520 (Dec. 28, 1961), J. D. Kendall, G. F. Duffin, and J. Voltz (to J. R. Geigy A.G.).

127. Belg. Pats. 593,877 (Aug. 31, 1960), 615,562 (April 13, 1962), R. Raue and E. H. Rohe (to Farbenfabriken Bayer A.G.).

128. Neth. Appl. Pat. 6,611,259 (Aug. 10, 1966) (to Ciba Ltd.).

129. U.S. Pat. 2,251,922 (Aug. 12, 1941), J. B. Dickey and J. B. Normington (to Eastman Kodak Co.).

130. A. Meyer and G. Bouchet, *Compt. Rend.* **227**, 345–347 (1948); **229**, 372–374 (1949).

131. Belg. Pat. 637,526 (Jan. 16, 1964), E. Grigat, K. G. Kieb, and R. Puetter (to Farbenfabriken Bayer A.G.).

132. Fr. Pat. 1,324,434 (April 19, 1963), A. Simonnet and P. Kienzle (to Compagnie Française des Matières Colorantes).

133. Ger. Pat. 627,902 (March 25, 1936), H. Krzikalla and K.-R. Jacobi (to I. G. Farbenindustrie A.G.).

134. R. N. Sen and B. N. Sen, *J. Indian Chem. Soc.* **7**, 965 (1930).

135. S. B. Dutt and J. D. Lewari, *J. Indian Chem. Soc.* **5**, 59 (1928); A. N. Dey and S. B. Dutt, *J. Indian Chem. Soc.* **5**, 535 (1928).

136. U.S. Tariff Commission, *Synthetic Organic Chemicals—U.S. Production and Sales, 1965*, TC Publ. 206, and *Imports of Benzenoid Chemicals and Products, 1966*, TC Publ. 216, U.S. Govt. Printing Office, Washington, D.C.

HUGO ILLY AND LANCE FUNDERBURK
Toms River Chemical Corp.

QUINONES

Quinones are colored dioxo derivatives of dihydroaromatic systems, the oxygen atoms occupying positions which are either ortho or para (or their equivalents in polycyclic compounds) to each other. Thus, benzene forms the nucleus for two quinones, o- and p-quinone (o- and p-benzoquinone) (**1** and **2**). Naphthalene should be able to form six quinones of which three are known, 1,2-, 1,4-, and 2,6-naphthoquinones (**3**, **4**, and **5**); anthracene could form eight, of which three are known (**6**, **7**, and **8**); phenanthrene could form more than a dozen, of which only one (**9**) is well known. Acenaphthene and chrysene, likewise, are each represented by only one well-known quinone (**10** and **11**). Quinones with more than six rings are described in the literature. Polynuclear quinones such as the diphenoquinones (**12** and **13**) and stilbenequinone (**14**) are also of interest.

The benzoquinones, naphthoquinones, and a few other quinones will be described here, but not anthraquinone (**8**) (see Vol. 2, pp. 431–533). Such dioxo compounds as "camphorquinone," which is actually a 1,2-diketone, will not be included. The conjugated-double-bond (quinonoid or quinoid) system characteristic of quinones can exist in many other cyclic compounds which contain other elements (such as N, S, C) instead of oxygen. These types are also excluded from this discussion except where they are used to characterize the parent compound (for example, oximes and hydrazones).

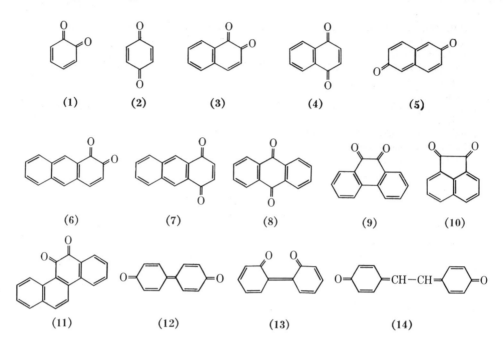

In the quinone imines (quinone monoimines and quinone diimines), also called quinone imides, one or both of the oxygen atoms in the carbonyl groups of quinone are replaced by =NH or =NR groups. The quinone imines are not prepared from quinones; p-benzoquinone imine, $O=C_6H_4=NH$, is prepared by the oxidation of p-aminophenol, and the diimine, $HN=C_6H_4=NH$, by the oxidation of p-phenylenediamine (qv). N-Aryl derivatives of quinone imines are often called anils, as quinone monoanil, $O=C_6H_4=NC_6H_5$, red crystals, mp 97°C, and quinone dianil, $C_6H_5N=C_6H_4=NC_6H_5$, mp 180°C. Indamine, indoaniline, and indophenol dyes and intermediates are derivatives of quinone imines (see Color photography).

Methylene quinones, of the type $O=C_6H_4=CH_2$, often called quinone methides, are formed as intermediates in the condensation of phenols and formaldehyde to produce resins (see Phenolic resins and plastics).

Although the simplest quinones, $O=C_6H_4=O$, are often called o- and p-quinone, the names o- and p-benzoquinone (in conformity with the present usage of CA will be used in this article to differentiate these compounds from quinones in general. Quinones derived from the polynuclear hydrocarbons have been named by CA in two ways: as quinones in the case of the better-known ones, as phenanthrenequinone for the 9,10-form (**9**), and as diones, eg 4,9 ($1H$, $4aH$)-phenanthrenedione.

Occurrence (1,2)

Many insects synthesize simple benzoquinones whose high vapor pressure and unpleasant odor and taste serve as a defense against predators. Plants such as tobacco, alfalfa, and wheat germ contain a variety of more highly substituted benzoquinones and their cyclization products (eg, tocopherols, etc). Cultures of a number of bacteria produce quinones of biological significance including coenzyme Q.

Naphthoquinones also are found in a variety of plants. Vitamin K_1 was found in plant life; vitamin K_2 was found in putrefied fish meal, apparently a product of bacterial action. Hydroxynaphthoquinones (juglones) are found in the leaves of henna and in the buds and green shells of the walnut tree; some of the polyhydroxy-naphthoquinones (echinochromes) give the red color to the spines or shells of some forms of sea life.

Among the phenanthrenequinones found in nature are pigments such as thele-phoric acid (permanganate color) which is found in fungi and lichens, and xylindein which is found as a green covering on the fallen branches of oak and other hard woods.

A number of other quinones found in nature are listed in Table 4.

Properties

Biological (1). Since many of the quinones are found in nature, it is obvious that they fit well into biological mechanisms. Some of the simpler quinones may be end products for defensive purposes, as stated earlier. Some may be intermediates for more highly cyclic biochemicals such as the tocopherols or may be decyclization products of the latter. Many have vitamin activity (K_1, K_2); some are bacteriostats (phthiocol); some are antimalarials (hydrolapachol); some are stimulants (plumbagin); some are paralyzants (plumbagin in large doses). Biologically active quinones, eg, plastoquinone (**15**) and ubiquinone (coenzyme Q) (**16**) have been shown to cat-

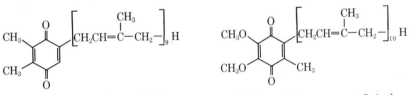

plastoquinone A or PQ9 (**15**)   ubiquinone 10 or coenzyme Q (**16**)

alyze some biochemical reactions in animals, plants, and microorganisms. They appear to be of suitable size, shape, and redox activity to transfer electrons to and from other coenzymes. There is considerable research activity on this topic and especially on the role of quinones or phosphorylated quinols in oxidative phosphorylation and in the respiratory cycle (3).

Ultraviolet and Visible Absorption Spectra. The uv absorption spectrum of *p*-benzoquinone shows more aliphatic than aromatic character and closely resembles that of a conjugated diketone. The major absorption is in the range of 240–250 nm (nanometer $\equiv$ mμ $\equiv$ 10^{-9}m) in solvents of widely varying polarity. A second peak occurs at 276–296 nm and minor absorption beyond 400 nm imparts yellow color to solutions. As conjugation is extended by fused benzene rings the secondary absorption is shifted toward and into the visible. Some of the echinochromes, by virtue of the auxochromic effect of hydroxyl groups on naphthoquinone have maximum absorptions near 550 nm and are thus red. As stated above, xylidein is green and therefore must have considerable absorption in the region of 400–500 nm and beyond 600 nm. The *o*-quinones are generally more highly colored than are the *p*-quinones. *o*-Benzoquinone has peak absorptions at 260 and 375 nm in the ultraviolet but has considerable absorption as far as 590 nm in the visible.

Redox Properties. The reduction of quinones is a reversible process such as that existing in inorganic chemistry with metals of variable valency. The oxidation-reduction potentials of a number of quinones have been studied in the determination of aromatic characteristics, particularly in fused-ring systems (4,5). Some of the

Table 1. Reduction Potentials of Quinones at 25°C

Quinone	Normal potential, E^0, volt	
	Aq soln	Alc soln
p-benzoquinone	0.699	0.715
o-benzoquinone	0.794	
1,4-naphthoquinone	0.470	0.484
1,2-naphthoquinone	0.555	0.576
2,6-naphthoquinone		0.76 (calcd)
1,4,5,8-naphthodiquinone		0.972 (estd)
diphenoquinone		0.954
stilbenequinone		0.854
9,10-phenanthrenequinone		0.460
1,4-phenanthrenequinone		0.523
1,2-phenanthrenequinone		0.660
3,4-phenanthrenequinone		0.621
9,10-anthraquinone		0.154
1,2-anthraquinone		0.490
1,4-anthraquinone		0.401
1,2-benz-9,10-anthraquinone (benz[a]anthracene-7,12-dione)		0.228
1,2-benz-3,4-anthraquinone (benz[a]anthracene-5,6-dione)		0.430
1,2,5,6-dibenz-9,10-anthraquinone (dibenz[a,h]anthracene-7,14-dione)		0.268
5,6-chrysenequinone (5,6-chrysenedione)		0.465
6,12-chrysenequinone (6,12-chrysenedione)		0.392

values are listed in Table 1 (4). Ring substituents have a significant effect on these potentials, and the course of many reactions is regulated by them (see p. 906).

Benzoquinone and anthraquinone with unsaturated side chains can yield polymers containing pendent quinone structures along the polymer chain (6). Similarly, formaldehyde polymers with a variety of hydroquinones yield oxidation-reduction polymers. These polymers can participate as do the monomers in redox systems and in acid-base reactions yet remain fixed in their media. Thus, they will not contaminate the ambient solution and, if necessary, can be filtered from a suspension or used to pack an ion-exchange column. As yet there is no startling application of such polymers but speculation and claims include their use for generation of hydrogen peroxide, for removal of oxygen from water, for antioxidants, for purification of water, for assisting in waste disposal, for assisting biochemical reactions where contamination by the redox agents is undesired, for treatment of gastrointestinal ulcers, and for nondiffusing reducing agents for color-photographic systems.

Benzoquinones

Quinone itself (p-benzoquinone) was discovered in 1838 by Woskresensky as an oxidation product of quinic acid, which had been extracted from cinchona bark. It is a chief oxidation product of hydroquinone (qv) in many applications of the latter.

Most p-benzoquinones are yellow-to-orange crystalline solids having relatively high sublimation pressures, and odors that are rather pungent and irritating. They are usually volatile with steam, whereas the o-benzoquinones are not. The latter, generally orange-to-red, are usually less stable than p-benzoquinones. Table 2 lists benzoquinones and their principal derivatives with some properties and uses (see also p. 912).

Table 2. Benzoquinones

Quinone	Properties	Uses
o-benzoquinone	usual form is bright red plates or prisms; also exists as unstable colorless prisms which go over to red form at 60–70°C	limited use as reagent for 1,2-diamines; determination of cysteine
p-benzoquinone	golden yellow prisms; mp 116°C; highly volatile	oxidizing agent; tanning agent
imine	colorless; very reactive	
chloromide (N-chloro-imine)	yellow crystals; mp 85°C; explodes before boiling	
monoxime (p-nitrosophe-nol)	yellow needles, mp 126°C (dec)	color reactions with proteins and amino acids; intermediate for dyes
dioxime	colorless or yellow needles; mp 240°C (dec)	bactericide; vulcanizer for rubber
2-chloroquinone	mp 57°C	bactericide
2,5-dichloroquinone	mp 161°C	bactericide
2,6-dichloroquinone	yellow prisms; mp 121°C; sublimes below 120°C	bactericide
2,3-dichloro-5,6-dicy-anoquinone (DDQ)	golden plates; mp 203°C (dec)	oxidation of phenols; dehydrogenation of steroids
2,5-dichloro-3,6-dihy-droxyquinone (chloranilic acid)	red leaflets; mp 284°C	analytical reagent
2,3,5,6-tetrachloroquinone (chloranil)	yellow prisms; mp 290°C in sealed tube	intermediate for dyes of dioxazine series; intermediate for other derivatives of quinone and hydroquinone; useful for dehydrogenation of hydro-aromatic compounds

REACTIONS

Having two carbonyl groups and two olefinic linkages which may function independently of each other, two independent and four dependent conjugated systems of four atoms each, and two long conjugated systems of six atoms each, the p-benzoquinones undergo a great variety of reactions. Many quinones give characteristic color reactions with aqueous alkali and with concentrated sulfuric acid. They are more readily reduced and both o- and p-benzoquinones undergo addition reactions more readily than open-chain α,β-unsaturated ketones. Though fairly stable under the proper conditions toward oxidizing agents, quinones can be destroyed if care is not taken. o-Benzoquinone gives oxalic acid on warming with potassium permanganate. p-Benzoquinone with potassium peroxydisulfate in the presence of silver sulfate is oxidized to maleic acid and some fumaric acid.

Carbonyl Reagents. The carbonyl groups of p-benzoquinone do not always exhibit the normal reactions of such groups. For example, with sodium bisulfite no addition product forms, but sulfonation occurs on a ring carbon with reduction to the hydroquinone (see Table 3). Cyanohydrins also do not form on reaction with hydrogen cyanide, but ring substitution occurs. The reaction of p-benzoquinone with nitrophenylhdrazines such as 2,4-dinitrophenylhydrazine gives the 4-arylazophenol. The latter is the tautomer of the hydrazone compound in the same sense that p-nitrosophenol is tautomeric with the monoxime of p-benzoquinone (see also Nitro and nitroso compounds; Oximes).

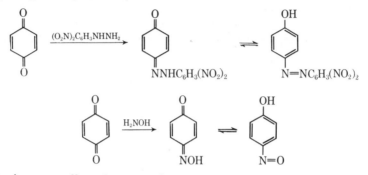

The dioxime as well as the monoxime of p-benzoquinone is readily prepared, but excess phenylhydrazine causes reduction to the hydroquinone. Aniline under certain conditions has been reported to yield the anil of dianilinoquinone; the chief products are, however, 2,5-dianilinohydroquinone and 2,5-dianilinoquinone formed by 1,4-addition (see p. 906).

o-Benzoquinone can be used to characterize 1,2-diamines by the formation of quinoxalines and phenazines. Larger o-quinones are, however, more useful since they more generally yield crystalline products.

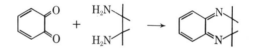

The reaction of p-benzoquinone with ethanethiol (ethyl mercaptan) has been reported to yield, in addition to the expected 2-ethylthiohydroquinone, a 1,1-bis-(ethylmercapto) derivative, which can be oxidized to a β-disulfone (14). The remaining carbonyl group is unreactive toward hydroxylamine and semicarbazide.

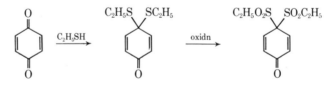

Phenylhydrazine does not form a hydrazone but reduces the system. Polynuclear quinones undergo the same types of reactions.

The Schmidt reaction with hydrazoic acid (normally applied to ketones) gives azepinediones (**20**). This reaction in concentrated sulfuric acid is effected in better

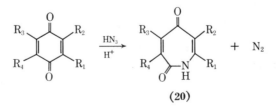

(**20**)

than 75–85% yield. The substituents are H, CH₃ and CH(CH₃)₂. Reaction takes place on the least hindered carbonyl of the quinone but electronic factors also influence the course of the reaction (13).

Reduction. *o*- and *p*-Benzoquinones are readily reduced in aqueous solution by sulfur dioxide to pyrocatechols (qv) and hydroquinones (qv), respectively. About 80% of the theoretical amount of hydroquinone is obtained, the remainder of the product being hydroquinonesulfonic acid formed by the addition of sulfurous acid to the quinone. Commercially, *p*-benzoquinone is reduced to hydroquinone by a slurry

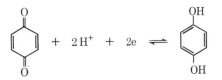

of iron dust in water (8). Other reducing agents such as excess phenylhydrazine, excess aqueous hydroxylamine, zinc dust and acetic acid, and hydrogen and catalyst have been used to advantage. Many of the addition reactions (see p. 906) result in formation of the substituted hydroquinone.

p-Benzoquinone is a very good oxidizing agent. It liberates iodine from hydriodic acid and is capable of oxidizing silver to silver ion, thus finding use as a bleach for silver in photographic processes.

During the reduction of *p*-benzoquinone by sulfur dioxide a green color develops owing to the formation of quinhydrone, $C_6H_4O_2 \cdot C_6H_4(OH)_2$, which has the composition of a molecular complex of quinone and hydroquinone. Quinhydrone is isolated from water as lustrous green needles, mp 171°C, and is used to determine the pH of solutions which are not more alkaline than pH 8. Quinhydrones, in general, may be formed by mixing equimolecular amounts of a quinone and hydroquinone. The reactants may be closely related or may be of entirely different families. For example, 1,4-naphthoquinone forms a quinhydrone very readily with hydroquinone.

Substitution. Substitution of the *p*-benzoquinone ring without reduction appears to occur in only two cases, both of which probably involve free-radical mechanisms. The reaction with diazonium salts gives the monoarylquinones, and the reaction of certain polysubstituted (alkylated, hydroxylated, halogenated) *p*-benzoquinones with

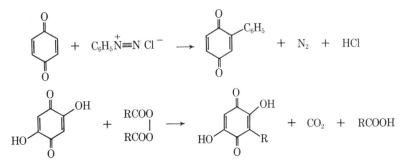

acyl peroxides results in further alkylation or arylation. The acyl peroxide may be formed in situ by the oxidation of the fatty acid with red lead and a promoter.

Additions Involving Ethylene Linkages. *p*-Benzoquinone adds halogen on the ethylenic atoms giving, for example, *p*-benzoquinone 2,3-dibromide, and 2,3,5,6-tetrabromide.

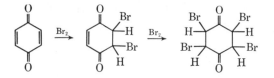

The addition of a diene to benzoquinone was one of the first known examples of the diene synthesis (Diels-Alder reaction). A tetrahydronaphthoquinone may be isolated; reaction of the latter with another molecule of butadiene gives an octahydroanthraquinone. These products may be dehydrogenated to the corresponding naphthoquinone and anthraquinone. 2-Methyl-1,4-naphthoquinone (vitamin K_3) can be prepared in this way in 84% yield (15) but the method is not commercially practical (see Vitamins).

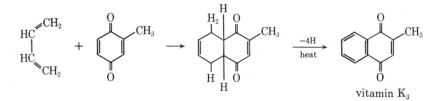

Additions Involving Ethylene and Carbonyl Linkages. The addition of compounds having active hydrogen atoms appears to occur in the 1,4-positions of the conjugated system of one carbonyl group and one ring double bond, the hydrogen attaching to the oxygen, followed by enolization:

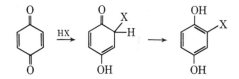

(The addition of hydrogen itself, giving unsubstituted hydroquinone, is a special case of this reaction.) If the substituted hydroquinone formed has a higher oxidation potential than p-benzoquinone, no further reaction occurs. If, on the other hand, its oxidation potential is lower than that of p-benzoquinone, oxidation of the product may occur, with the further addition of HX, giving 2,5-substitution; the latter hydroquinone may then be oxidized by p-benzoquinone, giving as the ultimate product the 2,5-disubstituted p-benzoquinone:

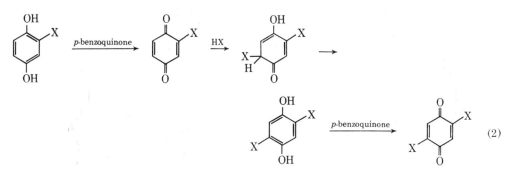

(2)

The reaction represented by equation 1 is effected only when X is a strong electron-attracting group such as halogen and sulfo, and the reaction represented by equation 2, when X is a strong electron-donating group such as amino and alkoxyl. The overall reaction in the latter case is:

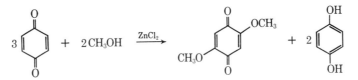

Table 3 lists examples of these reactions.

Table 3. 1,4-Addition to Quinones

Quinone	Reactant	Product
p-benzoquinone	hydrogen chloride	2-chlorohydroquinone
chloro-p-benzoquinone	hydrogen chloride	2,5-dichlorohydroquinone
p-benzoquinone	sodium bisulfite	2,5-dihydroxybenzenesulfonic acid
p-benzoquinonesulfonic acid	sodium bisulfite	2,5-dihydroxy-p-benzenedisulfonic acid
p-benzoquinone	sodium thiosulfate	hydroquinonethiosulfonic acid (2,5-dihydroxybenzenethiosulfonic acid)
p-benzoquinone	acetic anhydride (H$_2$SO$_4$)	1,2,4-triacetoxybenzene (1,2,4-benzenetriol triacetate)
p-benzoquinone	toluene (AlCl$_3$)	2,5-di-p-tolylhydroquinone
p-benzoquinone	benzenesulfinic acid	(phenylsulfonyl)hydroquinone (2,5-dihydroxydiphenyl sulfone)
thymoquinone (2,5-p-cymenedione)	benzenesulfinic acid	6-(phenylsulfonyl)thymohydroquinone (2,5-dihydroxy-6-isopropyl-3-methyldiphenyl sulfone)
p-benzoquinone	aniline	2-anilinohydroquinone, 2,5-dianilinohydroquinone, 2,5-dianilinoquinone
p-benzoquinone	acetaldehyde (sunlight)	2,5-dihydroxyacetophenone
p-benzoquinone	hydrogen cyanide	2,3-dicyanohydroquinone[a]
p-benzoquinone	methanol (ZnCl$_2$)	2,5-dimethoxybenzoquinone

[a] The cyano group to enter first is involved in the addition of the second molecule of hydrogen cyanide to the conjugated system (16).

PREPARATION

o-Benzoquinone has little practical value. However, the synthesis and properties of o-quinones in the benzene and naphthalene series have resulted in over two dozen papers by one research group (7). o-Benzoquinone is prepared by the oxidation of pyrocatechol in dry ether with silver oxide in the presence of a dehydrating agent (normally fused sodium sulfate).

p-Benzoquinone is prepared commercially (8) by the oxidation of aniline (qv) according to the following overall equation:

$$2\ \text{(aniline)}\ +\ 4\,MnO_2\ +\ 5\,H_2SO_4\ \xrightarrow{3-10^\circ C}\ 2\ \text{(benzoquinone)}\ +\ 4\,MnSO_4\ +\ (NH_4)_2SO_4\ +\ 4\,H_2O$$

After completion of the reaction the quinone is distilled with steam. The distillate may be passed into a reductor for conversion to hydroquinone or may be chilled, the benzoquinone separating in beautiful golden-yellow needles of a purity of 99–100%. The manganous sulfate and ammonium sulfate are recovered as described in Managanese compounds (Vol. 13, p. 40).

An older, but still widely used, commercial method of preparation involves oxidation of aniline or phenol with sodium dichromate and sulfuric acid. The vapor-phase oxidation of benzene itself to p-quinone is covered by several patents, though the method seems to be of little value. Many other oxidizing agents have been used commercially, for example, ferric chloride or sulfate on anilines.

Substituted anilines react likewise to give the corresponding substituted quinones: o- or m-toluidine gives toluquinone, and p-xylidine gives p-xyloquinone. Some amines having a methyl group para to the amino group form quinones with elimination of the methyl group. For example, mesidine (2,4,6-trimethylaniline) gives 2,6-dimethylquinone.

Anilines, p-aminophenols (qv), phenylenediamines (qv), hydroquinones, and their derivatives are frequently oxidized to the corresponding quinones in laboratory work (9). Useful oxidizing agents are sodium dichromate or lead dioxide with sulfuric acid, and sodium chlorate in very dilute sulfuric acid with a trace of vanadium pentoxide as a catalyst (10); potassium nitrosodisulfonate and some enzymes have also been used. p-Benzoquinone itself may be the oxidizing agent and a great many other agents have been used, even including halogens. For instance, chloranil is prepared from crude 2,4,6-trichlorophenol by passing chlorine into a solution of this chlorophenol in sulfuric acid monohydrate and chlorosulfonic acid at 85–90°C.

Naphthoquinones

In addition to the three known simple naphthoquinones, 1,2-, 1,4-, and 2,6- (3, 4, and 5), two diquinones are of interest, the 1,2,3,4- and 1,4,5,8-naphthodiquinones (26 and 27).

(26)　　　　　(27)

Properties. The naphthoquinones are generally yellow and only the 1,4 compounds are volatile with steam. 1,4-Naphthoquinone has an odor like that of p-benzoquinone and likewise sublimes easily.

Table 4 lists the properties and uses of the naphthoquinones which seem to be important.

Reactions. The naphthoquinones are somewhat less reactive than the benzoquinones. They are reduced less readily (see Table 1) and their carbonyl functions are more evident. While phenylhydrazine reduces p-benzoquinone, it reacts with 1,4-naphthoquinone to give the hydrazone or 4-benzeneazo-1-naphthol. The reduction of 1,4-naphthoquinone with sulfur dioxide is very slow; stannous chloride is apparently the best chemical reducing agent.

Table 4. Naphthoquinones

Compound	Properties	Uses
1,2-naphthoquinone	golden yellow needles, mp 145–147°C (dec); nonvolatile with steam; unstable in aqueous soln; stable in benzene	intermediate for phenazines
1,4-naphthoquinone	yellow needles; mp 125°C (after sublimation and distillation, mp 128.5°C); odor like p-benzoquinone, volatile with steam	
2,6-naphthoquinone	red-yellow or brick-red prisms; turns gray at 130–135°C; no mp reported; stable in air; nonvolatile; odorless; soluble, with decompn, in polar organic solvents	
1,2,3,4-naphthodiquinone	colorless crystals; mp 131°C	
1,4,5,8-naphthodiquinone	pale yellowish crystals, dec at 220°C; forms oximes, phenazines	
1,2-naphthoquinone derivatives		
1-oxime (1-nitroso-2-naphthol)	mp 110°C	bactericide; detection or determination of phenols, amines, as well as many inorganic ions, eg cobalt
2-oxime (2-nitroso-1-naphthol)	mp 162–164°C	analytical reagent for zirconium and cobalt
4-sulfo(2-nitroso-1-naphthol)		sodium salt gives pink color with indole in chloroform soln (Herter's reaction); intermediate for dyes
1,4-naphthoquinone derivatives		
2-methyl- (vitamin K_3)	mp 105–106°C	highest antihemorrhagic activity known; vitamin K_1 substitute
.NaHSO$_3$.3H$_2$O	loses water at 100°C, mp 154–157°C (dec)	high antihemorrhagic activity; commercially available in soln or tablet form with glucose
2-phytyl- (norvitamin K_1)	yellow oil	antihemorrhagic activity
2,3-dimethyl-	mp 126.5–127.5°C	high antihemorrhagic activity
2-methyl-3-phytyl- (vitamin K_1)	yellow oil, mp about −20°C	$\frac{1}{3}$ to $\frac{1}{2}$ antihemorrhagic activity of vitamin K_3
2-methyl-3-phytyl-, 2,3-oxide	nearly colorless oil	same order of antihemorrhagic activity as vitamin K_1
2,3-dichloro-	yellow needles, mp 193°C	agricultural and textile fungicide; intermediate for dyes

Naphthoquinones also undergo few substitution reactions. 1,2-Naphthoquinone can be brominated and nitrated in the 3-position, but other substitution reactions characteristic of aromatic compounds have not been reported. 1,4-Naphthoquinones react less readily than does p-benzoquinone with diazotized aniline; however, more reactive diazonium salts give the characteristic 2-aryl-1,4-naphthoquinone. The alkylation of 1,4-naphthoquinones with acyl peroxides proceeds very smoothly (see also Vol. 10, p. 755).

Addition reactions occur similar to those with p-benzoquinones, that is, ethylenic additions of halogen, Diels-Alder reactions with dienes, 1,4-additions, etc (5).

A quinhydrone of 1,2-naphthoquinone and 1,2-naphthalenediol has apparently not been reported. However, 1,4-naphthoquinone reacts with hydroquinone, giving dark green needles (ruby red transmission), mp 123–124°C, and with 1,4-naphthalenediol, giving dark purple crystals or bronze needles, mp >220°C (dec). 2,6-Naphthoquinone reacts with its hydroxy analog to give dark blue-green needles which lose their color at 124–125°C without melting.

Replacement of one or both halogen atoms of 2,3-dichloro-1,4-naphthoquinone is easily accomplished because of their high reactivity. In addition, a number of heterocyclic quinones have been prepared by reaction of certain ketones, phenols **or** naphthols, dithiocarbonates and amines with dichloronaphthoquinone in the presence usually of other agents. The first note of this type of reaction involved only dichloronaphthoquinone and resorcinol (17):

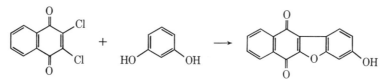

Reactions of this type were little studied until after 1940 when it was found that several heterocyclic quinones had attractive properties as dyes (18) (see under Uses).

Preparation. 1,2-Naphthoquinone and 1,4-naphthoquinone are prepared by the oxidation of the corresponding amino naphthols in high yield. The oxidation of 1-amino-2-naphthol hydrochloride with ferric chloride in dilute hydrochloric acid gives a 93–94% yield of 1,2-naphthoquinone. The action of potassium dichromate and sulfuric acid on 4-amino-1-naphthol hydrochloride gives a nearly quantitative yield of 1,4-naphthoquinone. The direct oxidation of naphthalene to 1,4-naphthoquinone appears to be of limited value; however, the oxidation of 2-methylnaphthalene to 2-methyl-1,4-naphthoquinone is of great commercial importance. 2,6-Naphthoquinone is prepared in rather low yield (20%) by shaking 2,6-naphthalenediol with dry lead dioxide in boiling anhydrous benzene. The diquinones are also formed by oxidation of hydroxy compounds. 1,2,3,4-Naphthodiquinone is formed in 85% yield by the oxidation of 2,3-dihydroxy-1,4-naphthoquinone with nitric acid in acetic acid, and 1,4,5,8-naphthodiquinone in 40% yield from 5,8-dihydroxy-1,4-naphthoquinone (naphthazarin) with lead tetraacetate.

Other Quinones

Quinones can increase in complexity by the fusion of other rings to the simple systems, as in naphthoquinones and phenanthrenequinones, or by extension of the conjugated system through substituent rings or carbon chains, as in 4,4'-dipheno-

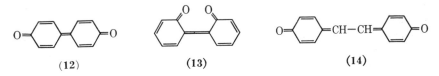

(12)   (13)   (14)

quinone (**12**), 2,2′-diphenoquinone (**13**), and 4,4′-stilbenequinone (**14**). The more complex quinones have physical properties similar to those of the simpler quinones. They have, generally, less odor and a lower volatility. Some of these quinones are listed in Table 5.

Table 5. Other Quinones

Quinone	Properties	Uses
4,4′-diphenoquinone (**12**)	stable form is golden yellow; mp 165°C (dec); nonvolatile; odorless	
4,4′-stilbenequinone (**14**)	bright red or brown needles, become colorless on heating	
phenanthrenequinone (**9**)	orange plates; mp 208°C	identification of *o*-diamines; detection of thiophenes in toluene
acenaphthenequinone (**10**)	yellow needles; mp 261°C	intermediate for dyes
chrysenequinone (11,12-chrysenedione) (**11**)	orange-red needles or plates; mp 235°C	

Phenanthrenequinone is formed by the oxidation of phenanthrene with potassium dichromate and concentrated sulfuric acid. Further oxidation gives diphenic acid:

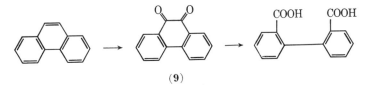

(9)

Acenaphthenequinone is prepared in 40–60% yield by the oxidation of acenaphthene, but a considerable amount of naphthalic acid is obtained also:

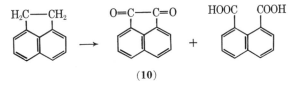

(10)

A yield of 60% of the quinone is obtained when an alcoholic hydrogen chloride solution of acenaphthene is treated with ethyl nitrite and the resulting dioxime is hydrolyzed (19). Chrysenequinone likewise is prepared by the oxidation of chrysene with sodium dichromate in acetic acid. Further oxidation with permanganate gives cleavage of the ring to the corresponding dicarboxylic acid.

Health and Safety Factors

p-Benzoquinone is an irritant, particularly dangerous to the eyes in solid, vapor, or dissolved state. In a few cases, there has been an appreciable loss of vision (8,20).

The toxic properties of *p*-benzoquinone and its derivatives have led to their use as bactericides, fungicides, and insecticides. Some quinones have carcinogenic activity, causing epitheliomas and papillomas when applied to the skin in benzene solution (21). On the other hand, some quinones containing ethylenimino groups are claimed to be antitumor agents (22).

Commercial Products and Uses

Listed in Table 6 are some of the quinones available in commerce. The prices are those given by catalogs such as Eastman Organic Chemicals List No. 44, the 1967–1968 catalog of the Aldrich Chemical Co. Inc., and the January 1, 1968, issue of the *Oil, Paint and Drug Reporter*.

A number of quinones are used as dyes or as dye intermediates. Chloranil is an intermediate for the dioxazine dye CI 51310 (CI Direct Blue 109). 6-Sulfo-1,2-naphthoquinone is an intermediate for CI 10020 (CI Acid Green 1). 2,3-Dichloro-1,4-naphthoquinone is an intermediate for a number of naphthofurandiones (17) (see p. 910). The latter are mostly yellow to red and are suitable as vat dyes for natural or synthetic fibers (18,27). Disperse and cationic dyes of this type may be obtained from the reaction of the 2,3-dichloro compound with 5-hydroxyquinoline (28). Acenaphthenequinone is an intermediate for CI 73860 (CI Vat Red 45). Some of the multiring quinones, such as the pyranthrones (CI 59700 (CI Vat Orange 9) and CI 59710 (CI Vat Orange 4)) and violanthrones (CI 59800 (CI Vat Blue 20) and CI 59825 (CI Vat Green 1)) appear to be produced in large amounts (see Table 6).

2,5-Dichloro-3,6-dihydroxy-*p*-benzoquinone (chloranilic acid) is useful in colorimetric analysis for inorganic cations and anions. Barium, silver, sodium, lanthanum, mercury, nickel, thorium, and zinc salts of chloranilic acid are commercially available (Distillation Products Industries). The lanthanum and thorium salts are specific for fluoride ion. 2,6-Dichloro-*p*-benzoquinone-chloroimide (Gibbs' reagent) is used to detect phenols in paper chromatography and in thin-layer chromatography. Quinonedioximes are used as vulcanization agents for rubber.

Many derivatives of hydroxy-1,4-naphthoquinones have been studied for antimalarial activity. A number are more active than quinone for avian malaria and some have antimalarial activity in man (see Therapeutic agents, protozoal infections). 2-Methyl-1,4-naphthoquinone is of major importance as one of the K vitamins (see

Table 6. Some Quinones of Commercial Importance

Quinone	Price
p-benzoquinone	$6/kg
p-quinonedioxime	$25/25 g[a]
2,3-dichloro-5,6-dicyanobenzoquinone	$11/25 g[b]
1,4-naphthoquinone	$14/kg
2,3-dichloronaphthoquinone	$3/100 g
Golden Orange GFD (CI 59700)[c]	$2.30/lb
Flaming Orange 4RD (CI 59710)[c]	$6.45/lb
Dark Blue BO (CI 59800)[c]	$2.28/lb
Jade Green NC (CI 59825)[c]	$1.75/lb

[a] $2.60/lb in ton lots (Uniroyal).

[b] $80/lb in 100 lb lots (Arapahoe Chemicals).

[c] Major producers of these vat dyes are American Cyanamid, Ciba, Du Pont, Geigy, and Imperial Chemical Industries.

Table 4 and Vitamins). A number of other biological effects of quinones have been observed. For example, embelin (2,5-dihydroxy-3-*n*-undecyl-*p*-quinone) is used as a remedy for tapeworms; plumbagin (5-hydroxy-2-methyl-1,4-naphthoquinone) has antibacterial and medicinal properties; juglone (5-hydroxy-1,4-naphthoquinone) is a powerful fungicide, though apparently not in commercial use.

Quinhydrone is a useful component of an electrode for the determination of hydrogen-ion concentrations at pH values lower than 8 (see Hydrogen-ion concentration); the glass electrode has, however, supplanted the quinhydrone electrode in most applications.

Bibliography

"Quinones" in *ECT* 1st ed., Vol. 11, pp. 410–424, by J. R. Thirtle, Eastman Kodak Company.

1. R. A. Morton, ed., *Biochemistry of Quinones*, Academic Press, Inc., New York, 1965.
2. R. H. Thomson, *Naturally Occurring Quinones*, Academic Press, Inc., New York, 1957.
3. R. A. Morton, "Quinones as Biological Catalysts," *Endeavour* **24** (92), 81 (1965).
4. L. F. Fieser, "Theory of the Structure and Reactions of Organic Compounds," in H. Gilman, ed., *Organic Chemistry*, Vol. 1, 2nd ed., John Wiley & Sons, Inc., New York, 1943, pp. 117–213.
5. L. F. Fieser and M. Fieser, *Organic Chemistry*, 3rd ed., Reinhold Publishing Corp., New York, 1956, pp. 710–731.
6. H. G. Cassidy and K. A. Kun, in N. G. Gaylord and H. F. Mark, *Linear and Stereoregular Addition Polymers*, Vol. 2 of H. F. Mark and E. H. Immergut, eds., *Polymer Reviews*, Interscience Publishers, a division of John Wiley & Sons, Inc., New York, 1965.
7. L. Homer and E. Geyer, "*o*-Quinones XXVII," *Chem. Ber.* **98,** 2016 (1965).
8. L. G. Davy and H. VonBramer, *Ind. Eng. Chem.* **44,** 1730 (1952).
9. J. Cason, in R. Adams, ed., *Organic Reactions Series*, Vol. 4, John Wiley & Sons, Inc., New York, 1948, pp. 305–361.
10. H. W. Underwood, Jr. and W. L. Walsh, "Quinone," in A. H. Blatt, ed., *Organic Syntheses*, Coll. Vol. 2, John Wiley & Sons, Inc., New York, 1947, p. 553.
11. A. Recsei, *Ber.* **B60,** 1836 (1927).
12. D. Bryce-Smith and A. Gilbert, *Proc. Chem. Soc.* **1964,** 87.
13. D. Misiti, H. W. Moore, and K. Folkers, *Tetrahedron Letters* **1965** (16), 1071.
14. F. M. Dean, P. G. Jones, R. B. Morton, and P. Sidisunthorn, *J. Chem. Soc.* **1964,** 411.
15. A. N. Grinev and A. P. Terent'ev, *Zhur. Obshchei Khim.* **28,** 75 (1958).
16. C. F. H. Allen and C. V. Wilson, *J. Am. Chem. Soc.* **63,** 1756 (1941).
17. C. Lieberman, *Chem. Ber.* **32,** 923 (1899).
18. M. F. Sartori, *Chem Rev.* **63,** 279 (1963); U.S. Pat. 2,893,998 (1959) and 2,995,579 (1961), M. F. Sartori (to E. I. du Pont de Nemours & Co., Inc.).
19. J. Avery et al., "Manufacture of Intermediates for Dyestuffs," *U.S. Dept. Comm. Office Tech. Serv. PB Rept.* 77764; *BIOS (British Intelligence Objectives Subcommittee) Final Rept.* 986.
20. N. I. Sax, *Dangerous Properties of Industrial Materials*, Reinhold Publishing Corp., New York, 1963.
21. J. L. Hartwell, *Public Health Service Publication*, No. 149.
22. Brit. Pat. 838,993 (June 22, 1960) (to Ciba, Ltd.).
23. Ger. Pat. 1,021,979 (Jan. 2, 1958), A. E. Brown (to Gillette Co.).
24. U.S. Pat. 3,041,244 (June 26, 1962), Jerome A. Feit and Aloysius J. Feit.
25. D. B. Andrews, et al., "German Dyestuffs and Dyestuff Intermediates," *Field Information Agency Tech. Rept.* No. 1313, Vol. 2, pp. 164, 198 (1948).
26. K. Venkataraman, *The Chemistry of Synthetic Dyes*, Academic Press, Inc., New York, 1952, Vol. 1, pp. 153–164; Vol. 2, pp. 796–802.
27. U.S. Pat. 2,862,931 (1959), 2,870,168 (1959), and 2,967,870 (1961), D. I. Randall and W. Schmidt-Nickels (to General Aniline & Film Corp.).
28. U.S. Pat. 3,121,086 (1964), M. F. Sartori (to E. I. du Pont de Nemours & Co., Inc.).

J. R. Thirtle
Eastman Kodak Company